42nd Edition

DIRECTORY OF

Pathology Training Programs 2010–2011

United States and Canada

A resource for training programs in anatomic pathology and clinical pathology and subspecialties

The Intersociety Council for Pathology Information, Inc.

Figure Legends:

1. Back Cover, Left. Heirarchical clustering of microarray gene expression data from different types of adenocarcinoma. Adapted from Bloom, G., Yang, I.V., Boulware, D., Kwong, K.Y., Coppola, D., Eschich, S., Quackenbush, J., and Yeatman, T.J. (2004), Multi-platform, multi-site, microarray-based human tumor classification, *The American Journal of Pathology*, 164:9-16.
2. Back Cover, Right. Telomeric Fluorscent *In Situ* Hybridization (FISH) of pleomorphic sarcomas displaying long and heterogeneous telomeres (arrows). Adapted from Montgomery, E., Argani, P., Hicks, J., De Marzo, A.M., and Meeker, A.K. (2004), Telomere length of translocation-associated and nontranslocation-associated sarcomas differ dramatically, *The American Journal of Pathology*, 164:1523-1529.
3. Front Cover, Right. Hematoxylin and eosin staining of normal breast terminal duct lobular units. Adapted from Meeker, A.K., Hicks, J.L., Gabrielson, E., Strauss, W.M., De Marzo, A.M., and Argani, P. (2004), Telomere shortening occurs in subsets of normal breast epithelium as well as in situ and invasive carcinoma, *The American Journal of Pathology*, 164:925-935.

Controlled distribution to medical schools, medical libraries and hospitals in the United States and Canada.

ISBN 978-0-937888-25-4

The Intersociety Council for Pathology Information, Inc.
9650 Rockville Pike
Bethesda, Maryland 20814-3993
Phone: (301) 634-7200
Fax: (301) 634-7990
E-mail: icpi@asip.org
Single copies may be purchased for $25 each prepaid including U.S. postage (book rate) and handling. Order forms are available at www.pathologytraining.org.

The *Directory of Pathology Training Programs* is edited and published annually for the Intersociety Council for Pathology Information by the American Society for Investigative Pathology. Mark E. Sobel, MD, PhD, Executive Officer; Donna Stivers, Administrator and Managing Editor. Visit ICPI's Web site at www.pathologytraining.org for a searchable version of this *Directory* online.

INTRODUCTION

We are pleased to present the 42nd Edition of the *Directory of Pathology Training Programs*, published annually by the Intersociety Council for Pathology Information (ICPI), a nonprofit organization sponsored by five national pathology societies. The *Directory's* purpose is to give medical students and graduate physicians a timely source of detailed information about the many options for pathology training in the United States and Canada. Publication is in June, a year in advance of the training period covered by each edition. Complimentary distribution to medical schools, medical libraries and teaching hospitals makes the *Directory* readily accessible for reference use. Medical students and residents may receive their own copy at no charge with a pathologist's countersignature. The information in this *Directory* is also available at www.pathologytraining.org.

This 2010-2011 edition includes geographically arranged descriptions of the facilities, residencies, remuneration, application requirements, and faculty at nearly all of the approved residency training programs for anatomic and clinical pathology in the United States, and more than half of the approved programs in Canada. Most programs also provide the names and research interests of their faculty members. This edition contains 480 descriptions of fellowship opportunities in specialized areas of pathology. A Training Staff Index makes it easy to determine the present location of about 7,000 pathologists. The individual institutions and organizations listed have provided the information in this *Directory*. ICPI is not responsible for its accuracy.

A section on "Information about Pathology" includes sources of information about pathology as a career in medicine; a description of the services and activities of the five charter member societies and associate members of ICPI; a summary of requirements and procedures for certification by the American Board of Pathology; and a list of members of the Intersociety Pathology Council, a forum representing major pathology organizations in North America.

Post-Sophomore Fellowships in Pathology for medical students are listed in a special section. This "year out" fellowship program is being offered in a number of medical schools, and the *Directory* provides descriptions of 10 programs with stipends and application requirements.

Participation in the *Directory* is voluntary for any accredited pathology residency and postgraduate program in the United States and Canada. The Intersociety Council for Pathology Information invites inquiries about participation in the next edition to be published in June 2010.

THE INTERSOCIETY COUNCIL FOR PATHOLOGY INFORMATION, INC.

The Intersociety Council for Pathology Information (ICPI) is a nonprofit educational organization sponsored by five national pathology societies to serve as a central source of information about pathology in the practice of medicine, in medical research, and to provide literature about pathology as a career. Members of the ICPI Board and the societies they represent are:

David S. Wilkinson, MD, PhD, *Chair*
Association of Pathology Chairs
Eric S. Wargotz, MD, *Vice Chair*
American Society for Clinical Pathology
Margaret M. Grimes, MD, *Secretary-Treasurer*
United States and Canadian Academy of Pathology
Ronald P. Spark, MD
College of American Pathologists
Jacob J. Steinberg, MD
American Society for Investigative Pathology

A Brief History of ICPI: In February, 1957, five pathologists, representing five national pathology societies (American Association of Pathologists and Bacteriologists, American Society for Experimental Pathology, American Society of Clinical Pathologists, College of American Pathologists, and the International Academy of Pathology) met to organize an effort to help pathologists improve public and professional appreciation of their specialty's contributions to medical practice and research, to recruit physicians for careers in pathology, and to educate pathologists about how to improve individual, community, and professional relationships. As a result of that meeting, the Intersociety Committee on Pathology Information (ICPI) was formally established. Since that time, the American Association of Pathologists and Bacteriologists and the American Society for Experimental Pathology merged to form what is now the American Society for Investigative Pathology; the American Society of Clinical Pathologists changed its name to the American Society for Clinical Pathology, the International Academy of Pathology changed its name to the United States and Canadian Academy of Pathology, and the Association of Pathology Chairs became a member in 1982. Since 2008, Associate member societies have joined ICPI and include:

American Association of Neuropathologists, Tarik Tihan, MD, *Delegate*
American Board of Pathology, Betsy D. Bennett, MD, PhD, *Delegate*
American College of Veterinary Pathologists, John M. Cullen, VMD, PhD, *Delegate*
Association of Molecular Pathology, Jan Nowak, MD, PhD, *Delegate*
Canadian Association of Pathologists, Jagdish Butany, MBBS, MS, FRCPC, *Delegate*
National Association of Medical Examiners, Scott Denton, MD, *Delegate*

ICPI was structured to be a continuing body consisting of one representative from each society, with the understanding that projects would be undertaken for the good of all pathology. The first chair of ICPI was William O. Russell. Other pathologists who served as chairs of ICPI during its first 25 years were Victor B. Buhler, Robert L. Breckenridge, Kenneth M.Brinkhous, F. Wells Brason, Rex B. Conn, Jr., William M. Christopherson, Robert B. Jennings, Thomas D. Kinney, David J. LaFond, E. Coye Mason, Henry D. Moon, Richard E. Palmer, Ernest E. Simard, Robert E. Stowell, and Martin J. Valaske. Dr. Herschel Sidransky served as Chair from 1984 to 2000, after which time Dr. Ronald P. Spark became Chair through 2007. Dr. David Wilkinson has served as Chair since 2008.

In the first decades of its existence, PR Associates (later incorporated as Information Services, Inc.), a Washington, D.C. firm experienced in public relations for health, scientific and educational projects, provided staff and headquarters for ICPI in Bethesda, Maryland. In 2000, ICPI moved its headquarters to the shared offices of ASIP and Universities for the Advancement of Research and Education in Pathology (UAREP). Since the dissolution of UAREP in 2002, ICPI has been managed by ASIP (Dr. Mark E. Sobel, Executive Officer). **In 2004, ICPI reincorporated in the State of Maryland as the Intersociety Council for Pathology Information, Inc**.

Currently, ICPI's major activity is the publication of this annual *Directory of Pathology Training Programs in the United States and Canada*. In 2001, a searchable web version of the *Directory* was developed on ICPI's website www.pathologytraining.org. ICPI also answers questions from pathologists and the lay public about pathology and pathology careers. In addition, ICPI distributes an illustrated color brochure "Pathology: a Career in Medicine," which describes the pathologist's role on the clinical team and intimate involvement in patient care problems, the variety of case material, the opportunities to do research and to teach, and the wide scope of career options. A free copy is available on request. A revised web version of the brochure is also available at www.asip.org. A new print edition of the brochure was printed in 2007. ICPI launched a Trainee Travel Award Program in 2007. Applications are available online at http://www.pathologytraining.org/Travel%20Award.pdf.

Intersociety Council for Pathology Information, Inc., 9650 Rockville Pike, Bethesda, MD 20814-3993
Phone: (301) 634-7200 • **Fax:** (301) 634-7990 • **E-mail:** icpi@asip.org
Web site: www.pathologytraining.org

CONTENTS

UNITED STATES RESIDENCY TRAINING PROGRAMS

IOWA

Iowa City

KANSAS

Kansas City

KENTUCKY

Lexington

Louisville

LOUISIANA

New Orleans

Shreveport

MARYLAND

Baltimore

Bethesda

MASSACHUSETTS

Boston

Pittsfield

Springfield

Worcester

MICHIGAN

Ann Arbor

Detroit

Royal Oak

PENNSYLVANIA

PUERTO RICO

RHODE ISLAND

SOUTH CAROLINA

TENNESSEE

TEXAS

UTAH

Salt Lake City

VERMONT

Burlington

VIRGINIA

Charlottesville

Richmond

WASHINGTON

Seattle

WEST VIRGINIA

Morgantown

WISCONSIN

Madison

Milwaukee

CANADIAN RESIDENCY TRAINING PROGRAMS

TRAINING IN SPECIALIZED AREAS OF PATHOLOGY

Clinical Microbiology (pp. 445-450)

Clinical Pathology/Laboratory Medicine (page 451)

Coagulation (see Blood Banking/Transfusion Medicine page 438)

Cytopathology (pp. 453-492)

Dermatopathology (pp. 493-510)

Immunopathology/Transplantation (page 571)

Informatics (pp. 573-574)

Laboratory Medicine (see Clinical Pathology/Laboratory Medicine page 451)

Molecular Genetic Pathology (pp. 575-588; also see Genetics pp. 529-530)

Molecular Pathology (page 589)

Neuropathology (pp. 591-609)

Soft Tissue Pathology (pp. 663-665)

Surgical Pathology (General) (pp. 666-698)

POST-SOPHOMORE FELLOWSHIPS IN PATHOLOGY

ADDITIONAL RESIDENCY PROGRAMS NOT LISTED IN THIS DIRECTORY

USA

California, University of, San Diego .... San Diego, CA
Danbury Hospital .... Danbury, CT
Lenox Hill Hospital .... New York, NY
Madigan Army Medical Center .... Tacoma, WA Missouri,
Missouri-Kansas City, University of .... Kansas City, MO
Nassau County Medical Center .... East Meadow, NY
National Capital Consortium .... Washington, DC
Naval Medical Center .... San Diego, CA
New York Medical College at Westchester Medical Center .... Valhalla, NY
St. Luke's-Roosevelt Hospital and Beth Israel Medical Center .... New York, NY
San Antonio Uniformed Services Health Educ .... Lackland AFB, TX
South Dakota, University .... Sioux Falls, SD
VA Greater Los Angeles Healthcare .... Los Angeles, CA

CANADA

Alberta, University of .... Edmonton, AB
Montreal, University of .... Montreal, QC
Ottawa, University of .... Ottawa, ON
Queen's University Medical Center .... Kingston, ON
Sherbrooke, University of .... Sherbrooke, QC
Western Ontario, University of .... London, ON

These programs provided no additional information.

INFORMATION ABOUT PATHOLOGY

Pathology is a medical specialty that provides the scientific foundation for medical practice. The pathologist works with all other medical specialties, using the tools of laboratory medicine to provide information essential to problem solving in clinical practice.

Many pathologists are generalists concerned with all facets of disease that can be examined in the laboratory; others specialize. Anatomic pathologists use information gathered from microscopic examination and concentrate on abnormal morphology; clinical pathologists obtain and interpret clinical laboratory data as needed for diagnosis and patient care. There are pathology specialties concerned with every category of disease. Graduate training in many of these specialties is described in this *Directory* under "Training in Specialized Areas of Pathology." Pathologists can be certified to practice in the following subspecialties in the United States:

Blood Banking/Transfusion Medicine
Chemical Pathology
Cytopathology
Dermatopathology
Forensic Pathology
Hematology
Medical Microbiology
Molecular Genetic Pathology
Neuropathology
Pediatric Pathology

Today's employment outlook for the newly graduated pathologist is very promising. The following 2007 career statistics were obtained from the American Medical Association FREIDA Online (www.ama-assn.org). The average salary for a resident was $43,881, and the average number of weeks of vacation was 3.2. Salaries for fellowships in specialized areas of pathology varied with the subspecialty and were at least $40,000. In 2007, of the 574 residents or fellows who completed training in anatomic and/or clinical pathology, 52 % of residents were female and 34.5% were international medical graduates. In 2007, 79.7% of residents completing a residency program decided to pursue additional training in specialized fellowships, 8.3% began a career in academic medicine (in pathology), 6.5% began practicing in the United States (65.6% of these went into group practice), 4.5% went into the military, and the remainder left the United States.

Data from the College of American Pathologists for the year 2007 show that on average, pathologists worked 50.1 hours per week (compared to 55 hours for all other specialties combined). Currently, approximately half of pathologists work in group practice, and the remainder work in solo practice, in a university medical school or hospital, in independent laboratories, in a multi-specialty group, and as coroners or medical examiners. More than half of pathology group practices have five or more pathologists (and one third of those in group practice work in larger groups of seven or more). Salaries for practicing pathologists vary with years of experience, type of practice and practice site. Further details can be obtained at http://www.pathologytraining.org/recruit.ppt (Residency Recruitment Tool).

The best sources of additional information about the personal and professional satisfaction of being a pathologist are pathologists in hospitals, medical schools, and private practice. For more information about residency and fellowship training, check the *Directory of Graduate Medical Education Programs*, the Accreditation Council for Graduate Medical Education's annual source book of all accredited programs. Reference copies are located in medical schools and medical libraries, and the information is also available online at www.acgme.org.

In this *Directory*, there is information about how physicians can be certified in pathology in the United States, provided by the American Board of Pathology. All the information in this *Directory* is available online, in searchable format by region, state, and institution, at www.pathologytraining.org.

Useful sources of information on the Web include:

Accreditation Council for Graduate Medical Education	www.acgme.org
American Association of Medical Colleges	www.aamc.org
American Board of Pathology	www.abpath.org
American Medical Association	www.ama-assn.org
American Society for Clinical Pathology	www.ascp.org
American Society for Investigative Pathology	www.asip.org
Association of Pathology Chairs	www.apcprods.org
College of American Pathologists	www.cap.org
Intersociety Council for Pathology Information	www.pathologytraining.org
United States and Canadian Academy of Pathology	www.uscap.org

AMERICAN SOCIETY FOR CLINICAL PATHOLOGY

The mission of the American Society for Clinical Pathology (ASCP) is to provide excellence in education, certification, and advocacy on behalf of patients, pathologists, and laboratory professionals. Founded in 1922, the Society is a professional medical specialty society with 130,000 members representing the entire laboratory team — Board-certified pathologists, pathology residents, laboratory professionals, and students.

ASCP serves as a principal resource for continuing medical education (CME) in pathology and laboratory medicine. ASCP is accredited with commendation by the Accreditation Council for Continuing Medical Education (ACCME) to provide CME for physicians. All ASCP CME activities are acceptable for the American Board of Pathology's Maintenance of Certification Program, Part II Lifelong Learning. Many also meet the requirements for Part II Self-Assessment Modules and/or Part IV Quality Assurance.

ASCP's Board of Registry (BOR) began certifying laboratory personnel in 1928 and has registered more than 400,000 laboratory professionals. The ASCP-BOR is now accredited by the American National Standards Institute (ANSI), which sets the benchmark of excellence in US voluntary standardization and conformity assessment systems. Through its advocacy efforts, the Society represents the interests of pathology and laboratory medicine on legislative and policy issues before Congress, the Administration, federal regulatory agencies, and state governments. ASCP also interacts with patient, allied health, laboratory and medical organizations to build coalitions to further the goals of ASCP in the interests of the profession.

ASCP membership is free to pathology residents. Resident members receive:

- online access to ASCP journals, ***LABMEDICINE***™ and the *American Journal of Clinical Pathology* (AJCP), and the ASCP Job Finder;
- discounts on the ASCP Annual Meeting, ASCP Teleconferences, and ASCP Weekends of Pathology;
- the ASCP quarterly member newsletter *Critical Values*, *Daily Diagnosis* custom e-mail briefs, ASCP e-NewsBriefs, ASCP e-Policy News, plus access to ASCP's e-Advocacy Center;
- discounted subscription to AJCP ($43) and ***LABMEDICINE***™ ($43)
- personal benefits such as group discounts on car insurance and rentals, online diagnostic tools, and credit card offers.

Residents may become active members of the ASCP and participate on a national level in organized pathology through the ASCP Resident Council. Resident members also are eligible to vote for members of the Resident Council.

Since 1983, the ASCP has offered the Pathology Resident In-Service Examination, which is taken by all pathology residents in United States training programs. The examination was developed to help both residents and training programs identify their weaknesses and strengths, thereby providing a continuous quality monitor for entrants into the profession. ASCP also offers a week-long Resident Review Course, which enables residents nearing the end of training to review the entire scope of pathology.

ASCP is based in Chicago and has offices in Washington, DC, and Indianapolis, IN.

American Society for Clinical Pathology
33 W. Monroe St. , Suite 1600
Chicago, IL 60603
Phone: (800) 267-2727, (312) 541-4999 • **Fax:** (312) 541-4998 • **E-mail:** info@ascp.org
Web site: www.ascp.org

AMERICAN SOCIETY FOR INVESTIGATIVE PATHOLOGY

The mission of the American Society for Investigative Pathology (ASIP) is to promote the discovery, advancement, and dissemination of basic and translational knowledge in experimental pathology and related disciplines by fostering investigation into the pathogenesis, classification, diagnosis, and manifestations of disease through meetings, publications, and educational activities. The Society is headquartered in the Washington, DC metropolitan area near the NIH campus in Bethesda, MD.

Divisions and Affiliates

ASIP invites appropriate groups to become semi-autonomous Divisions of the Society. Current Divisions are the International Society for Biological and Environmental Repositories (ISBER) and the Pulmonary Pathology Society (PPS). The Società Italiana di Patologia and the American College of Veterinary Pathologists (ACVP) are affiliate societies. ASIP is a cooperating society of the American Board of Pathology and a charter constituent society of the Federation of American Societies for Experimental Biology (FASEB).

Meeting and Educational Courses

Each year, ASIP meets together with other basic biomedical research societies at the Experimental Biology Meeting. This scientific meeting provides a forum for members to present their research findings in oral and poster sessions; symposia provide perspectives on advances in topic areas. Regular and emeritus members may sponsor abstracts. The annual business meeting and award presentations also take place during this meeting. The Divisions hold additional meetings each year. ASIP and its affiliate the Società Italiana di Patologia will hold a joint meeting in Italy in September 2010. The ASIP Summer Academy offers courses on the Molecular Mechanisms of Human Disease each year.

Publications

ASIP publishes **The American Journal of Pathology** (AJP), providing a scholarly forum for the dissemination of information about experimental and investigative pathology. This internationally recognized research journal is published monthly. ASIP and the Association for Molecular Pathology jointly publish **The Journal of Molecular Diagnostics,** which is published bimonthly and is devoted to original papers on translational research and validation of molecular discoveries in medicine into the clinical diagnostic setting. The ASIP Journal CME Program offers continuing medical education credits to the readership of the two journals. ASIP supports an active website at http://www.asip.org that lists upcoming scientific meetings and announces news of interest to society members. A special feature on the website is an adaptation of "Pathology: a Career in Medicine," ICPI's popular brochure for students and the lay public. ASIP also hosts a jobs board at www.PathologyJobsToday.org.

Awards and Honors

ASIP recognizes individuals at different stages in their careers. The Gold-Headed Cane is presented to a leader in academic pathology for long-standing contributions to investigative pathology, including meritorious research and outstanding teaching. The ASIP-Rous-Whipple Award recognizes a distinguished investigator with a long-standing and ongoing research program. The ASIP Outstanding Investigator Award for meritorious research in experimental pathology, the Cotran Established Investigator Award, and the Excellence in Science Award are presented to members who are at an earlier career stage. The Robbins Distinguished Educator Award recognizes a pathologist whose contributions to education have had a manifest impact on learning. The Society also honors pre- and post-doctoral trainees who are presenting papers at the annual meeting with Experimental Pathologist-in-Training Awards and Merit awards, trainee travel awards and minority trainee travel awards.

Public Affairs

Through its membership in FASEB and liaisons with other pathology organizations, ASIP is committed to promoting quality research and educational environments, including appropriate resources for research support, peer review procedures, and graduate curriculum in pathology.

For additional information, please contact:

Mark E. Sobel MD, PhD, Executive Officer
American Society for Investigative Pathology
9650 Rockville Pike
Bethesda, MD 20814
Phone: (301) 634-7130 • **Fax:** (301) 634-7990 • **E-mail:** ASIP@asip.org
Web site: www.asip.org

ASSOCIATION OF PATHOLOGY CHAIRS

The Association of Pathology Chairs (APC), Inc, originated in 1966-67 as the official organization representing departments of pathology and laboratory medicine in United States, Canadian and Puerto Rican schools of medicine that are accredited by the Liaison Committee for Medical Education. Full voting membership is limited to chairs and acting chairs of those departments.

The APC strives to nurture, enhance and represent academic pathology and laboratory medicine in all their aspects. In the late 1980s, a program directors section (PRODS) evolved to give a stronger voice to pathology residency directors both within and outside the APC membership (to include those pathology residency programs that aren't affiliated with schools of medicine) and to facilitate their interaction on a variety of issues related to resident training. There are 143 APC members and 232 PRODS members. In 2005, a section for medical course directors (UMEDS) was established. APC also has a section for department administrators (PDAS).

The APC is governed by a Council consisting of President, Past-President, President-Elect, Secretary-Treasurer, the Chairs of APC Committees, and a Councilor-at-Large. The APC Council meets several times a year with extended meetings in the winter and the summer. PRODS, UMEDS, and PDAS are each governed by a Council whose chairs are non-voting members of the APC Council.

The Chairs of APC's four standing committees facilitate the functions of APC, and most APC members serve on at least one committee. These committees focus on undergraduate medical education in pathology, graduate medical education in pathology, practice and management, and research.

The APC, PRODS, UMEDS, and PDAS have a national meeting each summer, at which time a variety of plenary sessions, panel discussions and workshops are held. Overall themes of the APC meeting emphasize undergraduate medical education (coordinated with UMEDS); graduate medical education (coordinated with PRODS); and the business aspects of pathology (coordinated with PDAS). The annual business meetings of APC, PRODS, UMEDS, and PDAS also occur during this time.

Each regional section of the APC (Northeast, Southeast, West/Midwest) meets annually as well, hosted by the respective regional APC chair. This permits opportunities to discuss items of local or regional interest and to transmit resolutions to the APC Council.

The activities of APC are conveyed through a regular APC newsletter, which reports items of current interest to academic pathology, including results of APC surveys and studies, workshop reports, committee reports, regulatory and legislative issues, etc. APC, PRODS, UMEDS, and PDAS each operate listservs for their members and sponsor a web page on the internet at http://www.apcprods.org. Of particular note, this website includes a Web Library with links to a number of sites of particular interest to someone interested in pursuing a career in pathology, including the American Board of Pathology, the Accreditation Council for Graduate Medical Education (ACGME), and to the online version of this *Directory*. APC sponsors the Pathology Honor Society, which recognizes medical students who have particular interest and ability in pathology.

For more information about APC contact:
Priscilla Markwood
Director of Scientific Affairs, Communications and Society Services
Association of Pathology Chairs
9650 Rockville Pike
Bethesda, MD 20814
Phone: (301) 634-7880 • **Fax:** (301) 634-7990 • **E-mail:** apc@asip.org
Web site: http://www.apcprods.org

COLLEGE OF AMERICAN PATHOLOGISTS

The College of American Pathologists is the leading organization of board-certified pathologists serving patients, pathologists and the public by fostering and advocating excellence in the practice of pathology and laboratory medicine. It is the world's largest association composed exclusively of pathologists and is widely considered the leader in laboratory quality assurance. The CAP is an advocate for high-quality and cost-effective patient care.

Since the College was founded in 1947, it has had more impact than any other organization on the standardization and improvement of clinical laboratory procedures. The College's *Laboratory Accreditation Program (LAP)* now accredits approximately 6,400 laboratories with deeming authority from CMS, and there are 23,000 subscribers in the *Surveys Program.*

Today, the more than 17,000 pathologists who are members of the College represent a diverse array of laboratory settings and discipline expertise. More than 70 percent of all board-certified pathologists are members of the College; more than 80 percent of all pathology residents are junior members.

Student and Resident Programs

The Residents Forum was formed in 1988 and meets face-to-face twice per year. It affords younger members the opportunity to network among themselves as well as with established pathologists in practice. For current information on the Residents Forum and ways to stay connected to other pathologists-in-training between the meetings, visit CAP for Residents at residents.cap.org.

A resident serves on every council, committee, and commission in the College including the Board of Governors. This opportunity to interact with the world's leading pathologists helps equip young pathologists for their professional careers. Other special services include the Online Career Center, which helps to match pathologists looking for jobs, the Residents Online Community and the receptions at the Annual Meeting, an opportunity to meet and talk with colleagues and pathology's leaders.

Medical students may find information about choosing pathology as a specialty, joining a medical student forum and finding pathology residencies on pathologistsaregroovy.org.

Founded in 1963, the *CAP Foundation* serves the pathology community by committing resources to publications and special conferences. The Foundation also has instituted new technology fellowships for residents to study disciplines that are not available at their own institutions and bring back that technology for their own benefit and that of their departments. The Foundation is also responsible for the *CAP Scholars Program,* which annually gives a $25,000 award to three pathologists who are engaged in research that will enable new technology to be transferred to the general practice of pathology.

Member Services

The College offers interactive education seminars during its annual meeting and in regional gatherings, and electronic, timely and relevant workshops and seminars. Management seminars address financial, organizational, and personnel issues related to the medical laboratory. Consensus conferences bring together CAP members with experts in other fields to study and develop consensus on scientific topics. The results of these may be published in *Archives of Pathology & Laboratory Medicine,* a scientific, peer-reviewed journal.

College publications such as *CAP TODAY®* and electronic newsletters such as *CAP@YourService* and *Statline* help members stay informed about issues that affect the practice of pathology.

Together with staff in Washington, DC, members actively advocate to expand access and improve the quality of health care for all Americans. Pathologists who participate in the *Political Advocacy Network* (PathNet) cultivate personal relationships with elected officials, are updated regularly with information about legislative issues, and host laboratory tours for elected officials designed to highlight the important role pathologists play in their communities while providing context for the College's advocacy efforts. The College's political action committee, *PathPAC,* focuses the efforts of member contributors on assuring that legislators are serving the best interests of the public and pathology.

More than 200 members who are trained as CAP Spokespersons inform their peers, the media, and the public about timely public health issues and events. Each year they are featured in print and broadcast pieces that reach more than 300 million people a year. The college's public affairs area also developed a new patient Web site, MyBiopsy.org, which provides information on nearly 30 of the most common cancers and cancer-related conditions. Pathologists also download these pages and attach them to their pathology reports at the time of diagnosis.

College of American Pathologists
325 Waukegan Road
Northfield, IL 60093
Phone: (847) 832-7000 or (800) 323-4040 • **Fax:** (847) 832-8000
Web site: www.cap.org

UNITED STATES AND CANADIAN ACADEMY OF PATHOLOGY

A distinguished body of educators: Drs William Osler, William Welch, William MacCallum, Maude Abbott and others founded the International Association of Medical Museums in 1906. The name was later changed to the International Academy of Pathology (the IAP) which became the parent organization of the United States and Canadian Academy of Pathology (the Academy). With an uninterrupted focus upon excellence in medical education, the IAP extended its geographic scope worldwide. There are currently 50 semi-autonomous, national divisions of the International Academy of Pathology, of which the US and Canadian Division is the largest, with membership greater than 10,600 pathologists.

It is the mission of the Academy to enrich, expand and disseminate knowledge that is relevant to human and comparative pathology and to do so through the promotion of research, the organization of scientific meetings, and the publication of scientific journals.

Our USCAP website - www.uscap.org - contains a wealth of pathology-based educational materials for your use for free. The Knowledge Hub offers approximately 50,000 pages, 100's thousands of up-to-date references, 10's of thousands of illustrations, tables and graphs. At present there are over 1900 different educational modules and 500 Virtual (Light Microscopic) Slides there for your use.

Also, we have launched the Anatomic Pathology Electronic Case Series (APECS) through the eAcademy. Real world, peer-reviewed cases in a dynamic, virtual technological environment that allows subscribers to learn about current trends and developments in the classification and prognosis of disease, and the appropriate selection and interpretation of ancillary tests in diagnostic evaluations. Best of all, it is accessible anytime, anywhere in the world from any internet connected computer, so CME/SAM credits can be earned on the go as personal schedules allow.

The Academy conducts an annual, week-long meeting, usually in March, that combines scientific presentations and a comprehensive didactic educational program. The focus is largely upon diagnostic anatomic pathology. This meeting, which is held in cities of the United States or Canada, attracts well over 3,300 registrants - not just from North America but from around the world. This is the largest gathering of physician-pathologists in the world. The Academy also conducts an annual update and review course in surgical pathology, entitled *Diagnostic Pathology,* which is scheduled in July-August, a Diagnostic Cytopathology course in January, and a Short Course review (Practical Pathology Seminars) in the late spring.

The Academy publishes two monthly scientific journals*:* *Laboratory Investigation* and *Modern Pathologg,* two of the top four or five general diagnostic and investigative pathology journals in the world by impact factor. The former is an instrument for the dissemination of the most current research observations that have relevance to human disease. *Modern Pathology* is a journal of anatomic pathology; its articles address the utilitarian needs of surgical and autopsy pathologists. Both are published by Nature Pub. Co.

The International Academy of Pathology holds a semi-annual, week-long Congress, hosted by one of its divisions. This congress brings together the scientific and educational programs that are worldwide in scope.

The qualifications for "Regular" membership in the United States and Canadian Academy of Pathology include a degree of Doctor of Medicine, or its international equivalent, and a minimum of four years of training and experience in pathology. "Junior" membership is available to individuals who hold the prerequisite degree in medicine and who are currently in a formal training program in pathology. The annual dues of $200 for "Regular" and $35 for "Junior" membership provide a subscription to one of the Academy's journals, decreased registration fees at the scientific meetings, and membership in the IAP.

For additional information, please contact:
Fred Silva, MD
Secretary-Treasurer & Executive Vice President
United States and Canadian Academy of Pathology
3643 Walton Way Ext
Augusta, GA 30909
Phone: (706) 733-7550 • **Fax:** (706) 733-8033 • **E-mail:** iap@uscap.org
Web site: http://www. uscap.org

THE AMERICAN BOARD OF PATHOLOGY
Certification in Pathology in the United States

Specialty certification for the medical practice of pathology in the United States is the responsibility of The American Board of Pathology. For the benefit of physicians planning to specialize in pathology, the ABP provides the following statement of its aims and requirements.

There are four steps in recognizing a pathologist by certification. The first step is completion of professional education in an approved medical school or college of osteopathic medicine and subsequent licensure in the United States or Canada.

The second step is specialty training in pathology of sufficient duration and quality to establish the required level of competence. The training must take place in a program accredited by the Accreditation Council for Graduate Medical Education (ACGME) or the Royal College of Physicians and Surgeons of Canada (RCPSC), which are responsible for inspecting and evaluating programs for quality and duration of the educational experience.

The third step is verification of the candidate's qualifications by the pathology training program director. The program director has the opportunity to observe the candidate's performance over the course of training and the responsibility to evaluate the candidate's overall educational advancement. Therefore, the pathology training program director is asked to verify to the ABP that the training has been appropriate and successfully completed and that the candidate is ready to take the certifying examinations. The ABP solicits written evaluations of the candidate's performance from the pathology training program director(s) and from other persons acceptable to the ABP for such evaluation. This evaluation is a critical factor considered by the ABP in determining the candidate's qualification for examination and certification.

The fourth and final step is successful completion of the objective written and practical examinations, designed to evaluate the candidate's factual knowledge of pathology and to assess practical problem solving skills, interpretive skills, and diagnostic abilities.

The ABP offers three primary certificates: combined anatomic pathology and clinical pathology, anatomic pathology only, and clinical pathology only. The examinations for each are to establish general competence in pathology. In addition, the ABP offers a number of examinations to assess expertise in subspecialty areas of anatomic pathology and clinical pathology.

Prerequisites for Examination

All candidates must have either (1) graduated from a medical school in the United States or Canada accredited by the Liaison Committee on Medical Education, (2) graduated from a college of osteopathic medicine accredited by the Bureau of Professional Education of the American Osteopathic Association, or (3) graduated from a medical school outside the United States or Canada acceptable to the ABP.

In addition, the candidate must hold a currently valid, full, and unrestricted license to practice medicine or osteopathy issued by one of the licensing agencies of the United States or Canada.

Pathology Training and Credentialing Requirements for Primary Certification
Pathology Training Requirements

A candidate must satisfactorily complete training in a program accredited by the ACGME or the RCPSC. The requirements are as follows:

a. For certification in combined anatomic pathology and clinical pathology (AP/CP) — four years of full-time, approved training in an accredited APCP-4 program that includes at least 18 months of structured training in anatomic pathology and 18 months of structured training in clinical pathology, plus a "flexible year (an additional 12 months of full-time, continued training in anatomic pathology and/or clinical pathology or 12 months full-time, approved training in other areas of pathology as part of the defined 4-year accredited AP/CP training program.

b. For certification in anatomic pathology (AP) only - Three years of full-time, approved training in anatomic pathology in an accredited APCP-4 or AP-3 program that includes at least 24 months of structured training in anatomic pathology, plus a "flexible year" that may be either an additional 12 months of full-time, continued training in anatomic pathology **or** 12 months of full-time, approved training in other areas of pathology as part of the defined accredited training program.

c. For certification in clinical pathology (CP) only - Three years of full-time, approved training in clinical pathology in an accredited APCP-4 program that includes at least 24 months of structured training in clinical pathology, plus a "flexible year" that may be either an additional 12 months of full-time, continued training in clinical pathology or 12 months of full-time, approved training in other areas of pathology as part of the defined accredited training program.

Subspecialty Certification

Candidates holding a primary certificate from the ABP, or in certain specific situations, from another member medical specialty board of the American Board of Medical Specialties, may qualify after one to two years of appropriate training to sit for a subspecialty certification examination in blood banking/transfusion medicine, chemical pathology, cytopathology, dermatopathology, forensic pathology, hematology, medical microbiology, molecular genetic pathology, neuropathology or pediatric pathology.

Maintenance of Certification

All certificates issued by the ABP on or after January 1, 2006 are time-limited and the diplomates holding such certificates are required to participate in the ABP Maintenance of Certification (MOC) program. Each certificate is valid for 10-years provided that the diplomate meets all requirements of MOC during that 10 year period. Successful completion of the 10-year cycle will result in a new certificate which will also be time-limited and subject to the same conditions. Please see the MOC Booklet of Information on the ABP web site for the latest updates.

Mission and Purpose

The mission of The American Board of Pathology (ABP), as a member of the American Board of Medical Specialties, is to promote the health of the public by advancing the practice and science of pathology.

The ABP accomplishes its mission through the following principal activities:

1. Establishing certification standards.
2. Assessing the qualifications of those seeking to practice the specialty of pathology.
3. Conducting voluntary primary and subspecialty certification examinations and awarding certificates to successful candidates.
4. Encouraging the maintenance of certification of those practicing pathology.
5. Participating in the review of pathology training programs and supporting the directors and trainees of these programs.
6. Maintaining communication with pathology and other medical organizations, with its diplomates, and with others as appropriate.
7. Encouraging the study of pathology.
8. Maintaining a registry of its diplomates.

The ABP does **not** seek special privileges for its diplomates, **nor** does it:

1. Confer an academic degree.
2. Confer a legal qualification or license to practice pathology.
3. Define hospital privileges.
4. Define the scope of specialty practice.
5. Delineate who may or may not engage in the practice of pathology.

Further Information

For more detailed and specific information on the requirements for certification, consult either the "Requirements for Certification" published in the Directory of Graduate Medical Education Programs or the Booklet of Information, FAQs, and Instructions for Candidates on the ABP web site (www.abpath.org). Additional questions may be directed to questions@abpath.org or send in writing to:

The American Board of Pathology
PO Box 25915, Tampa, Florida 33622-5915
Phone: (813) 286-2444 • **Fax:** (813) 289-5279
Web site: www.abpath.org

AMERICAN ASSOCIATION OF NEUROPATHOLOGISTS, INC

Neuropathology is a profession built around the principles that guide patient care, education, and research in order to promote human health. Neuropathology subspecialty is intricately connected to the practice of Anatomic Pathology, and is directly affected by the developments in Molecular Pathology and Neurosciences. The American Association of Neuropathologists (the Association) was founded in 1925 to advance the science, practice and teaching of neuropathology and is the principal advocate of the profession in the United States. The American Association of Neuropathologists, Inc. (AANP) began in the early 1930's as a professional and educational organization representing American neuropathologists. It was incorporated in the State of Pennsylvania in May 1960. The AANP's purpose is to advance the science, teaching and training of the diseases of the nervous system and the practice of neuropathology. Currently, AANP has more than 800 members.

Official Journal

Since 1981 the official forum of the AANP has been the Journal of Neuropathology & Experimental Neurology, one of the premier neuroscience journals in the world.

Annual Meeting

An annual meeting is held each year. The meeting includes a one-day Special Course on a topic of interest with invited faculty, two days of scientific sessions (platform and poster) in which members or their guests present original research, an evening Diagnostic Slide Session, and a half-day Presidential Symposium. The annual meeting has been approved by the Accreditation Council for Continuing Medical Education for category 1 CME on an hour-per-hour basis.

Become a Member

We encourage scientists from all disciplines to become members. AANP Membership is divided into **Affiliate** and **Active** categories with annual dues of $140 and $165, respectively. Membership privileges include, among others, a yearly subscription to the **Journal of Neuropathology & Experimental Neurology** and reduced registration fee to the annual meeting.

Organization Office and Administrator
Peggy Harris
Department of Pathology
Case Western Reserve University
2103 Cornell Road, WRB 5101
Cleveland, OH 44106
Phone: (216) 368-8964 • **E-mail:** aanp@case.edu

AMERICAN COLLEGE OF VETERINARY PATHOLOGISTS

The American College of Veterinary Pathologists (ACVP) is an organization of board-certified scientists that has been setting the standard for veterinary pathology since 1949. By promoting excellence in veterinary pathology, ACVP improves and protects human and animal health for the betterment of society.

Our Mission

The mission of the College is to foster excellence in veterinary pathology to protect and improve animal, human, and environmental health to benefit society. The College promotes the advancement and sharing of knowledge, life-long learning and professional competency through its certifying examinations, educational programs, and journal. Integrity and respect for diversity are core values of the College. The College's vision is to be an innovative and integral contributor to global health solutions by understanding disease.

The Organization

ACVP is a 501(c)(3) nonprofit organization governed by an eight-member elected Council. Incorporated in 1949, ACVP is the oldest veterinary specialty organization recognized by the American Veterinary Medical Association. Dedicated to furthering scientific knowledge, ACVP's activities include the peer-reviewed journal *Veterinary Pathology* and a renowned annual scientific meeting. Successful completion of ACVP's rigorous certifying examination ensures scientific prestige and strong employer demand. ACVP is working to ensure the future of veterinary pathology with veterinary student chapter support and scholarship programs. Both members and corporations support ACVP's activities with financial contributions.

The Membership

ACVP's 1,550 members, or diplomates, reside in 17 countries and have all passed the certifying examination in veterinary anatomic and/or clinical pathology. All ACVP members have completed a degree in veterinary medicine and at least three years of post-veterinary school training. Many of them specialize further with doctorates in toxicology, molecular biology or other scientific fields. They work in academia, diagnostic labs, industry or state or federal government agencies, carrying out a diverse range of activities including:

- Diagnosing disease in pet and food-producing animals
- Teaching future scientists and veterinarians
- Ensuring safety in food, pharmaceuticals and biological products
- Conserving wildlife and the environment
- Maintaining vigilance against outbreaks of new and emerging diseases
- Conducting research to understand the mechanisms of disease for the advancement of animal and human health.

Member Services

2009 ACVP ANNUAL MEETING
Date: December 5 - 8, 2009
Location: Monterey Convention Center
Hotel: Monterey Marriott Hotel, Monterey, CA
www.acvp.org

EDUCATIONAL
Certifying Exam Dates
Scheman Building, Iowa State Center
Iowa State University
Ames, Iowa
September 22, 23, 24, 2009

Executive Office Information

The American College of Veterinary Pathologists
2810 Crossroads Drive, Suite 3800 Madison, WI 53718USA
Phone: (608) 443-2466, ext. 149 • **E-mail:** info@acvp.org
Web site: www.acvp.org

ASSOCIATION FOR MOLECULAR PATHOLOGY

The Association for Molecular Pathology (AMP) is an international medical professional association representing approximately 1,600 physicians, doctoral scientists, and medical technologists who perform laboratory testing based on knowledge derived from molecular biology, genetics, and genomics. Since the beginning of our organization we have dedicated ourselves to the development and implementation of molecular diagnostic testing, which includes genetic testing in all its definitions, in a manner consistent with the highest standards established by Clinical Laboratory Improvement Act, the College of American Pathologists, the American College of Medical Genetics, and the United States Food and Drug Administration. Our members lead and work at the majority of clinical molecular diagnostic laboratories in the United States and laboratories in many other countries. We are frequently involved in the development of novel molecular tests, and in the validation of laboratory or commercially developed assays.

The Association realizes its commitment to the advancement of clinical molecular diagnostic and prognostic medicine through its various education and training activities. AMP supports the development of new technologies in molecular biology to be used in laboratory medicine, including diagnosis, treatment, and prognosis of genetic disorders, cancer, infectious diseases, identity and histocompatibility. AMP members and supporters participate in basic and translational research aimed at broadening the understanding of gene/protein structure and function, disease processes, and molecular diagnostics. AMP aims to inform and educate its members of advances in, and applications of nucleic acid-based diagnostics through its annual society meetings, publications (*The Journal of Molecular Diagnostics*, published jointly with the American Society for Investigative Pathology, and the *AMP Newsletter*), website (**www.amp.org**), listserv (CHAMP – Chat at AMP), webinars, and other venues. AMP routinely sponsors a Companion Meeting in conjunction with the USCAP Annual Meeting, a certification review course for trainees in Molecular Genetic Pathology fellowship programs, as well as a molecular pathology course offered jointly with the American Association for Clinical Chemistry.

Member Services

The AMP Annual Meeting is the preeminent forum in laboratory medicine and pathology for the presentation and discussion of molecular diagnostics. Membership benefits include reduced registration rates to the AMP Annual Meeting, free subscription to *The Journal of Molecular Diagnostics* (print and online), access to the society's Membership Directory, CHAMP listserv, Web Library and the *AMP Test Directory*. Through its various Committees, AMP works to represent the interests of its members in legislative and regulatory issues relevant to molecular pathology, as well as to promote the highest standards of clinical practice in the field of molecular diagnostics.

Student and Resident Opportunities

Associate Membership is open to students, postdoctoral fellows, and residents at a reduced rate and carries all the benefits of full membership except for holding elected office and voting in AMP elections. Associate members are eligible for Junior Membership on several AMP committees. Associate member candidates must include communication from their Program Director certifying the applicant's trainee status.

The *AMP Young Investigator Award* recognizes student, postdoctoral fellow, or resident trainees who present outstanding basic or applied research in poster format at the AMP Annual Meeting. The mission of the award is to encourage junior investigators to ask important original questions, to design sound, controlled experiments with a clear rationale, and to present the results clearly in a poster format. Trainees eligible for this award must be either Associate or Regular members of AMP. Each year three winners are selected to receive stipend awards.

Association for Molecular Pathology
9650 Rockville Pike
Bethesda, MD 20814-3993
Phone: (301) 634-7939 • **Fax:** (301) 634-7990
Web site: www.AMP.org

NATIONAL ASSOCIATION OF MEDICAL EXAMINERS

The National Association of Medical Examiners (NAME) is the premier organization of Board–certified forensic pathologists who investigate sudden, violent and suspicious deaths, related to public health and perform autopsies, serving the families of the deceased, the public, police, and the justice system. NAME was founded in 1966 with the dual purposes of fostering the professional growth of physician death investigators and disseminating the professional and technical information vital to the continuing improvement of the medical investigation of violent, suspicious and unusual deaths. Growing from a small nucleus of concerned physicians, NAME has expanded its scope to include physician medical examiners and coroners, medical death investigators and medicolegal system administrators from throughout the United States and other countries.

Activities and Programs

The evolution of excellence in the medicolegal investigation of death in the United States has been slow and arduous. NAME members provide the expertise to medicolegal death investigation that is essential to the effective functioning of the civil and criminal justice systems. In many jurisdictions the medical aspects of death investigation remain relegated to personnel without certification or medical training, or are performed by persons with little or no education in death investigation or forensic pathology. NAME serves as a resource to individuals and jurisdictions seeking to improve medicolegal death investigation by continually working to develop and upgrade national standards for death investigation. The published NAME Standards for a Modern Medicolegal Investigative System provide a model for jurisdictions seeking to improve death investigation. NAME aims to involve competent professional medicolegal death investigators in every jurisdiction in the United States. NAME, as an association and through its members, maintains active cooperative relationships with the College of American Pathologists, American Society of Clinical Pathologists, ACGME, and other professional organizations. NAME representatives participate and serve in an advisory capacity to federal, public and private organizations on numerous projects. As the official specialty association of physician medical examiners, the NAME promotes its vision of competent national death investigation from a seat in the House of Delegates of the American Medical Association.

Inspection and Standards

As part of its mission to improve the quality of death investigation nationally and to recognize excellence in death investigation systems, the NAME offers a voluntary inspection and accreditation program for medicolegal death investigative offices. This program is designed to offer expert evaluation and offer recommendations for improvement of functioning offices. Accreditation by NAME is an honor. For individual forensic pathologists, the NAME Forensic Autopsy Performance Standards set rules for the minimum proper performance of a forensic autopsy.

Education and Residents

The educational functions of NAME are simultaneously directed towards the development and improvement of efficient, cost effective death investigation systems. NAME further encourages members to participate in the training of residents, medical students, law enforcement officers, allied health professionals, paramedical personnel and others who interface with death cases. The educational activities of NAME are carried out at the week long annual meeting each Fall. The meeting's didactic sessions provide instruction on subjects of medicolegal interest while the scientific sessions provide a platform for individual presentation of scientific studies and research in a peer review setting. The Association meets for an interim half-day meeting each February in conjunction with the annual meeting of the American Academy of Forensic Sciences. NAME's Committee for Fellowship Training meets once per year with FP Residency Training Directors to proactively address training and recruitment issues of residents and fellows, aimed at improving our specialty for the future. Forensic Pathology Fellows are given the opportunity to join NAME during their fellowship year without paying dues, and have the annual NAME meeting registration fee waived once within two years of fellowship completion. A special reception is hosted each year by the President of NAME at the annual meeting just for medical students, residents and fellows.

Membership

The NAME is open to all physicians, residents, investigators, and administrators who are active in medicolegal death investigation. The annual dues of $305 include a subscription to the Association's official publication, the American Journal of Forensic Medicine and Pathology, and access to NAME-L, an active Internet Listserv.

For further information, contact:

Denise McNally, Executive Director
430 Pryor Street SW
Atlanta, GA 30312
Phone: (660) 734-1891 or (404) 730-4781

AMERICAN REGISTRY OF PATHOLOGY
Armed Forces Institute of Pathology

The American Registry of Pathology (ARP) is a non-profit corporation reflecting thirty-eight national societies, which sponsor registries within the Armed Forces Institute of Pathology (AFIP).

The Registry was created by Public Law 94-361 in 1976. Its governing body, the Board of Members, is composed of representatives of professional societies.

The ARP engages in cooperative enterprises in medical research and education in collaboration with the AFIP. It functions as a fiscal agent in the management of contracts, research grants and monies derived from tuition fees and consultations. It serves as a focus for the interchange between military and civilian pathology and encourages the participation of medical, dental and veterinary sciences in pathology for the mutual benefit of military and civilian medicine. It publishes the atlas of pathology and other publications.

The ARP provides funds in support of various fellowship programs. Additional information concerning the ARP may be obtained from the Executive Director.

Chair, Board of Directors
Ronald A. DeLellis, MD
Chair, Department of Pathology
Rhode Island Hospital
593 Eddy Street
Providence, RI 02903

Past Chair
Fred Gorstein, MD
Thomas Jefferson University Hospital
Chair, Department of Pathology
125 S. 11th Street, Suite 204
Philadelphia, PA 19107

Vice-Chair
A. Julian Garvin
Dept. of Pathology - Wake Forest Univ.
WFUSM
Bowman Gray Sch. Of Med.
Med. Ctr. Blvd.
Winston Salem, NC 27157-1072

Secretary/Treasurer
Ralph Eagle, Jr. MD
Wills Eye Hospital
900 Walnut Street
Philadelphia, PA 19107

Executive Director
William A. Gardner, MD
American Registry of Pathology
14th Street & Alaska Avenue, NW
Washington, DC 20306-6000

American Registry of Pathology
Armed Forces Institute of Pathology
Washington, D.C. 20306-6000
Phone: (202) 782-2102 • **Fax:** (202) 782-7883
Web site: www.afip.org

INTERSOCIETY PATHOLOGY COUNCIL

www.interpathcouncil.org

The Intersociety Pathology Council (IPC) is an unincorporated organization which serves as a central source of information about pathology in the practice of medicine, in medical research and education and provides a unified voice for the discipline of pathology in North America. The Council, formed in 1968, is presently composed of representatives of 27 pathology organizations. The secretariat for IPC is:

Intersociety Council for Pathology Information
9650 Rockville Pike
Bethesda, MD 20814
(301) 634-7200
www.pathologytraining.org
Executive Officer: Mark E. Sobel, MD, PhD

OFFICERS OF THE INTERSOCIETY PATHOLOGY COUNCIL

Chair
Gene P. Siegal, MD, PhD
University of Alabama Birmingham

Vice Chair
Valerie Murrah, DMD, MS
University of North Carolina

Secretary-Treasurer
Fred H. Rodriguez, Jr., MD
Southeast Louisiana Veterans
Health Care System

CONSTITUENT SOCIETIES

** denotes IPC Representative*

Academy of Clinical Laboratory Physicians and Scientists
www.aclps.org
C. Bruce Alexander, MD *President*
U Alabama at Birmingham Medical Center
619 S 19th St WP P220
Birmingham, AL 35249 7331
Phone: (205) 934-2219
Fax: (205) 934-5499
E-mail: cba@uab.edu

Mitchell G. Scott *President-Elect*
Washington University School of Medicine
Department of Pathology & Immunology
660 S. Euclid Avenue
Saint Louis, MO 63110
Phone: (314) 362-1503
Fax: (314) 362-1461
E-mail: mscott@pathbox.wustl.edu

*Jeffrey A. Kant MD, PhD *IPC Representative*
Univ of Pittsburgh Medical Center
Dept. of Pathology, RM S701
S 701 Scaife Hall
3550 Terrace Street
Pittsburgh, PA 15261
Phone: (412) 648-8519
Fax: (412) 383-9594
E-mail: kantja@upmc.edu

American Academy of Forensic Sciences (Pathology-Biology Section)
www.aafs.org
Thomas L. Bohan, PhD, JD *President*
MTC Forensics
54 Pleasant Avenue
Peaks Island, ME 04108
Phone: (207) 766-5184
Fax: (207) 776-5220
E-mail: tbohan2@maine.rr.com

Joseph P. Bono, MA *President-Elect*
Forensic and Inv. Sciences Program
Indiana University Purdue University Indianapolis
402 N Blackford Street
Indianapolis, IN 46202
Phone: (703) 303-3851
E-mail: josephpbono@hotmail.com

*Lynda M. Biedrzycki, MD *IPC Representative*
Waukesha County Medical Examiner's Office
515 West Moreland Blvd
Waukesha, WI 53188
Phone: (262) 548-7575
Fax: (262) 896-8079
E-mail: lbiedrzycki@waukeshacounty.gov

Anne Warren *Executive Director*
PO Box 669
Colorado Springs, CO 80901-0669
Phone: (719) 636-1100, Ext. 214
Fax: (719) 636-1993
E-mail: awarren@aafs.org

American Academy of Oral and Maxillofacial Pathology
www.aaomp.org
*Valerie A. Murrah, DMD *President and IPC Representative*
University of North Carolina
Oral & Maxillofacial Pathology Lab
2057 Old Dental Bldg, CB 7450
Chapel Hill, NC 27599-7450
Phone: (919) 966-2746
Fax: (919) 966-0705
E-mail: valerie_murrah@dentistry.unc.edu

Susan L. Zunt, DDS, MS *President-Elect*
Indiana University School of Dentistry
Oral Pathology, Medicine & Radiology
1121 W. Michigan Street, Room S110
Indianapolis, IN 46202-5186
Phone: (317) 274-5250
Fax: (317) 278-3018
E-mail: szunt@iupui.edu

Liz Lenard *Staff Liaison*
American Academy of Oral & Maxillofacial Pathology
710 E. Ogden Avenue, Suite 600
Naperville, IL 60563-8614
Phone: (888) 552-2667
Fax: (630) 369-2488
E-mail: LLenard@integrated-solutions.com

American Association of Neuropathologists
www.neuropath.org
George Perry, PhD *President and IPC Representative*
University of Texas at San Antonio
College of Sciences
One UTSA Circle
San Antonio, TX 78249-0661
Phone: (210) 458-4450
Fax: (210) 458-4445
E-mail: george.perry@utsa.edu

David N. Louis, MD *President-Elect*
Massachusetts General Hospital
Department of Pathology
55 Fruit Street, WRN 225
Boston, MA 02114
Phone: (617) 726-2966
Fax: (617) 726-7533
E-mail: louis@helix.mgh.harvard.edu

American College of Veterinary Pathologists
www.acvp.org
Wendy Coe
2810 Crossroads Drive
Suite 3800
Madison, WI 53718
Phone: (608) 443-2466 Ext. 149
Fax: (608) 443-2474
E-mail: wcoe@acvp.org

American Osteopathic College of Pathologists
www.aocp-net.org
Laura Michael, DO *President*
Monroe Adams, DO *President-Elect*
General Offices:
142 East Ontario Street
Chicago, IL 60611-8224
Phone: (312) 202-8197
Fax: (312) 202-8224

American Society for Clinical Pathology
www.ascp.org
Barbara J. McKenna, MD, FASCP *President*
University of Michigan
Dept of Pathology
1500 E Medical Center Dr - Box 0054
Ann Arbor, MI 48109-0054
Phone: (734) 615-7184
Fax: (734) 763-4095
E-mail: barbmcke@med.umich.edu

Mark H. Stoler, MD, FASCP *President-Elect*
University of Virginia Health System
Department of Pathology/Surgical Pathology
P.O. Box 800214
Charlottesville, VA 22908
Phone: (434) 982-0284
Fax: (434) 924-9492
E-mail: mhs2e@virginia.edu

*John R. Ball, MD, JD *IPC Representative*
33 West Monroe Street, Suite 1600
Chicago, IL 60603
Phone: (312) 541-4885
Fax: (312) 541-4767
E-mail:john.ball@ascp.org

American Society for Investigative Pathology
www.asip.org
Linda M. McManus, PhD *President*
Univ of Texas Health Science Center
Dept of Pathology
7703 Floyd Curl Dr, MSC 7750
San Antonio, TX 78229
Phone: (210) 567-4071
Fax: (210) 567-2303
E-mail: mcmanus@uthscsa.edu

Stanley Cohen, MD, *President-Elect*
UMDNJ-New Jersey Medical School
Dept of Pathology & Lab Medicine
185 S Orange Ave – MSB C579
Newark, NJ 07103-2714
Phone: (973) 972-4520
Fax: (973) 972-5909
E-mail: cohenst@umdnj.edu

*Mark E. Sobel, MD, PhD *Executive Officer and IPC Representative*
American Society for Investigative Pathology
9650 Rockville Pike
Bethesda, MD 20814-3993
Phone: (301) 634-7130
Fax: (301) 634-7990
E-mail: mesobel@asip.org

American Society of Cytopathology
www.cytopathology.org
Ann T. Moriarty, MD *President and IPC Representative*
AmeriPath Indiana
2560 Shadeland Avenue, Suite A
Indianapolis, IN 46219
Phone: (317) 275-8000
E-mail: amoriarty@ameripath.com

Hormoz Ehyam MD *President Elect*
Fox Chase Cancer Center
333 Cottman Avenue
Philadelphia, PA 11911
Phone: (215) 725-3675
E-mail: h_ehya@fccc.edu

Edmund S. Cibas, MD *Secretary-Treasurer*
Brigham & Women's Hospital
75 Frances Street
Boston, MA 02115
Phone: (617) 732-6797
Fax: (617) 739-6192
E-mail: ecibas@partners.org

Arthur Purdy Stout Society of Surgical Pathologists
www.apssociety.org
*Maria J. Merino, MD *President and IPC Representative*
NIH/NCI Lab of Pathology
Bldg 10 Room 2N212
Bethesda, MD 20892
Phone: (301) 496-2441
Fax: (301) 480-9488
E-mail: mjmerino@box-m.nih.gov

John Goldblum, MD *President-Elect*
Cleveland Clinic Foundation
9500 Euclid Ave
Cleveland, OH 44195
Phone: (216) 444-8238
Fax: (216) 445-6967
E-mail: goldblj@ccf.org

Michael L. Cibull, MD *Secretary*
University of Kentucky Med Center
Dept of Pathology
800 Rose Street
Lexington, KY 40536-0001
Phone: (859) 323-5425 Ext. 229
Fax: (859) 323-2094
E-mail: mcibull@uky.edu

Association of Directors of Anatomic and Surgical Pathology
www.adasp.org
Mark R. Wick, MD *President and IPC Representative*
Univ of Virginia Health Science Center
Box 800214, Dept of Pathology
Charlottesville, VA 22908
Phone: (434) 924-9038
Fax: (434) 924-9617
E-mail: mrw9c@virginia.edu

M. Timothy Smith, MD *Secretary/Treasurer*
Medical University of South Carolina
Anatomic Pathology
165 Ashley Avenue, Suite 309
Charleston, SC 29425
Phone: (843) 792-1092
Fax: (843) 792-8974
E-mail: smithti@musc.edu

Association for Molecular Pathology
www.amp.org
Jan Nowak, MD, PhD *President*
Northshore University Health System
Department of Pathology and Laboratory Medicine
2650 Ridge Avenue
Evanston, IL 60201-1783
Phone: (847) 570-2730
Fax: (847) 570-1938
E-mail: jnowak51@comcast.net

Karen Mann, MD, PhD *President-Elect*
Emory University
Department of Pathology and Laboratory Medicine
1364 Clifton Road, F143C
Atlanta, GA 30322
Phone: (404) 712-1264
Fax: (404) 712-0819
E-mail: kmann@emory.edu

Mark E. Sobel, MD, PhD *Executive Officer*
Association for Molecular Pathology
9650 Rockville Pike
Bethesda, MD 20814-3993
Phone: (301) 634-7130
Fax: (301) 634-7990
E-mail: mesobel@asip.org

*Mary S. Williams, MT(ASCP)SM *IPC Representative*
Association for Molecular Pathology
9650 Rockville Pike
Bethesda, MD 20814-3993
Phone: (301) 634-7921
Fax: (301) 634-7990
E-mail: mwilliams@amp.org

Association for Pathology Informatics
www.pathologyinformatics.org
Myra L. Wilkerson, MD *President and IPC Representative*
Geisinger Health System
100 North Academy Avenue, MC 01-31
Danville, PA 17822
Phone: (570) 820-6049
E-mail: mwilkerson@geisinger.edu

Association of Clinical Scientists
www.clinicalscience.org
Vincent A. DeBari, PhD *President*
School of Graduate Medical Education
Seton Hall University
400 South Orange Avenue
South Orange, NJ 07079
Phone: (973) 877-2813
Fax: (973) 877-5767
E-mail: debarivi@shu.edu

*Dani S. Zander, MD, *IPC Representative*
Penn State Milton Hershey Medical Center
Dept of Pathology & Lab Medicine
MC H083, PO Box 850
500 University Drive
Hershey, PA 17033-0850
Phone: (717) 531-8351
Fax: (717) 531-5021
E-mail: dzander@hmc.psu.edu

Association of Pathology Chairs
www.apcprods.org
J. Charles Jennette, MD *President and IPC Representative*
University of North Carolina - Chapel Hill
Department of Pathology & Laboratory Medicine
Manning Drive, CB # 7525
Chapel Hill, NC 27599-7525
Phone: (215) 662-6880
Fax: (215) 662-4063
E-mail: jcj@med.unc.edu

Tristram G. Parslow, MD, PhD *Secretary/Treasurer* Emory University Hospital
Dept of Pathology & Lab Medicine
1364 Clifton Road NE Rm H-182
Atlanta, GA 30322
Phone: (404) 727-8657
Fax: (404) 727-3133
E-mail: tparslo@emory.edu

*Mark E. Sobel, MD, PhD *Managing Officer and IPC Representative*
Association of Pathology Chairs
9650 Rockville Pike
Bethesda, MD 20814-3993
Phone: (301) 634-7130
Fax: (301) 634-7990
E-mail: mesobel@asip.org

Canadian Association of Pathologists
www.cap.medical.org
Jagdish Butany, MD *President and IPC Representative*
Canadian Association of Pathologists
774 Echo Drive
Ottawa, Ontario
Canada, K1S 5N8
Phone: (613) 730-6230
Fax: (613) 730-1116
E-mail: jagdish.butany@uhn.on.ca

Bruce Burns, MD, FRCPC *Secretary/Treasurer*
The Ottawa Hospital, Civic Campus
Department of Pathology and Laboratory Medicine
501 Smyth
Ottawa, Ontario
Canada, K1H 8L6
Phone: (613) 737-8899 Ext. 79041
Fax: (613) 737-8461
E-mail: bfburns@ottawahospital.on.ca

College of American Pathologists
www.cap.org
Jared N. Schwartz, MD, PhD *President*
Stephen N. Bauer, MD *President-Elect*
Gene N. Herbek, MD, FCAP *Secretary/Treasurer*

General Offices
College of American Pathologists
325 Waukegan Road
Northfield, IL 60093
Phone: (847) 832-7000
Fax: (847) 832-8500
E-mail: president@cap.org

National Association of Medical Examiners
www.thename.org
John D. Howard, MD *President*
Pierce County Medical Examiner's Office
3619 Pacific Avenue
Tacoma, WA 38418
Phone: (253) 798-6494
Fax: (253) 798-2893
E-mail: johnhoward@pol.net

Lakshmanan Sathyavagiswaran, MD *Vice President*
Los Angeles County Department of the Coroner
1104 N. Mission Road
Los Angeles, CA 90033
Phone: (323) 343-0512

*Lynda Biedrzycki, MD *IPC Representative*
Waukesha County Medical Examiner's Office
515 W. Moreland Boulevard
Waukesha, WI 53188
Phone: (262) 548-7575
Fax: (262) 896-8079
E-mail: lbiedrzycki@waukeshacounty.gov

Denise McNally *Executive Director*
National Association of Medical Examiners
430 Pryor Street SW
Atlanta, GA 30312
Phone: (404) 730-4781
Fax: (404) 730-4420
E-mail: denise.mcnally@thename.org

Papanicolaou Society of Cytopathology
www.papsociety.org
Martha B. Pitman, MD *President and IPC Representative*
Massachusetts General Hospital
55 Fruit Street
Boston, MA 02114
E-mail: mpitman@partners.org

Lester Layfield, MD *President-Elect*
University of Utah
Dept of Pathology
1950 Circle of Hope
Salt Lake City, UT 84112
Phone: (801) 581-2507
Fax: (801) 581-7035
E-mail: lesterlayfield@comcast.net

Pulmonary Pathology Society
www.pulmonarypath.org
*Don Guinee, MD *President and IPC Representative*
Virginia Mason Medical Center
Department of Pathology
1100 Ninth Avenue, C6-PTH
Seattle, WA 98111
Phone: (206) 223-6861
Fax: (206) 341-0525
E-mail: Donald.guinee@vmmc.org

Elisabeth Brambilla, MD *Vice-President*
CHU Grenoble
Centre Hospital Univ-Albert Michallon
Grenoble, Cedex 09, France
Phone: (33) 04-7676-5486
Fax: (33) 04-7676-5949
E-mail: ebrambilla@chu-grenoble.fr

Mark E. Sobel, MD, PhD *Executive Officer*
9650 Rockville Pike
Bethesda, MD 20814-3993
Phone: (301) 634-7130
Fax: (301) 634-7990
E-mail: mesobel@asip.org

Society for Pediatric Pathology
www.spponline.org
David Parham, MD *President*
University of Arkansas for Medical Sciences
Department of Pathology
4301 West Markham, #517
Little Rock AR 72205
Phone:(501) 686-5170
E-mail: parhamdavidm@uams.edu

Jeffrey Goldstein, MD *President-Elect*
Baptist Health of Northeast Florida
Pathology Department
800 Prudential Drive
Jacksonville, FL 32207
Phone: (904) 202-1882
Fax: (904) 202-3232

Theodore (Ted) Pysher, MD *IPC Representative*
Primary Children's Medical Center
Department of Pediatric Pathology
100 North Mario Capecchi Drive
Salt Lake City, UT 84112
Phone: (801) 662-2154
E-mail: theodore.pysher@imail.org

General Offices
Society for Pediatric Pathology
c/o USCAP
3643 Walton Way Extension
Augusta, GA 30909
Phone: (706) 364-3375
Fax: (706) 733-8033
E-mail: spp@uscap.org

United States and Canadian Academy of Pathology
www.uscap.org
*Victor E. Reuter, MD *President and IPC Representative*
Richard J. Zarbo, MD *President-Elect*
Fred Silva, MD, *Secretary/Treasurer*

General Offices
United States and Canadian
Academy of Pathology, Inc.
3643 Walton Way
Augusta, GA 30909
Phone: (706) 733-7550
Fax: (706) 733-8033
E-mail: fsilva@uscap.org

EX OFFICIO MEMBERS

American Board of Oral and Maxillofacial Pathology
www.abomp.org
Paul Freedman, DDS *President*
Oral Pathology Laboratory, Inc.
56-31 141st Street
Flushing, NY 11355
Phone: (718) 670-1520
Fax: (718) 445-4147
E-mail: pdf2001@nyp.org

*Craig B. Fowler, DDS Secretary-Treasurer and IPC Representative
Wilford Hall Medical Center
Department of Oral & Maxillofacial Pathology
59th DTS/SGDRM
2200 Bergquist Drive, Suite 1
Lackland AFB, TX 78236-5300
Phone: (210) 292-5505
Fax: (210) 292-2269
E-mail: craig.fowler@lackland.af.mil

Clarita Scioscia *Executive Officer*
PO Box 25915
Tampa, FL 33622-5915
Phone: (813) 286-2444 Ext. 230
Fax: (813) 289-5279
E-mail: clarita@abpath.org

American Board of Pathology
www.abpath.org
Rebecca Johnson, MD *President*
Berkshire Health Systems
725 North Street
Pittsfield, MA 01201
Phone: (413) 447-2565
Fax: (413) 447-2097
E-mail: rjohnson@bhs1.org

John V. Collin, MD *Vice-President*
El Camino Hospital
2500 Grant Road
Mountain View, CA 94040
Phone: (650) 964-4732
Fax: (650) 964-9388
E-mail: john_collin@elcaminohospital.org

*Betsy D. Bennett, MD, PhD *Executive Vice President and IPC Representative*
4830 W. Kennedy Boulevard, Suite 690
Tampa, FL 33609
Phone: (813) 826-2444
Fax: (813) 289-5279
E-mail: bdbennett@abpath.org

American Registry of Pathology
www.afip.org
A. Julian Garvin, MD, PhD *Chair*
Wake Forest University School of Medicine
Department of Pathology
Medical Center Blvd.
Winston-Salem, NC 27157-1072
Phone: (336) 716-2650
Fax: (336) 716-5437
E-mail: ajgarvin@wfubmc.edu

Ronald DeLellis, MD *Vice-Chair*
Lifespan AMC
Rhode Island Hospital
Department of Pathology
593 Eddy Street
Providence, RI 02903
Phone: (401) 444-5154
Fax: (401) 444-9038
E-mail: rdelellis@lifespan.org

*William Gardner, Jr, MD *Executive Director and IPC Representative*
American Registry of Pathology
Office of the Director
P.O. Box 8188
Washington, DC 20907
Phone: (202) 782-2102
Fax: (202) 782-7883
E-mail: gardnerw@afip.osd.mil

Armed Forces Institute of Pathology
www.afip.org
*Florabel Garcia Mullick, MD *Director and IPC Representative*
Col. Charles W. Pemble III *Deputy Director*
Armed Forces Institute of Pathology
6825 16th Street, NW

Department of Veterans Affairs Pathology and Laboratory Medicine Service
*Fred H. Rodriguez, Jr., MD *National Director and IPC Representative*
Southeast Louisiana Veterans Health Care System
Pathology and Lab Medicine (629/113)
1555 Poydras St, Suite 1300
New Orleans, LA 70112
Phone: (504) 565-4972
Fax: (504) 565-4951
E-mail: fred.rodriguez@va.gov

Intersociety Council for Pathology Information
www.pathologytraining.org
David S. Wilkinson, MD, PhD *Chair*
Virginia Commonwealth University
Dept of Pathology
1101 E Marshall St. Sanger - Room 4-011
Box 980662
Richmond, VA 23298-0662
Phone: (804) 828-0183
Fax: (804) 828-2869
E-mail: dswilkin@vcu.edu

Margaret Grimes, MD *Secretary-Treasurer*
Virginia Commonwealth University
Dept of Pathology
1200 E. Marshall Street, Gateway 6-210
P.O. Box 980662
Richmond, VA 23298-0662
Phone: (804) 828-9004
Fax: (804) 828-5055
E-mail: mmgrimes@vcu.edu

*Mark E. Sobel, MD, PhD *Executive Officer and IPC Representative*
9650 Rockville Pike
Bethesda, MD 20814
Phone: (301) 634-7130
Fax: (301) 634-7990
E-mail: mesobel@asip.org

The Intersociety Council for Pathology Information, Inc.

AMERICAN SOCIETY FOR CLINICAL PATHOLOGY • AMERICAN SOCIETY FOR INVESTIGATIVE PATHOLOGY
ASSOCIATION OF PATHOLOGY CHAIRS • COLLEGE OF AMERICAN PATHOLOGISTS
UNITED STATES AND CANADIAN ACADEMY OF PATHOLOGY

9650 Rockville Pike
Bethesda, Maryland 20814-3993

E-mail: icpi@asip.org
Web site: http://www.pathologytraining.org

Phone: (301) 634-7200
Fax: (301) 634-7990

Calendar of Events

AMERICAN SOCIETY FOR CLINICAL PATHOLOGY
2009 ASCP Annual Meeting
Sheraton Chicago Hotel
Chicago, IL
October 29-November 1

2010 ASCP Annual Meeting
San Francisco Marriott
San Francisco, CA
October 27-31

AMERICAN SOCIETY FOR INVESTIGATIVE PATHOLOGY
2009 Summer Academy: Molecular Pathobiology of Solid Tumors:
Transcripts, Tyrosine Kinases, and Therapeutics
Hilton Arlington
Arlington, VA
June 6-8

ASIP Annual Meeting at Experimental Biology 2010
The Anaheim Convention Center
Anaheim, California
April 24-April 28

ASIP Annual Meeting at Experimental Biology 2011
Washington DC Convention Center
Washington, DC
April 9-13

ASIP Annual Meeting at Experimental Biology 2012
San Diego Convention Center
San Diego, CA
April 21-25

ASSOCIATION OF PATHOLOGY CHAIRS
2009 APC Annual Meeting
Fairmont Olympic Hotel
Seattle, WA
July 15-17

COLLEGE OF AMERICAN PATHOLOGISTS
"The Pathologists' Meetings"
2009 CAP Annual Meeting
Gaylord National Resort
Washington, DC
October 11-14

2010 CAP Annual Meeting
Hyatt Regency Chicago
Chicago, Illinois
September 26-29

UNITED STATES AND CANADA ACADEMY OF PATHOLOGY
2010 USCAP Annual Meeting
Marriott Wardman Park
Washington, DC
March 22-28

2011 USCAP Annual Meeting
Riverfront & Riverwalk Hotels
San Antonio, TX
February 26-March 4

ASSOCIATION FOR MOLECULAR PATHOLOGY
2009 AMP Annual Meeting
Gaylord Palms Resort
Kissimmee, FL
November 19-22

2010 AMP Annual Meeting
San Jose McEnery Convention Center
San Jose, CA
November 17-20

AMERICAN ASSOCIATION OF NEUROPATHOLOGISTS
2009 AANP Annual Meeting
Texas Riverwalk Hotel
San Antonio, Texas
June 11-14

2010 AANP Annual Meeting
Lowes Philadelphia Hotel
Philadelphia, Pennsylvania
June 10-12

AMERICAN COLLEGE OF VETERINARY PATHOLOGISTS
2009 ACVP Annual Meeting
Monterey Marriott Hotel
Monterey, CA
December 5-8

2010 ACVP Annual Meeting
Marriott Baltimore Waterfront Hotel
Baltimore, MD
October 30-Novemebr 3

NATIONAL ASSOCIATION OF MEDICAL EXAMINERS
2009 NAME Annual Meeting
Hyatt Regency San Francisco
San Francisco, CA
September 11-16

42nd Edition

United States Residency Training Programs 2010–2011

All postgraduate specialty programs will be found in the section headed "Training in Specialized Areas of Pathology."

For information on certification in the United States see page 35.

The Intersociety Council for Pathology Information, Inc.

BAPTIST HEALTH SYSTEM

Birmingham, Alabama

PROGRAMS OFFERED

At Baptist Health System, emphasis is placed upon generalized training in all areas of anatomic and clinical pathology. The educational program includes 30 months of training in anatomic pathology and 18 months of training in clinical pathology.

REQUIREMENTS

Residents are required to complete one research activity per year.

TYPES AND NUMBERS OF APPOINTMENTS

Eight fully accredited positions in the four-year anatomic and clinical pathology residency program are available.

FACILITIES

Baptist Health System encompass 1,033 beds in two major hospitals, including a very large referral service. The laboratories examined approximately 18,000 surgical specimens and performed approximately 2.5 million clinical laboratory procedures in 2008. All major clinical subspecialties are represented on the medical staff, including neurosurgery and thoracic surgery. The staff includes more than 700 members. Clinical diagnostic equipment includes the full range of automated instrumentation. Education in every major area of clinical and anatomic pathology is provided. Numerous intra- and interdepartmental conferences form a major part of the educational program.

COMMUNITY

Metropolitan Birmingham has a population of approximately 1,000,000. Patient referrals are received not only from the area but from adjoining states as well. The city lies in the southern end of the Appalachian chain and is relatively near the Florida coast as well as the higher mountains to the north. The economy is mixed industrial, agricultural, and service oriented. The city administration is progressive and farsighted and economic conditions are well above the regional average. The climate is temperate with mild winters. Six universities and the University of Alabama Medical Center are located in the area. The medical school library as well as the hospital libraries are fully accessible to Baptist Health System resident physicians. Cultural opportunities include an art museum, numerous theaters as well as parks, city zoo and botanical gardens.

STIPENDS AND MAINTENANCE

Stipends vary depending on postgraduate year. Additionally, $250 maintenance allowance, malpractice and life insurance are provided. 75% of group health insurance premiums are paid by the hospital.

STAFF

Kim M. Parker MD (Univ Alabama 1990); **Gloria Hutchinson** MD (Univ Alabama 1983); **Mary Louise Guerry-Force** MD (Univ South Carolina 1980); **Alfred R. Rector** MD (Univ Alabama 1990); **Matthew Sheffield** MD (Med Col Georgia 1992); **Paul J. Biggs** MD (Indiana Univ 1977); **D. Scott Day** MD (Univ Louisville 1992); **Henning Proelss** PhD (Technical Univ Munich 1967).

APPLICATIONS

Applications are accepted through the Electronic Residency Application Service (ERAS) and should be received in our department prior to December 31 for the upcoming academic year. Satisfactory references are required. July 1 is the normal beginning date for residencies, but other times are open to consideration.

Address inquiries to:

Gloria K. Hutchinson, MD
Associate Director of Graduate Education in Pathology
Baptist Health System
800 Montclair Road
Birmingham, AL 35213
Phone: (205) 592-5052

Baptist Health System, Birmingham, Alabama

UNIVERSITY OF ALABAMA MEDICAL CENTER

Birmingham, Alabama

PROGRAMS OFFERED

The Department of Pathology at the University of Alabama Medical Center offers approved, flexible, individually tailored training programs in straight or combined anatomic and clinical pathology toward Board qualification in each area. Training in all areas focuses on the understanding of disease at the macroscopic, microscopic and molecular levels. Additional training opportunities include specialty fellowships, clinical research fellowships or other approved training to meet the needs of the individual. The educational experience of training is coordinated through the department's divisions of Anatomic Pathology, Laboratory Medicine, Neuropathology, Forensic Pathology, Pediatric Pathology and Molecular and Cellular Pathology. In-depth experience with each rotation is provided. In anatomic pathology, this experience is provided primarily in autopsy, surgical pathology and cytopathology. A resident has the opportunity to develop competence in specific systems in anatomic pathology (gastrointestinal, hepatobiliary, pulmonary, renal, cardiac, neurological, ob-gyn and orthopaedic) as well as special competence or added qualification in cytopathology, forensic pathology, hematopathology, dermatopathology, molecular genetics and neuropathology. The opportunity for training in laboratory medicine focuses on the acquisition of a knowledge base and experience to prepare for an active consultative role in laboratory medicine. An initial year in-depth core experience in immunohematology, clinical chemistry, microbiology, clinical immunology, endocrinology, clinical hematology and coagulation/hemostasis is provided. These rotations are integrated with an active on-call system and conferences with a variety of clinical subspecialties. Training in laboratory medicine after the initial year is tailored to the individual's career goals with emphasis on understanding disease at the molecular level and subspecialization. Appointments for one to three years of research in experimental pathology are available to all house officers and a combined residency/PhD is available for exceptional individuals. On-call duties and conference participation are an integral component of all phases of training and are in compliance with the 80 hour/week work limit.

TYPES AND NUMBERS OF APPOINTMENTS

There are 32 residency positions available. In addition, accredited training fellowships are offered in transfusion medicine, dermatopathology, neuropathology, cytopathology, hematopathology, molecular genetics and forensic medicine. One-year fellowship positions in surgical pathology and organ-specific pathology (e.g. renal pathology, bone and soft tissue pathology and gastrointentinal pathology) as well as transplantation pathology are available for persons who have completed a majority of their residency program in anatomic pathology.

FACILITIES

The University of Alabama Medical Center is located on the campus of the University of Alabama at Birmingham. It has recently been cited in US News and World Report as the best of the "up and coming" medical schools. It ranks 18th in the nation in overall NIH support of medical schools. The Medical Center complex includes approximately six city blocks. The patient care facilities within this area include Children's Hospital, Civitan Research Center, Cooper Green Hospital, Engel Psychiatric Day Treatment Center, Eye Foundation Hospital, Quarterback Tower, Russell Ambulatory Center, Smolian Psychiatric Clinic, Spain Rehabilitation Center, UAB Hospital-Center for Psychiatric Medicine, University Hospital, Veterans Affairs Medical Center and Wallace Tumor Institute. The Kirklin Clinic, a 150,000 square-foot outpatient care facility, was opened in June 1992. The pathology residents share the above facilities with over 800 other residents and fellows from accredited programs at UAB. Resources available to residents and fellows include Centers of Research in arthritis, bone, cancer, cardiovascular diseases, AIDS, macromolecular crystallography, oral biology, cystic fibrosis, diabetes, neuroscience and neurobiology as well as over 46,000- square-feet of research space within the department. In addition, faculty members from the Departments of Pathology, Medicine, Biochemistry, Microbiology, Cell Biology and Anatomy, Pharmacology, Physiology and Biophysics are available as potential mentors. Research is usually pursued after the first or second postgraduate year when the resident is in a straight anatomic or straight clinical program or later in the fourth and fifth year for combined residents in anatomic and clinical pathology. In the combined program, the research time may be for 6 months. Emphasis is also given to teaching and productive service work. Resources for this experience come in anatomic pathology from the autopsy service (388 accessions in 2008), forensic autopsies (491 accessions in 2008), surgical pathology (40,692 accessions in 2008), and cytopathology (22,157 accessions in 2008). The division of laboratory medicine draws from a data base of greater than one million patients (7.2 million tests at UAH in 2008 and combined 3.0 million tests at VA and Children's Hospital in 2008). Residents and fellows participate in over 250 conferences with other clinical and basic science departments at UAB. Teaching experience also includes participation in General Pathology and Correlative Pathology system courses.

COMMUNITY

Birmingham is a conveniently located Southeastern city of approximately one million individuals in the metropolitan area. Cultural and recreational facilities include the Birmingham Museum of Art, the Civil Rights Institute/Museum, the McWane Center, Discovery Place, a professional symphony, several performing theater groups, a ballet company and school, zoo and botanical gardens. It has recently been cited by Newsweek magazine as one of "America's Hottest Cities" and the US Conference of Mayors also voted Birmingham as "America's Most Livable City" based on its support of the arts and recreation.

STIPENDS AND MAINTENANCE

Salaries (2008-09) for postgraduates begin at approximately $43,010 in the first year with 15 days annual vacation. Hospital coats are furnished. Professional liability insurance and family leave benefits are provided.

STAFF

Professors

Kevin A. Roth MD, PhD (Stanford 1985) Chair, regulation of neuronal apoptosis; **C. Bruce Alexander** MD (Univ Virginia 1971) Vice Chairman; pulmonary, forensic and autopsy pathology; **Gene P. Siegal** MD, PhD (Univ Louisville 1974, Univ Minnesota 1979) Exec. Vice Chair and Director, Division Anatomic Pathology, experimental and surgical pathology; **Peter G. Anderson** DVM, PhD (Washington State Univ 1981, UAB 1986) cardiovascular pathology; **William H. Benjamin, Jr.** PhD (Univ Alabama at Birmingham 1985) clinical microbiology, *M. tuberculosis* epidemiology, diagnostic parasitology, diagnostic molecular biology; **Robert Brissie** MD (Univ South Carolina 1979) forensic pathology; **Ralph P. Bucy** MD, PhD (Univ Washington 1981) immunopathology, flow cytometry; **Xu Cao** PhD (Univ South Carolina 1991) transcriptional mechanisms in TGFâ signaling and their functions; **John T. Carpenter, Jr.** MD (Tulane Univ 1968) hematology; **Steven L. Carroll** MD, PhD (Baylor Col Med, 1988, 1986) neuropathology/ regeneration of injured nervous system; **Thomas L. Clemens** PhD, (Pennsylvania State Univ 1975, Univ. of London, England 1980) bone metabolism; **Michael G. Conner** MD (Univ Alabama Sch Med 1976) anatomic and gynecologic pathology; **William J. Cook** MD, PhD (Univ Alabama 1974, 1976) renal pathology; **David T. Curiel** MD (Emory Univ 1982) gene therapy; **Victor M. Darley-Usmar** PhD (Univ Essex, England 1980) molecular and cellular pathology, nitric oxide and control of cell function; **Isam-Eldin Eltoum** MD (Univ Khartoum, Sudan 1983) genitourinary pathology, cytopathology; **Ona Marie Faye-Peterson** MD (Univ Colorado Med Sch 1980) perinatal-pediatric pathology; **William E. Grizzle** MD, PhD (Johns Hopkins Univ 1977) surgical pathology, neuroendocrinology; **Shu T. Huang** MD (Univ Taiwan 1966) transfusion medicine; **Nirag Jhala** MD (BJ Med Col, India 1989) pathology, cytopathology, gastrointestinal and hepatobiliary tract pathology; **David R. Kelly** MD (Clinical) (Univ Tennessee 1974) Chief of Pathology, Children's Hospital; surgical pathology, pediatric pathology; **Hiromi Kubagawa** MD (Jutendo Univ, Tokyo 1971) immunology; **Robinna G. Lorenz** MD, PhD (Washington Univ 1990) cellular components of mucosal immune system and their interactions with gastrointestinal epithelium and luminal contents; **Marisa Marques** MD (Federal Univ Rio Grand Sul, Brazil 1983) hematopathology and transfusion medicine; **Jay M. McDonald** MD (Wayne State Univ 1969) Professor; pathogenesis of AIDS, bone biology, osteoporosis, apoptosis and cancer; **Joseph L. Messina** PhD (Univ Michigan 1982) molecular and cellular pathology, metabolic disease; **Stephen A. Moser** PhD (Ohio State Univ 1976) clinical microbiology/informatics; **Joanne E. Murphy-Ulrich** PhD (Univ Wisconsin 1983) extracellular matrix, cell adhesion, thrombospondin and control of cell function; **Moon H. Nahm** MD (Washington Univ 1974) vaccine biology; **Shin S. Oh** MD (Seoul National Univ 1960) neuropathology; **Cheryl A. Palmer** MD (Univ West Virginia 1986) neuropathology and neurology; **Selvarangan Ponnazhagan** PhD (Univ Madras, India 1989) adeno-associated virus-mediated gene therapy; **Vishnu V. B. Reddy** hematopathology, bone marrow; **Ralph D. Sanderson** Ph.D. (UAB 1986) cancer biology; **Johnny W. Scott** MD, PhD (Univ Alabama, 1970) toxicology, special chemistry; **Jere P. Segrest** MD, PhD (Vanderbilt Univ 1967) atherosclerosis; **John A Smith** MD, PhD, MMM, (Univ. Missouri 1974, Univ Melbourne, Australia 1978, Tulane Univ 1998) bioinformatics, clinical pathology; **Ken B. Waites** MD (Univ Alabama 1981) microbiology; **Casey T. Weaver** MD (Univ Florida 1984) transplantation and renal pathology, immune response and marker-assisted genetics; **Danny R. Welch** PhD (Univ Texas 1984) Leonard H. Robinson Endowed Professor, Molecular Basis of Tumor Progression and Metastasis.

Professor Emeritus

Sanford P. Bishop DVM, PhD (Cornell Univ 1960, Ohio State Univ 1968) experimental cardiovascular pathology.

Adjunct Professor

Cloyd A. Robinson, Jr. PhD (Univ Alabama 1971) biochemistry, forensic toxicology.

Associate Professors

Scott W. Ballinger PhD (Emory 1993) atherosclerosis and free radical mediated events; **Walter C. Bell** MD (Univ Mississippi Sch Med, 1994) surgical pathology; **Gregory G. Davis** MD (Vanderbilt Univ 1987) forensic pathology; **Mark H. Deierhoi** MD (Northwestern Univ 1976) histocompatibility; **Xu Feng** PhD (Univ Vermont 1994) cellular and molecular mechanisms of osteoclast differentiation and function; **Andra R. Frost** MD (Univ Alabama Sch Med, 1985) anatomic pathology/translational research in neoplasia; **Robert I. Garver, Jr.** MD (Johns Hopkins Univ 1981), molecular and cellular pathology; **Robert W. Hardy** PhD (Univ Toronto, 1988) clinical chemistry, insulin resistance and cancer cell proliferation; **Darshana Jhala** MBBS,MD (BJ Med Col, India 1988) lymphomas, breast pathology, pancreatic pathology, endoscopic ultrasound guided fine needle aspiration; **Dennis F. Kucik** MD, PhD (Washington Univ, 1991) transfusion medicine, biophysics of cell motility; **Upender Manne** PhD (Osmania Univ, India 1987) identification of molecular markers of Colorectal Adenocarcinoma to utilize in clinical applications; **Elizabeth C. Mroczek-Musulman** MD (Clinical) (Bialystok Univ, Poland 1972) pediatric cardiovascular disease; **Mitchell A. Olman** MD (NYU 1983) pulmonary medicine; **Rakesh Patel** PhD (Univ Essex, 1996) molecular and cellular biology; **Richard E. Powers** MD (Univ Kentucky Col Med 1976) neuropathology, geriatric psychiatry; **Nasser Said-Al-Narief** DDS (Marquette Univ Sch Dent 1989) oral pathology; **Ken R. Tilashalski** DMD (Southern Illinois Univ, 1991) oral pathology; **Thomas S. Winokur** MD (Washington Univ Sch Med 1979) surgical pathology of heart and soft tissue tumors.

Assistant Professors

Amy L. Adams MD (UAB 1993) surgical pathology, hematopathology; **Aleodor A. Andea** MD, (Victor Babes University 1995) dermatopathology; **Yabing Chen** PhD (Xiamen Univ 1996) mechanisms of apoptosis; **Patricia DeVilliers** DDS oral pathology; **Joanne T. Douglas** PhD (Univ Southampton 1995) gene therapy; **Maaike Everts** PhD (Groningen University Institute 2002) vascular; **Omar Hameed** MD (Baghdad Univ 1991) surgical pathology; **Robin D. Hatton** PhD (Univ Alabama at Birmingham 1996) immunology; **Zdenek Hel** PhD (McGill Univ, Quebec, 1997) mucosal immunity to SIV; **Piotr Kulesza** MD, PhD (Washington Univ. 1999) cytology; **Aimee Landar** PhD (Univ South Alabama 1998); **Silvio H. Litovsky** MD (Univ Buenos Aires 1977) autopsy, cardiovascular; **Lee Ann MacMillan-Crow** PhD (Univ Alabama Sch Med, 1994) molecular and cellular biology; **Lea Nowak** MD (Charles Univ. 1985) surgical pathology; **Larisa Pereboeva** PhD (Inst of Bioengin 1999); **Stephanie D. Reilly** MD (Louisiana State Univ Med Ctr 1981) autopsy pathology; **Yongsheng Ren** MD, PhD (Anhui Medical Univ China, Univ Texas, MD Anderson) molecular diagnostics; **Gary T. Simmons** MD (Univ Tennessee 1983) forensic pathology; **Marla C. Troughton** MD (Univ. Texas Galveston 2000) transfusion medicine; **Mei Wan** PhD (Hebei Med Univ, China 1997) cancer; **Yang Yang** MD, PhD (China Medical University 1982, China 1989) Tumor biology and gene therapy; **Majd Zayzafoon** MD, PhD (Dmascas Univ, Syria, Univ. Michigan) Bone Biology; **Jianhua Zhang** PhD (Univ. Texas Southwestern 1991); **Zeng-Bian Zhu** (Univ Nanjing Sch Med 1966) immunology, molecular biology.

Instructors

Keith J Micoli PhD (UAB 2001) Calmodulin, osteoclast differentiation, apoptosis; **John J Shacka** PhD (Med Col of Virginia 1997) mechanisms of cell death in the nervous system; **John J. Shacka** PhD (Med Col of Virginia, 1997) Neurobiology; **Chao Wan** MD, PhD (Shangdong Univ China 1995/Shanghai Sec. Med Univ China 2002) osteoclastogenesis, bone regeneration.

APPLICATIONS

Apply at least six months in advance.

Address inquiries to:

C. Bruce Alexander, MD, Residency Program Director
University of Alabama at Birmingham
Department of Pathology
619 South 19th Street, WP P220
Birmingham, AL 35233-7331
Phone: (205) 934-4303 • **Web site:** http://www.path.uab.edu

University of Alabama Medical Center, Birmingham

UNIVERSITY OF SOUTH ALABAMA

Mobile, Alabama

PROGRAMS OFFERED

The Pathology Residency Program provides thorough training in all aspects of anatomic and clinical pathology and laboratory management with the specifics of the program tailored to meet the needs of the individual. In addition to autopsies, surgical pathology, and cytopathology, the anatomic pathology program includes specialized training in neuropathology, dermatopathology, pediatric pathology, electron microscopy, and forensic pathology. Laboratory medicine includes clinical chemistry, toxicology, hematology, transfusion medicine, microbiology, and immunopathology. Research experience is encouraged and facilities are available for residents to learn standard and specialized research techniques and participate in projects independently or with faculty. Funds are available to support presentation of such projects at scientific meetings. The house staff participates actively in the educational activities of the department. This activity includes interdepartmental conferences and lectures to allied health personnel as well as participation in lectures, laboratories, case study assignments and discussion groups in the pathology/laboratory medicine course for second year medical students.

TYPES AND NUMBERS OF APPOINTMENTS

The program supports 13 residency positions. The department participates in the NRMP.

FACILITIES

The University of South Alabama (USA) is a major referral center for the Gulf Coast and is especially noted for its trauma center and high risk intensive care nursery. It currently includes an acute care hospital, the USA Medical Center, and the USA Children's and Women's Hospital; combined, these hospitals are licensed for over 550 beds. The new Mitchell Cancer Institute has just opened. Residents also routinely rotate at the 315 bed Infirmary West Hospital. Each facility has its own clinical laboratory, and these facilities provide a core experience in anatomic pathology involving about 11,000 surgical pathology specimens and 10,000 cytopathology specimens per year. In addition, senior residents have the opportunity to rotate with the private pathology group at Mobile Infirmary, a 704 bed acute care hospital with a much higher surgical pathology volume, augmenting the residency experience. Also located at the USA Medical Center, in a facility shared by the medical center and the state, is a division of the State Department of Forensic Sciences. This building houses the offices of the medical examiner and supporting services in forensic serology, trace evidence, ballistics, and toxicology. Teaching facilities are located on each hospital campus and in the Medical Sciences Building on the main university campus in west Mobile.

COMMUNITY

Mobile is a rapidly growing, yet traditional city of approximately 210,000 people (metropolitan population of 500,000). It was settled in 1502 by the French and was subsequently governed by Britain, Spain, the U.S., and the Confederacy before being retaken for the US by Admiral Farragut in 1864. Mobile's streets are shaded by a canopy of live oaks and the city features a mild climate with flowers blooming year round. Other attractions are the annual Mardi Gras festivities, Senior Bowl, and GMAC Bowl, as well as 12 months of fishing and sailing. The university sponsors Division I basketball and baseball, and is launching football along with a band program for the 2009 football season. Beaches at Gulf Shores and Dauphin Island are within an hour's drive. The Mobile metropolitan area is experiencing the greatest job growth of any area in the state. Major industries include computer hardware and software, textiles, seafood processing, oil and gas production, paper and lumber products, chemicals, aviation, shipbuilding, and tourism. Mobile is the deep-water port of the Tennessee-Tombigbee Waterway and a gateway to more than 16,000 miles of navigable rivers. With the community's strong growth comes an increased need for educational and medical services provided through the University of South Alabama.

STIPENDS AND MAINTENANCE

First-year postgraduates start at $45,656 (2009-2010 rate) plus malpractice insurance. Yearly increments exist.

STAFF

Professors

J. Allan Tucker MD (Vanderbilt Univ 1981) Louise L. Locke Professor and Chair, Director Anatomic Pathology, surgical pathology; **Elizabeth A. Manci** MD (Univ Alabama 1979) pediatric pathology, environmental pathology.

Adjunct Professors

LeRoy Riddick MD (Univ New Jersey 1969) forensic pathology; **Betsy Bennett** MD, PhD (Vanderbilt Univ 1976) clinical pathology.

Emeritus Professors

Edmund A. Dowling MD (Univ Col Cork, Ireland 1951) surgical pathology, cytopathology; **William A. Gardner, Jr.** MD (Univ South Carolina 1965) urologic pathology; **Song Wong** MD (Univ Burma 1962) forensic pathology, cytopathology, surgical pathology.

Associate Professors

Carole W. Boudreaux MD (Louisiana State Univ 1990) Director Cytopathology, surgical pathology; **J. Elliot Carter** MD (Univ Mississippi Sch Med 1995) Director Clinical Labs; Director Microbiology; cytopathology, surgical pathology; **Jacek Polski** MD (Med Acad Lublin, Poland 1990) Director Hematopathology.

Adjunct Associate Professors

Lloyd L. Gardner MD (Univ Alabama 1978); **Robert M. Donnell** MD (Univ South Alabama 1977); **John Krolikowski** MD (Tufts Univ Sch of Med 1972) forensic pathology.

Assistant Professors

Gary Carnahan MD, PhD (Vanderbilt Univ 1980) clinical pathology; **Andrea G. Kahn** MD (Univ Nac Cordoba 1990) Director Surgical Pathology, cytopathology; **M. Margaret O'Brien** MD (Univ South Alabama 1993) surgical pathology, autopsy; **Jeffrey Sosnowski** MD, PhD (Univ Louisville Hlth Sci Ctr 1998) Director Neuropathology, surgical pathology; **David O. Wood** PhD (Univ Georgia 1977) microbiology.

Adjunct Assistant Professors

Eugene Hart MD (Univ Miami, 1999) forensic pathology; **John Lazarchick** MD (Medical University of South Carolina 1986) dermatopathology, surgical pathology; **Kelly Roveda** MD (Univ South Alabama 1990) surgical pathology.

Lecturer

Michael Titford BS (Univ South Alabama 1987).

APPLICATIONS

Completed applications should be received by January 1, 2010 and are accepted through ERAS.

Address inquiries to:

Carole W. Boudreaux, MD
Director, Pathology Residency Program
University of South Alabama
2451 Fillingim Street
Mobile, AL 36617
Phone: (251) 471-7786 • **Fax:** (251) 471-7884 • **E-mail:** pathres@usouthal.edu

ST. JOSEPH'S HOSPITAL AND MEDICAL CENTER

Phoenix, Arizona

PROGRAMS OFFERED

The goal of the St. Joseph's Pathology Residency Training Program is to provide the resident physician with a broad educational experience in all aspects of general pathology, so that he or she will have the training and expertise to enter the community as a practicing pathologist or to pursue academic fellowship training. The residency training program in pathology is a combined, fully accredited program in Anatomic and Clinical Pathology. The Anatomic Pathology service offers training in surgical pathology, neuropathology, dermatopathology, cytopathology, immunohistochemistry, immunofluorescence microscopy, molecular diagnostics, electron microscopy, autopsy pathology and forensic pathology. The Clinical Pathology service offers training in clinical chemistry, hematopathology and flow cytometry, immunohematology/transfusion medicine, microbiology and virology, laboratory management and cytogenetics and molecular pathology. The pathology residents and staff physicians interact extensively with other hospital departments through conference presentations and interdepartmental teaching and research activities, as well as during daily patient care duties. For academic year 2008-2009, the Department of Pathology has 11 board-certified pathologists covering multiple specialty disciplines.

TYPES AND NUMBERS OF APPOINTMENTS

The AP/CP program is approved for up to 10 residency positions (at least 2 residents per academic year). The resident to faculty ratio is virtually 1:1. Our recent resident graduates have successfully found employment in private practice positions (mostly in the Phoenix area) or have been placed in fellowship positions of their choice.

FACILITIES

Located in the heart of Phoenix, Arizona, St. Joseph's Hospital and Medical Center is a 743-bed, not-for-profit hospital that provides a wide range of health, social and support services, with special advocacy for the poor and the underserved. Founded in 1895 by the Sisters of Mercy, St. Joseph's was the first hospital in the Phoenix area. The hospital is part of Catholic Healthcare West (CHW), one of the largest healthcare systems in the western U.S., with 42 hospitals in Arizona, California and Nevada. The medical center admitted 37,564 patients in 2007. Over 65,000 patients received care through the hospital's Emergency Services Department, which includes a level 1 trauma center. Recent renovations have expanded the main campus, including the new Neuroscience Tower and the renovated Heart and Lung Institute (HLI) tower. The St. Joseph's Medical Center specializes in neurologic diseases (Barrow Neurologic Institute), cardiovascular and pulmonary diseases (Heart and Lung Institute), women's and children's care and cancer diagnostics and therapeutics. During 2007, the Pathology Department at St. Joseph's Hospital examined 16,000 surgical pathology specimens, 21,000 gynecologic cytology specimens, 3500 non-gynecologic cytology specimens and 1900 fine needle aspirations. In addition, more than 1900 cases were seen in consultation from other hospitals and laboratories in the area. Over 60 autopsy examinations were performed.

COMMUNITY

The Phoenix metropolitan area offers year-round activities for its residents, with desert vistas, lakes, mountains and ski slopes within an easy drive of the city. The mean summer temperature is over 85 degrees and the mean winter temperature is 51 degrees. The Phoenix area has seen a recent expansion of cultural facilities, and is home to the Phoenix Symphony, Arizona Opera, Arizona Theatre Company, Phoenix Little Theatre, Phoenix Art Museum, Heard Museum, the Desert Botanical Garden and the Phoenix Zoo - making the ''Valley of the Sun'' a cultural center for the state. Athletes will find the many Valley golf courses, tennis courts, athletic clubs, hiking trails and swimming facilities to their liking. The Phoenix area has four major league professional sports teams (Cardinals, Coyotes, Diamondbacks and Suns) and several minor league teams, and is the home of Major League Baseball spring training and two college bowl games. The metropolitan area hosted Super Bowl 2008 and will be the site of the 2009 NBA All-Star Game. Other popular destinations are within easy reach. The Grand Canyon, San Diego beaches, Los Angeles area, Las Vegas and Mexico are a 3-6 hour drive from Phoenix. The Sky Harbor International Airport is centrally located and provides easy access for more distant travel opportunities.

STIPENDS AND MAINTENANCE

For the 2007-08 academic year the institution's resident stipends were: first-year, $46,550.40; second-year, $48,339.20; third-year, $50,564.80; and fourth-year, $53,081.60. Malpractice coverage is provided under the hospital's professional liability program. Health, dental and life insurance are provided for residents and their dependents as part of the standard benefits package for St. Joseph's professionals. Seventeen working days of paid vacation and five additional conference days are given to each resident per year. In addition to the above mentioned benefits, residents receive free parking, free lab coats, a book allowance and an educational travel fund.

STAFF

William D. Anderson MD (Univ Iowa 1979) surgical pathology, cytology, autopsy pathology, immunofluorescence microscopy; **Earle Smith Collum** MD (Univ South Carolina 1979) general clinical pathology, surgical pathology, laboratory management, autopsy pathology; **Stephen W. Coons** MD (Univ Arizona 1983) neuropathology, autopsy pathology, neuropathology research, skeletal muscle and peripheral nerve pathology; **Roy I. Davis** MD (Univ Witwatersrand, South Africa 1970) surgical pathology, cytology, electron microscopy, laboratory management; **Mary J. Fietz** MD (Univ Oklahoma 1986) surgical pathology, cytology, general clinical pathology, autopsy pathology, laboratory management; **Chadwick Haarer** MD (New York Med Col 2001) urologic pathology, oncologic pathology, general surgical pathology, autopsy pathology; **M. Frances Hahn** MD (Univ Arizona 1993) surgical pathology, general clinical pathology, cytology; **Jeffrey D. Oliver** MD (Univ Iowa 1983) hematopathology, lymph node pathology, surgical pathology, cytology; **Thomas Rhulen** MD (Univ Kansas 1976) general clinical pathology, cytology, autopsy pathology, pulmonary pathology, thyroid pathology; **Richard W. Trepeta** MD (Yale Univ 1978) dermatopathology, microbiology, surgical pathology, cytology; **Linda Zeien** MD (Univ Southern California 1987) surgical pathology, cytology, blood bank, autopsy pathology.

APPLICATIONS

Address inquiries to:

Rosanna M. Harrell, Program Coordinator
St. Joseph's Hospital and Medical Center
Department of Pathology
350 W Thomas Road
Phoenix, AZ 85013
Phone: (602) 406-6129 • **Fax:** (602) 406-7132 • **E-mail:** rharrel@chw.edu

ARIZONA HEALTH SCIENCES CENTER

Tucson, Arizona

PROGRAMS OFFERED

The department provides educational opportunities designed to produce both academic and practicing pathologists of the highest quality. The program is flexible and may lead to qualification for combined certification by the American Board of Pathology through a combined program in anatomic and clinical pathology. The training programs are integrated between University Medical Center and the Southern Arizona VA Health Care System, and comply fully with the special requirements for residency training programs in pathology established by the Accreditation Council for Graduate Medical Education. We also offer accredited fellowships in hematopathology and molecular genetic pathology and a non-accredited fellowship in surgical pathology.

TYPES AND NUMBERS OF APPOINTMENTS

Thirteen positions are available, three in any one year of the four-year program, or other combinations as special circumstances warrant. Medical graduates seeking their first year of graduate medical education (internship) are appointed through the National Resident Matching Program. Other candidates are appointed directly by the department.

FACILITIES

University Medical Center provides 375 beds and 40 bassinets. The caseload per year is 150 autopsies, 18,750 surgical specimens, 4,500 dermatopathology specimens, 9,300 cytology specimens, and 16 million weighted work units in the clinical laboratories. Seven miles southwest of the medical campus is the 250-bed Southern Arizona VA Health Care System, with a yearly caseload of 40 autopsies, 5,600 surgical specimens, 3,100 cytology specimens, and about 2 million billable laboratory tests per year. A new clinical lab was completed in 1999. The Pathology Department Clinical Laboratories are extensively automated and computerized, being fully equipped with modern service and research instruments. The Immunopathology, Immunology, and Cytogenetics Laboratories are newly renovated. The new medical school library, open 24 hours a day and located in University Medical Center, contains over 154,467 volumes and maintains 3,377 serial subscriptions. The main campus of the University of Arizona is three blocks south of the Health Sciences Center complex.

COMMUNITY

Tucson is a major cultural and resort city. It is located in a beautiful green desert valley between mountain ranges more than 9,000 feet high. There are 850,000 permanent area residents and thousands of visitors who enjoy the mild winter climate. Outdoor recreational opportunities such as hiking, tennis, golf and swimming are abundant. Mexico lies 65 miles to the south; Indian reservations and numerous historical sites are nearby. Theater performances, symphony concerts, opera productions and other cultural events are available at the university and the Tucson Community Center. The University of Arizona has over 35,000 students and 12,400 graduate students and faculty members.

STIPENDS AND MAINTENANCE

Salaries for the 2009-2010 fiscal year range from $46,036 for the first year in postgraduate medical education to $52,865 for the fourth year.

STAFF

Chairman

Achyut K. Bhattacharyya MD (Calcutta Univ 1976) Interim Chairman; anatomic pathology, gastrointestinal pathology, transplantation biology, telepathology.

Director of Residency Program

Richard E. Sobonya MD (Western Reserve Univ 1967) autopsy and pulmonary pathology.

Professors

Christopher Cunniff MD (Alabama 1984) cytogenetics; **John R. Davis** MD (Univ Iowa 1959) Emeritus, anatomic pathology, cytology, gynecologic pathology, and cytogenetics; **Barun De** PhD (Univ of Maryland 1979) chemistry; **Anna R. Graham** MD (Univ Arizona 1974) Emeritus, anatomic pathology, immunopathology, renal pathology; **Thomas M. Grogan** MD (George Washington Univ 1971) lymphoreticular pathology; **Douglas W. Huestis** MD (McGill Univ 1948) Emeritus; transfusion medicine; **Emmanuel Katsanis** MD (National Univ Athens, Greece, 1980) pediatric hematology/oncology; **Jack M. Layton** MD (Univ Iowa 1943) Emeritus; ophthalmic pathology; **Raymond B. Nagle** MD, PhD (Univ Washington 1964, 1967) anatomic pathology, immunopathology, and electron microscopy; Deputy Director, Arizona Cancer Ctr; **Mark A. Nelson** PhD (Washington State Univ 1989) cancer biology, toxicology; **Samuel H. Paplanus** MD (Vanderbilt Univ 1954) Emeritus; surgical pathology; **Naomi E. Rance** MD, PhD (Maryland Univ

1981, 1983) Associate Chairman; neuropathology; **C. George Ray** MD (Chicago 1960) micorbiology; **Stephen W. Renner** MD (Univ Texas 1976) clinical pathology; **Lisa Rimsza** MD (Univ Arizona 1992) hematopathology; **Kenneth J. Ryan** MD (Univ Washington 1966) Emeritus; bacteriology, clinical microbiology; **Ziad Shehab** MD (American Univ Beirut) virology, pediatric pathology; **Ronald S. Weinstein** MD (Tufts Univ 1965) telepathology, informatics, and cancer cell biology; **Wenxin Zheng** MD (Shanghai Med Univ 1983) gynecologic pathology.

Associate Professors

Leslie Boyer MD (Harvard, 1988) clinical toxicology, Director of Poison Center; **Margaret M. Briehl** PhD (Univ Arizona 1988) molecular genetics; **Ana Maria Lopez** MD (Jefferson PA Univ 1988) oncology; **Michael W. Riggs** PhD (Washington State Univ 1987) veterinary pathology; **Ronald B. Schifman** MD (Univ Kansas 1978) Chief, Laboratory Services VAMC; clinical pathology; **Ronald P. Spark** MD (Temple Univ 1967) microbiology; **Catherine M. Spier** MD (Univ North Dakota 1978) hematopathology and immunopathology; **Karen K. Steinbronn** MD (Univ Arizona 1975) anatomic and clinical pathology.

Assistant Professors

Osama Abdelatif MBBCh (Cairo Univ 1982) cytopathology, FNA; **Gail Barker** PhD (Kennedy Western Univ 2004) health administration; **Erika R. Bracamonte** MD (Univ Arizona 2003) anatomic pathology, renal pathology; **Jill Cohen** MD (Univ Michigan 1991) dermatopathology; **David Feldman** MD (SUNY Upstate Med Univ 1994) blood banking, clinical pathology; **Deborah Fuchs** MD (Univ Arizona 1998) hematopathology; **Olivia T. Garza** MD (Univ Texas Houston) cytopathology, FNA; **Lauren Grasso-LeBeau** MD (Wayne State Univ 2003) anatomic pathology, breast pathology; **Gregory L. Hess** MD (Med Col Wisconsin 1997) Pima County, forensic pathology; **Robert Klein** MD (Utah, 1997) anatomic pathology, medical informatics/database; **Fangru Lian** MD (Med Col Wisconsin 1997) dematopathology, anatomic pathology; **Bruce O. Parks** MD (Univ Arizona 1982) Chief Medical Examiner, Pima County; forensic pathology; **Eric Peters** (New York Med Col 1992) Pima County, forensic pathology; **Cynthia M. Porterfield** DO (Chicago Col Osteopathic Med 1989) Pima County, forensic pathology; **Anil Prasad** MD (Pondicherry India 1992) surgical pathology; **Margaret Rennels** MD (Univ Arizona 1983) anatomic and clinical pathology; **Monica Schmelz** PhD (Univ Germany 1989) electron microscopy, experimental pathology; **Katherine M. Scott** MD (Univ Oregon 1993) immunopathology, renal pathology; **Veena Singh** MD (Oregon Univ 2001) Pima County, forensic pathology; **Margaret Tome** PhD (Arizona 1996) experimental pathology; **David Winston** MD (South Carolina 1993) Pima County, forensic pathology; **Donna Wolk** PhD (Arizona 1999) molecular pathology, microbiology.

Lecturers

Judy Dye MA (Univ Phoenix) management; **Alison Stopeck** MD (Columbia Univ 1985) coagulation; **David A. Wheeler** MD (Univ Arizona 1981) anatomic and clinical pathology.

APPLICATIONS

Applicants must have an MD or DO degree from a school of medicine in the United States or Canada; or, if graduated from a foreign medical school, must have the qualifications required for admittance to a program in graduate medical education. Physicians may enter the program directly from medical school for their first year of graduate medical education. Applications are through ERAS (Electronic Residency Application System) and should be completed by December 31st for appointments to begin July 1.

Address inquiries to:

Richard E. Sobonya, MD
Department of Pathology
Arizona Health Sciences Center, 1501 N Campbell
Tucson, AZ 85724-5108
Phone: (520) 626-6830 • **Fax:** (520) 626-2521 • **E-mail:** rsobonya@umcaz.edu
Web site: http://residency.pathology.arizona.edu

Training at the University of Arizona: pathology in paradise.

UNIVERSITY OF ARKANSAS FOR MEDICAL SCIENCES AND AFFILIATED INSTITUTIONS

Little Rock, Arkansas

PROGRAMS OFFERED

The UAMS Department of Pathology offers a fully accredited residency training program. The residency training program is available in combined anatomic and clinical pathology only. In addition to the general program, elective time is available for the acquisition of special competence in the service and/or research aspects of cytopathology, musculoskeletal pathology, dermatopathology, immunohistochemistry, toxicology, immunopathology, hematopathology, microbiology, virology, transfusion medicine, gastrointestinal pathology, renal pathology, pediatric pathology, ophthalmic pathology, chemical pathology and molecular pathology. The diversity in background and philosophy of the individual faculty members is such that residents are afforded wide latitude toward the realization of their career goals, whether in academia or private practice.

TYPES AND NUMBERS OF APPOINTMENTS

A total of 18 positions are approved.

FACILITIES

UAMS Medical Center is the patient care network of the University of Arkansas for Medical Sciences (UAMS) and includes University Hospital, the Arkansas Cancer Research Center, Jones Eye Institute, Family Medical Center, Reynolds Center on Aging, Stephens Spine and Neuroscience Institute, Arkansas Children's Hospital, and numerous clinics located in the Outpatient Center. UAMS, the sole medical school in a state of 2,300,000 citizens, houses a medical library which contains over 150,000 volumes and subscribes to 4,236periodicals. State-of-the-art audiovisual and photographic educational facilities are available including a statewide telemedicine network. The 350-bed University Hospital is the leading referral center in the state. A major new wing of the hospital will open in 2009, including a new state-of-the-art surgical pathology grossing suite, signout facilities and much of the clinical laboratory operations. The Department of Pathology currently occupies 35,740 square feet in University Hospital and the anatomic and clinical laboratories contain state-of-the-art technology. The Arkansas Cancer Research Center is recognized around the world for research and treatment, particularly of multiple myeloma, and currently has more than 115,000 patient visits a year. The Reynolds Center on Aging is only the second geriatric department of its kind in the United States. The Central Arkansas Veterans Healthcare System is physically connected to the UAMS campus and is one of the largest, best appointed and equipped such hospitals in the country. UAMS physicians provide the majority of care offered at this facility. The nearby Arkansas Children's Hospital, with 300 beds and 35 specialty clinics, is the only pediatric care hospital in the state, and is staffed by the UAMS Department of Pediatrics. Total yearly workload in pathology for all contributing institutions is as follows: surgical accessions, 28,000; autopsies, 320; cytologic accessions, 22,000; clinical laboratory determinations, 8,000,000.

COMMUNITY

Little Rock, Arkansas' capital city with over 184,000 citizens, is situated along the southern bank of the scenic, serpentine Arkansas river. With its transfluvial sister city, North Little Rock, and surrounding suburbs and exurbs, the Little Rock area contains over 400,000 people. As it is the largest urban area in Arkansas and is centrally located, Little Rock is home to numerous restaurants, pubs and other urban attractions. The Clinton Presidential Library is adjacent to a revitalized and flourishing riverfront section of downtown Little Rock. Little Rock has resident ballet, symphony and local theatre companies, and hosts touring national theatre troupes as well. The natural beauty and geographic diversity of the Arkansas countryside affords its residents and visitors a variety of activities, and camping, sailing, scuba diving, water skiing, hunting, fishing, and mountain climbing opportunities may all be found within a radius of an hour's drive from Little Rock. Horse racing with pari-mutuel wagering is available in Hot Springs, only 40 miles away. Semi-professional and collegiate sporting events also take place here throughout the year. The mild climate (average annual temperature 62 F) allows for enjoyment of these natural resources and sporting events year-round.

STIPENDS AND MAINTENANCE

The following figures are for the fiscal year beginning July 1, 2009: PGY-1, $45,356; PGY-2, $46,638; PGY-3, $48,175; PGY-4, $49,456; PGY-5, $51,250; PGY-6, $53,813; PGY-7, $55,350. A benefits package includes a group major medical insurance plan with family coverage, term life insurance, malpractice insurance, lab coats with laundry privileges, and parking. Travel to selected national professional meetings and book allowance are also included.

STAFF

Bruce Smoller MD Professor and Chairman (Univ Cincinnati,1983); **Ila Bansal** MD (Meerut Univ, India 1993) Hematopathology; **William Bellamy** PhD (Univ Arizona 1988) molecular pathology; **Douglas Blackall** MD (Univ Arkansas Med Sci 1988) pediatric clinical pathology; **Joshua Bornhorst** PhD (Univ Colorado at Boulder, 2002) chemistry; **Harry Brown** MD Program Director (Vanderbilt Univ 1984) ophthalmic pathology; **Kari Caradine** MD (Univ Arkansas Med Sci 2002); **Neslihan Cetin** MD (Uludag Univ, Turkey 1990); **Warren J. Clingan** MD (Univ Arkansas Med Sci 2003); **Elena Davis** MD (Cayetano Heredia Peruvian Univ, Peru 1991); **Chun-Yang Fan** MD, PhD (Guangzhou Med Col, China 1983) head/neck pathology; **Michele Fox** MD (Univ Stockholm 1983) transfusion medicine; **Murat Gokden** MD (Univ Turkey 1986) Director of Cytopathology, neuropathology; **Neriman Gokden** MD (Dokuz Eylul Univ, Turkey 1986) renal pathology; **Leah Hennings** DVM (Washington State Univ 1999) veterinary pathology; **Kim Hiatt** MD (Georgetown Univ 1996) Director of Dermatopathology; **A.J. Hough, Jr.** MD (Vanderbilt Univ 1970); orthopedic pathology; **Emily Howard** MD, PhD (Univ Chicago, 1999) hematopathology; **M.M. Husain** MD (Dacca Univ 1967) neuropathology; **Michael Johnson** MD (Univ Arkansas Med Sci 1994) cytopathology; **Thomas Kelly** PhD (Univ North Carolina, 1988) experimental pathology; **S. Korourian** MD (Univ Vienna 1983) gynecologic pathology; **Laura Lamps** MD Director Anatomic Pathology (Vanderbilt Univ 1992) gastrointestinal pathology; **Robert Lorsbach** MD, PhD (Univ Kansas Sch Med, 1994) Director Hematopathology; **Ginell Post** MD, PhD (Univ of Chicago 1992) Hematopathology; **Ali Saad** MD (Lebanese Univ, Lebanon 1998); **J. Sawyer** PhD (Univ Florida Inst Technol 1984) cytogenetics; **Steven Schichman** MD, PhD (Univ Chicago 1982) molecular pathology; **Margie Scott** MD (Meharry Med Col 1988) microbiology; **Zeba Singh** MD (Univ of Rajashan, India 1988) Hematopathology; **Carmen Steigman** MD (Louisiana St. Univ Med Ctr 1983) autopsy and perinatal; **John Theus** MD (Univ Arkansas Med Sci 2001) Blood/Transfusion Medicine; **Gail Woods** MD Director Clinical Laboratory (Indiana Univ 1978) microbiology; **Marwan Yared** MD Associate Program Director (American Univ of Beirut, Lebanon 1991) Hematopathology; **Fengjuan Zhang** MD (Bethune Univ Med Sci 1988) cytopathology.

APPLICATIONS

Residency candidates must be graduates of accredited American or Canadian medical schools or must possess an ECFMG certificate. All applications must be received through ERAS. This program/institution is a member of NRMP.

Address inquiries to:

Renee' Gordon
Residency & Fellowship Program Manager
Department of Pathology, #517
University of Arkansas for Medical Sciences
4301 West Markham Street
Little Rock, AR 72205
Phone: (501) 603-1508 • **Fax:** (501) 686-5959 • **E-mail:** gordonreneen@uams.edu

LOMA LINDA UNIVERSITY MEDICAL CENTER

Loma Linda, California

PROGRAMS OFFERED

Loma Linda University Medical Center (LLUMC) offers a fully accredited four-year residency program in combined anatomic-clinical pathology. Anatomic pathology rotations involve all major areas of surgical pathology (including pediatric, renal, soft tissue, consultative and cardiopulmonary), cytopathology, neuropathology, electron microscopy, immunopathology, necropsy and forensic pathology. Clinical pathology involves chemistry, immunology (including immunophenotyping by flow cytometry), microbiology, transfusion medicine and cytogenetics. Most rotations are at LLUMC. Rotations at the Loma Linda Pathology Laboratory involve surgical specimens from doctors' offices, the Outpatient Surgery Center and Loma Linda Community Hospital. A large volume of gynecological, gastrointestinal, dermatological and breast material is seen. Each year, residents rotate through the Jerry L. Pettis Memorial Veterans Medical Center in a combined anatomic/clinical pathology service which gives the resident thc perspective of a general pathologist. All residents participate in daily conferences which provide a systematic overview of clinical and anatomic subspecialties by attending staff. Regular reviews of interesting current clinical and anatomic cases are conducted by residents and attending staff. A resident's exposure to forensic pathology is enhanced by LLUMC's affiliation with the San Bernardino County Coroner's Office. Residents also assist with the Medical School pathology labs and may participate in the lectures.

TYPES AND NUMBERS OF APPOINTMENTS

The department currently offers 15 residency positions including a Chief Resident and two to three one-year post-sophomore fellowship positions.

FACILITIES

The Residency Program at Loma Linda University Medical Center is integrated with the Loma Linda University Pathology Laboratory, California Tumor Tissue Registry, the Jerry L. Pettis Memorial Veterans Medical Center, the East Campus, Heart and Surgical Hospital, and the San Bernardino County Coroner's Office. With the exception of the Coroner's Office, all facilities are located within one mile of each other. LLUMC, a 797-bed tertiary care, private teaching hospital including the Loma Linda University Children's Hospital, is the only university medical center serving four counties. LLUMC is a state-approved center for transplantation and has achieved national visibility for its infant-heart transplantation program. Annual workflows through LLUMC and its affiliates are approximately 250 autopsies, 21,000 surgical specimens, 87,000 cytology specimens and 716,500 laboratory tests (raw count).

COMMUNITY

Loma Linda is located in the center of a wide assortment of unique Southern California attractions, both natural (warm beaches and snow-covered mountains with ski resorts) and man-made (Disneyland, Knott's Berry Farm, Magic Mountain and Universal Studios). Relatively affordable housing is available locally.

STIPENDS AND MAINTENANCE

The range of resident salaries is $47,063 to $52,599 per annum. Benefits include major medical coverage, including dental and optical, for residents (available to their families for a minimal monthly charge); four weeks of paid vacation (three weeks the first year); sick leave; maternity leave; family/parental leave; live insurance; disability insurance; white laboratory coats and laundering; free tuition (8 units per year); and professional liability insurance.

STAFF

Brian Bull MD Chairman & Resident Director, Pathology; **Ken Cantos** MD; **Jeffrey D. Cao** MD; **Donald R. Chase** MD; **Resa L. Chase** MD; **Evelyn Choo** MD; **Camilla Cobb** MD; **G. Gordon Hadley** MD; **Paul Herrmann** M.D., Ph.D.; **Darryl Heustis** MD; **Richard Hubbard** PhD; **John Lewis** PhD; **Roland Lonser** MD; **Kerby Oberg** MD, PhD; **James Pappas** MD; **Norman Peckham** MD; **Mia Perez** MD; **Ravi Raghavan** MD; **Donald Rankin** MD; **Anwar Raza** MD; **Heather Rojas** M.D.; **Edward Rowsell** MD, PhD; **G. William Saukel** MD; **Frank Sheridan** MD; **Fred Soeprono** MD; **Wesley Tait Stevens** MD; **Kevin Thompson** MD; **Steve Trenkle** MD; **Jun Wang** MD; **Bo Ying Wat** MD; **Pamela J. Wat** MD; **Craig Zuppan** MD.

APPLICATIONS

Applicants must be graduates of approved medical schools who are eligible for California licensure. First-year positions are chosen through the National Residency Matching Program with training usually beginning July 1.

Applications for first-year programs starting July 1 must be submitted by December 1 of the preceding year. Space permitting, positions may be filled throughout the year. Personal interviews are required.

Address inquiries to:

Brian S. Bull, MD
Chairman & Director of Pathology Residency Program
Department of Pathology
Loma Linda University Medical Center
11234 Anderson Street, Room 2516
Loma Linda, CA 92354
Phone: (909) 558-4094 • **Fax:** (909) 558-4189
Web site: http://www.llu.edu/llumc/residency/welcome.htm

Loma Linda University Medical Center

CEDARS-SINAI MEDICAL CENTER

Los Angeles, California

PROGRAMS OFFERED

The Department of Pathology and Laboratory Medicine Residency is a four-year, fully approved program in anatomic and clinical pathology whose strength is based on a combination of superb patient care material, faculty subspecialization with strength in anatomic and clinical pathology, sophisticated research programs, and the most advanced instrumentation. The Department runs a centralized service providing total laboratory support to the hospital, and has a robust outreach program in anatomic and clinical pathology. Residents participate in all areas of pathology including autopsy and surgical pathology, immunohistochemistry, EM, cytopathology, forensic pathology, clinical chemistry, toxicology, molecular pathology, cytogenetics/HLA, hematology, transfusion medicine, clinical immunology, and all aspects of microbiology and computerized laboratory management.

TYPES AND NUMBERS OF APPOINTMENTS

The program is approved for a total of 20 AP/CP residency trainees and in addition offers fellowships in surgical pathology, GU pathology, renal pathology, GI and liver pathology, transfusion medicine, hematopathology, and molecular genetic pathology.

FACILITIES

Cedars-Sinai is a nonprofit quaternary academic medical center with 969 beds, affiliated with UCLA through its teaching programs. There are approximately 50,000 surgical specimens, 100 autopsies, and 15,000 cytologic specimens annually. Besides having depth in general medical and surgical cases, we provide breadth by being a trauma center, a tertiary care center for all specialties with an NCI accredited cancer institute and an active organ transplant program. Well funded basic, translational and clinical research programs are integral to the Medical Center through numerous associated Institutes. For example, the Neurosurgical and Prostate Cancer Institutes are among the premier brain and prostate tumor programs in the country, providing a wealth of material for education and research. The clinical laboratories perform 5 million tests yearly utilizing state-of-the-art technology. We have molecular pathology laboratories in both anatomic and clinical pathology. The hospital's libraries contain more than 12,000 books and monographs and subscribe to over 600 journals. The Department of Pathology and Laboratory Medicine maintains its own library of pathology journals and text books.

COMMUNITY

The Cedars-Sinai Medical Center is located at the junction of the Beverly Hills and West Hollywood sections of Los Angeles. The area is renowned for its wide variety of social and recreational facilities and the excellent climate in which to enjoy them. In recent years, Los Angeles has become a major cultural center with superb museums, theaters, and musical events. Three medical schools are in the immediate area.

STIPENDS AND MAINTENANCE

The annual salary levels for residents for 2009-2010 are: PGY1 $48,140; PGY2 $49,685; PGY3 $51,639; PGY4 $53,432; PGY5 $55,275; PGY6 $57,546; PGY7 $59,266. All residents are provided with professional liability insurance, medical and dental benefits for the resident, spouse and children, and uniforms with laundry services.

STAFF

Mahul B. Amin MD Chairman, GU pathology; **Randa Alsabeh** MD hematopathology, immunopathology; **Bonnie Balzer** MD dermatopathology, GYN and bone pathology; **Serguei Bannykh** MD neuropathology; **Denise Barbuto** MD GYN pathology; **Catherine I Barry** DO, dermatopathology; **Kenneth E Bernstein** MD, experimental pathology; **Shikha Bose** MD cytopathology, breast pathology; **Arthur H. Cohen** MD renal pathology; **Justin Cole** MD, PhD microbiology, hematopathology, molecular pathology; **Farnaz Dadmanesh** MD breast and GYN pathology; **Mariza Deperalta-Venturina** MD surgical pathology, cytopathology; **Deepti Dhall** MD GI pathology; **Rena E Falk** MD cytogenetics; **Xuemo Fan** MD neuropathology; **Sergio J. Farber** PhD clinical chemistry; **David Frishberg** MD dermatopathology; **Stephen A. Geller** MD hepatic pathology, autopsy; **Mark Haas** MD, PhD renal pathology; **Jerry Hussong** MD hematopathology; **Melissa Kahn** MD GI pathology; **Ellen Klapper** MD transfusion medicine, point-of-care testing; **Stephen Lee** MD hematology, immunology; **Jean Lopategui** MD molecular pathology; **Daniel Luthringer** MD GU and cardiovascular pathology; **Alberto Marchevsky** MD pulmonary and mediastinal pathology; **Richard B. Mertens** MD, PhD GI and breast pathology; **Margie Morgan** PhD microbiology; **Cynthia C. Nast** MD renal pathology; **W. Stephen Nichols** MD microbiology, molecular pathology; **Samuel Pepkowitz** MD pediatric pathology, transfusion medicine; **Karen A. Scharre** MD breast pathology; **Rhona Schreck** PhD cytogenetics; **Elvio Silva** MD GYN pathology; **Elizabeth Spiteri** PhD cytogenetics; **Oxana Tcherniantchouk** MD coagulation; **Eleftehrios**

Vamvakas MD transfusion medicine; **Ann E. Walts** MD cytopathology; **Hanlin Wang** MD GI pathology; **Sijian Wang** MD GU pathology; **Jing Zhai** MD, PhD cytopathology.

APPLICATIONS

Candidates for the residency program who do not possess a California license must be within two years of graduation from an approved medical school in the USA or Canada. Graduates of foreign medical schools or more than two years post US graduation must be eligible for a California license. For further information regarding licensure, communicate with the Board of Medical Quality Assurance, 1430 Howe Ave, Sacramento, CA 95825.

Address inquiries to:

LeeTanya Marion-Murray, Program Coordinator
Eleftherios Vamvakas, MD, PhD or Cynthia Nast, MD, Residency Program Directors
Department of Pathology and Laboratory Medicine
Cedars-Sinai Medical Center
8700 Beverly Boulevard
Los Angeles, CA 90048
Phone: (310) 423-6941 • **E-mail:** leetanya.marion-murray@cshs.org
Web site: http://www.csmc.edu/5487.html

Cedars-Sinai Medical Center, Los Angeles, California.

LAC+USC MEDICAL CENTER/KECK SCHOOL OF MEDICINE AT THE UNIVERSITY OF SOUTHERN CALIFORNIA/VETERANS AFFAIRS GREATER LOS ANGELES HEALTHCARE SYSTEM

Los Angeles, California

PROGRAMS OFFERED

A fully accredited training program in anatomic and clinical pathology is offered over a four year period. In October 2003, the Pathology Residency Training Program at the Veterans Affairs Greater Los Angeles Healthcare System (VAGLAHS) underwent a merger with the LAC+USC Medical Center/Keck School of Medicine of the University of Southern California (LAC+USCMC) that was approved by the Pathology RRC. Occasionally, residents choose anatomic pathology alone but most complete an integrated AP/CP program. Training is offered in autopsy pathology, surgical pathology, oral pathology, dermatopathology, cytopathology, forensic pathology, neuropathology, hematopathology, microbiology, transfusion medicine, chemical pathology, toxicology, immunopathology, neuropathology, molecular pathology, cytogenetics, laboratory management, information science, electron microscopy, immunohistochemistry, immunofluorescence and other specialty areas. Graded responsibility is emphasized in all areas. LAC + USC Medical Center is the principal teaching hospital and provides experience with a broad and diverse spectrum of pathology. The residency program includes rotations at the VAGLAHS, USC University Hospital which is merging with the Norris Cancer Hospital that complement the experience at the Medical Center. In addition, as part of the core curriculum, forensic pathology is also provided at the Los Angeles County Coroner's Office. Fellowship positions are available in surgical pathology, hematopathology, neuropathology, and cytopathology. Postgraduate physicians actively participate in the teaching programs of the University of Southern California Schools of Medicine and Pharmacy. Research is strongly encouraged and teaching is expected.

TYPES AND NUMBERS OF APPOINTMENTS

A total of 40 positions are available to support the residency and fellowship positions. Twenty-eight (28) GY-1 to GY-4 AP/CP positions (20 funded by LAC+USC, 8 funded by VAGLAHS), 7 surgical pathology (5 funded by LAC+USC, 2 funded by Keck/USC), 4 cytopathology, 2 hematopathology, and 1 neuropathology fellowship positions are available. Admission to a fellowship is by application.

FACILITIES

The LAC+USC Medical Center has a capacity of 685 beds housed in two units on a single campus with more than 36,000 admissions and more than 562,000 outpatient visits per year. Patients of all ages, backgrounds and ethnic groups are cared for, representing a vast variety of diseases in such numbers that the rare becomes almost commonplace. A large modern laboratory with facilities in several buildings employs more than 414 laboratory personnel. Annually, approximately 54 autopsies (additional autopsy experience is incorporated into the program through the VAGLAHS and the Los Angeles County Coroner's Office), 22,360 surgical specimen examinations, 21,504 cytologic examinations (2,310 fine needle aspirations, 2,927 non-gynecologic, and 16,069 pap smears), and more than 7,832,054 total laboratory procedures. Research facilities are available for a wide variety of procedures including tissue culture, germ free techniques, molecular pathology and others. Teaching conferences for postgraduate physicians and students are held daily in several conference rooms including a departmental library and multidiscipline teaching laboratories. Extensive library facilities exist within the department, hospital, and the Norris Library of the Keck School of Medicine at the University of Southern California. Residents also have access to current computers with Pentium processors and internet access. The VAGLAHS is a 945-bed general healthcare system. Annually, the laboratory system performs over 3 1/2 million clinical laboratory tests, 48 autopsies, 10,421 surgical pathology specimens, 1,681 cytological specimens, approximately 179 fine-needle aspirations (FNAs), and 261 bone marrow biopsies. Each office is shared by two residents and is equipped with a fully loaded networked PC with flat screen monitors, and each resident has their own new microscope.

COMMUNITY

Los Angeles is a metropolitan community of 7,000,000 people with an unmatched year-round climate, readily accessible mountains, beaches, snow and surf, and as wide a variety of cultural, social, educational, recreational and sporting events as can be found anywhere in the world.

STIPENDS AND MAINTENANCE

The stipend for physicians, postgraduate 1 is $43,956.60. Physicians, postgraduate 2, 3, 4, and 5 receive $49,176.96, $53,284.08, $57,419.40, and $61,443.48, respectively. The base salary is the same, regardless of source of pay. However, benefits will differ from the County of Los Angeles and the VAGLAHS.

STAFF

Professors

Clive R. Taylor MD, PhD Chairman; immunopathology; **Russell K. Brynes** MD hematopathology; **Michael K.-M. Chan** PhD chemical pathology and toxicology; **Parakrama Chandrasoma** MD Chief, Anatomic and Surgical Pathology; gastrointestinal pathology; **Louis Dubeau** MD, PhD pathology and molecular pathology of tumors; **David B. Endres** PhD calcium metabolism; **Juan C. Felix** MD gynecologic pathology; **Kenneth A. Frankel** MD cytopathology; **David R. Hinton** MD neuropathology; **Gary C. Kanel** MD Chief of Autopsy; autopsy and liver pathology; **Anthony J. Keyser** PhD chemical pathology; **David V. Kon** MD cytopathology; **Michael N. Koss** MD renal and respiratory pathology, electron microscopy; **Michael R. Lieber** MD, PhD autopsy and DNA repair research in humans; **Carol A. Miller** MD neuropathology; **Wesley Y. Naritoku** MD, PhD Residency Program Director; surgical pathology and cytology; **Bharat N. Nathwani** MD hematopathology, computer expert systems; **Janice M. Nelson** MD transfusion medicine; **Peter W. Nichols** MD Director, Laboratories and Pathology, USC Univ Hosp and Norris Cancer Hosp; surgical pathology; **Lydia M. Petrovic** MD anatomic pathology; **Michael F. Press** MD, PhD gynecologic pathology, breast cancer; **Christopher Rogers** MD Medical Examiner-Coroner's Office; forensic pathology; **Lakshmanan Sathyavagiswaran** MD Chief Medical Examiner-Coroner's Office; forensic pathology; **Sunita Saxena** MD Medical Director, Comprehensive Health Cancer Laboratory Services; transfusion medicine and laboratory utilization; **Andy E. Sherrod** MD Associate Director, Laboratories and Pathology, Kenneth Norris Cancer Hosp; surgical pathology; **Darryl K Shibata** MD hematopathology and molecular pathology; **Ira A. Shulman** MD Vice Chairman; Director of Laboratories, LAC + USC Healthcare Network; Chief, Clinical Pathology; transfusion medicine.

Associate Professors

Roscoe D. Atkinson MD neuropathology; **Nancy J. Barr** MD immunohistology; **Camilla Cobb** MD cytopathology; **Deborah L. Commins** MD, PhD neuropathology and general surgical pathology; **Alexander N. Fedenko** MD, PhD Chief of Anatomic Pathology, USC Univ Hosp; orthopaedic pathology, pediatric tumor pathology; **Yanling Ma** MD anatomic and clinical pathology; **Sue Ellen Martin** MD, PhD cytology and immunohistology; **Anwar Raza** MD cytopathology; **Susan Selser** MD Medical Examiner-Coroner's Office; forensic pathology; **Gary D. Zeger** MD transfusion medicine.

Assistant Professors

Armine Baltayan MD surgical pathology and cytology; **Joel A. Chan** MD surgical pathology and hematopathology; **Wilson Chick** MD surgical pathology; **Adrian J. Correa** MD, MBA anatomic pathology; **Linda Koss Kelly** PhD electron microscopy; **Gene H. Kim** Dermatopathology; **Nancy E. Klipfel** MD surgical pathology and cytology; **Melanie Osby** MD clinical pathology and microbiology; **Raul G. Simental-Pizarro** MD anatomic pathology; **Lina Wang** MD, MS surgical pathology and cytopathology; **Yan Wang** MD surgical pathology and cytology; **Wenxue Xing** MD surgical pathology and cytology.

Clinical Instructors

Keane K.Y. Lai MD clinical pathology.

VAGLAHS Faculty

Farhad Moatamed MD Chief, Pathology and Laboratory Medicine, immunopathology and molecular pathology; **Tom E. Howard** MD, PhD Director, Hemostasis Laboratory; **Marc Chalet** MD dermatopathology; **Eugene C. Dinovo** PhD clinical chemistry and toxicology; **Richard E. Horowitz** MD autopsy pathology; **Min Huang** MD surgical pathology; **Celina Nadelman** MD surgical pathology and cytology; **Faramarz Naiem** MD hematopathology; **Gholam H. Pezeshkpour** MD anatomic pathology; **Sylvia Suzuki** MD cytology; **Jerome S. Wollman** MD anatomic pathology and dermatopathology.

APPLICATIONS

Residency candidates must be graduates of approved medical schools and must be eligible for licensure in California. (H1B visas are no longer sponsored.) Deadline for application for the AP/CP program through ERAS is December 1. Interviews must be completed by January 15. Residencies usually begin on July 1, but other starting times are considered under exceptional circumstances. Medical students applying for PGY-1 positions should do so through the NRMP. Only ERAS applications will be accepted for these students. A personal interview is required.

Address inquiries to:

Wesley Y. Naritoku, MD, PhD, Program Director or
Ms. Nan Norona, Program Coordinator
LAC+USC Healthcare Network, CT A7E, 7th Floor
1100 North State Street
Los Angeles, CA 90033-1084
Phone: (323) 409-7148 • **Fax:** (323) 441-8193
Web site: http://www.usc.edu/medicine/pathology

UCLA HOSPITAL CENTER FOR THE HEALTH SCIENCES

Los Angeles, California

PROGRAMS OFFERED

Fully approved training in both anatomic and clinical pathology is offered for residents, interns and fellows. The training is provided in all general and surgical pathology specialties, including cytology, fine needle aspiration, immunopathology, electron microscopy, neuropathology, gastrointestinal, and oral pathology. The forensic pathology requirement is fulfilled at the Los Angeles County Coroner's Office. The clinical laboratory program includes all subspecialties including molecular pathology and computer adaptations. Research opportunities are numerous, including molecular pathology, neuropathology, ophthalmic pathology, cancer cell biology, infectious disease, and immunology. The department also offers graduate education leading to a PhD in cellular and molecular pathology.

TYPES AND NUMBERS OF APPOINTMENTS

The department presently supports 20 PGY1-4 residency positions, two fellowships each in neuropathology, cytopathology, GI pathology, hematopathology, and three fellowships in dermatopathology. One fellowship position per year is available in ophthalmic pathology, clinical microbiology, cardio/pulmonary, molecular pathology, and transfusion medicine. Between three and five surgical pathology fellowships are available each year. We also offer post-sophomore/post-junior fellowships to students currently enrolled in accredited U.S. or Canadian medical schools.

FACILITIES

The UCLA Hospital has been consistently rated among the five best hospitals in patient care in the nation. It is a part of the Center for the Health Sciences of the University of California, Los Angeles. The Center includes the David Geffen School of Medicine, the School of Dentistry, the School of Public Health, the Jonsson Comprehensive Cancer Center, and UCLA Santa Monica Hospital. The hospital has 669 licensed beds. The approximate number of examinations annually is: clinical laboratory, 3,414,275; surgical, 30,000; cytology, 32,000 and autopsy, 200. The computer division is adjacent to the clinical laboratories. The Center is on the UCLA general campus, providing access to the main university library of approximately 3 million volumes. The Biomedical Library, which is located contiguous to the Pathology Department, contains more than 263,000 volumes and subscribes to more than 6,500 journals. A new, state-of-the-art hospital and medical center is currently under construction on a separate site on the campus. This new hospital is designed by the world-renowned architectural firm of I.M. Pei, and construction is nearing completion.

COMMUNITY

The UCLA Hospital and campus are situated on the western edge of the City of Los Angeles, adjacent to the City of Santa Monica which is on the Pacific Coast. Cultural and recreational facilities are numerous, including a wide variety on the campus itself. A broad spectrum of living accommodations is to be found within a radius of a few miles of the hospital. University-owned or sponsored housing is available at competitive prices.

STIPENDS AND MAINTENANCE

Stipends: PGY-1 thru PGY-4 Residents $44,200 to $49,347; chief resident approximately $48,127 to $51,815 (depending on year of training), including full hospitalization and medical care, as well as meal allowance, uniforms and laundry. Living quarters are not available within the Center and must be arranged for by the residents.

STAFF

Professors

Scott D. Binder MD (Univ Chicago 1985); **Linda G. Baum** MD, PhD (Duke Univ 1986); **Judith A. Berliner** PhD (Brown Univ 1969); **Sunita M. Bhuta** MD (Bombay Univ 1968); **Jonathan Braun** MD (Harvard Univ 1981) Professor and Chair; **David A. Bruckner** ScD (Johns Hopkins Univ 1972); **Michael Cecka** PhD (UCLA 1975); **Alistair J. Cochran** MD (Glasgow 1966); **Kenneth Dorshkind** PhD (Univ Washington 1980); **Thomas A. Drake** MD (Univ Pennsylvania 1977); **Rita B. Effros** PhD (Univ Pennsylvania 1978; **Michael C. Fishbein** MD (Univ Illinois 1971); **Richard A. Gatti** MD (St. Louis Univ 1962); **David Gjertson** PhD (UCLA 1989); **Ben J. Glasgow** MD (Johns Hopkins Univ 1979); **Wayne W. Grody** MD PhD (Baylor Col of Med 1981); **Oliver Hankinson** PhD (Cambridge Univ 1972); **Sharon L. Hirschowitz** MD (Univ Witwatersrand 1978); **Scott D. Nelson** MD (Univ Nevada 1987); **Elaine F. Reed** PhD (Columbia Univ 1984); **Jonathan Said** MD (Witwatersrand Univ 1971) Head, Anatomic Pathology; **Harry V. Vinters** MD (Univ Toronto 1976) Head, Neuropathology; **Elizabeth Wagar** MD (Michigan State Univ 1981) Director, Clinical Laboratories.

Associate Professors

Anthony Butch PhD (Wayne State Univ 1987); **David Chia** PhD (UCLA 1972); **Charles R. Lassman** MD, PhD (Univ Pittsburgh 1992); **Paul S. Mischel** MD (Cornell 1991); **Jianyu Rao** MD, PhD (Shanghai Med Univ 1984); **Nagesh P. Rao** PhD (Univ Notre Dame 1985); **Nora Rozengurt** DVM, PhD (Univ London 1967); **Peter Tontonoz** MD, PhD (Harvard Univ 1996).

Assistant Professors

Sophia K. Apple MD (Wright State Univ 1992); **Galen R. Cortina** MD, PhD (Med Col Wisconsin 1993); **David Dawson** MD (Northwestern Univ 1999); **Sarah Dry** MD, PhD (Univ Connecticut 1995); **Samuel W French** MD, PhD (Univ Pittsburgh 1996); **Nicole A Gillis** MD (Univ Cal-Los Angeles 1996); **Lee Goodglick** PhD (Oregon Hlth Sci Univ 1969); **Dean Harvey** MD; **Kathleen A Kelly** PhD (Ohio State 1990); **Ayyappan K. Rajasekaran** PhD (Indian Inst Sci, Bangalore); **Peter Shintaku** PhD (UCLA 1973) Academic Supervisor; **Sophie X Song** MD, PhD (Capital Univ of Med Sci Beijing 1986); **Michael Teitell** MD, PhD (Univ Cal-Los Angeles 1993); **George V Thomas** MD (Royal Col Surgeons Ireland 1991); **Alyssa Ziman** MD (Sackler Sch Med 1997).

APPLICATIONS

PGY-1 candidates and above must be graduates of approved medical schools in the U.S. or Canada. Graduates of foreign medical schools must have received an eligibility letter from the California Medical Board prior to applying. Satisfactory references are required. Applicants participating in the National Resident Matching Program should submit their application by November 31 and complete the interview process by January 31. Residency training applications are accepted through the ERAS system only (www.aamc.org). Receipt of the applicant's Dean's Letter is not required for the interview. Chief Resident/Surgical Pathology Fellowship applications should be received by February 1 for the chief residency/fellowship that begins in the following year on July 1.

Address inquiries to:

Charles R. Lassman, MD, PhD, Vice Chair for Clinical Education, Department of Pathology and Laboratory Medicine, David Geffen School of Medicine at UCLA, 10833 Le Conte Avenue, Room A7-149 CHS, Los Angeles, CA 90095-1732.
Residency Training and Fellowship Program Coordinator:
Ms. Annetta Pierro
Phone: (310) 825-5719 • **Fax:** (310) 267-2058
Web site: www.pathology.ucla.edu

The new UCLA Center for Health Sciences Hospital, to be completed in 2006.

UNIVERSITY OF CALIFORNIA, IRVINE

Orange, California

PROGRAMS OFFERED

Fully approved four-year integrated programs in anatomic and in clinical pathology are available. This program is unique in offering a variety of practice settings among the three hospitals—University of California Irvine Medical Center, Long Beach Memorial Medical Center, and Veterans Affairs Medical Center (Long Beach). Residents will rotate on a quarterly basis. The combined hospital programs offer a wide variety of experience in autopsy and surgical pathology, fine needle aspiration, dermatopathology, oral pathology, histochemistry, cytopathology, neuropathology, electron microscopy, pediatric pathology, immunopathology, clinical chemistry, toxicology including drug screening, hematopathology and coagulation, blood banking and blood donor and pheresis programs, microbiology including mycology, parasitology, and virology and laboratory computer systems. Ample opportunity exists for research and teaching for individuals pursuing an academic career. A curriculum for residents with an interest in a career in Forensic Pathology is also available. Hospital conferences cover a wide range of specialties.

TYPES AND NUMBERS OF APPOINTMENTS

The program is approved for a total of 20 residents and fellows. First-year positions are available in the NRMP.

FACILITIES

Beds	389	760	416
Necropsy	70	49	70
Surgical Pathology	12,000	30,500	5,500
Cytopathology	54,000	99,000	3,200
Clinical Pathology	2,000,000	5 million	2.5 million
Blood Bank (transfusions)	8,000	12,000	4,000
Bone Marrows	500	500	300

COMMUNITY

UCIMC is located in the heart of Orange County. Numerous cultural events are held in the Performing Arts Center and South Coast Repertory Theater. Several universities are located near by, and amusement parks such as Disneyland and Knott's Berry Farm are a short distance from the complex. LBMMC and VAMCLB are in the coastal city of Long Beach with its own commercial seaport, renowned beaches, marinas, international trade center, university, theater, arena, and attractions such as the Queen Mary, and Grand Prix. The mild, pleasant climate promotes a wide variety of outdoor recreational activities.

STIPENDS AND MAINTENANCE

The salary scale of the University of California will be paid and for the 2008-09 was: Post-MD I $45,659; Post-MD II $47,211; Post-MD III $49,095; Post-MD IV $50,987. Three weeks paid vacation, educational leave, and medical and professional liability insurance are provided.

STAFF

Michael Selsted MD, PhD Chair; microbiology and molecular diagnostics; **Gloria Bertucci** MD anatomic pathology and clinical chemistry; **Philip Carpenter** MD surgical pathology; **Jefferson Chan** MD, PhD molecular pathology; **Gracita Dacosta-Iyer** MD surgical pathology; **Luis de la Maza** MD, PhD microbiology; **Milton Drachenberg** MD, PhD hematopathology; **Robert Edwards** MD, PhD gastrointestinal pathology; **Jane Emerson** MD, PhD clinical chemistry; **Emanuel Ferro** DVM, MD, PhD blood banking and anatomic pathology; **Mai Gu** MD, PhD cytopathology and surgical pathology; **Melvin Hoshiko** MD microbiology; **Julio Ibarra** MD surgical pathology and cytopathology; **Martin Jadus** PhD immunopathology; **Suzanne Keel** anatomic pathology; **Ronald Kim** MD neuropathology; **Joyce King** MD anatomic pathology; **John Krolewski** MD, PhD molecular pathology; **Gary Kukes** MD, PhD clinical chemistry and autopsy pathology; **Nils Lambrecht** anatomic pathology; **Fritz Lin** MD surgical pathology and cytopathology; **Irina K Maramica** MD, PhD blood bank; **Dan Mercola** MD; **Donald S Minckler** ophthalmic pathology; **Edwin S. Monuki** MD, PhD neuropathology; **Navneet Narula** MD cardiac pathology; **Richard Newman** MD blood banking and coagulation; **Yi Ouyang** surgical pathology; **Ellena Peterson** PhD microbiology; **Ibrahim Ramzy** MD cytopathology and gynecologic pathology; **Sherif Rezk** hematopathology; **Savita Ries** MD surgical pathology; **W. Edward Robinson Jr** PhD, MD AIDS research; **Lowell Rogers** MD surgical pathology; **Stephen G. Romansky** MD pediatric pathology, muscle pathology, surgical pathology and electron microscopy; **Joanne Rutgers** MD gynecological pathology and general anatomic pathology; **Sandor Szabo** MD, PhD surgical pathology; **Jane Tongson-Ignacio** surgical and cytopathology; **Mark L Wu** MD, PhD gastrointestinal and surgical pathology; **Chisa Yamada** MD, Transfusion Medicine; **Xiaohui Zhao** MD, PhD hematopathology.

APPLICATIONS

Applications for a position through the NRMP should be submitted and completed in accordance with their deadlines. Positions not filled by the NRMP will be available after March of each year, and application for these positions may be submitted at any time and are evaluated as soon as they are received. Candidates must either be graduates of LCME accredited medical schools in the USA or Canada or International medical graduates with current ECFMG certification and current Medical Board of California letter of commencement. Applications will be accepted through ERAS.

Address inquiries to:

Irina Maramica, MD
Director, Pathology Residency Training Program
University of California Irvine Medical Center
101 The City Drive
Building 10, Route 40
Orange, CA 92868
Residency Training and Fellowship Program Coordinator: Diana Speaker
Phone: (714) 456-6411 • **Fax:** (714) 456-5873
Web site: http://www.ucihs.uci.edu/som/pathology/residencyProgram.html

UNIVERSITY OF CALIFORNIA, DAVIS

Affiliated Pathology Residency Program

Sacramento, California

PROGRAMS OFFERED

The University of California, Davis Health System (UCDHS) is located in Sacramento and is the sponsoring institution for the program. Residents are based primarily at the UC Davis Medical Center in Sacramento but also participate in scheduled and elective rotations at affiliated facilities primarily at the VA Sacramento Medical Center or Clinics. They may also rotate at the Blood Source, the regional blood bank.

The University of California, Davis Health System (UCDHS) offers a fully accredited and integrated four-year training program in anatomic and clinical pathology. Fundamental training in general surgical, cytologic, autopsy, and clinical pathology is enhanced by the broad geographic catchment area served by the UCDHS. Training experiences include autopsy, neuropathology, surgical pathology, cytopathology, fine needle aspiration, blood banking, hematopathology, cytogenetics, microbiology, pediatric pathology, electron microscopy, management, informatics, immunology, chemistry, toxicology, therapeutic drug monitoring, forensic pathology and molecular pathology. In addition, elective training in dermatopathology, transplant pathology, head and neck pathology, urologic pathology, gynecologic pathology, gastrointestinal pathology, and transfusion medicine are available. The program emphasizes scholarly and academic activities, and each resident is encouraged to undertake or participate in an original scientific project, with the goal of publication in a peer reviewed journal and/or presentation at a scientific meeting. Opportunities for clinically oriented research are plentiful, while basic science research may be undertaken in conjunction with our research faculty based in Sacramento or the Davis Campus at the California Primate Research Center, and the Center for Comparative Medicine. Proficiency in the field of pathology is achieved through service work, complemented by daily morning conferences which include a core didactic lecture series.

TYPES AND NUMBERS OF APPOINTMENTS

There are 12 postgraduate physician positions in pathology as well as fellowships in hematopathology, surgical pathology, and cytopathology.

FACILITIES

The residency is based at the UC Davis, Medical Center in Sacramento. In addition to serving the main hospital, Cancer Center and outpatient clinics, the UCDMC Laboratory also provides services to an extensive primary care network throughout California's Central Valley, and is one of the region's rapidly expanding reference laboratories. The VA supports resident positions with regular rotations in the VA Northern California Healthcare Systems at the VA Mather Field. Resident rotations in anatomic pathology, microbiology, and clinical chemistry are currently supported. Other UCDMC affiliations include The Sacramento County Coroner's Office.

COMMUNITY

Sacramento, California's capital, is a medium-sized city located midway between the Pacific Ocean and the scenic Sierra Nevada Mountains, in the heart of the Sacramento Valley. The area features a favorable climate and reasonable cost of living. Nearby Davis, 14 miles to the west, offers a small, university-town atmosphere with abundant family-oriented resources, an excellent public school system, and numerous cultural and scholarly events drawn by the University. Recreational opportunities are plentiful, with skiing, hiking and backpacking, the San Francisco Bay Area, the Napa Valley Wine Country, and the majestic Pacific Coast all within two hours of the Sacramento metropolitan area.

STIPENDS AND MAINTENANCE

The 2008-2009 annual salaries are as follows: first year $45,659, second year $47,193, third year $49,095, fourth year $50,975. Fringe benefits include sick leave, medical, dental, vision, disability, and life insurance, generous annual leave, professional liability insurance, laundry, on-call meals, and generous developement and travel funds.

STAFF

UCDHS

Lydia Howell MD, Acting Chair.

Residency and Fellowship Program Coordinator

Penny Young penny.young@ucdmc.ucdavis.edu.

Anatomic Pathology

Alaa Afify MD Director Cytopathology; **Michael Berry** MD Surgical Pathology; **John Bishop** MD Director Surgical Pathology; **Alexander Borowsky** MD Breast Pathology; **Dariusz Borys** MD Soft Tissue and Bone/Pediatric

Pathology; **William Ellis** MD Neuropathology; **Regina Gandour-Edwards** MD Head and Neck Pathology; **William Gilles** MD Surgical Pathology; **Claudia Greco** MD Neuropathology; **Lydia Howell** MD Cytopathology; **Lee-Way Jin** MD, PhD Neuropathology and Research; **Malathy Kapali** MD Breast and GYN pathology; **Thomas Konia** MD Dermatopathology; **Rajendra Ramsamooj** MD Director, Residency Training Program; **Boris Ruebner** MD Gastrointestinal; **Ramez M Saroufeem** MD Gastrointestinal and Hepatology; **Cindy Yu** MD Surgical Pathology.

Clinical Pathology

Sridevi Devaraj PhD Clinical Chemistry and Toxicology, Research; **Denis Dwyre** MD, Director Hematopathology Fellowship; **Leonor Fernando** MD Transfusion Medicine and Apheresis; **Ralph Green** MD Hematopathology and Research; **Jeffrey Gregg** MD Molecular, Molecular Research; **Hanne Jensen** MD Director Transfusion medicine; **Ishwarlal Jialal** MD, PhD Clinical Chemistry, Cardiovascular Research; **Gerald Kost** MD, PhD Clinical Chemistry; **Edward C Larkin** MD Hematopathology; **Carol Marshall** MD Transfusion Medicine; **Christopher Polage** MD, Director, Microbiology.

Consortium Members

Alfredo Asuncion MD - VA Mather; **Patricia Dalton** MD - VA Mather; **Ivan Meadows** MD - Acting Director, VA Mather.

Joint Appointments

Robert Cardiff MD, PhD Caner and Mouse Biology Research; **Jimmy Chen** MD Hematopathology, Director of LIS; **Hwai-Jong Cheng** MD, PhD Neuroscience Institute; **Maxwell Fung** MD Dermatology; **Michael Hogarth** MD Internal Medicine, Research Informatics; **Fred Meyers** MD Internal Medicine; **Jeanna Welborn** MD internal medicine.

Volunteer Clinical Faculty

Elizabeth A Albers MD Forensics - Sacramento County Coroners; **Kathleen M Enstice** MD, Forensics - Sacramento County Coroners; **Stephany E Fiore** MD Forensics - Sacramento County Coroners; **Mark A Super** MD Forensics - Sacramento County Coroners.

APPLICATIONS

Candidates must be eligible for licensure in the State of California. If there is any question regarding eligibility, inquiries should go directly to the Medical Board of California. We participate in the Electronic Residency Application Service (ERAS). All applications and accompanying materials must be filed through ERAS. First-year appointments will be made through the National Resident Matching Program. Appointments at advanced levels are occasionally available, and open filing is permitted. Following review of complete applications, interviews of selected candidates will be arranged. Foreign medical graduates are encouraged to pursue experience in a clinical setting within the US prior to applying.

In accordance with applicable State and Federal laws and University policy, the University of California does not discriminate in any of its policies, procedures or practices on the basis of race color, national origin, religion, sex, sexual orientation, handicap, age, veterans status, medical condition (cancer-related) as defined in Section 12926 of the California Government Code, ancestry, or marital status; nor does the University discriminate on the basis of citizenship, within the limits imposed by law or university policy. Inquiries regarding the university's equal opportunity policies may be directed to the vice chancellor of academic affairs-affirmative action officer and Title IX coordinator, 525 Mark Hall, (916) 752-2070. Speech or hearing impaired persons may dial 752-7320 (TTD).

In conformance with applicable law and university policy, the University of California is an affirmative action/equal opportunity employer.

Address inquiries to:

Penny Young, Residency and Fellowship Program Coordinator
Department of Pathology and Laboratory Medicine
University of California, Davis Health System
4400 V Street, PATH Building
Sacramento, CA 95817
Phone: (916) 734-2525
Web site: http://ucdmc.ucdavis.edu/pathology

UNIVERSITY OF CALIFORNIA, SAN DIEGO

San Diego, California

PROGRAMS OFFERED

The Department of Pathology offers an accredited, intensive, and flexible program leading to Board eligibility available in three distinct tracks: straight anatomic pathology, straight laboratory medicine (clinical pathology), and the combined anatomic pathology and laboratory medicine. A neuropathology residency and a surgical pathology fellowship program are also available. The tracks in straight anatomic pathology or straight laboratory medicine are designed to give in-depth education in these specialties with emphasis on research experience and preparation for an academic career. Straight tracks require 24 months of approved core training and 12 months of subspecialty training. The combined track requires a minimum 18 months of approved core anatomic pathology, a minimum18 months of approved core laboratory medicine, and approximately 12 months of flexible rotations (anatomic pathology and/or laboratory medicine). Anatomic pathology core includes autopsy, surgical pathology, forensic pathology, electron microscopy, neuropathology, cytogenetics and cytopathology. Laboratory medicine core includes laboratory management, informatics, clinical chemistry, hematopathology, transfusion medicine-immunohematology, histocompatibility and immunogenetics, immunopathology, coagulation, toxicology, microbiology, and virology. Additional rotations are available in pediatric pathology, dermatopathology, comparative pathology, and molecular pathology and informatics. Opportunity for investigative activity exists and is encouraged. The University department, together with the Howard Hughes Medical Institute, the Ludwig Institute for Cancer Research, the UCSD Moores Cancer Center, the Scripps Research Institute, the Salk Institute, the Burnham Institute, and numerous biotechnology programs, collectively constitute an international center for research in immunopathology, neurosciences, molecular biology and related disciplines. Other opportunities for rotations include the Kaiser Permanente Medical Center, the United States Naval Regional Medical Center, the Children's Hospital and Health Center, the County of San Diego Medical Examiner's office, Scripps Clinic, and Sharp Hospital. Residents participate in the medical student teaching program of the University of California, San Diego, School of Medicine, and divide service commitments between the UCSD Medical Center and Veterans Affairs San Diego Health Care System (VASDHCS).

TYPES AND NUMBERS OF APPOINTMENTS

The total number of trainees in the program is twenty-one (21). In addition, training programs for advanced research training preparatory for academic careers are available for interested individuals after one to two years of pathology training.

FACILITIES

The University of California, San Diego, Medical Center is composed of UCSD Medical Center-Hillcrest and the UCSD Medical Center-La Jolla. The latter includes the Thornton Hospital, the Perlman Ambulatory Care Center, the Shiley Eye Center, and the Ratner Children's Eye Center. The Veterans Affairs San Diego Health Care System is an affiliated "dean's committee" medical center on the UCSD La Jolla campus. The combined licensed bed capacity of UCSD Medical Center (Hillcrest and La Jolla) is 504 and that of the VA Medical Center is 238. The annual combined workload of the UCSD and VASDHCS Clinical Laboratories includes over 7,000,000 clinical pathology procedures, more than 26,000 surgical specimens, nearly 200 autopsies, close to 23,000 cytological examinations, and around 200 electron microscopy specimens. The UCSD Biomedical Library (with locations in both Hillcrest and La Jolla) provides access to over 1,000 elecronic textbooks (including Harrison's Online, and Scientific American Medicine Online). There is also access to MDConsult and STATRef and Medline/HealthSTAR, Current Contents, Web of Science, and many more. The UCSD Biomedical library contains a quarter of a million volumes with 2,300 journal subscriptions; the Medical Center Library houses approximately 500 periodical subscriptions and 27,000 volumes.

COMMUNITY

San Diego, the sixth largest city in the United States, is the center of a beautiful, livable, metropolitan region of approximately 2,500,000 people. UCSD, which includes the Scripps Institutions of Oceanography, is a center for biotechnological research and located near several other noted research institutes, including the Scripps Research Institute, the Salk Institute, and the Burnham Institute. San Diego's climate, ranked one of the best in the United States, is ideal for outdoor activities of all kinds. With no heavy industry, the region remains one of the cleanest urban areas of its size in the country. Recreational and cultural facilities abound countywide and include museums, art galleries, theaters, the San Diego Zoo, Mission Bay Aquatic Park (home to SeaWorld), beautiful beaches, breathtaking deserts and mountains, and nearby Mexico just 20 minutes from downtown.

STIPENDS AND MAINTENANCE

Post-MD I, $45,659, Post-MD II $47,211, Post-MD III $49,095 Post-MD IV $50,987 Post-MD V $52,905. There are four weeks of vacation time each year. Leave is available to attend scientific meetings, with travel compensation for residents who have first-authored papers to be presented. All house officers are provided with uniforms and laundry of uniforms. A University-paid insurance plan consists of medical, dental, basic life, basic disability, vision and professional liability. Housing is not provided; however, pleasant living accommodations are available close to either hospital. There is a one-time $1500 moving stipend, and initial educational stipends totaling $2000 the first year and $800 per year thereafter.

STAFF

Chairperson

Steven L. Gonias MD, PhD.

Residency Program Director

Brian Datnow MD (Witwatersrand Univ 1970) surgical pathology.

Full Rank Faculty

H. Elizabeth Broome MD (Univ Pennsylvania 1983) hematopathology; **Nigel Calcutt** PhD (Univ Nottingham, UK 1988) experimental neuropathology; **David A Cheresh** PhD (Univ Nottingham, UK 1988) Microbiology/immunology; **Lynette B. Corbeil** (Cornell Univ 1974) experimental infectious diseases; **Brian Datnow** MD (Witwatersrand Univ. 1970) Surgical Pathology; **Marilyn C. Farquhar** PhD (Univ Cal-Berkeley 1955) cell biology, experimental pathology; **Joshua Fierer** MD (NYU 1963) microbiology; **Steven L. Gonias** MD, PhD (Duke Univ 1983, 1984) coagulation, protease biochemistry, hemostasis; **Parviz Haghighi** MD (Shiraz Univ 1961) surgical pathology; **Lawrence Hansen** MD (Loyola Univ 1977) neuropathology; **David Herold** MD, PhD (Univ Utah 1979, 1982) clinical chemistry, mass spectrometry; **Michael Kalichman** PhD (Univ Toronto 1980) experimental neuropathology; **Mark P. Kamps** PhD (UC San Diego 1986) Director, Molecular Pathology Graduate Program; molecular pathology; **Michael J. Kelner** MD (Univ Minnesota 1981) special chemistry, toxicology; **Theo N. Kirkland III** MD (Univ Alabama 1975) microbiology; **Richard L. Klemke** PhD (Texas Tech Univ 1993) cell and developmental biology; **Henry Krous** MD (Univ of Nebraska, Omaha) Director of Pathology at Children's Hospital San Diego; **Thomas A. Lane** MD (Jefferson Med Col 1969) transfusion medicine; **Eliezer Masliah** MD (National Autonomous Univ Mexico 1983) Director Autopsy Service, UCSD Medical Center-Hillcrest; Alzheimer's disease research; **Ronald L. McLawhon** MD, PhD (Rush Med Col, Univ Chicago 1986, 1982) Director, Division of Laboratory Medicine; **Katsumi Miyai** MD, PhD (Keio Univ 1956, Univ Toronto 1967) hepatic and gastrointestinal pathology; **Andrew P. Mizisin** PhD (UC Irvine 1984) experimental neuropathology; **Henry C. Powell** MD, DSc (Univ Col, Dublin 1970) Head, Division Neuropathology; neuropathology; **Sharon L. Reed** MD (Harvard Univ 1978) microbiology, parasitology; **Douglas D. Richman** MD (Stanford Univ 1970) virology; **Sam Ridgway** PhD, DVM (Cambridge Univ 1974, Texas A&M Univ 1960) marine mammals; **Ahmed S. Shabaik** MD (Univ Cairo 1977) genitourinary pathology, fine-needle aspiration cytology; **Diane Shelton** DVM, PhD (UC Davis 1979, 1985) Director, Comparative Neuromuscular Disease Laboratory; neuromuscular disorders; **David Tarin** MD (Oxford Univ 1963) diagnostic surgical pathology, mechanisms of metastases; **Nissi M. Varki** MD (Christian Med Col 1975) glycobiology, histology; **Gernot Walter** PhD (Max Planck Inst Biochem, Munich 1965) molecular pathology; **Kenneth Watson** DO (Kansas City College of Ostepathic Medicine) Chief of Anatomic Pathology VA; **Noel Weidner** MD (Univ Rochester 1975) Director, Division Anatomic Pathology; surgical pathology; **Paul L. Wolf** MD (Univ Michigan 1952) autopsy pathology; **Dong-Er Zhang** Ph.D. (Univ of Houston, TX) Pathology and Molecular Biology.

Associate Rank Faculty

Lesley G Ellies PhD (Univ Toronto, Canada) MRC Group in Periodontal Physiology; **Robert Fitzgerald** PhD (Med Col Virginia 1989) mass spectrometry; **Dzung The Le** MD, PhD (Mount Sinai 1989, UC San Diego 1985) blood banking, coagulation; **Lauralynn Lebeck** PhD (Univ Illinois 1991) immunogenetics, transplantation immunology; **Celsa Spina** PhD (UC Davis 1976) experimental virology; **Ann M. P. Tipps** MD (Med Col Virginia 1987) surgical pathology; **Jessica Wang-Rodriguez** MD (Univ Nevada 1990) immunohematology, surgical pathology, flow cytometry.

Assistant Rank Faculty

Jack D. Bui MD, PhD (UC San Diego, 2001; 1999) immunology; **Farnez Hasteh** MD (Iran Univ Med Sci, 1995) surgical pathology; **Grace Lin** MD, PhD (Northwestern 2002) Anatomic Pathology; **Mana Parast** MD, PhD (University of Virginia, Charlottesville) Gynecologic and Perinatal Pathology; **Michael Peterson** MD, PhD (Univ California, San Diego) Gastrointestinal and Liver Pathology; **Christina J Sigurdson** DVM, PhD (Univ California, Davis, Colorado State) Anatomic Pathology; **Dwayne G. Stupack** PhD (Univ Manitoba, 1996) angiogenesis.

Emeritus Faculty

Nicholas M. Alexander PhD (UC Berkeley 1958) chemistry, thyroid; **Kurt Benirschke** MD (Hamburg Univ, Germany 1948) reproductive and comparative pathology, autopsy; **Colin M. Bloor** MD (Yale Univ 1960) cardiovascular pathology, endotheliology; **Charles E. Davis** MD (Texas Southwestern Med Sch 1958) microbiology and parasitology; **Cecil Hougie** MD (Univ London 1946) special coagulation; **Harvey Itano** MD, PhD (St. Louis Univ 1945, Caltech 1950) biochemistry, hematology; **Serafeim P. Masouredis** MD, PhD (Michigan 1948, UC Berkeley 1952) blood banking, immunohematology; **Michael N. Oxman** MD (Harvard Univ 1963) virology; **Samuel I. Rapaport** MD (USC 1945) special coagulation; **C. Ann Rearden** MD (McGill Univ 1971) Director, Clinical Laboratories, UCSD Medical Center-La Jolla; immunogenetics; **Sidney L Saltzstein** MD, MPH (Johns Hopkins Univ 1954) oncology and epidemiology; **Robert D. Terry** MD (Albany Med Col 1950) neuropathology; **Francis White** PhD (Georgia Inst Technol 1963) cardiovascular pathology.

APPLICATIONS

Internship and residency candidates must be graduates of approved medical schools in the United States or Canada, or meet licensure requirements in the State of California at the time of application. Inquiries concerning licensure should be made directly to the State Board of Medical Quality Assurance. Appointments are made through the National Resident Matching program. All applications will be accepted through ERAS and are due by Nov 1 each year. Interviews are completed by February 1 for the following July.

Address inquiries to:

Melissa Wahl, MPH, Pathology House Staff Coordinator
University of California San Diego Medical Center
200 West Arbor Street, Mail Code 8320
San Diego, CA 92103
Phone: (619) 543-5966 • **E-mail:** mmwahl@ucsd.edu
Web site: http://medicine.ucsd.edu/pathology/

UNIVERSITY OF CALIFORNIA, SAN FRANCISCO

San Francisco, California

PROGRAMS OFFERED

The Departments of Pathology and Laboratory Medicine offer programs in either anatomic or clinical pathology or a combined program in anatomic and clinical pathology. On average, eight to ten new positions are available each year. The combined program provides two years of training in anatomic pathology and two years in laboratory medicine. The straight programs in anatomic pathology or laboratory medicine provide opportunities for developing a degree of expertise in the general fields, as well as in-depth experience in specific aspects of anatomic pathology or clinical pathology. The programs in anatomic pathology offered to residents include training in fine-needle aspiration cytology, dermatopathology, neuropathology, immunohistochemistry, hematopathology, electron microscopy and renal pathology in addition to surgical and autopsy pathology, transplantation pathology, and exfoliative cytology. Research opportunities are available in such areas as dermatopathology, neuropathology, surgical pathology, immunology, and experimental pathology. The programs in clinical pathology (laboratory medicine) include training in clinical chemistry, hematology, microbiology, parasitology, immunology, transfusion medicine, molecular diagnostics, molecular genetics, laboratory management, and informatics. Research experience is available in all areas.

TYPES AND NUMBERS OF APPOINTMENTS

Twenty-nine resident positions: 17 anatomic pathology, 12 clinical pathology.

FACILITIES

Residents in the anatomic and clinical pathology training programs rotate among the three university or affiliated hospitals (UCSF Medical Center, San Francisco General Hospital, Veterans Affairs Medical Center), as well as the UCSF Comprehensive Cancer Center. In these varied settings, residents have ample opportunity to study a wide spectrum of diseases and become familiar with a broad range of diagnostic techniques.

COMMUNITY

San Francisco, with a population of almost 750,000, is located at the tip of the San Francisco Peninsula, facing the Pacific Ocean, the Golden Gate and San Francisco Bay. The UCSF Medical Center is within walking distance of Golden Gate Park, and San Francisco General Hospital is in the sun belt of the city, 15 minutes away by shuttle from UCSF Medical Center. The Veterans Affairs Medical Center, also 15 minutes from UCSF Medical Center, occupies scenic grounds overlooking the Golden Gate National Recreation Area and the Pacific Ocean. San Francisco is worldrenowned for its many culinary, recreational, artistic, and cultural opportunities.

STIPENDS AND MAINTENANCE

Stipends for house staff range between $45,659.00 and $50,987.00, determined by the year of training. New residents are given $2,400 for relocation. In addition, the departments provide an annual housing allowance of $4,000 for residents up to the PGY- 5 level as well as additional $7200.00/per annum paid for by the School of Medicine. Residents are provided $1,000 annually for professional expenses. Residents are provided professional liability insurance, long-term disability and life insurance, and medical/dental/vision insurance including coverage for family members. Uniforms and laundry service are also provided.

STAFF

Maria Serrano-Correa MD; **Annemike Van Zante** MD, PhD, cytopathology, surgical pathology.

Department of Laboratory Medicine

George F. Brooks, Jr. MD (Washington 1966) microbiology; **Michael P Bush** MD, PhD (Keck Sch Med 1982); **Farid F. Chehab** PhD (Beirut 1983) molecular diagnostics; **Lawrence W. Drew** MD, PhD (Jefferson Univ 1962, 1966) virology; **Joan E. Etzell** MD (Univ California 1992) Director Hematopathology Fellowship, hematology; **Eberhard Fiebig** MD (Univ Göettingen 1980) transfusion medicine, hematology; **Barbara Haller** PhD, MD (Minnesota 1983, St. Louis 1990) microbiology; **Christine Haller** MD (Univ California 1994) clinical pharmacology; **Timothy Hamill** MD (California 1983) Director Clinical Labs, UCSF Med Ctr; hematology; **Nora V Hirschler** MD (Rosario Univ 1970); **Linda Jeng** MD, Ph.D. Director of Molecular Genetics and Assistant Director of Cytogenetics; **William Karlon** MD, PhD (Univ Cal-Irvine 2002) Immunology; **Scott C. Kogan** MD (California 1991) hematology; **Theodore W. Kurtz** MD (Univ Michigan 1979) renal physiology, clinical chemistry; **Andrew Leavitt** MD (Harvard Univ 1984) transfusion medicine; **Jack Levin** MD (Yale Univ 1957) hematology; **Elizabeth St. Lezin** MD (Univ California 1987) transfusion medicine; **Clifford A. Lowell** MD, PhD (Johns Hopkins Univ 1984) Chair of Lab Medicine immunology; **Mark C Lu** MD, PhD (Tongji Med Univ 1988) hematology; **Steve Miller** MD, PhD (Albert Einstein Col Med 2003)

Inf. Disease/Microbial Pathogenesis; **Ashok Nambiar** MD (Sri Venkatesvara Univ 1985) transfusion medicine; **C. Diana Nicoll** PhD, MD (Univ London 1969, NYU 1975) Director, Clinical Laboratory, VAMC; clinical chemistry; **Herbert A Perkins** MD (Univ Cal-San Francsico, 1943) Dir. of Transfusion Medicine; **D. Lynn Pulliam** PhD (Univ California 1983) microbiology; **Imran Siddiqi** MD, Ph.D. Assistant Director, Clinical Hematology; **Enrique Terrazas** MD, MS (Univ California 1993) Director Residency Program, informatics; **Pearl T.C.Y. Toy** MD (Stanford Univ 1973) transfusion medicine; **Frederic M. Waldman** MD, PhD (NYU 1980) molecular cytogenetics; **Alan Wu** PhD (Univ Illinois 1980) clinical chemistry; **Maria Yiu** Phd Assistant Director Cytogenetics; **Jingwei Yu** PhD (Univ Cal-San Francisco 1997) Cytogenetics.

Department of Pathology

Joanna Phillips MD, Ph.D. neuropathology; **Bradley Stohr** MD, PhD; **Abul K. Abbas** MD (AIIMS, India 1968) Chair, Department Pathology; immunology; **Frederick Baehner** MD (Univ Kansas, 1997) cytology, surgical pathology; **Anna Berry** MD (Univ Nebraska 1995) molecular/cytopathology; **Andrew W. Bollen** DVM, MD (Univ California 1980, 1985) neuropathology; **Yunn-Yi Chen** MD (Univ Taiwan 1994) surgical pathology; **Lisa Coussens** PhD (UCLA 1993) Research Institute & Anatomic Pathology; **Darren Cox** DDS (Univ Louisiana 1990), Oral Pathology; **Teresa M. Darragh** MD (Cornell Univ 1986) cytology, surgical pathology; **Stephen J. DeArmond** PhD, MD (Med Col Pennsylvania 1972, 1975) neuropathology, experimental pathology; **Jayanta Debnath** MD (Harvard Med. School 1998) Autopsy, Cancer biology research; **Linda D. Ferrell** MD (Univ Kansas 1977) Director, Surgical Pathology; liver, gastrointestinal and surgical pathology; **Walter Finkbeiner** MD, PhD (Univ Illinois 1978) Chief Pathology, SFGH; **James P. Grenert** MD, PhD (Mayo Medical School 2000) surgical pathology; **Douglas K. Hanks** MD (Univ Nevada 1984) cytology; **Andrew Horvai** MD, PhD (Univ San Diego, CA 1998) surgical pathology; **Eric J. Huang** MD, PhD (Natl Taiwan Univ 1986, Cornell Univ 1993) neuropathology; **Gioia Iezza** MD (Univ degli studi Roma, 1995) cytology, surgical pathology; **Kirk D. Jones** MD (Univ California 1994) cytology, surgical pathology; **Richard Jordan** DDS, PhD (Univ Toronto 1986) Oral and Maxillofacial Pathology; **Sanjay Kakar** MD (Chandigarh, India 1994) surgical pathology; **Elham Khanafshar** MD (Tehran Univ 1997) cytopathology; **Grace Kim** MD (Loma Linda Univ 1995) pediatric pathology; **Max Krummel** PhD (California 1995) immunology; **Zoltan Laszik** MD, PhD (Univ Szege, Hungary 1980) Renal Pathology; **Philip E. LeBoit** MD (Albany Med Col 1979) dermatopathology; **Britt-Marie E. Ljung** MD (Karolinska Univ 1975) fine-needle aspiration cytology; **Marta Margeta** MD, PhD (Univ Zagreb 1991) neuropathology; **Timothy H. McCalmont** MD (Univ Iowa 1986) dermatopathology; **James H. McKerrow** PhD, MD (Univ California 1973, Stony Brook 1976) experimental pathology; **Theodore R. Miller** MD (Louisville Univ 1969) Director, Cytopathology; fine needle aspiration cytology, gynecologic pathology; **Stephen L. Nishimura** MD (Univ Vermont 1988) surgical pathology; **Scott Oakes** MD (Univ Connecticut 1998) autopsy pathology; **Jean Olson** MD (Univ Rochester 1974) renal pathology, electron microscopy; **Luke Perkocha** MD (Univ Hawaii 1983) dermatopathology; **Joseph Rabban** MD (Harvard 1998) surgical pathology; **Werner Rosenau** MD (California 1956) surgical pathology; **Beth Ruben** MD (Stanford Univ 1989) Dermatopathology; **Henry C. Sanchez** MD (USC 1985) autopsy pathology; **Jeffry Simko** MD, PhD (Univ North Carolina, 1996) surgical pathology; **Robert Stern** MD (Univ Washington 1962) experimental pathology; **Z. Laura Tabatabai** MD (Missouri 1995) cytology; **Tarik Tihan** MD, PhD (Istanbul Univ 1985) neuropathology; **Thea Tlsty** PhD (Washington Univ 1980) molecular biology; **Patrick A. Treseler** MD, PhD (Duke Univ 1985) Director, Residency Training Program; surgical pathology; **Philip C. Ursell** MD (Columbia 1976) cardiovascular pathology, developmental pathology; **Scott Vandenberg** MD, PhD (Stanford Univ 1979) neuropathology; **Martha L. Warnock** MD (Harvard Univ 1960) pulmonary pathology; **Tien-Sze Benedict Yen** PhD, MD (Duke Univ 1981, 1982) Director, Anatomic Pathology Service, VAMC; experimental pathology, renal pathology; **Charles J. Zaloudek** MD (Johns Hopkins Univ 1971) cytology, obstetrics and gynecology.

APPLICATIONS

Applicants must be graduates of approved allopathic or osteopathic medical schools in the United States or Canada, or be a foreign medical graduate with a current ECFMG certificate and an "Applicant Evaluation Status Letter" issued by the Medical Board of California. Residency applications are accepted only through the Electronic Residency Application System (ERAS), and must be received by December 15 for appointments beginning July 1 of the following year. First-year postgraduate training appointments are made through the National Resident Matching Program.

Address inquiries to:

Pathology Residency Training Program
University of California, San Francisco
Departments of Pathology and Laboratory Medicine
505 Parnassus Avenue
San Francisco, CA 94143-0506
Phone: (415) 353-7359 • **Fax:** (415) 353-7354 • **E-mail:** kirsten.jeworowski@ucsf.edu
Web site: http://pathology.ucsf.edu/education/residency/residency-index.html

STANFORD UNIVERSITY MEDICAL CENTER

Stanford, California

PROGRAMS OFFERED

The Pathology Department of Stanford University School of Medicine seeks to train outstanding academically-oriented candidates for leadership positions in pathology. The overall goal of our program is to provide in-depth training in all aspects of pathology leading to board certification in Anatomic Pathology (AP), Clinical Pathology (CP), combined AP and CP (AP/CP), combined AP and Hematopathology (AP/HP), or combined AP and Neuropathology (AP/NP), depending on the resident's career goals. We also offer accredited fellowships in several specialty areas and advanced training in Surgical Pathology (Fellowship in Surgical Pathology). See the separate descriptions of these opportunities. *Anatomic Pathology* (AP) consists of 24 months of structured training followed by 12 months of flexible training. The structured rotations include extensive surgical pathology and autopsy experience, as well as specialty training in cytopathology, dermatopathology, forensic pathology, hematopathology, immunohistochemistry and neuropathology. The third year of required training may be customized by the resident to meet her or his individual needs. A variety of research opportunities exist (see below). Those who would prefer an additional year of clinical training may apply for our Surgical Pathology fellowship or design an alternative year of AP in conjunction with the faculty in accord with the trainee's career plans. *Clinical Pathology* (CP) consists of 24 months of structured training and 12 months of flexible training, but not necessarily in that order. Structured training includes a core experience in chemistry, hematology, microbiology/virology, and transfusion medicine. This may begin when the resident starts training or, alternatively, after the resident has spent time establishing a basic, translational or clinical research project. Structured clinical training also includes integrated rotations in genetics (biochemical, cytogenetic and molecular), pediatric, coagulation and general laboratory medicine. *Combined AP/CP* (AP/CP) residency training at Stanford consists of a solid grounding in AP during the first two years; an introduction to the major areas of laboratory medicine during the third year; and an integrated final year during which residents are encouraged to synthesize all previous knowledge and solidify their ability to practice general diagnostic pathology. A fifth year of training, in AP, is guaranteed for / all/ AP/CP residents who wish to take advantage of this program. We believe that more than 2 years of training in AP is required for the practice of surgical pathology. Residents interested in this option may apply for our Surgical Pathology Fellowship or take an alternative year of AP training that will be designed in conjunction with the faculty in accord with the trainee's career plans. *Combined AP/Hematopathology* (AP/HP) residency training at Stanford consists of AP training, as described above, for the first two years followed by a third year of Hematopathology training with extensive exposure to both wet and tissue hematopathology, coagulation, flow cytometry, immunohistochemistry, cytogenetics and molecular pathology. The program also includes 12 months of flexible training. *Combined AP/ Neuropathology* (AP/NP) training at Stanford consists of AP training, as described above, for the first two years followed by 24 months of Neuropathology (NP). The first 12 months of NP training concentrates on diagnostic surgical and autopsy neuropathology, including extensive exposure to muscle pathology, FISH and other molecular diagnostic techniques, and specialized immunohistochemistry; in the second 12 months, the trainee develops a research project and/or acquires additional expertise in diagnostic NP, depending upon the ultimate career objectives of the trainee. *Research.* The department encourages all residents to pursue research projects, and we urge AP, CP, AP/Hematopathology or AP/Neuropathology residents planning careers in academic or experimental pathology and related fields to pursue an intensive experience in basic or translational research. In addition to the department's own research opportunities, which are extensive, there are also ample opportunities to work with investigators in other departments at the medical school or elsewhere in Stanford University. The research also could be conducted at UCSF, as long as the trainee continues her or his clinical activities at Stanford. The Department will assist our residents in finding a suitable laboratory for their research training. The flexible portion of the residency training period may be used to pursue research that can be extended into a period of subsequent postdoctoral training. Residents and mentors are expected to seek outside support (e.g., NIH K08, etc.) for such additional research experience. During this period, the trainee ordinarily will provide service work in their clinical area of interest at the 15 or 20% effort level. Until the external award is received, or if the external award does not provide salary support at the equivalent PGY level plus the standard housing benefit (see below), then the Department will supplement the trainee's salary to that level for up to three years. In most cases, those seeking NIH K08 awards will be appointed to the academic rank of Instructor in the Department of Pathology.

FACILITIES

Stanford University Medical Center (SUMC) is located on the campus of Stanford University in Palo Alto, California, 35 miles south of San Francisco. SUMC includes Stanford Hospital and Clinics, Lucile Packard Children's Hospital, Stanford University School of Medicine and the Lane Medical Library. Nearby is the Palo Alto Veterans Affairs (PAVA) Medical Center, a newly rebuilt 900-bed facility whose pathology service is an integral part of our department. Additional facilities fully occupy two buildings adjacent to the PAVA Medical Center. One houses new clinical laboratories for increased in-patient, out-patient and outreach laboratory testing. The other is the home of the Stanford Blood Center, that is part of the Department of Pathology, and houses some of the department's research laboratories.

COMMUNITY

Palo Alto, a community of about 61,200 inhabitants, is located 35 miles south of San Francisco on the San Francisco Bay. It is situated on the San Francisco Peninsula, which has a population of about one million. The city is within driving distance of many types of recreational areas including seaside resorts, skiing areas and numerous regional, state and national parks. The elementary and secondary school systems are outstanding, and the city provides a number of cultural and recreational facilities. Interns, residents, and their families, as members of the Stanford University community, can also take advantage of the abundant educational, cultural, and athletic activities of the University.

STIPENDS AND MAINTENANCE

Stipends are commensurate with experience, plus additional $8400 per year housing allowance.

STAFF

The pathology faculty consists of 75 full and part-time faculty members, of which 54 focus primarily on clinical and educational activities.

APPLICATIONS

Address inquiries to:

Diana Y. Chang
Department of Pathology
Stanford University Medical Center
Stanford, CA 94305-5324
Phone: (650) 725-8383 • **E-mail:** dianayc@stanfor.dedu
Web site: http://pathology.stanford.edu/

Stanford University Medical Center, Stanford, California.

HARBOR-UCLA MEDICAL CENTER

Torrance, California

PROGRAMS OFFERED

The Department of Pathology offers a fully accredited four year comprehensive training in Anatomic and Clinical Pathology, or three year training in Anatomic Pathology only. Our program accepts candidates who are new medical school graduates, and physicians with a transitional year internship or one year or more in another medical specialty. Experience in medical research is welcomed. The Anatomic Pathology core program features 22 months of rotations in surgical pathology, autopsy and forensic pathology, cytopathology, molecular biology, electron microscopy and neuropathology; the Clinical Pathology core rotations include 19 months of hematology, transfusion medicine, clinical biochemistry and toxicology, microbiology, immunopathology, and HLA/genetics. Laboratory management and administration topics are integrated into all rotations and offered as a periodic seminar series. Additional monthly rotations are performed in the third and fourth year as 3 or more months of electives of the resident's selection, Chief Resident supervision of intraoperative frozen sections and resident scheduling, and as a rotation in Junior Attending service. All residents participate in the educational conferences and significant case work review ongoing in all AP/CP rotations throughout their training. Resident participation in research activities and publication is strongly encouraged and supported. A fifth year of Surgical Pathology Fellowship experience is also offered to selected individuals.

REQUIREMENTS

Application (ERAS); self-statement; CV; 3 LOR; USMLE/COMLEX scores 1, 2 (3 if available); med school dean's letter; med school transcript. **For foreign applicants**: ECFMG certificate; Medical Board of CA Evaluation Status Letter. **Acceptable Visa Types**: The institution will not sponsor any visas. Only J-1 visas sponsored by ECFMG are allowed.

TYPES AND NUMBERS OF APPOINTMENTS

The program has 14 PGY1-PGY4 residents and 2 Surgical Pathology Fellows.

FACILITIES

Harbor-UCLA Medical Center is a 570 bed hospital providing comprehensive surgical and diagnostic care to Los Angeles County patients in southwestern Los Angeles County, and serving a population of over 2 million as a regional Trauma Center. It is the second largest of five Los Angeles County supported medical centers, as a branch of the UCLA School of Medicine. In-patient admissions exceed 22,000 yearly. Several large outpatient clinical services provide 250,000 patient visits per year. Residency programs in twelve other medical specialties are offered at this medical center. The hospital facilities have recently undergone clinic and resident on-call facilities expansion, and extensive renovation of other areas, including upgraded computer hospital information network and modern earthquake retrofitting. The Department of Pathology faculty is comprised of 10 full time physicians with academic appointments from the UCLA School of Medicine, an active group of associated pathologists, who have clinical teaching appointments from UCLA, a Ph.D. clinical chemist and a Ph.D. microbiologist. The Division of Surgical Pathology accessions 11,000 specimens yearly, from a full spectrum of patient demographics and clinical diagnoses. Autopsies number about 60 per year, with additional autopsy and forensic experience provided by a Los Angeles County Coroner's rotation. The Cytopathology Laboratory handles over 800 fine needle biopsy aspirations per year, with the majority of the aspiration procedures performed by pathology residents. Hematopathology cases number about 300 per year; flow cytometry is performed on-site. The Diagnostic Electron Microscopy laboratory processes about 250 specimens yearly. The Clinical Pathology Division processes over 4 million analytic procedure requests yearly. Clinical Chemistry, Microbiology, Hematology and Transfusion Medicine facilities are on-site, computerized and readily accessible for training. Transfusion Medicine training includes in-hospital donor center and plasmapheresis procedures. Other on-campus facilities include a comprehensive UCLA branch medical library and Department of Pathology computer teaching and reference libraries. The Harbor-UCLA LA BioMedical Research Institute provides extensive educational seminar programs accessible to all residents, as well as research facilities noted for basic and clinically-related research in a complex adjacent to the hospital.

COMMUNITY

Harbor-UCLA Medical Center is in the city of Torrance at the mid coastal edge of the Los Angeles metropolitan area. It is five miles from Pacific Ocean beaches, in a pleasant, largely residential area with close freeway access. Our sister LA County-USC Medical Center and UCLA School of Medicine main campus are each 20 freeway miles away, as is downtown Los Angeles' cultural center. The climate is mild and dry, typical of Southern California.

STIPENDS AND MAINTENANCE

Annual salary for a PGY1 is currently set at $43,957; PGY2 $49,177; PGY3 $53,284; PGY4 $57,420 and PGY5 $61,443. Residents benefits include professional liability coverage, health and disability insurance. Residents are provided uniforms with laundry, three daily meals, and parking without cost.

STAFF

Luciano Barajas MD (Univ Madrid, Spain 1956) Head, Autopsy Services and Pediatric Pathology; renal autoregulation; **James A Baker** MD (Univ Michigan 1961) hematopathology; **Marcia E. Cornford** MD, PhD (UCSD 1984) Head, Neuropathology; neuropathology of viral encephalitis; **Gloria B. Duane** (Ohio State Univ 1976), Cytopathology; **Samuel W. French** MD (UCSF 1952) Chief, Anatomic Pathology; Head, GI Pathology and EM; liver pathology; **Paul C. Fu** PhD (Univ Massachusetts 1968) Head, Clinical Biochemistry; enzymology, pharmacogenetics, biochemical instrumentation; **Thomas Hirose** (UCLA 1987) Transfusion Medicine; **Holli M. Mason** MD (Med College of Virginia 1995) Director, Transfusion Medicine and Serology; **Laron McPhaul** MD (Univ Minnesota, Minneapolis 1984) Co-director, Molecular Pathology; Head, GYN Pathology; molecular pathology; **Robert E. Morin** MD (UCSF 1960) Chairman; Head, Chemical Hematology; cholesterol and atherosclerosis; **Shi-Kaung Peng** MD, PhD (Natl Taiwan Univ 1966, Northwestern Univ 1971) Head, Surgical Pathology, Cardiovascular Pathology and Dermatopathology; lipid metabolism, atherogenesis, cardiac ultrastructure; **Beerelli Seshi** MD (Osmania, India 1977) Head, Hematopathology; proteomics and genomics of bone marrow stromal mesenchymal progenitor cells; **Nora C.J. Sun** MD (Shanghai Second Med Col 1961) hematopathology; **Rose Venegas** MD (UCLA 1983) Head, Cytopathology; fine needle aspiration; **Robert Yoshimori** PhD (UCSF 1971), Microbiology.

Attending Physicians Consultants

David Bernstein MD (Univ Connecticut 1983) anatomic pathology; **Arthur H. Cohen** MD (SUNY, Buffalo 1967) anatomic pathology; **Frank M. Hirose** MD (Univ Oklahoma 1951) anatomic pathology; **Hideo H. Itabashi** MD (Boston 1954) neuropathology; **Maria Perla Lamtenza-Vargas** MD (Cayeton Heredia Peruvian Univ 1986) anatomic pathology; **Moon Lee** PhD (Univ Hawaii 1979) virology; **Yun Lin** MD (Nat Taiwan Univ 1996) anatomic p athology; **Byron A. Myhre** MD (Univ Illinois 1953) blood banking; **Cynthia C. Nast** MD (New York Med Col 1979) anatomic pathology; **Joanne K. Rutgers** MD (UCSD 1981) gynecology pathology; **Walid Salahi** MD (Damascus Univ 1979); **Paul Shitabata** MD (Univ Hawaii, 1988) dermatopathology; **Lucilene F Tolentino** MD (Univ of Santo Tomas 1987) anatomic pathology; **Jun Wang** MD (Wannan Med Col 1982) hematopathology; **Harout Yaghsezian** MD (Yerevan State Med Inst 1981) cytopathology; **Chang Yue** MD (Second Univ Med Univ 1984) hematopathology.

APPLICATIONS

ERAS applications should be completed by December 1 for appointment beginning July 1 of the following year. Interviews will be scheduled before January 30 with faculty and residents to facilitate selection of residents.

Address inquiries to:

Holli M. Mason, MD
Director, Pathology Training Program
Department of Pathology
Harbor-UCLA Medical Center
1000 West Carson Street
Torrance, CA 90502
Phone: (310) 222-2643 • **E-mail:** adflores@dhs.lacounty.gov
Web site: www.harbor-ucla.org/pathology

UNIVERSITY OF COLORADO DENVER SCHOOL OF MEDICINE

Aurora, Colorado

PROGRAMS OFFERED

The Department of Pathology offers a comprehensive 4-year residency training program in anatomic and clinical pathology. The training curriculum and rotation experiences are based on the ACGME and RRC requirements. We seek to produce professional, educated residents who meet or exceed the competency requirements in pathology, have a broad knowledge of human and experimental pathogenesis and are curious, motivated, lifetime learners. Residents rotate through a variety of clinical settings staffed by Department of Pathology faculty including: the University of Colorado Hospital and Clinics, the Denver Veteran's Affairs Medical Center, The Children's Hospital, and Denver Health Medical Center. We encourage residents to explore areas of clinical sub-specialization through electives and fellowships to meet the increasing demands and complexity of modern pathology. Residents are also required to develop an academic (research) project and are supported to present that work at a national scientific meeting of their choice. The Department of Pathology is both a clinical and basic science department at UCDSOM. We also have Ph.D. faculty and a Ph.D. program in Cancer Biology. Our faculty have expertise in molecular pathology, cancer biology and pathogenesis, environmental carcinogenesis, comparative pathology/animal models of cancer, biochemistry, immunopathology, cytogenetics, proteomics, general surgical pathology, cytopathology, cytogenetics, dermatopathology, urologic and renal pathology, breast and gynecologic pathology, head and neck pathology, hematopathology, pulmonary pathology, pediatric pathology, forensic pathology, clinical chemistry, transfusion medicine and coagulation, immunopathology, lab management and informatics. We have post-residency fellowships in dermatopathology, general surgical pathology, transfusion medicine, and pediatric pathology.

Resident training will occur primarily at the new University of Colorado Hospital and the Children's Hospital in Aurora. The Denver Veterans Affairs Medical Center (moving to the Anschutz Medical Campus in 2011), and Denver Health Medical Center are in nearby Denver. These are connected for conferences through e-conferencing and web based systems.

TYPES AND NUMBERS OF APPOINTMENTS

A total of 23 ACGME-approved positions are available, with up to 7 first-year positions. Residents are expected to complete both AP and CP training, rather than subspecialize in one or the other. Applicants with an MD or MD/PhD degree are welcome to apply. A 5th year in laboratory research as part of the residency program may be negotiated for exceptional candidates. The department also supports fellowships in General Surgical Pathology (2), Dermatopathology (2), and Transfusion Medicine (1).

FACILITIES

The Anschutz Medical Center (AMC) is northeast of downtown Denver, in the city of Aurora. It has ready access to the Denver International Airport (DIA), the mountains (for winter and summer activities), and affordable housing in family-oriented communities. The Veterans Affairs Medical Center and Denver Health Medical Center are approximately 20 minutes away by car or shuttle, and are located within the city of Denver.

COMMUNITY

Metropolitan Denver (including Aurora) has a popultation over two million and is widely known for its restaurants, the arts and a youth-oriented culture. Although the weather is generally mild, our proximity to the Rocky Mountains provides year round access to a wide range of climates and activities.

STIPENDS AND MAINTENANCE

Stipends start at $45,487 per year for interns with increments of $1,500 annually. Residents receive medical insurance coverage for themselves and their families, as well as life insurance, professional liability insurance and disability insurance. Residents also receive some support for academic expenses, including travel to meetings, if they are presenting research findings.

STAFF

Professors

Ann D. Thor MD, Chair (Vanderbilt Univ 1981) cytopathology, gynecologic pathology, breast biology and cancer pathogenesis; **Steven Anderson** PhD (Rockefeller Univ 1981) molecular and development biology; **Geza Bodor** MD

(Semmelweis Med Univ, Hungary 1978) clinical chemistry, toxicology; **Bette K. DeMasters** MD (Univ Wisconsin 1977) neuropathology; **Wilbur A. Franklin** MD (Northwestern Univ 1968) surgical pathology, tumor markers; **Loren E. Golitz** MD (Univ Missouri 1966) dermatopathology; **Robert O. Greer** DDS, ScD (Howard Univ 1969, Boston Univ 1974) oral pathology; **Peter Henson** DVM, PhD (Univ Edinburgh, Cambridge, England 1967) immunology; **Jeffrey Holt** MD (Univ Michigan 1979) anatomic pathology, breast cancer research; **Richard Irons** PhD (Univ Rochester 1974) toxicology; **Ronald B. Lepoff** MD (Univ Rochester 1967) clinical pathology; **Stuart Lind** MD (NYU 1976) coagulation; **Steven K. Nordeen** PhD (Univ Rochester 1976) molecular biology, mechanism of hormone action; **Stephen Raab** MD (SUNY Syracuse 1988) cytopathology, quality/outcomes; **James O. Stevens** DVM, PhD (Univ Washington 1975) veterinary pathology; **Tsieh Sun** MD (Hunan Med Col, China 1956) immunopathology and flow cytometry; **Ruben Tuder** MD (Sao Paulo Univ SOM, Sao Paulo, Brazil 1979) pulmonary pathology; **Michael Wilson** MD (Univ Colorado 1984) clinical pathology, microbiology; **Xiao-Jing Wang** MD, PhD (Beijing Medical Univ 1984) molecular pathology of head and neck cancer.

Associate Professors

Mark Brissette MD (Loma Linda Univ 1983) hematopathology; **Mary Berg** MD (Medical College of Wisconsin 1991) transfusion medicine; **Carlyne Cool** MD (Univ Colorado 1992) pulmonary pathology; **Michael Dobersen** MD, PhD (Univ Colorado 1989, Univ Miami 1976) forensic pathology; **Robert Evans** PhD (Univ Pennsylvania 1975) cell biology, cytoskeleton; **Loretta Gaido** MD, PhD (Univ Honduras 1982, Emory Univ 1987) clinical microbiology, anatomic pathology; **Joseph Gal** PhD (Univ Cal-Davis) drug assay; **Dana Grzybicki** MD, PhD (UCLA 1990, Univ Iowa 1995) outcomes research, undergrad education; **Haihua Gu** PhD (Tufts 1995) mechanisms of breast cancer progression; **Ronald Harbeck** PhD (South Dakota 1971) immunology, immunodiagnostics; **Kenneth Iczkowski** MD (St Louis Univ 1992) genitourinary pathology, molecular mechanisms of prostate cancer; **Frank Jones** PhD (McMaster Univ Canada 1995) molecular biology of breast cancer; **Kevin Land** MD (Univ Texas SW Med Ctr 1992) bloodbanking, transfusion medicine; **Christina Leslie** PhD (Univ Georgia 1975) microbiology, immunology; **Xiayuan Liang** MD (Capital Univ Med Sci, China 1982) hematopathology, blood banking; **Mark Lovell** MD (Univ Colorado 1983) anatomic pathology, molecular diagnosis; **Robert L. Low** MD, PhD (Univ Chicago 1977, 1975) anatomic pathology, molecular diagnosis; **M. Scott Lucia** MD (Univ Colorado 1988) anatomic pathology, renal pathology, genitourinary pathology, growth factors; **Loris McGavran** PhD (Univ Denver 1976) cytogenetics; **Nancy Madinger** MD (UCLA 1994) clinical microbiology; **Samia Nawaz** MD (Punjab Univ, Pakistan 1976) surgical pathology, cytopathology; **David J. Orlicky** PhD (Univ Colorado 1986) molecular signalling mechanisms, growth regulation; **Edmund Orsini** MD (Univ Arkansas 1969) pediatric pathology; **Chitra Rajagopalan** MD (Armed Forces Med Col India 1978) transfusion medicine, blood banking; **Mona Rizeq** MD (Univ Sheffield Med Sch, England 1983) surgical pathology, cardiovascular pathology; **John Ryder** MD (Univ Colorado 1983) hematopathology, molecular biology; **M. Sherif Said** MD (Univ Cairo 1978) surgical pathology, head and neck; **Karen Swisshelm** PhD (Univ of Washington 1989) cytogenetics of cancer.

Assistant Professors

Gissou Azabdaftari MD (Univ Bologna, Italy 1994) surgical pathology, cytopathology, bone and soft tissue neoplasms; **Roberto Gianani** MD (Univ Rome, Italy 1989) diabetes research; **Lorne Holland** MD (Univ Illinois 2003) transfusion medicine, coagulation; **Paul Jedlicka** MD, PhD (McGill Univ 1999, Johns Hopkins 1996) pediatric pathology; **Ken Kassenbrock** MD, PhD (Univ of California, SF 1989) breast cancer biology; **Francisco G. La Rosa** MD (National Univ Federico Villarreal, Peru 1975) prostate pathology; **James Lambert** PhD (Univ Cal-Irvine 1995) molecular biology; **Tuan Le** MD (Univ Colorado 1993) transfusion medicine; **Bolin Liu** MD (Beijing Med Univ, China 1987) molecular mechanisms of breast carcinogenesis; **Amy Martin** MD (Ohio State Univ 1984) forensic pathology; **Daniel Merrick** MD (Univ Washington 1989) lung cancer; **J.L. Loes Nardi-Korver** MD (Vrije Univ, Netherlands 1995) anatomic pathology; **Sheila Nielsen-Preiss** PhD (SUNY 1993) bone tumors; **Miriam Post** MD (Thomas Jefferson Univ 2004) gynecologic pathology, neonatal pathology; **Jennifer Richer** PhD (Colo State Univ 1992) molecular mechanisms of hormone-dependent carcinogenesis; **Amy Storfa** MD (Univ Colorado 2003) surgical pathology; **James W. Wahe** MD (Univ Nebraska 1971) forensic pathology; **Priya Werahera** PhD (Colorado State Univ 1994) application of bioengineering in prostate cancer diagnosis; **Joshua Wisell** MD (Univ Colorado 2003) surgical pathology, dermatopathology.

Instructors

Susan Edgerton MA (Central Michigan Univ 1981) breast cancer research; **Ralph Giorno** MD (Univ Colorado 1974) surgical pathology; **Patricia Skavlen** DVM (Univ Oklahoma 1981) veterinary pathology; **Kathleen Torkko** PhD (Univ Colorado 2005) epidemiology/genetic risk for prostate cancer; **Adriaan vanBokhoven** PhD (Univ Nijmegen, Netherlands 2004) prostate cancer metastasis.

APPLICATIONS

Candidates must be graduates of American Allopathic or Osteopathic Medical Schools or have passed the ECFMG examinations. Completed applications should be submitted through ERAS and be received by November 1 for appointments beginning July 1 of the following year.

Address inquiries to:

Robert L. Low, MD, PhD
Residency Program Director
E-mail: robert.low@uchsc.edu
or
Patricia Braund
Residency Program Coordinator
E-mail: patricia.braund@uchsc.edu
Web site: http://www.uchsc.edu/pathology

Anschutz Centers for Advanced Medicine (Photo furnished by Lisa Litzenberger)

PENROSE HOSPITAL

Colorado Springs, Colorado

PROGRAMS OFFERED

The fully approved four-year Penrose training program in combined anatomic and clinical pathology is uniquely appropriate for independent individuals interested in academic residency training in a tertiary care referral hospital. The goal of the program is to equip anatomic and clinical pathologists with specific skills in management and teaching in order to become leaders in clinical practice, whether ultimately university or community based. The Division of Anatomic Pathology offers training in autopsy, surgical and cytopathology including all subspecialties thereof. The outpatient and multihospital program provides a well-balanced caseload including all types of pulmonary, cardiovascular, gastrointestinal, neurologic, pediatric, neonatal, ophthalmologic, nose and throat, gynecologic and urologic pathology. Fluorescence microscopy is extensively used in both anatomic pathology and diagnostic microbiology and serology. Extensive immunopathologic techniques are employed using immunoperoxidase, immunofluorescence, 3- and 4-color flow cytometry, and DNA probe techniques for solid tumor and hematopoietic malignancies. Transmission electron microscopy is performed for both diagnostic and research purposes. Forensic pathology exposure and experience are provided through collaboration with the El Paso County Coroner's Office and the Medical Examiner's System for the State of New Mexico. The Division of Clinical Pathology provides training in all phases of general and special clinical chemistry, toxicology, hematology, blood coagulation, transfusion medicine, microbiology, serology, parasitology, virology, and cytogenetics. Residents actively participate in the research and development of new procedures throughout the laboratory. Both practical and didactic teaching are conducted in the areas of laboratory management, biostatistics, test and methodology evaluation, and laboratory computers. Residents at all levels of training are actively involved in the teaching of departmental and hospital-wide conferences.

TYPES AND NUMBERS OF APPOINTMENTS

Six pathology residency positions are currently available, with planned expansion by 2011 to eight positions. The program includes: 42 months of anatomic and clinical rotations; 1 month each in molecular biology/cytogenetics, forensic pathology, and flow cytometry; and 3 months of electives.

FACILITIES

The Penrose-St. Francis Health Care System consists of two hospitals, Penrose Hospital and the new St. Francis Hospital, opened in 2008 both located in Colorado Springs. Penrose Hospital provides services of medicine, surgery and subspecialties thereof. St. Francis Hospital provides similar services with the addition of obstetrics, pediatrics, and neonatology. The total number of beds for both hospitals is 522. The average combined daily census is 247 with annual admissions of 23,409 (excluding newborns). In 2004, there were 3,092 births at Penrose Community Hospital. There are 643 physicians on the active medical staff of the Penrose-St. Francis hospitals, consisting of Board-certified specialists and subspecialists. The hospital has a hospitalist program for inpatient care. In 2008, there were 31 autopsies, 19,099 surgical pathology specimens (including 456 bone marrows biopsies, most of which are performed by residents and staff from the Department of Pathology), 11,974 cytology specimens (including 2162 non-gynecological specimens), 2459 flow cytometrical evaluations, 948 fluorescence in situ hybridization studies, 3338 molecular studies, 1215 chromosome analyses, and 269 electron microscopy cases (including 251 renal biopsies). The autopsy suite has been completely redesigned and remodeled and includes shower and dressing areas. The highly automated clinical laboratory has a staff of 197 technical and nontechnical personnel. Each resident is provided with a private study carrel in the residents' office area. A medical librarian staffs the hospital library with 200 annual subscriptions and a fine textbook and monograph section. An intradepartmental library with emphasis on surgical pathology is provided in the laboratory.

COMMUNITY

Colorado Springs is a young, urban area with a population of approximately 517,000. The city, at an elevation of 6,000 feet, is located on the eastern side of 14,000-foot Pikes Peak, 65 miles south of Denver. The University of Colorado at Colorado Springs, Colorado College, the Air Force Academy, and Pikes Peak Community College are located here. The Olympic Training Center, Fine Arts Center, Broadmoor International Center, and Pikes Peak Center for the Performing Arts offer a wide variety of cultural, recreational and social events. Year round mountain activities including hiking, mountain climbing, hunting, fishing, kayaking, cycling and skiing are within easy driving distance. Athletic facilities and locker rooms are available on the hospital campus. A two-mile-long creek-side city park begins two blocks from the hospital complex.

STIPENDS AND MAINTENANCE

Resident salaries: First-year residents $44,605; second year $46,040; third year $46,169; fourth year $48,954. Additional benefits include professional liability and health insurance, laboratory coats, laundry, breakfast and lunch meals, educational assistance for medical meetings, and tuition assistance for the MBA degree. A stipend is given for moving expenses.

STAFF

Jerome Myers MD, PhD (Boston Univ 1990) Anatomic and Clinical Pathology; hematopathology; **Cosimo G. Sciotto** MD, PhD (Case Western Reserve Univ 1976) Anatomic and Clinical Pathology; hematopathology, leukemia cytochemistry, coagulation, cytogenetics, immunopathology; **Tobias Kircher** MD (Harvard Univ 1976) Anatomic and Clinical Pathology; clinical chemistry, epidemiology, autopsy pathology, GI pathology, laboratory management; **Barry Lawshe** MD (New Mexico Univ 1981) Anatomic and Clinical Pathology; laboratory computers and information management; **Eileen Nobles** MD (Univ Colorado 1985) Anatomic and Clinical Pathology; hematology, coagulation, toxicology; **Douglas Franquemont** MD (Univ Colorado 1987) Anatomic and Clinical Pathology; cytology, surgical pathology, laboratory management; **Richard Rupkalvis** MD (Rush Univ 1989) Anatomic and Clinical Pathology; cytology and surgical pathology; **Sigurd Torgerson** MD (Univ Iowa 1993) Anatomic and Clinical Pathology, dermatopathology, surgical pathology; **David Newton** MD (Loma Linda 1999) Anatomic and Clinical Pathology, hematopathology; **Tim Drumheller** PhD (Wayne State Univ 1995) Molecular Biology/Genetics, (Yale 1997) Fellowship in Clincal Cytogenetics; **Daniel C. Mayes** MD (Vanderbilt Univ 1986) Anatomic and Clinical Pathology, dermatopathology.

APPLICATIONS

Candidates must be graduates of approved medical schools in the U.S. or Canada and be eligible for a Colorado state medical license at the end of the first postgraduate year. The last week of June is the normal beginning date for residency, but other times may be available. Applications are accepted through the ERAS program.

Address inquiries to:

Daniel C. Mayes, MD, Department of Pathology
Penrose Hospital
2222 N Nevada Ave
Colorado Springs, CO 80907
Phone: (719) 776-5816 • **Fax:** (719) 776-2108
Web site: http://www.penrosepathologyresidency.org

View of Pikes Peak from Colorado Springs

HARTFORD HOSPITAL

Hartford, Connecticut

PROGRAMS OFFERED

Hartford Hospital is an 867-bed general and tertiary care teaching hospital and transplantation center affiliated with the University of Connecticut School of Medicine. Hartford Hospital also provides all pathology services for Connecticut Children's Medical Center, a separate 128-bed pediatric hospital on the Hartford Hospital campus. Fully approved program in anatomic and clinical pathology is designed for the training of either academic or community hospital-based pathologists. Anatomic pathology includes rotations through autopsy, surgical pathology, cytology, immunohistochemistry, pediatric pathology and forensic pathology. Clinical pathology rotations include clinical chemistry, cytogenetic and molecular pathology, microbiology, hematology and transfusion medicine. Clinical pathology rotations are performed at Hartford Hospital and Clinical Laboratory Partners, LLC, a reference laboratory that provides outpatient laboratory services through over thirty outpatient facilities in Connecticut. Structured training in anatomic pathology, clinical pathology and laboratory management consists of both weekly didactic lectures and working conferences (AP Unknown Slide Conference and CP Laboratory Working Rounds). Housestaff also actively participate in intra and interdepartmental conferences and are encouraged to take advantage of opportunities in the Department for clinical or basic research. The program is generally divided into 27 months spent in anatomic pathology and 19 months in clinical pathology with 2 months allotted for rotation of electives in another discipline.

TYPES AND NUMBERS OF APPOINTMENTS

A total of twelve resident positions are offered in pathology. These are distributed over a four year period with, in general, three first year positions available. Fellowships are available for one year in surgical pathology, hematopathology and cytopathology. (See Specialized Area Section).

FACILITIES

The Department of Pathology and Laboratory Medicine processed 37,250 surgical tissues including 3,900 intraoperative consultations. In addition, there was over 4700 Hematology cases and 1700 outside consultations. The cytology division handled approximately 70,000 gyn specimens and 6,000 non-gyn specimens in 2007. There is a very active fine needle aspiration biopsy service, which evaluates samples from all body sites. There were 115 medical autopsies preformed in 2007 and 1,740medicolegal autopsies/examinations at the Office of the Chief Medical Examiner in Farmington, CT. The clinical laboratories are well equipped and automated and all have active research and development sections. Over 2.8 million tests were performed in the Hartford Hospital laboratories during 2007 with active Hematology, Transfusion and Molecular Pathology services. Personal computers are provided for resident use. Career counseling and seminars in practice management, stress and risk are provided. Parking is free for residents. In addition to the excellent departmental library, the hospital library contains more than 12,000 books and bound volumes, including 850 journal titles. There is also access to the libraries of the Hartford Medical Society and the University of Connecticut Medical Center, as well as an extensive electronic library. A hospital maintained gymnasium is available for resident use.

COMMUNITY

Hartford is the state capital of Connecticut, and as such offers extensive cultural opportunities. Hartford is located in the north central portion of Connecticut and is midway between Boston and New York. Hartford's population is 124,000.

STIPENDS AND MAINTENANCE

Salaries for the 2008-09 academic year are: first year $46,200; second year $48,500; third year $51,300; fourth year $52,500; fifth year $53,500; sixth year $54,600. Medical insurance coverage is available for single house officers as well as married with dependents, and malpractice insurance is provided by the hospital. Apartments and single rooms (hospital owned) are available at cost. Privately owned apartments are present in the immediate neighborhood.

STAFF

William T. Pastuszak MD, Chairman, Pathology; hematopathology; **Evelyn Abernathy** MD, anatomic pathology, clinical pathology, hematopathology; **Desiderio Arce** MD, anatomic pathology, clinical pathology; **Jaber Aslanzadeh** PhD, microbiology; **Margaret Assaad** MD, surgical pathology,cytopathology,gynecological pathology; **Fabiola Balarezo** MD, anatomic pathology, pediatric pathology; **Adrienne Berke** MD, Consultant, dermatopathology; **Richard Cartun** PhD, immunopathology; **Thomas Ciesielski** MD, anatomic pathology, neuropathology; **Joseph A. DiGiuseppe** MD, hematopathology, anatomic pathology; **Jonathan Earle** MD, molecular pathology; **Ellen Eisenberg** DMD, Consultant, oral and maxillofacial pathology; **Mary Fiel-Gan** MD, anatomic pathology, cytology, pulmonary pathology; **Jane M. Grant Kels** MD, Consultant, dermatopathology; **Diane Hoss** MD, Consultant, dermatopathology; **Vijay Joshi** MD, Consultant, pediatric pathology; **Saverio Ligato** MD, anatomic pathology, cytology, clinical pathology; **Mark**

E. Ludwig MD, anatomic pathology, cytology, gynecologic pathology; **Gregory Makowski** PhD, chemistry; **Srinivas Mandavilli** MD, anatomic pathology, clinical pathology, cytology; **Edward T. McDonough III** MD, Consultant, forensic pathology; **Laila Mnayer** PhD, cytogenetics and molecular genetics; **Richard Muller** MD, anatomic pathology, cytology; **Michael Murphy** MD, Consultant, dermatopathology; **William N. Rezuke Jr.** MD, hematology, hematopathology, blood banking; **Andrew Ricci, Jr.** MD, anatomic pathology; **Bradford Sherburne** MD, clinical pathology, hematopathology; **Yanjun Su** MD, surgical pathology, cytology; **Dean F. Uphoff** MD, anatomic pathology, neuropathology; **Theresa Voytek** MD, anatomic pathology, cytopathology; **Rebecca Williams** MD, anatomic pathology; **Harold T. Yamase** MD, Consultant, renal pathology.

APPLICATIONS

Candidates must be graduates of approved medical schools in the United States or Canada or graduates of foreign schools with an ECFMG certificate. Applications are accepted only via ERAS with a deadline of November 1st.

Address inquiries to:

Rebecca N. Williams, MD
Director, Graduate Medical Education
Department of Pathology and Laboratory Medicine
Hartford Hospital
80 Seymour St.
Hartford, CT 06102-5037
Phone: (860) 545-6113 • **E-mail:** cdavids @clpct.com
Web site: http://www.harthosp.org/education

Hartford Hospital, Hartford, Connecticut.

YALE-NEW HAVEN MEDICAL CENTER

New Haven, Connecticut

PROGRAMS OFFERED

PROGRAM(S) Yale University School of Medicine and Yale-New Haven Hospital provide training for residents seeking Board certification in Anatomic Pathology (AP), Clinical Pathology (CP), and both Anatomic and Clinical Pathology (AP/CP). The Residency Program's mission is to provide comprehensive post-graduate training in anatomical and clinical pathology, and to prepare physicians for leadership in clinical practice, research, and academia. We produce world-class physicians and physician-scientists capable of fulfilling the role of the pathologist as a diagnostic consultant and of advancing the field of pathology. Training in Pathology is provided by both the Department of Pathology and the Department of Laboratory Medicine, coordinated into a single Residency Program. Working together, the two departments assure strong training in both Anatomic and Clinical Pathology. Rotations at the West Haven campus of the Veterans Administration Healthcare System (VA) and at Bridgeport Hospital in Bridgeport, CT, broaden the training experience. Residents acquire a fundamental knowledge and understanding of the various subspecialties of anatomic and clinical pathology. The core AP training is 24 months. Core CP training is 18 months. Combined training provides several options for the sequence of the core training, which is then supplemented with six months of flexible training opportunities, including transitional ''fellowship-level'' training and basic research (experimental pathology). In anatomic pathology, approximately 50,000 surgical specimens, 100,000 cytology specimens, and 230 autopsies are studied yearly. The laboratory medicine program provides training in clinical chemistry, hematology, immunology, transfusion medicine, and microbiology/virology. Molecular diagnostics experience, both formal and informal, is integrated into both anatomic and clinical pathology training. Opportunities for in-depth experience with research are available for those interested, and may be pursued not only within the two Departments, but also with mentors in other basic science or clinical departments in the School of Medicine, School of Public Health, and Yale University. Pathology residents are responsible for the presentation of cases at interdepartmental conferences, and participate in Pathology and Laboratory Medicine course laboratories for second-year medical students.

TYPES AND NUMBERS OF APPOINTMENTS

A total of 29 resident positions are available. Of these, 6-8 are first-year positions. Residents may arrange a program comprising straight anatomic (AP), straight clinical (CP), or a combination of anatomic and clinical pathology (AP/CP). Please be sure to specify your track preference when applying. Within each track, residents can pursue one of two career paths: ''diagnostic practice'' or ''physician scientist''.

STIPENDS AND MAINTENANCE

For 2008-2009 the range of resident salaries was $50,200 to $58,000 per annum. Chief residents receive an additional stipend. Benefits include medical, dental, disability, professional liability, life insurance, vacation, sick leave, prescriptions, and an annual professional allowance. To maintain the quality of our staff, Yale-New Haven Medical Center feels it is essential to recruit and employ the people best prepared and committed to serve; therefore, drug testing is a condition of employment.

STAFF

All faculty members of the Departments of Pathology and Laboratory Medicine have appointments at Yale University School of Medicine.

Department of Pathology

Jon S. Morrow MD, PhD (Yale Univ 1976) Professor, Chairman and Chief. Research: protein chemistry; **Young J. Choi** MD (Seoul Natl Univ Col Med 1966) Professor and Vice Chair. Research: immunopathology and molecular pathology; **José Costa** MD (Univ Barcelona 1967) Professor and Vice Chair. Research: tumor pathology and molecular genetics of tumors; **A. Brian West** MD (Univ Dublin, Trinity Col 1979) Professor and Vice Chair; Director of Anatomic Pathology. Research: non-neoplastic gastrointestinal and liver disease; **Adebowale Adeniran** MD University of Ibadan, Nigeria, 1995, Assistant Professor; **Veerle Bossuyt** MD (Vrije Univ 2002) Assistant Professor. Research: molecular markers as an adjunct to cytologic and histologic examination; **Demetrios Braddock** MD, PhD (Univ Chicago 1996) Assistant Professor. Research: structural biology of protein complexes in cancer; **Guoping Cai** Wenzhou Medical College, Zhhejaiang, China, 1983, Assistant Professor, Research: Fine needle aspiration (FNA), cytology and urologic pathology; **Robert Camp** MD, PhD (Yale Univ 1997) Associate Research Scientist. Research: Quantitative Pathology; **David Chhieng** MD, (Univ Hong Kong, 1987, Professor and Director, Research: Gynecologic cytology, thyroid and pancreas fine needle aspiration biopsy, breast pathology, and immunohistochemistry; **Jan K. Czyzyk** MD (Warsaw Med Sch 1992) Associate Research Scientist. Research: signal transduction in T cells; **Paul Cohen** MD Columbia Univ., College of Physicians and Surgeons, 1981, Assistant Professor, Research: general surgical pathology, pulmonary pathology, and general pathology; **Steve E. Downing** MD (Yale Univ 1956) Professor Emeritus. Research: cardiac pathology and pathophysiology; **James Gill** MD (Univ CT 1992) Assistant Clinical Professor. Research: forensic pathology; **Earl Glusac** MD (Michigan State Univ 1987) Professor. Research: cutaneous T cell lymphoma/mycosis fungoides; melanocytic neoplasms; epithelioid cell histiocytoma; **Kenneth G. Haines III** MD (Ohio State Univ 1987) Associate Professor. Research: mechanisms of inflammation, arthritis; **Liming Hao** MD (Beijing Med Col 1983) Associate Professor. Research: GI pathology; **Malini Harigopal** MD (Osmania Univ 1985) Assistant Professor. Research: quantitative protein expression in breast cancer and prediction of therapeutic response; **Robert J. Homer** MD, PhD (Yale Univ 1987) Associate Professor. Research: experimental pulmonary pathology; **Pei Hui** MD, PhD (Xian Med Col 1984) Associate Professor. Research: molecular oncogenesis; **Anita Huttner** MD, PhD (Friedrich-Alexander Univ Erlangen-Nurnberg 1998) Assistant Professor. Research: neuropathology; **Dhanpat Jain** MD (Mysore Univ India 1986) Associate Professor. Research: GI and liver disease; **Michael Kashgarian** MD (Yale Univ 1958) Professor Emeritus. Research: renal pathophysiology; **Sihem Khelifa** MD (School of Medicine, Annaba, Algeria, 1985), Research: breast and gynecologic pathology; **Jung Kim** MD (Pusan Natl Univ 1964) Professor Emeritus. Research: neuropathology; **Steven Kleinstein** PhD (Princeton Univ 2002) Assistant Professor. Research: computational immunology, systems biology, statistical and model-based analysis of experimental and clinical data; **Diane P. Kowalski** MD (Med Col Georgia 1994) Assistant Professor. Research: head and neck tumors; **Michael O. Krauthammer** MD, PhD (Univ of Zurich 1995) Assistant Professor. Research: biomedical informatics, computational biology; **Themis R. Kyriakides** PhD (Washington State Univ 1993) Assistant Professor. Research: vascular biology, wound healing, bioengineering; **Angelique Levi** MD (Univ Rochester Med Coll, 1997) Instructor. Research: cytopathology and genitourinary and gynecologic pathology; **Paul M. Lizardi** PhD (Rockefeller Univ 1972) Professor. Research: cancer genetics/epigenetics; **Joseph A. Madri** MD, PhD (Indiana Univ 1975) Professor. Research: vascular biology, connective tissue biology, and immunobiology of autoimmunity; **Vincent T. Marchesi** MD, PhD (Yale Univ 1963) Professor. Research: membrane biochemistry; **Robert Means** PhD (Harvard Univ 1999) Assistant Professor. Research: viral oncology and immune evasion; **Wang Min** PhD (Univ of Wales 1993) Associate Professor. Research: vascular biology; **Kisha Mitchell** MD (Univ West Indies 1998) Assistant Professor. Research: gastrointestinal and liver pathology; **Gilbert Moeckel** MD, PhD (Ludwig Maximilians Univ 1989) Associate Professor. Research: renal pathology/nephrology; **Vinita Parkash** MD (Lady Hardinge Med Col 1988) Associate Professor. Research: gynecologic neoplasms and gestational trophoblastic disease; **Marguerite Pinto** MD (St Johns Med Sch India 1971) Assistant Professor. Research: tumor markers in cyst fluids, effusions and FNA breast pathology; **David Rimm** MD, PhD (Johns Hopkins Med Inst 1989) Professor. Research: tissue biomarkers, tissue microarrays; **Michael Robek** PhD (Washington Univ 2000) Assistant Professor. Research: virus-host interactions; viral immunology; hepatitis viruses; interferon; **Marie Robert** MD (Univ Michigan 1988) Associate Professor. Research: inflammatory bowel disease; **John K. Rose** PhD (Stanford Univ 1973) Professor. Research: viral assembly and viral vectors as vaccines; **Ozlen Saglam** MD (Marmara Univ Med Sch, Istanbul, Turkey 1982), Assistant Professor. Research: breast and gynecologic pathology Rochester Med College, 1997) Instructor. Research: cytopathology and genitourinary and gynecologic pathology; **Gerald S. Shadel** PhD (Texas A&M Univ 1991) Associate Professor. Research: mitochondrial gene expression and disease; **John Sinard** MD, PhD (Johns Hopkins Med Inst 1990) Professor; Director of the Residency Training Program. Research: pathology informatics; **Jeffrey Sklar** MD, PhD (Yale Univ 1977) Professor. Research: molecular diagnostics, molecular oncology, immunogenetics; **David F. Stern** PhD (Univ California 1983) Professor. Research: growth factor receptors in carcinogenesis and DNA checkpoint signaling; **Fattaneh Tavassoli** MD (St Louis Univ 1968) Professor. Research: breast and female genital tract tumors; **Constantine Theoharis** MD (Univ Illinois 1997) Assistant Professor. Research: molecular diagnostic techniques in cytopathology and surgical pathology; **David P. Tuck** MD (Univ Vermont 1985) Assistant Professor. Research: bioinformatics, computational biology; **Zenta Walther** MD, PhD (Weill Med Col Cornell Univ 1995) Assistant Professor. Research: epithelial cell polarity and the cytoskeleton; **Raymond Yesner** MD (Tufts Univ 1941) Professor Emeritus; Research: lung tumors; **Eduardo Zambrano** MD, MS (Univ Catolica de Santiago de Guayaquil, Ecuador 1992) Assistant Professor. Research: perinatal and pediatric pathology.

Secondary Appointments

Shawn E. Cowper MD (Michigan State Univ 1990) Assistant Professor. Research: nephrogenic fibrosing dermopathy; **Anjela Galan** MD (N Testimitanu Kishinev State Med Inst 1991) Instructor. Research: dermatopathology; **Christine Ko** MD (New York Univ 1999) Assistant Professor. Research: cutaneous and adnexal neoplasms; **Rossitza Lazova** MD (Higher Med Univ Bulgaria 1985) Associate Professor. Research: dermatopathology; **Jennifer McNiff** MD (Univ Vermont 1986) Professor. Research: dermatopathology and immunofluorescence; **Antonio Subtil-Deoliveira** MD, MBA (Federal Univ Goias 1996) Assistant Professor. Research: cutaneous lymphoproliferative disorders and melanocytic lesions.

Department of Laboratory Medicine

Brian R. Smith MD (Harvard Univ 1976) Professor and Chair. Research: flow cytometry, cell adhesion, bone marrow transplantation; **Marie Landry** MD (Georgetown Univ 1974) Professor and Vice Chair. Research: diagnostic and molecular virology; **Sheldon Campbell** MD, PhD (Baylor Col Med 1987) Associate Professor. Research: microbiology; **Stephen Edberg** PhD (SUNY Upstate 1971) Professor. Research: medical microbiology, waterborne pathogens; **Brigitte Griffith** PhD (Strasbourg Univ, France 1974) Clinical Professor. Research: experimental virology, viral pathogenesis;

Michael Hodsdon MD, PhD (Washington Univ 1997) Associate Professor. Research: protein structure and biochemistry; **J. Gregory Howe** PhD (Univ Cal-Davis 1983) Assistant Professor. Research: molecular diagnostics, virology; **Peter I. Jatlow** MD (SUNY Downstate 1961) Professor. Research: clinical chemistry, clinical psychopharmacology, toxicology; **Paula M. Kavathas** PhD (Univ Wisconsin 1980) Professor. Research: molecular immunology and immunogenetics; **Diane Krause** MD, PhD (Univ Pennsylvania 1990) Professor. Research: stem cell biology and transplantation; **Herbert Malkus** PhD (Iowa State Univ, 1968) Assistant Clinical Professor. Research: cardiac injury; **John McClaskey** MD (Yale Univ 1981) Assistant Professor. Research: endocrine assay development, thyroid cytology; **R. Rodian Rathbone** MD (Yale Univ 1979) Assistant Clinical Professor. Research: automation and computation, biomedical engineering; **Henry M. Rinder** MD (Univ Vermont 1984) Associate Professor. Research: platelet function and coagulation; **Mark Shlomchik** MD, PhD (Univ Pennsylvania 1989) Professor. Research: B cell immunology, auto immune disease; **Edward L. Snyder** MD (New York Med Col 1973) Professor. Research: transfusion medicine, platelet function; **Gary Stack** MD, PhD (Univ Wisconsin 1983, MD Johns Hopkins Med Inst 1984) Associate Professor. Research: transfusion medicine; **Peter Tattersall** PhD (Univ London 1971) Professor. Research: molecular genetics, virology; **Yan Yun Wu** MD, PhD (Tulane Univ 1996) Assistant Professor. Research: transfusion medicine, stem cell transplantation.

APPLICATIONS

Candidates must be graduates of accredited medical schools in the United States or Canada or have passed the USMLE and hold a current ECFMG certificate. U.S. medical student applicants must be enrolled in the National Resident Matching Program. Applications should be completed by October 31 for appointments the following July. Applications will be accepted via ERAS only.

THE GEORGE WASHINGTON UNIVERSITY

Washington, District of Columbia

PROGRAMS OFFERED

A fully accredited 4-year combined anatomic and clinical pathology training program is offered. First-year appointments may begin the first year out of medical school or at a later date. In the combined AP-CP program, anatomic and clinical pathology rotations are fully integrated throughout the 4 years of training and are generally divided into 2 or 3 month blocks. A highlight of the program is the excellent balance between anatomic and clinical pathology training. Most rotations occur at the University Hospital, with a minority at the Washington Veterans Affairs Medical Center. Rotations in pediatric anatomic and clinical pathology take place at the Children's National Medical Center. Rotations in forensic pathology take place at the DC Medical Examiner's Office. Major departmental conferences are held throughout the week, and departmental research seminars and special lectures are held periodically. Other teaching conferences (hematology, neuropathology, medical and surgical death conferences, tumor conferences, breast conference, gastrointestinal conference, renal conference, head and neck conference, etc.) are held in conjunction with various clinical departments. Exposure to emerging new technologies such as molecular diagnostics is provided. Residents actively participate in the research and teaching activities of the department. Residents have 4 months of elective time in anatomic pathology, clinical pathology and/or research. The elective time allows trainees to focus on areas of special interest and may include work at any of the affiliated hospitals or other institutions outside of the university (NIH, AFIP, etc.). Optional training toward an MPH degree is available in the GWU School of Public Health.

TYPES AND NUMBERS OF APPOINTMENTS

A total of 15 appointments is offered, divided among each year of training. Fellowships in cytopathology and surgical pathology are also available in the department. Most beginning residency appointments are at the first-year level; however, advanced appointments may be arranged. Other specialties account for some 450 internships and residencies at the University Hospital, the Veterans Affairs Medical Center, the Children's National Medical Center, and other affiliated hospitals.

FACILITIES

The George Washington University Hospital is a general hospital of 371 beds, admitting approximately 16,700 patients annually. The hospital is located in a new state-of-the-art building opened in August, 2002. The Veterans Affairs Medical Center is also a general hospital with a bed capacity of 252 beds and admits about 7,500 patients annually. The Children's National Medical Center is a pediatric hospital of 260 beds and admits approximately 22,000 patients annually. The professional staffs at the three hospitals all have faculty appointments in the University Medical Center. The material available for the residents' study is diverse and covers practically all fields. At the three hospitals there are some 120 autopsies annually, 25,000 surgical pathology accessions, 8,000 cytopathology accessions, 2,000 intraoperative consultations, and approximately 3,200,000 clinical pathology tests. More than 20 additional autopsies are usually performed by each resident while at the DC Medical Examiner's office. A fine needle aspiration clinic is located in the Cytopathology service. An electron microscopy suite is present in the department. The clinical pathology division includes laboratories for hematology, clinical chemistry, microbiology, blood bank, flow cytometry, and molecular diagnostics. The residents take part in all these activities, with particular emphasis on providing consultation to clinicians. An excellent collection of current textbooks and clinical case study sets is maintained in the department.

COMMUNITY

Washington, DC offers many cultural, social, recreational, religious and educational opportunities. In addition, Washington is frequently host to important national and regional medical meetings. Residents in pathology attend many of these meetings and participate in special courses in pathology available in the area, especially those at the Armed Forces Institute of Pathology (AFIP) and NIH.

STIPENDS AND MAINTENANCE

In academic year 2008-2009, first-year trainees received $46,249 and second-year trainees $48,024 per annum, with an incremental increase of about $2,000 per annum for each subsequent year. Salary levels for academic year 2009-2010 were not yet available at press time. Each year, all house officers receive three weeks vacation and up to one week administrative leave with pay. White coats are provided. Free parking is available. House staff members provide their own meals and quarters. University tuition benefits and a variety of health insurance and other benefit plans are available. The hospital provides professional liability insurance.

STAFF

Anatomic Pathology: Professors

Donald S. Karcher MD (Louisiana State Univ 1974) Chair; **Christian C. Haudenschild** MD (Univ Basel, Switzerland 1969) cardiovascular pathology; **Jack H. Lichy** MD, PhD (Albert Einstein Coll Med 1984) anatomic pathology, molecular diagnostics; **Jan M. Orenstein** MD, PhD (SUNY Downstate 1969, 1971) electron microscopy, autopsy pathology, surgical pathology; **Arnold M. Schwartz** MD, PhD (MIT 1973, Univ Miami 1978) surgical pathology, experimental pathology; **Sana O. Tabbara** MD (American Univ Beirut 1984) surgical pathology, cytopathology.

Anatomic Pathology: Associate Professors

Robert V. Jones MD (Univ Virginia 1977) neuropathology, surgical pathology; **Patricia S. Latham** MD (Univ Southern California, 1972) experimental pathology, autopsy pathology, surgical pathology.

Anatomic Pathology: Assistant Professors

Suman Chauhan MD (Rajasthan Univ, India 1988) surgical pathology, cytopathology; **Wen Chen** MD (Beijing Univ 1993) surgical pathology, dermatopathology; **Samantha E Easley** MD (SUNY Sch Med at Buffalo 2003) surgical pathology; **David E. Kardon** MD (Albert Einstein Col Med 1995) renal pathology; **Minling Liu** MD, PhD (Shangai Med Univ 1984, Univ Iowa 1994) surgical pathology; **Edina E. Paal** MD (Semmelweis Univ Med, Budapest 1996), surgical pathology, cytopathology; **Masoumeh Rezaei** MD (Univ Med Sci Yazd, Iran 1992) surgical pathology, cytopathology; **Michael D Stamatakos** MD (Uniformed Services Univ Health Sci 1987) surgical pathology.

Clinical Pathology: Professors

Joseph M. Campos PhD (Univ Cal-Berkeley 1976) pediatric clinical microbiology; **Louis A. DePalma** MD (Univ Naples, Italy 1982) hematology, molecular diagnostics; **D. Robert Dufour** MD (Med Col Wisconsin 1975) clinical chemistry; **Donald S. Karcher** MD (Louisiana State Univ 1974) hematology, flow cytometry; **Naomi C. Luban** MD (Mount Sinai 1972) pediatric hematology; **Sylvia Silver** DA (Catholic Univ 1977) clinical laboratory science program.

Clinical Pathology: Associate Professors

John F. Keiser, Jr. MD, PhD (Penn State Univ 1974) microbiology; **Steven A. Schonberg** PhD (Cornell Univ 1980) clinical cytogenetics.

Clinical Pathology: Assistant Professors

Elsie S. Lee MD (SUNY Hlth Sci Ctr at Syracuse 1990) blood banking, transfusion medicine; **David Leitenberg** MD, PhD (Univ Iowa 1990) pediatric clinical immunology; **Minling Liu** MD, PhD (Shanghai Med Univ 1984, Univ Iowa 1994) hematology; **Edina E Paal** MD (Semmelweis Univ Medicine, Budapest 1996), blood bank, transfusion medicine; **Carol Smith** MS (Virginia Commonwealth Univ 1981) clinical laboratory science; **Edward C.C. Wong** MD (Washington Univ 1989) blood banking, transfusion medicine.

APPLICATIONS

Residency candidates must be graduates of approved medical schools in the U.S. or Canada, or, in the case of graduates of foreign medical schools, must have an ECFMG certificate. Letters from three physicians familiar with the candidate's work must be submitted as references. Appointments normally become effective July 1, but residency service may begin on other dates. Applications for appointments to begin in July 2010 will be processed by ERAS.

Address inquiries to:

Donald S. Karcher, MD, Chair
Department of Pathology, Room 502
The George Washington University Medical Center
2300 Eye Street, NW
Washington, DC 20037
Phone: (202) 994-3391 • **Fax:** (202) 994-2618
Web site: http://www.gwumc.edu/dept/path

GEORGETOWN UNIVERSITY HOSPITAL

Washington, District of Columbia

PROGRAMS OFFERED

A fully accredited and broadly based program of anatomic pathology and clinical pathology. The Department of Pathology is a component of the Georgetown University Hospital, a major referral base that includes strong clinical services and the Lombardi Cancer Center, a National Cancer Institute designated comprehensive cancer center. We are committed to offer a flexible program tailored to meet the academic needs of the individual resident. The program provides training in surgical pathology, cytopathology, autopsy pathology, neuropathology, hematopathology, nephropathology, and gynecological pathology. Specialized diagnostic laboratory training in anatomic pathology is available in our electron microscopy, immunohistochemistry and molecular diagnostics laboratories. A full clinical pathology program is provided and includes rotations through Clinical Chemistry, Hematology, Blood Banking, Microbiology and Laboratory Management. Research in the Department of Pathology comprises a variety of creative scientific approaches in the fields of DNA tumor virology, molecular genetics of cancer, gene regulation and molecular immunology. The Molecular Diagnostics Laboratory of the Department of Pathology is a comprehensive diagnostic service facility which uses new, probe-based approaches for diagnostic pathology. Residents are exposed to the techniques of molecular biology, flow cytometry, immunohistochemistry, *in situ* hybridization and polymerase chain reaction. Residents assist in the teaching of the pathology course to the sophomore medical student class.

TYPES AND NUMBERS OF APPOINTMENTS

Twelve AP/CP positions.

FACILITIES

The Department of Pathology provides diagnostic pathology service to the Georgetown University Hospital. The University Hospital is the principal clinical facility for patient care and undergraduate and graduate teaching of the Georgetown University Hospital. In fulfilling its service responsibilities, the Department of Pathology annually performs approximately 50 autopsies, analyzes 15,000 surgical pathology specimens, 3,000 molecular diagnostic tests and 6,000 cytology specimens, including fine needle aspirations (FNA).The Department of Pathology is centrally housed in the **Medical Dental Building** of the Georgetown University Hospital and occupies additional new research facilities adjacent to the Medical Library. The Clinical Laboratories, Surgical Pathology suite, Histopathology Laboratory and Division of Cytopathology are housed in the University Hospital and Lombardi Cancer Center and provide excellent facilities for conducting diagnostic studies and residency training.

COMMUNITY

The Georgetown University Hospital is located on the main campus of Georgetown University which overlooks the Potomac River and is in the heart of the Georgetown residential district. The campus is near the cosmopolitan cultural environment of Washington, DC including its many museums, Kennedy Center, restaurants and parks and is within commuting distance of nearby residential areas of Washington, DC and the Maryland and Virginia suburbs. The academic pathology environment of the Washington, DC area is remarkable for its strength and diversity with many nationally recognized pathologists not only at Georgetown University but also the government research institutions: Armed Forces Institute of Pathology (AFIP) and the National Institutes of Health (NIH).

STIPENDS AND MAINTENANCE

The range of salaries for residents is approximately $45,500.00 - $57,790.72

STAFF

Norio Azumi MD, PhD Clinical Chair; **Pedro DeBrito** MD Director, Cytology and Surgical Pathology; **Mary A. Furlong** MD Program Director, Director, Medical Student Pathology Course; **David F. Garvin** MD Medical Director, Laboratory Medicine; **Dan-Paul Hartmann** PhD Scientific Director, Molecular Diagnostics Lab; **Bhaskar V Kallakury** MD Director, Molecular Diagnostics/EM/Renal; **Craig Kessler** MD, Chief, Hematology/Oncology; **Metin Ozdemirli** MD, PhD Director, Hematopathology; **Stephen M. Peters** PhD Director, Infectious Diseases, Immunology and MDL; **Sandra Rosen-Bronson** PhD Histocompatibility; **S. Gerald Sandler** MD Director,Transfusion Medicine, Blood Bank; **C. Richard Schlegel** MD, PhD, Academic Chair; **Mary K. Sidawy** MD, Director, Anatomic Pathology.

Adjunct Faculty

Richard J Benjamin MD, PhD; **Robert DuFour** MD; **Michael Lewin-Smith** MD; **Florabel Mullick** MD; **Elisabeth Rushing** MD; **Sina Sabet** MD, Ophthamology; **Jacqueline Wieneke** MD.

APPLICATIONS

Candidates must have graduated from an approved medical school in the United States or Canada and residents must be eligible for licensure to practice medicine in the District of Columbia. Graduates of foreign medical schools must hold an ECFMG certificate. Applications must be received by **November 15th** for appointments to begin July 1st of the following year.

Address inquiries to:

Janetta E. Epps, Program Coordinator
Department of Pathology
Georgetown University Hospital
3900 Reservoir Road,
Medical Dental Bldg. #SW211
NW Washington, DC 20007
Phone (202) 687-7020 • **E-mail:** eppsj@gunet.georgetown.edu
Web site: http://www.georgetown.edu/departments/pathology/

HOWARD UNIVERSITY MEDICAL CENTER

Washington, District of Columbia

PROGRAMS OFFERED

A four-year combined anatomic and clinical pathology training program, leading to American Board of Pathology qualification in anatomic and clinical pathology, is offered. The program is designed to provide an integrated experience in morphologic pathology and laboratory medicine and to allow time for the trainee to pursue individual interests or research. Supervised experience is provided in surgical and autopsy pathology, immunohistochemistry, cytopathology/ fine needle aspiration, hematology, and flow cytometry, transfusion medicine/blood banking, immunoserology, clinical chemistry and microbiology. The program is structured to provide progressive training with emphasis on resident responsibility and development. There is an active departmental educational program consisting of scheduled lectures, in addition to conferences and seminars where the theory and practice of anatomic and clinical pathology are systemically reviewed. Research in varied areas within the department and in collaboration with individuals in the Howard University Cancer Center provide opportunities for resident participation.

Forensic pathology and forensic toxicology training is provided through a rotation in the Office of the Medical Examiner in Baltimore, Maryland. Training in apheresis, HLA typing and transplantation is provided at the National Institutes of Health (NIH). Residents rotate at Children's National Medical Center for pediatric surgical pathology and pediatric hematology and the Veterans Administration Medical Center for chemical pathology. The pathology program is also affiliated with the Armed Forces Institute of Pathology (AFIP) where the residents rotate in any of the following various subspecialty areas.

TYPES AND NUMBERS OF APPOINTMENTS

A total of eight house officer positions are offered in pathology. These are distributed over a four-year period. In general, two first-year positions are available. Applications from prospective graduates of approved medical schools in the United States and Canada and/or physicians who have postgraduate training in clinical medicine/research, and foreign medical graduates with ECFMG ertificate are accepted.

FACILITIES

Howard University Hospital, located on the main university campus, is a comprehensive general hospital, Level I trauma center with a bed capacity of 350. Annual accessions in the Department of Pathology include approximately 50-80 necropsies; 6,000-7,000 surgical specimens; 4,000-5,000 cytologic cases and 850,000 clinical laboratory examinations. The diagnostic laboratories of the Department of Pathology occupy a total of 15,000 sq. ft. in the University Hospital, which is connected to the College of Medicine. In addition to departmental library facilities, the Louis B. Stokes Medical Library a recently built, state-of-the art, facility that has approximately 110,000 bound volumes and 2,000 current journal subscriptions. Full access is provided to all facilities of Howard University.

COMMUNITY

Howard University Medical Center is located in the northwest section of Washington, DC. The nation's capitol is a beautiful vibrant city which offers a variety of cultural, educational and social opportunities. The surrounding Virginia and Maryland countryside invites the enthusiast interested in history and recreation. Three other local medical schools, the Armed Forces Institute of Pathology, the National Institutes of Health and the National Library of Medicine are easily accessible.

STIPENDS AND MAINTENANCE

First-year house officers receive approximately $42,000 annually. Stipends increase each subsequent year. House staff is provided with the following benefits: major medical coverage, employee assistance program, free uniforms/ laundry service, subsidized meals, free parking, and malpractice.

STAFF

Howard University Staff

Edward L. Lee MD Professor and Chair; GI pathology, surgical pathology, autopsy pathology; **Lekidelu Taddesse-Heath** MD Assistant Professor; hematopathology, flow cytometry, surgical pathology; **Hassan Brim** PhD Assistant Professor; research; **Diana Davis** MS, Assistant Laboratory Manager; quality assurance and performance improvement; **Marie Fidelia-Lambert** MD Associate Professor; autopsy pathology, surgical pathology; **William R. Green** MD Associate Professor; ultrastructural pathology, autopsy pathology; **Josephine J. Marshalleck** MD Associate Professor; surgical pathology, cytopathology/fine needle aspiration; **Tammey J. Naab** MD Associate Professor, surgical pathology, microbiology, immunoserology, immunohistochemistry; **Babak Shokrani** MD Assistant Professor; cytopathology, surgical pathology.

Consulting Staff

Ema Berbescu MD, cytopathology, surgical pathology; Virginia Commonwelath University; **Esther Blinderman-Childers** DDS, oral and maxillofacial pathology; Howard University; **Allen Burke** MD, cardiopathology; Armed Forces Institute of Pathology; **Cathy Conry-Cantilena** MD, immunohematology/transfusion medicine; National Institutes of Health; **D. Robert Dufour** MD, chemistry pathology, hepatopathology; Veterans Affairs Medical Center; **David R. Fowler** MD, forensic pathology; Office of the Chief Medical Examiner; **Jasmine Hijazi** MD, cytopathology, immunohistochemistry, Quest Diagnostics Nichols Institute; **Alexander T. Ocampo** MD, dermatopathology; Howard University; **Charles Repetti** PhD, flow cytometry; Quest Diagnostics Nichols Institute; **Christine Reyes** MD, pediatric surgical pathology; Childrens National Medical Center; **Mary Ripple** MD, forensic pathology; Office of the Medical Examiner; **Susan Roseff** MD, Associate Professor; Virginia Commonwealth University; **Elisabeth Rushing** MD, neuropathology; Armed Forces Institute of Pathology; **Steven Schonberg** PhD, cytogenetics; Quest Diagnostics Nichols Institute; **David Stroncek** MD, immunohematology/transfusion medicine; National Institutes of Health; **Guanghua Wang** MD, molecular pathology; Armed Forces Institute of Pathology; **Edward Wong** MD, pediatric hematology/transfusion medicine; Childrens National Medical Center.

APPLICATIONS

Candidates must be graduates of approved medical schools in the U.S. or Canada. Graduates of foreign medical schools must hold an ECFMG certificate and valid visa. All applicants must have successfully passed USMLE, Steps 1 and 2. Applicants for postgraduate positions should be enrolled in NRMP. Applications for PGY1 positions are only accepted through ERAS.

Address inquiries to:

Edward L. Lee, MD
Director, Residency Training Program
E-mail: ellee@howard.edu
or
Lekidelu Taddesse-Heath, MD
Associate Director, Residency Training Program
E-mail: ltaddesse-heath@howard.edu
or
Vernicka M. Irving
Residency Training Program Coordinator
E-mail: virving@howard.edu
Department of Pathology
Howard University College of Medicine
520 "W" Street N.W.
Washington, DC 20059
Phone: (202) 806-6306

Howard University Hospital, Washington, D.C.

WASHINGTON HOSPITAL CENTER

Washington, District of Columbia

PROGRAMS OFFERED

The Department of Pathology and Laboratory Medicine at the Washington Hospital Center offers a fully accredited four-year program leading to certification by the American Board of Pathology in Anatomic and Clinical Pathology. The philosophy of the program is to prepare residents for pathology practice by exposing them to the wide spectrum of case material (routine and unusual) seen in clinical and anatomic pathology at a large tertiary care teaching center, and to teach a logical diagnostic approach to clinical situations and problems. The program provides training in surgical pathology, cytopathology, autopsy pathology, neuropathology, hematopathology, electron microscopy, immunohistopathology, molecular pathology, forensic and pediatric pathology. A full clinical pathology program is provided and includes rotations through clinical chemistry, hematology and coagulation, transfusion medicine and blood donor center, microbiology, laboratory management and informatics, transplantation, virology, parasitology, diagnostic immunology, and flow cytometry. The residents are active participants in both inter- and intradepartmental teaching conferences. Each resident is required to participate in research, including Residents' Research Day.

TYPES AND NUMBERS OF APPOINTMENTS

Ten resident positions are offered in Anatomic and Clinical Pathology.

FACILITIES

Washington Hospital Center (WHC) is one of the busiest tertiary care hospitals in the country with 907 beds. The Department of Pathology and Laboratory Medicine processes approximately 22,000 surgical cases, 120 autopsies and over 3 million billable clinical tests, annually. The Department has a fine needle aspiration clinic and a growing outreach laboratory program. WHC employs approximately 4,900 people and has a medical and dental staff of 2,500. Extensive resources include the region's only burn center for adults, a regional referral center for critical medical and surgical emergencies (MedSTAR), as well as active programs in cancer care (Washington Cancer Institute), cardiac and vascular surgery, and transplantation. In addition to WHC, rotations are provided through the Children's Hospital National Medical Center, State of Maryland Medical Examiner's Office, Armed Forces Institute of Pathology (AFIP), Georgetown University Medical Center, and Franklin Square Hospital Center.

COMMUNITY

The Washington Hospital Center is located in the northwest section of Washington, DC in a hospital campus which also includes the Veterans Affairs Medical Center, Children's Hospital National Medical Center, National Rehabilitation Hospital, Washington Cancer Institute at Washington Hospital Center, and the MedStar Research Facility. The nation's capital offers a variety of educational, historical, cultural and social opportunities. The adjacent states include Virginia and Maryland. Easily accessible to the hospital are the Armed Forces Institute of Pathology (AFIP), the National Institutes of Health (NIH), and the National Library of Medicine.

STIPENDS AND MAINTENANCE

Resident salaries range from $45,500 to $51,000 for PGY1 to PGY4, respectively.

STAFF

Thomas A. Godwin MD Chairman (Pulmonary Pathology;GI/Hepatopathology); **Kirsten Alcorn** MD Residency Program Director, Microbiology Program Director, Director of Transfusion Medicine and Donor Center; **Ernest Lack** MD Director of Anatomic Pathology; **Lisa Beaudet** MD Director of Cytopathology; **Thomas Deng** MD Hematopathology; **Jayashree Krishnan** MD Director of Molecular Pathology, Hematopathology and Chemistry; **Dhruv Kumar** MD Director of Autopsy Pathology; **Wen Lee** MD Cytopathology; **Yolanda Oertel** MD Director of FNA Services; **Jeffrey Seidman** MD Director of Gynecologic Pathology; **John C. Rees** PhD Immunology, Flow Cytometry, Molecular Pathology, and Research Projects.

Additional Faculty

Joseph Catlett MD Clinical Hematology; **David Fowler** MD Forensic Pathology; **Bhaskar Kallakury** MD Electron Microscopy; **Vera Malkovska** MD Clinical Hematology; **Jeanne Meck** PhD Cytogenetics; **Elizabeth Rushing** MD Neuropathology; **Margo Smith** MD Clinical Microbiology; **Melissa Withrow** PhD Gyn-Cytology; **Edward Wong** MD Anatomic Ped Path.

APPLICATIONS

Residency candidates must be graduates of accredited medical schools in the United States or Canada or, in the case of graduates of foreign medical schools, must have an ECFMG certificate. Residency positions usually become effective July 1, but residency service may begin on other dates. Applications must be submitted through ERAS by November 1.

Address inquiries to:

Jennifer Pottinger, Program Coordinator
Department of Pathology and Laboratory Medicine
Washington Hospital Center
110 Irving Street, NW
Washington, DC 20010
Phone: (202) 877-5613 • **Fax:** (202) 877-3820

Washington Hospital Center

UNIVERSITY OF FLORIDA COLLEGE OF MEDICINE

Gainesville, Florida

PROGRAMS OFFERED

The ACGME-accredited residency training program in pathology and laboratory medicine is designed to train pathologists of the highest caliber in preparation for academic or private practice. Through an organized educational experience, pathology residents acquire a broad understanding of anatomic pathology (AP), clinical pathology (CP), investigational pathology, and the role of the pathologist as a physician. Residents generally pursue combined training in AP and CP over a four-year program of study. Training takes place at Shands Hospital at the University of Florida and at the North Florida/South Georgia Veterans Health System located adjacent to the University of Florida Health Science Center complex; rotations at the nearby Shands at Alachua General Hospital also are available.

The training program includes a large and varied case mix. In 2006-2007, Shands at the University of Florida, the Department of Pathology's Diagnostic Reference Laboratories, and the North Florida / South Georgia Veterans Health System performed 308,513 anatomic pathology procedures, which included 152,130 surgical pathology/histology procedures, and 120,744 (42,444 gynecologic and 79,300 medical) cytology procedures. There were nearly 11 million clinical pathology tests performed, including 8 million chemistry, 2 million hematology, and 100,000 immunology. Nearly 200,000 blood bank workups were conducted. Over 300 regular autopsies were performed, and over 600 forensic autopsy cases in the Medical Examiners Office, managed and staffed by the department. Specialized laboratories for cytogenetics, transplant medicine, hematopathology, and molecular pathology round out this full complement of laboratory services. Laboratory marketing and sales, regulatory compliance, billing and collections and quality management are covered as well.

Many outstanding educational program components exist at the University of Florida, including: gynecologic, breast, urogenital, and otolaryngologic pathology, cytopathology, gastrointestinal and hepatic pathology, neuropathology, bone and soft tissue pathology, hematopathology, pediatric pathology, integrated anatomic and clinical pathology at North Florida/South Georgia Veterans Health System and at Alachua General Hospital, immunology and histocompatibility, clinical pathology and laboratory management, electron microscopy, cytogenetics, flow cytometry, forensic pathology, forensic toxicology, and molecular pathology rotations. The program also provides training in informatics, laboratory management principles, laboratory consultation, and leadership. The department is home to the Maples Center for Forensics, with programming in forensic toxicology, forensic anthropology, and forensic pathology.

Strong research programs in the department include immunology programs in diabetes, HIV, HCV, autoimmunity, and the genetic basis of autoimmune diseases, and programs in stem cell biology, cell signaling and differentiation, kidney stone disease, liver regeneration and carcinogenesis, hematology and hematopathology, molecular pathology, toxicology, and neurodegenerative diseases. The University of Florida College of Medicine is home to the Center for Immunology and Transplantation, the Diabetes Center, the Cancer Center, the McKnight Brain Institute, the Aging Institute, the Genetics Institute, the Center for Mammalian Genetics and the Center for Gene Therapy. There are outstanding investigational opportunities for residents through involvement with faculty in the department and College of Medicine. Residents are encouraged to pursue either clinical or basic research during some period of their residency, and will present original scholarly work on at least two occasions during training. There are regular opportunities for resident leadership through participation in work rounds, interdepartmental conferences, weekly teaching conferences, journal clubs, slide conferences, and national participation in pathology societies. Conversely, faculty provide a systematic program of didactic resident teaching that contributes to the well-rounded foundation that residents acquire while in the program. The latest description of our program can be found at http:/www.pathology.ufl.edu/.

TYPES AND NUMBERS OF APPOINTMENTS

There are 16 residency positions and 4 ACGME-accredited fellowship positions (hematopathology, dermatopathology, neuropathology, cytopathology) funded by Shands Hospital and the North Florida/South Georgia Veterans Health System. The program provides four years of training to meet all requirements for AP/CP Board certification.

FACILITIES

Shands Healthcare comprises nine hospitals and more than eighty primary and specialty practices across North Central Florida, and employs over 12,500 people. 88,519 patients were admitted to the 1,953 licensed beds and over 1.1 million hospital based outpatient visits were encountered. Shands Hospital at the University of Florida has 636 beds and over 28,000 admissions each year. Shands Hospital is the major teaching and referral center for north, west and central Florida and south Georgia, and draws patients from throughout the Southeastern United States and the Caribbean. The University of Florida College of Medicine is affiliated with the 251 bed North Florida / South Georgia Veterans Administration Health System, directly across the street from Shands Hospital. This VA group supported over 120,000 unique patients and experienced over 1.3 million outpatient visits in 2006. The Shands HealthCare System includes the Alachua General Hospital, a community-based hospital located 1-mile from Shands Hospital, and the Shands/Jacksonville Medical Center in Jacksonville, Florida. The Health Science Center campus includes the Colleges of Dentistry, Nursing, Pharmacy, Allied Health Professions and Veterinary Medicine. The Health Science Center Library has 344,966 volume texts, subscribes to 4,200 on-line journals, and has 6,944 resource audiovisuals. The College of Medicine has over 1,000 faculty members responsible for 135 medical students per year.

COMMUNITY

Gainesville is located in north central Florida, and has all of the advantages of a large university (e.g., the arts, theater, music, dance, sports) in the setting of a smaller but growing community (population 125,000). Gainesville's beautiful climate allows year-round opportunities for outdoor recreational activities. There are a large number of nearby parks, lakes, and springs. The warm waters of the Gulf of Mexico and Atlantic Ocean are close at hand. Orlando is only a two-hour drive to the south. Gainesville was voted the number one city in the United States by Money Magazine in 1994 and consistently ranks in the top 20. The University of Florida enrolls nearly 50,000 students yearly and has all of the scientific, artistic, cultural and athletic programs expected of a large university community.

STIPENDS AND MAINTENANCE

For the 2008-2009 year, the PGY-1 yearly salary will be $43,964, PGY-2: $45,277, PGY-3: $46,897, PGY-4: $48,690, PGY-5: $50,475, PGY-6: $52,390, PGY-7+: $54,079. Salaries usually increase 2-3% per year. Health, life, accidental death and dismemberment, and disability insurance are provided. A book and travel allowance is provided.

STAFF

Michael J. Clare-Salzler MD Professor and Interim Chair; Director Center for Immunology and Transplantation, immunology and endocrinology, diabetes; **Edward J. Wilkinson** MD Professor and Vice Chair; gynecological pathology, cytopathology, surgical pathology; **John D. Reith** MD Associate Professor; Director Residency Program; Director Section of Soft Bone and Tissue; surgical pathology, orthopaedic oncology; **Lisa R. Dixon** MD Assistant Professor; Associate Director Pathology Residency Program, gastrointestinal and liver pathology; **Mark A. Atkinson** PhD Professor; immunology, diabetes; **Martha L. Campbell-Thompson** DVM, PhD Professor and Director; Molecular Pathology and Immunology Core Laboratory; Associate Director Experimental Pathology; **Byron P. Croker** MD, PhD Professor; Chief, VA Pathology Service; surgical and renal pathology; **William H. Donnelly Jr.** MD Adjunct Professor and Professor Emeritus; surgical pathology, autopsy pathology, pediatric pathology; **Bruce A. Goldberger** PhD Professor; Director William R. Maples Center for Forensic Medicine; Director Forensic and Clinical Toxicology; **Maureen M. Goodenow** PhD Professor; immunology of HIV infection; **Ralph R. Grams** MD Professor; informatics, laboratory information systems; **Nancy S. Hardt** MD Professor; Senior Associate Dean for External Affairs; OB/GYN, women's health, government relations; **Glen L. Hortin** MD, PhD Professor; chemistry, hematology, coagulation; **Judith A. Johnson** PhD Professor; Microbiology, emerging pathogens; **Saeed R. Khan** PhD Professor; oxalate stone disease; **Laurence M. Morel** PhD Professor; Director Experimental Pathology; autoimmune diseases; **Sigurd J. Normann** MD, PhD Adjunct Professor and Professor Emeritus; cardiac pathology; **Ammon B. Peck** PhD Professor; autoimmune diseases, oxalate stone disease; **Kenneth H. Rand** MD Professor; Director Clinical Pathology; microbiology and virology; **Juan C. Scornik** MD Professor; immunogenetics and transplantation immunology; **Vladimir Vincek** MD, DMSc Professor of Pathology; Director Dermatopathology; Medical Director Diagnostic Reference Laboratories (DRL); **William E. Winter** MD Professor; Director of Education; clinical chemistry, diabetes; **Anthony T. Yachnis** MD Professor; Director Anatomic Pathology; Chief Neuropathology; neuropathology, pediatric neuropathology, gynecologic pathology; **William L. Clapp III** MD Associate Professor; surgical and renal pathology; **Peter A. Drew** MD Associate Professor; cytopathology and surgical pathology; **Robert W. Freel** PhD Associate Professor; intestinal physiology; **William F. Hamilton** MD Associate Professor; Chief Medical Examiner; anatomic pathology; **Marguerite Hatch** PhD Associate Professor; oxalate stone disease, intestinal transport; **Chen Liu** MD, PhD Associate Professor; gastrointestinal and hepatic pathology; **Clayton E. Mathews** PhD Associate Professor; immunology, diabetes; **Wayne T. McCormack** PhD Associate Professor; Director Interdisciplinary Progam in Biomedical Sciences; Associate Dean for Graduate Education; **Bryon E. Petersen** PhD Associate Professor; hepatic regeneration, stem cells; **Miguel V. Tellado-Fente** MD Associate Professor; ophthalmic pathology, cytopathology; **Naohiro Terada** MD, PhD Associate Professor; cell cycle regulation and cellular differentiation; **LiJun Yang** MD Associate Professor; hematopathology, stem cell biology; **Roberto T. Zori** MD Associate Professor; Chief Clinical Cytogenetics; **Samer Z. Al-Quran** MD Assistant Professor; Director Breast Pathology, hematopathology; **Robert W. Allan** MD Assistant Professor; hematopathology; **Martha J. Burt** MD Assistant Professor; Associate Medical Examiner; Director Autopsy; forensic pathology; **Hui-Jia Dong** PhD Assistant Professor; Technical Director Molecular Diagnostic Laboratory, molecular pathology; **Frederick L. Glavin** MD Assistant Professor; dermatopathology; **Neil S. Harris** MD Assistant Professor; Director Clinical Chemistry; coagulation; **Jacquelyn A. Knapik** MD Assistant Professor; gynecological pathology, cytopathology, orthopeadic pathology, surgical pathology; **Ying Li** MD, PhD Assistant Professor; Director Hematopathology; flow cytometry; **Li Lu** MD, PhD Assistant Professor; surgical and autopsy pathology, pulmonary pathology; **Tisha C. Netzel** MD Assistant Professor; Director of Blood Bank; **David A. Ostrov** PhD Assistant Professor; immunology, structural basis of immune recognition; **Demaretta S. Rush** MD Assistant Professor; surgical pathology, cytopathology; **Marco M. Salemi** PhD Assistant Professor; molecular evolution; **Dongqi Tang** MD, PhD Assistant Professor; diabetes and regenerative medicine research; **Changqing Xia** MD, PhD Assistant Professor; immunology; **Li Yin** MD, PhD Assistant Professor; HIV and immune deficiency; **Robin M. Foss** PA Associate in Pathology; surgical pathology; **Gerald A. Phipps** PA Associate in Pathology; anatomic pathology; **Trevor L. Jorgensen** BS Assistant in Pathology; surgical pathology; **Catherine M. Ketcham** PhD Assistant in Pathology; tissue bank; **Kerwin M. Kolheffer** MS, PA Assistant in Pathology; anatomic pathology; **Clive H. Wasserfall** MS Assistant in Pathology; immunology, diabetes; **Melanie C Zona** BS, PA Assistant in Pathology; anatomic pathology; **Jing Chen** MD, PhD Assistant Scientist; diabetes; **Yuansha Chen** PhD Assistant Scientist; enteric microbiology; **Takashi Hamazaki** MD Assistant Scientist; stem cell biology and cellular differentiation; **Shi W. Li** PhD Assistant Scientist; diabetes; **Seh-Hoon Oh** PhD Assistant Scientist; experimental pathology; **Larry L. Bedore** Assistant Director Medical/Health Administration; FEMORS; Director of Investigations; **David L. Pittman** Facilities Management and Diagnostic Reference Laboratories Coordinator; **Naomi R. Williams** Diagnostic Reference Laboratories Administrator.

APPLICATIONS

Candidates from the United States, Canada and Puerto Rico must be graduates of LCME-approved medical schools. PGY-1 candidates are chosen through the National Resident Matching Program (NRMP). Graduates of international medical schools must present their valid ECFMG certificate, USMLE steps 1, 2 and 3 scores, Clinical Skills Assessment examination and TOEFL. Applications must be submitted through ERAS (The Electronic Residency Application Service). Interviews are required and should be completed prior to February 1. Applications will be acted upon following receipt and review. Appointments usually begin July 1.

Address inquiries to:

John D. Reith, MD
Director, Residency Training Program
University of Florida College of Medicine
Department of Pathology, Immunology & Laboratory Medicine
Box 100275
Gainesville, FL 32610-0275
Phone: (352) 265-0432 • **Fax:** (352) 265-6987 • **E-mail:** residency@pathology.ufl.edu
Web site: http://www.pathology.ufl.edu

UNIVERSITY OF FLORIDA COLLEGE OF MEDICINE JACKSONVILLE DIVISION

Jacksonville, Florida

PROGRAMS OFFERED

The University of Florida College of Medicine-Jacksonville pathology residency is based at Shands Jacksonville, which is the Urban Campus of the University of Florida College of Medicine. The program offers four-year training programs in anatomic pathology, clinical pathology, or both. The program and faculty are committed to excellence and producing graduates capable of entry into academic or private practice. The program schedule is flexible and may be designed to fit the resident's interests. Anatomic pathology training includes autopsy and surgical pathology, cytology and fine needle aspiration biopsy, image analysis, forensic pathology, immunohistochemistry, fluorescent and electron microscopy. Clinical pathology training includes chemistry, endocrinology, blood banking, hematology and flow cytometry, microbiology, clinical microscopy, immunology, and immunoassays. Some of these new technologies are integrated in the Tumor Analysis Laboratory at Shands Jacksonville, which is a reference laboratory devoted to special diagnostic and prognostic testing. Residents participate in the teaching programs of the department's ASCP-approved School of Medical Technology. Investigative studies and research are expected and the faculty assist and support the residents in these efforts. Pathology residents and medical students from Gainesville may elect rotations in pathology in Jacksonville. Our program is unique in several ways. Our professional staff and volume of material are large enough to provide diverse exposure, yet the program is small enough for extensive one-to-one contact between faculty and residents. Our program's emphasis is on pathology as a general specialty that interacts strongly with all areas of clinical practice; we stress the critical interaction between pathologists and clinicians. The program does permit, however, the pursuit of subspecialization in pathology as well. We also offer two cytopathology fellowship positions. The cytopathology fellowship training includes primary sign-out as well as performing fine needle aspiration biopsies, utilization of immunocytochemistry, electron microscopy, flow cytometry and image analysis in cytologic material. Requirements include Board eligibility in anatomical pathology and interest in research activity. Finally, our unique relationship with both an academic center and a large community of practicing pathologists, offers residents a broad exposure to the types of practice available, so they have an opportunity to determine first-hand what type of practice best suits their goals.

REQUIREMENTS

Each applicant must provide the following (some items may not apply): MD degree (original and English translation); ECFMG certificate; CSAtest passed; USMLE 1 & 2 passed with scores of 78 and above with a maximum of 2 attempts; Preferably taken and passed step 3 with the exception of those coming directly from medical school (Once in program must pass by the time a resident is finished with their 2nd year of training); No previous clinical US experience needed; No more than 5 years graduated from medical school.

Our deadline date for applications is December 31(interviews slots may be full before deadline date). Apply on line through ERAS for all positions. For visa sponsorship please go to www.hscj.ufl.edu/gme/brochure under the Eligibility and Selection Criteria.

TYPES AND NUMBERS OF APPOINTMENTS

Eight residency positions are available, one or two in each year. Two fellowship positions are available each year.

FACILITIES

Shands Jacksonville is a major affiliate hospital and Urban Campus for the University of Florida Health Science Center. It is operated as a not-for-profit corporation, and has, as its basic charge, the care of the medically indigent of this region. There is also a growing referral practice from North Florida and South Georgia. The hospital has 696 beds, large outpatient clinics, and is equipped with the most modern facilities available. Annual laboratory procedures include 14,000 surgicals, 90 autopsies, 33,000 cytologies, and 1,500,000 laboratory examinations. The department provides full anatomical and clinical pathology services including electron microscopy, immunopathology studies, as well as flow cytometric analyses for the entire community. The Borland Health Science Library is an extension of the University of Florida Health Science Center Library, so that access to more than 187,000 volumes, including 42,000 books and 1800 journals, is available.

COMMUNITY

The consolidated city of Jacksonville has a population approaching 1,000,000 and the standard metropolitan statistical area is over 100,000. The city is located 15 miles from the Atlantic Ocean on the St Johns River. The city serves as a port and regional distribution, commercial and insurance center for this area of the southeastern United

States. The usual cultural and recreational advantages of a city of this size are present. The nearby beaches are the site of considerable leisure and recreational activity such as boating, swimming, surfing and fishing.

STIPENDS AND MAINTENANCE

First-year house officers receive $43, 964.00 per year, with 3-6% increases-normally determined at the beginning of each academic year. Hospital scrubs are provided and laundered without charge. The residents will receive two labcoats a year. A special Humana plan is provided for the resident and his family at no extra charge.

STAFF

Shahla Masood MD (Shiraz Univ, Iran 1973) Professor and Chair; Chief Pathology; Director Pathology Residency and Fellowship Programs; Medical Director of Shands Jacksonville Breast Health Center; anatomic, clinical pathology, cytopathology; **Agnes Aysola** MD (Semmelweis Univ Med, Hungry 1980) Clinical Assistant Professor, Anatomic and clinical pathology; **Roger L. Bertholf** PhD (Univ Virginia 1985) Professor; Chief Clinical Chemistry and Toxicology; clinical and forensics toxicology; **Azita Djalilvand** MD, (Fac Med Tours, France) Clinical Assistant Professor, anatomic and clinical pathology and molecular pathology; **Raafat Makary** MD, PhD (MD-Ain Shams Univ 1976, PhD-Zagazig Univ, Egypt -1988) Clinical Assistant Professor, anatomic & clinical pathology; **Yvette S. McCarter** PhD (Med Col Virginia 1990) Clinical Professor; Director Clin Microbiology; Associate Program Director for the pathology residency program; **Carmela B. Monteiro** MD (Fac Med, Univ Estado da Guanabara, Brazil 1974) Clinical Associate Professor; anatomic pathology, pediatric pathology; **Ronald Rhatigan** MD (Univ Iowa Col of Med 1961) Clinical Professor, Director of Autopsy; **Marilin Rosa** MD (Universidad Autonoma de Ciencias Medicas de centro America, Costa Rica 1999) Clinical Assistant Professor; Breast pathology and cytopathology; **Sania Shuja** MD, PhD (King Edward Med Col, Pakistan 1981) Clinical Associate Professor; anatomic pathology and cytopathology; Director of Neuropathology; **Bruce H. Villas** MD (UMDNJ-Rutgers Univ 1985) Clinical Associate Professor; Director Hematology; anatomic, clinical pathology, hematopathology; **David J. Wolfson** MD (Univ Florida Col Med 1988) Clinical Assistant Professor, Director of Transfusion Medicine; anatomic & clinical pathology and cytopathology.

APPLICATIONS

Residency candidates must be graduates of medical schools in the United States and Canada or graduates of foreign medical schools approved by the Florida Board of Medicine. Please refer to our requirements for more detailed information. Interviews are by invitation and will begin shortly after the National Residency Matching Program (NRMP) has opened, in which we participate in.

Address inquiries to:

Shahla Masood, MD
Director, Pathology Residency & Fellowship Programs
c/o Rebel Jones, GME Program Assistant/Resident Coord.
University of Florida College of Medicine - Jacksonville
Department of Pathology
655 W. 8th Street
Jacksonville, FL 32209-6511
Phone: (904) 244-4889 • **Fax:** (904) 244-4060 • **E-mail:** rebel.jones@jax.ufl.edu
Web site: http://www.hscj.ufl.edu

JACKSON MEMORIAL HOSPITAL
JACKSON HEALTH SYSTEM

In affiliation with the University of Miami School of Medicine

Miami, Florida

PROGRAMS OFFERED

The Jackson Memorial Health System Pathology Residency Training Program is a four-year intergrated program in anatomic pathology and clinical pathology. Over 30 full-time faculty members participate in the educational pogram of the Department of Pathology. Training in anatomic pathology includes autopsy pathology, general and subspeciality surgical pathology, cytopathology as well as rotations in pediatric pathology, neuropathology, hematopathology, dermatopathology, immunopathology and forensic pathology. Training in clinical pathology includes rotations in chemical pathology, hematology, medical microbiology, immunology, coagulation, and blood banking/transfusion medicine. Included in the clinical pathology training program is experience in virology, radioimmunoassay, flow cytometry, cytogenetics and molecular biology. The Department of Pathology stresses active involvement with the clinical staff in patient care, along with participation in intra- and interdepartmental conferences, medical student teaching, and research. This training program fulfills the current requirements of the American Board of Pathology.

The Department of Pathology also offers fellowships in cytopathology, hematopathology, immunopathology/ transplant pathology, pediatric pathology and surgical pathology subspecialities (see fellowship program descriptions).

TYPES AND NUMBERS OF APPOINTMENTS

Twenty-four pathology residencies and fellowships.

FACILITIES

The program utilizes the facilities of Jackson Memorial Hospital (1,500 beds), the Veterans' Affairs Hospital (900 beds), the University of Miami Sylvester Comprehensive Cancer Center, and the Dade County Medical Examiner's Office, all of which are located within an 8-square block of downtown Miami. For both hospitals combined, there are approximately 71,000 admissions; 350 autopsies; 41,000 surgical specimens; 35,000 cytology examinations, and over 8,000,000 laboratory tests yearly. Adjacent to the medical complex, the University of Miami Medical School Library offers 70,000 volumes, more than 119,000 journals and full computerized informational services. Library privileges are also extended by the main campus of the University (1,800,000 volumes).

COMMUNITY

Miami and surrounding Dade County, with its semitropical climate and international flavor, is a city of 1,700,000 people. Sailing on Biscayne Bay, jogging the "Vita Courses" in the parks, and bicycling on the extensive bikeway system are year-round activities. Symphony orchestra, professional opera, live theater, and a variety of tourist attractions are offered.

STIPENDS AND MAINTENANCE

Annual stipends in 2008-9: first year residents: $46,566.29, second year residents: $48,682.49, third year residents: $50,796.31, fourth year residents: $53,256.92 and fifth year residents: $ 56,131.12. Hospitalization insurance is provided for the resident, spouse and children. Disability, life, and professional liability insurance are covered by the hospital, as is ambulatory medical care. Residents are also furnished with professional uniforms (white laboratory coats), parking and on-call meal tickets.

STAFF

Richard J Cote Chairman of Pathology and Director of Laboratories (Univ of Chicago, 1980), genitourinary pathology, nanotechnology; **David M. Andrews** MD (Univ Miami 1991) transfusion medicine and coagulation; **Pablo A. Bejarano** MD (Javeriana Univ 1986) anatomic pathology and liver transplant pathology; **Michael D. Bell** MD (Dartmouth Med Col 1985) forensic pathology; **Jocelyn Bruce** MD (St Tomas Univ 1969) anatomic pathology, neuropathology; **Gerald E. Byrne, Jr.** MD (St Louis Univ 1963) hematopathology, clinical pathology; **Timothy J. Cleary** PhD (Univ Cincinnati 1969) microbiology; **Margarita De La Ossa** MS (Pontificia Universidad Javeriana 1995) Hemepath Anatomic Clinical; **Parvin Ganjei-Azar** MD (Tehran Univ 1973) anatomic pathology, cytopathology; **Monica T Garcia** MD (Escuela Colombiana de Medicina 1989) anatomic/clinical pathology, cytopathology; **Zeina Ghorab** MD (Tichreen Univ 1984) Hemapath, Cytopath, Surg Path, Anatomic Clinical Path; **Carmen Gomez-Fernandez** MD (Univ Miami 1991) anatomic pathology, cytopathology; **Bruce A. Hyma** MD (Wayne State Univ 1982) forensic pathology; **Merce Jorda** MD, PhD (Univ Barcelona 1983) anatomic pathology, cytopathology; **Clara Milikowski** MD (Univ Miami 1983) anatomic/clinical pathology; **Azorides R. Morales** MD (Univ Madrid 1958) Professor and former Chairman, Jackson Memorial Hospital; anatomic pathology, cardiovascular pathology; **Mehrdad Nadji** MD (Univ

Tehran 1969) anatomic pathology, molecular pathology; **Michael D. Norenberg** MD (Univ Rochester 1965) neuropathology; **Carol K. Petito** MD (Columbia Univ 1967) neuropathology, anatomic pathology; **Rebeca Porto** MD (Univ Miami 1982) anatomic and clinical pathology; **Jacinto J. Regalado** MD (Med Col Georgia, 1985) anatomic/clinical pathology; **Philip G. Robinson** MD (Univ Miami 1975) anatomic pathology, bone pathology; **Maria M. Rodriguez** MD (Univ Havana 1976) pediatric pathology; **Phillip Ruiz** MD, PhD (George Washington Univ 1985) immunopathology, transplant pathology; **Sherry Shariatmadar** MD (Ross Univ 1992) transfusion medicine; **Bernard Steele** MD (Univ Minnesota 1970) clinical chemistry, clinical pathology; **Rafael Valenzuela** MD, PhD (Seville Univ 1969) immunopathology, nephropathology, anatomic/clinical pathology; **Stephen Vernon** MD (USF 1974) anatomic pathology, cytology; **Vladimir Vincek** MD, PhD (Rijeka Univ 1984) dermatopathology; **Clarence C. Whitcomb** MD (Univ Vermont 1968) clinical pathology, hematopathology, hematology; **Christian Wunsch** MD, PhD (Northwestern Univ 1970) computer services.

APPLICATIONS

Applicants must have graduated from approved medical schools and have successfully passed USMLE Step I and II and clinical skills examinations or their equivalent. Foreign students must have an ECFMG certificate. Training programs usually begin June 24th and applications should be received the previous year by October 31. Appointments are made upon review of a completed ERAS application, letters of reference from Dean of applicant's medical school and from two physicians who supervised applicant during internship or recent training programs, transcript of medical school record, and brief biographical sketch with attached photo. Physical examination and immunization program mandatory upon reporting.

Address inquiries to:

Director, Residency Training Program
Department of Pathology
Jackson Memorial Hospital
1611 NW 12 Avenue, Holtz Center, Room 2053
Miami, FL 33136
Phone: (305) 585-8381 • **Fax:** (305) 585-5497 • **E-mail:** jsilva@med.miami.edu
Web site: http://path.med.miami.edu

MOUNT SINAI MEDICAL CENTER OF GREATER MIAMI

Miami Beach, Florida

PROGRAMS OFFERED

Fully approved one-to four-year training programs for interns, residents and fellows are available in anatomic and clinical pathology. The Department of Anatomic Pathology offers training in autopsy, surgical pathology and cytology. Rotation is mandatory through the Medical Examiner's Office for training in forensic pathology. The Department of Clinical Pathology offers training in clinical chemistry, hematology, blood banking and microbiology. Special training is also provided in research methodology, histochemistry, flow cytometry and molecular techniques.

TYPES AND NUMBERS OF APPOINTMENTS

Eight pathology residencies are offered. There are AMA-approved residencies in internal medicine, emergency medicine, radiology, surgery, and podiatry. Fellowships in pathology, cardiology, interventional cardiology, breast imaging and surgical oncology are also offered. Additional residents and fellows rotate from the University of Miami School of Medicine in anesthesiology, dermatology, family practice, gastroenterology, geriatrics, infectious disease, neurosurgery, plastic surgery and thoracic and cardiovascular surgery. Medical students, along with residents in medicine, surgery and podiatry rotate through the Department of Pathology.

FACILITIES

Mount Sinai Medical Center is a 955-bed (plus 52 bassinets for newborns) non-profit hospital with an average daily census of 440 adults, 10 newborns and 22,364 admissions per year. The hospital is affiliated with the University of Miami School of Medicine and the Florida International University College of Medicine. Number of autopsies 132 total number of tests performed 1,050,639 number of surgical specimens 17,254 number of cytology specimens 2,073. The clinical laboratories are modern, highly automated, and the staff includes 129 technical and nontechnical personnel. Facilities are available for research programs, including those for histochemistry, flow cytometry and DNA phenotyping, phase and interference microscopy, immunopathology, cytology and experimental pathology. A modern 33,000-square-foot free-standing animal research facility is available, ALLAC accredited.

The Library-Audiovisual Service provides a collection of over 5,000 medical books, current subscriptions of 400 journal titles and over 300 on-line journals, audio CDs, and a large number of books on CD ROM format, covering the total health sciences program of the medical center. In addition, our Medical Library is a member of the Medical Library Association and part of the National Network of Libraries of Medicine.

COMMUNITY

The hospital is centrally located in the residential section of Miami Beach, a famous resort vacation community whose population is swelled yearly by visitors and winter residents. Their physicians refer many of these people from other areas and as a consequence, a highly varied pathology is represented in the hospital census. The community supports an opera company and symphony presentations. A variety of entertainment is offered and abundant facilities for spectator and participant athletic events are available. The University of Miami, Florida International University and the Miami-Dade Community College system offer a wide range of cultural and educational opportunities.

STIPENDS AND MAINTENANCE

First-year resident salaries per annum, as of 2009-2010, are $47,962, second-year residents receive $50,143, third-year residents, $52,320, fourth-year residents, $54,885 and fifth-year residents, $57,815. All residents and their immediate families are provided with hospitalization and medical care. Uniforms are provided.

STAFF

Robert Poppiti, Jr. MD, AP and CP, Chairman, Department of Pathology; **John Alexis** MB, ChB, AP and CP, Dermatopathology; **Lydia Howard** MD, AP and CP, Transfusion Medicine and Program Director; **Antonio E. Martinez** MD, AP and CP, Hematopathology; **Monica Recine** MD, AP and CP, Cytopathology; **Morton J. Robinson** MD, AP and CP, Autopsy Pathology; **Vathany Sriganeshan** MD, AP and CP, Hematopathology; **Yumna Omarzai** MD.

Consulting Staff

Carole Brathwaite MD, AP and CP, Pediatric Pathology; **Eva Gyori** MD, NP, Neuropathology; **Bruce Lenes** MD, Transfusion Medicine; **Harry Lumerman** DDS, Oral Pathology; **Kalai Mathee** PhD, Molecular Microbiology and Immunology; **Steven Melnick** PhD, MD, AP and CP, Molecular and Pediatric Pathology; **Hadi Yaziji** MD, AP and CP, Molecular and Immunopathology.

APPLICATIONS

Residency candidates must be graduates of approved medical schools in the U.S. or Canada. Graduates of foreign medical schools must have an ECFMG certificate. Satisfactory references are required.

Address inquiries to:

Lydia H. Howard, MD
Program Director, Department of Pathology and Laboratory Medicine
Mount Sinai Medical Center
4300 Alton Road Miami Beach, FL 33140
Phone: (305) 674-2277 • **E-mail:** lhoward@msmc.com

Mount Sinai Medical Center of Greater Miami, Miami Beach, Florida.

ORLANDO REGIONAL HEALTHCARE SYSTEM

Orlando, Florida

PROGRAMS OFFERED

The Department of Pathology of Orlando Regional Healthcare offers training programs as recommended by the American Board of Pathology. The programs are comprehensive, well-organized and fully approved both in anatomic and clinical pathology. There is a gradual increase in responsibility from the first through the last year, and the development of personal initiative is stressed with opportunities for presenting case reports, disease summaries, research papers, etc. The Department of Pathology conducts an active intradepartmental teaching program, including clinical and surgical pathology conferences, and specialized review conferences in such areas as hematology, clinical chemistry, immunology, toxicology dermatopathology, neuropathology, electron microscopy, cytology, cytogenetics, parasitology, virology, molecular biology and blood banking, so that at the end of the training period, the resident should have comprehensive knowledge. All surgical tissues, necropsies and frozen are reviewed by the resident and a pathologist. In addition, training includes experience in management, computer procedures, data processing, and interpretative clinical pathology.

TYPES AND NUMBERS OF APPOINTMENTS

Ten pathology residencies are offered.

FACILITIES

Orlando Regional Healthcare is a 1,450-bed general hospital complex, one of the largest private nonprofit medical complexes in the Southeast. The medical complex in downtown Orlando includes Orlando Regional Medical Center, Arnold Palmer Hospital for Children, Winnie Palmer Hospital for Mothers and Babies, MD Anderson Cancer Center and Lucerne Hospital for Internal Medicine. ORH also has three other facilities providing services throughout the community. In 2008, there were 168 autopsies and approximately 54,000 surgical cases; 4,800 frozen sections; 330 electron microscopy cases; 8,700 cytology preparations; 1600 fine needle aspirations, 4,029 flow cytometric studies and 2,300,000 laboratory procedures. The M.D. Anderson Cancer Center - Orlando provides additional diagnostic teaching material. The department is affiliated with the District Nine Medical Examiner's Office, and although the resident has no direct responsibility for the performance of legal autopsies, the material is available and utilized for teaching purposes. The clinical laboratories are well equipped, automated and provide a full range of procedures in clinical chemistry, toxicology, hematology, coagulation, diagnostic microbiology, molecular pathology, and immunopathology, each under the supervision of one or more pathologists. The laboratory has a comprehensive computer system with on-line instrumentation.

COMMUNITY

Orlando is the cultural center of central Florida with a full-time symphony orchestra, art and science museums, and well-endowed library. The University of Central Florida, Valencia Community College, Rollins College, excellent private and public schools are located here. There are numerous opportunities for year-round outdoor recreation with 32 lakes, public tennis courts, golf courses, and country clubs in the Orlando city limits. World famous beaches and many fine attractions, including Walt Disney Epcot Center, Sea World, MGM, Universal Studios, and Cypress Gardens are only a short distance away.

STIPENDS AND MAINTENANCE

The current stipend is $43,368-$48,256.

STAFF

Lizardo Cerezo MD Associate Director Medical Education; hematopathology, surgical pathology, electron microscopy; **Raymond B. Franklin** MD, PhD Chairman; virology and microbiology, molecular and surgical pathology; **Jan Garavaglia** MD forensic pathology; **Orlando Gonzales** MD surgical pathology, pediatric pathology; **Christopher Hornsby** MD Dermatopathology, surgical pathology; **Shuan C. Li** MD Director Medical Education Pathology; surgical pathology, gastrointestinalpathology; **Mike Magill** MD Dermatopathology, surgical pathology; **John Maksem** MD, Cytopathology, Surgical Pathology; **Julia Martin** Forensic Pathology, autopsy; **Gary Pearl** MD, PhD Assistant Director Medical Education; neuropathology, immunopathology, surgical pathology; **Andrew Sloman** MD oncologic pathology, urologic pathology, surgical pathology; **Anthony Walsh** PhD microbiology.

APPLICATIONS

Further information on the program may be found by visiting our web site at www.orlandohealth.com then go to the Residency/Medical Clerkship link.

Address inquiries to:

Chelle Kozy, Academic Program Manager
1414 Kuhl Avenue, Pathology 2B
Orlando, Fl 32806
Phone: (321) 841-8933
E-mail: pathres@orlandohealth.com

UNIVERSITY OF SOUTH FLORIDA COLLEGE OF MEDICINE

Tampa, Florida

PROGRAMS OFFERED

The Department of Pathology at the University of South Florida College of Medicine offers a fully accredited residency program in combined anatomic and clinical pathology. Comprehensive preparation for either community or academic practice is achieved through a basic core curriculum (22 months AP and 20 months CP) complemented by a broad choice of well-defined resident-chosen electives (6 months). The program emphasizes progressive responsibility in patient care in a variety of practice settings, as well as ample opportunity for supervised research and medical student teaching. These activities are integrated with an extensive lecture and conference series in all aspects of anatomic and clinical pathology. This program follows the guidelines of the Accreditation Council for Graduate Medical Education and is structured to lead to eligibility for certification in anatomic and clinical pathology by the American Board of Pathology. Anatomic pathology rotations encompass training in autopsy and surgical pathology, cytopathology, pediatric pathology, dermatopathology, forensic pathology, immunopathology, histochemistry, ultrastructural pathology, and molecular biology. Clinical pathology rotations encompass training in microbiology, immunopathology, transfusion medicine, chemistry, cytogenetics, hematology, coagulation, toxicology, medical microscopy, molecular biology, and laboratory administration.

TYPES AND NUMBERS OF APPOINTMENTS

The program is currently approved for a total of 18 residents. Applications for positions at all levels are considered. Most positions are filled at the PGY-1 level through the NRMP. One-year fellowships in oncologic surgical pathology, hematopathology, post-sophomore and cytopathology are available at H. Lee Moffitt Cancer Center and Research Institute. Fellowships are also available in pediatric pathology at Tampa General Hospital, and in forensic pathology at the Hillsborough County Medical Examiner's Office.

FACILITIES

The Department of Pathology at the University of South Florida College of Medicine is located within the USF Health Center on the main Tampa campus. The USF Health Center is home to the medical school which began in 1971 and currently accepts 100 freshman medical students each year. The USF Health Center includes a large and active multidisciplinary outpatient clinic and the Medical Center Library, which has current holdings of 28,436 books, receives 1,720 on-line printed journals, and has a network computer lab, with databases for medical literature retrieval, and word processing, Internet, e-mail and graphics applications. Located immediately adjacent to the USF Health Center and entirely staffed by University of South Florida College of Medicine faculty are the James A. Haley VA Medical Center and the H. Lee Moffitt Cancer Center and Research Institute. Tampa General Hospital, located in downtown Tampa, serves as a general teaching hospital for the College of Medicine and the Department of Pathology and Cell Biology. Rotations are also available at several large affiliated hospitals and specialized sites including the Hillsborough County Medical Examiner's Office, Florida Blood Services, Bay Pines VA Medical Center, and Bayfront Medical Center. Tampa General Hospital is a 1,000-bed county-supported institution located in downtown Tampa which serves as a primary teaching facility for the College of Medicine. A total of 220 autopsies in addition to 200 embryo and early fetal autopsies, 14,000 surgical specimens, and 7,500 cytology samples are examined annually. The hospital has active kidney, liver, lung, pancreas and heart transplant programs, a Level 1 Trauma Center, a Regional Cardiovascular Center, and is the base for airborne adult and pediatric emergency teams. The clinical laboratory performs more than 3 million tests per year. H. Lee Moffitt Cancer Center and Research Institute is a 162-bed NCI designated comprehensive cancer center on the campus of the University of South Florida adjacent to the College of Medicine. Comprehensive in-patient and outpatient services are available through interdisciplinary groups in which pathology plays a vital role. Each year the laboratory accessions 10,300 surgicals, 9,200 consultation/review cases, 8,200 cytology specimens, 1,300 bone marrow biopsies, 1,700 fine needle aspiration biopsies, and 30 autopsies. The laboratory also offers a full range of clinical pathology services and has facilities for immunohisto - chemistry, transmission and scanning electron microscopy, and image analysis. The James A. Haley Veterans Hospital is a 309-bed hospital with an adjoining 180-bed nursing unit and a research building. The hospital is linked to the College of Medicine by an overpass. It has an active Ambulatory Care Service encompassing all medical and surgical specialties. The Laboratory Service is staffed by full-time faculty members. In 2006, there were approximately 31,225 surgical specimens, 62 autopsies, 8,102 regular cytology and 691 fine needle aspiration specimens, 250 electron microscopic studies, 202 bone marrow examinations and approximately 2 million clinical laboratory tests. There are facilities for electron microscopy, immunohistochemistry, flow cytometry and image analysis.

COMMUNITY

The Tampa campus of the University of South Florida is located in the rapidly growing "New Tampa" area in Northeast Tampa. Housing is affordable and readily available in several pleasant local neighborhoods with easy access to the University, beaches of the Gulf of Mexico, and cultural activities of downtown Tampa. Tampa is home to Busch Gardens, the Florida Symphony, the Florida Aquarium, the Tampa Bay Buccaneers, the Tampa Bay Lightning hockey team and a mecca for spring professional baseball training. The American Board of Pathology is also located in Tampa. Tampa's climate and location allow year-round outdoor recreational activities including game fishing, boating, tennis, and golf.

STIPENDS AND MAINTENANCE

The 2008-2009 schedule of remuneration for trainees is $43,800 for the first postgraduate year, $45,600 for the second year, $47,200 for the third year, $48,900 for the fourth year and $50,600 for the fifth postgraduate year.

STAFF

University of South Florida Department of Pathology, James A. Haley VA Hospital, H. Lee Moffitt Cancer Center and Research Institute

Santo V. Nicosia MD Professor and Chairman; Chief Cytopathology; reproductive biology; **Geza Acs** MD Associate Professor, Surgical pathology, breast pathology, gynecologic pathology; **Steven Agosti** MD Associate Professor; clinical pathology; **Nazeel Ahmad** MD, Associate Professor; surgical pathology, cytopathology, genitourinary pathology; **Soner Altiok** MD, PhD, Associate Professor, Anatomic Pathology, Thoracic Oncology; **Orhan Arslan** MD Associate Professor, Cell Biology; **Wenlong Bai** PhD Associate Professor; molecular endocrinology and ovarian oncology; **Kaaron Benson** MD Associate Professor; transfusion medicine; **Andrew A. Borkowski** MD Associate Professor, Molecular Diagnostic; **Marilyn Bui** PhD Assistant Professor, surgical pathology; **Don Cameron** PhD Professor, Cell Biology; **Barbara A. Centeno** MD Associate Professor; cytopathology; **Jin Q. Cheng** PhD, Professor; molecular genetics of ovarian cancer; **Shang-Tian Chuang** DO Assistant Professor, Anatomic Pathology; **Domenico Coppola** MD Professor, Cell Biology; **Hernani Cualing** MD Associate Professor, Hematopathology; **Shohreh Dickinson** MD Assistant Professor, immunohistochemistry; **Nicole Esposito** MD, Assistant Member, Anatomic Pathology; **Philip R. Foulis** MD, MPH Associate Professor; clinical pathology; **Ardeshir Hakam** MD,MBA Associate Professor; cytopathology, GYN, GI, GU, surgical pathology; **Don Hilbelink** PhD Professor, Cell Biology; **Jean M. Johnson** MD Assistant Professor; gynecologic pathology, virology; **Loveleen Kang** MD Assistant Professor, Hematopathology; **Farah Khalil** MD, Assistant Professor, Surgical Pathology; **Patricia A. Kruk** PhD Associate Professor; molecular ovarian oncology; **Gabor Legradi** PhD Assistant Professor, Cell Biology; **Leah Strickland Marmol** MD Assistant Professor; surgical pathology; **Tomasz Marzec** MD, Assistant Professor, Surgical Pathology; **Stephen M. Mastorides** MD Assistant Professor; Chief, Pathology and Laboratory Medicine; **Jane L. Messina** MD Associate Professor; dermatopathology; **Michael B. Morgan** MD Professor; dermatopathology; **Lynn Moscinski** MD Professor; hematopathology, molecular biology; **Karl Muffly** PhD Associate Professor, Cell Biology; **Carlos Muro-Cacho** MD, Professor, Anatomic Pathology; **Aejaz Nasir** MD Assistant Professor, cytopathology; **Michael Nolan** PhD Professor, Cell Biology; **Rola Pigeon** MD, Assistant Members, Anatomic Pathology; **Dahui Qin** MD, PhD, Assistant Professor, Molecular & Clinical Pathology; **Jennifer L. Reed** MD Assistant Professor, surgical pathology; **Amyn Rojiani** MD, PhD Professor; neuropathology; **Ramon Sandin** MD Associate Professor; microbiology; **Samuel Saporta** PhD Professor, Cell Biology; **Prudence Smith** MD Assistant Professor; cytopathology, surgical pathology; **Jianguo Tao** Assistant Professor, Hematopathology; **Vesna Vrcel** MD Assistant Professor, surgical pathology; **Don E Wheeler** MD Associate Professor, renal pathology; **Marzenna Wiranowska** PhD Associate Professor, Cell Biology; **Ling Zhang** MD, Assistant Member, Hemato Pathology.

Tampa General Hospital

Stephen Brantley MD Clinical Assistant Professor; anatomic pathology; **Irwin L. Browarsky** MD Clinical Associate Professor, Director Pathology; hematopathology, anatomic pathology; **Enid Gilbert-Barness** MD Professor; pediatric pathology; **Americo A. Gonzalvo** MD Clinical Associate Professor; anatomic and clinical pathology; **Sivaselvi Gunasekaran** MD Clinical Assistant Professor; anatomic pathology; **David Shields** MD Clinical Assistant Professor, anatomic pathology.

Bay Pines VA Hospital

Friedrich W. Klutzow MD Clinical Associate Professor; **John W. Mason** MD Assistant Professor; **Rehana Nawab** MD Clinical Associate Professor; **Theodore Strickland** MD Clinical Assistant Professor; **Myron Tannenbaum** MD Professor.

Consulting Faculty

Vernard Adams MD Associate Professor, Hillsborough County Medical Examiner; **John U Balis** MD Emeritus Professor, anatomic pathology, pulmonary pathophysiology; **Larry J. Davis** MD Clinical Assistant Professor; Director Pathology, Bayfront Medical Center; **Peter J. Dawson** MD Emeritus Professor; **William H. Hartmann** MD Clinical Professor, American Board of Pathology; **German Leparc** MD Clinical Assistant Professor, Florida Blood Services;

David T. Rowlands MD Emeritus Professor; **Eugene H. Ruffolo** MD Clinical Professor, Humana Women's Hospital of Tampa; **Paul J. Schmidt** MD Professor, Florida Blood Services.

APPLICATIONS

Residencies in pathology are open to graduates of approved medical schools in the United States and Canada. Graduates of foreign medical schools must have an ECFMG certificate. Completed applications should be received prior to December 1.

Address inquiries to:

Santo V. Nicosia, MD, Professor and Chairman
Director, Pathology Residency Program
University of South Florida Health
Department of Pathology & Cell Biology
12901 Bruce B. Downs Blvd Box 11
Tampa, FL 33612-4799
Phone: (813) 974-0535 • **Fax:** (813) 974-5536

Jamie Shutter, MD, Assistant Professor
Associate Director, Pathology Residency Program
University of South Florida Health
Department of Pathology & Cell Biology
12901 Bruce B. Downs Blvd Box 11
Tampa, FL 33612-4799

EMORY UNIVERSITY AND AFFILIATED HOSPITALS

Atlanta, Georgia

PROGRAMS OFFERED

The Department of Pathology and Laboratory Medicine of Emory University is one of the largest training centers for pathologists in the United States, and has a full-time faculty: resident ratio of about 2:1. The patient population, faculty interests and physical resources of the Emory Healthcare system permit the training of residents with a wide range of career goals. A general track, including four years of combined AP and CP training, prepares pathologists for practice in either an academic or private setting. A program in anatomic pathology with intensive training in specific areas is available for those who desire a career in an academic setting. A fully established program in clinical pathology is also offered. Regardless of the type of training, the faculty is dedicated to the promotion of confidence in one's abilities through graded responsibilities and increasing independent activities, as well as to the achievement of knowledge, during the training program. Post-residency fellowship training is offered in surgical pathology, hematopathology, cytopathology, transfusion medicine, neuropathology, dermatopathology, GI pathology, soft tissue pathology, forensic pathology, clinical microbiology, clinical chemistry and molecular genetic pathology. A fellowship in infectious disease pathology is co-sponsored by the Center for Disease Control (CDC) and Emory. Training in each of these areas is included in the AP and CP residency years.

TYPES AND NUMBERS OF APPOINTMENTS

The Emory program encompasses training in Anatomic Pathology and Clinical Pathology. There are 40 AP-CP positions, accredited by the ACGME, at PG levels 1 through 4. Applications are considered for training in AP only and CP only. Fellowships are described elsewhere in this book.

FACILITIES

The Robert W. Woodruff Health Sciences Center of Emory University is the major health care center of the Atlanta area and is also a referral center for patients from all parts of the world. The Emory University Hospital (523 beds), the School of Medicine, the Children's Hospital of Atlanta (216 beds), and the Yerkes Regional Primate Center are located on the university campus. Nearby are the Atlanta Veterans Affairs Medical Center (450 beds), and the Centers for Disease Control. Grady Memorial Hospital (667 beds), and Emory University Midtown Hospital (455 beds), are located in downtown Atlanta, approximately 6 miles from campus. Annually, there are approximately 511 autopsies, 63,394 surgical pathology examinations, 992 electron microscopic examinations, 90,000 cytology specimens, and over 8 million clinical laboratory tests. In downtown Atlanta is the Fulton County Medical Examiner's Office, through which residents rotate, where 1,000 autopsies are performed. Emory University is a major center for transplantation of bone marrow, kidney, heart, lung, pancreas, and liver. The Winship Cancer Institute has major programs in breast, genitourinary, lung, head and neck, brain and hematopoetic malignancies. There are extensive facilities for research, and investigators collaborate with the CDC and Yerkes Regional Primate Center. The facilities and patient population offer one of the most comprehensive pathology educational programs in the world.

COMMUNITY

The Emory University Campus occupies 550 acres in a quiet, residential area about 15 minutes northeast of downtown Atlanta. The campus has an outstanding multifunction athletic center, an active theater, and many musical performances. In midtown Atlanta, only 15 minutes away, is the Woodruff Arts Center which houses the Atlanta Symphony Orchestra, the Alliance Theatre, and the High Museum of Art.

STIPENDS AND MAINTENANCE

In 2008-2009, first-year residents earn approximately $44,464, and fourth-year residents earn $50,670. Travel funds up to $2,500 are provided for residents attending national meetings. A $1,000 annual book allowance is provided. Residents are provided with professional liability, health, life and disability insurance. Health insurance for dependents is available at low cost.

STAFF

Tristram G. Parslow MD, PhD William Patterson Timmie Professor and Chairman; pathology, microbiology, immunology; **N.V. Adsay** MD, Professor and Vice Chair, Anatomic Pathology; **A.M. Caliendo** MD, PhD, Professor and Vice Chair, Clinical Pathology.

Professors

C.R. Abramowsky MD pediatric pathology; **G.M. Benian** MD experimental pathology, molecular genetics; **D.J. Brat** MD, PhD neuropathology; **R.A. Bray** PhD clinical pathology; **C. Cohen** MB, ChB surgical pathology, immunohistochemistry, dermatopathology; **A.A. Gal** MD anatomic pathology; **H.M. Gebel** PhD clinical pathology; **R.L. Hanzlick** MD forensic pathology; **C.D. Hillyer** MD transfusion, blood banking; **W. Lewis** MD cardiovascular pathology; **A. Lukacher** MD, PhD immunology, molecular pathology; **B.N. Majmudar** MD gynecologic pathology; **J.E. McGowan, JR** MD infectious diseases; **A. S. Neish** MD immunology; **A. Nusrat** MD gastrointestinal pathology; **C.A. Parkos** MD, PhD gastrointestinal pathology & hepatopathology; **C.W. Sewell** MD neoplastic diseases, breast pathology; **D.R. Weathers** DDS oral pathology; **S.W. Weiss** MD; soft tissue pathology.

Associate Professors

G.G. Birdsong MD cytopathology; **S.D. Budnick** DDS oral pathology; **E.M. Burd** PhD microbiology; **H.E. Grossniklaus** MD ocular pathology; **J. Guarner** MD pediatric pathology; **C. Hao** MD, PhD neuropathology; **R. Hennigar** MD, PhD nephropathology; **J.T. Holden** MD hematopathology; **S.B. Hunter** MD neuropathology; **D.L. Jaye** MD hematopathology; **C.D. Josephson** MD pediatric transfusion medicine; **D.D. Koch** PhD clinical chemistry; **M. Lewis** MD cytopathology; **S. Li** MD, PhD hematopathology; **S. Logani** MD cytopathology, surgical pathology; **L. Logdberg** MD, PhD transfusion medicine; **K.P. Mann** MD, PhD molecular genetic pathology, hematopathology; **S. Muller** DMD oral pathology, molecular diagnostics; **A.S. Neish** MD molecular diagnostics; **J.C. Ritchie Jr.** PhD clinical chemistry; **J.D. Roback** MD, PhD transfusion medicine; **B. Shehata** MD pediatric pathology; **M. Siddiqui** MD, Cytopathology; **T.S. Tadros** MD cytopathology,surgical pathology; **V.A. Varma** MBBS gastrointestinal pathology, electron microscopy; **I.R. Williams** MD, PhD immunology; **A.N. Young** MD, PhD clinical pathology, molecular diagnostics.

Assistant Professors

A. L. Adams MD breast pathology; **A.B. Carter** MD informatics; **A.T. Deyrup** MD, PhD soft tissue, surgical pathology; **A.S. Duncan** MB, ChB immunohematology; **C.R. Fantz** PhD clinical chemistry; **X. Gao** MD cytopathology; **M. Heninger** MD forensic pathology; **C.E. Hill** MD, PhD molecular genetic pathology; **K.L. Hillyer** MD transfusion medicine; **C. Katzen** MD surgical and administrative pathology; **S.K. Lau** MD cytopathology, surgical pathology; **H. Liang** MD gastrointestinal pathology; **J.V. Little** MD surgical pathology; **R. J. Molinaro** PhD clinical chemistry; **R.J. Morris** MD dermatopathology, anatomic pathology; **M. Mosunjac** MD surgical pathology; **M.I. Mosunjac** MD forensic, autopsy & anatomic pathology; **G.M. Oprea** MD cytopathology; **A.O. Osunkoya** MD genitourinary pathology; **S.I. Park** MD pediatric hematopathology; **D.C. Parker** MD, DDS surgical pathology, dermatopathology; **D. Saxe** PhD molecular genetic pathology; **S. Sharma** MD gastrointestinal pathology & hepatopathology; **B.H. Shaz** MD transfusion medicine; **M. Stauffenberg** MD forensic pathology; **Y.F. Wang** MD, PhD microbiology; **B.A. Webber** MD clinical pathology; **J.C. Zimring** MD, PhD immunology.

APPLICATIONS

Applicants must be graduates of approved medical schools. Graduates of schools outside the U.S. must have valid ECFMG certificates. Only ERAS applications will be accepted for first year positions.

Address inquiries to:

Shobha Sharma, MD, Assistant Professor and Director, Pathology Training Programs
Daniel J. Brat, MD, PhD Professor and Co-director
Charles Hill, MD, PhD Assistant Professor and Co-director
Mary Lou Mojonnier, Pathology Education Coordinator
Phone: (404) 727-4283 • **E-mail:** mmojonn@emory.edu
Web site: www.emory.edu/PATHOLOGY/

MEDICAL COLLEGE OF GEORGIA HOSPITAL AND CLINICS

Augusta, Georgia

PROGRAMS OFFERED

The Medical College of Georgia (MCG) offers a four-year ACGME-accredited combined Anatomic Pathology (AP) and Clinical Pathology (CP) residency program. The faculty are committed to the education and training of residents to ensure that they are adequately prepared to pursue a career in either academics or private practice. The residency program focuses on providing broad, yet in-depth training in diagnostic anatomic and clinical pathology leading to eligibility for certification by the American Board of Pathology. Residents rotate both at the Medical College of Georgia and the Charlie Norwood VA Medical Center and are exposed to a wide range of complex specimens. The Children's Medical Center provides exposure to pediatric solid tumor and leukemia/lymphoma cases. Residents have supervised experience in autopsy/neuropathology and surgical pathology, cytopathology/fine needle aspiration, dermatopathology, microbiology, clinical chemistry, hematology (including flow cytometry), transfusion medicine, cytogenetics and molecular pathology. The forensic pathology rotation is provided in collaboration with the Georgia Bureau of Investigation (GBI) in Atlanta. Additional subspecialty rotations in dermatopathology, renal and molecular pathology are available. There is a regularly scheduled core didactic curriculum both in anatomic and clinical pathology throughout the year. The residents participate in departmental and multidisciplinary conferences. Opportunities exist for clinical research with faculty in the department as well as basic science research in the Georgia Esoteric and Molecular Laboratory and the MCG Cancer Center. Funds are available to present data from projects at scientific meetings. Both on- and off campus elective rotations are available in the third and fourth year. One surgical pathology fellowship and one transfusion medicine fellowship are offered.

TYPES AND NUMBERS OF APPOINTMENTS

The program is currently approved for 14 residency positions, 1 surgical pathology fellow, and 1 transfusion medicine fellow. Current 2008-2009 house staff/fellows total 15 (residents: 12; fellows: 3).

FACILITIES

The Medical College of Georgia is an independent unit of the University System of Georgia. The Medical College of Georgia Hospital and Clinics and its Children's Medical Center are an integral part of the College, serving as a referral center for the state. Combined they are a 632 bed teaching hospital. The adjacent 420-bed Veterans Affairs Medical Center is fully integrated into the teaching and residency programs. Our laboratory provides support for active bone marrow and renal transplant programs. We have acquired the Aperio ScanScope System that can archive digitized slides which can then be used for telepathology, teaching and presentations. The department also maintains its own scanning and transmission electron microscopes and a laser capture microdissection microscope. In addition to the departmental library being kept very current, the campus library has an online subscription to most common pathology journals that are available to the residents. The pathology department and laboratories are housed in well equipped facilities that are modern and comprehensive.

COMMUNITY

Augusta is the metropolitan center of the more than 400,000 area population. Augusta's mild climate has average temperatures of 45 in winter and 82 in summer. The city has an active cultural life including symphony and ballet organizations, a choral society, theater groups and Augusta State University, a four year state-supported liberal arts university. Nearby Thurmond Lake has 1,000 miles of shoreline for recreation; the Atlantic Coast and the Great Smokey Mountains are three hours away by automobile. The yearly Masters Golf Tournament is a special attraction.

STIPENDS AND MAINTENANCE

For fiscal year 2008-2009, first-year post-MD graduates receive $44,057, with increases each successive year. Hospital benefits include free life and professional liability insurance. There are three weeks paid vacation yearly. Current departmental policies include: off-call time during Christmas holidays, sponsorship at one national scientific meeting yearly (if presenting) and a book-journal allowance.

STAFF

Full-Time Senior Staff

Rafik Abdelsayed DDS (Indiana Univ Sch Denistry 1993) oral pathology; **Paul W. Biddinger** MD (Univ Cincinnati 1979) Chief, Section of Anatomic Pathology, Director Autopsy Services, Director Immunopathology, Director Surgical Pathology; **Michael Boyd** MD (Univ California at Davis 1985) pathologists' assistant; **Lloyd O. Cook** MD (Indiana Univ 1974) clinical pathology; Director Blood Bank; **John H. Crosby** MD (Univ Tennessee 1967) anatomic pathology, cytopathology; **Yehia A Daaka** PhD (Univ South Florida Coll of Med 1995) Vice Chair Translational Research; **D. Greer Falls** MD (Med Univ South Carolina 1979) anatomic pathology; Director Pathology Residency Program; **Anita S. Kulharya** PhD (Univ North Texas 1990) anatomic pathology; Director Cancer Cytogenetics Laboratory; **Jeffrey R. Lee** MD (Northwestern Univ 1975) Chief, Laboratory Service, Veterans Affairs Hospital, Augusta; **Elizabeth J. Manaloor** MD (Christian Med Col India, 1968) clinical pathology; Director Hematology-Hemostasis Laboratory and Flow Cytometry Laboratory; **Richard A. McIndoe** PhD (Univ Florida, 1991) Center for Biotechnology & Genomic Medicine; **Nidia Messias** MD (Faculdade de Medicina da Universidade Federal do Ceara 1988) anatomic pathology; **Cuong Nguyen** MD (Uninformed Services Univ Health Sciences, The F. Edward Hebert School of Medicine 1994) anatomic pathology; **Preetha Ramalingam** MBBS (Rajah Muthiah Med Col, India 1992) anatomic pathology; Associate Director Pathology Residency Program; **Michelle D. Reid-Nicholson** MBBS (Univ West Indies 1995) anatomic pathology; Director Cytopathology; **Suash Sharma** MD (All India Inst of Med Sci 1992) anatomic pathology, Director Neuromuscular Laboratory; **Jin-Xiong She** PhD (Univ Montpellier, 1987) Director, Center for Biotechnology & Genomic Medicine; **Daniel Sheehan** MD (Washington Univ Sch Med 2001) dermatopathology; **Xingming Shi** PhD (Univ South Carolina 1996) Institute of Molecular Medicine and Genetics; **John C. H. Steele, Jr.** PhD, MD (Duke Univ 1978) Interim Chairman, Chief, Section of Clinical Pathology, Director Microbiology, Vice Chairman Academic Affairs; **Diane Turnbull** EdD (Univ Georgia 1995) Director Undergraduate Education in Pathology; **Cong-Yi Wang** MS (Tongji Med Univ 1989) molecular genetics & functional genomics, Center for Biotechnology & Genomic Medicine.

Visiting Senior Staff

D. L. Booker MD (Univ Georgia 1982) Pathologist, St Joseph's Hospital, Augusta; **Daniel K. Brown** MD (American Univ Caribbean 1989) forensic pathology, Georgia Bureau of Investigation, Augusta; **V. E. Dube** MD (Halle Univ, Germany 1961) Medical Director, Walter Shepeard Community Blood Center, Augusta; **Mark G. Hanly** MB,ChB (Univ Zimbabwe, 1983) Pathologist, Brunswick Biomedical Laboratories, Brunswick, GA; **S. C. Mullins** MD (Univ Georgia 1982) Pathology Laboratory, Augusta; **J. S. Sexton** MD (Univ South Carolina 1968) Pathologist, Newberry County Memorial Hospital, Newberry, SC; **K. B. Sharma** MD (Jaipur Univ, India 1968) Pathologist, University Hospital, Augusta; **F. Silva** MD (Univ Oklahoma 1972) Executive Director, USCAP, Augusta; **Kris L. Sperry** MD (Univ Kansas 1978) Chief Medical Examiner, GBI Crime Lab, Decatur.

APPLICATIONS

ERAS applications accepted.

Address inquiries to:

Shannon Williford, Program Coordinator
Medical College of Georgia
Department of Pathology
1120 15th Street, BA-2576
Augusta, GA 30912
Phone: (706) 721-5118 • **Fax:** (706) 721-7781 • **E-mail:** swillifo@mcg.edu
Web site: http://www.mcg.edu/som/pathology

UNIVERSITY OF HAWAII

Honolulu, Hawaii

PROGRAMS OFFERED

The University of Hawaii Pathology Residency offers a fully accredited and integrated four-year training program in combined anatomic and clinical pathology. We seek to produce professional, educated residents who meet or exceed competency requirements through a curriculum that is structured yet sufficiently flexible for them to pursue his or her area of interest. Residents learn core foundation skills that become the basis for increased responsibility as he/she progresses through training. Required rotations throughout the four years include, in anatomic pathology: a general AP rotation - autopsies and surgicals, forensic pathology, cytogenetics, cytology, and electron microscopy; in clinical pathology: hematology, blood banking/transfusion medicine, immunopathology, chemistry, including toxicology, and microbiology. Elective time is provided in anatomic and clinical areas and elective research projects may include cardiovascular pathology, experimental bacterial infections, ultrastructure of renal disease, alcoholic cirrhosis, neuropathology, cytogenetics and molecular biology, and immunopathology. The program regularly sponsors visiting professors and consultants to enhance residents' training.

Besides the usual duties expected of each rotation, residents prepare and participate in formal and informal presentations for departmental and interdepartmental conferences, journal clubs and research conferences and are involved in teaching medical students throughout their four years. Residents are required to pursue either clinical or basic research during some period of their residency and the program supports presentations at state and national meetings.

TYPES AND NUMBERS OF APPOINTMENTS

The Program is approved for a total of 10 residency positions.

FACILITIES

The major participating institutions, The Queen's Medical Center, Kaiser Foundation Hospital (Moanalua) and Kapiolani Medical Center for Women and Children, contain a total of 1,000 hospital beds and large outpatient clinics; yearly there are approximately 140 autopsies, 71,000 surgical accessions, over 150,000 cytologic specimens and almost 5.3 million clinical laboratory tests. The Medical Examiner's office provides an additional 400+ autopsies per year. In all centers, laboratory facilities are modern with largely automated equipment and ample technical staff. Honolulu serves as a health referral center for the entire Pacific Basin, affording a wealth of interesting and often unique pathologic material. The staff at all major hospitals has special expertise in surgical pathology, clinical pathology, blood banking/ transfusion medicine, hematopathology, cytopathology, microbiology, dermatopathology and neuropathology. Queen's Medical Center Genetics Lab offers valuable training in cytogenetics and molecular pathology while Kapiolani Medical Center for Women and Children offers pediatric and ob-gyn pathology. Affiliate institutions such as the Medical Examiner's office, Blood Bank of Hawaii, Diagnostic Laboratory Services, Inc. and Clinical Laboratories of Hawaii, LLP. contain capabilities for blood processing, tissue culture, rapid viral identification techniques and various chromatographic (gas, TLC, HPLC) techniques. Each hospital department has its own library and there are three comprehensive, readily accessible reference libraries available. The Health Sciences Library, Hamilton Library of Science and Technology and the Hawaii Medical Library maintain a collection that includes more than 300,000 bound volumes of books and journals, over 2,500 electronic journals, 600 books online, and over 60 online medical databases.

COMMUNITY

Hawaii enjoys one of the most benign climates in the world. Honolulu is a center of Pacific-wide activities in health, business, trade, aviation and education. Recreational and cultural opportunities in Honolulu are abundant and well-recognized. The cost of living in Honolulu is equivalent to other popular major metropolitan areas, similar to San Francisco but better than New York.

STIPENDS AND MAINTENANCE

Annual stipends start at $48,352 for first-year trainees and increase in subsequent years. Included in benefits are state licensure fees, lab coats, health, life and professional liability insurance, book and educational travel allowance as well as reimbursement of up to $1,950 to assist with initial relocation costs to Hawaii. Vacation is 3 weeks per academic year.

STAFF

Michele Carbone MD, PhD, Pathology Chair; **Peter K. Bryant-Greenwood** MD, Vice Pathology Chair, gen pathol, cytopathol, Dir of Clin Proteomics; **David M. Shimizu** MD, Program Director; gen pathology; **Jeffrey L. Killeen** MD, Assoc Clin Prof; gen pathol, cytopathol; **Wesley J. Kim** MD, Asst Prof; gen pathol; **Stacey A. Honda** MD, PhD, Assoc Clin Prof; gen pathol; **Steven T. Komura** MD, Asst. Clinc Prof; gen pathol; **Kanthi De Alwis** MD,

Chief Med Examiner, Asst Clin Prof; gen/forensic pathol; **Timothy A. Donlon** PhD, MS; Adj Assoc Prof; molecular pathol; **Muhammad S. Rahman** MD, Assoc Clin Prof; gen pathol; **Matthew J. Bankowski** PhD, MS; Asst Prof; med microbiology; **Christina P. Belnap** MD, Asst Clin Prof; anatomic pathol; **N.V. Bhagavan** PhD, MS; Prof, Dept Biochemistry; medical technology, clin pathol, molecular biophysics; **Karen L. Burmeister** MD, Asst Clin Prof; gen pathol, transfusion med; **Randal B. Covin** MD, Asst Clin Prof; blood bank, transfusion med, informatics; **Wael ElShamy** PhD, MS; Asst Prof; medical biochemistry; **Judy H. Freeman** MD, Asst Clin Prof; cytopathol; **Glenn H. Furuya** MD, Assoc Clin Prof; gen pathol; **David A.T. Goo** MD, Assoc Clin Prof; gen pathol, hematopathol; **William W. Goodhue Jr.** MD, Asst Clin Prof; gen/forensic pathol; **Francis M. Gress** MD, PhD, Assoc Clin Prof; gen pathol, hematopathol; **Kirk Y. Hirata** MD, Assoc Clin Prof; gen pathol, hematopathol; **David H. Horio** MD, Assoc Clin Prof; gen pathol; **Brock J. Kaya** MD, Assoc Prof; gen pathol, neuropathol; **Kenton J. Kramer** PhD, MS; Asst Clin Prof; Sch Tropical Med; **Christopher-Allan Lum** MD, Asst Clin Prof; dermpath; **Anthony A. Manoukian** MD, Assoc Clin Prof; gen/forensic pathol; **Thomas S. Namiki** MD, Assoc Clin Prof; gen pathol, cytopathol; **James J. Navin** MD, Assoc Clin Prof; gen pathol, cytopathol; **Ana M. Ortega Lopez** MD; Asst Clin Prof, blood bank; **Thomas S. Reppun** MD, Assoc Clin Prof; gen pathol, hematopathol, blood bank; **Carlos N. Rios** MD, Assoc Clin Prof; gen pathol, hematopathol; **Gayle F. Suzuki** MD, Asst Clin Prof, gen/forensic pathol; **Pamela S. Tauchi-Nishi** MD, Assoc Clin Prof; gen pathol, cytopathol; **Karen S. Thompson** MD, Assoc Prof; surgical/pediatric pathol; **Jane H. Uyehara-Lock** MD, Assoc Clin Prof; gen pathol, neuropathol; **Haining Yang** PhD, Asst Prof; molecular biology; **Robyn S.L. Yim** MD, Assoc Clin Prof; clin pathol.

APPLICATIONS

Residency applications are accepted through Electronic Residency Application System (ERAS) only, and must be received by December 15 for appointments beginning July 1 of the following year. Dean's letter/transcript, a minimum of three reference letters and official USMLE transcripts are required. Applicants must be graduates of approved medical schools in the U.S./Canada or include ECFMG verification. International graduates will ideally have pursued experience in a U.S. clinical setting and provide letters of reference from U.S. physicians with whom they have worked. Only U.S. citizens, U.S. permanent residents and only J1-Visa candidates are accepted. Appointments are made through the National Resident Matching Program.

Address inquiries to:

David M. Shimizu, MD, Program Director
University of Hawaii Pathology Residency Program
John A. Burns School of Medicine, MEB
651 Ilalo St. #401A
Honolulu, HI 96813
Phone: (808) 692-1131 • **Fax:** (808) 692-1256 • **E-mail:** pathres@hawaii.edu
Web site: http://hawaiiresidency.org

McGAW MEDICAL CENTER OF NORTHWESTERN UNIVERSITY

Northwestern Memorial Hospital, Children's Memorial Hospital

Chicago, Illinois

PROGRAMS OFFERED

The affiliated hospitals of the McGaw Medical Center of Northwestern University, together with the Department of Pathology, Northwestern University Feinberg School of Medicine, offer two distinct training programs. Candidates wishing to prepare for a career centered on diagnostic pathology can choose either *combined AP/CP or single-track AP or CP training*. This program offers intense training in general pathology and the subspecialty areas of anatomic and/or clinical pathology. The emphasis is on producing outstanding diagnosticians and clinical consultants, with a strong background in the current literature and experience in translational research. A *basic science investigator track* is available for MD, PhD candidates. This track allows extended time for basic science research with a faculty member, and focused clinical training in either anatomic or clinical pathology. All trainees and fellows are expected to be actively involved in interdepartmental conferences and in medical student teaching.

TYPES AND NUMBERS OF APPOINTMENTS

A total of 22 pathology residency positions is available.

FACILITIES

The closely affiliated hospitals, Northwestern Memorial Hospital and Children's Memorial Hospital, contribute over 1,000 beds, more than 200 autopsies, 40,000 surgical specimens, 37,000 gyne and 13,500 non-gyne cytology specimens examined microscopically, and more than 4 million laboratory determinations to the training program. Each hospital laboratory is under the direction of a full-time faculty member under whom the trainees work and study. Research facilities based in the hospitals and the Medical School are available to trainees. There is a departmental library as well as the Galter Health Science Library.

COMMUNITY

Chicago is a vibrant city of more than 3.5 million people and a medical center of worldwide reputation. Feinberg School of Medicine is situated on the shores of Lake Michigan near the Gold Coast / Magnificent Mile and within walking distance of the Loop. There are numerous scientific and world class cultural institutions as well as major professional sports and other recreational facilities available in the city.

STIPENDS AND MAINTENANCE

First-year trainees receive $46,865 per year, second-year trainees $49,048, third-year trainees $51,575, and fourth-year trainees $54, 774. In addition to the stipend, trainees are provided with the following additional support including: Group health, dental, term life and accidental death and dismemberment insurance, short and long term disability, professional liability insurance and legal defense while on formal training assignments, a 401k plan, three weeks vacation with stipend and two weeks sick time with stipend. Additional information may be found at: http://gme.northwestern.edu.

STAFF

Professors

Eileen Bigio MD neuropathology; research: Alzheimer's disease; **Jayme Borensztajn** MD, PhD clinical chemistry; research: lipoprotein metabolism and atherosclerosis; **Amy Chadburn** MD, hematopathology; research; leukemias/lymphomas; **Pauline Chou** MD pediatric pathology; **Charles Clevenger** MD, PhD cytopathology; research; breast pathology; **Denise DeFrias** MD cytology; research: cytologic/pathologic correlation; **David M. Engman** MD, PhD diagnostic molecular biology; research: molecular parasitology, autoimmunity; **Charles Goolsby** PhD flow cytometry; research: BCLL biology; **Kathleen Green** PhD research: gene regulation of cell-cell interaction; **Yashpal S. Kanwar** MD, PhD anatomic pathology, renal pathology, immunology; research: structure and function of basement membrane; **William J. Karpus** PhD flow cytometry; research: autoimmunity, cytokines; **William A Muller** MD, PhD Chairman Anatomic Pathology; research: inflammation; **Jill Pelling** PhD research: molecular mechanisms of cutaneous carcinogenesis and cancer chemoprevention; **Elizabeth Perlman** MD pediatric pathology; research: biologic characterization of pediatric germ cell tumors; **LoAnn Peterson** MD hematopathology; research: biology and cytogenetics of B-cell chronic lymphocytic leukemia; **Glenn Ramsey** MD blood banking; research: platelet transfusion; **Sambasiva Rao** MD surgical pathology, gastrointestinal pathology; research: chemical carcinogenesis; **Janardan K. Reddy** MD research: experimental pathology, chemical carcinogenesis; **Kurt Reed** MD medical microbiology; **Jian-Jun Wei** MD, surgical pathology; research; leiomyomas; **Ximing Yang** MD, PhD surgical pathology; research: prostate pathology.

Associate Professors

William Laskin MD surgical pathology; research: soft tissue pathology; **Paul Lindholm** MD blood banking; research: prostate cancer; **Jon Lomasney** MD cardiovascular pathology; research: molecular basis for function of adrenergic receptors; **Ritu Nayer** MD cytopathology; research: fine needle aspiration, quality assurance; **Beverly Nelson** MD hematopathology; research: lymphoproliferative disorders; **Dennis Solt** DMD, PhD oral pathology; research: chemical carcinogenesis; **Barbara Susnik** MD Surgical Pathology; research; breast pathology; **Daina Variakojis** MD hematopathology; research: lymphoreticular diseases; **Guang-Yu Yang** MD, PhD surgical pathology; research; gastrointestinal and liver transplant pathology; **Anjana Yeldandi** MD surgical pathology/pulmonary; research: experimental pathology, chemical carcinogenesis; **Xiaotian Zheng** PhD pediatric pathology/medical microbiology.

Assistant Professors

Katrin Carlson PhD pediatric pathology/cytogenetics; **Yi-Hua Chen** MD hematopathology; **Zongming Chen** MD, PhD surgical pathology; **Anjen Chenn** MD, PhD medical microbiology; research: neuroscience; **Linda Ernst** MD autopsy, surgical pathology, perinatal; **Numa R. Gottardi-Littell** MD neuropathology; research: pathogenesis of human neurodegenerative diseases; **Susan Hasegawa** MD, PhD pediatric pathology; **Marina Ivanovic** MD cytopathology; research; cytopathology; **Lawrence Jennings** MD, PhD pediatric pathology; **Pacita Keh** MD surgical pathology; research: gynecologic pathology; **Xiaoqi Lin** MD, PhD cytopathology; **Hector Melin-Aldana** MD pediatric/hepatology pathology; **Maria Proytcheva** MD pediatric pathology/hematopathology/transfusion medicine; **Chao Qi** PhD clinical microbiology, research; blood culture system; **Carol Schiller** MD surgical pathology; research; ob-gyne pathology; **Nedjema Sustento-Reodica** MD surgical pathology; **Warren Tourtellotte** MD, PhD neuropathology; research: molecular neurobiology; **Yijun Zhu** MD, PhD cytogenetics; research: nuclear receptor coactivators and breast cancer.

APPLICATIONS

Trainees are accepted through ERAS. Graduates of International medical schools must have passed USMLE step 1 and step 2 with scores of 85 or better, and passed the English language examination. Appointments are for a one year period with automatic continuation of the appointment if the resident's work is satisfactory. Applications must be received via ERAS prior to November 1.

Address inquiries to:

Beverly P. Nelson, MD
Director, Pathology Residency Training Program
C/O Irene Galace
Department of Pathology
McGaw Medical Center of Northwestern University Feinberg School of Medicine
303 East Chicago Avenue, Ward 3-140, Chicago, IL 60611
Phone: (312) 503-8223
Web site: http://www.feinberg.northwestern.edu/pathology/

RUSH UNIVERSITY COLLEGE OF MEDICINE

Chicago, Illinois

PROGRAMS OFFERED

Rush Medical College offers a fully approved integrated residency program in anatomic and clinical pathology at Rush University Medical Center. The program is flexible and tailored to the career goals of the individual trainees. A large and enthusiastic staff, with major commitments to service, teaching and research, serve as the faculty for the program. The program is designed to give residents learning opportunities in a large university tertiary care center, Rush University Medical Center. This provides the broad range of experiences which residents need to complete their formal education and finalize their career goals.

TYPES AND NUMBERS OF APPOINTMENTS

Sixteen positions for residents in pathology are offered.

FACILITIES

Rush University Medical Center is located on a 33-acre campus which houses 14 major buildings. Included are Rush University Medical Center, a facility with 674 beds and Rush University housed in a 192,000-square-foot Academic Facility which contains classrooms, research facilities and the University Library. There are over 600 residents currently training at the Medical Center and approximately 500 medical students enrolled in Rush Medical College. The Department of Pathology at the Medical Center serves as the academic department for Rush Medical College. It is centrally located near the geographic center of the complex, which connects the patient care areas and the Academic Facility. The Department performed 144 autopsies, and examined 31,511 surgical pathology specimens and 13,172 cytopathology specimens in 2008. Over 2,000,000 clinical laboratory tests are done each year.

COMMUNITY

Rush University Medical Center is just west of downtown Chicago. The City of Chicago is a major cultural center with many fine art museums, a superior resident opera company, the famed Chicago Symphony Orchestra, outstanding ethnic restaurants, and several major professional sports teams.

STIPENDS AND MAINTENANCE

PGY-1 stipends for 2008-2009 begin at $45,644. This increases progressively in subsequent years to $50,987 in the fourth year. The house staff is provided with uniforms and laundry of uniforms. Free parking is also provided. The house staff is protected with malpractice insurance and receives hospitalization and medical care for themselves and their immediate family.

STAFF

Robert De Cresce MD Chairman.

Professors

Carlos Bedrossian MD Surgical Pathology; Cytopathology; **Pincas Bitterman** MD Director Gynecologic Pathology; **John S. Coon IV** MD, PhD Director Molecular Diagnostics; Immunopathology; **Paolo Gattuso** MD Director Anatomic Pathology; Cytopathology; **Stephanie A. Gregory** MD Hematology; **Jerome R. Kuszak** PhD Electron Microscopy; **Yvonne Lange** PhD Membrane Biogenesis; **Bruce C. McLeod** MD Blood Transfusion; **Theodore Oegema** PhD Biochemistry; **Vijaya B. Reddy** MD Dermatopathology; **Melvin M. Schwartz** MD Renal Pathology; **Russell Tomar** MD Immunology; **Paul Wong** MD Genetics.

Associate Professors

Elizabeth J. Cochran MD Director Autopsy Services, Residency program, Neuropathology; **Shriram Jakate** MD Director Laboratory Services; GI Pathology; **Jerome M. Loew** MD Hematopathology, Pediatric Pathology; **Julie Scheider** MD, Neuropathology; **Kalliopi Siziopikou** MD, PhD Breast Pathology.

Assistant Professors

Thomas Betlej MD Surgical Pathology; **Valerie Arangelovich** MD Forensic Pathology; **Lela Buckingham** PhD Molecular Diagnostics; **Richard J. Grostern** MD Ophthalmology; **Mary Hayden** MD Director Microbiology Section, Rush Medical Laboratories; **Wei-Tong Hsu** MD Genetics; **Michel Humilier** MD Forensic Pathology; **Larry F. Kluskens** MD, PhD Director Cytopathology; **Ira Miller** MD, PhD Hematopathology; **Mark Pool** MD Surgical Pathology, Transfusion Medicine; **Lester Raff** MD Surgical Pathology; **Noman Siddiqui** MD Surgical Pathology; Cytopathology; **Kamaljit Singh** MD Infectious Disease; Microbiology; **Eric Staros** MD; **Abbas Zarif** MD.

APPLICATIONS

Applications are accepted via ERAS System. Candidates must be graduates of approved medical schools and be eligible for licensure to practice medicine in the State of Illinois. Graduates of foreign medical schools must have a valid visa and hold a current ECFMG certificate. Applications should be received by November 15th for appointments beginning July 1st of the next year.

Address inquiries to:

Elizabeth J. Cochran, MD
Director of Education and Residency Training Program
Department of Pathology
1653 W. Congress Parkway
Chicago, IL 60612-3864
Phone: (312) 942-8850 • **Fax:** (312) 942-3434 • **E-mail:** rush_pathology_residency@rsh.net
Web site: http://www.rush.edu/professionals/gme/pathology/index.html

Rush University Medical Center, Chicago, Illinois.

THE UNIVERSITY OF CHICAGO MEDICAL CENTER PRITZKER SCHOOL OF MEDICINE

Chicago, Illinois

PROGRAMS OFFERED

The University of Chicago offers a training program leading to certification in both anatomic and clinical pathology. The program is flexible and adapted to individual needs. It includes rigorous and pragmatic training in all of the standard areas. In-depth training is available in most subspecialties including hematopathology, cytopathology, neuropathology, molecular genetics, gastrointestinal pathology, renal pathology, bone and soft tissue pathology, and transfusion medicine, among many others. There are six regularly held teaching conferences each week in the department. Numerous other conferences within and outside the department are also available. Often pathology residents prepare and present the pathologic aspects of case conferences held in other departments. Required and elective experience in teaching is available. The program provides a core of required rotations and ample time for elective subspecialty training. Excellent opportunities for investigative work at clinical, applied, and basic levels are also available. Most residents conduct clinical, translational, or basic research during their training and publish findings with faculty advisors. Involvement in basic research is also encouraged and the department underwrites two years' of salary for those interested in doing full time bench research in laboratories within or external to the department. Graduates are well prepared for academic careers in diagnostic pathology or experimental pathology depending on the individual's interests and elective experience in the program.

TYPES AND NUMBERS OF APPOINTMENTS

There are 23 pathology resident positions. Typically 6 residents are accepted every year. These include those seeking AP/CP, AP only, and CP only training. Residents may enter the program at advanced levels. The department offers accredited fellowships in cytopathology, hematopathology, and blood banking, and additional fellowships in surgical pathology and most other surgical pathology subspecialties. Advanced training in other specialty areas of pathology and research may also be arranged.

FACILITIES

The University Medical Center is located on the University of Chicago campus. It consists of interconnected hospitals with a total of 631 beds, a large outpatient department, and a busy emergency room. The Anatomic Pathology service is on one floor and includes a newly renovated surgical pathology wing with state-of-the-art diagnostic laboratories, biospecimen banking facility, and offices for house staff. There are approximately 29,000 surgical pathology cases analyzed annually, including 900 renal and over 1,900 bone marrow specimens. In addition, there are 6,000 dermatopathology accessions, 25,000 cytology specimens (11% are nongynecologic) and 1,800 FNA samples examined annually; approximately 200 autopsies are performed every year. Forensic pathology experience is provided at the Cook County Medical Examiner's Office. The modern, spacious Clinical Pathology laboratories occupy 30,000 square feet and utilize advanced instrumentation and methodology. Three million clinical laboratory tests are performed on patient specimens annually. Including quality control and other procedures, this accounts for approximately 12 million CAP weighted workload units performed. The John Crerar Library, located adjacent to the Medical Center, is home to more than 1.3 million volumes in the biomedical and physical sciences as well as the history of science and medicine. About 15,000 reference volumes are available, as well as current journals. The library subscribes to the online versions of all major medical journals.

COMMUNITY

Located on the shores of Lake Michigan, the City of Chicago offers some of the nation's finest museums, a renowned symphony orchestra, and numerous theaters and restaurants of all varieties. The University of Chicago campus is near the lake and less than 15 minutes from downtown. A high proportion of the faculty and house staff live in the immediate neighborhood, Hyde Park. This area provides much of the best of urban living in a university community, with an easy walk to work, and an outstanding university-run school with subsidized tuition.

STIPENDS AND MAINTENANCE

House staff stipends for 2007/2008 were $44,200 - $50,000 per annum. Housestaff are provided with malpractice insurance, hospitalization and medical care.

STAFF

Professors

Albert Bendelac MD, PhD molecular immunology; **Paul Chang** MD, radiology, informatics; **Richard DeMay** MD, Director Cytopathology; **Yang-Xin Fu** MD, PhD transfusion medicine, immunology; **Godfrey S. Getz** MB, BCh,

Dphil (Oxon) atherosclerosis, chemical pathology; **John Hart** MD, gastrointestinal and liver pathology, liver transplant pathology; **Aliya N. Husain** MD, surgical pulmonary and pediatric pathology; pathology education; **Thomas Krausz** MD, FRCPath, Director Anatomic Pathology, general surgical pathology, soft tissue pathology; **Vinay Kumar** MBBS,MD,FRCPath Chairman; cellular and molecular immunology; **James L. Madara** MD, Dean, Biological Sciences Division; gut epithelial biology; **Stephen C. Meredith** MD, PhD autopsy pathology, pathology education, protein biochemistry; **Jonathan Miller** MD, PhD Vice Chairman and Director of Clinical Labs; hemostasis; pathology education; **Anthony Montag** MD, general surgical pathology, bone and gynecologic pathology; **Hans Schreiber** MD, PhD tumor immunology; **Stuart Schwartz** PhD, molecular diagnostics; **Jerome Taxy** MD, surgical pathology, urologic pathology,neoplastic pathology; **Jerrold R. Turner** MD, PhD, gastrointestinal surgical pathology, gut epithelial biology; **James Vardiman** MD, hematopathology; **Martin Weigert** MD, PhD autoimmunity; **Robert Wollmann** MD, PhD neuropathology; **KT Jerry Yeo** PhD, Director Clinical Chemistry Laboratories and UC Med Labs.

Associate Professors

John Anastasi MD, Residency Program Director; hematopathology; **Beverly W. Baron** MD, Director Blood Bank and Transfusion Medicine; **Alexander V. Chervonsky** MD, PhD immunology; **Thomas Gajewski** MD, PhD T cell activation, tumor immunology, cancer vaccines; **Barbara L. Kee** PhD, immunology; **Mark Lingen** DDS, PhD oral pathology, cancer biology; **Susana Marino** MD, PhD histocompatibility, immuno genetics; **Shane Meehan** MD, renal pathology; **Amy Noffsinger** MD, surgical pathology and gastrointestinal; **Ting-Wa Wong** MD, PhD pathology education.

Assistant Professors

Anthony Chang MD, Residency Program Associate Director; renal pathology; **Karen Frank** MD, PhD, Residency Program Associate Director; clinical microbiology; **Hikmat Al-Ahmadie** MD, genitourinary pathology, oncologic pathology; **Elizabeth Hyjek** MD, PhD, hematopathology; immunohistochemistry; **Loren Joseph** MD, PhD, clinical chemistry and molecular diagnostics; **Ivan Moskowitz** MD, PhD, cardiac pathology; **Peter Pytel** MD, neuropathology; **Husain Sattar** MD, breast pathology; **Rosie Xing** PhD, cancer biology.

Instructors

Elie Richa MD, transfusion medicine.

Clinical Associates

Cyril Abrahams MD, pulmonary pathology, autopsy pathology; **Jerome Dickstein** MD, PhD hematopathology; **Ward Reeves** MD, cytopathology; **Elizabeth Sengupta** MD, electron microscopy.

APPLICATIONS

Candidates must be graduates of approved medical schools or hold an ECFMG certificate. Candidates must be eligible for licensure to practice medicine in the State of Illinois. Application deadline is December 1.

Address inquires to:

John Anastasi MD, Director, Residency Training Program
Anthony Chang MD, Associate Director, Residency Training Program
Karen Frank MD, PhD, Associate Director, Residency Training Program
Department of Pathology
The University of Chicago Medical Center
5841 S Maryland Avenue, MC 3083
Chicago, IL 60637
Phone: (773) 834-7708 • **E-mail:** lcleland@bsd.uchicago.edu

The University of Chicago Medical Center, Chicago, Illinois.

UNIVERSITY OF ILLINOIS COLLEGE OF MEDICINE

Chicago, Illinois

PROGRAMS OFFERED

The University of Illinois College of Medicine at Chicago offers a fully-accredited residency training program in Anatomic Pathology (AP) and Clinical Pathology (CP). The residency seeks to provide the educational opportunities and thoughtful guidance that allow a first-year resident to develop into a competent and confident pathologist equipped to embark upon any of a variety of post-residency experiences. Rotation sites include the University of Illinois Medical Center at Chicago (UIMC), Advocate Lutheran General Hospital (ALGH), Advocate Illinois Masonic Medical Center (AIMMC), and Jesse Brown Veterans Affairs Medical Center (JBVAMC) (formerly West Side Veterans Affairs Hospital). The affiliation of a university tertiary-care medical center with community-based institutions and a federally-funded hospital broadens the residency experience by providing varied practice models, and the variety of training environments offers diverse patient populations from which to learn.

Anatomic Pathology and Clinical Pathology rotations are provided throughout each of the four years of a combined AP/CP residency. AP training includes surgical pathology rotations that offer the resident extensive exposure to a wide variety of specimens (including an emphasis at UIMC on ophthalmic, soft tissue, hepatic, gastrointestinal, and transplantation pathology). Cytopathology rotations include interpretation of gynecologic and non-gynecologic specimens, as well as performance and interpretation of fine-needle aspiration specimens. Forensic pathology education is provided at the Office of the Medical Examiner of Cook County. CP rotations provide experience in all of the major disciplines of clinical pathology practice: Clinical Chemistry (including core laboratory services, immunoserology, toxicology); Microbiology (including bacteriology, mycology, parasitology, virology, and mycobacteriology); Transfusion Medicine (including donor, transfusion service, and therapeutic apheresis/stem cell collection training); and Hematopathology (including bone marrow and lymph node interpretation, clinical hematology services, and coagulation). Residents also rotate through subspecialty areas, such as Cytogenetics, Molecular Pathology, and Tissue Typing/HLA. Residents participate frequently in hospital-wide multidisciplinary conferences, intra-departmental conferences, and medical student teaching.

Resources for diagnostic purposes and investigative activities include flow cytometry, immunohistochemistry, electron microscopy, laser capture microdissection, cytogenetics, image analysis, and molecular diagnostic services. Digital pathology is available for educational and research purposes. Participation in a range of scholarly activities is required, and research experiences are strongly encouraged. The Division of Pathology Research focuses on Molecular Epidemiology. Research programs and projects are also ongoing throughout the Department's other divisions.

The program stresses progressive responsibility under supervision, commensurate with the level of training and ability.

TYPES AND NUMBERS OF APPOINTMENTS

28 PGY I through PGY V residents (which includes seven PGY I positions) are participating in the 2009-2010 academic year. Seven PGY I positions are anticipated for the 2010-2011 academic year. Fellowship training is also available of UIMC in Blood Banking/Transfusion Medicine, Hematopathology, and Surgical Pathology.

FACILITIES

The Department of Pathology is an academic unit of the University of Illinois College of Medicine and is composed of six major divisions: Surgical Pathology, Cytopathology, Transdisciplinary Pathology (including Autopsy Pathology), Clinical Pathology, Pathology Research, and Pathology Education. UIMC and JBVAMC provide approximately 700 hospital beds with 16,000 surgical specimens, 5,500 gynecologic and 1,000 non-gynecologic cytology specimens, 600 fine needle aspirations, 3,000,000 clinical laboratory determinations, and 100-130 autopsies yearly. AIMMC and ALGH provide over 1000 hospital beds with over 40,000 surgical specimens, 25,000 cytological specimens, nearly 3,000,000 clinical laboratory tests, and approximately 120 autopsy cases per year. Library and computer facilities are available in each institution, and access to the University of Illinois at Chicago library is available to all residents. Medical students from the University of Illinois and residents from multiple disciplines are present at each rotation site.

UIMC and JBVAMC are within a few minutes walk from each other in the Illinois Medical District (IMD). AIMMC is approximately 20 minutes from the IMD, and ALGH, located in the northwest Chicago suburbs, is approximately 20 miles from the IMD. Multiple conferences are available at each rotation site, and bidirectional videoconferencing provides distance teaching / learning opportunities.

COMMUNITY

Chicago is an exciting and beautiful city of cultural diversity and rich history. The city and surrounding counties are home to approximately 8 million people. The stunning architecture, numerous museums, interesting landmarks, theatrical and cinema offerings, and musical venues make Chicago a stimulating place to visit and a superb place to live. Housing is readily available near all sites, and multiple transportation options are available via an extensive public transit system.

STIPENDS AND MAINTENANCE

Annual stipends for fiscal year 2009-2010 range from $45,420 for PGY 1 trainees to $51,720 for PGY 4 trainees. The website of the Graduate Medical Education Office (http://www.uic.edu/com/gme/) contains additional specific information regarding stipends and benefits.

STAFF

Frederick Behm MD, Prof, Interim Head, Hematopathology, UIC; **Brain Adley** MD, Clin Asst Prof, Assoc Attending, Surgical Pathology, ALGH; **A. Ali** MD, Surgical Pathologist, ALGH; **I. Almanaseer** MD, Clin Asst Prof, Chair, Hematopathology and Molecular Pathology, ALGH; **C. August** MD, Clin Asst Prof, Director of Anatomic Pathology, Flow and Image Cytometry, AIMMC; **A. Balla** MD, PhD, Prof, Director of Transdisiplinary Pathology, UIC; **N. Baumann** PhD, Asst Prof, Director of Chemical Pathology, UIC; **C. Booth** MD, Clin Asst Prof, Director of Cytogenetics, ALGH; **M. Braniecki** MD, Dermatopathology, ALGH; **R.J. Buschmann** PhD, Assoc Prof, JBVAMC; **Julio Cabrera** MD, Clin Asst Prof, Assoc Attending, Surgical Pathology & Renal, ALGH; **S. Campbell-Lee** MD, Asst Prof, Director of Transfusion Medicine, UIC; **G. Chejfec** MD, Prof, Emetrius, UIC; **M. Costello** PhD, Clin Asst Prof, Immunology, Molecular Pathology, ALGH; **O. David** MD, MPH, Asst Prof, Director of Cytopathology, UIC; **D. Fretzin** MD, Clin Prof, Dermatopathology, UIMC; **S. Gaitonde** MD, Clin Asst Prof, Hematopathology, UIC; **P. Gann** MD, ScD, Prof, Director of Pathology Research, UIC; **M. Gonzalez** MD, Clin Asst Prof, Site Coordinator, ALGH; **M. Guo** MD, Asst Prof Clin Path, Cytopathology, UIC; **G. Guzman-Hartman** MD, Asst Prof, Liver, GI, Pancreas Pathology and Gynecologic Pathology, UIC; **I. B Harris** PhD, Prof, Pathology Medical Education, UIC; **W. M. Janda** PhD, Assoc Prof, Microbiology, UIC; **S. Kadkol** MD, PhD, Asst Prof, Director Molecular Pathology, UIC; **J. L. Kennedy** MD, Clin Assoc Prof, Chief Lab Service, JBVAMC; **G. Kirshenbaum** MD, Clin Assoc Prof, Assoc Chairman, Director of Chemistry, Immunopathology, AIMMC; **Amy Lin** MD, Asst Prof, Opthalmic Pathology, UIC; **V. Lindgren** PhD, Assoc Prof, Director Cytogenetics, UIC; **Z. Malecki** MD, Clin Instructor, Surgical Pathology, AIMMC; **R. Murray** PhD, Clin Asst Prof, Biochemistry, ALGH; **J. Nowak** MD, PhD, Clin Assoc Prof, Molecular Pathology and Cytopathology, ALGH; **Michael Pins** MD, Clin Asst Prof, Assoc Attending, Surgical Pathology, ALGH; **J. W. Ryoo** MD, PhD, Clin Asst Prof, General Pathology, JBVAMC; **L. Sabatini** PhD, HCLD, Technical Director, Molecluar Pathology, ALGH; **A. Segovia** MD, Clin Assoc Prof, Deputy Chief Medical Examiner of Cook County; **S. Setty** MD, Asst Prof, Molecular Surgical Pathology and Renal, UIC; **R. Sirota** MD, Surgical Pathology, Hematopathology, ALGH; **S.D. Sosler** MS, Asst Prof, Blood Bank, UIC; **M. Utset** MD, PhD, Asst Prof, Director of Neuropathology, Stroger Cook County Hospital; **T. Valyi-Nagy** MD, PhD, Asst Prof, Director of Neuropathology, UIC; **V. Vidanovic** MD, Asst Prof of Clinical Pathology, UIC; **E. Weisenberg** MD, Visiting Clin Prof, Assoc Program Director, Surgical Pathology and Hematopathology, AIMMC; **C. M. Weldon-Linne** MD, Clin Asst Prof, Chairman, Microbiology and Virology, AIMMC; **E. Wiley** MD, Prof, Director of Surgical Pathology, UIC.

APPLICATIONS

Applications will be accepted only through the Electronic Residency Application Service (ERAS). By the time of beginning residency, all applicants must be a graduate of an accredited allopathic or osteopathic medical school in the United States or Canada, or, if a graduate of a medical school outside of the United States or Canada, must hold a valid ECFMG certificate and a valid temporary Illinois medical license, or a permanent and unrestricted medical license in the State of Illinois. Personal interviews are required. Applications should be received no later than December 31 for appointments beginning July 1.

Address inquiries to:

Corey J. Parker, MPA
Education Division Coordinator
University of Illinois at Chicago (MC 847)
840 South Wood Street, Suite 130 CSN
Chicago, IL 60612
Phone: (312) 996-7250 • **Fax:** (312) 996-7586
Web site: pathology.uic.edu

EVANSTON HOSPITAL

Evanston, Illinois

PROGRAMS OFFERED

Evanston Hospital, a teaching affililate of the University of Chicago, offers fully accredited training in anatomic and clinical pathology for 12 residents as University of Chicago (NorthShore) Pathology at Evanston Hospital (AAMC ID 1051274). The residency emphasizes thorough and balanced training in anatomic and clinical pathology, and there is opportunity and support for supervised research within and outside the department. Trainees actively participate in all departmental functions with teaching and mentoring from members of the attending staff. The program includes departmental seminars and teaching conferences as well as seminars conducted by other departments. Advanced trainees may rotate to other services and educational activities of the medical school and other institutions. Trainees also participate in numerous professional activities in Chicago, such as meetings of local and national medical societies and symposia in the medical schools. All residents rotate to Children's Memorial Hospital and to the Medical Examiner's Office in Chicago.

REQUIREMENTS

Applicants must be graduates of approved allopathic and osteopathic medical schools with minimum USMLE and COMLEX scores of 80 or above (parts I and II), passing on the first attempt. Temporary or permanent Illinois license to practice medicine is mandatory. Graduates of foreign medical schools must have an ECFMG certificate and a valid visa. Satisfactory references are required.

TYPES AND NUMBERS OF APPOINTMENTS

We offer 12 accredited residency positions. Residents generally choose a combined AP/CP experience.

FACILITIES

NorthShore University HealthSystem consists of Evanston Hospital in Evanston, Glenbrook Hospital in Glenview, Highland Park Hospital in Highland Park, and Skokie Hospital in Skokie, Illinois (added in 2009). The hospitals have a combined total of 1026 licensed beds. Evanston Hospital is a specialty institution, providing leadership in cancer and cardiac care with specialized cancer services at The Kellogg Cancer Care Center, comprehensive heart care at the Cardiovascular Care Center, and adult medical genetics at The Center for Medical Genetics. The Women's Hospital is the regional center for high-risk obstetrics with access to the latest technology and a highly-trained staff. The hospital is also a licensed Level I Trauma Center and a Level 3 NICU. There is a house staff of 160 and more than 2000 affiliated physicians. Most staff physicians have teaching appointments at the University of Chicago, and University of Chicago residents and medical students spend part of their training at Evanston Hospital every year.

The pathology training program is centered at Evanston Hospital. In 2007 there were 38,316 admissions at the three hospitals. The Department of Pathology and Laboratory Medicine is located in laboratories completed in 1977 and remodeled in 1995 and 2004. In 2008 the department performed 259 autopsies and processed approximately 60,000 surgical, including 27,100 outreach tissue specimens, and 62,000 cytology specimens, including FNA. The clinical laboratories performed approximately 3.3 million examinations in the various divisions and outreach program. The Glenbrook and Highland Park Hospital laboratories are available for rotation in the final year for those who wish to experience a community hospital environment.

COMMUNITY

Evanston, an established residential community of approximately 80,000, is located on Lake Michigan immediately north of Chicago. Evanston Hospital is near the main campus of Northwestern University. Evanston offers the unique combination of a lake front residential area and the social and cultural activities of a large university in proximity to a large metropolis and important medical center with six medical schools, active local medical societies and a meeting place for national societies. Fast and easy transportation makes all the professional, recreational, and cultural facilities of the nation's third largest city readily available.

STIPENDS AND MAINTENANCE

First-year trainees received an annual salary of $45,550 (2008-2009) with graduated increases up to $51,500 at the fourth-year level. Benefits are competitive. Four weeks of paid vacation are allowed during each year of training.

STAFF

Faculty

Thomas A. Victor MD PhD, Chairman, Professor Pathology; surgical pathology, dermatopathology; **Karen L. Kaul** MD, PhD, Director Residency Program, Director Division of Molecular Pathology, Professor Pathology and

Urology; molecular biology; **Irene J. Check** PhD, Director Clinical Pathology, Director Immunology, Professor Clinical Pathology; lymphocyte markers; **Thomas Cibull** MD; surgical pathology, dermatopathology; **Susan Crawford** DO; perinatal and pediatric pathology; **Mark Dieterich** MD, Director Cytology, Assistant Professor Pathology; gynecologic and infectious diseases pathology; **James C. Dohnal** PhD, Director Biochemistry, Assistant Professor Pathology; fetal lung maturation and informatics; **Mohamed Eldibany** MD, Director Hematology, Assistant Professor Pathology; diagnostic hematopathology, hemostasis, and thrombosis; **Barbara M. Golden** MD, Assistant Professor Pathology; surgical pathology; **Robert A. Goldschmidt** MD, Assistant Professor Pathology; ploidy in malignancy, immunochemistry; **Curtis R. Hall** MD, Assistant Professor Pathology; surgical pathology; **Igor Jovanovic** MD PhD; surgical pathology, cytopathology; **Michael W. Kaufman** MD, Director Autopsy Pathology, Assistant Professor Pathology; diagnostic and forensic pathology; **Lin Liu** MD; surgical pathology, cytopathology; **Mary Milano** MD; surgical pathology; **Jan Nowak** MD, PhD, Director Molecular Diagnostics Lab; molecular biology; **James L. Padgett** MD, JD MBA, Assistant Professor Pathology; surgical pathology; **James T. Perkins** MD, Director Blood Bank, Medical Director School Medical Technology, Assistant Professor Pathology; **Lance R Peterson** MD, Professor of Pathology and Medicine; medical microbiology, clinical infectious diseases; **Robert Rosecrans** PhD, Director Clinical Pathology Glenbrook and Highland Park Hospitals, Assistant Professor of Pathology; **Antoinette Thomas-Cibull** MD; surgical pathology, hematopathology; **Richard B. Thomson, Jr.** PhD, Director Microbiology and Virology, Professor Pathology; antimicrobial testing; **William G. Watkin** MD, Director Anatomic Pathology, Assistant Professor Pathology; gynecologic neoplasia.

Consulting

Veena Rajaram MD, Assistant Professor of Pathology; neuropathology; **Ira S. Salafsky** MD, Assistant Professor Pediatrics; cytogenetics.

APPLICATIONS

Applications should be received by December 1 for appointments starting July 1 of the next year.

Address inquiries to:

Karen Kaul, MD, PhD
Department of Pathology
Evanston Hospital
2650 Ridge Avenue
Evanston, IL 60201-1783
Phone: (847) 570-2052

LOYOLA UNIVERSITY MEDICAL CENTER

Maywood, Illinois

PROGRAMS OFFERED

The combined facilities of the Pathology Departments and Clinical Laboratories of the Stritch School of Medicine and Foster G. McGaw Hospital of Loyola University of Chicago and Hines VA are approved for resident training in anatomic and clinical pathology for a four-year program. The residents will rotate through the various divisions of the Clinical Laboratories, the Autopsy Service and Surgical Pathology sections at both hospitals. The training program is flexible so that individual programs may be designed for those with interests in community hospital practice or academic careers in pathology (with opportunities for subspecialization and research). The anatomic pathology component of the program provides training in surgical pathology, autopsy pathology, cytopathology, dermatopathology, neuropathology, forensic pathology, pediatric pathology, electron microscopy, immunopathology, molecular pathology, cytogenetics, and immunohistochemistry. The clinical pathology component of the program offers training in chemistry, hematology, blood bank, microbiology, molecular pathology, virology, immunology/immunoserology, laboratory management and computer science. Electives are available for additional training in subspecialty areas of interest. There is opportunity for investigative work in experimental pathology with special emphasis on molecular biology and molecular pathology. Outstanding residents will be offered special research opportunities which should be a stepping stone to an academic career in pathology. There will be opportunities to teach medical students, medical technologists, graduate students and postgraduates in departmental and interdepartmental conferences and seminars. Also, numerous additional conferences are available at other medical centers within the area which will be supplemental to the training at Loyola. Fellowships are available in surgical pathology, hematopathology,cytopathology and GI pathology.

TYPES AND NUMBERS OF APPOINTMENTS

The combined program is approved for 16 residents.

FACILITIES

The two facilities, having a total of 1,568 beds, occupy the same grounds and are immediately adjacent to one another. Between both institutions 150 autopsies, 30,000 surgicals, 25,000 cytologies and 20,000,000 laboratory procedures are performed annually. The clinical laboratories in both institutions are well staffed, highly sophisticated, and very well equipped, including extensive computerization of services. Specialized areas include information systems, electron microscopy, neuropathology, quantitative cytology, histology, immunopathology, molecular biology, and a highly developed research area in hemostasis, coagulation, neurosciences, and skin diseases.

COMMUNITY

Maywood is located about 10 miles west of downtown Chicago. It is readily accessible to interstates, public transportation, many beautiful suburban areas, parks, forest preserves, and many cultural activities, including the Chicago Symphony, Ballet and Opera, in addition to numerous fine museums and cultural centers. Major professional sports teams include the Bulls, Bears, Black Hawks, White Sox and Cubs.

STIPENDS AND MAINTENANCE

Stipends range from $42,897.00 (first year) to $48,417.00 (fourth year) and are adjusted on July 1 of each year. Additional benefits include individual coverage in Blue Cross/Blue Shield, Major Medical, Dental Insurance, Malpractice, Workman's Compensation.

STAFF

Full-Time

Guliz Barkan MD, Assistant Professor; **Maurizio Bocchetta** PhD, Assistant Professor, Research; **Henry Brown** MD, PhD, Associate Professor, Director of Autopsy & Neuropathology; **Lee Cera** DVM, PhD Assistant Professor, Veterinary Pathology Services and Research; **Madhu Dahiya** MD, Assistant Professor; **Phillip DeChristopher** MD, PhD, Professor, Director of Blood Bank & Transfusion Medicine; **Mitchell Denning** PhD, Professor, Research; **Cagatay Ersahin** MD, PhD, Assistant Professor; **Jawed Fareed** PhD, Professor, Research; **Kimberly Foreman** PhD Associate Professor, Research; **Earle Holmes** PhD Professor, Clinical Chemistry, Endocrinology; **Walter Jeske** PhD Associate Professor, CV Surgery; **Stephen Kahn** PhD, Professor, Vice-Chair of Anatomic Pathology; **Umesh Kapur** MD, Assistant Professor; **Ameet Kini** MD, PhD, Associate Professor, Director, Flow Cytometry; **Caroline Le Poole** PhD, Assistant Professor, Research; **John M. Lee** MD, PhD, Professor, Neuropathology; **Swati Mehrotra** MD, Assistant Professor; **Debra Moorman** PhD, Associate Professor, Research; **Brian Nickoloff** MD, PhD, Vice- Chair Research; Professor, Dermatopathology; **Gladell Paner** MD, Assistant Professor; **Maria Picken,** MD, PhD, Professor, Director of Renal Pathology; **Margaret Prechel** PhD, Assistant Professor, Research; **Prabha Rajan** MD, Associate Professor, Breast Pathology; **Alia Salhadar** MD, Associate Professor, Director, Cytopathology; **Paul Schreckenberger** PhD, Professor, Director of Microbiology; **Milind Velankar** MD, Assistant Professor Hematopathology; **Razan Wafai** MD, Associate Professor, Cytopathology & Surgical Pathology; **Jeanine Walenga** PhD, Professor, Thoracic & CV Surgery & Pathology; **Eva M. Wojcik** MD, Professor, Chair, Director, Resident Training; **Sherri Yong** MD, Associate Professor, Surgical Pathology.

APPLICATIONS

Applicants to the program should have an MD degree from an approved Medical School. Residency candidates must be eligible to be licensed to practice medicine in the State of Illinois. Residencies and fellowships begin July 1.

Address inquiries to:

Vicki Baertschi
Education Coordinator
Department of Pathology
Loyola University Medical Center
2160 South First Avenue
Maywood, IL 60153
Phone: (708) 216-5591
Web site: http://www.stritch.luc.edu/depts/path/index.htm

INDIANA UNIVERSITY SCHOOL OF MEDICINE

Indianapolis, Indiana

PROGRAMS OFFERED

The Department of Pathology and Laboratory Medicine of Indiana University School of Medicine offers approved pathology training programs at Clarian Methodist Hospital, Clarian University Hospital, Clarian Riley Children's Hospital, Wishard Memorial Hospital and the Veterans Hospital, all of which are located in downtown Indianapolis. The residency program is a combined anatomic and clinical pathology program. In the combined program, residents gain experience in surgical pathology, including frozen section diagnosis, diagnostic cytopathology, forensic pathology, necropsy pathology, pediatric pathology, dermatopathology, neuropathology, electron microscopy, and immunopathology. Cytopathology includes fine needle aspiration procurement and analysis. Also, there are opportunities for acquisition of skills in flow cytometry, histochemistry and special techniques in pathologic diagnosis. In clinical pathology, residents rotate through laboratories of hematology, chemistry, microbiology, blood bank, and genetics. The laboratories offer comprehensive experience including frozen blood program, white cell transfusions, molecular biology, virology, clinical toxicology/drug monitoring, endocrinology, and computer information handling. Residents complete 6 months of anatomic and 6 months of clinical pathology training annually for the first 3 years. The final year may be concentrated in a single discipline or used to become more proficient in several areas. Opportunities for research are available, and research activity is encouraged in conjunction with members of the staff or independently if desired. Residents participate in teaching of medical students and medical technology students. In addition, a variety of advanced courses in basic medical sciences are available. Departmental conferences include all areas of anatomic and clinical pathology. Interdepartmental conferences are held regularly as are state- and city-wide pathology meetings. Fellowships are offered in: Clinical Microbiology, Neuropathology, Cytopathology, Surgical Pathology, Hematopathology, Dermatopathology, and Forensic Pathology.

TYPES AND NUMBERS OF APPOINTMENTS

There are 20 residency positions and approximately 5 are filled each year. In 2008-09 our house staff included 7 graduates from Indiana University, 10 from other states and 3 foreign medical graduates. In addition to the residency program, in 2008-09 we had 8 fellows training in 5 subspecialties.

FACILITIES

Complete facilities exist for anatomic and clinical pathology services and are directed by physicians who are members of the faculty. Extensive research facilities include those for electron microscopy, molecular biology, tissue culture and highly diversified instrumentation for clinical and experimental pathology studies. In May 2006, a new centralized laboratory facility opened located midway between the medical school campus and Methodist Hospital. Numbers of procedures in various areas are summarized below.

	Clarian Health Partners Methodist/IU/Riley	Wishard Hospital	Veterans Hospital
Beds	MH899/IU379/RI279	350	150
Autopsies	160	17	18
Forensic necropsies	1000	0	0
Surgical pathology	59,260	9,889	8,330
Frozen sections	4,903	362	170
Cytopathology	44,569	25,521	2,789
Fine Needle Aspiration	3,612	205	459
Chemistry	1,850,237	624,712	1,991,479
Hematolog	1,117,650	694,353	105,950
Microbiology	232,235	212,616	64,366
Blood Bank	92,228	55,993	7,562

COMMUNITY

Indianapolis is a forward-looking city of 1,000,000 situated in the center of Indiana. The city has an extensive park system with excellent public golf courses, sailing facilities, art museums, children's museum, symphony orchestra, opera, ballet, and several theaters. There are professional sports teams and two major annual auto races. In amateur athletics, the city frequently hosts national championships in track and field, gymnastics, swimming and diving, and basketball.

STIPENDS AND MAINTENANCE

Stipends for 2009-2010 are as follows: postgraduate level one $46,146; level two $46,846; level three $47,746; level four $48,846; level five $50,146; level six $51,646.

STAFF

John N. Eble MD Chairman; urologic pathology; **David Grignon** MD Vice Chair, Clinical Programs, urologic pathology; **Kenneth W. Ryder** MD, PhD Clarian Laboratory Director; clinical chemistry; **Narasimhan Agaram** MD surgical pathology, cytopathology, soft tissue pathology; **Stephen D. Allen** MD microbiology; **Caroline S. An** MD anatomic pathology, hematopathology; **Biagio Azzarelli** MD Emeritus Professor neuropathology; **Sunil Badve** MD surgical pathology; **John C. Baenziger** MD clinical chemistry, newborn screening; **Jose M. Bonnin** MD neuropathology, surgical pathology, liver pathology; **Jey-Hsin Chen** MD, PhD surgical pathology, gastrointestinal pathology, hematopathology; **Liang Cheng** MD urologic pathology, molecular pathology; **Harvey Cramer** MD cytopathology; **Oscar W. Cummings** MD surgical pathology, transplantation pathology; **Magdalena Czader** MD, PhD hematopathology; **Constance F. Danielson** MD, PhD transfusion medicine; **Darrell Davidson** MD, PhD cytopathology; **Thomas E. Davis** MD, PhD surgical pathology, microbiology; **Rosen Dimitrov** MD cytopathology; **Robert Emerson** MD surgical pathology, cytopathology; **Rong Fan** MD pediatric pathology; **Philip Faught** MD pediatric pathology; **Bernardino Ghetti** MD neuropathology; **Steven Gregurek** MD transfusion medicine; **Eyas Hattab** MD surgical pathology, neuropathology; **Dean A. Hawley** MD autopsy, forensic pathology; **Kurt Hodges** MD surgical pathology, cytopathology; **Meredith T. Hull** MD surgical pathology; **Muhammad Idrees** MD surgical pathology, cytopathology; **Raymond Konger** MD chemical pathology, research; **Lisbeth G. Larsson** MD anatomic pathology, pulmonary pathology; **Chao-Hung Lee** PhD molecular pathology; **Diane Leland** PhD virology, serology; **Leo J. McCarthy** MD Emeritus Professor Pathology; **Helen B. Michael** MD surgical pathology, gyn pathology; **William Moores** MD dermatopathology; **Paul Musto** MD surgical pathology; **Mehdi Nassiri** MD hematopathology, informatics; **Carrie Phillips** MD nephropathology, electron microscopy; **John E. Pless** MD Emeritus Professor pathology; **Ramesh Ramanathan** MBBS cytopathology, surgical pathology; **Kathryn Rizzo** DO, PhD hematopathology, cytopathology; **Lawrence M. Roth** MD Emeritus Professor pathology; **Romil Saxena** MD surgical pathology, liver pathology; **Daniel S Smith** MD transfusion medicine; **J.W. Smith** MD Emeritus Professor Pathology; **Thomas M. Ulbright** MD surgical pathology, urologic pathology; **Saeed T. Vakili** MD surgical pathology, neuropathology; **Xiaoyan Wang** MD surgical pathology, cytopathology; **Simon Warren** MD dermatopathology.

APPLICATIONS

First-year appointments are made in accordance with policies of the National Resident Matching Program when applicable, and training usually begins on July 1. Applications should be received by December 1 for appointment beginning July 1 of the following year. References and personal interviews are required.

Address inquiries to:

Carrie L. Phillips, MD
Director, Residency Program
Indiana University School of Medicine
Clarian Pathology Laboratory, Rm 4090
350 W. 11th Street
Indianapolis, IN 46202
Phone: (317) 491-6350
Web site: http://pathology.iupui.edu

Clarian Pathology Laboratory

View of Downtown Indianapolis

BALL MEMORIAL HOSPITAL

Muncie, Indiana

PROGRAMS OFFERED

The Department of Pathology and Laboratory Medicine offers a combined anatomic and clinical (AP/CP) four-year program. An approved Medical Technology School is sponsored by the Department. The pathology resident is an active teacher and consultant for family medicine, internal medicine and transitional residents with a total of 60 physicians in training. The pathology resident has direct contact with medical students since the Muncie Center for Medical Education is a branch of the Indiana University School of Medicine. Our program offers the optimal blend of academics and "private practice" pathology. A coordinated, three-year core curriculum lecture series is offered twice a week in AP/CP. We have a very close relationship with the medical staff and often directly affect patient care. We feel it is important to be trained as a consultant in laboratory medicine since this is an important role of the pathologist.

TYPES AND NUMBERS OF APPOINTMENTS

The program is currently approved for 12 residents in combined AP/CP training.

FACILITIES

Ball Memorial Hospital is a destination health facility for some of the most advanced healthcare available to the citizens of Central Indiana and the only facility between Fort Wayne and Indianapolis that offers a full range of services including cardiology, open heart, cancer, OB/GYN, prenatal and neonatal services. Founded in 1929, Ball Memorial Hospital serves as a regional tertiary referral center and teaching hospital and the largest non-government employer in East Central Indiana. The laboratory performs over 2.8 million procedures per year. These include 33,008 surgical specimens, 234 autopsies (hospital and forensic), 1,071 fine needle aspirations, 260 bone marrows and more than 81,897 cytologic specimens per year. We have "State of the Art" instrumentation including an 18-headed microscope, digital cameras and digital projectors. Each pathology resident is given an ample work area with a personal telephone, microscope, dictation equipment, personal laptop computer and PDA with wireless internet access. The hospital library subscribes to print journals and online journals. Free computerized literature searches, internet and free photocopying are available. The library and computer facilities are available 24 hours a day. The hospital has an adjacent five story Outpatient Medical Pavilion that has brought positive changes in healthcare delivery to East Central Indiana residents. This Medical Pavilion houses outpatient services including ambulatory surgery, physician offices representing a variety of medical specialties, resident offices and conference rooms. Also on campus is a renal dialysis center, cancer center and Medical Education Building. This facility houses state-of-the-art outpatient clinics and support facilities for medical education.

COMMUNITY

Muncie, Indiana is a university community with both an industrial and agricultural base (population 115,000). Ball State University has an enrollment in excess of 18,000 students. Many sporting, musical and cultural activities are available through the University. For example, a world-renowned Human Performance Laboratory is based at the indoor sports facility. A year-round schedule of theater, opera and dance performances by companies from all over the world, along with several popular touring concerts and comedians perform in the acoustically designed Emens Auditorium. Muncie is located in East Central Indiana, approximately 50 minutes from Indianapolis, Indiana. Housing costs and cost of living are among the lowest in the nation. Two convenient major airports are located in Dayton, Ohio, and Indianapolis.

STIPENDS AND MAINTENANCE

Stipends are $44,027 for PGY-1 positions, $45,088 for PGY-2 positions, $46,149 for PGY-3 positions, and $47,210 for PGY-4 positions. Meals are provided free of cost. Health, dental and life insurance are provided at a shared cost to the resident. Twenty-eight paid days off (inclusive of vacation, sick days, and holidays) and also a week for medical meetings are other benefits. Additional benefits include a $4,000 flexible account that can be used for moving, housing, books and meetings. Residents are also provided with personal laptop computers and PDAs that have wireless internet access.

STAFF

Janet E. Roepke MD, (Indiana Univ 1992), PhD (Indiana Univ 1993) AP/CP; Subspecialty Boards in Hematology; Director Hematology Department; Director Pathology Residency Program; **James R. Baldwin** MD (Indiana Univ 1974) AP/CP; **George E. Branam** MD (Indiana Univ 1957) AP/CP; Subspecialty Boards in Hematology and Nuclear Medicine; **Tarik M. Elsheikh** MD (Univ Alexandria, Egypt 1981) AP/CP; Subspecialty Boards in Cytopathology; **Rudy Gangadhar** MD (Bangalore Med Coll Hosp 1965) AP/CP; **Jennifer N. Jones** MD (Univ Southern Illinois 1998) AP/CP; Subspecialty Boards in Cytopathology; **Thomas A. Kocoshis** MD (Indiana Univ 1974) AP/CP; Subspecialty

Boards in Hematology; **M. Joseph Ma** MD, PhD (Taipei Medical Univ, Taiwan 1985) AP; Subspecialty Boards in Neuropathology; Consultant in Neuropathology; **Paul F. Mellen** MD, DMJ (London) (Boston Univ 1984) AP/CP; Subspeciality in Forensic Pathology; **Richard W. Pearson** MD (Indiana Univ 1977) AP/CP; Subspecialty Boards in Hematology; **Howard H. Wu** MD (Kaohsiung Medical Univ, Taiwan 1984) AP/CP; Subspecialty Boards in Cytopathology.

APPLICATIONS

Residency applicants must be graduates of approved medical schools in the United States or Canada or must have an ECFMG certificate. Applicants are accepted through ERAS. A temporary permit to practice medicine in Indiana is available through the Indiana State Board of Medical Registration for residencies in Indiana.

Address inquiries to:

Janet E. Roepke, MD, PhD, Director
Ball Memorial Hospital Pathology Residency
2401 W. University Avenue
Muncie, IN 47303
Phone: (765) 751-2702 • **Fax:** (765) 747-4466
Web site: http://www.ballhospital.org/html/pathology.htm

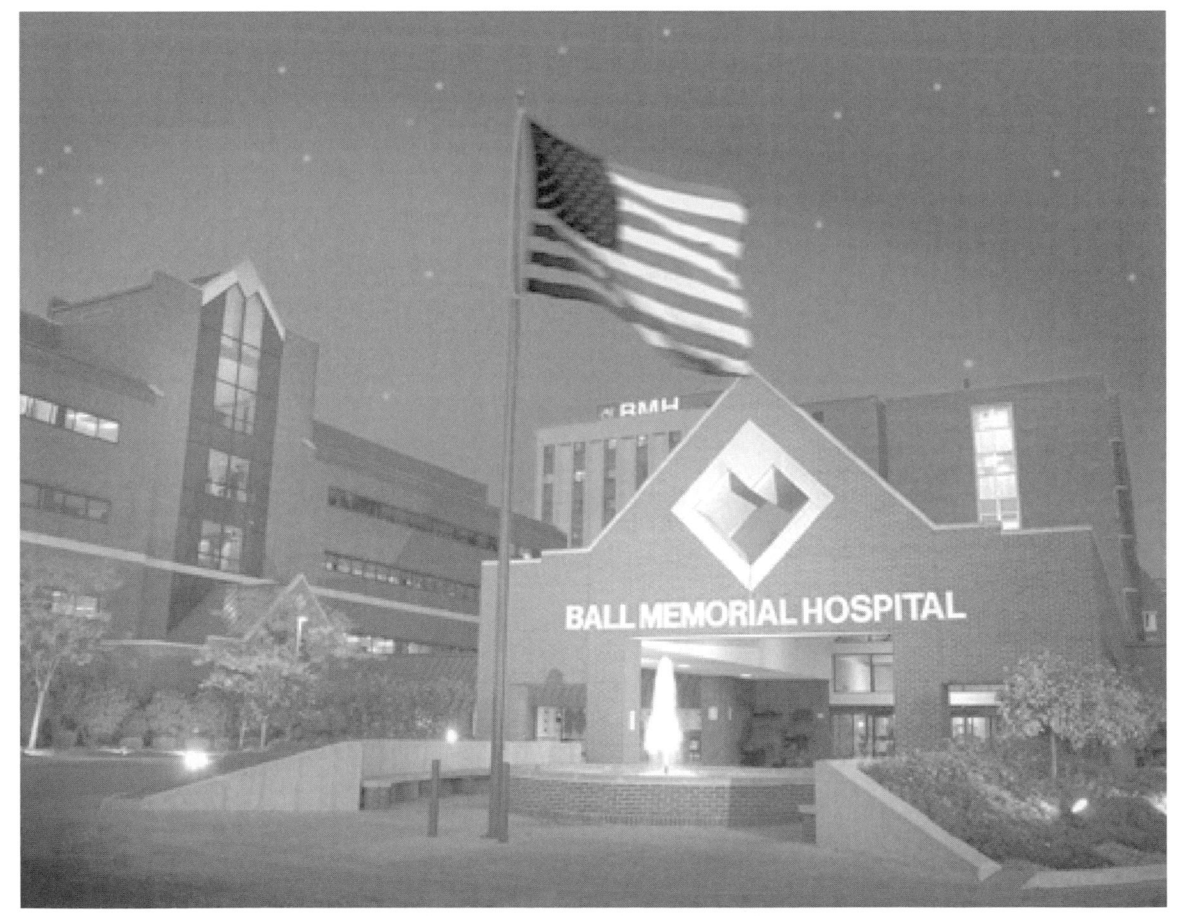

Ball Memorial Hospital, Muncie, Indiana

UNIVERSITY OF IOWA HOSPITALS AND CLINICS

Iowa City, Iowa

PROGRAMS OFFERED

The department offers approved training for residents in anatomic pathology, clinical pathology and combined anatomic and clinical pathology. Rotations for combined anatomic and clinical pathology training are fully integrated. Flexibility is maintained in straight and combined programs to meet the special interests of the residents. Residents are involved in many intra- and interdepartmental subspecialty conferences, and emphasis is placed on training the pathologist as a clinical consultant. Residents are encouraged to become involved in research. Active research areas within the department include immunopathology, hematopathology, hemostasis and thrombosis, neuropathology, surgical pathology, cytopathology, transfusion medicine, microbiology, clinical chemistry, cellular and molecular immunology, and cell and tumor biology. Residents participate in teaching medical technology students, allied health students and medical students.

TYPES AND NUMBERS OF APPOINTMENTS

Twenty pathology residency positions and 7 subspecialty fellowship positions are available, generally with 5 residents in each year of training. The number of residents apportioned to straight versus combined training is flexible.

FACILITIES

The University of Iowa Hospitals and Clinics (UIHC) have approximately 700 beds. Last year, the UIHC performed and processed 301 autopsies; 3,365,838 laboratory determinations; 34,750 surgical specimens; 1,190 bone marrow examinations; 18,009 gynecologic cytology specimens, 6,344 nongynecologic cytology specimens including 2,000 fine needle aspirations. The Pathology Department maintains flow cytometry, EM, fluorescence microscopy, histology, animal pathology, and digital image cores for its investigators. The Department also purchases and supports shared equipment including a chemiluminescent digital capture unit, a real-time PCR thermocycler, a continuous wavelength plate reader, and both beta and gamma counters. In addition, the College of Medicine operates state-of-the-art research cores including DNA, microscopy, flow cytometry, protein analysis (X-ray crystallography, ESR, NMR), gene vector, and mouse transgenic and gene targeting facilities. The clinical and research laboratories at the nearby 93-bed Veterans Affairs Medical Center are affiliated with the residency program at the University of Iowa. Annually, this laboratory performs approximately 1,289,813 laboratory determinations, 4,215 surgical pathology examinations and 26 autopsies, and processes 814 gynecologic cytology specimens, 1,300 nongynecologic cytology specimens and 150 bone marrow examinations.

COMMUNITY

Greater Iowa City has a population of over 80,000. The university is a dominant influence in the community, and cultural activities and opportunities in Iowa City abound. A fine arts complex includes a 2,700 seat performing auditorium, two theaters, a new music classroom and recital building, and an excellent art museum. The school system is excellent, and there are 18 parks and playgrounds within the city, many of them small neighborhood parks for children. Excellent recreational facilities are also provided by the University of Iowa Athletic Department and Lake MacBride State Park on the Iowa River. The community is served by two radio stations, two daily newspapers and a National Educational Television station. Four conveniently located shopping centers supplement the downtown business district, which has recently been rebuilt.

STIPENDS AND MAINTENANCE

The following levels were offered for 2008-09: first year $45,800; second year $47,400; third year $49,200; fourth year $51,100; fifth year $52,900. Residents are provided with professional liability insurance, and white coats. Resident physicians and their dependents are granted free inpatient and outpatient service at University Hospitals.

STAFF

Michael B. Cohen MD (Univ Albany 1982) Department Head and Professor cytology; **Leslie A. Bruch** MD (Univ Iowa 1992) Assoc Professor neuropathology; **Gary L. Baumbach** MD (Univ Iowa 1976) Professor neuropathology; **Jo A. Benda** MD (Univ Iowa 1975) Professor surgical pathology; **Aaron D Bossler** MD, PhD (Univ Iowa 2001) Asst Professor molecular pathology; **Robert T. Cook** MD, PhD (Univ Kansas 1962, 1967) Professor pathology; **Laila Dahmoush** MD (Alexandria Sch Med, Egypt 1983) Assoc Professor anatomic pathology; **Morris O. Dailey** MD, PhD (Univ Chicago 1977, 1976) Assoc Professor flow cytometry; **Fred R. Dee** MD (Univ Iowa 1967) Professor hematopathology; **Barry R. De Young** MD (Georgetown Univ 1991) Professor surgical pathology; **Daniel Diekema** MD (Vanderbilt Univ 1989) Assoc Professor microbiology (secondary); **Yasuko Erickson** MD (Univ Utah 2003) Asst

Professor clinical pathology; **Ronald D. Feld** PhD (Univ Wisconsin 1974) Assoc Professor clinical chemistry; **Thomas H. Haugen** MD, PhD (Univ Iowa 1983; Univ Cal-Davis 1976) Assoc Professor microbiology; Director, VA Hospital Laboratories; **Jonathan W. Heusel** MD, PhD (Washington Univ 1995) Asst Professor molecular pathology; **Michael S. Icardi** MD (Univ Miami 1995) Asst Professor immunopathology; **Chris S. Jensen** MD (Univ Iowa 1989) Assoc Professor cytopathology; **George F. Johnson** PhD (Iowa State Univ 1969) Professor clinical chemistry; **John D. Kemp** MD (Univ Indiana 1975) Professor immunopathology; **Patricia A. Kirby** MD (Univ South Africa 1979) Professor anatomic pathology; **J. Stacey Klutts** MD, PhD (Univ Arkansas, 2002) Asst Professor clinical pathology; **C. Michael Knudson** MD, PhD (Univ Iowa 1992) Assoc Professor transfusion medicine; **Vincent Liu** MD (Univ Pennsylvania 1996) Asst Professor dermatopathology (secondary); **Charles T. Lynch** MD, PhD (Univ Iowa 1979, 1984) Assoc Professor autopsy pathology (secondary); **Frank A. Mitros** MD (Univ New Jersey 1969) Professor surgical pathology; **Steven A. Moore** MD, PhD (Univ Indiana 1982, 1980) Professor neuropathology; **Peter L Nagy** MD, PhD (Univ Pecs, Hungary 1989; Purdue Univ 1995) Asst Professor molecular pathology; **Ramesh Nair** MD (Calicut Medical College, India 1987) Asst Professor renal pathology; **Marcus B. Nashelsky** MD (Univ Nebraska 1989) Assoc Professor forensic pathology; **Vishala Neppalli** MBBS (Siddhartha Med College, Univ of Health Sci, Andhra Pradesh, India 1994) Asst Professor hematopathology; **Thomas J. Raife** MD (Univ Iowa 1989) Assoc Professor transfusion medicine; **Sandra S. Richter** MD (Univ Missouri 1996) Assoc Professor microbiology; **Robert A. Robinson** MD, PhD (Univ Missouri 1976; Univ Minnesota 1982) Professor anatomic pathology; **Nancy S. Rosenthal** MD (Univ Pennsylvania 1983) Professor hematopathology; **Annette J. Schlueter** MD, PhD (Univ Illinois 1991, 1993) Assoc Professor transfusion medicine; **Mary S. Stone** MD (Baylor Col Med 1981) Assoc Professor dermatopathology (secondary); **Brian L. Swick** MD (Univ Iowa 2001) Asst Professor dermatopathology (secondary); **Nasreen A. Syed** MD (Univ Missouri 1990) Asst Professor ocular pathology (secondary); **Sergei I. Syrbu** MD, PhD (State Univ of Med, Chishinau 1982, All Union Cardiology Research Cntr, Moscow 1987) Asst Professor hematopathology, immunopathology; **Thomas Waldschmidt** PhD (Univ Texas Southwestern Med Ctr 1984) Professor flow cytometry.

APPLICATIONS

Applicants must be graduates of approved medical or osteopathic schools. Graduates of international medical schools must have an ECFMG certificate. Application is through ERAS.

Address inquiries to:

Leslie A. Bruch, MD
Director, Pathology Residency Program
University of Iowa
Department of Pathology
200 Hawkins Dr, 5232A RCP
Iowa City, IA 52242
Web site: http://www.healthcare.uiowa.edu/pathology

UNIVERSITY OF KANSAS MEDICAL CENTER

Kansas City, Kansas

PROGRAMS OFFERED

We offer a four-year combined AP/CP program or a three-year program in either AP or CP only. The AP/CP program consists of a 40-month core program consisting of 20 months of AP, 20 months of CP. The faculty works with the residents to design an elective program that will provide a sound educational experience in the resident's chosen area of concentration, as well as to adapt flexibly to the resident's level of expertise and career goals. During the elective time, residents are encouraged to spend time in research or in subspecialty training electives. We encourage residents to elect a combined program in AP/CP because we feel that there is a considerable overlap between many of the traditional areas of anatomic pathology and laboratory medicine. We also feel that residents with combined Board certification have more flexible future career options.

TYPES AND NUMBERS OF APPOINTMENTS

Sixteen resident training positions are available.

FACILITIES

The University of Kansas Medical Center (KUMC) consists of the University of Kansas Medical School, a School of Nursing, and School of Allied Health. The University of Kansas Hospital is a university teaching hospital of 508 active beds with clinical facilities accommodating 474,165 outpatient visits per year. Annually, the clinical laboratory at KUMC performs approximately 1,800,000 laboratory determinations, processes 16,750 surgical pathology and 18,500 cytology specimens. Approximately 500 autopsies are performed each year, a large number of which are medical legal autopsies. Additional hospital affiliations include a 125-bed general Veterans Affairs Medical Center integrated with the program at the KU Hospital. The laboratory at the VA performs approximately 1,700,000 clinical laboratory determinations and processes 6,500 surgical pathology cases a year. The Dykes Medical Library contains an outstanding collection of more than 104,100 volumes and 2,175 periodicals as well as a nationally renowned history of medicine library. A much used modern student center and fitness center provide areas for relaxation and conferences. The Department of Pathology and Laboratory Medicine consists of resident and trainee offices, a departmental library, conference rooms, modern and well-equipped autopsy and surgical pathology suites, and expanded clinical laboratory facilities. Numerous research laboratories include facilities for electron microscopy, fluorescence microscopy, photomicroscopy, biochemistry, infectious diseases, immunopathology, virology, comparative pathology, tissue culture, *in situ* hybridization, molecular biology, autoradiography, histochemistry, cancer research, forensic pathology, bone pathology and renal pathology. Computer facilities are readily available.

COMMUNITY

Kansas City is a metropolitan area with a population of 1,980,000. Its beautiful rolling hills and woodlands with numerous parks provide both land and water recreation. Several colleges and universities offer excellent educational opportunities. Numerous cultural facilities include museums, opera, theater and symphony. A variety of amateur and professional sports and outdoor activities are available. Cost of living is reasonable and the region has been considered historically as an ideal location.

STIPENDS AND MAINTENANCE

Pathology resident stipends for 2008-2009 ranged from $42,773 for first year residents to $46,918 for fourth year. Apartments and reasonably priced houses are plentiful within a convenient distance from the medical center. Fringe benefits also include professional liability insurance, personal health insurance, uniform laundry, parking, and a travel and book allowance.

STAFF

H. Clarke Anderson MD (Univ Louisville 1958) Professor Emeritus; mineralization, skeletal differentiation, skeletal pathology; **Barbara F. Atkinson** MD (Thomas Jefferson Univ 1974) Professor; Executive Dean Sch Med; cytopathology, education; **Rachel Cherian** MD (Christian Med Col, India 1968) Associate Professor; surgical pathology and hematopathology, VA Med Ctr; **Mark T. Cunningham** MD (Univ Minnesota 1989) Associate Professor; hematopathology; **Ivan Damjanov** MD, PhD (Zagreb Univ, Yugoslavia 1964) Professor; surgical pathology, electron microscopy, immunopathology, early mammalian embryology and embryo-derived tumors; **Katie Dennis** MD (Univ Kansas Medical Center 2008) Assistant Professor; surgical pathology, cytopathology; **Fang Fan** MD, PhD (Univ Shanghai 1989) Associate Professor; Director Cytopathology; breast and gynecologic pathology, cytopathology; **James L. Fishback** MD (Univ Kansas 1983) Associate Professor; anatomic pathology and infectious disease; Medical Student Course

Director; **Garth Fraga** MD (Univ Chicago 1994) A&C Pathologist; Dermatopathology; **Rebecca Horvat** PhD (Univ Kansas, 1987) Associate Professor; clinical microbiology and virology; **Rashna Madan** MD, (Kasturba Med Coll 1996) Assistant Professor; cytopathology, surgical pathology; **Sharad C. Mathur** MD (All-India Inst Med Sci, New Delhi 1994) Associate Professor; anatomic pathology, hematopathology and transfusion medicine VA Med Ctr; **Douglas H. McGregor** MD (Duke Univ 1966) Professor; anatomic pathology, VA Med Ctr; **Kathy L. Newell** MD (Univ Kansas 1992) Assistant Professor; dementia, neuropathology; **Maura O'Neil** MD (Univ Kansas Med Ctr 2008) Assistant Professor; surgical pathology, cytopathology; **Diane L. Persons** MD (Univ Kansas, 1987) Professor; Residency Program Director, Director of Cytogenetics, clinical cytogenetics, molecular cytogenetics, anatomic pathology; **David M. Pinson** DVM, PhD (Univ Georgia 1978) Research Professor; infectious disease, veterinary, comparative pathology and medicine; Associate Director Laboratory Animal Resources; **Maria Romanas** MD, (Univ Kansas Med Center 1996); clinical instructor, VA Medical Center; **Ossama Tawfik** MD, PhD (Univ Cairo 1978, Kansas 1987) Professor; Director Surgical Pathology; reproductive immunology and biology, cytokine biology, surgical pathology, cytology; **Patricia Thomas** MD, MA (NYC 1986) Chair; Professor; Director Cytopathology Fellowship Program; Associate Dean Office of Cultural Enhancement and Diversity; FNA, cancer, health disparieties, diversity; **Lowell L. Tilzer** MD, PhD (Univ Kansas 1976) Professor; transfusion medicine, clinical laboratory med; **Ozlem Ulusarac** MD (Istanbul Univ 1993) Director, Clinical Chemistry & Mirobiology/Immunology; **Da Zhang** MD (Shandong Med Univ, China 1985) Assistant Professor; surgical pathology, education.

APPLICATIONS

Trainees must be graduates of approved medical schools in the U.S. or foreign countries at the time they begin training. ECFMG certification is necessary for foreign graduates. Satisfactory references are required. Personal interviews are required. Applications should be received by November 15, 2009 for appointments beginning July 1, 2010. Applications should be submitted through the Electronic Residency Application System (ERAS).

Address inquiries to:

Charla Tunget, M.Ed.
Residency Coordinator
Department of Pathology and Laboratory Medicine
2006 Wahl Hall West, MS 3045
University of Kansas Medical Center
3901 Rainbow Blvd,
Kansas City, KS 66160-7410
Phone: (913) 588-7076 • **Fax:** (913) 588-7073 • **E-mail:** ctunget@kumc.edu
Web site: http://www2.kumc.edu/Pathologypathweb/Residency/info.html

UNIVERSITY OF KENTUCKY MEDICAL CENTER

Lexington, Kentucky

PROGRAMS OFFERED

The residency training program in the Department of Pathology and Laboratory Medicine of the College of Medicine is based in the University Hospital and the adjacent and contiguous Lexington Veterans Affairs Medical Center. A four-year program looking forward to certification in both pathologic anatomy and clinical pathology is approved by the American Board of Pathology. Each year of pathology training is balanced equally between anatomic pathology and laboratory medicine for those desiring preparation in both disciplines. Training in anatomic pathology includes 18-months of surgical pathology, 3-months of autopsy/forensic pathology, 4-months of cytology, 3-months community hospital based rotations, and 2-months of electives. Multiple elective rotations are available including dermatopathology and neuropathology. Training in clinical pathology aims to develop in each resident the competence to lead a hospital laboratory and provide effective consultation to physicians in all areas of laboratory medicine. In addition to mastering laboratory methodology, residents will become familiar with personnel organization and qualifications, scheduling, processing technology, data handling and computer applications, quality control and in-service training programs, and supply and support services. Training in CP includes 3-months Transfusion Medicine, 3-months Chemical Pathology (including routine and special clinical chemistry, toxicology), 1-month Cytogenetics, 3-months Hematopathology, 1-month Laboratory Management, 3-months Microbiology and Serology, 1-month Immunopathology, 1-month Molecular Pathology, and 3-months clinical pathology electives. Elective rotations are available in advanced Blood Banking, advanced Clinical Chemistry, advanced Microbiology, advanced Immunopathology, and advanced Hematopathology.

REQUIREMENTS

Qualifying applicants must have taken and passed Step I and Step II of the USMLEs with a minimum 2 digit score of 80. You must have graduated from Medical School within the last ten years. For IMG applicants, eligibility for J-1 student visa status is strongly preferred because of institutional requirements. Also, the university requires ECFMG certification prior to ranking in the "Match." If you meet these criteria, we would be very happy to consider your application for residency training with us and look forward to hearing from you.

TYPES AND NUMBERS OF APPOINTMENTS

A total of 16 postgraduate pathology positions are available, four for each year of training.

FACILITIES

The Department of Pathology and Laboratory Medicine is housed in the College of Medicine, the University Hospital of the Albert B. Chandler Medical Center, and UK HealthCare Good Samaritan Hospital. It supplies full pathology service to University Hospital, a modern 489-bed Level I trauma center, including a 117-bed Kentucky Children's Hospital, the 209-bed Veterans Affairs Medical Center, and the 302-bed UK Good Samaritan, the principal clinical facilities for both undergraduate and graduate teaching of the College of Medicine. In fulfilling its service responsibilities at UK and VAMC, the department performs approximately 150 autopsies and processes over 27,000 surgical specimens. In addition, approximately 21,000 smears are received for cytologic study. This volume represents a broad range of pathologic material. An additional 741 medicolegal autopsies are performed at the centralized lab facility in Frankfort by three medical examiners, all faculty members who are available for residents' education. The Department of Pathology and Laboratory Medicine is also responsible for pathology services at St. Claire Medical Center in Morehead, KY, a 159-bed acute care community hospital. Pathology residents spend two to three months of training at this facility that is staffed by two full-time faculty members.

COMMUNITY

Lexington is a culturally diverse university city of approximately 260,000. Lexington and the surrounding Bluegrass Region are rich in historical interest and scenic beauty. Extending to the Cumberland Mountains and crossed by the Kentucky River, this region offers a fresh and enjoyable experience to all. It is a land of rolling plains, lakes, streams, woodlands, productive farms, and comfortable homes. Fishing, boating, swimming, water skiing, hiking, and camping are within easy reach of Lexington. Excellent inns noted for their traditional food are found throughout the area. Kentucky's fine system of state parks provides for enjoyable weekends and short vacations.

STIPENDS AND MAINTENANCE

As of July 2008, stipends range from $46,348 per year for first year trainees to $51,753 for fourth year trainees. Benefits include 10-days paid vacation (15-days for the second through fourth-year), UK Credit for plan and coverage level chosen hospitalization insurance, life insurance, professional liability insurance, lab coats and laundry, and $1,200 per year available for attending meetings and purchasing books. Additionally, funding is available for residents presenting research findings at national meetings.

STAFF

Paul Bachner MD (Columbia Univ 1963) Professor and Chairman, Clinical Pathology; **Kimberly Absher** MD (East Tennessee State Univ 1993) Assistant Professor, Anatomic Pathology; **Michael Blechner** MD (Dartmouth 1998) Assistant Professor, Medical Informatics; **Yolanda M. Brill** MD (Univ Kentucky 1988) Associate Professor, Director Cytopathology; **Michael Cibull** MD (Univ Illinois 1973) Professor, Surgical Pathology and Hematopathology; **Gregory Davis** MD (Univ Tennessee 1985) Professor, Program Director, Forensic Pathology; **Jeffrey Ellis** MD (Louisville 1988) Associate Professor, Anatomic and Clinical Pathology, Morehead; **John Hunsaker III** MD, JD, MA (Univ Kentucky 1977) Professor, Forensic Pathology; **C. Darrell Jennings** MD (Univ Kentucky 1977) Professor, Immunopathology; **Rouzan Karabakhtsian** MD, PhD (Yerevan State Med Univ Armenia 1978) Assistant Professor, Anatomic Pathology; **Melissa Kesler** MD (Univ Kentucky 1999) Assistant Professor, Director Hematopathology; **Eun Lee** MD (Kyung Hee Univ, Korea 1978) Professor, Director Surgical Pathology, GI Pathology; **Charles Lutz** MD, PhD (Univ Chicago 1982) Professor, Immunopathology; **Ewa Marciniak** (Univ Wroclaw, Poland 1951) Professor, Hematology; **William Markesbery** MD (Univ Kentucky 1964) Professor, Neuropathology; **Bonnie Mitchell-Clark** MD (Univ Washington 1976) Professor, Renal Pathology, Veterans Affairs Medical Center; **Paul Murphy** MD (Massachusetts 1982) Assistant Professor and Course Director, PAT823; **Peter Nelson** MD, PhD (Univ Chicago 1998) Assistant Professor, Neuropathology; **William N O'Connor** MB BCh BAO (Ireland 1972) Professor, Anatomic Pathology; **Peter Oeltgen** PhD (Loyola Univ 1973) Professor, Clinical Chemistry; **Timothy Overman** PhD (Univ Cincinnati 1971) Associate Professor, Clinical Microbiology; **Elpidio Pena** MD (Dominican Republic 1985) Assistant Professor, Director Transfusion Medicine; **Anjana Pettigrew** MD (Baylor Col Med 1983) Associate Professor, Director Cytogenetics; **William Porter** PhD (Vanderbilt Univ 1970) Professor, Clinical Chemistry; **Joseph Pulliam** MD (Univ Kentucky 1994) Assistant Professor, Molecular Genetics and Hematopathology; **Julie Ribes** MD, PhD (Univ Rochester 1990) Associate Professor, Clinical Microbiology; **Cristin Rolf** MD (Toledo Univ 1991) Assistant Professor, Forensic Pathology; **Luis Samayoa** MD (Univ El Salvador 1991) Assistant Professor, Anatomic Pathology, Veterans Affairs Medical Center; **Robert Sloss** MD (Univ Louisville 1974) Associate Professor, Anatomic and Clinical Pathology, Morehead; **Ronald Whitley** PhD (Georgia Inst Tech 1975) Professor, Director Clinical Chemistry; **Dianne Wilson** MD (Univ Kentucky 1977) Associate Professor, Surgical Pathology and Neuropathology.

APPLICATIONS

First year postgraduate applications are handled through the Matching Plan, NRMP #184830 0C0. Deadline for receiving completed applications is November 30. We are participating in ERAS-the Electronic Residency Application Service from the Association of American Medical Colleges.

Address inquiries to:

Gregory J. Davis, MD, Director of Residency Program
University of Kentucky College of Medicine
Department of Pathology
800 Rose St., Ste MS-117
Lexington, KY 40536-0298
Phone: (859) 323-6183 • **Web site:** http://www.mc.uky.edu/pathology

UNIVERSITY OF LOUISVILLE SCHOOL OF MEDICINE

Louisville, Kentucky

PROGRAMS OFFERED

A fully approved program in anatomic and clinical pathology is available. The AP/CP program requires four years and includes autopsy, surgical and cytopathology, pediatric pathology, hematology, microbiology, toxicology, clinical chemistry and immunohematology. In addition, rotations in electron microscopy, immunohistochemistry, dermatopathology, tissue typing, neuropathology, molecular diagnostics and lab management are included. Residents are given opportunities and encouraged to participate in research and teaching activities. Approved fellowships in forensic pathology, cytopathology, transfusion medicine, surgical pathology and clinical chemistry (two-year) are also offered.

TYPES AND NUMBERS OF APPOINTMENTS

A total of 12 pathology resident positions offered. The remainder of the house staff consists of over 500 residents in medicine, surgery, obstetrics-gynecology, pediatrics, diagnostic radiology, therapeutic radiology, family practice, emergency medicine, anesthesiology, ophthalmology, psychiatry, and the major subspecialties in medicine, pediatrics and surgery.

FACILITIES

University of Louisville Hospital, Department of Veterans Affairs Medical Center, Kosair-Children's Hospital, Norton Hospital and Jewish Hospital are utilized in the program. There are 1,500 beds in the combined hospitals. Approximately 70 autopsies, 15,000 surgicals, 9,600 cytologics, and over three million laboratory procedures are performed annually. The Medical Examiner's services are utilized in the training program, accounting for over 1,000 additional autopsies. The Department is located within the Health Sciences Center with a library of 135,000 volumes and 1,300 journal subscriptions.

COMMUNITY

Louisville was settled in 1778, at the Falls of the Ohio River. The University of Louisville was established in 1798. The metropolitan area has a population of about one million. Louisville is renowned for its pioneering work in medicine, and for its cultural activities (Actors Theatre of Louisville, the Louisville Orchestra, the Kentucky Opera Association, the Louisville Bach Society, Louisville Ballet, etc.). The city offers many recreational opportunities with over 35 major parks, fishing in river and park lakes, golf, water sports and horse racing.

STIPENDS AND MAINTENANCE

The salaries for trainees are as follows: PG-1 $47,323; PG-2 $48,804; PG-3 $50,658; PG-4 $52,586; PG-5 $55,241; PG-6 $57,551; PG-7 $59,551; and PG-8 $61,551. Professional liability insurance, uniforms, laundry service, parking and hospitalization insurance are provided. Housing is available at moderate rates in the immediate vicinity.

STAFF

Professors

Ronald J. Elin MD, PhD Professor and Chairman; Director, Division Laboratory Medicine; **Joseph C. Parker, Jr.** MD Professor and Director of GME; neuropathology; **Robert W. Bendon** MD Clinical Professor; anatomic pathology; **Mark L. Bernstien** DDS Clinical Professor; **John J. Buchino** MD Professor; pediatric pathology, electron microscopy; **Tracey S. Corey** MD Clinical Professor; forensic pathology; **Susan Coventry** MD Clinical Professor; **Jayne L. Hollander** MD Clinical Professor; immunohematology, transfusion medicine; **Stanley S. Levinson** PhD Professor; clinical chemistry; **William B. Lockwood** PhD, MD Clinical Professor; transfusion medicine; **Alvin W. Martin** MD Professor; immunohistochemistry, flow cytometry; **James J. Miller** PhD Professor; clinical chemistry; **Rawhi A. Omar** MD, PhD Professor; molecular pathology; **James W. Snyder** PhD Professor; microbiology; **Roland Valdes, Jr.** PhD Professor; clinical chemistry and toxicology; **Vaclav Vetvicka** PhD Professor; **Barbara Weakly-Jones** MD Clinical Professor; forensic pathology; **Lung T. Yam** MD Professor; medicine.

Associate Professors

Douglas Ackerman MD Associate Clinical Professor; **Amy Burrows-Beckham** MD Associate Clinical Professor; forensic pathology; **Cindy A. Corrigan** MD Associate Clinical Professor; anatomic pathology, transfusion medicine; **Karen M. Cost** PhD Associate Clinical Professor; immunology; **Rafael Fernandez** PhD Associate Professor; **Sandra C. Hollensead** MD Associate Professor; Director, Hematology and Coagulation Laboratories; **Linda G. Korfhage** MD Associate Clinical Professor; anatomic pathology; **Mark W. Linder** PhD Associate Professor; toxicology; **Claire Meena-Leist** MD Associate Clinical Professor; **Dennis M. O'Connor** MD Associate Clinical Professor; OB/GYN, anatomic pathology; **Stephen D. Slone** MD Associate Professor; hematology; **Donna M. Stewart** MD Associate Clinical Professor; forensic pathology.

Assistant Professors

Houda Alatassi MD Assistant Professor, anatomic Pathology; **Robert L. Barker** PhD Assistant Clinical Professor; molecular biology; **George E. Buck** PhD Assistant Clinical Professor; **Carolyn D. Burns** Assistant Clinical Professor; **Emily Craig** PhD Assistant Clinical Professor; **Robert Debski** MD Assistant Clinical Professor; **Hanan Farghaly** MD Assistant Professor; head and neck pathology, surgical pathology; **Yenshen Hseuh** MD Assistant Clinical Professor; **Saeed Jortani** PhD Assistant Professor; clinical toxicology; **Janine Malone** MD Assistant Clinical Professor; dermatopathology; **Grace D. Moore** MD Assistant Professor; anatomic pathology; **Muhammad Nadeem** MD Assistant Professor; **Michael Nowacki** MD Assistant Clinical Professor; **John R. Parker** MD Assistant Clinical Professor; neuropathology; **William C. Ralston III** MD Assistant Clinical Professor; **Kristen Reynolds** PhD Assistant Clinical Professor; clinical chemistry; **Sunati Sahoo** MD Assistant Professor; cytopatholgy, breast pathology, surgical pathology; **Saad P. Shaheen II** MD Assistant Professor; hematology; **Bennie C. Slucher** MD Assistant Clinical Professor; cytopathology.

APPLICATIONS

An application, CV, documentation of USMLE scores and three or more letters of recommendation accepted only though ERAS. Trainees must be graduates of approved medical schools in the United States or foreign countries. ECFMG and Visa Qualifying Examination certifications are necessary for foreign graduates. Applications must be received by **November 1** for appointments beginning July 1 of the following year.

Address inquiries to:

Joseph C. Parker, Jr., MD
Director, Residency Program
Department of Pathology and Laboratory Medicine
University of Louisville
Louisville, KY 40292
Phone: (502) 852-8203 • **E-mail:** lacowh01@gwise.louisville.edu

University of Louisville Health Sciences Center Complex

LOUISIANA STATE UNIVERSITY SCHOOL OF MEDICINE

New Orleans, Louisiana

PROGRAMS OFFERED

Pathology residencies provide supervised, thorough training in all aspects of anatomic and clinical pathology. Anatomic pathology includes autopsy and surgical pathology, diagnostic cytology, forensic pathology and neuropathology. Clinical pathology consists of clinical chemistry, molecular diagnostics, medical microbiology, parasitology, virology, serology, hematology, immunology, medical microscopy, cytogenetics and blood banking. Experience in teaching and research methodology is offered in addition to the basic training in anatomic and clinical pathology.

TYPES AND NUMBERS OF APPOINTMENTS

The program is approved for 8 residency positions. Residents may enter the program in the first postgraduate year or after a year of clinical training. Entrance at an advanced level is possible.

FACILITIES

The Pathology Residency Program at Louisiana State University School of Medicine in New Orleans is integrated into several community hospitals in the greater New Orleans area. These include Interim LSU Public Hospital, West Jefferson Medical Center and Ochsner Foundation Hospital. These facilities provide comprehensive health care and training in all major medical specialties as well as training in all areas of anatomic and clinical pathology. Training in Pediatric Pathology is provided through Children's Hospital. Forensic pathology training is provided through the Office of the Coroner of Jefferson Parish. Research activities in the Pathology Department cover a wide spectrum of studies involving human disease and animal experimentation. Close correlation with allied sciences such as microbiology, biochemistry, and immunology are emphasized.

STIPENDS AND MAINTENANCE

The current annual salary for first year House Officers at the Interim LSU Public Hospital is $42,757. Professional liability insurance, parking, and a 3-week paid vacation are provided. Meals are available at nominal cost. Housing is not provided but can be readily found in the New Orleans area.

STAFF

Grace Athas PhD (Tulane Med Ctr 1994) hematology, molecular pathology; **James Barbeau** MD JD (Case Western Reserve Univ Sch Med 1999) transfusion medicine, microbiology; **Frederick Brazda** MD (Louisiana State Univ 1970) clinical chemistry; **James E Brown, Jr** MD (Louisiana State Univ 1984) surgical pathology; **Tom Carson** MD (Univ Cincinnati 1978) blood banking, pediatric pathology; **Randall Craver** MD (Univ Arkansas 1979) pediatric pathology; **Carmen Espinoza** MD (Univ San Marcos, Peru 1969) surgical pathology, dermatopathology; **Barton Farris** MD (Tulane Medical Center 1975) anatomic pathology; **Herman Gaumer** PhD (Univ North Carolina 1971) immunology; **Gary Lipscomb** MD (Univ Tennessee 1975) hematology, surgical pathology; **Jane Lipscomb** MD (Univ Tennessee 1975) cytopathology, surgical pathology; **William H Luer** MD (Tulane Med Ctr 1976) clinical chemistry, surgical pathology; **Mark Luquette** MD (Louisiana State Univ 1985) pediatric pathology; **Robin McGoey** MD (Louisiana State Univ 2000) autopsy pathology, genetics; **William Newman III** MD (Louisiana State Univ 1967) primatology, anatomic pathology; **F. Avery Ragan** PhD (Univ Alabama 1977) clinical pharmacology, toxicology; **Bernardo Ruiz** MD, PhD (Univ del Valle 1983) cytopathology, surgical pathology; **Douglas Scheer** PhD (Louisiana State Univ 1976) clinical chemistry; **Jack Strong** MD (Louisiana State Univ 1951) atherosclerosis; **Dana Troxclair** MD (Louisiana State Univ 2000) autopsy pathology, forensic pathology; **Arthur Zieske** MD (Louisiana State Univ 1993) hematopathology, surgical pathology.

APPLICATIONS

Candidates for residency training must meet the requirements as outlined in the LSU School of Medicine House Officer Manual (http://www.medschool.lsuhsc.edu/medical_education/graduate/HouseOfficerManual/HOM0809Revised.pdf). First-year positions are chosen through the National Resident Matching Program. Appointments ordinarily begin on July 1; however, space permitting, positions may be available at any time during the year. A personal interview is required. Applications should be submitted through the Electronic Residency Application Service (ERAS) from the Association of American Medical Colleges.

Address inquiries to:

Gary E. Lipscomb, MD
Pathology Residency Director
Department of Pathology
Louisiana State University
Medical Education Building
1901 Perdido Street
New Orleans, LA 70112-1393
E-mail: glipsc@lsuhsc.edu
Web site: http://www.medschool.lsuhsc.edu/pathology/residency.aspx

TULANE UNIVERSITY HEALTH SCIENCES CENTER SCHOOL OF MEDICINE

New Orleans, Louisiana

PROGRAMS OFFERED

A fully accredited combined training program for residents in anatomic and clinical pathology is offered. The anatomic pathology division offers training in autopsy and surgical pathology, as well in the subspecialties of forensic pathology, neuropathology, dermatopathology, nephropathology, hepatopathology, cytopathology, electron microscopy, immunopathology, cytogenetics, molecular and experimental pathology. The division of clinical pathology offers training in molecular diagnostics, flow cytometry, bacteriology, parasitology, virology, mycology, immunology, serology, clinical chemistry, endocrinological chemistry, toxicology, hematology, coagulation, pheresis, blood banking, computer science and laboratory administration. The program is structured to meet the requirements of the American Board of Pathology, but flexible for special interests of residents in selected areas. Many conferences with pathology staff and clinicians are integrated into the training program. Residents have opportunities to participate in teaching of medical students as well as in defined research projects to investigate disease processes by modern techniques and instruments.

TYPES AND NUMBERS OF APPOINTMENTS

The program has a total of 8 residency positions for the four years of training.

FACILITIES

Tulane University Hospital and Clinic is a 235-bed university hospital located in downtown New Orleans that houses the clinical and anatomical laboratories with state-of-the-art equipment and laboratory information system. Annually, there are 21,354 admissions, over 13,250 surgical pathology accessions, 5,825 cytopathology accessions and over 50 autopsies. Over 1,000,000 clinical pathology determinations are performed annually. Residents participate in patient care, teaching and research. Our specialties range from diagnostic surgical pathology and subspecialty training, to technologically advanced computerized clinical laboratories and molecular pathology. Tulane residents also rotate at Ochsner Medical Center and West Jefferson Medical Center. These facilities provide training in all areas of anatomical and clinical pathology. Each resident is provided office space, a microscope and computer. The department maintains a working library with subscriptions to the major pathology journals as well as e-journals. The medical school library contains over 148,000 books and 1,300 journal subscriptions.

COMMUNITY

The population of the Greater New Orleans metropolitan area is above 250,000. It is one of the major port cities of the United States with a wide variety of social, cultural and recreational activities. It is internationally recognized for its rich culture, arts, architecture, varied and excellent cuisine, French Quarter, jazz, annual Mardi Gras celebration, and the Superdome facility for spectator sporting and other events.

STIPENDS AND MAINTENANCE

Our current stipends begin at $44,168 for first year House Officers. Residents are provided a four-week paid vacation (1st year three weeks) annually, free parking, free comprehensive health coverage, life, disability and malpractice insurance, textbooks of surgical pathology and clinical pathology on entering the program, paid junior membership in the ASCP and Greater New Orleans Pathology Society, and funds for attendance of scientific meetings. In addition, moving expenses are provided to first-year residents.

STAFF

J.R. Krause MD (Univ Pittsburgh, 1966) Chairman; clinical pathology, hematopathology, flow cytometry; **B. E. Crawford** MD (Louisiana State Univ, New Orleans, 1976) surgical pathology; **P.J. Daroca, Jr.** MD (Tulane Univ, 1968) pulmonary pathology, surgical pathology; **S. Dash** PhD (All India Inst of Med Sci New Delhi, 1986) hepatitis research; **E.K. Flemington** PhD (Louisiana State Univ, 1987) cancer research; **S. Haque** MD (Univ Dacca Med Col, Bangladesh, 1978) GI pathology, hepatopathology; **R. Jetly** (Netaji Subhash Chandra Bose Med College & Hospital, India, 1996) surgical pathology, hematopathology; **M. Li** (Tongji Med Univ, China, 1983) cytogenetics; **Z. Lin** MD, PhD (Peking Univ HSC, 2000, Tulane Univ Sch of Med, 2005) cancer research; **W.H. Luer** MD (Tulane Univ, 1976) clinical pathology; **E. J. Martin, Jr** MD (Tulane Univ, 1986) surgical pathology; **S. Meleg-Smith** MD (Javeriana Univ, Columbia, 1964) nephropathology; **K. Moroz** MD (Academy Med, Poland, 1984) cytopathology, surgical pathology; **G.F. Morris** PhD (Florida State Univ, 1982) transcriptional regulation, neoplastic transformation; **E. Occhipinti** MD (Louisiana State Univ Sch of Med, New Orleans, 2001) clinical pathology, hematopathology; **T. Peterson**

MD (Louisiana State Univ Sch of Med, New Orleans, 1990) clinical pathology, blood bank; **L. Rajan** MD, MPH (All India Institute of Medical Sciences, New Delhi, 1988) microbiology; **J.L. Schmid** MD (Univ Minnesota, 1993) clinical pathology, transfusion medicine and hematology; **J. W. Scott** MD, PhD (University of L'Aquila, School of Medicine L'Aquila, Italy, 1985) clinical pathology, blood bank, transfusion medicine; **A.R. Wang** MD, PhD (China Med Univ, Shenyang, 1982) dermatopathology; **Z. Xiong** MD, PhD (Hengyang Medical College, P.R. China, 1982) surgical pathology, neuropathology; **Q. Yin** PhD (Chinese Academy of Sciences, P.R. China, 2000) cancer research; **H. Zhang** PhD (State Univ of New York, Roswell Park Cancer Institute, 1999) cancer research.

APPLICATIONS

Applications should be submitted through the Electronic Residency Applications System (ERAS) and received by November 30 for appointment the following July. Applicants must be graduates of approved medical schools. Graduates of international medical schools must have an ECFMG certificate.

Address inquiries to:

Bea Delucca
Residency Program Coordinator
1430 Tulane Ave. SL-79
New Orleans, LA 70112
Phone: (504) 988-2436 • **Fax:** (504) 988-7389 • **E-mail:** bdelucc@tulane.edu
Web site: http://www.som.tulane.edu/departments/pathology/resident/resident.html

LOUISIANA STATE UNIVERSITY HEALTH SCIENCES CENTER

Shreveport, Louisiana

PROGRAMS OFFERED

The Pathology Residency Program at Louisiana State University Health Sciences Center-Shreveport (LSUHSC-S) is fully accredited for training in anatomic and clinical pathology. The anatomic pathology rotations include autopsy pathology, surgical pathology, cytopathology, nephropathology, electron microscopy, forensic pathology, pediatric pathology, and neuropathology. Clinical pathology rotations include hematology, coagulation, urinalysis, blood bank, clinical chemistry, microbiology, cytogenetics, immunopathology, molecular pathology, virology, toxicology, nuclear medicine, blood gases, endocrinology, rheumatology, and laboratory management. Residents attend daily sign-out conference with the entire surgical pathology staff using a multi-headed microscope and are expected to participate in yearly research projects with staff members. In addition to conducting conferences for residents and medical students, opportunities for teaching medical students are available.

TYPES AND NUMBERS OF APPOINTMENTS

The four-year Anatomic Pathology/Clinical Pathology Program is approved for 12 residents.

FACILITIES

LSU Hospital is the main teaching institution with 478 beds. Per year, the Pathology Department processes 18,000 surgical specimens, 60,000 cytology specimens, and 1,500,000 clinical laboratory tests. In 2008, yearly autopsies averaged 407 and are expected to increase to 500 in 2009. Residents have the opportunity to rotate at the Willis-Knighton Medical Center. The Willis-Knighton Medical Center has 335 beds, 60,000 surgical specimens per year, 45,000 cytology specimens per year, and 2,200,000 clinical laboratory tests per year. Many recent department improvements have enhanced the learning environment for residents, including the purchase of individual and library textbooks, updated microscopes, and personal computers. A newly remodeled sign-out room is available with six internet connections, microscopes with cameras for digital imaging, and a comfortable study area.

COMMUNITY

The Shreveport/Bossier City metropolitan complex has a population of approximately 400,000. Public schools are excellent. There is an abundance of permforming arts, including the Shreveport Symphony Orchestra and several theatrical groups. Other leisure options include numerous galleries, museums, and festivals. The Louisiana Boardwalk, situated along the Red River offers over 50 unique outlet stores, a 14-screen Regal Cinema, Cajun Cuisine, and many other amenities. There is easy access to several excellent lakes for fishing and water sports. The climate is pleasant and traffic in Shreveport/Bossier City flows smoothly.

STIPENDS AND MAINTENANCE

The salary range for 2009-2010 is $44,167.71 to $49,030.43. Chief residents and fourth year residents receive an additional stipend. Other benefits include: $250 monthly meal allowance; $900 book allowance; free labcoats and monogramming, free scrubs, free parking, and paid airfaire/travel expenses to present research. Malpractice and disability insurance are paid in full. A variety of medical and dental insurance benefits are available. First year residents receive three weeks paid annual leave and four weeks beginning in their second year. Also, all residents receive ten paid days of both sick leave and educational leave.

STAFF

Stephen M. Bonsib MD, AP/CP, Chairman of the Department of Pathology, renal pathology, male genitourinary, surgical pathology, electron microscopy; **Marjorie Fowler** MD, AP/NP, Director Residency Program, Director of Anatomic Pathology, electron microscopy, neuropathology, endocrine pathology, surgical and anatomic pathology; **James D. Cotelingam** MD, AP/CP/HP, Director Clinical Pathology Division; hematopathology; **Fleurette Abreo** MD, AP/CP, Cytopathology Fellowship Director; cytopathology, surgical and anatomic pathology, breast pathology, fine needle aspiration; **James G. Traylor, Jr.** MD, Director of Autopsy Pathology, forensic pathology; **Diana Veillon** MD, AP/CP/HP, molecular pathology, cell flow cytometry, hematopathology; **Patrick Adegboyega** MD, Director of Immunopathology and research, surgical pathology, tissue bank; **Xin Gu** MD, AP/CP, GU and renal pathology, electron microscopy, surgical pathology; **Songlin Zhang** MD, cytopathology, surgical pathology; **Chris Kevil** PhD, cell adhesions and inflammatory response, leukocyte trafficking, transgenic animal models; **Mary Lowery-Nordberg** PhD, molecular pathology, cytogenetics, flow cytometry, FISH, gene amplification, leukemia/lymphomas; **Janice Matthews-Greer** PhD, Director of the Diagnostic Virology Laboratory, HPV-CMV laboratory; **Kevin McCarthy** PhD, Acting Director Research Division; diabetic nephropathy, glomerulosclerosis, renal extracellular matrix, PPAR-gamma signaling, digital microscopy; **R. P. Misra** MD, PhD AP/CP, ophthalmic pathology; **Leonard Prouty** PhD, genetics; **William Jay Russell** PhD, molecular pathology and research, extracellular matrix, growth factors; **Krishna Yanamandra** PhD, genetics; **Marie E Beckner** MD, PhD, molecular pathology, neuoropathology; **Jaiyeola Thomas-Ogunniyi** MD, Director of Surgical Pathology; cytopathology.; **Edward L. Chan** PhD, FCCM, D(ABMM), Director of Microbiology; **Menchu G. Ong** MD, Medical Director of Transfusion Medicine Services.

APPLICATIONS

Applications must be submitted through the Electronic Residency Application System (ERAS) and received prior to December 1 for appointments the following July. Applicants must be graduates of approved medical schools and must be able to obtain a Louisiana license. Graduates of foreign medical schools must have an ECGMG certificate.

Address inquiries to:

Lisa LaChance, BA
Program Coordinator
LSUHSC-Shreveport, Department of Pathology
PO Box 33932
Shreveport, LA 71130-3932
Phone: (318) 675-7822 • **E-mail:** llacha@lsuhsc.edu
Web site: http://www.sh.lsuhsc.edu/pathology

LSU School of Medicine, Shreveport, LA

JOHNS HOPKINS MEDICAL INSTITUTIONS

Baltimore, Maryland

PROGRAMS OFFERED

The Department of Pathology at Johns Hopkins provides in-depth training in anatomic pathology (AP) and clinical pathology (CP) either combined or separately to newly graduated MD's and to MD's with previous postdoctoral experience. Anatomic pathology training includes autopsy and autopsy supervision, surgical pathology, cytopathology, forensic pathology, and multiple opportunities for training in the pathology of specific systems, including breast pathology, dermatopathology, gastrointestinal/liver pathology, gynecological pathology, molecular pathology, neuropathology, pediatric-perinatal pathology, renal pathology, and for electron microscopy, immunohistochemistry, special electives, and research. Clinical pathology training includes rotations in clinical chemistry, cytogenetics, molecular pathology, immunology, hematology/coagulation, hematopathology, informatics, medical microbiology, transfusion medicine and management of clinical laboratories. The emphasis is on interaction with clinical services, technical methods, quality assurance, utilization, instrumentation, information systems and management. Additional training consists of rotations and electives that provide advanced experience in selected areas and opportunities for research. Clinically relevant rotations are integrated throughout, and residents attend and present at departmental and interdepartmental conferences. Residents selecting combined AP and CP training have a fully integrated training program developed for their particular interest. Two senior residents serve each year as chief residents in AP and CP. **Post-Residency:** Fellowship programs or junior faculty positions are offered for training in breast pathology, cardiovascular pathology, clinical chemistry, cytopathology, gastrointestinal/liver pathology, gynecologic pathology, hematopathology, immunopathology, informatics, medical microbiology, molecular pathology, neuropathology, renal pathology, surgical pathology, transfusion medicine, urologic pathology and as ad hoc arrangements for research. All training programs are maximally customized to individual needs. For more information, please call or write. (See fellowship descriptions.)

TYPES AND NUMBERS OF APPOINTMENTS

Anatomic Pathology and Clinical Pathology: Seven or eight first-year positions in AP and/or CP are available with up to 26 additional residency positions (second year and beyond). All residents receive appointments as fellows in The Johns Hopkins University School of Medicine and residency staff appointments in The Johns Hopkins Hospital.

FACILITIES

The Johns Hopkins Hospital is a 975-bed general hospital that is a component of the Johns Hopkins Health Systems(JHHS). Training in anatomic and clinical pathology is integrated in the Department of Pathology, which each year performs approximately 381 autopsies, approximately 78,329 surgical and 39,136 cytopathology evaluations, and over 5,000,000 laboratory tests. Laboratories are well-equipped for electron microscopy, fluorescence microscopy, flow cytometry, immunohistochemistry, biochemical and molecular biology, as well as modern automated diagnostic services. The department has seventeen (17)divisions including autopsy, cardiovascular pathology, clinical chemistry, cytopathology, gastrointestinal-liver pathology, genitourinary pathology, gynecologic pathology, hematologic pathology, immunology, informatics, medical microbiology, molecular pathology, neuropathology, pediatric pathology, pulmonary pathology, surgical pathology, and transfusion medicine. All divisions are engaged in basic research and development of new diagnostic methods. The Department of Pathology is also a teaching and research department in the School of Medicine, with approximately 65,000 square feet of research space. A new surgical pathology suite was opened in the Fall of 2000 as part of the Weinberg Comprehensive Cancer Center. Pathology residents may also spend time at the Johns Hopkins Bayview Medical Center (JHBMC), another JHMI component located two miles from The Johns Hopkins Hospital, which is staffed by full-time Johns Hopkins faculty members.

COMMUNITY

The Johns Hopkins Hospital, The Johns Hopkins University School of Medicine and the Johns Hopkins Bayview Medical Center are in the eastern part of downtown Baltimore, convenient to shopping and cultural centers and only 15-20 minutes by car from suburban residential areas. The nearby Chesapeake Bay and Atlantic Coast are favorite sites for boating, fishing and swimming.

STIPENDS AND MAINTENANCE

Annual stipends of at least $45,518 for first-year trainees increasing in subsequent years. Professional liability insurance is provided at no charge. Medical, dental, disability and malpractice insurance are paid in full. Uniforms and laundry are supplied.

STAFF

Faculty

J. Brooks Jackson MD, MBA, Baxley Professor and Director Pathology, Johns Hopkins Univ Sch Med; Pathologist-in-Chief, Johns Hopkins Hospital; **Michael J. Borowitz** MD, PhD, Professor and Deputy Director, Education and

Clinical Affairs; **Ralph H. Hruban** MD, Professor and Deputy Director, Program Development; **Donald L. Price** MD, Professor, Deputy Director, Research Affairs; **Edward F. McCarthy** MD, Professor and Director, Residency Training Program; **Patrizio Caturegli** MD, MPH, Associate Professor and Co-Director, Residency Training Program.

Autopsy Pathology

Barbara J. Crain MD, PhD Associate Professor; **Ralph H. Hruban** MD Professor; **Grover M. Hutchins** MD Professor; **William H. Westra** MD Professor; **Marc K. Halushka** MD Assistant Professor.

Cardiac Pathology

Charles Steenbergen MD, PhD Professor; **Marc K. Halushka** MD, PhD Assistant Professor.

Clinical Chemistry

Daniel W. Chan PhD Professor; **Edward W. Gabrielson** MD Professor; **Paul W. Ladenson** MD Professor Medicine and Pathology; **Lori Sokoll** PhD Associate Professor; **William Clarke** PhD Assistant Professor.

Cytogenetics

Constance A. Griffin MD Professor Oncology, Medicine and Pathology; **George H. Thomas** PhD Professor Pediatrics and Pathology; **Denise Batista** PhD Assistant Professor.

Cytopathology

Douglas P. Clark MD Professor; **Brigitte Ronnett** MD Professor; **Syed Z. Ali** MBBS Associate Professor; **Mostafa Fraig** MD V. Associate Professor; **Karen S. Gustafson** MD, PhD Assistant Professor; **Qing Kay Li** MD, PhD Assistant Professor; **Zahra Maleki** MD, Instructor.

Dermatopathology

Jacqueline Junkins-Hopkins MD Associate Professor; **Grant J. Anhalt** MD Professor Dermatology and Pathology; **Gary Warnock** DDS Associate Professor, Dermatology Pathology and Oral Pathology.

Forensic Pathology

Mary G. Ripple MD Instructor; **James L. Locke** MD Lecturer; **Tasha Z Greenberg** MD, Lecturer.

Gastrointestinal-Liver

Ralph H. Hruban MD Professor; **John K. Boitnott** MD Professor; **Michael S. Goggins** MD Professor; **Scott E. Kern** MD Professor Oncology and Pathology; **Elizabeth A. Montgomery** MD Professor; **Belur S. Bhagavan** MD Associate Professor; **James R. Eshleman** MD, PhD Associate Professor; **Christine Iacobuzio-Donohue** MD, PhD Associate Professor; **Anirban Maitra** MD Associate Professor; **Michael Torbenson** MD AssociateProfessor; **Robert A. Anders** MD, PhD Assistant Professor.

Gynecologic Pathology

Robert J. Kurman MD, Professor Pathology and Gynecology and Obstetrics; **Brigitte Ronnett** MD Professor; **IeMing Shih** MD, PhD Professor; **T. C. Wu** MD, PhD Professor; **Richard B. S. Roden** PhD Associate Professor; **Russell Vang** MD Associate Professor; **Anna V. Yemelyanova** MD Assistant Professor.

Hematopathology

Michael J. Borowitz MD, PhD Professor; **Thomas S. Kickler** MD Professor; **Paul M. Ness** MD Professor; **Chi V. Dang** MD, PhD Professor Medicine and Pathology; **Christopher D. Gocke** MD Associate Professor; **Kathleen H. Burns** MD, PhD Assistant Professor; **Milena Vuica-Ross** MD Assistant Professor.

Immunopathology

Michael J. Borowitz MD, PhD Professor; **Noel R. Rose** MD, PhD Professor; **Jonathan P. Schneck** MD, PhD Professor; **T. C. Wu** MD, PhD Professor; **Barbara Detrick** PhD Associate Professor; **C. Lynne Burek** PhD Associate Professor; **Richard L. Humphrey** MD Associate Professor Pathology; **Scheherazade Sadegh-Nasseri** PhD Associate Professor; **Patrizio Caturegli** MD Associate Professor; **Maria Theresa Lee** MD Assistant Professor; **Barbara A. Wasowska** PhD Assistant Professor.

Informatics

John K. Boitnott MD Professor; **Robert E. Miller** MD Associate Professor Pathology and Biomedical Engineering; **Norman J. Barker** MS, RBP Associate Professor.

Kidney-Urologic Pathology

Jonathan I. Epstein MD Professor; **Angelo DeMarzo** MD, PhD Professor; **Lorraine C. Racusen** MD Professor; **Serena M. Bagnasco** MD Associate Professor; **David M. Berman** MD, PhD Associate Professor; **George Netto** MD, Associate Professor; **G. Steven Bova** MD Assistant Professor; **Tamara Lotan** MD, Assistant Professor.

Microbiology

Karen Carroll MD Professor; **Richard F. Ambinder** MD, PhD Professor Oncology, Pharmacology and Pathology; **Patricia Charache** MD Professor; **Douglas P. Clark** MD Professor; **J. Stephen Dumler** MD Professor; **Mary G.**

Fowler MD Professor; **J. Brooks Jackson** MD Professor; **William G. Merz** PhD Professor; **Alexandra Valsamakis** MD, PhD Associate Professor; **Nicole Parrish** PhD Assistant Professor; **Megan Reller** MD Assistant Professor.

Molecular Pathology

Constance A Griffin MD Professor; **Daniel W. Chan** PhD Professor; **Patricia Charache** MD Professor; **Edward Gabrielson** MD Professor; **Francis Kuhajda** MD Professor; **Lee J Martin** PhD Professor; **Drew M. Pardoll** MD, PhD Professor Oncology and Pathology; **Donald L. Price** MD Professor; **Saraswati Sukamar** PhD Professor Oncology and Pathology; **Philip C-Y Wong** PhD Professor; **James R Eshleman** MD, PhD Associate Professor; **Christopher D Gocke** MD Associate Professor; **Michael K. Lee** PhD Associate Professor; **Kathleen Murphy** PhD Associate Professor; **Denise Batista** PhD Assistant Professor.

Musculoskeletal

Edward F. McCarthy, Jr. MD Professor.

Neuropathology

Donald L. Price MD Professor; **Peter C. Burger** MD Professor; **Walter E. Kaufmann** MD Professor; **Lee J. Martin** PhD Professor; **Juan C. Troncoso** MD Professor; **Philip C-Y. Wong** PhD Professor; **Barbara J. Crain** MD, PhD Associate Professor; **Charles G. Eberhart** MD, PhD Associate Professor; **Vassilis E. Koliatsos** MD Associate Professor; **Michael K. Lee** PhD Associate Professor; **Alena Savonenko** MD, PhD, Assistant Professor.

Ophthalmic Pathology

Charles G Eberhart MD, PhD Associate Professor.

Pediatric Pathology

Frederic B. Askin MD Professor; **Michael J. Borowitz** MD, PhD Professor; **Grover M. Hutchins** MD Professor; **Walter Kaufmann** MD Professor; **Belur S. Bhagavan** MD Associate Professor.

Pulmonary Pathology

Frederic B. Askin MD Professor; **Edward Gabrielson** MD Professor; **Grover M. Hutchins** MD Professor; **William H. Westra** MD Professor; **Mostafa Fraig** MD V. Associate Professor; **Peter Illei** MD Assistant Professor.

Surgical Pathology

Jonathan I. Epstein MD Professor; **Pedram Argani** MD, Professor; **Frederic B. Askin** MD Professor; **Peter C. Burger** MD Professor; **Mark Haas** MD Professor; **Ralph H. Hruban** MD Professor; **Robert J. Kurman** MD Professor Pathology and Gynecology and Obstetrics; **Edward F. McCarthy** MD Professor; **Lorraine C. Racusen** MD Professor; **William H. Westra** MD Professor; **Peter B. Illei** MD Assistant Professor; **Hind Nassar** MD Assistant Professor.

Transfusion Medicine

Paul M. Ness MD Professor; **Susan H. Eshleman** MD, PhD Professor; **J. Brooks Jackson** MD Professor; **Thomas S. Kickler** MD Professor; **James R. Eshleman** MD, PhD Associate Professor; **Karen King** MD Associate Professor; **Hua Shan** MD, PhD Associate Professor; **William Savage** MD, Assistant Professor.

Johns Hopkins Bayview Medical Center

Frederic B. Askin MD, Professor, Chief of Pathology; **Edward Gabrielson** MD, Professor; **Francis P. Kuhajda** MD, Professor; **Mostafa Fraig** MD, V Associate Professor; **Stefan Reidel** MD, PhD Assistant Professor; **Zahra Maleki** MD, Instructor.

APPLICATIONS

All applicants receive appointments through the National Resident Matching Program: the usual time schedule is followed. Candidates must be graduates of approved U.S. or Canadian medical schools, or have USMLE (formerly FMGEMS) certification. The program will be using the Electronic Residency Application Service (ERAS). Foreign applicants must contact ECFMG office in order to access ERAS. We only accept electronically submitted documents. Applications must be completed by December 1, 2009. The Johns Hopkins University does not discriminate on the basis of race, color, sex, religion, national or ethnic origin, age, handicapped or veteran status in any student program or activity administered by the University or with regard to admission or employment. Drug Free and Smoke Free.

Address Inquiries to:

Terry R. Aman
Educational Programs Manager
Johns Hopkins Medical Institutions
Department of Pathology, Rm 401
600 N. Wolfe St., Baltimore, MD 21287-6417
Phone: (410) 955-3439 • **Fax:** (410) 614-9011
Web site: http://pathology.jhu.edu/

UNIVERSITY OF MARYLAND

Baltimore, Maryland

PROGRAMS OFFERED

The University of Maryland Medical System/Hospital and its affiliated hospitals, Veterans Affairs Medical Center/ Baltimore, and the Medical Examiner's Office/State of Maryland, offer fully approved four year programs for residents in anatomic pathology, clinical pathology, or both. Residents are provided a mandatory three-year core program in the basic principles of anatomic and clinical pathology. Rotations also include hematopathology, neuropathology, dermatopathology, renal pathology and molecular diagnostics. Individuals pursuing an interest in academic pathology with emphasis on research will be encouraged to begin their research activities in the second and/or third year of training. Advanced training allows the opportunity for elective time in order to encourage individual potential interests; to meet requirements adapted to individual needs and experience; as well as to meet requirements of the American Board of Pathology. Electives may include unique opportunities in which to train among specialists in the University of Maryland Cancer Center, Shock Trauma Center, the Armed Forces Institute of Pathology (Washington DC), and the National Cancer Institute's Laboratory of Human Carcinogenesis (Bethesda, MD). Senior training (yr 3-4) includes rotations at the affiliate hospitals, the Medical Examiner's Office, electron microscopy, and cytogenetics. The Medical Examiner's Office also offers a fully accredited one-year training program in forensic pathology for those who have completed anatomic pathology training. Fully accredited cytopathology training program is also available, as is fellowship training in hematopathology and transplantation pathology.

FACILITIES

The department has on-site advanced molecular biology, cell and tissue culture laboratories, hematopathology, electron microscopy, and image analysis workstations, as well as advanced immunology research laboratories. The Department of Pathology occupies well developed and expanding laboratories in the University of Maryland affiliated hospitals. These are the laboratories of the University of Maryland Medical Center and Baltimore Veterans Affairs Medical Center with a yearly rate of 270 autopsies, 31,800 surgical and 18,560 cytology specimens, and 3,766,212 clinical laboratory tests. In addition, 3,300 forensic cases are seen in the Medical Examiner's Office adjacent to the University Hospital complex. The Health Sciences Library has more than 200,000 bound volumes and receives more than 3,500 journals.

COMMUNITY

Baltimore, the eleventh largest city in the U.S., is on the western shore of Maryland at the northern extent of the Chesapeake Bay, a famous site for fishing, sailing and swimming. The Baltimore- Washington area has a great variety of universities, colleges and medical centers, and offers many galleries and museums, symphony orchestras, professional athletic teams in all major sports, a variety of legitimate theaters, and other cultural advantages of a large metropolitan area.

STIPENDS AND MAINTENANCE

We have 15 pathology residency positions from first to fourth year levels. Residents in the first year of graduate training receive approximately $43,919 with an approximate $1,500 increase each following year. Contracts are on an annual basis. All residents are provided with parking, uniforms, uniform laundry, malpractice insurance coverage, and hospitalization and dental insurance premiums. Residents also receive $1000 per year book/travel stipend. Travel expenses are also paid for Residents who present at national and/or international conferences.

STAFF

University Hospital Full-Time Faculty

Tehmina Z Ali Assistant Professor (GU Pathology); **Allen B Burke** Assistant Professor (Cardiac Pathology); **Rudolph Castellani** Professor (Neurpathology); **Qing Chen** MD, PhD Associate Professor (Hematopathology); **Robert Christenson** PhD Professor (Clinical Chemistry); **Neil T. Constantine** PhD Professor (Research); **Louis J. DeTolla, Jr.** VMD, PhD Associate Professor, CAF Director (Research); **Cinthia I. Drachenberg** MD Professor (Renal Pathology, Immunohistochemistry, Electron Microscopy, Transplantation Pathology); **Show-Hong Duh** PhD Assistant Professor (Clinical Chemistry); **Bennett B. Edelman** MD Associate Professor; Director, Clinical Laboratories; **Amy Fulton** PhD Professor; **Anne W. Hamburger** PhD Professor, Director of Graduate Program (Cell Culture-Oncology); **John Hess** MD Associate Professor (Blood Bank); **Olga Ioffe** MD Associate Professor (Surgical Pathology, Gynecologic and Breast Pathology); **Raymond T. Jones** PhD Professor (Cell Injury, Environmental Pathology, Electron Microscopy); **Dean L. Mann** MD Professor; Director Immunogenetics; (Transplantation Immunology, Tumor Immunology, Immunology of Viral Infection); **A. James Mixson** MD Assistant Professor (Gene Therapy); **Nahid Nananji** Assistant Professor (Hematopathology); **Yi Ning** PhD Assistant Professor (Cytogenetics); **John C. Papadimitriou** MD Professor (Surgical Pathology, Immunology, Transplantation Pathology); **Antonio Passaniti** PhD Assistant Professor (Microbiology); **Hong**

Peng MD Visiting Assistant Professor; **Abulkalam M. Shamsuddin** MD, PhD Professor (Autopsy, Colon); **Steven G. Silverberg** MD Professor (Surgical Pathology, Breast Pathology, Gynecologic Pathology); **Sanford A. Stass** MD Professor and Chair; Director, University of Maryland Medical System Laboratories of Pathology (Hematopathology, Molecular Biology, Molecular Diagnosis); **Chen-Chih J. Sun** MD Professor; Director Autopsy Services (Pediatric Pathology); **William S Twaddell** Assistant Professor (GI Pathology); **Richard Venezia** PhD Professor (Clinical Microbiology); **Frank Zhao** MD, PhD Assistant Professor (Hematopathology); **Richard Zhao** PhD Associate Professor (Molecular Diagnostics).

Veterans Affairs Medical Center

Gladys Alonsozana MD Director, Surgical Pathology; **Lawrence Brown** MD Assistant Professor; **Judith A. Johnson** PhD Associate Professor; **Dong Lee** MD Chief, Pathology; **William Moore** MD, PhD Associate Professor; **Andrew Saladino** MD Associate Professor; **Wenle Wang** MD (GI Pathology); **Harris Yfantis** MD Chief, Anatomic Pathology & Cytopathology.

Medical Examiner's Office

David Fowler MD Chief Medical Examiner.; **Barry S. Levine** PhD Associate Professor; **Mary G Ripple** Deputy Chief.

APPLICATIONS

Candidates may be graduates of approved medical schools in the U.S. and abroad. Resident positions are available through the mechanisms of the National Matching Program generally for first-year training.

Address inquiries to:

Olga B. Ioffe, MD
Director, Residency Training Program
Department of Pathology
University of Maryland School of Medicine
22 South Greene Street
Baltimore, MD 21201
Phone: (410) 328-5555

CLINICAL CENTER NATIONAL INSTITUTES OF HEALTH

Bethesda, Maryland

PROGRAMS OFFERED

The Laboratory of Pathology (LP) conducts a fully ACGME accredited AP3 program for residents in Anatomic Pathology at the National Institutes of Health. A fourth year is fully funded to expand research opportunities. The program provides diversified exposure to all areas of anatomic pathology. Diagnostic specimens are derived from patients enrolled in over 3000 clinical research protocols conducted by 27 institutes and centers.The clinical protocols encompass a broad range of diseases in such areas as cancer, autoimmune disease, infectious disease, immunodeficiency, digestive and kidney diseases,metabolic disorders, andneuromuscular diseases. In addition, the LP receives more than 3,000 extramural consultation cases each year.

The philosophy of the training program is to provide broad and in-depth exposure to the subject matter of anatomic pathology, with an emphasis on clinical correlation, relationships to disease mechanisms, and exposure to investigational opportunities. The educational program is enhanced by the internationally recognized faculty, who are acclaimed in many areas of Anatomic Pathology and are committed to excellence in the teaching program. Exposure to the diverse daily case load is supplemented by didactic sessions to explore all topics of Anatomic Pathology. Because the clinical programs are integrated with the research activities of the NIH, residents are exposed to information regarding the pathogenesis and pathophysiology of diseases that they are diagnosing on a regular basis. This insight into the basic disease mechanisms of pathology enhances the educational experience.

Clinical training in the Anatomic Pathology Program includes three years of rotations and subspecialty training. The program provides for diversified experience in surgical pathology, cytopathology, autopsy pathology, dermatopathology, hematopathology, neuropathology, molecular pathology and cytogenetics. Separate one-month subspecialty rotations in forensic pathology, surgical pathology, and pediatric pathology offered at affiliated institutions broaden the training offered at the NIH. Residents in the third year gain more authority in making diagnostic decisions and supervising other residents in both surgical and postmortem pathology. The program offers generous opportunities for elective rotations, both intramurally and extramurally, during all three years. The fourth year may be devoted to full time research, or fellowship-level training in several subspecialty areas.

Residents are exposed to, and encouraged to participate in, clinical and laboratory research throughout the program. Residents may select a research mentor from any of the world-renowned scientists inthe NCI or the other NIH institutes.Residents have access to state of the art research facilities and cores. These include laser capture dissection, high resolution imaging, genetic, genomic and proteomic core laboratories.

For additional program information, please see the following links:

NIH GME programs; http://www.cc.nih.gov/training/gme/programs.html

Laboratory of Pathology residency; http://www.cc.nih.gov/training/gme/programs/anatomic_pathology.html

Laboratory of Pathology Home Page and Research Directory; http://home.ccr.cancer.gov/LOP/Clinical/default.asp http://ccr.cancer.gov/labs/lab.asp?labid=106

REQUIREMENTS

Residency candidates must be graduates of approved medical schools of the U.S. or Canada, or must hold an ECFMG certificate. Candidates must have passed Parts 1 & 2 of the USMLE prior to enrollment. Applicants with research experience or a PhD degree are given priority.

TYPES AND NUMBERS OF APPOINTMENTS

Nine positions are approved for AP training. Three PGY1 positions are open to new applicants each year. Anoptional fully funded fourth year research or clinical year is offered to residents enrolled in the program.

FACILITIES

The Laboratory of Pathology of the National Cancer Institute provides complete services in anatomic pathology for the Clinical Center, a 280-bed research hospital, which in turn serves all the Institutes of the National Institutes of Health. Most of the patients admitted to the Clinical Center are enrolled in clinical protocols. Although there is a numerical preponderance of patients admitted from the National Cancer Institute, the broad research interests of the other Institutes provide an unusually stimulating abundance of pathological material of all types for diagnosis and study in the Laboratory of Pathology. Hospital and departmental conferences are held regularly. A schedule of lectures, seminars and meetings is published each week and includes speakers of national and international note in all fields of biomedical science. The National Library of Medicine is located on the grounds of the National Institutes of Health and all its services are available. The Clinical Center has itself one of the most complete medical libraries in the country. In addition to the departmental library, electronic access to virtually all scientific publications is available.

COMMUNITY

The National Institutes of Health is a research complex in Bethesda, Maryland, a pleasant residential community just ten miles from the center of Washington, DC. All of the historic, social and cultural advantages of the nation's capital are close at hand. There are five University Medical Centers in the area as well as the Armed Forces Institute of Pathology.

STIPENDS AND MAINTENANCE

Residents receive appointments as clinical associates (Civil Service). Starting salary at the PGY1 level is $56,812. Residents holding a Ph.D. degree receive a supplemental bonus. Additional benefits include the NIH Loan Repayment Program and moving expenses to the Washington, DC area. No living quarters are provided, but homes and apartments at all price levels are available in the immediate vicinity.

STAFF

J. Carl Oberholtzer MD, PhD, Laboratory Chief; neuropathology; **Elaine S. Jaffe** MD, Program Director; hematopathology; **Diane Arthur** MD, cancer cytogenetics; **Carl Baker** MD, PhD, cellular regulation and virology; **Michael Emmert-Buck** MD, PhD, cancer genetics and technology development, laser capture microscopy; **Armando Filie** MD, cytopathology; **Stephen Hewitt** MD PhD, molecular profiling and high throughput technolgies; **David E. Kleiner** MD, PhD, hepatic and renal pathology, surgical and post-mortem pathology; **Chyi-Chia Richard Lee** MD, PhD, dermatopathology; surgical pathology; **David L. Levens** MD, PhD, molecular biology and gene regulation; **Susan M. Mackem** MD, PhD, developmental biology; **Maria J. Merino** MD, renal cancer, surgical pathology; **Stefania Pittaluga** MD, PhD, hematopathology & immunopathology; **Martha Quezado** MD, surgical pathology, neuropathology; **Mark Raffeld** MD, molecular biology and immunopathology; **David D. Roberts** PhD, angiogenesis and cell biology; **Jere B. Stern** MD, dermatopathology; **Maryalice Stetler-Stevenson** MD, PhD, hematopathology, flow cytometry; **Mary L. Stracke** PhD, tumor cell biology and angiogenesis; **Maria Tsokos** MD, pediatric pathology, ultrastructural pathology, and tumor biology; **Liqiang Xi** MD, molecular diagnostics; **Constance Yuan** MD, flow cytometry & hematopathology.

APPLICATIONS

Applicants may apply online through the Association of American Medical Colleges, Electronic Residency Application Service: https://services.aamc.org/eras/myeras2005/

Address inquiries to:
Elaine S. Jaffe, MD
Anatomic Pathology Residency Training Program
National Cancer Institute
National Institutes of Health
Building 10, Room 2N208
10 Center Drive, MSC-1500
Bethesda MD 20892-1500
Phone: (301) 402-3990 • **Fax:** (301) 402-0043 • **E-mail:** hostlers@mail.nih.gov

Campus of the National Institutes of Health, Bethesda, Maryland.

BETH ISRAEL DEACONESS MEDICAL CENTER HARVARD MEDICAL SCHOOL

Boston, Massachusetts

PROGRAMS OFFERED

Pathology is the branch of medicine that deals with the basic mechanisms of disease. At Beth Israel Deaconess Medical Center, we train residents in all areas of diagnostic pathology and encourage scholarly activity in clinical and basic research. Consequently, our focus is on four-year residency training programs in combined anatomic and clinical pathology. Also available is a three-year program in anatomic pathology only and a three-year program in clinical pathology only.

Combined Program

Our goal is to provide the framework for a successful career as physician, consultant, and teacher. Rapid changes in the delivery of health care require that residency training in pathology be grounded in the traditional disciplines, but, at the same time, be up-to-date and flexible. We offer a two-step approach. First, there are core curricula in the established areas of anatomic and clinical pathology. Then, there is a period of review, integration and synthesis, in part designed by the residents themselves, with graduated clinical responsibility and research opportunities.

First Year: Anatomic Pathology

PGY-1 is devoted entirely to anatomic pathology. Residents are involved with surgical pathology about 75% of the time, alternating rotations with autopsy pathology. Ours is a high-volume service of considerable breadth and depth, with over 50,000 surgical specimens, 50,000 cytopathology specimens and 150 autopsies per year. Subspecialty exposure is enhanced by both a weekly lecture series and by a large variety of departmental specialty conferences. Residents are exposed to the broad range of specimens on each cutting day; there is no division of specimens into subspecialties except for dermatopathology and, to a limited extent, gastrointestinal pathology. This allows maximum exposure to all types of diagnostic problems. Residents perform their own independent analysis before signing out with the staff person. They are involved in every operating room consultation, and follow their cases through to the final diagnosis, coordinating the results of all special studies.

Second Year: Laboratory Medicine

In PGY-2, residents move to the clinical laboratories. The year begins with two month basic rotations, in each of the four core laboratory areas. At the end of the year, the residents revisit each laboratory for one month advanced rotations with greater consultative responsibilities. Training in clinical chemistry includes many basic issues such as principles and philosophies of laboratory analysis; method evaluation; reference ranges; quality control; sensitivity, specificity, and predictive value. The wide range of testing used in both health screening and the management of critical medical situations is covered. In hematology, the focus is on blood cell morphology and coagulation testing. Concurrent training in hematopathology emphasizes lymphoma and leukemia. The resident takes responsibility for bone marrow and lymph node biopsies, coordinating the results of immunohistochemistry, flow cytometry, cytogenetics and molecular diagnosis. Microbiology training includes basic aspects of culturing bacteria and viruses; antimicrobial sensitivity testing; direct detection of microorganisms (including PCR and other methods of amplification); and infectious disease serology. Transfusion medicine provides a comprehensive introduction to blood banking. The focus is on the basic immunology of the blood group systems and the management of blood component therapy; solid organ, bone marrow and stem cell transplantation; and apheresis.

Years Three and Four: Putting It Together

The resident enters the second half of the program with a solid grounding in anatomic pathology and a comprehensive introduction to laboratory medicine. Some integration has already occurred. In the first year, residents attend teaching conferences and a lecture series in clinical pathology. In this way, they begin to develop a vocabulary for the clinical laboratory issues that will confront them during the second year. Conversely, during the second year, residents attend teaching conferences and a lecture series in anatomic pathology, to maintain their expertise in surgical and autopsy pathology. During the third year, six months are spent in anatomic pathology and six months are spent in the clinical laboratories, but the residents are encouraged to integrate their knowledge bases. Laboratory rotations are designed both to review laboratory problem-solving as well as to view the laboratory test in the context of the overall diagnostic problem. Required rotations include one month of laboratory administration/informatics, two months of cytopathology, and one month of cytogenetics/molecular diagnostics. Four months of elective are also available to gain some additional experience in an area of interest or to pursue a project with one of the individual staff members. Finally, in the fourth year, residents complete their training. They spend six months in anatomic pathology, assuming increased responsibility and reviewing specialized areas such as forensic pathology (one staff member is approved as a medical examiner), pediatric pathology, advanced cytopathology with FNA experience, and ultrastructural diagnosis. They may also customize three months of elective time to meet their individual needs. Formal electives are offered that are uniquely designed to integrate the various laboratory disciplines and clinical services, but the resident may also opt to spend time in one of the department's experimental pathology laboratories. Major research themes include angiogenesis; the remodeling of the extracellular matrix; and the molecular biology of allergic and other immunologic responses. There are also many opportunities for translational research, particularly in the areas of breast, gastrointestinal, genitourinary, and skin pathology.

Anatomic Pathology Program

The first year is the same as in the combined program. The activities in anatomic pathology continue in the second and third years, and include rotations in pediatric and forensic pathology, cytopathology, cytogenetics, hematopathology, further exposure to other subspecialties, and opportunity for research. The program in the third year can be modified to suit the needs of the resident.

Clinical Pathology Program

The first year is the same as the clinical pathology core year in the combined AP-CP program. The second year includes rotations in Molecular Pathology and Cytogenetics, additional rotations in the four basic laboratory modules, and time for extensive subspecialty training in a laboratory medicine discipline.

Physician-Scientist Track

This pathway prepares residents for the role of physician-scientist by emphasizing basic science research during pathology training in the context of an AP or CP only training pathway.

TYPES AND NUMBERS OF APPOINTMENTS

There are 32 residency positions available with 7-9 first-year positions available yearly. Also, there are separate one-year fellowship positions available in breast pathology, cytopathology, dermatopathology, gastrointestinal pathology, hematopathology, molecular pathology, surgical pathology and transfusion medicine. Preference for these positions is given to residents already enrolled in our program.

FACILITIES

Beth Israel Deaconess Medical Center is the result of the 1996 merger of Beth Israel Hospital and New England Deaconess Hospital. The department has three major divisions: Anatomic Pathology (with recently constructed cutting rooms; intra-operative laboratories; automated immunohistochemistry instrumentation; transmission and scanning electron microscopes; and a core molecular facility); Laboratory Medicine (with newly reorganized clinical laboratories); and Experimental Pathology (with extensive molecular biology facilities including a transgenic animal facility in newly constructed space and laser capture microscopy). Each resident has her or his own microscope. There are updated extensive interactive laboratory information systems, with a completely new HBO® system. In addition, the hospital information system offers on-line access to the *Paperchase®* medical library search system (developed at Beth Israel Deaconess) and all the resources of the Harvard Medical Library. The department maintains several computer work stations for resident use, each with both Macintosh and IBM-compatible systems, color scanners, presentation software, and direct server access to the Internet. Beth Israel Deaconess Medical Center is one of the primary teaching hospitals of Harvard Medical School and houses the newly created Harvard Medical School Center for Clinical Education. Pathology residents at all levels of their training are actively encouraged to participate in medical student education in a variety of settings. All residents receive an academic appointment at Harvard Medical School and access to the Countway Medical Library.

COMMUNITY

Boston is a great city. The neighborhoods adjacent to the medical center are Brookline, Fenway, and Jamaica Plain, and it is a short commute from Beacon Hill, Back Bay, or any of several Boston suburbs.

STIPENDS AND MAINTENANCE

2009-2010 salaries: $53,051.64 (PGY-1); $55,011.98 (PGY-2); $57,481.51 (PGY-3); $60,487.08 (PGY-4); and $63,601.55 (PGY-5). Health and professional liability insurance and uniforms provided. Chief residents receive an additional stipend.

STAFF

Donald A. Antonioli MD consultant, gastrointestinal pathology, especially Barrett's esophagus and inflammatory bowel disease; **Matthew Anderson** MD neuropathology; **Karoly Balogh** MD bone pathology, especially metabolic bone disease; head and neck pathology; **Nicole Belsley** MD surgical pathology, cytopathology; **Laura Benjamin** PhD vascular biology research; **Andes Berg** MD, PhD clinical chemistry; **Parul Bhargava** MD hematopathology; **Mark Boguski** MD, PhD bioinformatics; **Lawrence F. Brown** MD surgical pathology, angiogenesis research; **Justine M. Carr** MD coagulation disorders, especially fibrinolytic; appropriate utilization of laboratory resources; **Tracy Challies** MD surgical pathology; gastrointestinal pathology; **David Cohen** MD surgical pathology, pulmonary pathology, cytology; **Laura Collins** MD surgical pathology; breast pathology and cytopathology; **James L. Connolly** MD Director, Residency Training Program; breast pathology and endocrine pathology; **Ann M. Dvorak** MD ultrastructural analysis of basophil and mast cell degranulation, diagnostic electron microscopy; **Harold F. Dvorak** MD Director, Center for Vascular Biology; **Beverly Faulkner-Jones** MD, PhD dermatopathology; **Deborah Fleischhacker** MD surgical pathology; **Yineng Fu** MD surgical pathology, cytopathology; **Elizabeth Genega** MD surgical pathology, genitourinary pathology; **Hannah Gilmore** MD surgical pathology, breast pathology; **Harvey Goldman** MD Vice Chief of Department; gastrointestinal pathology; **Jeffrey Goldsmith** MD surgical pathology; pancreas and soft tissue pathology; **Richard Haspel** MD, PhD transfusion medicine; **Jonathan Hecht** MD surgical pathology; gynecologic pathology; autopsy pathology and cytopathology; **Gary L. Horowitz** MD markers of coronary artery disease, cholesterol and related lipids, therapeutic drug monitoring and toxicology; **Marie-Helene Jouvin** MD molecular and cellular biology of high affinity IgE receptor, particularly of mononuclear cells in asthmatic patients; **Sarah Kane** MD cytopathology; surgical pathology; **Jean-Pierre Kinet** MD molecular biology of membrane receptors involved in immune defense and in genesis of allergic reactions; **James Kirby** MD microbiology; **Olivier Kocher** MD, PhD Director Molecular Diagnostics Laboratory; surgical pathology, genetic changes responsible for malignant transformation; **Jack Lawler** PhD thrombospondin research; **Shu-Ling Liang** PhD clinical chemistry; **Takashi Maki** MD tissue typing; **Rajan Mariappan** MD, PhD hematopathology; **Cynthia Morton** PhD cytogenetics; **Janice A. Nagy** PhD mechanisms by which tumor cells induce ascites, particularly angiogenesis and altered hemostasis in peritoneum; **Imad Nasser** MD surgical pathology and cytopathology; **Henry Nields** MD PhD Interim Chief Medical Examiner; **Pier Paolo Pandolfi** MD, PhD cancer genetics program; **German Pihan** MD Director, Hematopathology; **Amy Powers** MD aphoresis and infusion medicine; **Qiafang Qian** MD, PhD microbiology; **Seymour Rosen** MD diagnostic surgical pathology and renal pathology, basic mechanisms of hypoxic nephrotoxicity; **Angela Ruiz** MD surgical pathology; **Jeffrey E. Saffitz** MD, PhD Chairman, Department of Pathology; cardiac pathology; **Stuart J. Schnitt** MD Director, Anatomic Pathology; surgical pathology, breast pathology; immunohistochemistry; **Donald R. Senger** PhD molecular biology of osteopontin and VPF/VEGF in tumor angiogenesis and neovascularization; **Su-Jean Seo** MD, PhD dermatopathology; **Alireza Sepehr** MD dermatopathology; **Isaac E. Stillman** MD surgical pathology; renal pathology, electron microscopy; **Steven R. Tahan** MD Director, dermatopathology; **Lynne Uhl** MD bone marrow and stem cell cryopreservation, transfusion medicine; **Helen H. Wang** MD, DrPH Director, cytopathology; surgical pathology, epidemiology; **Mary Jane Zimerowski** MD dermatopathology.

APPLICATIONS

All applicants receive appointments through the National Resident Matching Program. All applicants must either be graduates of approved medical schools in the United States or Canada, or hold a certificate of ECFMG certificate. Applications accepted via ERAS only.

Address inquiries to:

Joan Allin
Residency and Fellowship Training Programs Coordinator
Department of Pathology - Room SH177
Beth Israel Deaconess Medical Center - East Campus
330 Brookline Avenue
Boston, MA 02215
Phone: (617) 667-7284 • **Web site:** http://www.bidmc.org/pathology

BOSTON UNIVERSITY MEDICAL CENTER PROGRAM

Boston, Massachusetts

PROGRAMS OFFERED

This is a fully accredited program that offers a combined pathway to American Board of Pathology certification. *Combined Anatomic and Clinical Pathology*: This program consists of 24 months anatomic pathology and 18 months clinical pathology. The remaining 6 months of the program may be spent doing either anatomic pathology or clinical pathology, depending on the resident's particular interests. Residents alternate between AP and CP at yearly and six-month intervals.

TYPES AND NUMBERS OF APPOINTMENTS

There are 10 positions available in the program, including up to 3 first-year positions. Fellowships in cytopathology are also available. The program actively seeks to recruit minority physicians.

FACILITIES

The Boston Medical Center is a modern tertiary care 547-bed facility with a distinguished tradition in academic medicine. The Medical Center is immediately adjacent to and flanks the campus of the Boston University School of Medicine. The Department of Pathology, housed in Biosquare 3 on the campus of Boston University Medical Center, is the department of anatomic pathology for both campuses and is an integral part of the department of pathology at the School of Medicine. More than 19,000 surgical specimens, 20,000 cytology specimens and 100 autopsies are performed at the combined facilities in anatomic pathology. The Laboratory at the Boston Medical Center supports the Clinical Pathology program and performs approximately 3.5 million tests annually. A large PhD program in pathology at BUSM is associated with the program. that has an enrollment of 27 students and shares facilities and some academic programs with the residency program.

COMMUNITY

Boston is a lively cultural center with a fine arts museum, numerous art galleries, the Boston Symphony Orchestra, theater, many of its own experimental theater groups, opera and a heavy concentration of educational institutions. The New England countryside is easily accessible and there are opportunities for a wide variety of winter and summer sports.

STIPENDS AND MAINTENANCE

Residents receive not less than $52,258 per annum (2008) with stipends increasing approximately $1,800 for each additional year of training. Medical and dental insurance is available at low group rates. The hospital provides malpractice insurance.

STAFF

Department of Anatomic Pathology, Boston Medical Center (Mallory Institute of Pathology)

Daniel G Remick MD, Chairman and Professor of Pathology and Laboratory Medicine, Boston Univ Sch Med; **Michael J. O'Brien** MD, MPH Chief, Anatomic Pathology; Professor, Boston Univ Sch Med; GI and liver disease; **Sandra Cerda** MD, Assistant Professor, Boston Univ Sch Med; surgical pathology and cytopathology; **Antonio de las Morenas** MD, Chief, Cytopathology; Assistant Professor, Boston Univ Sch Med; **Ivana Delalle** MD, PhD Assistant Professor, Boston Univ Sch Med; neuropathology; **Rachel Factor** MD, Assistant Professor, Boston Univ Sch Med; surgical pathology, cytopathology; **Jianmin Gan** MD, Staff Pathologist, Surgical Pathology and Cytology; **Lija Joseph** MD, Assistant Professor; surgical pathology, cardiovascular pathology and clinical hematology; **Carl J. O'Hara** MD, Chief, Surgical Pathology and Hematopathology; Professor, Boston Univ Sch Med; **Walther Pfeifer** MD, Assistant Professor, Boston Univ Sch Med; surgical pathology, hematopathology; **Robert W. Pistey** MD, Assistant Professor, Boston Univ Sch Med; surgical pathology and cytopathology; **Carmen Sarita-Reyes** MD, Assistant Professor, Boston Univ Sch Med; surgical pathology, pediatric pathology; **Huihong Xu** MD, Assistant Professor, Boston Univ Sch Med; surgical pathology, cytopathology.

Department of Laboratory Medicine, Boston Medical Center

Martin Kroll MD, Chief, Laboratory Medicine; Professor, Boston Univ Sch Med; **Steven Bogen** MD, PhD Assistant Professor, Boston Univ Sch Med; immunology; **Nancy S Miller** MD, Assistant Professor, Boston Univ Sch Med; microbiology; **Eugene Pearlman** MD, Associate Professor, Boston Univ Sch Med; Laboratory Outreach, Chemistry; **Karen Quillen** MD Assistant Professor, Boston Univ Sch Med; blood bank.

Consultant Staff

Randolp Byers MD, Consultant, Dermatopathology; **Meera Mahalingam** MD, Consultant, Dermatopathology.

Scientific/Research Staff

Christopher D Andry PhD, Administrative Director Anatomic Pathology, Electron Microscopy, Assistant Professor, Boston Univ Sch. Med.; **Jan K. Blusztajn** PhD, Assistant Professor, Boston Univ Sch Med; **Raphael Breuer** MD, Adjunct Assistant Professor pulmonary disease; **Bohdana Burke** MD, flow cytometry and imageanalysis; **Thomas G. Christensen** PhD, Associate Professor, Boston Univ Sch Med; pulmonary disease, electron microscopy; **Jiyoun Kim** PhD, Assistant Professor Boston Univ Sch Med; Asthma; **Shinichiro Kurosawa** MD, PhD, Associate Professor, Boston Univ Sch Med; Sepsis & Inflammation; **Mary Jo Murnane** PhD, Associate Professor, Boston Univ Sch Med; genetics; **Jacqueline Sharon** PhD, Assistant Professor, Boston Univ Sch Med; molecular genetics; **Barbara Slack** PhD, Assistant Professor, Boston Univ Sch Med; **Debbie Stearns-Kurosawa** PhD, Assistant Professor, Boston Univ Sch Med; Sepsis & Inflammation; **Cyrus Vaziri** PhD, Associate Professor, Boston Univ Sch Med; DNA Repair.

APPLICATIONS

Residency candidates must be graduates of approved medical schools in the U.S. or Canada. Graduates of foreign medical schools must have an ECFMG certificate. Applicants must apply through ERAS for this program. The deadline for submission of applications is November 1 for appointments beginning the following July.

Address inquiries to:

Carl J. O'Hara, MD
Residency Training Program
670 Albany St., 3rd Floor, Biosquare 3
Boston, MA 02118
Phone: (617) 414-5314 (Mr Foley)

BRIGHAM AND WOMEN'S HOSPITAL HARVARD MEDICAL SCHOOL

Boston, Massachusetts

PROGRAMS OFFERED

The Brigham and Women's Hospital offers a fully-accredited program in anatomic and clinical pathology. Residents may elect to take a combined AP/CP program, or to limit their training to either AP or CP. Core AP training consists of 24 months and core CP 18 months. Additional training to satisfy Board certification is flexible and is planned to fit the career objectives of the individual resident. In the AP program, residents assume increasing responsibility under staff supervision in autopsy and surgical pathology. There are advanced rotations in pediatric and gynecologic/obstetrical, perinatal pathology, cytology, forensic pathology, neuropathology, dermatopathology, and hematopathology. There is also training in specialty fields such as renal, breast, liver, and gastrointestinal pathology, cardiac and pulmonary pathology, soft tissue pathology, genitourinary pathology, cytogenetics and immunocytochemistry, flow cytometry and molecular pathology. The CP training program provides core rotations in chemistry, microbiology, hematology and blood banking, and permits concentrated work in the subspecialties. There are diverse opportunities for research and a departmental research training program. Interests of the faculty include: pathophysiology and molecular cell biology of vascular, renal, pulmonary, cardiovascular, and gastrointestinal diseases; immunopathology; molecular immunology; molecular biology of cancer, biochemical cell injury, soft tissue tumors, and hematopathology. Programs conducted jointly with the basic science departments at Harvard Medical School and affiliated hospitals include many other areas of research. Residents participate in the teaching program at Harvard Medical School. Separately approved training and fellowships are offered in cytopathology, obstetrical and gynecologic pathology, hematopathology, dermatopathology, blood bank/transfusion medicine, molecular gentic pathology and neuropathology (see specialty listings).

TYPES AND NUMBERS OF APPOINTMENTS

There are 35 positions in the Anatomic and Clinical Pathology Program. Of these, 10-12 are first-year positions. Fellowships in the subspecialties and research fellowships are also available.

FACILITIES

The Brigham and Women's Hospital is a primary affiliate of Harvard Medical School and is situated in the "Longwood Medical Area." The following institutions are within a 5-minute walk: Harvard Medical School, Countway Library of Medicine, Children's Hospital, Dana Farber Cancer Institute, Beth Israel/Deaconess Medical Center, and the Joslin Research Foundation. The Brigham and Women's Hospital has 746 licensed beds, 100 bassinets, a professional staff of some 2,400 members, and a house staff of over 800 residents and fellows. Each year the AP Program examines nearly 250 autopsies, 70,000 surgical specimens and 65,000 cytological specimens. The combined clinical laboratories perform over 3,000,000 examinations per year. The following hospitals are associated with the program: Dana Farber Cancer Institute, Children's Hospital, and Faulkner Hospital.

STIPENDS AND MAINTENANCE

First-year residents, $52,064 per year; 2nd-year residents, $52,568; 3rd-year residents, $55,089; Chief Resident, PG year + $2,000 per year (figures as of July, 2008). Stipends for research fellows depend on level of training.

STAFF

Chairman and Executive Vice-Chairman

Michael A. Gimbrone, Jr. Elsie T. Friedman Professor of Pathology and Chairman; Director, Vascular Research Division; **Frederick J. Schoen** Professor and Executive Vice-Chairman; Chief, Cardiac Pathology.

Division Directors and Service Chiefs

Edmund S. Cibas Associate Professor; Director, Cytopathology Division; **Christopher P. Crum** Professor; Director, Women's and Perinatal Pathology Division; **David M. Dorfman** Associate Professor; Medical Director, Hematology Laboratory; Associate Director, Clinical Laboratories Division; hematopathology; **Christopher D.M. Fletcher** Professor; Director, Surgical Pathology Division; soft tissue and oncologic pathology; **Rebecca D. Folkerth** Associate Professor; Director, Neuropathology Division; **John J. Godleski** Associate Professor; Chief, Pulmonary Pathology; **Petr Jarolim** Associate Professor; Medical Director, Chemistry Laboratory; **Richard M. Kaufman** Assistant Professor; Medical Director, Transfusion Medicine; **Jeffrey F. Krane** Assistant Professor; Chief, Head and Neck Pathology; surgical pathology and cytology; **Frank C. Kuo** Assistant Professor; Director, Pathology Information Technology Division; hematopathology; **Susan C. Lester** Assistant Professor; Chief, Breast Pathology; surgical and breast pathology; **Janina A. Longtine** Associate Professor; Chief, Molecular Diagnostics; hematopathology; **Cynthia C. Morton** Professor of Pathology and William Lambert Richardson Professor of Obstetrics, Gynecology, and Reproductive

Biology; Director, Cytogenetics Division; **George F. Murphy** Professor; Chief, Dermatopathology Division; **George L. Mutter** Associate Professor; Medical Director, Reproductive Endocrinology Laboratory; women's and perinatal pathology; **Vania Nose** Associate Professor; Associate Director, Surgical Pathology Division; endocrine pathology; **Robert D. Odze** Associate Professor; Chief, Gastrointestinal Pathology; **Andrew B. Onderdonk** Professor; Medical Director, Microbiology Laboratory; **Geraldine S. Pinkus** Professor; Chief, Hematopathology; **Helmut G. Rennke** Professor; Chief, Renal Pathology; **David B. Sacks** Associate Professor; Director, Clinical Pathology Training Program; **Arlene H. Sharpe** Professor; Director, Immunology Research Division; virology, molecular biology; **Leslie E. Silberstein** Professor; Director, Joint Program in Transfusion Medicine; **Milenko J. Tanasijevic** Associate Professor; Director, Clinical Laboratory Division; **Gayle L. Winters** Associate Professor; Director, Residency Training Program; Director, Autopsy Division; cardiac pathology.

Faculty

Jon C. Aster Professor; hematopathology; **Aleksandar M. Babic** Instructor; transfusion medicine; **Andrew Bellizzi** Instructor; gastrointestinal pathology; **Frederick R. Bieber** Associate Professor; teratology, embryology and genetics; **Vanesa Bijol** Instructor; renal pathology; **Stephen C. Blacklow** Associate Professor; structural biology; **Manfred Brigl** Instructor; Associate Medical Director, Microbiology Laboratory; **Jane E. Brock** Instructor; breast pathology; **Lynn Bry** Assistant Professor; Associate Medical Director, Microbiology Laboratory; **Ruben D. Carrasco** Assistant Professor, hematopathology; **Li Chai** Instructor; Associate Director, Adult Transfusion Medicine; **Lucian R. Chirieac** Assistant Professor; surgical and oncologic pulmonary pathology; **Joseph M. Corson** Professor Emeritus; oncologic pathology, rheumatic diseases; **Paola Dal Cin** Associate Professor; cytogenetics; **Umberto De Girolami** Professor; neuropathology; **Deborah A. R. Dillon** Assistant Professor; breast pathology; **Ronny I. Drapkin** Assistant Professor; oncologic pathology research; **Mel B. Feany** Associate Professor; neuropathology and neurogenetics; **Jonathan A. Fletcher** Associate Professor; tumor cytogenetics; **Christopher A. French** Assistant Professor; cytopathology; **Eleonora G. Galvanek** Assistant Professor; renal pathology, cytopathology; **Anne B. Giersch** Assistant Professor; cytogenetics; **Scott R. Granter** Associate Professor; dermatopathology; **Joel M. Henderson** Instructor; renal pathology; **Michelle S. Hirsch** Assistant Professor; women's and perinatal pathology; genitourinary pathology; **Jason L. Hornick** Associate Professor; surgical pathology, gastrointestinal pathology and hematopathology; **Mei-Yu Hsu** Assistant Professor; dermatopathology; **Tan A. Ince** Assistant Professor; women's and perinatal pathology; **David W. Kindelberger** Instructor; Assistant Director, Residency Training Program; cytopathology, women's and perinatal pathology; **Lester Kobzik** Professor; pulmonary pathology; **Jeffery L. Kutok** Associate Professor; hematopathology and molecular diagnostics; **Natalia T. Leach** Instructor; cytogenetics; **Charles Lee** Associate Professor; cytogenetics; **Kenneth R. Lee** Associate Professor; cytopathology; **Franz von Lichtenberg** Professor Emeritus, Pathology; host-parasitic relationships, schistosomiasis; **Andrew H. Lichtman** Associate Professor; immunological research; **Azra H. Ligon** Assistant Professor; cytogenetics; **Keith L. Ligon** Assistant Professor; neuropathology; **Neal I. Lindeman** Assistant Professsor; Assistant Director, Residency Training Program; molecular diagnostics, clinical chemistry; **Massimo Loda** Professor; urologic and surgical pathology; oncologic pathology research; **Chance John Luckey** Assistant Professor; transfusion medicine, research; **F. William Luscinskas** Associate Professor; vascular research; **Tanya Mayadas-Norton** Associate Professor; vascular research; **Stacy E. F. Melanson** Assistant Professsor; Associate Medical Director, Chemistry Laboratory; **Danny A. Milner** Assistant Professor; Assistant Medical Director, Microbiology Laboratory; **David S. Milstone** Assistant Professor; vascular research; **Richard N. Mitchell** Associate Professor; cardiac pathology, immunopathology; **Alessandra F. Nascimento** Assistant Professor; surgical pathology and hematopathology; **Marisa R. Nucci** Associate Professor; gynecologic and surgical pathology; **Shuji Ogino** Associate Professor; molecular diagnostics; **Robert F. Padera** Assistant Professor; cardiac, pulmonary and autopsy pathology; **Xiaohua Qian** Instructor; cytopathology, surgical pathology; **Bradley J. Quade** Associate Professor; women's and perinatal pathology; **Heidi L. Rehm** Assistant Professor; molecular genetics; **Andrea Richardson** Assistant Professor; breast pathology; **Scott J. Rodig** Assistant Professor; hematopathology; **Sandro Santagata** Instructor; neuropathology; **William C. Schoene** Associate Professor; neuropathology; **Lynette M. Sholl** Instructor; molecular diagnostics, pulmonary pathology and surgical pathology; **Sabina Signoretti** Associate Professor; translational cancer research; **Sara O. Vargas** Associate Professor; pulmonary pathology; **Elsa F. Velazquez** Assistant Professor; dermatopathology; **Jo-Anne Vergilio** Assistant Professor; hematopathology and hematology; **William R. Welch** Associate Professor; gynecologic and surgical pathology; **Stanislawa Weremowicz** Assistant Professor; cytogenetics; **Tad J. Wieczorek** Instructor; cytopathology; **Jacqueline M-L William** Instructor; hematopathology; **Sheng Xiao** Assistant Professor; solid tumor cytogenetics.

Consultants

Matthew P. Anderson neuropathology; **Theonia K. Boyd** pediatric pathology; **Gilbert L. Brodsky** surgical pathology; **Carlo Brugnara** clinical pathology; **James Connolly** breast pathology; **Ivana Delalle** neuropathology; **Patricia Devine** clinical pathology; **Robert L. Ehrmann** cytology; **Mark D. Fleming** hematopathology; Chief of Pathology, Children's Hospital, Boston; **Matthew P. Frosch** neuropathology; **Hannah C. Kinney** neuropathology; **Hart Lidov** neuropathology; **Gifford Lum** clinical pathology, West Roxbury VA Med Ctr.; **Kilmer S. McCully** Director, Boston Area Clin Labs, VA Med Ctr; **Imad A. Nasser** cytopathology; **Rolf Pfannl** neuropathology; **Drucilla Roberts** pediatric pathology; **Andrew Rosenberg** bone pathology; **Lynda Rushing** cytopathology, Mt. Auburn Hospital;

Stuart Schnitt breast pathology; **Gerald Shklar** oral pathology, Harvard School of Dental Medicine; **Juliana Szakacs** surgical pathology, Chief of Pathology, Harvard Pilgrim Health Center; **Helen Wang** cytopathology, Beth Israel Deaconess Medical Center; **Sook-Bin Woo** oral pathology.

APPLICATIONS

Only applications received via ERAS by November 1 will be considered. Residency positions begin July 1 of the following year. Medical school seniors receive appointments through the National Resident Matching Program. An interview is mandatory.

Address inquiries to:

Gayle L. Winters, MD
Pathology Residency Program Director
Brigham and Women's Hospital
75 Francis Street
Boston, MA 02115
Phone: (617) 732-8613

MASSACHUSETTS GENERAL HOSPITAL HARVARD MEDICAL SCHOOL

Boston, Massachusetts

PROGRAMS OFFERED

The Pathology Department offers resident training programs toward American Board of Pathology certification in anatomic pathology (AP), anatomic and clinical pathology (AP-CP), clinical pathology (CP), dermatopathology (DP), neuropathology (NP), cytopathology, hematopathology and transfusion medicine. AP residents dissect and interpret surgical pathology specimens, including frozen sections, and perform autopsies under the supervision of the attending pathologists. In addition, the residents present pathologic findings to other departments and services at conferences. AP residents follow a two-year core that includes rotations in autopsy, bone and soft tissue pathology, breast pathology, cardiac pathology, cytopathology, dermatopathology, ear, nose and throat pathology, forensic pathology, gastrointestinal pathology, genitourinary pathology, gynecologic pathology, hematopathology, obstetric and perinatal pathology, pulmonary pathology, and renal pathology. Basic training in electron microscopy, cytogenetics, and molecular biology is also included. The residents attend daily conferences in general surgical and subspecialty pathology, twice weekly Autopsy conferences, weekly Grand Rounds, and the weekly New England Journal of Medicine Case Records of the Massachusetts General Hospital Conference. CP residents rotate through the Laboratories in microbiology (bacteriology, virology, parasitology), clinical chemistry (general chemistry, toxicology, endocrinology), coagulation, hematology, hematopathology, clinical immunology, and the Blood Transfusion Service (Blood Bank, Donor Center, therapeutic apheresis, tissue typing). Residents participate in daily lectures by the professional staff of the various laboratories. Residents have clinical responsibility for an active consult service and signout of narrative interpretation for certain test panels. Residents may take advanced rotations in CP to acquire skills necessary to direct a specific clinical laboratory. At the Massachusetts General Hospital, all attending pathologists have Harvard Medical School appointments. All residents are appointed as Clinical Fellows in Pathology at Harvard Medical School, and are encouraged to participate in the teaching of pathology to medical students.

TYPES AND NUMBERS OF APPOINTMENTS

There are 35 in AP, AP-CP and CP. Fellowship positions include neuropathology (2), dermatopathology (2), cytopathology (3), hematopathology (2), and one transfusion medicine fellowship. The number of positions for first-year residents varies between eight and ten. Research and clinical fellowships in special areas of pathology are also offered on a selective basis subject to available funding. The department has an NIH Research Training Grant that supports 5 fellows per year.

FACILITIES

The Massachusetts General Hospital, founded in 1811, is Harvard Medical School's original teaching hospital. Its bed capacity is 907. During 2008, the Pathology Department examined approximately 64,957 surgical pathology specimens, 63,000 cytopathology specimens (14,800 nongynecologic), 4,000 fine needle aspirations, and 410 autopsies were performed. In addition, the staff of the Department receives over 9,000 unusual surgical pathology cases each year in consultation from hospitals throughout the world. The MGH also performs more than 10,000,000 laboratory studies per year, including many highly esoteric tests requiring substantial expertise for interpretation. Library facilities include the Department's Mallory Library, the Hospital's Treadwell Library and Harvard Medical School's Countway Library, which is among the world's largest medical reference libraries. The Department has research facilities at the MGH main campus and at MGH East in Charlestown. MGH East is a 400,000-square-foot research complex, which includes the Cancer and Neuroscience Centers.

COMMUNITY

The hospital is situated in the center of Boston. The numerous communities of the greater Boston area have a total population of over two million, and the area offers a wide variety of cultural and educational opportunities. The geographic location is favorable from a recreational viewpoint, with proximity to forests, lakes, mountains, and beaches.

STIPENDS AND MAINTENANCE

As of July 2008, first-year residents were paid $52,064, second-year residents $52568, third-year residents $55,089, fourth-year residents $57,623, fifth-year residents $60,617, sixth-year residents $66,000 and chief residents $2,500 over residency level. Uniforms, laundry, malpractice insurance, travel and book allowances and rent deposit guarantee are provided. Health insurance, long-term disability and life insurance are provided at a reasonable cost. Parking is provided at a reduced rate. Housing facilities are not provided.

STAFF

David N. Louis MD, Chief; **W. Stephen Black-Schaffer** MD, Associate Chief, Pathology Education; **Kent Lewandrowski** MD, Associate Chief, Clinical Services.

Autopsy Pathology Service

Eugene Mark MD Director; **Atul Bhan** MD; **John Grabbe** MD; **E. Tessa Hedley-Whyte** MD; **Katharine Kosinski** MD; **Richard Kradin** MD; **Esther Oliva** MD; **Eva Patalas** MD; **Drucilla Roberts** MD; **Rex Neal Smith** MD, PhD; **James Stone** MD; **Rosemary Tambouret** MD.

Blood Transfusion Service

Christopher Stowell MD, PhD Director; **Walter Dzik** MD Co-director; **Robert Makar** MD, PhD.

Clinical Immunology Laboratory

Mandakolathur Murali MD Director; **Anand Dighe** MD, PhD.

Core Laboratory

Anand Dighe MD, PhD Director; **James Flood** PhD; **Kent Lewandrowski** MD; **Aliyah Rahemtullah**; **Patrick Sluss** PhD; **Elizabeth Van Cott** MD.

Cytopathology Service

David Wilbur MD Director; **Ronald Balassanian** MD; **W. Stephen Black-Schaffer** MD; **Elena Brachtel** MD; **Vikram Deshpande** MD; **John Eichhorn** MD; **William Faquin** MD; **John Grabbe** MD; **Frederick Koerner** MD; **Joseph Misdraji** MD; **Rebecca Osgood** MD; **Martha Pitman** MD; **Jian Shen** MD; **Rosemary Tambouret** MD; **Elizabeth Zulinska** MD.

Flow Cytometry Laboratory

Frederic Preffer PhD Director.

Histocompatibility Laboratory

Susan Saidman PhD Director; **Ronald Balassanian** MD.

Immunopathology Laboratory

Mandakolathur Murali MD Director; **Anand Dighe** MD, PhD.

Informatics

John Gilbertson MD, PhD Director; **Yukako Yagi** PhD.

Microbiology Laboratory

Mary Jane Ferraro PhD, MPH Director; **John Branda** MD; **Eric Rosenberg** MD; **Eric Rosenberg**.

Molecular Pathology Unit

Jae Keith Joung MD, PhD Director; **Bradley Bernstein** MD, PhD; **Dora Dias-Santagata** PhD; **Matthew Frosch** MD, PhD; **Kevin Haigis** PhD; **A. John Iafrate** MD, PhD; **David Louis** MD; **Gayatry Mohapatra** PhD; **Catherine Nutt** PhD; **Sandra Orsulic** MD; **Miguel Rivera**; **Dennis Sgroi** MD.

Pathology Residency Program

W. Stephen Black-Schaffer MD, Director; **Matthew P. Frosch** MD, PhD, Associate Director, Resident Research; **Robert Hasserjian** MD, Associate Director, Resident Recruitment; **Frederick C. Koerner** MD, Associate Director, Resident Scheduling; **Esther Oliva** MD, Associate Director, Anatomic Pathology.

Surgical Pathology - Perinatal Pathology

Drucilla Roberts MD Director; **Esther Oliva** MD; **Rosemary Tambouret** MD.

Surgical Pathology - Bone and Soft Tissue Pathology

Andrew Rosenberg MD Director; **Vikram Deshpande** MD; **G. Petur Nielsen** MD.

Surgical Pathology - Breast Pathology

Dennis Sgroi MD Director; **Elena Brachtel** MD; **John Eichhorn** MD; **Frederick Koerner** MD; **Melinda Lerwill** MD.

Surgical Pathology - Cardiovascular Pathology

James Stone MD, PhD Director; **Stuart Houser** MD; **Richard Kradin** MD; **Eugene Mark** MD; **Rex Neal Smith** MD, PhD.

Surgical Pathology - Dermatopathology

Lyn M. Duncan MD Director; **Mai Hoang**; **Martin Mihm Jr.** MD; **Jian Shen** MD.

Surgical Pathology - Ear, Nose and Throat Pathology

Ben Pilch MD Director; **William Faquin** MD; **Peter Sadow**; **Chin-Lee Wu** MD, PhD.

Surgical Pathology - Gastrointestinal Pathology

Gregory Lauwers MD Director; **Kamran Badizadegan** MD; **Vikram Deshpande** MD; **Fiona Graeme-Cook** MB FRCPI; **Robert Hasserjian** MD; **Mari Mino-Kenudson** MD; **Joseph Misdraji** MD; **Martha Pitman** MD; **Lawrence Zukerberg** MD.

Surgical Pathology - Genitourinary Pathology

Robert Young MD Director; **G. Petur Nielsen** MD; **Esther Oliva** MD; **Ben Pilch** MD; **Chin-Lee Wu** MD, PhD.

Surgical Pathology - Gynecologic Pathology

W. Stephen Black-Schaffer MD; **John Eichhorn** MD; **Melinda Lerwill** MD; **Esther Oliva** MD; **Drucilla Roberts** MD; **Rosemary Tambouret** MD; **David Wilbur** MD; **Robert Young** MD Director.

Surgical Pathology - Hematopathology

Nancy Lee Harris MD Director; **Judith Ferry** MD; **Robert Hasserjian** MD; **Frederic Preffer** PhD; **Lawrence Zukerberg** MD.

Surgical Pathology - Neuropathology

Matthew Frosch MD, PhD Director; **E. Tessa Hedley-Whyte** MD; **David Louis** MD; **Anat Stemmer-Rachamimov** MD.

Surgical Pathology - Pulmonary Pathology

Eugene Mark MD Director; **Richard Kradin** MD; **Rex Neal Smith** MD, PhD.

Surgical Pathology - Renal Pathology

Robert Colvin Director; **Eveline Schneeberger** MD; **Rex Neal Smith** MD, PhD.

Surgical Pathology Service

Gregory Lauwers MD Co-director.

APPLICATIONS

Applications should be completed by December 1 for appointment the following July and must be submitted through the Electronic Residency Application System (ERAS). All applications must include a personal statement, a medical school transcript, and three letters of recommendation. Graduates of accredited medical and osteopathic schools in the United States and Canada must submit copies of the score on part I of the USMLE (or equivalent). Graduates of international medical schools must submit copies of scores on parts 1 and 2 of the USMLE or NBME and a valid ECFMG certificate. An interview is mandatory and is by invitation only.

Address inquiries to:
Robert P. Hasserjian, MD
Associate Director for Recruitment, Residency Training Program
Pathology Service, Warren Building, Room 219
Massachusetts General Hospital
55 Fruit Street
Boston, MA 02114-2696
Phone: (617) 724-6355 • **E-mail:** mghpath@partners.org
Web site: http://path.mgh.harvard.edu/residency/resid.html

TUFTS MEDICAL CENTER

Boston, Massachusetts

PROGRAMS OFFERED

This comprehensive program offers fully accredited training in an integrated anatomic pathology/clinical pathology program 4 years and in anatomic pathology only 3 years, with the opportunity to work at Tufts Medical Center the principal clinical affiliate of Tufts University School of Medicine. The training program is flexible so that individual programs may be designed for those with interests either in community hospital practice or academic careers, with opportunities for subspecialization and research. The anatomic pathology component of the program provides training in surgical and autopsy pathology, diagnostic exfoliative cytology, fine needle aspiration biopsy, neuropathology and dermatopathology. Subspecialty training is available in a wide range of fields, including pediatric pathology, hematopathology, renal, obstetrical/gynecological, gastrointestinal, ophthalmologic, forensic and comparative pathology. Training in molecular biology and electron microscopy is available, and a wide range of research programs may be conducted jointly with members of the department. In addition to departmental surgical and autopsy conferences, trainees participate in weekly or biweekly clinical subspecialty conferences. A well-structured clinical pathology program provides training in blood banking, clinical chemistry, hematology, immunology and microbiology. Subspecialty electives are available in all fields of pathology. Residents have a five to six month rotation at Lahey Clinic, where they participate in the evaluation of diverse surgical, cytologic and autopsy material with an emphasis on areas of tumor and breast pathology, hematopathology, and flow cytometry. Residents also participate in the teaching of medical students and hold appointments at Tufts University School of Medicine.

TYPES AND NUMBERS OF APPOINTMENTS

Thirteen residency training positions are available in combined anatomic pathology/clinical pathology and in anatomic pathology. Three first-year positions are available per year.

FACILITIES

The Tufts Medical Center, the principal teaching hospital of Tufts University School of Medicine, is a specialized diagnostic and referral center which provides full service inpatient and outpatient care. Conveniently located in the heart of downtown Boston, the Center is within walking distance of the Boston Common, the waterfront district and the Faneuil Hall Marketplace. The Tufts Medical Center subway stop on the Orange Line is located directly across from the hospital's main entrance. The Floating Hospital for Infants and Children is the pediatric hospital of the Center. The Center has approximately 442 adult medical/surgical, pediatric and obstetric beds together with extensive outpatient facilities. The Medical Center has attracted a group of nearly 400 full-time physicians who are committed to providing an integrated, interdisciplinary approach to patient management. The proximity to other area hospitals and universities facilitates trainee attendance at numerous interhospital conferences, lectures and symposia. The Department of Pathology at the Center processes approximately 19,000 surgical specimens, 15,000 cytologic samples and 85 autopsies per year. Total laboratory procedures exceed 2,300,000.

Lahey Clinic in Burlington, Massachusetts is a major teaching hospital of Tufts University School of Medicine with over 317 beds and active outpatient facilities. The Pathology Department processes over 28,993 surgical specimens, 37,000 cytology specimens and 60 autopsies. It serves a broad population of patients attracting a diverse case mix.

STIPENDS AND MAINTENANCE

The range of pathology trainee stipends is $47,267 to $54,712 per annum. A variety of health insurance plans are available in addition to professional liability insurance, three weeks paid vacation, and uniform/laundry service.

STAFF

Tufts Medical Center/Tufts University School of Medicine

Stephen P. Naber MD, PhD Pathologist-in-Chief, Associate Chair, TUSM Pathology; **Henry H. Wortis** MD Professor; Chairman, TUSM Pathology, Director, Immunology Graduate Training Program; immunogenetics; **Barbarajean Magnani** PhD, MD; Chief, Clinical Laboratory Services; Chemistry and Toxicology; **Joseph Alroy** DVM Associate Professor; metabolic disease; **Ina D. Bhan** MD Associate Clinical Professor; pediatric pathology; **Peter H. Brodeur** PhD Assistant Professor; immunoglobulin gene organization, TUSM pathology; **Raymond L Comenzo** MD, Director, Blood Bank and Stem Cell Processing Laboratory; **Maria L. Garcia-Moliner** MD, Associate Clinical Professor; Director, Residency Training Program;pulmonary pathology; **Brigitte T. Huber** PhD Associate Professor; superantigen characterization and T cell activation, TUSM pathology; **Thereza Imanishi-Kari** PhD TUSM pathology; **Michael Kahn** DDS; Oral Pathology; **Paul Kwan** PhD Research Assistant Professor; effects of hormones on target tissues, TUSM pathology; **Nora Laver** MD Assistant Professor; Director, Cytology Laboratory;cytology, surgical pathology, ophthalmologic pathology; **Miercio Pereira** MD Professor, TUSM pathology; **Rolf Pfannl** MD, Associate Clinical Professor, Neuropathology, TUSM, Director, Neuropathology and Autopsy Service; **Monika Pilichowska** MD PhD Associate Clinical Professor, TUSM; Assistant Director, Hematology; **Arthur R. Rabson** MD Professor; Director, HLA Laboratories; **David E. Ricklan** MD, PhD, Director, Anatomic Pathology; surgical pathology, cytology; **Naomi**

Rosenberg PhD Professor; development of RNA tumor virus, TUSM pathology; **Ananda Roy** PhD Associate Professor, TUSM pathology; **Igor B. Rozenvald** MD;Associate Clinical Professor; Director, Clinical Hematology/Microscopy Laboratory; **Homa Safaii** MD Associate Clinical Professor; OB/GYN pathology; **Robert N. Salomon** MD Assistant Clinical Professor; autopsy pathology, molecular and cardiac pathology; **Erik Selsing** PhD Associate Professor; B cell differentiation, TUSM pathology; **Miguel J. Stadecker** MD, PhD Professor; dermatopathology, immunology; **Natalie Sutkowski** Assistant Research Professor; TUSM pathology; **David A. Thorley-Lawson** PhD Associate Professor; Epstein-Barr virus, transformation and latency, TUSM pathology; **Arthur S. Tischler** MD Professor; neuroendocrine tumors; **Angelo A. Ucci** MD, PhD Associate Professor; renal pathology, uropathology, and electron microscopy; **Barbara J. Weinstein** MD, Assistant Clinical Professor; surgical pathology and cytology.

Lahey Clinic

Mark L Silverman MD, Chairman; Ear, Nose, Throat; Gastrointestinal; Urological Disorders; **Christine B Thomas** MD, Vice Chair, Program Director; Brain Tumors; **Namrata Anand** MD, Cytopathology; Hematopathology; Liver Pathology; **Eric J Burks** MD; Hematopathology, Soft Tissue Pathology; **K. Greg Chang** MD, Dermatopathology; **John M Dugan** MD, Cytopathology; **Lisa Gallagher** MD, Surgical Pathology; **Atoussa Goldar-Najafi** MD, Gastrointestinal; Liver Pathology; Surgical Pathology; **Urmila Khettry** MD, Hepatobiliary/Pancreatic and Liver Transplantation Pathology; Surgical Pathology; **Bruce S Tronic** MD, Hematopathology.

APPLICATIONS

Candidates must be graduates of approved medical schools in the United States or Canada or graduates of foreign schools with an ECFMG certificate based on passing USMLE steps I and II. Applicants must be eligible for a Massachusetts limited or full license under the provisions of the Massachusetts Board of Registration in Medicine. CSA exam required. Three (3) satisfactory letters of reference are required. Applications should be completed by November 15 for appointments beginning July 1 of the following year. An interview is mandatory. Applicants must apply through ERAS.

Address inquiries to:

Raymond P. Anderson, BA
Residency Program Coordinator
Tufts Medical Center
750 Washington Street
Boston, MA 02111
Phone: (617) 636-1112 • **Fax:** (617) 636-8302 • **E-mail:** randerson@tuftsmedicalcenter.org
Web site: http://www.nemcpath.org

BERKSHIRE MEDICAL CENTER
Pittsfield, Massachusetts

PROGRAMS OFFERED

ACGME accredited, four year residency training program is available leading to American Board of Pathology qualification in anatomic and clinical pathology. Training in anatomic pathology includes autopsy pathology, surgical pathology, dermatopathology, immunohistochemistry, forensics, cytology, analytical cytometry, molecular pathology, and cytogenetics. Training in clinical pathology includes hematology, coagulation, transfusion medicine/blood banking, microbiology, clinical chemistry, toxicology, clinical immunology, medical microscopy, informatics, administration and management. Each rotation is under the guidance of a specialized pathologist. The role of the pathologist as a clinical consultant is emphasized. There is an active molecular pathology laboratory and molecular diagnosis is stressed throughout. There are opportunities for scholarly, investigative activities, with some sources of funding available. The pathologists are medical examiners so the program offers a solid experience in forensic pathology. There are daily conferences in all disciplines in which the residents participate either as presenters or discussers. There are accredited Medical Technology and Cytotechnology training programs in the department, providing teaching and learning opportunities for residents.

TYPES AND NUMBERS OF APPOINTMENTS

There are 8 residency positions. Residents from other programs and medical students have elective rotations in the department. Other house staff includes 3 dental, 38 internal medicine, 13 surgical, and 4 psychiatry residents.

FACILITIES

Berkshire Medical Center is a major affiliate of the University of Massachusetts Medical School and the University of New England College of Osteopathic Medicine. The annual workload consists of over 3.4 million tests, 100 autopsies, 19,000 surgical specimens and over 21,000 cytology accessions, including about 600 aspiration cytologies. The laboratory occupies new facilities, is highly automated, including robotics, and has state-of-the art information systems. The library contains 50 journals and about 2,000 books. Other resources include the medical library and internet services. All residents have their own office, microscope, and laptop computer with connections to the hospital information systems and internet.

COMMUNITY

Pittsfield is located in the Berkshires, a culturally rich year-round vacation area. There are numerous music, theater and dance venues including the Tanglewood Music Festival of the Boston Symphony Orchestra. Summer and winter sports, skiing, tennis, golf, sailing, hiking, etc. are readily available. There are excellent schools and reasonable cost of living. Pittsfield is about 2 1/2 hours drive from Boston, 3 hours from New York City and 4 1/2 hours from Montreal.

STIPENDS AND MAINTENANCE

Salaries for 2009-2010 residents are: first year $49,950; second year $51,893; third year $54,027; fourth year $56,179 (this pay scale is subject to change). There is a generous benefits package, including discretionary funds for books, meetings and professional dues. Residents are provided uniforms and laundry services.

STAFF

Rebecca L. Johnson MD (Southern Illinois Univ 1978) Chair and Medical Director, Pathology and Clinical Laboratories; anatomic and clinical pathology. Professor, Pathology, Univ Massachusetts Med Sch; Certified AP/CP, Immunopathology and hematopathology; Research: hematopathology and immunopathology; **Charles L Abbott** MD (Univ of Sheffield, England 1997). Director Hematopathology, Flow Cytometry, Molecular Pathology, and Microbiology. Asst. Prof. Univ Mass Med Sch, Medical Examiner Berkshire County, Certified AP/CP, Hematology; **Deborah August** MD (Univ Massachusetts Med Sch 1988) Consultant, Forensic Pathology; Medical Examiner, Berkshire County; Certified AP/CP; **Daniel J. Carter** MD (Med Col Wisconsin 1984) Director, Anatomic Pathology; Asst Prof Pathology, Univ Mass Med Sch; Medical Examiner, Berkshire County; Certified AP/CP, dermatopathology and cytopathology; Research: immunohistochemistry; **Teri L. Cooper** MD (Univ Louisville Sch Med 1981) Director, Cytopathology; Asst Prof Univ Mass Med Sch; Certified AP/CP and cytology; Research: FNA of head and neck; **Gerard Demers** MT (ASCP) SBB, Instructor Blood Bank / Transfusion Medicine; **Michael R DiSiena** DO (New York Col of Osteopathic Medicine, 1994), Asst Prof of Surgery and Pathology Univ Mass Med Sch. Certified AP and General Surgery; **Ethan A. Flynn** MD (Louisiana State Univ 1995) Director Autopsy Pathology, Clinical Chemistry. Medical Examiner Berkshire County, Asst. Prof. Univ Mass Med Sch. Certified AP/CP; **Benjamin Glick** MD (Univ Southern California 1965) Consultant, Forensic Pathology; Medical Examiner, Berkshire County; Certified AP/CP; **Richard Intres** PhD (Wesleyan Univ 1986). molecular biology, Asst Prof Molecular Genetics and Microbiology, Univ Mass Med Sch; Research: molecular biology of visual cycle and molecular diagnostics; **Jessica D. Krochmal** MD (Univ Iowa 2002) Director

Blood Bank/Transfusion Med; Asst Prof Univ Mass Med Sch, Certified AP/CP, Cytopathology; **Judith R Shaffer** BS, SCT (ASCP) (Univ Vermont 1990); Instructor cytopathology; **Michael Sikirica** MD (SUNY Buffalo 1989) Consultant; Certified AP/CP, neuropathology and forensic pathology; **Thomas D. Smith** MD (Cornell Univ 1972) Consultant; Neuropathology; Prof Pathology and Neurology, Univ Mass Med Sch; Certified AP, Neuropathology; Research: neurodegenerative diseases; **Lawrence Spatz** PhD (Columbia Univ 1966). Biochemistry; Asst Prof Pharmacology, Univ Mass Med Sch; Diplomate clinical chemistry; Research: biological membranes; **Jon M. Valigorsky** MD (Univ Maryland 1968) hematology and transfusion medicine; Assoc Prof Pathology, Univ Mass Med Sch. Certified AP/CP, blood banking/transfusion medicine and hematopathology; Research: iron metabolism, sideroblastic anemias.

APPLICATIONS

Applicants must be graduates of approved medical schools in the United States or Canada. Graduates of foreign medical schools are required to have a valid ECFMG certificate. Applications are received only through ERAS. Interviews are required. Only J-1 visas are offered.

Address inquiries to:

Debby Rathbun
Pathology Residency Program Coordinator
Berkshire Health Systems
725 North Street
Pittsfield, MA 01201
Phone: (413) 447-2133
Web site: http://www.berkshirehealthsystems.com.

Berkshire Medical Center, Pittsfield, Massachusetts.

BAYSTATE MEDICAL CENTER
TUFTS UNIVERSITY SCHOOL OF MEDICINE
Springfield, Massachusetts

PROGRAMS OFFERED

The residency program in anatomic and clinical pathology at Baystate Medical Center (BMC) is designed to provide an organized educational experience for physicians seeking to practice pathology. The program offers residents a broad experience, with graduated responsibilities, in anatomic and clinical pathology (AP/CP) including the latest applications of molecular biology to the diagnosis of human disease. The curriculum emphasizes the consultative role of the pathologist in patient care. Twenty full-time faculty provide subspecialty expertise in patient care and house staff education. House staff are actively involved in intradepartmental and interdepartmental conferences. Teaching conferences form a core curriculum in many subspecialty areas, including quality improvement and laboratory management, to enable graduates to practice either in a community hospital or in an academic medical center. The AP/CP-4 program includes an integrated 18 months of AP combined with 18 months of CP. Training in AP includes autopsy and surgical pathology, cytology/image-analysis, special techniques in surgical pathology, and forensic pathology. Elective subspecialty training is available in a variety of areas, including pediatric pathology, neuropathology, hematopathology/flow cytometry, renal, gynecological, gastrointestinal/hepatic pathology, dermatopathology and molecular pathology & genetics. Training in CP includes all traditional areas, with an emphasis on clinical consultation and clinical rounds in the areas of transfusion medicine, hematology and microbiology. Since faculty and facilities are all housed in one large facility within one institution, an integrated program in AP/CP allows residents to be exposed to the multiple aspects of pathology almost concurrently, and they maintain and apply the knowledge and skills acquired in each special area throughout their training. The 36-month core curriculum is followed by the 4th year, in which rotations in AP/CP or research are offered. The remaining time is devoted to electives in AP and/or CP and any special requirements. ACGME-approved fellowships are also available in transfusion medicine and cytopathology. Residents are eligible to participate in the BMC-University of Massachusetts Amherst (UMass) collaborative program in biomedical research comprised of three components: (1) collaborative research projects, (2) molecular medicine course given in the spring, and (3) biomedical scholars program which can lead to graduate degrees at the doctorate and masters levels. Clinical and transitional research within the department is also strongly encouraged throughout the training. Faculty are dedicated not only to house staff training but also to the career development of individual residents.

REQUIREMENTS

-USMLE scores 80th percentile or above
-Graduation from medical school within the past 5 years
-Applications only accepted through ERAS

TYPES AND NUMBERS OF APPOINTMENTS

The residency program is fully accredited and approved for 16 positions in AP/CP. Applications will be considered for the combined AP/CP program and for training exclusively in AP or CP under special circumstances. The program welcomes graduates directly from medical school as well as residents in later postgraduate years who wish to transfer from other disciplines.

FACILITIES

Baystate Medical Center is the premier tertiary care facility in Western Massachusetts and the Western Campus of Tufts University School of Medicine. All staff academic appointments are at Tufts University School of Medicine. The medical center has approximately 600 beds and is the third largest acute care hospital in New England. The Department of Pathology examines approximately 45,000 surgical specimens, 74,000 cytopathologic specimens and performs 100 autopsies per year. In Clinical Pathology, over 5 million lab tests are performed. Facilities include a large open laboratory with modern instrumentation applying traditional and state-of-the-art techniques in all aspects of clinical pathology. State-of-the-art media equipment, computers, and printers are available in the department. Internet access is widely available. There is a conference room with a 14-headed microscope and slide projection facilities for informal case presentations and discussion. The most frequently used pathology journals, texts and teaching sets are available in the departmental Ralph N. Otto Library as well as in the main medical center library located on campus.

COMMUNITY

Baystate Medical Center is located in beautiful Western Massachusetts within a short drive of many recreational, cultural, and historical sites including Tanglewood, Jacob's Pillow, Old Sturbridge Village, Old Deerfield, the Connecticut shore, Vermont and Berkshire ski areas, and at least a dozen colleges and universities including Smith, Mount Holyoke, Amherst, and UMass at Amherst.

STIPENDS AND MAINTENANCE

Stipends (2009/2010) are: 1st year $51,000, 2nd year $53,000, 3rd year $56,000, 4th year $58,500. The medical center benefit package consists of medical, dental, life, long-term disability insurance, and professional liability insurance, a pension plan, and worker's compensation. Vacation is four weeks per year.

STAFF

Richard Friedberg MD, PhD Professor and Chairman; transfusion medicine; **Carol Rauch** MD, PhD Assistant Professor and Chief, Division Clinical Pathology; microbiology; **David L. Gang** MD Professor and Chief, Division Anatomic Pathology; pediatric/gastrointestinal/hepatic pathology; **James Mueller** MD Associate Professor and Chief, Division Molecular Pathology and Genetics; molecular diagnostics; **Rukmini Modem** MD Assistant Professor; Medical Director, Mary Lane Hospital; Surgical Pathologist and Cytopathologist, Baystate Health System; **Chester Andrzejewski Jr.** PhD, MD Assistant Professor, Medical Director, BloodBank and Transfusion Medicine Service; transfusion medicine; **Q. Jackie Cao** MD, PhD Assistant Professor; gynecology and cytopathology; **Giovanna M. Crisi** MD, PhD Assistant Professor; breast, renal and transplant; **Wayne Duke** MD Associate Director, Dermatopathology; dermatopathology; **Roxanne Florence** MD Assistant Professor and Associate Director, Cytopathology; cytopathology; **Katya Ford** MD Assistant Professor; gastrointestinal, liver and cytopathology; **Jonathan Freeman** MD Assistant Professor and Medical Director, Hematology Laboratory; hematopathology/ gastrointestinal/renal pathology; **Robert Goulart** MD Assistant Professor and Director, Cytopathology; cytopathology and breast pathology; **Jean Henneberry** MD Assistant Professor; Director, Dermatopathology and Director, Residency Program; dermatopathology; **Vandita Johari** MD hematopathology, coagulation, transfusion medicine; **Luis Moral** MD Assistant Professor and Director, Autopsy/Neuropathology Services; neuropathology; **James Nichols** PhD Director, Clinical Chemistry; clinical chemistry; **Christopher Otis** MD Associate Professor Pathology and Obstetrics and Gynecology; Director, Surgical Pathology and Director, Immunohistochemistry; obstetrical/gynecological pathology; **Liron Pantanowitz** MD Assistant Professor and Director Informatics, cytopathology, transfusion medicine; **Solveig Pflueger** PhD, MD Assistant Professor Obstetrics & Gynecology and Director, Medical Genetics; medical genetics.

APPLICATIONS

Applicants must be graduates of an approved school of medicine in the United States or hold ECFMG certification, if from a foreign school. Satisfactory references and personal interviews are required.

Address inquiries to:

Jean Henneberry, MD
Director, Residency Program
Department of Pathology
Baystate Medical Center
759 Chestnut Street
Springfield, MA 01199
Phone: (413) 794-5085 • **Fax:** (413) 794-5893

UNIVERSITY OF MASSACHUSETTS MEDICAL SCHOOL

Worcester, Massachusetts

PROGRAMS OFFERED

A four-year fully ACGME-accredited training program in anatomic and clinical pathology (AP/CP) and three-year programs in straight anatomic pathology (AP) or straight clinical pathology (CP). The Department of Pathology and Laboratory Medicine provides a comprehensive training in all aspects of pathology with the primary goal of training residents for careers in academic and hospital pathology and leading to Board certification in AP, CP or combined AP and CP. In-depth training in anatomic pathology includes autopsy and surgical pathology, cytopathology, gastrointestinal pathology, genitourinary pathology, gynecologic and perinatal pathology, head and neck pathology, bone and soft tissue pathology, neuropathology, dermatopathology, hematopathology, pediatric pathology, renal pathology, electron microscopy, immunohistochemistry, molecular diagnostics and forensic pathology. In-depth training in clinical pathology includes chemistry, hematology, transfusion medicine, immunology, microbiology, cytogenetics, HLA and tissue typing, and toxicology. A broad range of elective time is available including in-depth experiences in selected areas of general and subspecialty pathology. Clinical research with financial support from the department is arranged for interested residents. The department also offers formal accredited fellowship training in surgical pathology, dermatopathology, cytopathology and hematopathology.

TYPES AND NUMBERS OF APPOINTMENTS

The department presently supports sixteen PGY 1-4 residency positions, two fellowships in surgical pathology and one fellowship each in dermatopathology, cytopathology and hematopathology. We also offer two post-sophomore fellowship positions to medical students currently enrolled in accredited U.S. or Canadian medical schools.

FACILITIES

UMass Memorial Medical Center is the largest health care system in Central and Western Massachusetts. There are approximately 1,500 physicians as members of our active medical staff, and 13,000 employees. In total, our hospitals have 1,093 beds. In 2006, we treated 58,762 inpatients, and counted more than one million outpatient visits. The pathology department is equipped with state-of-the-art laboratories, modern resident and conference rooms, and seminar facilities all in a central and spacious building. During the past year, there were 57,000 surgical pathology specimens, 64,000 cytology specimens and 107 autopsies. The clinical laboratories performed more than seven million laboratory tests that are utilized by laboratories throughout the New England area. Library facilities include the University of Massachusetts Medical School library with over 60,000 volumes and 2,000 journals, and the library of the Memorial Campus with more than 200 periodicals and an extensive collection of textbooks. All UMass online library journals and publications can be accessed from the comuters in the resident room.

COMMUNITY

Our medical center is located in Worcester, which is 45 minutes from Boston by expressway, and less than a two-hour drive from Cape Cod. Worceser is a city of 170,000 people and serves as a vibrant cultural and economic center of Worcester County, which has a population of over 600,000 people. A world-famous art museum is a focal point of the cultural activities. There is an active musical community, which includes the Worcester Symphony Orchestra, Opera Worcester, Inc., and the Annual Music Festival. Several local theater groups offer a variety of presentations. A Civic Center with a capacity for 14,000 spectators was completed in 1982. The Convention Center recently completed is now fully operational. Beautiful mountains and lakes provide you year-round activities including hiking, fishing, kayaking, cycling and skiing. Extensive athletic facilities are available within thirty minutes of the hospital and include ski resorts, golf courses, and ice skating facilities.

STIPENDS AND MAINTENANCE

Resident salaries: First-year residents $48,862; second year $50,695; third year $53,180; fourth year $55,366. Chief residents receive an additional stipend. Additional benefits include medical, dental, disability, malpractice and life insurance, vacation, sick leave and $1,250 yearly book and travel allowance.

STAFF

Kenneth Rock MD Professor and Chairman; **Bruce A. Woda** MD Professor and Vice Chairman; Director Anatomic Pathology and Hematopathology; **L. Michael Snyder** MD Professor and Chairman Hospital Laboratories and Clinical Pathology; **Zhong Jiang** MD, FCAP Professor, Director Pathology Residency Program; Director GU Pathology; **Patricia Miron** PhD Clinical Associate Professor, Director Cytogenetics; Associate Director Pathology Residency Program; **Gamze Ayata** MD Assistant Professor; GI Pathology; **George Behonick** PhD Assistant Professor,

Forensic Toxicology; **Ediz Cosar** MD Assistant Professor, Director Diagnostic Molecular Oncology; **April Deng** MD, Associate Professor, Director Dermatopathology Fellowship Program; **Richard Evans** MD Associate Professor; Medical Examiner; Forensic Pathology; **Andrew Fischer** MD, Professor, Director of Cytopathology; **Armando E. Fraire** MD Professor; Director Autopsy Pathology; Pulmonary Pathology; **Rujing Han** MD, Assistant Professor of Pathology, Dermatopathology; **Suyang Hao** MD Clinical Associate Professor, Director Flow Cytometry, Director Hematopathology Fellowship; **Dina Kandil** MD Assistant Professor; **Ashraf Khan** MD, FRCPath Professor; Director Surgical Pathology; Endocrine and Breast Pathology; **Charles Kiefer** PhD Associate Professor; Director Andrology; **Di Lu** MD Associate Professor, Cytopathology, GYN Pathology; **Stephen Lyle** MD Staff Pathologist Dermatopathology; Assistant Professor Cancer Biology; **Michael Mitchell** MD Assistant Professor, Director Clinical Microbiology; **Nader Morad** MD, Professor of Pathology; **Liberto Pechet** MD Professor; Hematology; **Lan Peng** MD Assistant Professor; GI Pathology; **Lokinendi Rao** MD Assistant Professor; CP/Chemistry; **Thomas W. Smith** MD Professor; Neuropathology; **Jerzy Sobota** MD Assistant Professor; Attending Pathologist; **Guy M. Vallaro** PhD Director Clinical and Forensic Toxicology, Hospital Laboratories; Chief of Toxicology, Office of Medical Examiner; **Vijay Vanguri** MD Instructor of Pathology; **Xiaofei Wang** MD Instructor of Pathology; **Robert Weinstein** PhD Director of Transfusion Medicine; **James Yang** MD Surgical Pathology; **Neng Yu** MD Assistant Professor, Director HLA and Tissue Typing.

APPLICATIONS

Residency candidates must be graduates of approved medical schools in the United States or Canada. Graduates of foreign medical schools must have an ECFMG certificate. Three current satisfactory references are required. Residents must be eligible to practice medicine in the Commonwealth of Massachusetts. The customary starting date for residencies is July 1. Applicants must be submitted through ERAS (Electronic Residency Application Service).

Address inquiries to:

Patti Davis
Residency Coordinator
Department of Pathology
UMass Memorial Health Care
One Innovation Drive
Biotech Three
Worcester, MA 01605
Phone: (508) 793-6156
E-mail: Patricia.Davis@umassmemorial.org

University of Massachusetts Medical School, Worcester, Masschusetts.

THE UNIVERSITY OF MICHIGAN HOSPITALS

Ann Arbor, Michigan

PROGRAMS OFFERED

The Residency Training Program in the Department of Pathology at The University of Michigan Hospitals provides training in anatomic pathology (AP), clinical pathology (CP), or combined anatomic and clinical pathology (AP/CP), depending on the candidate's career objectives. Research training is available either exclusively as postdoctoral fellowship training or can be linked with clinical training. Newly created divisions of Translational Research and Pathology Informatics highlight some of the exciting new initiatives in the department. While the University of Michigan Hospitals in Ann Arbor represent the chief training facilities, educational experiences also involve the Ann Arbor Veterans Affairs Medical Center located approximately 0.6 miles from the University Hospitals. Together, these resources represent approximately 65,000 surgical pathology specimens, 70,000 cytology specimens (including PAPs and FNAs) and 350 autopsies including 75 forensic cases annually. The AP training provides specialized training in cytology and multiple sub-specialty areas including gastrointestinal, dermatologic, genitourinary, breast, pulmonary, renal, pediatric, endocrine, opthalmologic and neuropathology. The Clinical Pathology program provides specialized training in chemical pathology, microbiologic pathology, blood banking and apheresis, coagulation, cytogenetics, tissue typing, clinical immunopathology and informatics. In addition, the Department has developed multiple core facilities (i.e., flow cytometry, molecular diagnostics, proteomics, image analysis, immunochemistry as well as cDNA, protein and tissue microarray analysis facilities), which serve as resources for both clinical and research training. Fellowship training in cytopathology, dermatopathology, hematopathology, molecular genetic pathology, blood bank, pathology informatics, surgical pathology and subspecialty areas of gastrointestinal, breast, genitourinary and pulmonary pathology are available. Postdoctoral research positions for individuals with MD, PhD, or other relevant backgrounds are available through funding from NIH training grants, individual investigator research grants and Departmental sources. Particular research strengths include molecular oncology, epigenetics, regulatory mechanisms of the inflammatory and immune response, pathology informatics, bioinformatics and proteomics. Many of the research programs in the Department of Pathology have close links to research activities within the University of Michigan Cancer Center Unit, other clinical departments as well as the School of Dental Medicine and School of Engineering.

FACILITIES

In addition to clinical facilities and activities described above, The University of Michigan Hospitals includes the University Hospital, the Mott (Children's)/Women's/Holden Hospitals, comprising nearly 900 beds with 45,000 patient admissions and 1.6 million outpatient visits per year. Clinical and anatomic pathology are located primarily in 32,000 sq. ft. within the University Hospital. Additional faculty offices and the experimental pathology programs are located in the Department's own four-story building containing approximately 40,000 sq. ft. of space. Currently, approximately 25,000 sq. ft. are devoted to modern, well equipped research laboratories, with additional research laboratories located in the Biomedical Sciences Research Building, Howard Hughes Medical Institute, Cancer and Geriatric Center and Life Sciences Institute. These physical resources provide an excellent environment with state-of-the-art facilities for support of both clinical and research programs in the Department of Pathology. Planning for a new building to house all of the Department's clinical and research activities is currently underway.

COMMUNITY

Ann Arbor (population 115,000) offers many advantages of a large city, with few of the disadvantages. The University of Michigan and the city of Ann Arbor provide a wide variety of cultural, social, and recreational activities.

STIPENDS AND MAINTENANCE

First-year house officers receive approximately $45,889 per year. Stipends increase each subsequent year. Residents receive vacation/sick/personal time as well as medical, dental and disability insurance per the House Officer Association contract (http://www.med.umich.edu/medschool/hoa/). Policies governing house officer employment are described at the following **Website:** http://www.med.umich.edu/medschool/gme/.

STAFF

Jay L. Hess MD, PhD Carl V. Weller Professor and Chair of Pathology; hematopathology, molecular oncology; **Gerald D. Abrams** MD Professor Emeritus; anatomic pathology, cardiac pathology; **Anuska Anjelkovic-Zochowska** MD, PhD Assistant Professor; inflammation; **Thomas M. Annesley** PhD Professor; Director Drug Analysis and Toxicology; **Henry D. Appelman** MD MR Abell Professor; gastrointestinal and liver pathology; **Ulysses G.J. Balis** MD Associate Professor; Director of Division of Pathology Informatics; **Bryan L Betz** PhD Assistant Professor, Molecular Diagnostics; **Mila Blaivas** MD, PhD Associate Professor; anatomic pathology and neuropathology; **Priscilla**

Chamberlain MD Instructor; anatomic and clinical pathology; **Stephen Chensue** MD, PhD Professor; anatomic and clinical pathology; **Arul M. Chinnaiyan** MD, PhD Professor; bioinformatics, molecular pathology, Director, Research Informatics; **Kathleen Cho** MD Professor; gynecologic pathology; **Laura L. W. Cooling** MD Associate Professor; Associate Director Blood Bank and Transfusion Medicine; **Kitrina G. Cordell** MD Assistant Professor of Oral Medicine, Pathology and Oncology; **Constance D'Amato** BS Assistant Professor Emeritus; neurobiology; **Nisha J. D'Silva** MD Assistant Professor of Dentistry and Pathology; **Robertson D. Davenport** MD Associate Professor; Director Blood Bank and Transfusion Medicine; **Yali Dou** PhD Assistant Professor, histone lysine methyltransferases MLL1 (mixed lineage leukemia protein) and its interacting partners; **Gregory R. Dressler** PhD Professor; research programs; **Colin Duckett** PhD Associate Professor; research programs; **Kojo SJ Elenitoba-Johnson** MD Associate Professor, hematopathology, molecular genetic pathology, Director, Division of Translational Pathology; **Victor Elner** MD, PhD Associate Professor; ophthalmology; **Joseph C. Fantone** MD GD Stobbe Professor in Pathology Education; **Eric R. Fearon** MD, PhD Emanuel N Maisel Professor of Oncology; **David Ferguson** MD, PhD Assistant Professor, molecular pathology; **William G. Finn** MD Professor; Associate Director, Clinical Pathology Laboratories,; **Andrew Flint** MD Professor; anatomic pathology, pulmonary pathology; **Bruce A. Friedman** MD Professor Emeritus; pathology informatics; **Douglas R. Fullen** MD Associate Professor; dermatopathology; **Donald A. Giacherio** PhD Associate Professor; Director Chemical Pathology Section; **Paul Gikas** MD Professor Emeritus; anatomic pathology; **Thomas J. Giordano** MD, PhD Associate Professor; endocrine/molecular pathology; **David Gordon** MD Professor; cardiac pathology; **Joel Greenson** MD Professor; gastrointestinal and liver pathology; **Cory Hogaboam** PhD Associate Professor; research programs; **Jeffrey M Jentzen** MD, PhD Professor, anatomic pathology, forensic pathology; **Xin Jing** MD Assistant Professor, anatomic pathology, cytopathology; **Kent J. Johnson** MD Professor; renal pathology, immunopathology; **Paul D. Killen** MD, PhD Associate Professor; renal pathology; **Celina Kleer** MD Associate Professor; breast pathology; **Stewart Knoepp** MD, Assistant Professor, cytopathology; **Lakshmi Kunju** MD Assistant Professor; cytopathology; **Steven L. Kunkel** PhD Endowed Professor in Pathology Research; immunopathology. Co-Director, Division of Sponsored Programs; **Andrew P. Lieberman** MD, PhD Associate Professor; neuropathology; **Richard Lieberman** MD Assistant Professor; gynecologic pathology; **Megan S. Lim** MD Associate Professor, hematopathology, Director, Hematopathology; **Lori Lowe** MD Professor; Director Dermatopathology; **David Lucas** MD Professor; bone and soft tissue pathology; **Peter Lucas** MD Assistant Professor; research programs; **Nicholas W. Lukacs** PhD Professor; research programs. Director, Graduate Program.; **Linglei Ma** MD, PhD Assistant Professor, dermatopathology; **Steven Mandell** MD, Assistant Professor, Director, MLabs, anatomic and clinical pathology; **Jonathan B. McHugh** MD Head and Neck Pathology; **Paul E. McKeever** MD, PhD Professor; Director Neuropathology; **Barbara J. McKenna** MD Associate Professor; gastrointestinal pathology, cytology; **Claire W. Michael** MD Associate Professor; Director Cytology; cytopathology; **Richard Miller** MD, PhD Professor; immunopathology; **Hedwig Murphy** MD Assistant Professor; anatomic pathology, immunopathology; **Jeffrey L. Myers** MD A.James French Professor of Pathology; Director of Division of Anatomic Pathology; **Bernard Naylor** MD Professor Emeritus; cytology; **Alexey Nesvizhskii** PhD Assistant Professor; computational biology, proteomics; **Duane Newton** PhD Assistant Professor; microbiology/virology; Director, Microbiology/Virology.; **Gabriel Nunez** MD Paul H. deKruif Professor; anatomic pathology and molecular biology; **Stephen H Olsen** MD Assistant Professor, anatomic pathology, dermatopathology; **Sem H. Phan** MD, PhD Professor; anatomic pathology, immunopathology; **Carl L. Pierson** PhD Assistant Professor Emeritus; **Peter J. Polverini** Dean and Professor of Dentistry, Professor of Pathology; **Stephen R. Ramsburgh** MD Assistant Professor; anatomic pathology, Director, Autopsy Service; **Rodolfo F.H. Rasche** MD Assistant Professor; Associate Director M-Labs; **Charles Ross** MD Associate Professor; Director Flow Cytometry; hematopathology; **Diane Roulston** PhD Associate Professor; Director Clinical Cytogenetics Lab; **Bertram Schnitzer** MD Professor Emeritus; hematopathology; **Rajal B. Shah** MD Associate Professor; genitourinary pathology; **Eugene M. Silverman** MD Clinical Associate Professor Emeritus, anatomic and clinical pathology; **Douglas M Smith** MD, PhD, HLA Tissue Typing, blood banking; Director, Histocompatability Laboratory; **Lauren B Smith** MD Assistant Professor, clinical pathology, hematopathology; **Lloyd M. Stoolman** MD Professor; anatomic and clinical pathology, hematopathology, flow cytometry; **James Varani** PhD Professor; cell biology, microbiology virology; **Daniel W Visscher** MD Professor; surgical pathology, breast pathology, Director, Surgical Pathology; **Peter A. Ward** MD Godfrey D. Stobbe Professor immunopathology; **Jeffrey S. Warren** MD Professor; Director Division Clinical Pathology; immunopathology; **Thomas E. Wilson** MD, PhD Asociate Professor; research programs, Director, Molecular Diagnostics.

APPLICATIONS

House officer candidates must be graduates of approved medical schools in the United States. Graduates of foreign medical schools must have an ECFMG certificate and J-1 visa status if not a permanent resident. A minimum of two reference letters are required. Applications are considered for AP and CP training, as well as research training. Applications must be received by **November 8** for appointments beginning July 1 of the following year.

Address inquiries to:

Joseph C. Fantone, MD
Director, Resident Program
Department of Pathology
University of Michigan Medical School
M4211 Medical Science I
1301 Catherine
Ann Arbor, MI 48109-5602
Web site: http://www.pathology.med.umich.edu

HENRY FORD HOSPITAL

Detroit, Michigan

PROGRAMS OFFERED

A fully accredited program in anatomic and clinical pathology is offered with tracks in combined AP/CP, straight AP, or straight CP. The resident may enter the program after a year of approved clinical training or directly from medical school. Rotations include autopsy and surgical pathology, neuropathology, electron microscopy, molecular pathology, diagnostic cytology, forensic pathology, clinical chemistry, microbiology, serology, immunopathology, hematology, blood banking, urinalysis and cytogenetics. The basics of pathology are learned during core rotations in the various disciplines of anatomic and clinical pathology in the first two years. These concepts are expanded upon during the latter years of the program during which time the trainee also has the opportunity for elective rotations in areas of particular interest. Research opportunities are available in a variety of disciplines including surgical pathology, immunopathology, molecular pathology, cytogenetics and pathology informatics. An additional educational forte is the subspecialization of the anatomic and clinical pathology senior staff pathologists.

TYPES AND NUMBERS OF APPOINTMENTS

Sixteen resident positions are offered in anatomic and clinical pathology.

FACILITIES

Henry Ford Hospital and Health Network is made up of a 903 bed main hospital, 17 story clinic building, and a satellite clinic system of 24 regional medical centers.There is a 7-story Education and Research Building devoted primarily to basic research. It also houses clinical laboratories, classrooms and various support services. A 190-unit apartment building is available for house staff officers and families and medical students. The Department of Pathology at Henry Ford Hospital is founded upon a mission of service to patients, medical staff, and the community. The Department is composed of 35 senior staff pathologists and clinical PhD scientists and over 400 technical staff. Currently, it is the 15th largest hospital based laboratory in the United States. The department in 2008 accessioned 160 autopsies; 48,905 surgical specimens; 2,225 frozen section consultations; 66,489 cytology specimens (5,536 non-gyn and 1,893 fine needle biopsies); and 700 bone marrow samples. Over 6 million tests were performed in various laboratories. The hospital library contains 50,000 volumes and subscribes to over 1,000 medical journals in addition to the excellent interlibrary loan department and access to internet resources.

COMMUNITY

Henry Ford Hospital is located near the center of the City of Detroit and 10 minutes from its famed Detroit Renaissance Center and the Canadian border. The city has a robust athletic heritage offering 4 profession sports teams. Detroit hosted the 2005 MLB All Star Game at Comerica Park, the 2006 Super Bowl at Ford Field and is home to the 2004 NBA Champion Detroit Pistons. The metropolitan area, with a population of more than 3 million, lies near the heart of the Great Lakes megalopolis. The city has an excellent museum of fine arts, a noted symphony orchestra and 10 other museums of art, science and history. Nearby scenic parks, lakes, rivers, beaches and a cageless zoo provide numerous outdoor recreational opportunities. The University of Detroit and Wayne State University are within the city, the University of Michigan is located in nearby Ann Arbor, and Michigan State University is little more than an hour away at East Lansing. There are excellent drama departments at Wayne State and at nearby Oakland University and numerous amateur and semiprofessional dramatic musical groups.

STIPENDS AND MAINTENANCE

First-year residents receive $44,138, second-year residents $46,553, third-year residents $48,604, fourth-year residents $50,814, fifth-year residents $52,944. Insurance coverage includes hospitalization, dental, optical, disability, life, travel, malpractice and worker's compensation. There are vacation and tax shelter benefits. Third-year residents and above are eligible for professional meeting time. Relicensure fee and uniform laundry are provided. Apartments are available.

STAFF

Senior Staff

Richard J. Zarbo MD Chairman, Department Pathology; **John L. Carey** Vice Chairman, Clinical Pathology - Immunopathology, Hematology; **Kedar Inamdar** MD, PhD -Division Head, Hematopathology, Associate Program Director; **Osama Al-Assi** MD - anatomic pathology, cytopathology; **John Anagli** PhD - cancer research, proteomics; **Gary Assarian** DO - Clinical Chemistry; **Milena Cankovic** PhD - molecular pathology; **Marsha Chaffins** MD - dermatopathology; **Dhananjay Chitale** MD - Anatomic Pathology - Molecular; **Carolyn S. Feldkamp** PhD - clinical chemistry; **Arthur Gaba** MD - anatomic pathology, cytopathology; **Nilesh Gupta** MD - Anatomic Pathology; **Jorge**

A. Gutierrez MD - neuropathology; **Robert C. Hawley, Jr.** MD - clinical pathology, hematology; **Bruce A. Jones** MD - Anatomic Pathology, Med. Dir. HFWBH; **Sudha R. Kini** MD - cytopathology; **Min W. Lee** MD - anatomic pathology; **Norman Lehman** MD - Director of Neuropathology; **Michael D. Linden** MD - anatomic pathology; **Ileana Lopez-Plaza** Division Head, Transfusion Medicine; **Veronica Luzzi** PhD - Clinical Chemistry; **Chan K. Ma** MD - anatomic pathology; **Koichi Maeda** MD - clinical pathology, hematology; **Theodore Mayer** MD - Anatomic Pathology - Clinical Pathology; **Fredrick A. Meier** MD - anatomic pathology, regional medical laboratories; **Adrian Ormsby** MD - Divison Head, Anatomic Pathology; **Usha B. Raju** MD - anatomic pathology; **Sundara B.K. Raman** MD - clinical pathology, hematology; **Linoj Samuel** PhD - Clinical Microbiology; **Daniel Schultz** MD - anatomic pathology, cytopathology; **Veena Shah** MD - anatomic pathology; **Chad H. Stone** MD - anatomic pathology, cytopathology; **Robert Tibbetts** PhD - Clinical Microbiology; **Frank X Torres** MD - anatomic pathology; **J. Mark Tuthill** MD - pathology informatics; **Eve VanEgmond** MD - Anatomic Pathology.

APPLICATIONS

Residency candidates must be graduates of approved medical schools in the United States and Canada. Graduates of foreign medical schools must have ECFMG certification. Satisfactory references are required and a personal interview. Applications accepted through the Electronic Residency Application Service (ERAS) and must be received by November 10.

Address inquiries to:

Richard J. Zarbo, MD, DMD
Chairman, Department of Pathology
Program Director
Henry Ford Hospital
2799 W Grand Boulevard
Detroit, MI 48202
Phone: (313) 916-3194 • **Fax:** (313) 916-2385
or
Kedar Inamdar, MD, PhD
Associate Program Director
Department of Pathology, K-6
Henry Ford Hospital
2799 W Grand Boulevard
Detroit MI, 48202

ST JOHN HOSPITAL AND MEDICAL CENTER

Detroit, Michigan

PROGRAMS OFFERED

The Department of Pathology at St John Hospital and Medical Center offers a fully accredited four year program leading to certification by the American Board of Pathology in anatomic and clinical pathology. The major goal of the residency training program is to produce physicians who will be in demand because of their expertise in the field of Laboratory Medicine and their ability to make a significant contribution to patient care. The resident educational experience includes autopsy and surgical pathology, cytopathology, diagnostic electron microscopy, neuropathology, forensic pathology, dermatopathology, cytogenetics, hematopathology, transfusion medicine, immunopathology and flow cytometry, molecular pathology, clinical chemistry and ligand assay, microbiology and virology, and toxicology. During the clinical pathology rotations, the resident works directly under the supervision of an expert pathologist in each of the subspecialty areas. Likewise, in anatomic pathology, every organ or organ system has a subspecialist available. Residents are able to develop leadership abilities through management lectures and by exposure to administrative problems. The hospital provides facilities and funds for resident research.

TYPES AND NUMBERS OF APPOINTMENTS

Eight resident positions are available, two at each year level.

FACILITIES

St John Hospital and Medical Center is a 800-bed acute care teaching facility servicing Detroit and its eastern suburbs, including Macomb County. St John is a recognized Trauma Center and Regional Level III Perinatal Center. There have been recent updates to include the new Van Elslander Pavilion Cardiology Tower, renovations to the ER, as well as upgrades to the Van Elslander Cancer Center. The Pathology Department and Clinical Laboratories occupy 28,000 square feet in the Concentrated Care Building, serving as the core laboratory for a seven-hospital health system. The laboratory processes over four million tests per year, including 40,000 surgical specimens, 95,000 cytology specimens, 400 bone marrow examinations, and 100 autopsies. State-of-the-art instrumentation, automation systems and computer systems are used throughout the laboratory. The St John Laboratory provides advanced immunohistochemical diagnostic technology, flow cytometry, molecular pathology, and electron microscopy. The hospital and departmental libraries provide an extensive collection of textbooks and journals. All residents have hospital-provided Internet access, and MedLine.

COMMUNITY

The hospital is located at the junction of Detroit and Grosse Pointe, thus offering the resident the attractive pairing of cosmopolitan big city life and the tranquility, housing, and beauty of a well known suburban community. Downtown Detroit, with its varied attractions, is only 15 minutes away, and Lake St Clair, the setting for Grosse Pointe, is only 3 minutes away.

STIPENDS AND MAINTENANCE

Stipends range from $45,067.00 for PGY I to $50,585.00 for PGY IV. Residents receive three weeks paid vacation and leave for educational conferences. Hospitalization and dental insurance for resident and family, life, malpractice, and long-term disability insurance, as well as a stipend for educational conferences and free meals while on duty, are provided. One- and two-bedroom hospital-owned apartments are available a few blocks from the hospital.

STAFF

Martha J. Higgins MD Chief, Department of Pathology; Immunohematology/Transfusion Medicine, Hematopathology, Pediatric Pathology; **Basim M. Al-Khafaji** MD Program Director, Cytopathology, Surgical pathology; **Robert D. Danforth** MD Director, Anatomic Pathology, Cytopathology, Surgical Pathology; **Daniel Snower** MD Director, Clinical Pathology, Hematopathology,Surgical Pathology; **Paul F. Mazzara** MD Director Cytopathology, Surgical Pathology, Cytopathology; **Cheryl Aslakson** PhD Immunology, Flow Cytometry; **Michelle L. Bonnett** MD Surgical Pathology, Hematopathology; **Laurence E. Briski** MD Microbiology, Surgical Pathology; **Roger R. Calam** PhD Clinical Chemistry; **Lamia Fathallah** MD Surgical Pathology, Cytopathology; **Paul J. Kowalski** MD Surgical Pathology; **Noel S. Lawson** MD Clinical Chemistry, Medical Informatics, Endocrine Pathology, Surgical Pathology; **Cheryl Loewe** MD Forensic Pathology; **Daniel Ockner** MD Surgical Pathology; **Hong Qu** MD Surgical Pathology, Urologic Pathology, Medical Kidney, Electron Microscopy; **Richard K. Wesley** DDS, MSD Oral Pathology.

APPLICATIONS

Address inquiries to:

Basim M. Al-Khafaji, MD, Program Director
Department of Pathology
St John Hospital and Medical Center
22101 Moross Road
Detroit, MI 48236
Phone: (313) 343-3864
Web site: http://www.stjohn.org/StJohnHospital/CME-Residency/GME/Pathology/

St John Hospital and Medical Center, Detroit, Michigan

WAYNE STATE UNIVERSITY SCHOOL OF MEDICINE AND AFFILIATED HOSPITALS

Detroit, Michigan

PROGRAMS OFFERED

The Department of Pathology, Wayne State University School of Medicine, and affiliated hospitals offer an ACGME accredited competency based combined four-year training program in anatomic and clinical pathology or three-year program in anatomic pathology alone. The programs include instruction in experimental pathology and the opportunity for residents to participate in original research. The affiliated hospitals comprise Harper-Hutzel Hospital, Karmanos Cancer Institute, Detroit Receiving Hospital and University Health Center, Children's Hospital of Michigan, Sinai-Grace Hospital, Wayne County Medical Examiner's Office, and the John D. Dingell VA Medical Center. Emphasis is placed on the resident assuming increasing diagnostic responsibilities under faculty supervision, interaction with clinical specialists, and application of recent technological developments to diagnostic medicine. The diverse spectrum of hospital affiliations allows each resident to receive training from pathologists with special interest and expertise in subspecialty areas. Numerous electives offering specialized training are available in diverse fields including research, subspecialties, and molecular biology. The goal of this program is the preparation of individuals for the practice of anatomic and clinical pathology as well as for careers in research and education. A certificate of training from Wayne State University School of Medicine is awarded upon completion of the program.

TYPES AND NUMBERS OF APPOINTMENTS

Twelve house staff positions are available, with three first-year positions that may be entered at the PGY-1 level or after training in another medical specialty. Fellowship training is offered in cytopathology, hematopathology, pediatric pathology, and surgical pathology.

FACILITIES

The Detroit Medical Center complex comprises the Wayne State University School of Medicine (Gordon H. Scott Hall of Basic Medical Sciences, Louis M. Elliman Research Building and Helen V. Prentis Lande Building for Medical Research), Harper-Hutzel Hospital, Detroit Receiving Hospital/University Health Center, Children's Hospital of Michigan and Sinai-Grace Hospital. The University Health Center serves as the ambulatory care center for these institutions and is the centralized facility for the clinical laboratories. Total necropsies, 300; total laboratory analyses, 9,000,000; total surgicals, 40,000; cytologic specimens, 100,000. The diagnostic laboratories are modern, highly automated and computerized. Research facilities are fully equipped and include electron microscopes, freeze-fracture apparatus, cell culture facilities, cytogenetics laboratories, flow cytometers, and state-of-the-art molecular biology and molecular diagnostics facilities.

COMMUNITY

Wayne State University School of Medicine and Affiliated Hospitals are located in the cultural center of Detroit, a metropolitan area with population in excess of 4.0 million. Extensive cultural facilities include symphony orchestras, an opera house, museums, and theaters. Professional football, baseball, hockey, and basketball are readily available. Excellent housing is available. Interstate highways provide rapid transportation to the splendid recreation areas of the upper and lower peninsulas of Michigan and adjacent Southern Ontario.

STIPENDS AND MAINTENANCE

Stipends are available as follows: first post-MD year $45,715. second $47,087. third $48,499. fourth $49,955. and fifth $51,453. Residents receive two weeks vacation in the first year and three weeks each year thereafter. Hospitalization and life insurance are included.

STAFF

The staff of the School of Medicine and its affiliated hospitals, and their specialty areas are as follows:

Wayne State University, Detroit Receiving Hospital and University Health Center

Wael A. Sakr MD Professor and Chairman, Anatomic Pathology; **B. J. Anderson** MD, Administrative Medical Director Core Laboratory; **J-W. Chu** PhD clinical chemistry; **J. D. Crissman** MD surgical pathology; **M. Fairfax** MD, PhD microbiology and virology; **W. Neeley** MD Detroit Medical Center University Laboratories; **K. C Palmer** PhD pulmonary pathology; **M. Palutke** MD hematopathology and immunogenetics; **E. V. Perrin** MD Emeritus pediatric pathology; **A. Sima** MD, PhD neuropathology.

Harper-Hutzel Hospital

R. Ali-Fehmi MD surgical pathology and gynecologic pathology; **S. Bandyopadhyay** MD, anatomic pathology; **G. Bentley** MD hematopathology and coagulation; **M. Bluth** MD,PhD, clinical pathology; **H. Budev** MD Vice Chief Anatomic Pathology, gynecologic and ophthalmic pathology; **M. E. Dan** MD Medical Director, Clinical Pathology; blood bank, immunohematology; **S. Ebrahim** MD, cytogenetics; **O. Fagoaga** PhD associate director HLA; **G. Feldman** MD, PhD molecular pathology; **J. Feng** MD, PhD, surgical pathology and cytopathology; **T. Giorgadze** MD, anatomic pathology; **R. Grier** PhD Director, Biochemical Genetics Lab; **M. Herawi** MD, anatomic pathology; **M. Husain** MD Chief of Pathology and Director of Cytopathology, gynecologic and cytopathology; **S. M. Jacques** MD, anatomic/perinatal and obstetrical pathology; **H. Jaratli** MD, anatomic pathology, hematopathology; **W. J. Kupsky** MD neuropathology; **F. Lonardo** MD surgical pathology and pulmonary oncologic pathology; **A. Mohamed** MD cytogenetics; **F. Nahhas** PhD, Technical Director, molecular genetics lab; **S. L. Nehlsen-Cannarella** PhD Director, HLA; **B. O'Malley** MD, clinical pathology; **F. Qureshi** MD Director, Obstetrical and Perinatal Pathology; **W. Sakr** MD, Anatomic Pathology; head and neck pathology, urological pathology; **D. Shi** MD, anatomic pathology; **Xu Zheng** MD, PhD Director, Nephropathology.

Children's Hospital of Michigan

J. Poulik MD pediatric pathology; **R. Rabah-Hammad** MD pediatric pathology; **H. Salimnia** PhD molecular microbiology.

John D. Dingell VA Medical Center

R. S. Vander Heide MD, PhD Director, Laboratories; cardiovascular pathology; **D. Hatfield** PhD electron microscopy; **N. Khoury** MD surgical pathology; **E. Levi** MD surgical pathology and hematopathology; **P. Sochacki** MD surgical pathology.

Wayne County Medical Examiner's Office

C. J. Schmidt MD, Chief Medical Examiner, forensic pathology; **F Diaz** MD Forensic Pathology; **B. Hepler** PhD toxicology; **L. Hlavaty** MD forensic pathology; **D. Isenschmid** PhD forensic pathology; **C. Loewe** MD forensic pathology; **B. Pietak** MD forensic pathology.

Sinai-Grace Hospital

H. Saleh MD, MBA Chief of Pathology; **D David** MD surgical pathology and cytopathology; **M. El-Fakharany** MD, clinical pathology; **B. Jin** MD surgical pathology and cytopathology; **S. Zaidi** MD surgical pathology, oncologic pathology and hematopathology.

APPLICATIONS

Residency candidates must be graduates of approved medical schools in the United States or Canada or of foreign medical schools and possess an ECFMG certificate and eligibility for licensure in the state of Michigan. References and a personal interview are required. Applications should be submitted through ERAS.

Address inquiries to:

William J. Kupsky, MD, Director of Resident Training; c/o Ms. Janet Watycha, Department of Pathology
Wayne State University School of Medicine
540 East Canfield
Detroit, MI 48201
E-mail: path-res@med.wayne.edu
Web site: http://www.med.wayne.edu/Pathology/residencytraining.htm

WILLIAM BEAUMONT HOSPITAL

Royal Oak, Michigan

PROGRAMS OFFERED

The Pathology Departments of William Beaumont Hospital offer a comprehensive fully accredited four year training program in combined Anatomic and Clinical Pathology. The anatomic curriculum includes autopsy pathology, general surgical pathology, cytopathology, dermatopathology, neuropathology, pediatric pathology, immunopathology, and forensic pathology. The anatomic pathology program is strengthened by affiliations with the Detroit Children's Hospital and Wayne County Medical Examiner's Office. The clinical pathology curriculum includes hematopathology, hemostasis, transfusion medicine, clinical chemistry, analytical cytometry, image analysis, microbiology, virology, immunology, cytogenetics and molecular pathology. Residents are instructed and develop experience in techniques of fine needle aspiration biopsy and bone marrow biopsy and aspiration. The staff-to-resident ratio provides optimal supervision and guidance in all areas of pathology. Our high patient volume and case mix provides excellent material to develop skill, experience and efficiency. In addition to structured training, time and departmental support are available for independent study and investigation.

TYPES AND NUMBERS OF APPOINTMENTS

Three first-year positions are available in a combined four-year anatomic and clinical pathology program.

FACILITIES

William Beaumont Hospital is a 1,061-bed tertiary care general hospital with a 226-bed satellite family care hospital, servicing several large suburban communities in Oakland County, 13 miles north of Detroit. Beaumont is a teaching hospital with over 350 residents and fellows in essentially all of the specialties and subspecialties of medicine. Anatomic Pathology is staffed by 16 pathologists, 1 PhD, and 6 pathology assistants. Surgical specimens currently number over 72,436 per year and autopsies number approximately 119 per year. Cytology specimens approximate 86,951 per year, of which 8,894 are obtained from nongynecologic sites, 74,672 from gynecological sites and 3,385 are fine needle aspirates. Muscle biopsy specimens number 165 and kidney biopsies number 350 annually. There are dedicated electron microscopy, immunohistochemistry and molecular laboratories. The Clinical Pathology Laboratory handles 8,000,000 tests annually. It occupies new facilities totaling 53,000 square feet, and is staffed by 11 pathologists and five Ph.D's. There are also 3,560 square feet of research space. Both departments are well equipped with state of the art automated instrumentation and are supported by advanced dedicated computer systems. There are well stocked hospital and departmental libraries maintaining a collection of current standard and specialty textbooks and specialty journals.

COMMUNITY

Royal Oak offers comfortable residential suburban living with easy access to cultural and sports facilities in the nation's sixth largest city just 13 miles away. Summer and winter recreational activities can be found in Michigan as well as Ontario, Canada within a 50-mile radius of William Beaumont Hospital.

STIPENDS AND MAINTENANCE

Residents' salaries range from $47,200 yearly for the first postgraduate year to $53,700 per annum for the fourth postgraduate year. Uniforms/laundry, and health and malpractice insurance are paid for by the hospital. Comfortable apartments for house staff members and their families are available on the 112-acre hospital campus.

STAFF

John C. Watts MD Chairman of Anatomic Pathology; Surgical Pathology; **Edward G. Bernacki Jr.** MD Vice Chairman, Anatomic Pathology and Director of Cytopathology; **Mark D. Kolins** MD Chair, Clinical Pathology; **Elizabeth Sykes** MD Vice Chairman, Clinical Pathology, Medical Director, Chemistry and Special Testing; **Mitual B. Amin** MD Director, Autopsy Service, Surgical Pathology and Immunopathology; **Ali-Reza Armin** MD Director, Surgical Pathology; Dermatopathology; **Kimberley G. Crone** Dermatopathology; **Mohanpal S. Dulai** MD Neuropathology; **Maryam A. Farinola** MD Surgical Pathology and Urologic Pathology; **Robert Folberg** MD Eye Pathology; **Tomi J. Kuntzman** DO Director, Cytopathology Fellowship; Surgical Pathology and Cytopathology; **Rajwant K. Malhotra** MD Surgical Pathology and Dermatopathology; **Mark A. Micale** PhD Director of Cytogenetics; **Michele T. Rooney** MD Director, Residency Training in Pathology; Surgical Pathology and Cytopathology; **Deborah L. Shuster** Surgical Pathology and Neuropathology; **Jacqueline K. Trupiano** MD Surgical Pathology and Pediatric Pathology, Associate Director, Residency Training in Anatomic Pathology; **Alison L Uzieblo** MD Surgical Pathology and Dermatopathology; **Jon D. Wilson** MD Director of Neuropathology; Surgical Pathology; **Ping L. Zhang** Nephropathology and Surgical Pathology; **Ann Marie Blenc** MD, Medical Director, Hematopathology; **Bobby L. Boyanton** MD Medical Director, Microbiology and Associate Director, Residency Training in Clinical Pathology; **Domnita Crisan** MD, PhD

Medical Director, Molecular Pathology; **Vonda Douglas-Nikitin** MD Medical Director, Flow Cytometry; **James Huang** MD, Associate Medical Director, Flow Cytometry; **Helen Jeon** MD Associate Director, Transfusion Medicine; **Raymond E. Karcher** PhD Bioscientific Staff, Automated Chemistry; **Gabriel Maine** PhD Director, HLA Blood Bank; **Peter A. Millward** Ph.D. Medical Director, Transfusion Medicine; **Yvonne Posey** MD Clinical Chemistry; **Barbara Robinson-Dunn** PhD Bioscientific Staff, Microbiology; **Marc D. Smith** MD Medical Director, Coagulation; **John Wilson** PhD Bioscientific Staff, Toxicology.

APPLICATIONS

Brochure and program description are available online.

Address inquiries to:

Michele T. Rooney, MD
Director, Resident Training in Pathology
William Beaumont Hospital
3601 West Thirteen Mile Road
Royal Oak, MI 48073-6769
Phone: (248) 898-9060 • **Fax:** (248) 898-9054
Web site: http://www.beaumonthospitals.com/gme

William Beaumont Hospital, Royal Oak, Michigan.

UNIVERSITY OF MINNESOTA AFFILIATED HOSPITALS

Minneapolis, Minnesota

PROGRAMS OFFERED

The Department of Laboratory Medicine and Pathology at the University of Minnesota offers outstanding ACGME accredited training programs in anatomic pathology, clinical pathology, and combined anatomic and clinical pathology. The program draws additional strength from opportunities at our affiliated hospitals, including the University of Minnesota Medical Center, a divison of Fairview, Abbott Northwestern Hospital, Hennepin County Medical Center, Veterans Affairs Medical Center, Hennepin County Medical Examiners Office, the North Central blood Services of the American Red Cross and the Memorial Blood Centers of Minnesota. The core program in anatomic pathology incorporates histology with state of the art biotechnology in diagnosing surgical, autopsy and cytopathology cases. Cytopathology training includes evaluation of gynecologic, body fluid, and fine needle aspiration specimens. Clinical pathology training includes clinical chemistry, molecular diagnostics, transfusion medicine, hematopathology, medical microbiology/virology, coagulation, cytogenetics and immunopathology. On-going training in laboratory management and health informatics is an integral part of the program. As the specialty of pathology involves continual learning and the sharing of this knowledge, the residents regularly participate in service related conferences and medical student teaching. Beyond the core curriculum, residents pursue either a community or academically oriented practice track. While not required, our residents are encouraged to explore and participate in basic or clinical research with a spectrum of opportunities in immunology, molecular genetics, cancer biology, cancer cytogenetics, environmental pathology, cell biology, health informatics, and others.

TYPES AND NUMBERS OF APPOINTMENTS

The program includes 26 resident positions. In addition to strong basic residency training, competitive fellowship programs are available in transfusion medicine/blood bank, molecular genetics, hematopathology, and cytopathology.

FACILITIES

The University of Minnesota Medical Center, a division of Fairview is located in the Health Sciences Complex on the main university campus in Minneapolis. This University Hospital is a state of the art general and subspecialty care facility with 743 beds. The University services have a workload of 17,000 surgical specimens, 2,500 blood and bone marrow evaluations, 5,000 dermatopathology specimens, 59,000 cytopathology cases, 120 autopsies and over 2,700,000 clinical pathology assays annually. The VA Medical Center has a 361 bed capacity in addition to a full spectrum of clinics. The VA has 9,400 surgical specimens, 2,800 cytopathology cases, 300 blood and bone marrow evaluations, 180 autopsies, and more than 2,100,000 clinical pathology assays. The University of Minnesota Medical Center and the VA Hospital both have active on site blood bank donor centers. Hennepin County Medical Center, a 360 bed community hospital has 8,200 surgical specimens, 1,400 blood and bone marrow evaluations, 18,000 cytopathology accessions, 108 autopsies, and more than 1,800,000 clinical pathology assays. Abbott Northwestern Hospital, 642 bed community hospital, has 16,500 surgical specimens, 500 blood and bone marrow evaluations, 89,200 cytopathology accessions, 84 autopsies, and 230,000 clinical pathology assays. Residents also rotate at the Hennepin County Medical Examiner's Office, which performs more than 550 forensic autopsies per year.

COMMUNITY

The Twin Cities of Minneapolis and St. Paul are a thriving metropolitan area with over 3 million people. They are rich in what makes cities exciting without the big city drawbacks. The most appealing activity for many is also the simplest; enjoying the great outdoors. There are five large and numerous smaller lakes with beaches, bike trails, walking paths and parkways in Minneapolis alone. Near the St. Paul Campus, you will find the Como Park Zoo, the Conservatory, amusement parks, additional lakes and picnic areas. The Minnesota Zoological Garden, an open habitat for animals, is located on the southern edge of the metropolitan area. Among the most popular summer activities are swimming, canoeing, sailing, water skiing, hiking and bicycling. By December, Minnesota waters are frozen, and favorite pastimes switch to ice skating, cross country and downhill skiing, snow boarding and winter camping. Cultural activities abound in the Twin Cities. The riverfronts in both cities host several ethnic, art, and music festivals each year. Fine dining and shopping are abundant in the Twin Cities area, including the Mall of America. The Minnesota Symphony Orchestra and the Grammy Award winning St. Paul Chamber Orchestra make their homes in the Twin Cities. The Minneapolis Institute of Arts, Walker Art Center, Minnesota Museum of Art and the Science Museum of Minnesota with its Omnitheater are major attractions. The theater has long thrived in the Twin Cities, which support seven professional groups, including the famous Guthrie Theater. In addition to the University Big Ten intercollegiate teams, major league sports fans can catch the action with the Minnesota Twins baseball, Minnesota Wild hockey, Vikings football, Lynx women's basketball and Timberwolves men's basketball.

STIPENDS AND MAINTENANCE

First year postgraduate trainees receive competitive stipends and benefits, including life, long and short term disability, health and dental insurance. See our web page at http:// residency.pathology.umn.edu for current stipend and benefit information.

APPLICATIONS

Applicants should have a strong academic record, a demonstrated interest in the art of pathology, and a current understanding of clinical medicine. Applicants should see our program web site at http://residency.pathology.umn.edu for specific application requirements. All applications are accepted through ERAS.

Address inquiries to:

Alan Rose, MD, Program Director
Department of Laboratory Medicine and Pathology
University of Minnesota Medical School
420 Delaware St SE / MMC 76
Minneapolis, MN 55455-0392
Fax: (612) 273-1142
Web site: http://residency.pathology.umn.edu

MAYO SCHOOL OF GRADUATE MEDICAL EDUCATION

Rochester, Minnesota

PROGRAMS OFFERED

ACGME accredited residencies are offered in combined anatomic and clinical pathology. Residency training includes specific rotations in all aspects of anatomic and clinical pathology including autopsy, neuropathology, surgical pathology, dermatopathology, cytology, clinical biochemistry and immunology, microbiology, hematopathology, transfusion medicine, cytogenetics, molecular pathology and coagulation. One year of research support is available to highly qualified applicants. Clinician investigator residency positions are available for candidates who wish to participate in two years of research in combination with their residency.

TYPES AND NUMBERS OF APPOINTMENTS

The total number of residents is 20, generally with 5 appointments per year. Thirty-three fellowship appointments are available for qualified individuals for subspecialty training in clinical biochemical genetics, clinical chemistry, clinical cytogenetics, clinical microbiology, clinical molecular genetics, hematopathology, molecular genetic pathology, transfusion medicine, and anatomic pathology (including surgical pathology, bone and soft tissue pathology, cardiovascular pathology, cytopathology, GI and liver pathology, neuropathology, pulmonary pathology).

FACILITIES

The Mayo School of Graduate Medical Education in Rochester is a free-standing, degree-granting institution. The faculty is composed from the permanent staff of Mayo Clinic (3300 physicians and medical scientists). Approximately 2700 clinical residents and fellows are in training at any one time. Mayo Clinic has an annual registration of 520,000 patients. Two affiliated hospitals in Rochester are staffed exclusively by Mayo physicians: Saint Marys Hospital with 1157 beds and Rochester Methodist Hospital with 794 beds. Approximate annual numbers of pathologic examinations are: 500 autopsies, 250,000 surgical and consult specimens, 76,000 cytology specimens, and 17,000,000 laboratory tests. Completely equipped, modern laboratories are available for routine and research work in all areas listed. The professional staff in the Department of Laboratory Medicine and Pathology totals 125. The technical and nontechnical staff of these sections totals 3000. The Mayo medical library contains nearly 400,000 volumes and 5000 medical and scientific journal subscriptions of which 3500 are accessible electronically on the Mayo campus.

COMMUNITY

Rochester offers the advantages of a cosmopolitan center combined with the friendliness and informality of a small community. Located in southeastern Minnesota, Rochester is 80 miles southeast of Minneapolis and 275 miles northwest of Chicago. The permanent population is more than 125,000. Each year the city is host to several hundred thousand patients and visitors. Rochester provides indoor and outdoor athletic and recreational facilities, a symphony orchestra, a civic art center, and a civic theater, as well as numerous religious, social and cultural organizations.

STIPENDS AND MAINTENANCE

The annual stipends are: first postdoctoral year $46,063, second postdoctoral year $47,907, third postdoctoral year $49,890, fourth postdoctoral year $51,976, fifth postdoctoral year $54,218. Group hospitalization and major medical expense insurance, disability insurance, and group life insurance are available at low rates.

STAFF

Department of Laboratory Medicine and Pathology

F.R. Cockerill III MD Chair.

Anatomic Pathology

G.L. Keeney MD Division Chair, cytopathology, gynecologic and gastrointestinal pathology; **M.C. Aubry** MD autopsy, cardiovascular, pulmonary and transplant pathology; **D.A. Bell** MD cytopathology and gynecologic pathology; **V.S. Chandan** MBBS autopsy, gastrointestinal and liver pathology; **B. Chen** MD breast pathology; **J.C. Cheville** MD gastrointestinal and urologic pathology; **A.C. Clayton** MD gynecologic and cytopathology; **L.D. Cornell** MD renal pathology; **A. Dogan** MD hematopathology; **W.D. Edwards** MD autopsy, cardiovascular, and transplant pathology; **L.A. Erickson** MD dermatopathology and endocrine pathology; **A.L. Feldman** MD hematopathology; **M.E. Fidler** MD renal pathology; **T.J. Flotte** MD dermatopathology; **A.L. Folpe** MD bone and soft tissue pathology and breast pathology; **C. Giannini** MD neuropathology and ophthalmologic pathology; **J.P. Grande** MD renal pathology; **K.L. Grogg** MD hematopathology; **M.R. Henry** MD cytopathology and gynecologic pathology; **K.R. Hobday** MD gastrointestinal pathology; **C.Y. Inwards** MD cytopathology, bone and soft tissue, and head and neck pathology; **R. Jimenez**

MD breast and urologic pathology; **K.J. Kaplan** MD gastrointestinal and liver pathology; **P.J. Kurtin** MD hematopathology; **J.E. Lewis** MD head and neck pathology; **R.V. Lloyd** MD endocrine and molecular pathology; **W.R. Macon** MD hematopathology; **F. Medeiros** MD gynecologic and molecular pathology; **A.G. Nascimento** MD bone and soft tissue, and head and neck pathology; **A. Nassar** MD breast pathology; **L.T. Nelsen** MD gastrointestinal pathology; **A.M. Oliveira** MD molecular, bone and soft tissue pathology; **J.E. Parisi** MD autopsy pathology and neuropathology; **E.A. Pfeifer** MD autopsy, forensic, and transplant pathology; **E.D. Remstein** MD hematopathology; **C.A. Reynolds** MD breast, ophthalmologic, and transplant pathology; **F.J. Rodriguez** MD neuropathology; **D.R. Salomao** MD cytopathology and ophthalmologic pathology; **S.O. Sanderson** MD gastrointestinal, liver, and urologic pathology; **B.W. Scheithauer** MD neuropathology; **D. Schembri-Wismayer** MD head and neck pathology; **T.J. Sebo** MD cytopathology and urologic pathology; **S.N. Sethi** MD, PhD renal pathology; **T.C. Smyrk** MD cytopathology, gastrointestinal and liver pathology; **T.T. Wu** MD gastrointestinal and liver pathology; **J. Yi** MD pulmonary pathology; **J. Zhang** MD cytopathology, endocrine and urologic pathology.

Clinical Biochemistry and Immunology

S.K. Grebe MD Division Chair, endocrine testing, tumor markers, immunoassays, molecular endocrinology; **R.S. Abraham** PhD cellular and molecular immunology; **A. Algeciras-Schimnich** PhD automated immunoassay and endocrine testing; **L.M. Baudhuin** PhD molecular cardiovascular laboratory medicine, pharmacogenomics; **A. Dispenzieri** MD protein immunology; **A.S. Jaffe** MD cardiovascular laboratory medicine, cardiac risk markers; **J.A. Katzmann** PhD protein and cellular immunology; **D.H. Lachance** MD neuroimmunology; **L.J. Langman** PhD drug monitoring, pharmacogenomics, drug toxicity; **V.A. Lennon** MD, PhD neuroimmunology; **T.P. Moyer** PhD drug monitoring, pharmacogenomics, trace elements, metals; **D.J. O'Kane** PhD endocrine testing, tumor markers, pharmacogenomics; **L.K. Oliver** PhD clinical trials, trace elements/metals; **S.J. Pittock** MD neuroimmunology; **R.J. Singh** PhD endocrine testing, tumor markers, mass spectrometry, molecular endocrinology; **C.L. Snozek** PhD toxicology and drug monitoring; **M.R. Snyder** PhD allergy, autoimmunity and immunology.

Clinical Core Laboratory Services

A.S. Jaffe MD, MS Division Chair; **B.S. Karon** MD, PhD; **G.G. Klee** MD, PhD; **T.S. Larson** MD; **J.C. Lieske** MD; **J.P. McConnell** PhD; **L. Oliver** PhD; **A.K. Saenger** PhD.

Clinical Microbiology

J.E. Rosenblatt MD Division Chair, anaerobic bacteriology, parasitology; **M.J. Binnicker** PhD infectious diseases serology, mycology/mycobacteriology; **F.R. Cockerill III** MD bacteriology; **T. Grys** PhD infectious disease serology, virology; **R. Patel** MD bacteriology, initial processing; **B.S. Pritt** MD parasitology, virology; **G.D. Roberts** PhD mycology/mycobacteriology; **T.F. Smith** PhD virology; **N.L. Wengenack** PhD mycology/mycobacteriology; **J.D. Yao** MD hepatitis/HIV.

Experimental Pathology and Laboratory Medicine

G.G. Klee MD, PhD Divison Chair informatics, cardiovascular markers, and prostate cancer; **F.J. Couch** MD molecular biology and breast/pancreatic cancer; **J.M. Cunningham** PhD genotyping and genomics; **A.B. Dietz** PhD cell therapy/bioinformatics; **J.P. Grande** PhD renal fibrogenesis; **S.K. Grebe** MD, PhD molecular pathogenesis of thyroid cancer; **K.C. Halling** MD laboratory genetics; **R.B. Jenkins** MD, PhD cancer genetics, neuro-oncology, prostate cancer; **W.L. Lingle** PhD molecular biology, gynecological, and breast cancer; **R.V. Lloyd** MD, PhD endocrine tumor pathogenesis; **R. Lupu** PhD breast/pancreatic cancer; **P.L. Nguyen** MD supportive care in cancer, myelodysplastic syndromes; **H. Scrable** PhD aging and neuro-oncology; **V. Shridhar** PhD ovarian/breast cancer; **D.I. Smith** PhD molecular genetics; **S.N. Thibodeau** PhD cancer genetics, prostate and colon cancer; **D.L. Van Dyke** PhD molecular genetics.

Hematopathology

W.G. Morice MD Division Chair; **D. Chen** MD, PhD; **A. Dogan** MD, PhD; **A.L. Feldman** MD; **K.L. Grogg** MD; **C.A. Hanson** MD; **J.A. Heit** MD; **J.L. Herrick** MD; **J.D. Hoyer** MD; **D. Jevremovic** MD PhD; **P.J. Kurtin** MD; **W.R. Macon** MD; **R.F. McClure** MD; **P.L. Nguyen** MD; **W.L. Nichols Jr** MD; **R.K. Pruthi** MBBS; **E.D. Remstein** MD; **D. S. Viswanatha** MD.

Laboratory Genetics

D.B. Dawson PhD Division Chair; molecular genetics of inherited disorders; **M.J. Ferber** PhD clinical molecular genetics; **D.K. Gavrilov** MD, PhD inborn errors of metabolism; **K.C. Halling** MD, PhD molecular oncology; **W.E. Highsmith** PhD molecular genetics of inherited disorders, mutation detection technology; **J. Hodge** PhD cytogenetics; **R.B. Jenkins** MD, PhD molecular cytogenetics; **R.P. Ketterling** MD cytogenetics, FISH; **J.A. Lust** MD hematopathology; **D. Matern** MD inborn errors of metabolism, newborn screening; **D. Morbeck** PhD fertility testing; **D. Oglesbee** PhD inborn errors of metabolism; **K.M. Raymond** MD inborn errors of metabolism; **P. Rinaldo** MD, PhD biochemical genetics, inborn errors of metabolism, and newborn screening; **S.N. Thibodeau** PhD cancer genetics and mutation detection methodologies; **E.C. Thorland** PhD molecular cytogenetics; **S. Tortorelli** MD, PhD inborn errors of metabolism, newborn screening; **D.L. Van Dyke** PhD cytogenetics; **G.V. Velagaleti** PhD cytogenetics.

Transfusion Medicine

J.R. Stubbs MD Division Chair, transfusion serology, adverse reactions, blood component therapy, quality system; **A.B. Dietz** PhD human cellular therapy; **M.J. Gandhi** MD blood donations, tissue typing; **D.A. Gastineau** MD clinical stem cell transplants, clinical hematology, human cellular therapy; **P.J. Santrach** MD tissue typing, autotransfusion; **C. van Buskirk** MD blood components; **J.L. Winters** MD blood and stem cell donations, therapeutic apheresis, education.

APPLICATIONS

Residencies are open to graduates of approved medical schools in the United States or Canada and international medical graduates who have passed the qualifying examinations. Deadline for application is November 15 for training beginning the following July 1. Appointments are made through the National Resident Matching Program. Applications must be submitted through ERAS to be considered.

Address inquiries to:

Mary E. Fidler, MD
Director, Pathology Residency Program
Mayo Clinic
Hilton Building, 11th Floor
Rochester, MN 55905
Phone: (507) 284-1196 • **Fax:** (507) 538-3267 • **E-mail:** pathologyeducation@mayo.edu
Web site: http://www.mayo.edu/msgme/labmed-programs.html

UNIVERSITY HOSPITAL THE UNIVERSITY OF MISSISSIPPI MEDICAL CENTER

Jackson, Mississippi

PROGRAMS OFFERED

The Department of Pathology at the University of Mississippi Medical Center offers an integrated four-year training program in anatomic and clinical pathology. The residency program is designed to teach the changes occurring in human disease and the laboratory methods used in demonstrating these changes. Training will include surgical pathology, autopsy, cytopathology, electron microscopy, immunopathology, forensic pathology, neuropathology, pediatric pathology, hematology, coagulation, clinical chemistry, toxicology, microbiology, immunology, blood banking, molecular biology and cytogenetics. Electives provide the opportunity for extra, in-depth experiences in the above areas. Research activities, under faculty supervision, are encouraged.

TYPES AND NUMBERS OF APPOINTMENTS

The program is approved for 12 positions. Normally, two to three first-year positions are available each year through the matching program.

FACILITIES

The Medical Center occupies a 164-acre tract of University-owned land in the heart of Jackson. The original eight-story building is now the nucleus of a major academic health sciences complex. The Schools of Medicine, Nursing, Dentistry and Health Related Professions (SHRP) all have their own buildings on campus. The largest expansion project in the Medical Center's history, totalling $211 million, was completed in 1999. The project included a new children's hospital (the Blair E. Batson Hospital for Children), a women and infants' hospital (the Winfred L. Wiser for Women and Infants), imaging center, two parking garages and a student center (the Norman C. Nelson Student Union). A second construction phase has been completed. It includes the Wallace Conerly Hospital for Critical Care, a 256-bed adult hospital; a two-story expansion of the children's hospital, a classroom addition, and an expansion to the Arthur C. Guyton Research Complex. The Veterans Affairs Medical Center in Jackson, with 136 general medical and surgical patient beds and 120 nursing home beds, and the Mississippi State Hospital at Whitfield, with 2,066 licensed beds, cooperate in the teaching programs of the University of Mississippi Medical Center. The McBryde Memorial Rehabilitation Center for the Blind, completed in 1972, adjoins the University Hospital, as does the Methodist Rehabilitation Center which opened in 1975. Clinical material in anatomic pathology available to residents consists of over 17,981 surgical specimens, 143 autopsies and 64,447 cytology specimens. The Division of Laboratory Medicine performs over 3,348,020 tests annually. Residents rotate through the clinical pathology laboratories which encompass all subspecialty areas including blood banking, chemistry, hematology, immunology and microbiology.

STIPENDS AND MAINTENANCE

Stipends for the 2009-2010 year start at $45,331 annually for PGY I and $49,011 anually for PGY IV. Fringe benefits, including tax-deferred retirement plan, are the same as for all state employees.

STAFF

Israh Akhtar MD (Kashmir, Govt. Med Col 1994) Cytopathology; **Bret C. Allen** MD (Univ Texas Medical Branch 1981) Director, Surgical Pathology; **Kay G. Allen** MD (LSU 1980) Surgical Pathology; **Ayman Asfour** MD (Alexandria Univ 1978) Director, Blood Bank/Transfusion Medicine; **Mithra Baliga** MD (Kasturba Med Col 1972) Director, Cytopathology and Fellowship Program; **Steven A. Bigler** MD (Univ Utah 1986) Chairman, Department of Pathology; **Alexandra Brown** MD (LSU 2002) Surgical Pathology; **John P. Coleman** DO, PhD (Michigan State Univ 1994) Director, Microbiology; **Julius Cruse** MD, PhD (Univ Tennessee 1964, 1966) Director, Immunopathology, Transplant/Immunology; **William P. Daley** MD (Univ Mississippi 1998) Director, Clinical Chemistry and Toxicology; **Elizabeth R. Flowers** MD (Univ Mississippi 1989) Cytopathology; **Jonathan D. Fratkin** MD (SUNY-Downstate 1970) Director, Neuropathology; **Jeffrey R. Henegar** PhD (Univ Missouri 1996) Director, Electron Microscopy; **Courtney C. Jackson** MD (Tulane Univ 1999) Hematology and Surgical Pathology; **Patrick B. Kyle** PhD (Univ Mississippi 2006) Associate Director, Clinical Chemistry and Toxicology; **John T. Lam** MD (Tulane Univ 1990) Director, Hematology; **Jack R. Lewin** MBBCh (Witwatersrand Univ 1971) Surgical Pathology; **Robert Lewis** PhD (Univ Mississippi 1974) Director, Immunopathology, Transplant/Immunology; **Bruce Mitchell** PhD (Univ Mississippi 1976) Laboratory Management; **Luminita Rezeanu** MD (Univ de Medicina Si Farm Grigore T. Popa 1985) Surgical Pathology; **William A. Rock** MD (LSU 1969) Director, Clinical Laboratory; **Anwer M. Siddiqi** MD (Dow Med Col 1994) Director, Residency Training Program; **Charu Subramony** MD (Univ New Delhi 1972) Director, Autopsy Services; **Jun Ming Wang** PhD (Antwerp Univ 1996) Research.

APPLICATIONS

All applicants must hold an MD or DO degree, or equivalent, and be a graduate of an approved American or Canadian medical school; or a graduate of a foreign medical school approved by the Mississippi Board of Medical Licensure and ECFMG certified. All applicants must be eligible for Mississippi licensure.

Address inquiries to:

Anwer M. Siddiqi, MD
Associate Professor, Pathology
Director, Pathology Residency Training Program
University of Mississippi Medical Center
2500 North State Street
Jackson MS 39216-4505
Phone: (601) 984-1879 • **E-mail:** pathresprogram@pathology.umsmed.edu
Web site: http://pathology.umc.edu

The University of Mississippi Medical Center is an Equal Opportunity Employer, M/F/D/V.

UNIVERSITY OF MISSOURI COLUMBIA HEALTH SCIENCES CENTER

Columbia, Missouri

PROGRAMS OFFERED

Our approved program is a four-year integrated experience in anatomic (AP) and clinical pathology (CP). When vacancies occur, residents trained elsewhere may be accepted at advanced standing for a combined program. AP includes experience in autopsy and surgical pathology, neuropathology, dermatopathology, forensic pathology, renal pathology, exfoliative and aspiration cytology, and immunohistochemistry. CP includes experience in hematology, coagulation, blood bank, flow cytometry, immunopathology, clinical chemistry, microbiology, molecular pathology, toxicology and transplantation immunology. All house staff actively participate in teaching medical students. Research and other teaching opportunities are available.

TYPES AND NUMBERS OF APPOINTMENTS

There are 11 RRC-approved positions in our integrated AP-CP program, which most of our residents pursue. A background in general AP and CP is provided by a series of required rotations totaling 42 months. The remaining months are used for elective experiences or research. Programs for those admitted with advanced standing are adjusted according to their previous experience. Initial rotations emphasize technical skills, methodology, disease mechanisms and the relationship of laboratory measurements to clinical problems. Subsequent rotations emphasize skills in consultation, quality assurance, and management. Specific learning objectives and laboratory inspection activities help guide the resident in becoming a competent pathologist.

FACILITIES

All training programs are under the direction of the University. University facilities include a 268-bed University Hospital, including a Children's Hospital, and Outpatient Clinics, the Medical Sciences Building, the Diabetes and Eye Research Centers, and the Health South Rehabilitation Center. Residents also rotate to Columbia Regional Hospital, a community hospital now owned by the University of Missouri. The closely affiliated 104-bed Harry S Truman Memorial Veterans Administration Hospital is across the street. The University also operates Ellis Fischel State Cancer Center three miles away. Our blood bank, coagulation and HLA laboratories are located at the Regional Red Cross Unit one-half mile from the University Medical Center and are directed by faculty of the Department of Pathology. Specimens processed yearly approximate: surgical pathology 13,483, clinical pathology 900,000, cytology 16,723 including an active fine needle aspiration service, FNAs 477, bone marrows 245, and hospital autopsies 47. Over 250 Medical Examiner's cases are also used for resident training. The Medical Examiner's Office is directed by the acting Medical Examiner, Dr. Edward Adelstein. Research facilities within the department include transmission electron microscopes, macro- and micro-computers, flow cytometry, DNA laboratories, including probe analysis, molecular diagnostic laboratory, an excellent immunoperoxidase laboratory and a nationally funded DNA microarray laboratory. Excellent, large cross-referred photographic files, paraffin tissue blocks, and glass slide collections go back three decades. All residents have unlimited Internet access.

COMMUNITY

Columbia is a college community, the home for over 150 years of the University of Missouri, the oldest Land-Grant campus west of the Mississippi, and two colleges. Lectures, concerts, art exhibits, dramatic productions and other activities on the three campuses are open to the public. Sports fans enjoy Big Twelve athletics. Within walking distance of the Medical Center are the University golf course, bowling lanes, tennis courts, gymnasia, including a large new student-faculty athletic center, and indoor-outdoor swimming pools. Fine restaurants and night spots are plentiful and accessible. The pace of a medium-small city (84,500 plus a 25,000 student population), recognized for its excellent overall quality of life, with moderate housing costs and excellent public schools, is combined with easy access to attractions in urban settings. Kansas City and St Louis are both 120 miles from Columbia.

STIPENDS AND MAINTENANCE

Residents in their first year of postgraduate training receive a stipend of $45,081, while 4th year residents receive $50,073. Residents receive malpractice coverage and a life insurance policy in the amount of their annual salary at no cost. A dental plan and several forms of health insurance are available through payroll deduction. Tax-deferred annuity plans are also available. Residents receive an $1200 annual travel and book stipend and four-weeks vacation per year.

STAFF

*Indicates faculty with major appointments in other departments or institutions.

Douglas C. Anthony MD, PhD (Duke Univ 1984) Professor and Chairman; anatomic and neuropathology; **Edward Adelstein** DVM, MD (Univ Missouri 1962, 1969) Associate Professor; Chief Pathology, VA Hospital; tumor immunopathology and microbiology; **William F Birkby** MD* (Creighton Univ 1973) Clinical Assistant Professor; **Charles W. Caldwell** MD, PhD (Univ Missouri 1976, 1983) Professor; Director Laboratories, Ellis Fischel Cancer Center; hematopathology and flow cytometry; **Robert F. Cheek** MD* (Univ Missouri 1990) Clinical Assistant Professor, dermatopathology; **Michael D Curry** MD* (Univ Oklahoma 1980) Clinical Associate Professor; **Alberto A. Diaz-Arias** MD (Univ Missouri 1985) Associate Professor, anatomic and clinical pathology.; **Madga Esebua** MD, (Tbilisi State Medical University, Tbilisi, Republic of Georgia) Assistant Professor, Anatomic and Clinical Pathology, Cytology; **Darcy D Folzenlogen** MD* (Univ Cincinnati 1976) Clinical Assistant Professor, antinuclear antibody laboratory; **Shellaine R Frazier** DO (Kirksville Col Osteopathic Med, 1998) Clinical Instructor, anatomic & clinical pathology; **Ann D Havey** MD (Southern Illinois Univ 1977) Clinical Assistant Professor, medical school teaching; **Ellis A. Ingram** MD (Univ Michigan 1974) Associate Professor, cytopathology, anatomic pathology; **Angela Konrad** DO (Des Moines University, Osteopathic Medical Center), Assistant Clinical Professor, Anatomic and Clinical Pathology, surgical pathology and pulmonary pathology; **Randie R. Little** PhD (Florida State Univ 1977) Research Associate Professor, diabetes; **Timothy S. Loy** MD (Univ Southern Illinois 1983) Associate Professor, anatomic pathology, immunohistochemistry, and electron microscopy; **Alan M. Luger** MD (Duke Univ 1971) Associate Professor, nephropathology with electron microscopy, transplantation immunology, anatomic pathology; Residency Program Director and Director Clinical Laboratories; **Judith Miles** PhD, MD* (Univ Indiana 1970, Univ Missouri 1975) Associate Professor, cytogenetics, genetic disease; **Douglas C. Miller** MD, PhD (University of Miami School of Medicine, Miami, Fl), Clinical Professor, Anatomic Pathology and Neuropatholgy; **Ranadhir Mitra** PhD (Univ Missouri 1971) Associate Professor, radioimmunoassay; **Marian Petrides** MD (Dartmouth Univ 1974) Clinical Associate Professor, pathology and anatomical sciences; **David L. Pittman** MD(Univ Nebraska Med Coll), Vice Chair of Clinical Affairs, Anatomic & Clinical Pathology, Cytopathology, Blood Banking/Transfusion Medicine; **Gordon C Sharp** MD* (Johns Hopkins Univ 1957) antinuclear antibody laboratory; **Linda Spollen** MD (Univ Kansas 1975) Associate Professor, neuropathology and anatomic pathology; **Carl C. Stacy** MD (Univ Oklahoma), Assistant Professor of Clinical Pathology, Anatomic & Clinical Pathology, Forensic Pathology; **Sara E Walker** MD* (Univ Texas Med Branch 1964) Professor Emeritus, antinuclear antibody laboratory; **Michael Wang** PhD, MD (Lanzhou Med Col Assistant Professor, Clinical Pathology, hematology, molecular genetic pathology.

APPLICATIONS

Candidates should be graduates of approved schools of medicine in the U.S. or Canada. Graduates of foreign medical schools must have an USMLE and/or ECFMG certificate and be eligible for Missouri licensure. Satisfactory references are required. Normal starting date is July 1. Applications must be submitted through ERAS by December 1st to be considered for the program.

Address inquiries to:

Alan M. Luger MD, Residency Program Director
Department of Pathology
University of Missouri-Columbia Medical Center
Columbia, MO 65212
Phone: (573) 882-1201

SAINT LOUIS UNIVERSITY SCHOOL OF MEDICINE

St. Louis, Missouri

PROGRAMS OFFERED

The Department of Pathology at Saint Louis University School of Medicine offers a four-year program leading to combined certification in Anatomic and Clinical Pathology. The emphasis in this program is on broad training within a university medical school environment for the resident interested in the hospital practice of anatomic and clinical pathology. Subspecialty training for all residents is provided in diagnostic electron microscopy, immunopathology, cytopathology, coagulation, microbiology, blood banking, cytogenetics, neuropathology, forensic pathology, hematopathology, molecular pathology, and pediatric pathology. Participation by residents in research and teaching is encouraged and expected.

FACILITIES

Five principal hospitals provide exposure to a full range of pathology. All are teaching hospitals affiliated with Saint Louis University: Saint Louis University Hospital with 356 beds, Cardinal Glennon Children's Hospital with 190 beds, St Mary's Health Center with 460 beds, the John Cochran VA Hospital with 218 beds, and Belleville Memorial Hospital with 340 beds. Department faculty is responsible for the Medical Examiner's Offices in the City and the County. A total of approximately 145 hospital autopsies, 400 forensic autopsies, 30,800 surgical specimens, 26,000 cytologies, and 2,800,000 laboratory tests are performed each year. Currently, 1,100 fine needle aspirates are interpreted in Cytopathology. The department also serves as a referral center for evaluation of hereditary bleeding and thrombophilic disorders, inherited metabolic diseases, muscle biopsies, renal biopsies, toxicology, immunohistochemistry, immunohematology and electron microscopy. There are three electron microscopes available for residents use: a JEOL 5800 scanning electron microscope equipped with an energy dispersive X-ray analysis system, a JEOL 100CX scanning transmission instrument, and a JEOL 1200 transmission electron microscope. A Flow Cytometry Laboratory houses two Beckman Coulter FC 500 flow cytometers. Active research programs exist in the department on molecular pathology and pediatric pathology, renal and dermatopathology, oncogenes and cytokines, molecular immunology, RNA metabolism in normal and tumor cells, platelet function, endothelial cell-neutrophil interaction, the pathology and treatment of lysosomal storage disease, forensic toxicology, signal transduction, phospholipid metabolism, atherogenesis, transplant pathology, molecular biology of ovarian neoplasia, molecular mechanisms of hepatic fibrogenesis, chemoprevention of colon cancer, and phospholipase activation.

COMMUNITY

St Louis is the urban center for a metropolitan region with a population of over two million. Cultural opportunities include the St Louis Art Museum, numerous art galleries, the St Louis Symphony Orchestra, an acclaimed opera company, several professional theaters, the Science Center,Âand a superb zoo. The Wagih Bari Society of St Louis Pathologists sponsors gatherings of the community of pathologists in the region for the enjoyment of scientific discourse. Opportunities abound for tennis, softball, golf, jogging, ice skating, handball, and other sports in the numerous parks in the city and adjacent county suburbs. A well-equipped recreation center is available on the University campus with an indoor track and swimming pool. Rivers within a one-day drive provide canoeing and float trips. There is sailing on nearby lakes. Professional sports are represented by the baseball Cardinals, the Rams football team, and the hockey Blues. Saint Louis University fields nationally competitive Billiken teams in basketball and soccer.

STIPENDS AND MAINTENANCE

Resident stipends for 2009 are as follows: first year $47,635, second year $48,036, third year $48,444, and fourth year $49,644. Fringe benefits include malpractice insurance and health coverage for residents and their families and a generous book and travel allowance.

STAFF

Saint Louis University Hospital and School of Medicine

Ritu Bhalla MD cytopathology; **Anping Chen** MD molecular mechanisms of hepatic fibrogenesis, chemoprevention of colon cancer; **Michael Creer** MD laboratory medicine, signal-activated phospholipases, molecular mechanisms of atherosclerosis, hematopoietic stem cell banking; **George Eliceiri** MD, PhD molecular biology, neoplasia; **Nancy Galvin** PhD electron microscopy, functional domains of proteins; **Judy Grishaber** DO laboratory medicine, transfusion medicine; **Leonard Grosso** MD, PhD flow cytometry, molecular pathology, immunopathology; **Bisong Haupt** MD surgical pathology; **Necat Havlioglu** MD neuropathology, surgical pathology; **Jacki Kornbluth** PhD molecular immunology; **Beth Levy** MD neuropathology, surgical pathology; **Mary Mayo** PhD laboratory medicine, chemistry; **Jane McHowat** PhD phospholipid metabolism, ischemia-induced activation of phospholipases, signal transduction; **Kiyoko**

Oshima MD GI and liver pathology; **Nancy Phillips** MD surgical pathology, ovarian neoplasia; **Ratna Ray** PhD transcriptional regulation, cell growth and development, oncogenesis; **Alice Rickard** MS experimental pathology; **Jan Ryerse** PhD electron microscopy, morphogenetics; **Ella Swierkosz** PhD laboratory medicine, microbiology, virology.

Cardinal Glennon Children's Hospital

Jacqueline R. Batanian PhD cytogenetics; **David Brink** MD pediatric pathology; **Cirilo Sotelo** MD pediatric pathology; **Ella Swierkosz** PhD laboratory medicine, microbiology, virology; **Carole Vogler** MD pediatric pathology, metabolic disease.

Belleville Memorial Hospital

E. Stephen Bolesta MD anatomic and clinical pathology.

St Mary's Health Center

Alexander Babich MD surgical pathology, anatomic and clinical pathology; **Gloria Merenda** MD surgical pathology, cytopathology; **Mona Mirkhaef** MD surgical pathology; **Sumati Rao** MD anatomic and clinical pathology; **Janusz Wolaniuk** MD cytopathology, anatomic and clinical pathology.

John Cochran VA Hospital

Hyung Chung MD neuropathology; **Sandra F. Gibson** MD laboratory medicine, clinical microbiology; **Detlef Ritter** MD laboratory medicine, clinical pathology; **Rudolph Yanuck** MD hematopathology.

Medical Examiner's Office, St Louis City and County

Phillip Burch MD forensic pathology; **Mary E. Case** MD forensic pathology, neuropathology; **Mary Fran Ernst** BLS forensic science; **Michael Graham** MD forensic pathology, cardiac pathology; **Christopher Long** PhD forensic toxicology, effects of drugs on neuronal transmission in central nervous system; **Jane Turner** MD, PhD forensic pathology.

APPLICATIONS

Residency candidates must be graduates of medical schools in the United States or Canada or graduates of foreign medical schools certified by the ECFMG. Applications accepted through the Electronic Residency Application Service (ERAS).

Address inquiries to:

Carole Vogler, MD
Director, Residency Training Program
Department of Pathology
Saint Louis University School of Medicine
1402 South Grand Blvd., St Louis, MO 63104
Phone: (314) 577-8694 • **Fax:** (314) 268-5641 • **E-mail:** voglerca@slu.edu
Web site: http://path.slu.edu

WASHINGTON UNIVERSITY MEDICAL CENTER

St. Louis, Missouri

PROGRAMS OFFERED

The Department of Pathology and Immunology at Washington University School of Medicine, in conjunction with Barnes-Jewish Hospital, and the St Louis Children's Hospital, offers fully approved training programs in Anatomic Pathology, Clinical Pathology, combined training in both fields, and training in subspecialty areas of pathology. These training programs include instruction and experience in experimental pathology with the unique opportunity for the trainee to undertake original investigation in his field of interest. Clinical emphasis is placed on specialization, with the trainee assuming increasing diagnostic responsibility under expert supervision in the subspecialties of anatomic pathology or of laboratory medicine after basic training in the selected branch of pathology. The goal of the program is to train individuals who will be expert in their area of interest and will be prepared for a career in research, teaching and the practice of pathology. The anatomic pathology program offers training in general pathology and the subspecialty areas of surgical pathology, cytology, neuropathology, pediatric pathology, endocrine pathology, molecular pathology, obstetrics and gynecological pathology, oncology, cardiovascular pathology, renal pathology, immunopathology, dermatopathology, liver and gastrointestinal pathology, hematopathology, environmental pathology and bone pathology. The clinical pathology program offers training in clinical chemistry, clinical immunology, clinical microbiology, blood banking/transfusion medicine and immunohematology, histocompatability and immunogenetics, hematology and hemostasis, and computer sciences. Post-doctoral research fellowship positions are available in all of the above areas. All trainees hold appointments at Washington University and participate in the teaching of medical students.

TYPES AND NUMBERS OF APPOINTMENTS

Forty-two house staff positions are available with 10 first-year positions which may be entered at the intern level or after training in another medical specialty.

FACILITIES

Barnes-Jewish Hospital and St Louis Children's Hospital: 1,277 beds; 358 autopsies; 45,000-50,000 surgical accessions and 4 million laboratory test requests. Research facilities are fully equipped for biochemical, metabolic and morphologic investigations in the fields of cellular immunology, immunopathology, transplantation immunology, histocompatibility typing and human diseases, immunopathology of virus infection, chemical carcinogenesis, viral carcinogenesis, neoplasia, tumor specific antigens, immunology of plasmacytomas, diabetes, endocrine pathology, hormone action, hormone secretion, coagulation, experimental production of emphysema, microchemistry of the CNS, bone metabolism and pathology, molecular pathology, and environmental pathobiology. There are three well stocked medical libraries within the department as well as easy access to the Medical School library. Graduate courses may be taken at the Medical School or main University campus.

COMMUNITY

The Washington University Medical Center is located at the western edge of the City of St Louis, adjacent to St Louis County and to Forest Park, one of the world's finest public parks. A system of highways or buses and the new Metrolink light rail system provide easy access to the Center with reasonable housing available in nearby residential areas. The community provides an excellent zoo, art museum, science center, skating rink and tennis courts, all in Forest Park, as well as a world- renowned symphony orchestra, professional sports and excellent theatre.

STIPENDS AND MAINTENANCE

House officers and trainees begin at $45,680 and increase each year thereafter.

STAFF

Herbert W. Virgin MD, PhD Mallinckrodt Professor and Chairman; use of molecular and immunologic tools to study herpesvirus latency.

Professors of Pathology and Immunology and their research fields

Paul M. Allen PhD immunobiology and biochemistry of antigen presentation by accessory cells; **D. Craig Allred** MD development, progression, and prognosis of human premalignant breast disease; **Jacques U. Baenziger** MD, PhD autopsy pathology, biochemistry of cell membrane; **Elizabeth Brunt** MD surgical pathology and liver/GI pathology; **Hugh Chaplin Jr.** MD Professor Emeritus laboratory medicine, quantitative erythrocyte and plateletserology, immunoglobulins and complement subcomponents; **Marco Colonna** MD human and murine innate responses against pathogens; **Janet Connolly** PhD T lymphocyte recognition of MHC Class I; **Erika C. Crouch** MD, PhD pulmonary pathology, biology of collagen; **Louis Dehner** MD surgical pathology, pediatric pathology; **W. Michael Dunne** PhD laboratory medicine, microbiology; **Jeffrey I. Gordon** MD Director, Center for Genome Sciences; **Ted Hansen** PhD antigen presentation by MHC-1 proteins to T cells; **Peter A. Humphrey** MD, PhD Director, Anatomic and Molecular Pathology, surgical pathology, urologic pathology; **John M. Kissane** MD autopsy pathology, pediatric pathology; **Michael Kyriakos** MD surgical pathology, bone pathology; **Jack H. Ladenson** PhD laboratory medicine, metabolism of ionized calcium, sodium and potassium; **Helen Liapis** MD surgical pathology; renal pathology; **Douglas Lublin** MD, PhD laboratory medicine, transfusion medicine; **Michael L. McDaniel** PhD microchemistry, islet cell metabolism; **Jeffrey D. Milbrandt** MD, PhD laboratory medicine, developmental expression of genes regulated by nerve growth factor; **Kenneth M.M. Murphy** MD, PhD molecular biology of immune system; **Arie Perry** MD neuropathology, clinicopathologic and genetic markers of prognosis in gliomas and meningiomas; **John D. Pfeifer** MD, PhD Associate Chief Anatomic and Molecular Pathology, surgical pathology, molecular diagnostics, molecular genetic testing; **Robert Schmidt** MD, PhD Director Neuropathology; neuropathology, diabetic autonomic neuropathy; **Robert D. Schreiber** PhD molecular immunology, immunobiology and immunopathology, biochemistry and molecular biology of macrophage activating lymphokines; **Mitchell G. Scott** PhD laboratory medicine, study of human B cell development; **Andrey S. Shaw** MD Director of Immunobiology, molecular biology of T cell activation; **Barry Sleckman** MD, PhD DIrector, Division Laboratory and Genomic Medicine, developmental immunology; **Carl H. Smith Jr.** MD Professor Pediatrics; Co-director Chemistry Section Core Laboratory, Children's Hospital; **Steven L. Teitelbaum** MD anatomic pathology; bone metabolism and pathology; **John W. Turk** MD, PhD laboratory medicine; phospholipids as mediators; **Emil R Unanue** MD immunobiology and immunopathology; **Barbara Zehnbauer** PhD laboratory medicine, DNA-based diagnostics.

Associate Professors of Pathology and Immunology and their research fields

Morey Blinder MD laboratory medicine; hematology; **Kyunghee Choi** PhD hematopoiesis, biology and regulation; **George Despotis** MD hematology; **Charles Eby** MD hematology/coagulation; **Samir El-Mofty** MD surgical pathology, oral pathology; **Daved Fremont** PhD structural biology of T-cell receptor and histocompatibility molecules; **Ann Gronowski** PhD Medical Director Clinical Chemistry, Serology and Immunology;maternal fetal medicine & women's health; **Phyllis C. Huettner** MD Director, Residency Training Program; surgical pathology; GYN pathology; **Rakesh Nagarajan** MD, PhD bioinformatics; **Jon Ritter** MD surgical pathology, pulmonary pathology; **Wojciech Swat** PhD regulation of lymphocyte development and function; **Mark Watson** MD, PhD laboratory medicine; Director Tumor Repository; **Francis V. White** MD surgical pathology, pediatric pathology; **Nabeel Yaseen** MD PhD Director, Hematopathology; molecular pathogenesis of acute myeloid leukemia.

Assistant Professors of Pathology and Immunology and their research fields

Deepta Bhattacharya PhD; **Dengfeng Cao** MD, PhD surgical and GYN pathology; **Joseph Corbo** MD, PhD neuropathology; **Jamie Donnelly** MD surgical pathology; **John Frater** MD hematopathology; **Anjum Hassan** MD hematopathology; **Yina Huang** PhD molecular mechanisms of lymphocyte activation and development; **Friederike Kreisel** MD hematopathology; **Hannah Krigman** MD surgical pathology, GYN Pathology; **Shashikant Kulkarni** PhD Cytogenetics; molecular characterization of chromosomal anomalies in human development and cancer; **James Lewis** MD surgical pathology; ENT pathology; **Anne Lind** MD dermatopathology; **Dongsi Lu** MD, PhD surgical pathology; dermatopathology; **Mark Miller** PhD immunology; **Jason C Mills** MD, PhD molecular biology and bioinformatics of gut stem cells; **TuDong Nguyen** MD PhD hematopathology; **Andres Roma** MD surgical pathology, GYN Pathology; **Thaddeus Stappenbeck** MD, PhD intestinal epithelial stem cell biology; **Lourdes Ylagan** MD surgical pathology; cytopathology; **Lijuan Zhang** PhD, heparan and chondroitin sulfate in FGF/FGFR signaling and in immunology.

APPLICATIONS

Address inquiries to:

Dr. Phyllis C. Huettner, MD, Director, Pathology Residency Program
Department of Pathology & Immunology
Washington U School of Medicine
660 S Euclid Ave
Box 8118
St Louis, MO 63110
Phone: (314) 362-7472
Web site: http://pathimmuno.wustl.edu/

for Anatomic Pathology and combined AP/CP
Barry Sleckman, MD, PhD, Director. Division of Laboratory and Genomic Medicine
Washington U School of Medicine
660 S Euclid Ave
Box 8118
St Louis, MO 63110
Phone: (314) 362-3110
Web site: http://pathimmuno.wustl.edu/
for Laboratory Medicine (CP)

CREIGHTON UNIVERSITY AND AFFILIATED HOSPITALS

Omaha, Nebraska

PROGRAMS OFFERED

The Department of Pathology offers a training program in anatomic and clinical pathology. Anatomic pathology includes training in autopsy and surgical pathology, forensics, neuropathology, immunopathology, cytology and electron microscopy. Clinical pathology includes training in hematology, coagulation, cytogenetics and molecular genetics, transfusion medicine, diagnostic immunology, flow cytometry, clinical chemistry, toxicology, and microbiology. Initial rotations emphasize technical skills, methodology, basic disease mechanisms, and relationships to clinical problems, and later rotations emphasize development of consultative and management skills. All house staff actively participate in teaching medical students, pharmacy students and other junior house staff. Research is an important part of our program and all residents can apply for research funds. Preceptors from among the faculty are available to assist with project selection and completion.

TYPES AND NUMBERS OF APPOINTMENTS

Eleven pathology resident positions are available. The residency is 18 months of core anatomic pathology and 18 months of core clinical pathology broken into variably interspersed blocks. The final 12 months are elective months.

FACILITIES

All training programs are under the direction of Creighton University. The primary teaching hospital of Creighton University is the 242-bed Creighton University Medical Center. Opened in 1977, the six-level hospital combines modern medical facilities with a tradition of community service that has distinguished Creighton University Medical Center for more than a century. The western portion of the Hospital building is leased to the Creighton Health Professions Center which has classrooms, offices, and outpatient clinics and examination rooms for faculty members. The Medical Center also includes the Boys Town National Research Hospital; the School of Dentistry; and the Health Sciences Library and Bio-Information Center. The Department of Pathology operates the Creighton Medical Laboratories, an outreach service that provides laboratory services to Creighton clinics, community physicians, and rural hospitals and clinics. The Hospital and the residency program work closely with the Midwest Regional Blood Center, American Red Cross. The Hospital clinical laboratories are modern and well-equipped to provide comprehensive service and training in all areas of laboratory medicine. The Medical Center has 12,000 admissions annually, with 312 autopsies, 16,000 surgicals, 25,447 cytologies, and over 1,536,257 billable tests or profiles performed. Resident rotations at the American Red Cross Blood Center, Nebraska Forensic Institute, Omaha Veterans Affairs Medical Center and Children's Hospital are integrated into the pathology training program.

COMMUNITY

Omaha is located on the west bank of the Missouri River and is part of an extensive transportation and trading network. Its beautiful rolling hills and woodlands provide both land and water recreation. Numerous cultural facilities include museums, theatre, opera, ballet, and symphony. Omaha has excellent school systems and several other institutions of higher education. With a metropolitan population of about 700,000, it captures the advantages of a large city along with the relaxed nature and pride of a small town.

STIPENDS AND MAINTENANCE

First-year residents in 2008-2009 received $48,250 annually with an increase for each subsequent year. Malpractice, life, health and disability insurance, and laboratory coats are provided.

STAFF

Professor and Chairman (Pathology)

Roger A. Brumback MD (Penn State Univ 1971) Neuropathology, Residency Training Program Director.

Emeritus (Pathology)

James C Healy MD (Creighton Univ 1984) Consultant; **Hal C. Lankford** PhD (St Louis Univ 1959) Consultant Creighton Medical Laboratories; **Herbert J. Quigley, Jr.** MD (Univ Pennsylvania 1962) Omaha VA Med Ctr.

Professors (Pathology)

Robert C Allen MD, PhD (Tulane Univ 1977) Medical Director Creighton Medical Laboratories; **Chhanda Bewtra** MBBS (India Inst Med Sci 1972) Anatomic Pathology; Director Cytology, Surgical Pathology, OB-GYN pathology; **Zoran Gatalica** MD, DSc (Univ Zagreb, Coatia 1984) Director Anatomic Pathology, Director Cytopathology,

Tumor Pathology; **William J. Hunter** MD (Creighton Univ 1971) Director, Electron Microscopy, Renal Pathology; **Deba Sarma** MBBS (Dacca (Dhaka) Univ, Bangladesh 1969) Dermatopathology.

Associate Professors (Pathology)

Edward D. Adickes DO (Des Moines Univ 1977) Associate Chief of Veteran Affairs Medical Center, Surgical Pathology, Neuropathology; **Richard J. Baltaro** MD, PhD (Catholic Univ, Rome 1983, Univ Rome 1983) Director Clinical Chemistry and Immunology; **Stephen J. Cavalieri** PhD (Univ West Virginia 1981) Director Microbiology, Virology/Serology; **Joseph A Knezetic** PhD (Univ Cinicinnati 1986) Molecular Pathology; **Henry C. Nipper** PhD (Univ Maryland 1971) Director, Toxicology.

Assistant Professors (Pathology)

Caishu Deng MD (Hunan Med Col, Changsha, China, 1986) Cytopathology; **Donald A. Giger** PhD (Tulane Univ 1977) Omaha VA Med Ctr, microbiology; **Qinglong Hu** MD (Sun Yat-sen Univ Med Sci 1982) Hematopathology; **Hina Naushad** MBBS (Univ Punjab, Pakistan, 1996) Director, Hematopathology; **Poonam Sharma** MD (Lady Hardinge Med Col, Univ of Delhi, India 1991) Gastrointestinal Pathology; **Susan K Repertinger** MD (Univ Iowa Col Med) May 1995, Associate Residency Training Program Director; **Lisa N Tyler** MD (Univ Arkansas Med Sci 1981) Director, Transfusion Medicine; **Qingmei Xie** MD (Tongji Med Univ, China, 1987), Hematopathology.

Associate Clinical Professor (Pathology)

Matthias I. Okoye MD, JD (Univ Lagos, Nigeria and Conjoint Board England, U.K. 1974) forensic pathology.

Assistant Clinical Professors (Pathology)

Deborah Perry MD (Univ Nebraska 1983) pediatric pathology; **Ram Reddy** MD (Kurnool Med Col, India 1972) Medical Director Red Cross; **Jonathon W Rouse** MD (Creighton Univ Sch Med, May 1986), Surgical Pathology; **Thomas A. Ruma** MD (Creighton Univ 1973) surgical pathology.

APPLICATIONS

Address inquiries to:

Roger A. Brumback, MD
Director, Pathology Residency Training Program
Creighton University Medical Center
601 North 30th Street
Omaha, NE 68131
Phone: (402) 280-3436 • **Fax:** (402) 280-5247 • **E-mail:** rbrumback@creighton.edu

UNIVERSITY OF NEBRASKA MEDICAL CENTER

Omaha, Nebraska

PROGRAMS OFFERED

The Department of Pathology & Microbiology at the University of Nebraska Medical Center offers a fully accredited, four-year residency program in anatomic and clinical pathology (AP/CP) in addition to fellowship training in hematopathology and surgical pathology. Our residency program is designed to provide a broad-based education that meets the requirements of the American Board of Pathology and prepares residents for pathology careers in either private practice or academics. Our flexible program consists of core rotations through each of the basic AP and CP disciplines, followed by advanced rotations and electives including molecular diagnostics, cytogenetics, flow cytometry, forensic pathology, pediatric pathology as well as other subspecialty areas including transplant pathology, dermatopathology, neuropathology, hematopathology and others. Knowledge and skills are gained through service rotations, a didactic AP/CP core curriculum, numerous subspecialty and interdisciplinary conferences and teaching activities for medical students as well as allied health students. With the guidance of a large full-time faculty, residents gradually assume greater responsibility for pathology service and activities as they progress through the residency. Research in investigative pathology including diagnostic, molecular and experimental pathology is encouraged. Many research opportunities are available for residents within the department and institution. During the past year, extramural grants totaling in excess of 10 million dollars supported the research efforts in our department.

TYPES AND NUMBERS OF APPOINTMENTS

The program is approved for a total of 12 AP/CP residency positions, in addition to two fellowship positions in hematopathology and one surgical pathology fellowship.

FACILITIES

The University of Nebraska Medical Center (UNMC) is the only public health science center in the state. UNMC serves as both a primary care facility and as a tertiary referral center and is recognized as one of the country's leading centers in cancer (particularly hematopoietic malignancies), transplantation biology, bioterrorism preparedness, neurodegenerative disease, cardiovascular diseases, genetics and biomedical technology. The Nebraska Medical Center is the hospital partner of UNMC. It is Nebraska's largest teaching hospital licensed for 735 beds and approximately 26,000 discharges annually. The department annually processes approximately 32,000 surgical specimens, 25,000 cytology specimens, 160 autopsies and over 5 million clinical laboratory tests. Over 400 forensic autopsies are done at the Douglas County Coroner's Office yearly. In addition to the departmental library, the Library of Medicine on campus has over 175,000 books and 2,400 journals. It is a partner of the Midcontinental Regional Library, which serves seven states and is affiliated with the National Library of Medicine.

COMMUNITY

Omaha is a metropolitan center of more than 750,000 people that is strategically located within a day's drive to the Rocky Mountains, Minneapolis, Kansas City and Chicago. It has affordable housing and excellent school systems as well as several other institutions of higher education. In Omaha you can enjoy world-class theatre, symphony, opera, art galleries, malls and more. The trendy Old Market area is a popular gathering spot with exciting shops and nightlife. Whether you are walking the forests trails or the corridors of museums, our city's diversity will surprise you.

STIPENDS AND MAINTENANCE

First-year residents will receive approximately $46,130 with increases for subsequent years (subject to approval by the Board of Regents). An appointment provides generous fringe benefits including four weeks paid vacation and five days educational leave per year as well as malpractice insurance, lab coats, book and journal allowances, lunches, comprehensive health insurance and funds to attend national meetings when presenting.

STAFF

Professors

Steven H Hinrichs MD (Univ North Dakota, 1980) Chairman; microbiology, molecular biology; **Julia A Bridge** MD (Univ Nebraska, 1984) cytopathology, tumor cytogenetics; **Steven D Carson** PhD (Rice Univ, 1978) coagulation; **Wing-Chung Chan** MD (Univ Hong Kong, 1973) hematopathology; **Samuel M Cohen** MD, PhD (Univ Wisconsin, 1972) urologic pathology, chemical carcinogenesis; **Timothy C Greiner** MD (Univ Iowa, 1986) hematopathology, molecular pathology; **Sonny L Johansson** MD, PhD (Univ Göteborg, 1972) surgical pathology, urologic pathology, chemical carcinogenesis; **Audrey Lazenby** MD (Johns Hopkins Univ, 1982) surgical pathology, gastrointestinal pathology; **Rodney S Markin** MD, PhD (Univ Nebraska, 1983) hepatic pathology, informatics and laboratory automation;

Rodney D McComb MD (Univ Rochester, 1976) neuropathology; **Samuel Pirruccello** MD (Univ Nebraska, 1982) immunopathology, clinical chemistry, flow cytometry; **Stanley J Radio** MD (Univ Iowa, 1983) cardiovascular, transplantation, cytopathology; **Dennis D Weisenburger** MD (Univ Minnesota, 1974) hematopathology; **James Wisecarver** MD, PhD (Univ Nebraska, 1982) transplantation and molecular pathology.

Associate Professors

Patricia Aoun MD, MPH (Johns Hopkins Univ, 1985) hematopathology; **John J Baker** MD (Univ Nebraska, 1979) cytopathology, surgical pathology; **James Booth** PhD (Univ Nebraska, 1975) microbiology; **Paul D Fey** PhD (Creighton Univ, 1995) bacterial pathogenesis, antibiotic resistance; **Peter Iwen** PhD (Univ Nebraska, 2001) microbiology; **Jerry Jones** MD (Emeritus) (Univ Cincinnati, 1958) forensic pathology; **James D Landmark** MD (Univ Minnesota, 1971) transfusion medicine; **Subodh M Lele** MD (Univ Bombay, 1991) surgical pathology, gynecologic & urologic pathology, cytopathology; **Deborah Perry** MD (Clinical) (Univ Nebraska, 1984) pediatric pathology; **Douglas Stickle** PhD (Univ Texas Hlth Sci Ctr at Houston, 1989) clinical chemistry; **William W West** MD (Univ Nebraska, 1977) cytopathology, pulmonary pathology, breast pathology.

Assistant Professors

Dominick DiMaio MD (Univ Texas, 1995) surgical pathology, dermatopathology; **Kirk W Foster** MD (Univ Maryland, 1977) renalpathology, autopsy pathology; **Kai Fu** MD (Tianjin Med Univ, 1990) hematopathology; **Syed Ali Jaffar Kazmi** MD (Univ Karachi, Pakistan, 1989) neuropathology, surgical pathology, autopsy pathology; **Geoffrey A Talmon** MD (Univ Nebraska, 2007) surgical pathology, renal pathology, transplantation pathology.

APPLICATIONS

Residency is open to graduates of approved medical or osteopathic schools in the United States or Canada and International Medical Graduates who have an ECFMG certificate. Only applications submitted through the Electronic Residency Application Service (ERAS) will be considered. Preference for interviews will be given to applications received before November 15th for appointments beginning July 1 of the following year.

Address inquiries to:

Subodh M. Lele, MD
Pathology Residency Program Director
Department of Pathology and Microbiology
University of Nebraska Medical Center
983135 Nebraska Medical Center
Omaha, NE 68198-3135
Phone: (402) 559-7726 • **Fax:** (402) 559-6018 • **E-mail:** slele@unmc.edu
Web site: http://www.unmc.edu/Pathology

DARTMOUTH-HITCHCOCK MEDICAL CENTER DARTMOUTH MEDICAL SCHOOL

Lebanon, New Hampshire

PROGRAMS OFFERED

The Department of Pathology offers broad-based training in both anatomic and clinical pathology, either in preparation for the general practice of pathology or as a foundation for further specialty training. An organized three-year core program provides the basis for the general training and encourages increasing responsibility as residents gain experience and competence. Anatomic pathology offers training in autopsy and surgical pathology, cytology, dermatopathology, forensic pathology, neuropathology, electron microscopy, and immunohistochemistry. The clinical diagnostic laboratories cover blood bank and transfusion medicine, microbiology, clinical chemistry, hematology, radioisotope techniques, instrumentation, clinical decision analysis, molecular pathology/genetics, and flow cytometry. Residents interested in an academic career have an excellent opportunity to participate in teaching and research at the Dartmouth Medical School. In the Department there is research in medical informatics, cell culture, cytogenetics, diagnostic molecular genetics, gene mapping, experimental carcinogenesis, flow cytometry, vascular biology, neuropathology and neuroimmunology, pediatric developmental pathology, molecular parasitology, electron microscopy, immunoperoxidase techniques, and tumor biology.

TYPES AND NUMBERS OF APPOINTMENTS

The institution is approved for 14 residents in pathology. Appointments are made on an annual basis. Residencies are offered in surgery, medicine, neurosurgery, orthopedics, otolaryngology, urology, dermatology, psychiatry, neurology, diagnostic radiology, palliative medicine, pediatrics, anesthesiology, child psychiatry, obstetrics/gynecology, plastic surgery, vascular surgery, family practice, and leadership preventive medicine.

FACILITIES

The Dartmouth-Hitchcock Medical Center (DHMC) is comprised of the Mary Hitchcock Memorial Hospital (MHMH), the Dartmouth-Hitchcock Clinic (DHC), the Dartmouth Medical School (DMS), and the nearby Veterans Affairs Medical Center in White River Junction, VT. DHMC is a modern, state-of-the-art facility in a spectacular setting two miles from the Dartmouth College campus. The pathology faculty and all clinical and research laboratories are located on contiguous floors in the same building. MHMH has a bed capacity of 380, plus ICN and Nursery. In 2008 there were 23,048 inpatient admissions; 1.9 million laboratory tests; 66,024 surgical specimens; 35,673 cytology specimens; 158 autopsies. Residency training at MHMH provides in-depth experience and graded responsibility, as well as broad, general training in anatomic and clinical pathology. The faculty of the Department of Pathology at Dartmouth Medical School has excellent facilities for pathologic investigation. The Dana Biomedical Library houses medical and biological references: 260,000 volumes and 3,000 periodicals, and 7,000 audio-visual microcomputer software programs. The departmental library provides books and journals applicable to all phases of pathology. Residents have full access to on-line journals. Each resident is provided with a computer and microscope.

COMMUNITY

The Medical Center is located in Lebanon, two miles from downtown Hanover, a small rural New England college town 130 miles north of Boston and 300 miles from New York City, connected by interstate highways 89 and 91. Hanover is the home of Dartmouth College and the center of cultural activities usually found only in metropolitan centers. The area is noted for year-round recreational activities. Lebanon, NH has been cited as one of the best small communities in the country.

STIPENDS AND MAINTENANCE

Approximate 2009-2010 stipends: $45,860 (GL1); $48,360 (GL2); $51,070 (GL3); and $53,500 (GL4). Rental housing for single and married physicians is readily available within the area. Comprehensive health care coverage is provided for the resident, spouse and children at minimal cost to the house officer. Life insurance, disability income protection, and professional liability insurance are also provided by the Medical Center. Optional dental insurance is available at minimal cost. Each resident is registered with the New Hampshire Board of Registration in Medicine permitting practice within the program.

STAFF

Thomas A. Andrew MD (Univ Cincinnati 1982) Assoc Prof, forensic pathology; **Candice C. Black** DO (Nova Southeastern Univ 1996) Assoc Prof and Director of Residency Program, surgical and oncologic pathology; **Jeoffry B. Brennick** MD (Harvard 1991) Asst Prof, dermatopathology; **Larry J. Dumont** PhD (Univ Colorado 2005) Asst Prof, transfusion medicine research; **Jennie V. Duval** MD (McGill 1992) Asst Prof, forensic pathology; **Margaret A. French** MD PharmD (Dartmouth 1985) Asst Prof, clinical pathology; **Jorge L. Gonzalez** MD (Univ Miami 1985)

Asst Prof, cytopathology, gynecologic pathology; **James D. Gorham** MD, PhD (NYU 1992) Assoc Prof, transfusion medicine; research: immunology, molecular and cell biology; **Edward J. Gutmann** MD, AM (Albert Einstein Col Med 1983) Assoc Prof, cytopathology; **Brent T. Harris** MD, PhD (Georgetown 1995) Asst Prof, neuropathology; research: ALS, motor neuron survival; **William F. Hickey** MD (Univ Vermont 1977) Prof, neuropathology; research: neuroimmunology; **Prabhjot Kaur** MBBS (Assam Med Col 1995) Asst Prof, hematopathology; **Hong Kee Lee** PhD (National Univ Singapore 2000) Asst Prof, medicinal chemistry; interests: clinical chemistry, toxicology, and pharmacogenomics; **Norman B. Levy** MD (Univ Michigan 1976) Assoc Prof, hematopathology; research: diagnostic molecular genetics, flow cytometry; **Vincent A. Memoli** MD (Tufts 1976) Prof, anatomic pathology; research: neuroendocrine pathology; **T.K. Mohandas** PhD (McGill 1972) Prof, cytogenetics; research: genes of the X-chromosome; **Kim Ornvold** MD (Univ Copenhagen 1975) Assoc Prof, anatomic and pediatric pathology; **Vijayalakshmi Padmanabhan** MBBS MD (Kasturba Med Col 1986) Asst Prof, surgical pathology and cytopathology; research: genitourinary pathology; **Ann E. Perry** MD (Florida 1985) Assoc Prof, dermatopathology; **Nora R. Ratcliffe** MD (Univ Colorado 1991) Assoc Prof, transfusion medicine; research: autoimmune myocarditis; **C. Harker Rhodes** MD, PhD (Rockefeller-Cornell Univ 1982) Assoc Prof, neuropathology; research: biology of glial tumors; **Kathryn L Ruoff** PhD (Cornell Univ 1975) Assoc Prof, microbiology; interest: microbiology; **Alan R. Schned** MD (Columbia Univ 1975) Prof, anatomic pathology; research: uropathology; **Joseph D. Schwartzman** MD (Harvard 1974) Prof, microbiology; research: *Toxoplasma gondii*; **Amitabh Srivastava** MBBS (King George's Med Col 1990) Asst Prof, gastrointestinal pathology; **Craig A Storm** MD (Univ Minnesota 1996) Asst Prof, dermatopathology; **Arief A. Suriawinata** MD (Univ Indonesia, 1995) Assist Prof, anatomic/GI pathology; research: GI/transplant pathology; **Zbigniew M. Szczepiorkowski** MD, PhD (Med Acad Warsaw, 1991) Assoc Prof, transfusion medicine; research: stem cells; **Gregory J Tsongalis** PhD (UMDNJ 1990) Assoc Prof, molecular pathology and diagnostics; **Wendy A. Wells** MD (St Thomas's Hosp Med Sch, London 1982) Prof and Chair, cytopathology; research: breast pathology, image analysis; **Shaofeng Yan** MD, PhD (Peking Union Med Col 1994) Asst Prof, dermatopathology.

APPLICATIONS

Eligibility and application requirements are provided on our web site. References and personal interviews are required. Applications must be submitted through the Electronic Residency Application Service (ERAS) by November 1.

Address inquiries to:

Candice C. Black, DO, Residency Program Director
c/o Susan C. Hawk, Program Coordinator
Department of Pathology
Dartmouth-Hitchcock Medical Center
Lebanon, NH 03756-0001
Phone: (603) 650-8623
Web site: http://www.dhmc.org/dept/pathology

View of new Dartmouth-Hitchcock Medical Center campus in Lebanon, New Hampshire

SAINT BARNABAS MEDICAL CENTER

Integrated Pathology Residency Program

Livingston, New Jersey

PROGRAMS OFFERED

This is an ACGME- accredited four-year postgraduate training program in anatomic and clinical pathology. It is an integrated program with Saint Barnabas Medical Center in Livingston, NJ, Newark Beth Israel Medical Center in Newark, NJ, and Monmouth Medical Center in Long Branch, NJ, all members of the Saint Barnabas Health Care System. The integrated program in pathology offers the resident the opportunity to train in diverse hospital practice settings from suburban to urban community hospital settings. The trainee is exposed to a wide variety of cases reflecting the various demographic populations of the communities served. The program is fully integrated among the three institutions with specific rotations at designated centers or at selected off-site locations covering all aspects of anatomic and clinical pathology. All rotations are structured with specific goals and objectives. Evaluations of the trainee, the faculty members and rotations are carried out regularly. These evaluations are reviewed with the trainees in a constructive manner and followed up by the program director. It is the fundamental belief of the program faculty that trainees should be involved in everyday practice as members of the healthcare team with graduated responsibility, thereby giving them the opportunity to evolve into responsible pathologists able to serve the community in either a private practice or university setting. Residents are involved in intra and extradepartmental teaching conferences as well as research endeavors. There is the opportunity to conduct research during the training period and grant funding is available. Publication in peer-reviewed journals is encouraged by the faculty.

REQUIREMENTS

Passage of USMLE steps 1 and 2 are necessary prior to the start of training. In addition, it is institutional policy that all trainees must have successfully completed USMLE step 3 prior to being allowed to progress to PGY 3.

TYPES AND NUMBERS OF APPOINTMENTS

There are a total of 18 positions available in the four-year AP/CP program (averaging between four and five PGY 1 positions per year).

FACILITIES

The clinical laboratories of the three institutions combined have an aggregate total of over 50,000 surgical accessions, 26,000 cytology specimens, 130 autopsies and over 4,000,000 clinical tests annually. These facilities draw from over 75,000 annual admissions and a capacity of 1,700 hospital beds. There are numerous residency programs within the system with over 400 residents promoting interdisciplinary interaction between programs. Each institution has up-to-date library facilities with access to medline and subscriptions to most peer-reviewed journal publications. Each medical center has specific areas of excellence such as the Saint Barnabas Burn Center, the Monmouth Medical Cancer Center, and the Heart and Lung Transplant Program at Newark Beth Israel Medical Center. The Saint Barnabas HealthCare System is a major teaching affiliate of the Mount Sinai Medical School, New York, NY.

COMMUNITY

The three institutions geographically encompass the northern and central portions of the state. Saint Barnabas Medical Center and Newark Beth Israel Medical Center are situated in Essex County and are in a suburban and urban community respectively. The northern part of the state affords quick access to New York City by car, bus or train. There are also cultural and entertainment spots in the immediate vicinity including the Center for Performing Arts in Newark. Monmouth Medical Center, located in Monmouth County, is at the New Jersey shore. The town of Edison is roughly equidistant between the major institutions and offers a good school system and diverse population. Summer and winter sports are readily available within the state as well as in neighboring Pennsylvania affording an enjoyable lifestyle.

STIPENDS AND MAINTENANCE

At the first-year graduate training level (PGY 1) the annual stipend is $44,959. This amount increases at an increment of $2,000 per year until the fourth year. There is no supplemental pay for a chief resident. Additional benefits include medical and dental insurance for house staff (with a small weekly contribution by resident)and eligible dependents, medical liability, life insurance, on-call meal allowances, book allowances, lab coats and four weeks vacation per year.

STAFF

Saint Barnabas Medical Center

Selwyn J. Baptist MD Chairman (Bangalore Univ, 1969) AP/CP; **Emelie H. Ongcapin** MD Associate Chairman (Far Eastern Univ, 1964) AP/CP; **Errol L. Berman** MD (Univ Louisville, 1968) AP/CP; **Michael Dardik** MD (Univ

Pennsylvania, 1996) AP/CP; **Dae Un Kim** MD (Seoul National, 1965) AP/CP; **Marietta Kintiroglou** MD (Athens, 1969) AP cytopathology; **Jonathan F. Lara** MD Program Director (Far Eastern Univ, 1984) AP/CP cytopathology; **Teresita M.C. Redondo** MD (Univ Phil, 1972) AP/CP/IP; **Ellen Romanowski** MPA, MT (ASCP) (Clarion Univ Pennsylvania, 1983); **Marlene Sabbath-Solitaire** PhD (Columbia Univ, 1978).

Monmouth Medical Center

Louis J.M. Zinterhofer MD Chairman (Tulane Univ, 1967) AP/CP chem. pathology/RP; **Yong Kong** MD (Shanghai Med Univ, 1984), AP/CP; **Plamen Kossev** MD (Higher Inst, Bulgaria, 1988) AP; **Wendy T. Shertz** MD (MCP Hahnemann Univ, 1980) AP/CP; **Arpad Szallsi** MD, PhD (Hungary, 1984), AP/CP.

Newark Beth Israel Medical Center

Patricia Tsang MD, MBA (Boston Univ, 1992), Chairman, AP, Hematopathology; **Cyril D'Cruz** MD Vice Chairman (Baroda Med Col, 1967) AP/CP pediatric pathology; **Ludmilla Olesnicky** MD (Univ Innsbruck, 1973) AP; **Panayot Panayotov** MD, PhD (Med Acad, Sofia, Bulg., 1976), AP/CP, BB; **Fang Qian** MD (Beijing Med Sch, 1991) AP/CP.

Consultants

Daniel Albert MD (Univ Pennsylvania) ophthalmic pathology; **MaryAnn B. Clayton** MD (UMDNJ, 1981) forensic pathology; **Vijay V. Joshi** MD, PhD (Grant Med Col, 1962) AP pediatric pathology; **Calvin E. Oyer** MD (Indiana Univ, 1952) AP/CP pediatric pathology; **Gilbert B. Solitaire** MD (Yale Univ, 1957) AP neuropathology.

APPLICATIONS

Applicants must be graduates of medical schools from the United States or Canada or recognized medical schools from other countries with a valid ECFMG certificate. All applicants must have completed USMLE steps 1 and 2, preferrably with a minimum score of 85. Three letters of recommendation, and a medical school transcript (copy acceptable) should accompany a complete application thru ERAS and all other necessary and appropriate documents. Applications are accepted until December 1 of the preceding year and interviews are required. The usual starting date is July 1.

Address inquiries to:

Jonathan F. Lara, MD
Residency Program Director
E-mail: jlara@sbhcs.com
or
Ms. Margee Gearhart
Residency Program Coordinator
Department of Pathology
Saint Barnabas Medical Center
94 Old Short Hills Road
Livingston, NJ 07039
Phone: (973) 322-5760 or 5762 • **Fax:** (973) 322-5564
E-mail: mgearhart@sbhcs.com

The Saint Barnabas HealthCare System is an equal opportunity employer.

Saint Barnabas Medical Center (Top)
Monmouth Medical Center (Middle)
Newark Beth Israel Medical Center (Bottom)

ROBERT WOOD JOHNSON MEDICAL SCHOOL

UNIVERSITY OF MEDICINE AND DENTISTRY OF NEW JERSEY

New Brunswick, New Jersey

PROGRAMS OFFERED

Approved training in anatomic (AP) and clinical pathology (CP) is available with flexible, clinical or research pathways in pathology. The program provides training in autopsy and surgical pathology, including hematopathology, dermatopathology, pediatric pathology, neuropathology, cytopathology, cytogenetics, molecular biology, renal pathology, transplant pathology, electron microscopy and immunopathology. The CP segments of the program feature clinical chemistry, hematology, flow cytometry, blood banking/transfusion medicine and microbiology. Residents participate in teaching at the Medical School and are encouraged to develop their teaching and research interests.

TYPES AND NUMBERS OF APPOINTMENTS

Eight residency positions and one fellowship position are available, distributed through the four years of the combined program. The post-residency fellowship position is available in the area of hematopathology.

FACILITIES

The Robert Wood Johnson Medical School began in the early 1960s as Rutgers Medical School and is closely associated with Rutgers University. In the early 1970s, a separate statewide University of Medicine and Dentistry of New Jersey (UMDNJ) was established. In time Rutgers Medical School was placed under UMDNJ and its name changed to the UMDNJ- Robert Wood Johnson Medical School. Robert Wood Johnson was a major figure in the development of Johnson & Johnson and an important coordinator of American industrial efforts in World War II. The Busch Campus of Rutgers University and its undergraduate and graduate faculty in Biology, Pharmacology, Chemistry, Physics, Mathematics, Computer Science and Engineering surround the Piscataway campus of the Medical School. The Center for Advanced Biotechnology and Medicine and the Environmental and Occupational Health Sciences Institute are located adjacent to the Medical School. The major clinical facilities are the Robert Wood Johnson University Hospital, Bristol Myers Squibb Children's Hospital at Robert Wood Johnson University Hospital, St Peter's University Hospital, the Cancer Institute of New Jersey located in New Brunswick,the Child Health Institute of New Jersey, located in New Brunswick, and Cooper Hospital located in Camden, New Jersey. These clinical facilities and the research laboratories of the department in Piscataway and New Brunswick comprise the base of a flexible residency program. Robert Wood Johnson University Hospital is a 584 bed tertiary care teaching hospital with residency programs and fellowships in virtually all areas of academic medicine. There is an annual access to over 20,000 surgicals, 10,000 cytology specimens, and approximately 175 autopsies. A large volume of traditional, as well as complex, clinical tests including flow cytometry, tumor surface markers, gene rearrangements, clinical immunology, complex serology, diagnostic molecular pathology, complex clotting problems, fertility studies, cytogenetics, clinical virology, diagnostic electron microscopy tranplantation pathology and immunohistopathology are available.

The Medical School has an interdisciplinary PhD program affiliated with the Graduate School of Rutgers University. Residents interested in an academic career may obtain advanced training in areas such as molecular biology, cell and developmental biology, bioengineering, biochemistry and computer science. Departmental faculty is engaged in research in funded programs in Structural Biology, Cell and Developmental Pathology, Bioimaging, and Biomaterials. The Bioimaging program applies techniques in digitized image capture and analysis to three-dimensional ultrastructural reconstructions and complex image-generation methodologies.

COMMUNITY

New Brunswick experienced major urban and economic rejuvenation in the 1980s. It is the northern hub of an academic, pharmaceutical and arts axis in central New Jersey with Princeton as the southern hub. There are three theatres in New Brunswick, which provide excellent programs in all areas of the performing arts. For individuals who wish to be in New York City or Philadelphia, travel by train from New Brunswick to either city takes about an hour. The entire northeastern corridor from Boston to Washington is readily accessible by car, train or plane. The Jersey Shore with Atlantic City, the Pine Barrens of Southern New Jersey, Revolutionary War battlefields, the Delaware Water Gap and the Pocono Mountains in eastern Pennsylvania and the Catskills in New York are all within a two-hour drive.

STIPENDS AND MAINTENANCE

Resident salaries: first year $49,328; second year $52,671; third year $55,895; fourth year $59,159; and fifth-year $60,730. Fringe benefits include four weeks annual leave for all residents, hospitalization and major medical insurance.

STAFF

Peter S. Amenta MD, PhD immunohistopathology, anatomic pathology, matrix biology; **Renee Artymyshyn** MD cytopathology; **Hana Aviv** PhD cytogenetics; **Nicola Barnard** MBBS cytopathology, surgical pathology; **Evan Cadoff** MD Interim Chair, clinical chemistry, therapeutic monitoring; **Jeanette M. Camacho** MD Cooper Hospital, anatomic and clinical pathology; **Bethany Carlisle** DO, surgical pathology and cytopathology; **Chavela M. Carr** MD membrane fusion; **Wilfredo Causing** MD anatomic and clinical pathology; **Marina Chekmareva** MD, surgical pathology; **Malik Deen** MD anatomic/clinical pathology, cytopathology; **Hongbing Deng** MD, anatomic and clinical pathology; **David Foran** PhD medical informatics; **Billie S Fyfe-Kirschner** MD Director residency program, autopsy service and transplant pathology; **Janusz Godyn** MD anatomic and clinical pathology; **Lauri Goodell** MD hematopathology, clinical immunology, Director Hematopathology Fellowship; **Vito Gulli** MD anatomic and clinical pathology; **Anup Hazra** MD anatomic and clinical pathology; **Parisa Javidian** MD surgical pathology; **Bruce I. Kane** MD Cooper Hospital, clinical pathology; **Thomas Kirn** MD, Clinical Microbiology; **Sunita Kramer** PhD genetic research; **Mercy Kuriyan** MD transfusion medicine; **Shaohua Li** MD molecular and cell biology; **Eugene G. Martin** PhD information processing, PCR testing; **Michael May** MD, anatomic and clinical pathology; **Nagy Mikhail** MD anatomic and clinical pathology; **Zaida E. Olmo-Durham** MD St. Peter's University Hospital, cytopathology, anatomic pathology; **You-Wen Qian** MD, Hematopathology; **Christopher Quinn** PhD neural development; **Arnold Rabson** MD molecular pathology; **William Rafferty** MD Cooper Hospital, surgical pathology; **Roy Rhodes** MD neuropathology; **Carlos Ricart** MD anatomic and clinical pathology; **Eric Richfield** MD neuropathology; **Shelonita Rose** MD anatomic and clinical pathology; **Amrik Sahota** PhD molecular pathology; **Gratian Salaru** MD heamtopathology; **Roland Schwarting** MD Chairman Pathology, Cooper Hospital; hematopathology; **Mubina Shah** MD transfusion medicine; **Richard Siderits** MD anatomic and clinical pathology; **Frederick Silver** PhD biomaterials; **Martha Soto** PhD *C. elegans* research; **Grace Tenorio** MD Transfusion Medicine; **Robert L. Trelstad** MD matrix cell biology, anatomic pathology; **William G. Wadsworth** PhD developmental genetics; **Melvin P. Weinstein** MD clinical microbiology; **David Weissmann** MD hematopathology education; **Donald A. Winkelmann** PhD structural biology and bioimaging; **Dong Hua Yang** PhD, matrix cell biology pertaining to renal diseases; **Peter D. Yurchenco** MD, PhD matrix cell biology, anatomic pathology.

APPLICATIONS

Candidates for the program must be graduates of approved medical schools. Foreign medical graduates must be less than 10 years from graduating, hold valid ECFMG certificates, be permanent residents of the United States or have J1 clinical visas and Step 3 is strongly encouraged. Applications are accepted through ERAS only and should be submitted by December 31st for positions beginning July 1 of the following year.

Address inquiries to:

Billie Fyfe-Kirschner, MD
Director, Pathology Residency Program
UMDNJ-Robert Wood Johnson Medical School
One Robert Wood Johnson Place, MEB 212
New Brunswick, NJ 08903-0019
Phone: (732) 235-8121

UMDNJ-NEW JERSEY MEDICAL SCHOOL

Newark, New Jersey

PROGRAMS OFFERED

The program, which utilizes a consortium of three teaching hospitals, is approved for four years of combined training in anatomical and clinical pathology. NJMS-Department of Pathology and Laboratory Medicine encourages resident participation in the research activity of the Department. Residents also participate in teaching of medical students. Two years of the program involve training in autopsy and surgical pathology, including cytopathology, neuropathology, forensics, and cyto- and histochemistry, and two years are devoted to clinical pathology with rotations in the Divisions of Clinical Chemistry, Blood Bank, Microbiology, Coagulation, Tissue Typing, Serology, Immunology, Flow Cytometry, Molecular Pathology, Hematology, and Cytogenetics. However, a more prolonged period in an area of special interest, or research, can be substituted for one or two rotations. Elective subspecialty training is available to interested individuals in areas of surgical pathology, pediatric pathology, dermatopathology, neuropathology, blood banking and other areas of clinical pathology. A residency appointment in the program involves rotational assignments through University Hospital and the affiliated institutions during the four-year training period. The integrated program, utilizing the particular strengths at each of the hospitals, exposes the trainees to a wide variety of material, expertise and practice settings.

TYPES AND NUMBERS OF APPOINTMENTS

The program has 13 residents for 4 year training in anatomic and clinical pathology.

FACILITIES

UMDNJ-New Jersey Medical School Integrated Residency Program in Pathology includes three major teaching affiliates of the University of Medicine and Dentistry of New Jersey: UMDNJ-University Hospital, Hackensack University Medical Center and Veterans Affairs Medical Center in East Orange. The faculty at each of the participating units holds academic appointments at UMDNJ-NJMS. Combined hospital bed capacity of the affiliates is 1,650, the annual number of autopsies is 350 (excluding still births), surgical pathology specimens 46,373, and cytopathology specimens 25,096. The New Jersey Medical School and Veterans Affairs Medical Center have active research programs and fully staffed and well established electron microscopy, neuropathology, toxicology, immunofluorescence, molecular diagnostics, forensic pathology, cellular immunology, cellular and subcellular cancer research, and tissue culture facilities.

COMMUNITY

The University of Medicine and Dentistry, Newark campus, is in the major cultural, educational, commercial, transportation and population center of New Jersey and is a short distance from New York City.

STIPENDS AND MAINTENANCE

Salary is commensurate with the level of postgraduate training and ranges from $47,891 to $57,436 for PGY-1 through 4 with a chief resident supplement of $2,700, as of 2007-2008. An appointment provides generous fringe benefits including 4 weeks vacation, a State Health Benefits Program including medical, dental, and drug prescription coverage, and a book allowance.

STAFF

UMDNJ-New Jersey Medical School

Stanley Cohen MD Professor and Chair; **Seena C. Aisner** MD Professor and Vice Chair; Chief, Laboratory Services; Director, Anatomic Pathology; Director, Residency Program; **B. Bachl** MD Assistant Professor; Director, Clinical Chemistry; Chief, Laboratory Medicine; **Patricia Bocarsly-Fitzgerald** PhD Associate Professor; **Michele Burday** PhD Assistant Professor; Director, Microbiology; **Eun Sook Cho** MD Associate Professor; **Frederick Coffman** PhD Assistant Professor; **Marion Cohen** PhD Associate Professor; **Norman Ende** MD Professor; **Anthony Grygotis** MD Assistant Professor; Director, Informatics; **JoAnne Habermann** MD Assistant Professor; Director, Autopsy; **Meera Hameed** MD Professor; Director, Surgical Pathology and Molecular Diagnostics; **Debra S. Heller** MD Professor; Associate Director, Anatomic Pathology; **Kenneth K. Klein** MD Professor; **Ranie Koshy** MD Assistant Professor; Director, Blood Bank and Transfusion Medicine; **Muriel Lambert** PhD Professor; **W. Clark Lambert** MD, PhD Professor; Director, Dermatopathology; **Ronald M. Maenza** MD Professor Emeritus; **Fermina Mazzella** MD, Associate Professor; Director, Hematopathology; **Neena Mirani** MD Associate Professor; Director, Cytopathology; Vice Chair, Clinical Coordination; **James M. Oleske** MD Professor; Director, Pediatric Immunology; **Nicholas M. Ponzio** PhD

Professor and Vice Chair; **Elizabeth S. Raveche** PhD Professor; **Leroy R. Sharer** MD Professor; Director, Neuropathology; **George P. Studzinski** MD PhD Professor.

Hackensack University Medical Center

Joseph M. Lombardo MD, PhD Clinical Associate Professor and Chair; **Stephen R. Peters** MD Clinical Assistant Professor and Vice Chair; Director, Residency Program; **Pritish K. Bhattacharyya** MD Clinical Assistant Professor; Director, Hematopathology and Molecular Pathology; **Carol Fehmian** MD Clinical Assistant Professor; Director, Blood Bank; **Michael J. Goldfischer** MD Clinical Assistant Professor; Director, Autopsy Service; **Min Woo Han** MD Clinical Assistant Professor; **Sami Harawi** MD Clinical Associate Professor; **Patrice Hassoun** MD Clinical Assistant Professor; **Christopher Koenig** MD Clinical Assistant Professor; **Marlene Lengner** MD Clinical Assistant Professor; **Ciaran Mannion** MD Clinical Assistant Professor; **Xiao Y. Yang** MD PhD Clinical Assistant Professor.

East Orange VA New Jersey Health Care System

Clara N. Finch-Cruz MD Chief, Pathology Laboratory Medicine Service; **Shahida Ahmed** MD Director, Blood Bank; **Jin K. Choe** MD DMSc Clinical Associate Professor; **Sharon M. Smith** PhD Associate Professor; Director, Microbiology.

APPLICATIONS

Candidates must be senior medical students or graduates of an LCME/AOA approved medical school in the U.S. or Canada or, if a foreign medical graduate, hold a valid ECFMG certificate at the time of application. Applicants should include a curriculum vita and 3 letters of reference. All applications must be received no later than November 15 and only through ERAS. Candidates who are not American citizens must present documentation of permanent resident status.

Address inquiries to:

Seena C. Aisner, MD
Director of Pathology Residency Program
Department of Pathology and Laboratory Medicine
UMDNJ-New Jersey Medical School
185 South Orange Avenue
Newark, NJ 07101-1709
Phone: (973) 972-5722
Web site: http://njms.umdnj.edu/departments/pathology/index.cfm

UNIVERSITY OF NEW MEXICO AFFILIATED HOSPITALS

Albuquerque, New Mexico

PROGRAMS OFFERED

The Department of Pathology is committed in equal measure to education, patient care and scholarly investigation, preparing physicians for diverse career opportunities in both academic and private practice pathology. Most residents elect a four-year program of combined training in anatomic and clinical pathology. Anatomic pathology training includes extensive exposure to general surgical pathology, cytology, autopsy pathology, forensic pathology, and immunohistology. UNM clinical pathology faculty provide medical direction for TriCore Reference Laboratories, jointly owned by UNM, which is a large regional laboratory serving both UNM University Hospital, community hospitals and the state. This offers excellent training for the resident, under the supervision of the faculty, in all aspects of clinical pathology with a focus on patient care and the consulting role of the pathologist to both primary care and specialty clinicians. The Department is on the cutting edge in many areas of scientific investigation; equipment, research space and financial support are provided for those residents engaged in research. Advanced postresidency subspecialty training is offered in hematopathology, transfusion medicine, cytopathology, forensic pathology, molecular genetics and surgical pathology.

TYPES AND NUMBERS OF APPOINTMENTS

The current house staff includes 19 residents, 3 hematopathology fellows, 4 forensic pathology fellows, 1 molecular genetics fellow and 1 predoctoral fellows. Four first year residency positions are usually available each year.

FACILITIES

The University of New Mexico Hospital and the New Mexico Federal Regional (NMFR) Medical Center are the primary teaching hospitals used by the University of New Mexico Health Sciences Center. Anatomic pathology rotations at one affiliated community hospital and at the Office of the Medical Investigator, which performs 1,800 forensic autopsies per year, provide the resident with a total of 78,312 surgical pathology specimens; 123,000 cytopathology specimens; 992 bone marrows; and 150 hospital autopsies per year. Faculty of the Department of Pathology are involved in many research projects and programs offering research opportunities for residents. Many have joint appointments in the Cancer, Research, and Treatment Center where NCI-sponsored SWOG and POG activities are housed under the direction of Dr Cheryl Willman in Pathology. Other programs in which pathology faculty are involved include, among others, a UNM center of excellence in molecular and cellular diagnostics (Dr Willman), an NIH-funded Specialized Center for Research (SCOR) in asthma (Dr Lipscomb, PI), and an NCI sponsored Surveillance, Epidemiology and End Results (SEER) Program.

COMMUNITY

Albuquerque is frequently mentioned as one of the most desirable urban communities in the United States. As a bustling city of 766,000, Albuquerque serves as a center of education, commerce, and tourism for the mountain Southwest. The city's high desert location affords it a moderate climate with plentiful sunshine and mild temperatures year-round. Opportunities for numerous outdoor activities abound. New Mexico's natural beauty and cultural amenities draw visitors from around the world.

STIPENDS AND MAINTENANCE

2009 salaries will be comparable to 2008 salaries, which began at $43,886. Malpractice insurance, paid vacation, sick leave and health insurance (nominal copayment) are provided. Generous funds for educational resources and travel are provided. Good housing is readily available.

STAFF

Thomas M. Williams MD (Univ New Mexico) Prof, gene regulation, molecular pathology; **Marc Barry** MB (Univ College of Dublin, Ireland) Asst Prof, renal pathology; **Michelle Barry** MD, (Univ Oregon HSC) Asst Prof, forensic pathology; **Claire Bartolo** PhD (Ohio State Univ) Asst Prof, molecular oncology; **William C. Black** MD (Univ Colorado) Prof Emeritus, surgical pathology; **Therese Bocklage** MD (Med Col Ohio) Prof, surgical pathology/ cytology; **Lisa Cerilli** MD (Emory Univ) Assoc Prof, surgical pathology; **I-Ming Chen** DVM (National Taiwan Univ) Assoc Prof, flow cytometry; **Lida A. Crooks** MD (Univ New Mexico) Prof, surgical pathology; **Kendall P. Crookston** MD, PhD (Univ Virginia) Assoc Prof, transfusion medicine and coagulation; **Bruce Edwards** PhD (Univ Colorado) Prof, flow cytometry and adhesion biology; **Edgar G. Fischer** MD, PhD (Heidelberg Univ Med Sch, Germany) Asst Prof, surgical pathology; **M. Kathryn Foucar** MD (Ohio State Univ) Prof, hematopathology; TriCore Ref Lab; **Philip J. Garry** PhD (Ohio State Univ) Prof, chemistry; **Brian L. Hjelle** MD (Johns Hopkins Med Inst) Professor, molecular biology, virology; **John Hozier** PhD (Florida State Univ) Prof, cytogenetics; **Kristin Hunt** MD (Univ of Nebraska)

Asst Prof, hematopathology; TriCore Ref Lab; **Glynnis Ingall** MD, PhD (Univ Iowa) Assoc Prof, clinical chemistry; **Rebecca Irvine** MD (McMaster Univ) Asst Prof, forensic pathology; **Nancy Joste** MD (Univ New Mexico) Prof, surgical pathology/cytopathology; **Charles R. Key** MD, PhD (Univ Oklahoma) Prof, cardiovascular pathology; **Walter Kisiel** PhD (Univ North Dakota) Prof, coagulation; **Mario Kornfeld** MD (Zagreb) Prof Emeritus, neuropathology; **Richard Larson** MD, PhD (Harvard Univ) Prof, molecular pathology/hematopathology; **Mary F. Lipscomb** MD (Louisiana State Univ) Prof, immunology, pulmonary pathology; **Lesley C Lomo** MD (Wayne State Univ) Asst Prof, surgical pathology/cytology; **Matthew Luke** MD (Univ Utah) Assoc Prof, informatics; **Larry W. Massie** MD (Creighton Univ) Prof, microbiology; **Barbara Masten** PhD (Texas Tech Univ) Assoc Prof, immunology; **Rafael Medina-Flores** MD (La Salle Univ SOM, Mexico City) Asst Prof, surgical pathology/neuropathology; **Shakil H Merchant** MD (Seth GS Med Col, India) Asst Prof, anatomic pathology; **Jeffrey Nine** MD (Northeastern Ohio Univ) Assoc Prof, forensic pathology; **Kurt B. Nolte** MD (Albert Einstein Col Med) Prof, forensic pathology; **Deborah J Novak** MD (Univ Nebraska) Asst Prof, clinical pathology; **Janet M. Oliver** PhD (Univ London, England) Prof, cell biology; **Gary Overturf** MD microbiology; **Ian Paul** MD (McGill Univ, Montreal) Asst Prof, forensic pathology; **Kaari Reichard** MD, (Tufts Univ) Asst Prof, Hemepath; **Ross Reichard** MD, (Univ Louisville-Kentucky) Asst Prof, forensic pathology; **Kari T Rigg** PA Clinical Instructor, surgical pathology; **Larry A. Sklar** PhD (Stanford Univ) Prof; Director, flow cytometry; **Mohammad Vasef** MD (Univ Tehran, Iran) Assoc Prof, hematopathology; **Angela Wandinger-Ness** PhD (Univ Cal-Los Angeles) Prof, intracellular membrane transport; **Julie Wilder** PhD (Univ Iowa) Asst Prof, pulmonary immunology; **Wilbur L. Williams** MD (Univ New Mexico) Assoc Prof, hematopathology; **Cheryl L. Willman** MD (Mayo Med School) Prof, hematopathology and molecular biology; **Bridget Wilson** PhD (Univ New Mexico) Prof, signal transduction; **Carla Wilson** MD, PhD (Univ New Mexico) Prof, hematopathology; **Steve Young** PhD (Univ New Mexico) Prof, virology/microbiology; **Qian-Yun Zhang** MD, PhD (West China Univ of Med Sciences) Assoc Prof, hematopathology; **Myra C Zucker** PA(ASCP) Clin Instructor, surgical pathology; **Ross E. Zumwalt** MD (Univ Illinois) Prof and Chief Medical Investigator, forensic pathology.

Volunteer Clinical Faculty

Andrew Horvath MD Presbyterian Pathology Associate/Chief Medical Officer, TriCore Reference Laboratories; **Peter Appenzeller** MD; **Michael Crossey** MD, PhD; **Emily P DeSantis** MD; **Richard Feddersen** MD; **Robyn Gaffney** MD; **Ronnie Garner** MD; **Janet Griego** MD; **Jeffrey Huser** MD; **Mehraboon Irani** MD; **Cordelia Sever** MD; **Jim Spigel** MD; **Omar Yousef** MD; Pathology Associates of Albuquerque, Presbyterian Hospital.

APPLICATIONS

We will accept applications exclusively through the ERAS Program. For information on ERAS, U.S., and Canadian students should contact their school of graduation, and foreign students should contact ECFMG. For other information about the residency program, contact us at the address below or see our website.

Address inquiries to:

Ms. Jeanne Lay, Coordinator
UNM Department of Pathology
1 University of New Mexico MSC08-4640
Albuquerque, NM 87131-0001

Phone: (505) 272-3696
Coordinator, Jeanne Lay
E-mail: j lay@salud.unm.edu
Web site: http://hsc.unm.edu/pathology/residency/

Happy Hour is a long-standing tradition among the residents.

ALBANY MEDICAL COLLEGE
ALBANY MEDICAL CENTER HOSPITAL

Albany, New York

PROGRAMS OFFERED

An accredited four year residency is offered in combined anatomic and clinical pathology. The program provides broad, diverse training in all aspects of anatomic and clinical pathology. The training in anatomic pathology includes autopsy and surgical pathology, cytopathology, dermatopathology, molecular diagnostics, neuropathology, hematopathology, renal pathology, electron microscopy, forensic pathology and immunopathology. The program in clinical pathology provides training in clinical chemistry, clinical microbiology, hematology, immunohematology, blood banking, clinical immunology, toxicology, flow cytometry, cytogenetics, hemostasis, laboratory management and computer applications. The research program of the department emphasizes cancer molecular biology. Residents are expected to assume graduated professional responsibilities consistent with their level of experience and training.

TYPES AND NUMBERS OF APPOINTMENTS

There are 15 pathology residency positions divided among the four years.

FACILITIES

Albany Medical Center is the primary teaching hospital. Residents also rotate at the Veterans Affairs Medical Center Hospital. The case load available to the residents includes 110 hospital autopsies, 620 forensics autopsies, 55,000 surgical accessions, 35,000 cytology specimens, and clinical laboratory tests in excess of five million per year. Affiliated supplemental rotations in special areas of virology, mycology, parasitology, advanced hemostasis, cytogenetics, blood bank management and research are available at the nearby New York State Public Health laboratories.

COMMUNITY

Albany Medical Center is located in the capital of the Empire State, a medium-sized city of 120,000. As part of the tri-cities metropolitan area (Troy is nine miles to the northeast and Schenectady 13 miles to the northwest) with a combined population of half a million, Albany offers many of the advantages of a big city with few of its shortcomings. The Capital District is within one or two hours of many ski resorts of New York, Vermont, and Massachusetts. Mountains and lakes are close by, abounding in excellent facilities for outdoor activities. New York City is two and a half hours away by car, Boston only minutes farther. Saratoga Springs, with its racetracks and Performing Arts Center, the summer home of the Philadelphia Symphony Orchestra and New York City Ballet, is thirty minutes away. The Berkshires offer many cultural activities including Tanglewood, summer home of the Boston Symphony Orchestra.

STIPENDS AND MAINTENANCE

First-year postgraduate $48,500 per annum, second-year postgraduate $49,000, third-year postgraduate $49,500, fourth-year postgraduate $50,000, fifth-year postgraduate $50,500. Selected fifth-year postgraduates may be offered instructorships. An annual three-week paid vacation is included, as well as malpractice and health insurance.

STAFF

Anatomic Pathology

Jeffrey S. Ross MD Professor; Department Chairman; administration, surgical pathology, autopsy pathology, molecular diagnostics, and pharmacogenomics; **Ann Boguniewicz** MD Associate Professor; Director, AP/CP Residency Program; Director Cytopathology; cytopathology, surgical pathology, breast pathology, and gynecologic pathology; **J. Andrew Carlson** MD Professor; dermatopathology; **Martha Farber** MD Associate Professor; ophthalmic pathology; **Llewellyn Foulke** MD Assistant Professor; perinatal pathology, pediatric pathology, pulmonary pathology, cytopathology, and surgical pathology; **Alida Hayner-Buchan** MD Assistant Professor; renal pathology, electron microscopy, genitourinary pathology, hematopathology, and surgical pathology; **Timothy A. Jennings** MD Professor; Director Anatomic Pathology; surgical pathology, autopsy pathology, thyroid and head and neck pathology; **David Jones** MD Assistant Professor; surgical pathology, dermatopathology, and gastrointestinal pathology; **C. Y. Lee** MD, PhD Professor; electron microscopy, surgical pathology, and autopsy pathology; **Tipu Nazeer** MD Professor; Director Surgical Pathology, Director Hematopathology Fellowship Program; surgical pathology, genitourinary pathology, and hematopathology; **Jiang Qian** MD, PhD Associate Professor; neuropathology and surgical pathology; **Donald Rice** MD Associate Professor; Chief VA Laboratory Service; surgical pathology; **Merrill Ross** BS Instructor; informatics; **Christine Sheehan** BS Administrative Director of Research; **Michael Sikirica** MD Clinical Assistant Professor; forensic pathology; **An-Ya Wu** MD, PhD Associate Professor; administration and surgical pathology.

Clinical Pathology

Jeffrey S. Ross MD Professor and Chairman; administration; **Adrienne Frank** PhD Assistant Professor; administration; **Mary George** MD Assistant Professor; microbiology; **Amy Hahn** PhD Assistant Professor; transplantation immunology; **Susan Harrington** PhD Assistant Professor; microbiology; **Robert J. Laffin** PhD Professor; immunopathology and medical microbiology; **C.Y. Lee** MD, PhD, Professor; clinical chemistry, toxicology, and laboratory endocrinology; **Stanley Mudzinski** PhD Assistant Professor; immunology; **Mark Preissler** PhD Assistant Professor; immunology; **Thomas Rosano** PhD Professor and Director Division Laboratory Medicine; administration, chemical pathology and forensic toxicology; **Kathleen Stellrecht** PhD Associate Professor; microbiology and immunology; medical microbiology; **Thomas A. Swift** PhD Associate Director Clinical Chemistry Laboratory; **George Wilner** MD Professor; Medical Director, Laboratory Medicine; **An-Ya Wu** MD, PhD Associate Professor; Director VA Transfusion Services; Head Hematology Division.

APPLICATIONS

All residency and internship candidates must be graduates of approved medical schools; graduates of foreign medical schools must have an ECFMG Certificate. Satisfactory references are required. Applications are best submitted by November 15 for positions beginning July 1 of the following year.

Address inquiries to:

Kareen Maxwell
Residency Program Coordinator
Department of Pathology, Mail Code 81
Albany Medical College
47 New Scotland Avenue
Albany, NY 12208
Phone: (518) 262-5436
E-mail: maxwelk@mail.amc.edu

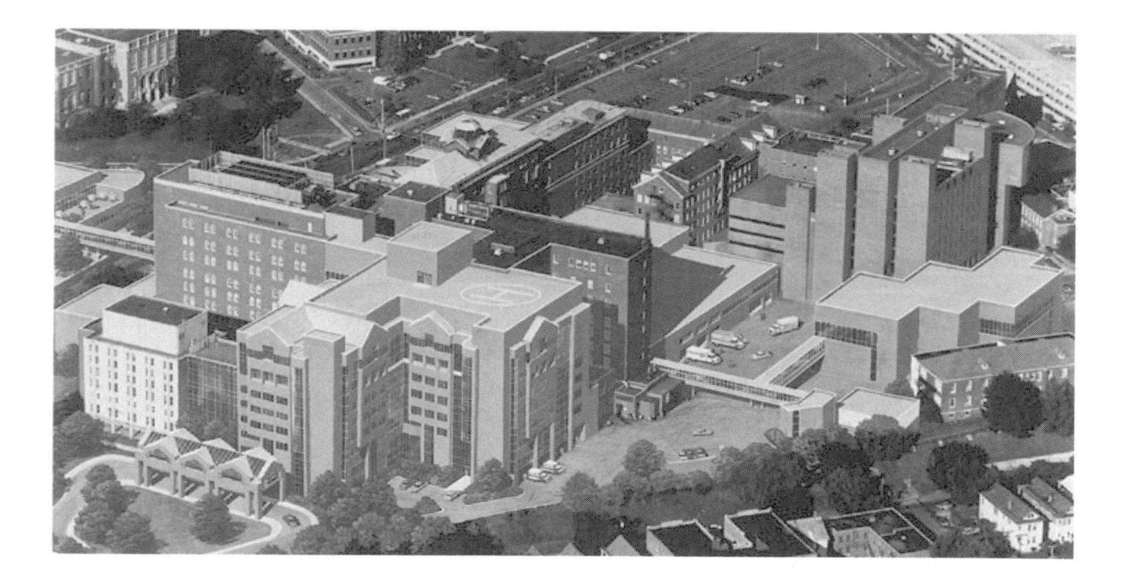

ALBERT EINSTEIN COLLEGE OF MEDICINE AND MONTEFIORE MEDICAL CENTER

Bronx, New York

PROGRAMS OFFERED

Clinical Training: The Department of Pathology offers a Training Program that leads to certification in either or both anatomic and clinical pathology. Training is available in autopsy pathology, surgical pathology, cytopathology, neuropathology, and all the subspecialties of clinical pathology including hematology, chemistry, virology, microbiology, serology, parasitology, blood banking, molecular diagnostics and cytogenetics. The AP/CP Residency typically includes a core curriculum of 18 - 20 months each of anatomic and clinical pathology plus ample elective time in numerous specialties. Clinical liaison experience is provided through rotations in the critical care units and hematology, infectious disease, rheumatology and endocrinology services. CP residents interact with staff physicians from all services in their roles of laboratory clinicians. In depth training is provided in all AP subspecialties including cytopathology, neuropathology, cardiac pathology, renal pathology, transplant pathology, pediatric pathology, pathology of infectious diseases, bone pathology, hematopathology and gynecologic pathology. A wide variety of regularly scheduled teaching conferences are conducted in all the various subspecialties of pathology, as well as with relevant clinical departments. Trainees are offered "hands-on" experience in immunocytochemistry, molecular diagnostics, cytogenetics, and electron microscopy. Residents learn to employ these techniques in both diagnostic and investigational work. Research: All resident trainees are encouraged to undertake at least one research project. Most residents publish and present at national meetings. The Department of Pathology has active ongoing research in many areas. These include studies of neuro-degenerative diseases; demyelinating disease; AIDS, and other infectious diseases; molecular parasitology; cytokine-mediated inflammation; cell biology of endothelial cells; automated cytopathologic diagnostics; perinatal pathology; immunology and pathology of HPV infection in the pathogenesis of cervical cancer; cardiac pathology; radiation and environmental medicine; pathobiology of aging; cytogenetics and mechanisms of metastasis. Work is also in progress on the role of cytoskeleton in liver and neurologic diseases as well as in endothelial cell function. The Department has established laboratories of molecular cytogenetics and a molecular diagnostic facility. Departmental research is supported by extramural research funding in excess of $6,000,000 annually. The Albert Einstein College of Medicine is an internationally recognized research institution with strength in many basic disciplines. Interdepartmental research programs are emphasized and trainees are encouraged to participate in collaborative projects with other clinical and basic science departments in the Medical School. Montefiore Medical Center is a large "state-of-the-art" modern medical facility which offers training in many areas of medicine. The Pathology training program offers a unique educational experience in the environment of an outstanding medical center and an outstanding research institute. The Pathology Department Seminar Series brings outstanding pathologists and scientists to Montefiore and Einstein and emphasizes resident contact. Residents are encouraged to spend elective time in research and to participate in the education of both medical students and graduate students. Management Training: To meet the needs of the new generation of pathologists and laboratory directors, intensive didactic training in laboratory management is offered. The course emphasizes theories of management as well as personnel, finance and human resource management. In addition, the role of the laboratory director in the hospital organization as well as legal concerns and risk management are covered. Informatics and telepathology are important and growing presences. Lastly, residents have access to modern digital equipment and computers to assist them in their academic and clinical growth and development.

TYPES AND NUMBERS OF APPOINTMENTS

A total of 29 resident and fellowship positions are offered. Fellowships are available in surgical pathology, hematopathology, gynecologic pathology, dermatopathology neuropathology, cytopathology (http://www.cytology.-com), combined orthopedic/surgical pathology, and other subspecialties of interest. A combined residency-postdoctoral fellowship is available to qualified applicants. Sabbath observing positions are available. Post-sophomore year and fellowships are also available. The program works closely with each resident to develop a training track that will meet his/her future goals.

FACILITIES

The hospitals of this medical center are Montefiore Medical Center, Moses Division and Einstein/Weiler Division, and Bronx Lebanon Medical Center with a total of 1,575 beds. The clinical laboratories perform in excess of 7.3 million tests annually. One hundred fifty three autopsies are performed per year; 38,032 surgical specimens are processed; 47,742 cytological specimens including fine needle aspirations are examined. The libraries of the Montefiore Medical Center and College of Medicine are large, accessible, computerized and current. The Department's extensive research laboratories are located on the grounds of the Albert Einstein College of Medicine in the Forchheimer Building, Ullmann Research Center, Chanin Institute for Cancer Research and Kennedy Center for Mental Retardation and Human Development, and in the Moses Research Institute at Montefiore. The laboratories are fully equipped for all areas of research in pathology from molecular to organ levels. Specialized equipment and research laboratory facilities include an extensive series of laboratories with full support facilities, micro-array, LASER capture dissection, advanced imaging, molecular biology, computer morphology, cytogenetics, electron microscopy, chemical laboratories and common equipment rooms equipped with ultracentrifuges, scintillation counters, spectroscopy equipment, etc. There are several laboratories fully equipped for tissue culture. Feel free to visit our web site (http://www.aecom.yu.edu and www.montefiore.org)

COMMUNITY

We are located on a large, attractive campus in a suburban environment in the northeast Bronx. The hospitals are adjacent to Westchester County suburbs, Riverdale, and City Island where the America's Cup racers are built. Excellent boating and seafood are nearby. Apartments and homes are sizable, and affordable around the medical center. Shopping malls are easily accessible, including all major department and discount stores. Houses of worship of all denominations are within walking distance. Fine public and parochial schools and child-care centers are ample. Modern playgrounds, softball and tennis courts are either on campus or close by. Horseback riding is available within walking distance of the hospital, the oldest public golf course in the U.S. with driving range, the New York Botanical Garden and the Bronx Zoo are only a five-minute drive. and Yankee Stadium is nearby. The Medical School has an athletic center, with a full gym, track, swimming pool, and Nautilus equipment. Express transportation reaches Manhattan in 25 minutes, with direct access to Fifth Avenue museums, shopping and theaters. Discount and free tickets to Broadway shows, the Philharmonic, opera, music, ball games, and discotheques, and excellent restaurants of every type are available. Professional activities in the field of pathology include two particularly active pathology societies (The New York Pathological Society and The Pathologists' Club).

STIPENDS AND MAINTENANCE

First-year trainees receive $50,250 per year and an increment is offered for each of the additional years (Year Four = $58,000). In addition, house staff members are provided with professional liability insurance, hospital and medical care. Housing is available, including Riverdale.

STAFF

Michael B. Prystowsky MD, PhD Professor and Chairman Department Pathology; genomic and proteomic approaches to predicting tumor behavior in head and neck cancer; **Peter Barland** MD Professor; rheumatologic diseases; **Thomas J Belbin** PhD, Associate Professor, rose of aberrant DNA methylation in head and neck cancer; **Joan W. Berman** PhD Professor; mechanisms of NeuroAIDS; **Margaret Brandwein-Gensler** MD General Surgical Pathology; Head & Neck Pathology; **Celia F Brosnan** PhD Professor; Inflammation in CNS, pathogenesis of multiple sclerosis; **Edward R. Burns** MD, Professor and Executive Dean; **Antonio Cajigas** MD Associate Clinical Professor; cytopathology; **Tina M. Calderon** PhD Assistant Professor; NeuroAIDS and substance abuse; **Barbara Cannella** PhD Assistant Professor, Operations Director, Histopathology Shared Resource, evaluation of animal models in human disease; **Linda Cannizzaro** PhD Professor; molecular cytogenetics; **Tylis Chang** MD Assistant Professor, molecular diagnostics and chemistry; **Geoffrey Childs** PhD, Professor, microRNA mediated gene silencing in head and neck cancer; **Peter Davies** PhD Professor; neurochemical, studies in Alzheimer's disease; **Howard D. Dorfman** MD Professor; bone pathology; **Eliseo A. Eugenin** MD, Assistant Professor, HIV neuropathology; **Michelle Ewart** MD Attending, Anatomic Pathology; **Susan Fineberg** MD General Surgical Pathology; breast pathology; **Amy Fox** MD Associate Clinical Professor; virology; **Philip Gialanella** MS Associate; microbiology; **James Gill** MD Deputy Chief, New York Medical Examiner; forensic pathology and sciences; **Cheryl Goss** MD Attending Blood Bank; **Thomas Harris** PhD, Assistant Professor, analysis of chromosomal copy number variations in oropharyngeal cancer; **Rachel Hazan** PhD, Associate Professor, role of cell adhesion and growth factor signaling in breast cancer; **Tiffany M. Hebert** MD Attending Surgical Pathology; **Larry Herbst** DVM, PhD, Associate Professor, Director of Institute for Animal Studies; **Asao Hirano** MD Professor; neuropathology, Parkinsonism dementia and motor neuron diseases; **Huan Huang** MD, Associate Professor, pathogenesis of chagas' disease and mechanisms of Trypanosoma cruzi differentiation; **Mark Jacobson** MD Director, Dermatopathology; **Zaven Kaprielian** PhD Professor, axon guidance and dendritic branching in the CNS and spinal cord; **Arthur Karmen** MD Professor, Laboratory Medicine; clinical pathology; **Christian Keller** MD Attending Neuropathology; **Samer Khader** MD Attending Cytopathology; **Leopold G. Koss** MD Professor and Chairman Emeritus; surgical pathology, cytopathology, cell research; **Sunhee C. Lee** MD Professor; neuropathology, neuroimmunology of demyelinating disease; **Michael Levi** ScD Associate Clinical Professor; microbiology; **Maomi Li** MD, PhD Associate Professor; surgical pathology and molecular diagnostics; **Qiang Liu** MD Attending Surgical Pathology; **Josefina Llena** MD Associate Professor; neuropathology; **Emily J Lloyd** MD Attending Anatomic Pathology; **Joseph Locker** MD, PhD Professor; basic research in molecular biology of transcription and liver development, and clinical research in tumor progression; **Fernando Macian** MD,PhD, Assistant Professor, molecular mechanisms responsible for induction of tolerance in T cells; **Panna Mahadevia** MD Associate Clinical Professor; surgical pathology; **John C. McKitrick** PhD Clinical Professor; Director Microbiology; **Christine McMahon** MD Attending Hematopathology; **Kala Mohandas** MD Assistant Professor; blood banking, apheresis; **Lejla Music-Aplenc** MD Blood Bank & Transfusion Medicine; **Phyllis Novikoff** PhD, Associate Professor, cellular, metabolic, genetic and proteomic phenotypes of preinvasive and invasive stages of liver cancer; **Maja Oktay** MD, PhD Assistant Professor; cytopathology, fine needle aspiration, cell research; **Amos Orlofsky** PhD Assistant Professor; cytokines in immune responses; **Qiulu Pan** PhD Technical Director/ Molecular Pathology; **James Pullman** MD, PhD Clinical Professor; Director Anatomic Pathology, Moses; surgical pathology, renal pathology, cytopathology; **K.H. Ramesh** MD Associate Director/Cytogenetics; **Jacob Rand** MD Professor; laboratory and clinical hematology, blood coagulation, hemostasis and thrombosis; **Howard Ratech** MD Clinical Professor; hematopathology and molecular diagnostics; **Sandra Reznik** MD, PhD Assistant Professor; reproductive and developmental pathology; **Herbert Rose** PhD Assistant Professor; clinical chemistry; **Pearl Rosenbaum** MD Clinical Professor; ophthalmic pathology; **Leonarda B. Sablay** MD Assistant Professor; renal and autopsy pathology; **Moshe Sadofsky** MD, PhD Associate Professor; molecular immunology; **Laura Santambrogio** MD, PhD, Associate Professor, antigen processing and pesentation in dendritic cells; **Kathie J. Schlesinger** MD Assistant Professor; cytopathology; **Klaus Schreiber** MD Clinical Professor; cytopathology; **Daniel Schwartz** MD, MSIS, Assistant Professor, Associate Director of Translational informatics, use of standardized ontologies to classify specimens and development of tissue repositories.; **Rani Sellers** DVM, PhD, Scientific Director, Histopathology Shared Resource, evaluation of animal models of human disease; **Andew Seymour** MD Attending Cytopathology; **Bridget Shafit-Zagardo** PhD Professor; molecular organization ad expression of brain specific mRNAs during development, regional localization of transcripts within the brain; **Jacob J. Steinberg** MD Professor; Director Residency Training Program; autopsy pathology, environmental sciences; **Mark J. Suhrland** MD Clinical Professor; Director Cytology, MMC; aspiration biopsy, pathology, cytopathology; **Yuhua Sun** MD Attending Anatomic Pathology; **Martin Surks** MD Professor; endocrinologic disorders; **Ira I. Sussman** MD Professor; Vice Chairman; hemostasis and thrombosis; **Kathryn Tanaka** MD Associate Clinical Professor, Surgical Pathology; **Herbert Tanowitz** MD Professor; parasitology and infectious diseases, pathogenesis of Chagas' disease; **Tom Tong** MD Anatomic Pathology; **Joan Uehlinger** MD Associate Clinical Professor; Director, Clinical Pathology Training Program, blood banking, apheresis; **Ljijana Vasovic** MD Blood Bank & Transfusion Medicine; **Esperanza Villanueva-Siles** MD Attending Physician Department of Pathology; **Yanhua Wang** MD Attending Anatomic Pathology; **Yihong Wang** MD Attending Anatomic Pathology; **Karen Weidenheim** MD Clinical Professor; Director Neuropathology; studies of autism; **Louis M Weiss** MD, Professor, biology of microsporidosis and taxoplasmosis; **Kathleen D. Whitney** MD Associate Professor; Director Anatomic Pathology Training and Student Education; surgical pathology, lung and breast pathology, autopsy pathology; **Murray Wittner** MD, PhD Professor; parasitology, cell biology, and cellular physiology of parasites; **Changcheng Zhu** MD, PhD Assistant Professor, Attending Pathologist.

Laboratory ResearchTeam

Michael B. Prystowsky MD, PhD head & neck cancer program; **Tom Belbin** Ph, DNA, methylation in head and neck cancer; **Joan Berman** PhD, mechanisms of NeuroAIDS; **Celia Brosnan** PhD, pathogenesis of multiple sclerosis; **L. Cannizzaro** PhD genemapping-renal cell carcinoma; **Peter Davies** PhD, Alzheimer's disease, dementia; **Rachel Hazan** PhD, breast cancer research; **Huan Huang** MD, parasitology and infectious diseases; **Zaven Kaprielian** PhD, PhD, neurodevelopment, CNS and spinal cord; **Sunhee Lee** MD, neuropathology; **Joseph Locker** MD, PhD, gene expression and transcription factors in liver cancer; **Fernando Macian** MD, PhD, anergy in T cell; **Amos Orlofsky** PhD, cytokines in immune responses; **Moshe Sadofsky** MD, PhD, molecular immunology; **Laura Santambrogio** MD, PhD Antigen processing and presentation in dendritic cells; **Bridget Shafit-Zagardo** PhD molecular neurobiology; **J. Steinberg** MD environmental sciences, DNA adducts and carcinogenesis; **Herbert Tanowitz** MD, parasitology and infectious diseases; **K. Weidenheim** MD neuropathology, neurodevelopment; **Louis Weiss** MD, parasitology and infectious diseases; **M. Wittner** MD, PhD molecular parasitology.

APPLICATIONS

First-year candidates must apply through the ERAS website (www.aamc.org).

The candidate must be a graduate of an approved medical school in the United States or Canada*. Three references (US), a Dean's letter and medical school grades are required. Fellowship applications may be obtained from the Department by letter with a CV, stating your medical school, home address and telephone number and e-mail, and should be submitted before January 1, although applications for future years or fellowship positions are acceptable for consideration beyond this date.

*Only graduates of a foreign medical school with outstanding USMLE scores and credentials will receive acknowledgment for their application.

Address inquiries to:

Jacob J. Steinberg, MD
Director, Residency Training Program
Department of Pathology (Central 410)
Montefiore Medical Center
111 East 210th Street
Bronx, NY 10467
Phone: (718) 920-6573 **Fax:** (718) 547-8349
E-mail: steinber@aecom.yu.edu or jsteinbe@montefiore.org
Web sites: http://www.aecom.yu.edu and http://www.montefiore.org
Ms. Betty Edwards, Residency Coordinator
E-mail: beedward@montefiore.org

STATE UNIVERSITY OF NEW YORK DOWNSTATE MEDICAL CENTER

Brooklyn, New York

PROGRAMS OFFERED

Our fully accredited program in Anatomic and Clinical Pathology based at Downstate Medical Center, the only academic medical center in Brooklyn, offers an outstanding training experience. Trainees are exposed to an exciting mix of case material in our three teaching affiliates: University Hospital of Brooklyn, Kings County Hospital Center, and the New York Harbor Healthcare System (mainly at the Brooklyn Veterans Affairs Medical Center). Fully accredited fellowship training also is available in Neuropathology and Dermatopathology.

The main objective of our program is to train physicians to be competent practitioners of Anatomic and Clinical Pathology in a variety of settings, e.g., academic medical centers, community hospitals, and referral laboratories. Residents are expected to develop knowledge, skills, and aptitudes consistent with the six ACGME General Competencies.

Our faculty has broad-based and nationally recognized expertise in all major areas of pathology. They oversee a comprehensive didactic program that includes case and special topic presentations and lectures, textbook review, unknown slide conferences, and journal clubs. Anatomic Pathology rotations and exposures include training in autopsy pathology, surgical pathology, renal pathology, dermatopathology, forensic pathology, neuropathology, cytopathology, pediatric pathology, and electron microscopy. Clinical pathology includes training in transfusion medicine, molecular pathology, clinical chemistry, hematopathology, immunology, microbiology, laboratory management, and interpretive analysis of laboratory test results. Elective rotations offering opportunity for more in-depth training and/or clinical or basic research are available at advanced levels of training.

Trainees are encouraged to conduct clinical or basic science research, present their work at national and regional meetings, and contribute to the scientific literature. The diverse array of clinical material is ideal for case studies and other clinical research. In addition, residents may work in basic science laboratories; investigators within the department have active research programs in infrared spectroscopic imaging and diffuse optical tomography; memory, learning and neurodegenerative disorders such as Alzheimer's disease; cancer-related peptides and therapeutics, and immunologic aspects of asthma and HIV infection.

TYPES AND NUMBERS OF APPOINTMENTS

There are 23 residency positions. Residents may choose either a combined 4-year AP/CP, a 3-year AP only or 3-year CP only program. A combined anatomic and neuropathology (AP/NP) program also is offered.

FACILITIES

Our facilities include approximately 1403 beds at the three hospitals. The laboratories are staffed by faculty members of the Department of Pathology of SUNY Downstate Medical Centers. The clinical material reflects the diversity of our hospitals and communities. Both forensic and medical autopsies are performed at the modern facility of the Brooklyn Office of the Chief Medical Examiner of New York City on our campus. Investigators in the department maintain research laboratories in the Basic Sciences Building of the College of Medicine as well as at the New York Harbor Healthcare System (mainly at the Brooklyn Veterans Affairs Medical Center). The HSCB library is one of the largest medical libraries in the United States and features extensive computer facilities.

COMMUNITY

The large variety of cultural, recreational and educational opportunities available in New York City are well known. Perhaps less well known are the extraordinary entertainment, recreational and cultural opportunities in Brooklyn. In addition, the student center has lounges, a large gym, pool, squash and tennis courts, a sauna and music rooms.

STIPENDS AND MAINTENANCE

Currently, PGY-1 residents receive a stipend of approximately $52,143 - $53,710. Residents are provided with professional liability, medical care and hospitalization insurance, dental insurance, meals allowance and four weeks of vacation.

STAFF

Suzanne S. Mirra MD Professor and Chair; neuropathology; **Khaled I. Abu-Lawi** PhD Clinical Associate Professor; microbiology; **Juan Marcos Alarcon** PhD Assistant Professor; neuroscience; **Teresa M. Alasio** MD Assistant Professor; surgical pathology, cytopathology; **Virginia Anderson** MD Associate Professor; pediatric pathology; **Thomas Athanassiades** MD Associate Professor; immunology; **Constantine A. Axiotis** MD Professor; surgical pathology, oncology; **Randall Barbour** PhD Professor; optical imaging; **Stephen J. deRoux** MD Assistant Professor; forensic pathology; **Fidelina DeSoto** MD Clinical Assistant Professor; surgical pathology; **Helen G. Durkin** PhD Associate Professor; immunology; **Elena T. Estuita** MD Clinical Assistant Professor; surgical pathology, cytopathology; **Elizabeth Gloster** MD Professor; blood banking, coagulation, pediatric pathology; **Susan R.S. Gottesman** PhD, MD Professor; hematopathology; **Raavi Gupta** MD Assistant Professor; surgical pathology, hematopathology; **Edward Heilman** MD Associate Professor; dermatopathology; **A. Ivan Hernandez** PhD Assistant Professor; neuroscience; **Joan H. Howanitz** MD Professor; clinical pathology, chemical pathology; **Peter J. Howanitz** MD Professor; clinical pathology, chemical pathology; **Y.D. Kim** MD Assistant Professor; surgical pathology; **Felicitas Lacbawan** MD Associate Professor; molecular pathology; **Jenny M. Libien** MD, PhD Assistant Professor; neuropathology, autopsy pathology; **Josef Michl** MD Associate Professor; cellular immunology; **Anthony Nicastri** MD Professor; surgical pathology, nephropathology; **Maja Nowakowski** PhD Associate Professor; immunology; **Matthew R. Pincus** MD, PhD Professor; clinical pathology; **Padmanabha R. Pulakhandam** MD Clinical Assistant Professor; hematopathology; **Chandrakant Rao** MD Clinical Professor; neuropathology; **Martin Salwen** MD Distinguished Service Professor; clinical pathology; **Janet A. Schneller** MD Clinical Professor; surgical pathology, cytology; **Charles Shao** MD, PhD Clinical Associate Professor; neuropathology; **Haseeb A. Siddiqi** PhD Assistant Professor; parasitology; **Marshall P. Solomon** DDS Professor; oral pathology; **Carl Vinciguerra** MD Assistant Professor; blood banking, hematology; **Rosemary Wieczorek** MD Clinical Professor; surgical pathology, immunopathology; **Carmencita Yudis** MD Assistant Clinical Professor, surgical pathology.

APPLICATIONS

Residency candidates must be graduates of approved medical schools in the United States or Canada or must have a valid ECFMG certificate. A curriculum vitae (CV), three letters of reference, USMLE transcript and a personal interview are required. All applications for PGY-1 positions are accepted through ERAS and should be received by December 15 for appointments beginning July 1 of the following year.

Address inquiries to:

Peter J. Howanitz, MD, Residency Program Director
Phone: (718) 270-4522 • **E-mail:** pathologyresidency@downstate.edu
or
Elizabeth Snypes, Education Coordinator
Department of Pathology
SUNY Downstate Medical Center
450 Clarkson Avenue, Box 25
Brooklyn, NY 11203
Phone: (718) 270-8173 • **E-mail:** pathologyresidency@downstate.edu
Web site: www.downstate.edu/pathology/

State University of New York Downstate Medical Center, Brooklyn, NY

UNIVERSITY AT BUFFALO THE STATE UNIVERSITY OF NEW YORK

Buffalo, New York

PROGRAMS OFFERED

The Department of Pathology at the State University of New York at Buffalo presently offers programs which are accredited by the Accreditation Council for Graduate Medical Education (ACGME) in Anatomic and Clinical Pathology (AP/CP, four years) or Anatomic Pathology (AP, three years). Residents in the AP/CP program receive training allowing them to either do general pathology, or to follow a more academic track through additional fellowship and/or research experience. The program in AP only is centered at the Buffalo General Hospital-Roswell Park Cancer Institute complex, with rotations of varying duration through other affiliated hospitals for additional experience in forensic pathology, cytogenetics, specialized surgical pathology and pediatric pathology. A didactic core lecture series is held weekly. In the first year, training in AP is emphasized along with an introduction to basic CP. Concentration in CP occurs during the second and third years with rotations in chemistry, microbiology, hematology, and blood banking. More advanced training in CP includes parasitology, virology, toxicology, tissue typing, and molecular diagnostics. Research opportunities are readily available.

REQUIREMENTS

For specific program requirements, access the University at Buffalo Department of Pathology **Website:** http://www.smbs.buffalo.edu/path/residency_appl.htm

TYPES AND NUMBERS OF APPOINTMENTS

The pathology program has a total of 15 residency positions. There are also five oncologic surgical pathology fellowships through Roswell Park Cancer Institute (RPCI).

FACILITIES

The University Department of Pathology is centered at the SUNY-Buffalo Medical School campus. The Buffalo General Hospital (BGH) is a major referral center for surgical pathology for the Kaleida Health System's five hospitals and outreach program. The Women's and Children's Hospital of Buffalo (WCHOB) is the main resource for pediatric pathology, with additional resources in obstetrical, breast and gynecological pathology. The Erie County Medical Center (ECMC) participates in advanced microbiology training. The Erie County Medical Examiner's Office shares the same campus site with the ECMC. Roswell Park Cancer Institute (RPCI) is a nationally renowned comprehensive cancer center and offers a unique opportunity for study and research in neoplastic diseases. The VA Western NY HealthCare System at Buffalo (WAWNYHS) serves as a regional consultation center for other VA hospitals in the district. In 2008, more than 145 autopsies were performed, not including over 1,200 forensic autopsies; more than 50,000 surgical and 60,000 cytology specimens were processed; and more than 10 million clinical laboratory examinations were performed in these hospitals.

COMMUNITY

Metropolitan Buffalo, with a population over 900,000, offers a wide range of activities for the sporting enthusiast in boating and snow skiing, and in its professional sport teams. Cultural activities including a major symphonic orchestra, excellent theatrical and musical presentations, and historic architectural treasures are available in the area. Niagara Falls and Canada are within a short drive.

STIPENDS AND MAINTENANCE

Stipends range from approximately $42,500 for PGY 1 residents to approximately $44,500 for PGY IV residents. Professional liability and medical insurance, lab coats, free parking and meal stipends are among the benefits provided.

STAFF

Medical School

Reid Heffner MD, Chairman, University Department of Pathology and Anatomical Sciences; **Amy Sands** MD, Residency Program Director; **Christopher Cohan** PhD, Neuroanatomy; **John Cotter** PhD, Anatomy; **Cynthia Dluguos** PhD, Neurobiology; **Samuel Gallant** PhD, Endocrine Pathology; **Chester Glomski** PhD, Hematology/Anatomy; **Robert Hard** PhD, Cell Biology; **Tracey A. Ignatowski** PhD, Neuroimmunology; **John Kolega** PhD, Cell Biology; **Frank Mendel** PhD, Functional Anatomy; **Peter A. Nickerson** PhD, Cell Biology; **Charles Severin** PhD, Neurobiology; **Michael Stachowiak** PhD, Cell Biology; **Judy Tamburin** PhD, Anatomy; **Linda M. Wild** MD, AP, Medical Education.

Kaleida Health System

Reid R. Heffner MD, University Department of Pathology, Chairman; Neuropathology; **Samuel Goodloe, Jr.** MD, Clinical Surgical Director; Surgical Pathology, Dermatopathology, Microbiology; **Lalarukh Aftab** MD, AP/CP, Hematopathology; **Lucia L. Balos** MD, Surgical Pathology, Neuropathology; **Frank Barbarossa** MD, AP/CP, Chemistry; **Frank Chen** MD, Surgical Pathology, Cytopathology; **Richard Erbe** MD, Cytogenetics, Molecular; **John Fisk** MD, Surgical Pathology, Transfusion Medcine; **Janet Fleck** MD, Surgical Pathology, Transfusion Medicine; **Mary George** MD, Surgical Pathology; **Federico Gonzalez-Fernandez** MD, PhD, Ophthalmic Pathology; **Brigid Hannahoe** MD, Surgical Pathology, Cytopathology; **Robert Hertzog** MD, Cytopathology, Surgical Pathology; **Susan Howard** MS, Chemistry; **Abdur R. Khan** MD, Pediatric Pathology, Surgical Pathology; **Rafal Kozielski** MD, Pediatric Pathology, Surgical Pathology; **Keith Krabill** MD, Clinical Pathology, Transfusion Services; **Wilfrido Mojica** MD, Surgical Pathology; **Marianne B. Murphy** MD, Surgical Pathology; **Hassan Nakhla** MD, Surgical Pathology; **Theodore Ondracek** MD, Surgical Pathology; **Peter Ostrow** MD, PhD, Neuropathology; **Joyce Paterson** MD, Surgical Pathology, GI Pathology; **Amy M. Sands** MD, Hematopathology, Cytopathology; **Georgirene Vladutiu** PhD, Biochemical Genetics; **Edit Weber-Shrikant** MD, Surgical Pathology, Renal Pathology.

Erie County Medical Center

James J. Woytash DDS, MD,Chief Medical Examiner and Director AP; Oral Pathology, Forensic Pathology; **Daniel Amsterdam** PhD, Director Laboratories; Microbiology; **Paul J. Hissin** MD, PhD, Chemistry; **Leorosa Lehman** MD, Hematology/Transfusion Service; **Jonrika Malone** MD, Forensic Pathology; **Robert J. Osiewicz** PhD, Toxicology; **Dianne Vertes** MD,PhD, Forensic Pathology.

Roswell Park Cancer Institute

Richard T. Cheney MD, Chairman, RPCI Department of Pathology; Dermatopathology; **Maurice Barcos** MD, Hematopathology; **Joanne Becker** MD, Transfusion, Laboratory Medicine; **AnneMarie W. Block** PhD, Cytogenetics; **Paul Bogner** MD, Pulmonary Pathology; **George Deeb** MD, Surgical Pathology, Hematopathology; **Helena Hwang** MD, Breast Pathology; **Thaer Khoury** MD, PhD, Breast Pathology; **Charles LeVea** MD, PhD, Surgical Pathology; GI Pathology; **Mihai Merzianu** MD, Head and Neck Pathology, Hematopathology; **Paulette Mhawech-Fauceglia** MD, GYN Pathology; **Carl Morrison** MD, Molecular Pathology; **Maria Enriqueta R. Nava** MD, Cytopathology; **Remedios B. Penetrante** MD, GI & GU Pathology, Breast Pathology; **Petr Starostik** MD, Molecular Diagnostics; **Paul Wallace** PhD, Flow Cytometry; **Shaozeng Zhang** MD, PhD, GU Pathology.

VA Western New York Healthcare System at Buffalo

Rana Samuel MD, Director, VAMC Department of Pathology and Laboratory Medicine; **Ayesha Arshad** MD, Surgical Pathology; **Fady Baddoura** MD, Hematopathology, Molecular Diagnostics; **David Crossland** MD, Anatomic Pathology, GI Pathology; **Federico Gonzalez-Fernandez** MD, PhD, Ophthalmic Pathology.

APPLICATIONS

Applications are accepted via the Electronic Residency Application Service (ERAS) only. For specific program requirements, access the University at Buffalo Department of Pathology website: http://www.smbs.buffalo.edu/path/residency_appl.htm.

WINTHROP-UNIVERSITY HOSPITAL

Mineola, New York

PROGRAMS OFFERED

The pathology laboratories occupy 19,700 square feet of space. These modern facilities are equipped with extensive automated equipment and a state-of-the-art computer system for the storage and retrieval of lab results. Averaged annual statistics over the last two years show 3,700,000 examinations in clinical pathology, 3,260 cytologies, 20,000 anatomic surgical specimens and an active autopsy service. The department houses a learning resource center consisting of a pathology library with a laser disc collection. The Department Chair is also the Program Director. Members of the department hold faculty positions at the State University of New York at Stony Brook. Pathologists and residents participate in teaching activities on the campus. Residents are encouraged to participate in research by utilizing all departmental resources. In anatomic pathology, the teaching faculty includes the Chairman of the department, Chief of Anatomic Pathology, seven full-time, and one part time Board certified pathologists who provide one-on-one supervision in all aspects of surgical and autopsy pathology. Instruction in neuropathology is provided by a full-time staff neuropathologist. Part-time specialists provide additional instruction in orthopedic pathology, pediatric pathology, renal pathology, pulmonary pathology, and dermatopathology. All sign-outs are performed over double-headed microscopes. Five pathologist assistants provide aid and backup to ensure that residents are not overwhelmed by grossing surgicals and have adequate opportunity to attend teaching conferences and examine and follow up their cases. Residents assume an important role on the frozen section service. A multi-headed video microscope is utilized to examine the histopathology of all interesting cases in regularly scheduled conferences. The cytopathology service is directed by a pathologist with specialty boards in cytopathology, and residents participate in obtaining high quality FNA material. Immunohistochemistry and Flow Cytometry laboratories are present on site. In clinical pathology, the teaching faculty includes the Department Chair, Blood Bank Director and one PhD faculty member, as well as many skilled and experienced technical supervisors. The clinical relevance of abnormal lab findings is stressed and residents participate actively in lab management including an on-call consultative component. A comprehensive lecture series covers all aspects of clinical pathology. Training in molecular diagnostic techniques is provided. Our residents have a consistent track record of involvement in scholarly activities leading to published articles. The Cytogenetics laboratory is under the auspices of pathology, and is directed by a PhD cytogeneticist. This lab employs FISH technology in addition to standard chromosomal studies.

TYPES AND NUMBERS OF APPOINTMENTS

The residency training program is approved for eight positions and is accredited for four years of combined training in anatomic and clinical pathology and for three years in anatomic pathology. Residents from other institution-approved programs, e.g. obstetrics and gynecology, are assigned to pathology rotations.

FACILITIES

Winthrop-University Hospital is widely acknowledged to be a rapidly growing, premier center of clinical and academic excellence. It is a 591-bed, fully accredited voluntary, nonprofit institution. Serving an important strategic hub of Nassau County since 1896, Winthrop-University Hospital has been extensively modernized in recent years. Winthrop-University Hospital is a major affiliate teaching hospital of the School of Medicine, State University of New York at Stony Brook. The hospital provides a generous allowance for attendance at local and national meetings.

COMMUNITY

Ideally situated in the heart of Nassau County, Winthrop-University Hospital offers access to all the elements that give the region one of the highest quality of life ratings in the country. Residents of the area have at their fingertips all the advantages of urban, suburban, and rural living. The hospital is situated minutes from the Long Island Railroad which provides a 40-minute ride to Manhattan and that great city's cultural resources. In stark contrast to the city, Long Island's hilly North Shore offers lush foliage, attractive villages and farther east, the inlets, coves and farm country of the North Fork. The sandy expanses of the South Shore feature some of the finest beaches on the Eastern Seaboard. Montauk Point, the eastern tip of Long Island's South Fork, is famous for its deep sea fishing. In Winthrop-University Hospital's immediate vicinity are abundant shopping and recreational facilities. All of these elements contribute to an ambiance that makes a residency at Winthrop-University Hospital a distinctly upscale experience.

STIPENDS AND MAINTENANCE

PGY-1: $46,147; PGY-2: $49,852; PGY-3: $52,168; PGY-4: $54,485. Subsidized housing is available.

STAFF

V. M. Donovan MD Department Chair/Program Director; Chief, Clinical Pathology; **Barbara Arendash,** MD Associate Pathologist; **Candace Bergen** Residency Coordinator; **J. Chiofolo** MD Director, Blood Bank; **S.A. Drexler**

MD Staff Pathologist; Neuropathologist; **A. Flieder** MD Attending Pathologist; **M. Gupta** MD Staff Pathologist; Chief, Cytopathology; **Iman Hanna** MD, Attending Pathologist; **P. Khullar** MD Attending Pathologist;Medical Director Molelcular Pathology; **P. Koduru** PhD Cytogeneticist; **R. Rivera** MT Administrative; Director, Pathology; **P.E. Schoch** PhD Microbiologist; **Elena Selbs** Attending Pathologist; **G.K. Turi** MD Chief, Anatomic Pathology; **Jen Zhou**, MD Attending Pathologist.

APPLICATIONS

Applicants for residency may obtain information from the Chairman's office by phoning (516) 663-2450.

Address inquiries to:

Virginia M. Donovan, MD
Chairman, Department of Pathology
Winthrop-University Hospital
222 Station Plaza North, Suite 620
Mineola, NY 11501

Main Entrance - Winthrop-University Hospital

NSLIJHS-ALBERT EINSTEIN COLLEGE OF MEDICINE AT LONG ISLAND JEWISH MEDICAL CENTER PROGRAM

New Hyde Park, New York

PROGRAMS OFFERED

The NSLIJHS-Albert Einstein College of Medicine at Long Island Jewish Medical Center is a merged Pathology Residency Program that incorporates the former North Shore University - New York University Medical School program. This fully accredited residency program offers combined training in anatomic and clinical pathology including its subspecialties of neuropathology, pediatric pathology, obstetric-gynecologic pathology, oral and maxillofacial pathology, cytopathology, dermatopathology, genitourinary pathology, forensic pathology, renal pathology, gastrointestinal pathology, hepatic pathology, clinical biochemistry, clinical microbiology, cytogenetics, molecular pathology, hematology and blood banking/transfusion medicine. Specialized training is also provided in research methodology which includes, among other techniques, electron microscopy, flow cytometry, fluorescent *in situ* hybridization and immunopathology. Residents may participate in the teaching programs of the Albert Einstein College of Medicine. We also have an accredited fellowship program in cytopathology.

REQUIREMENTS

Residency candidates must be graduates of approved medical schools in the United States or Canada. Graduates of foreign medical schools must have ECFMG certification. Satisfactory references are required.

TYPES AND NUMBERS OF APPOINTMENTS

The program has 16 pathology residency positions, 4 at each PGY level.

FACILITIES

Long Island Jewish Medical Center serves as the Long Island Campus for the Albert Einstein College of Medicine and comprises a voluntary nonprofit short-term 429-bed general hospital, a voluntary nonprofit psychiatric institution of 223 beds and a 140-bed children's hospital. In 2008, there were 2,130,392 billable tests, 36,185 surgical specimens, 27,387 cytology specimens and 125 autopsies. The laboratory facilities are modern and highly automated and the staff includes over 250 FTE professional, technical and non-technical personnel. The library has 9,300 medical texts including 460 e-books, subscribes to 50 print journals with online access to 3,800 unique journal titles, and stocks over 15,000 bound volumes of journals. AECOM has over 4,000 electronic journals to which LIJ has a paid subscription to access.

North Shore University Hospital comprises an 825-bed hospital that along with LIJMC are 2 of 3 tertiary care hospitals of a total of 16 hospitals that comprise the North Shore-Long Island Jewish Health System, the nation's third largest healthcare system. There are over 160 FTE professional, technical and non-technical personnel. The Don Monti Cancer Center and Ambulatory Surgery Center make NSUH one of the major cancer centers in the country. In 2008, there were 1,548,522 billable tests, 27,583 surgical specimens, 9,840 cytopathology specimens and 84 autopsies. A highly automated core laboratory for the Health System performs over 6.5 million tests per year, including specialized testing in many laboratory areas such as Molecular Diagnostics. The library has 3,737 medical texts, 173 print journals, and some 10,000 bound volumes of journals with access to 5,222 e-journals. The Department of Pathology at both campuses maintains a large, comprehensive working library of books and journals most frequently used by pathologists.

Participation and presentations by residents at regional and national pathology meetings is supported.

COMMUNITY

The LIJMC clinical campus is located in the New Hyde Park-Lake Success area of Long Island. The NSUH campus is just 4 miles away on the North Shore of Long Island with the main campus near Manhasset Bay. The location of both hospitals, about 10 miles east of New York City, offers easy access to the cultural and entertainment attractions for which the city is famous, as well as to the extensive recreational facilities of Long Island.

STIPENDS AND MAINTENANCE

Stipends effective as of 7/1/09 are as follows: (PGY-1) $58,000; (PGY-2) $60,000; (PGY-3) $62,000; (PGY-4) $63,500. Chief Residents receive an additional stipend of $1,500. Included in the benefits package: $1,800 housing stipend for qualified trainees, health and life insurance coverage and the supply and laundering of House Staff uniforms.

STAFF

Staff primarily based at LIJ

Michael J. Esposito MD (Northeastern Ohio Univ Col Med 1989) Program Director; Chief, Autopsy Pathology; **James M. Crawford** MD, PhD (Duke Univ School of Med 1982; Duke Univ Graduate School 1981) Chair, Pathology and Laboratory Medicine, Sr. VP of Laboratory Services; **Tawfiqul A. Bhuiya** MD (Dhaka Med Col, Bangladesh 1980) Vice Chairman, Pathology; **Cynthia Bowman** MD (Vanderbilt Univ Med Sch 1974) Vice Chairman, Laboratory Medicine; **Ayala Aviram** PhD (Sackler School of Med, Israel 1990) Chief, Cytogenetics; **Elsje C. Barendswaard** MD, PhD (Univ of Leyden Faculty of Med, the Netherlands 1985 and 2002) Gastrointestinal Pathology; **Theresa Y. Chan** MD (Cornell Univ Med Col 1995) Urologic Pathology; **Sheng Chen** MD (Hunan Med Univ, China 1984) Chief, Dermatopathology; **Morris Edelman** MD (Witwatersrand Univ, South Africa 1989) Chief, Pediatric Pathology; Cytopathology; **John E. Fantasia** DDS (Emory Univ 1975) Chief, Oral and Maxillofacial Pathology; **Alexander S. Fuchs** MD (Buenos Aires Univ, Argentina 1973) Chief, Immunopathology; Hematopathology; **Benjamin Greco** MD (Univ of the East, Philippines 1986) Associate Chief, Blood Banking/Transfusion Medicine; **Kathleen Grima** MD (Northwestern Univ 1981) Blood Banking/Transfusion Medicine; **Peihong Hsu** MD (Fujian Med Col, China 1982) Chief, Hematology; **Leonard B. Kahn** MBBCh (Witwatersrand Univ, South Africa 1960) Former Chairman, Pathology - NSUH and LIJ; **Robert D. Kelsch** DMD (Univ Connecticut 1992) Oral and Maxillofacial Pathology; **James E. Louie** MD (NYU 1978) Blood Banking/Transfusion Medicine; **Yvonne A. Lue** PhD (Columbia Univ Graduate School 1976) Chief, Microbiology; **Nora J. Morgenstern** MD (Buenos Aires Univ, Argentina 1989) Cytopathology; **Mansoor Nasim** MD, PhD (Univ Punjab, Pakistan 1987; Univ of London, United Kingdom 1993) Neuropathology; **Dilip V. Patel** MBBS (Baroda Med Col, India 1979) Hematology/Oncology; **Kanti Rai** MD (Jaipur, India 1955) Chief, Hematology/ Oncology; **Silvat Sheikh-Fayyaz** MBBS (Univ Punjab, King Edward Med Col, Pakistan 1982) Hematopathology; **Farnaz C. Tahmasebi** MD (Tehran Univ Med Sciences, Iran 1998) Gynecologic Pathology; **Elsa Valderrama** MD (Univ Colombia, South America 1968) Chief Emeritus, Pediatric Pathology; Renal Pathology; **Patricia G. Wasserman** MD (Buenos Aires Univ, Argentina 1982) Chief, Cytopathology; **Ding Wen Wu** MD (Shanghai Second Med Univ, China 1982) Chief, Blood Banking/ Transfusion Medicine.

Staff primarily based at NSUH

James M. Crawford MD, PhD (Duke Univ School of Med 1982; Duke Univ Graduate School 1981) Chair, Pathology and Laboratory Medicine, Sr. VP of Laboratory Services; **Lucien E. Nochomovitz** MBChB (Univ Cape Town, South Africa 1970) Vice Chairman, Pathology; **James H. Brassel** MD (Tufts Univ Sch Med 1973) Vice Chairman, Laboratory Medicine; **Jela Bandovic** MD (Univ of Tuzia, Bosnia and Herzegovina 1982) Hematopathology, Gastrointestinal Pathology; **Loring Bjornson** PhD (Univ of California 1970) Chief, Clinical Chemistry Lab; **Frank Breuer** MD (Emavnd Univ Gveifswald, Germany 1990) Surgical Pathology; **Judith P. Brody** MD (Feinberg Sch Med, Northwestern Univ 1976) Chief, Hematopathology; **Douglas A. Charney** MD (New York Med Col 1991) Renal Pathology; **Qiang H. Chen** MD (Tongji Med School, China 1984) Surgical Pathology; **Peter M. Farmer** MD (Jefferson Med Col 1969) Neuropathology; **Christine C. Ginocchio** PhD (SUNY at Stony Brook 1993) Microbiology; **Marina Ionescu** MD (Univ of Bucharest, Romania 1986) Gynecologic Pathology; **Leonard B. Kahn** MBBCh (Witwatersrand Univ, South Africa 1960) Former Chairman, Pathology - LIJ and NSUH; **James R. Kelson** PhD (Cleveland State Univ 1977) Clinical Chemistry; **Prasad R. Koduru** PhD (Andhra Univ, India 1979) Chief, Genetics; **Kathleen A. Leonard** MD (George Washington Univ School Med 1986) Blood Banking/Transfusion Medicine; **Jian Y. Li** MD, PhD (North China Med Coal Univ, China 1991; The Chinese Univ of Hong Kong, China 1998) Chief, Neuropathology; Molecular Pathology; **Maria D. Navarro** MD (NY Med Col 1992) Autopsy Pathology; **Ilan Reder** MD (Sackler School Med 1982) Chief, Cytopathology; **Saul Teichberg** PhD (Columbia Univ 1972) Electron Microscopy; **Xiaotong Wang** MD (China Med Univ, China 1990) Renal Pathology; **Albert Yeh** MD (National Taiwan Univ Col of Med, Taiwan (Republic of China) 1989) Pediatric and Perinatal Pathology; Urologic and Renal Pathology; Molecular Pathology; Cytogenetics; **Xinmin Zhang** MD (Qingdao Med Col, China 1989) Hematopathology.

APPLICATIONS

Applications will only be accepted via ERAS (Electronic Residency Application Service). Program criteria may be obtained via **E-mail:** sullivan@lij.edu. All applications and accompanying documentation must be received by December 31, 2009 for appointments beginning July 1, 2010.

Address inquiries to:

Michael J. Esposito MD, Director
Pathology Residency Program
Long Island Jewish Medical Center
270-05 76 Avenue, Room B-67
New Hyde Park, NY 11040
Phone: (718) 470-7709
Web site: http://www.northshorelij.com

The Long Island Jewish Medical Center, New Hyde Park, New York

North Shore University Hospital, Manhasset, New York

MOUNT SINAI SCHOOL OF MEDICINE

New York, New York

PROGRAMS OFFERED

The Mount Sinai School of Medicine offers approved postgraduate training programs in Anatomic Pathology, Anatomic and Clinical Pathology, and Anatomic and Neuropathology, leading to Board Certification in Pathology. Training programs are individually tailored to suit the needs of physicians preparing for careers in investigative pathology or clinical practice. Training is offered principally at the Mount Sinai Medical Center, comprised of the Mount Sinai Hospital and Mount Sinai School of Medicine, and the affiliated institutions, the Bronx Veterans Affairs Medical Center, Elmhurst Hospital Center, Englewood Hospital, and the Office of the Chief Medical Examiner of the City of New York. A graduate program in the biomedical sciences is sponsored by the Graduate School of Biological Sciences of Mount Sinai School of Medicine is also offered, leading to the PhD degree. The teaching staff includes more than 70 doctoral faculty with MD, PhD, or MD/PhD degrees, representing broad spectrum of interests and expertise in all phases of investigative and subspecialty pathology. Major investigative programs exist in molecular pathology, gene therapy, HIV, neurodegenerative diseases, and organ transplantation, with ample opportunities for resident participation in research. Each resident is assigned an individual faculty preceptor. Residents actively participate in the instruction of medical students at the Mount Sinai School of Medicine, including student laboratories, seminars, and electives. Residents are encouraged to complete an academic project in the laboratory or case study during their training and support is available for presentation at a national meeting. Fellowship opportunities are available to residents completing their training and are offered in dermatopathology, neuropathology, cytopathology, surgical pathology, obstetric and gynecologic pathology, gastrointestinal pathology, liver and transplantation pathology, and molecular genetic pathology.

REQUIREMENTS

Applicants must be graduates of approved medical schools in the United States or Canada or international graduates holding a valid ECFMG certificate.

TYPES AND NUMBERS OF APPOINTMENTS

There are 24 approved residency positions in anatomic or anatomic and clinical pathology.

FACILITIES

The Mount Sinai Medical Center, comprised of the Mount Sinai Hospital and Mount Sinai School of Medicine, is a world class academic medical center with an international reputation for biomedical research and advanced patient care. The Mount Sinai Hospital, founded over 150 years ago, has a long and distinguished record in medical research, teaching, and service to the community. The new Guggenheim Pavilion, a prototype for 21st century hospital care, designed by internationally renowned architect I.M. Pei, provides over 900 hospital beds for patient care, teaching, and research. The Lillian and Henry M. Stratton-Hans Popper Department of Pathology occupies the 15th floor of the Annenberg Building, which houses the Mount Sinai School of Medicine, the Gustave L. and Janet W. Levy Library, and research facilities. The department occupies over 60,000 square feet of space with facilities for transmission and scanning electron microscopy, image analysis, histochemistry, flow cytometry, immunohistochemistry and medical photography. The clinical laboratories, including automated robotic facilities, are located in the adjacent Icahn Medical Institute. Affiliated facilities, including the Bronx Veterans Affairs Medical Center, Elmhurst Hospital Center, Englewood Hospital, and the Office of the Chief Medical Examiner, assure the resident exposure to a wide variety of pathology problems. Shuttle bus service is provided to the affiliated institutions. Each year over 135,000 surgical specimen examinations, 7,000 operating room consultations, 49,000 cytopathology examinations, 300 autopsies, and 13,000,000 clinical laboratory procedures are performed in the combined programs. The facilities of the medical school, including the Gustave L. and Janet W. Levy Library, with a print collection of over 165,000 books and periodicals, more than 1,200 current journal subscriptions, and access to over 12,000 online periodicals and over 60 online databases, are available to the residents. The New York Academy of Medicine, housing one of the nation's largest medical libraries, is located adjacent to the medical center.

COMMUNITY

The Mount Sinai School of Medicine and the Mount Sinai Hospital occupy an eight block campus extending from 98th to 102nd street and from Fifth Avenue to Park Avenue on Manhattan's upper East side. The neighborhood, adjacent to Central Park, is renowned for its restaurants, museums, shopping, and cultural activities. Other New York City attractions are a short bus or subway ride away.

STIPENDS AND MAINTENANCE

The stipends in 2008-2009 ranged from $51,604 for PGY1 residents to $59,612 for PGY4 residents and $62,112 for chief residents. Funds for books and meeting travel are provided. A comprehensive benefits package, including malpractice insurance, health insurance, life insurance, dental, optical, and prescription plans, short and long term disability insurance, and workers' compensation insurance, is provided. On-campus parking is available. Rent-subsidized housing in the vicinity of the medical center is available.

STAFF

Mount Sinai Hospital, New York, New York

Alan L. Schiller MD (Chicago Med Sch, 1967) Chair, orthopedic pathology; **James A. Strauchen** MD (NYU, 1972) Vice Chair, Pathology Residency Program Director, hematopathology; **Mary Beth Beasley** MD (Tulane, 1993) pulmonary pathology; **Andrew D. Bergemann** PhD (Univ Melbourne, 1990) research pathology; **Miriam Birge** MD (Albert Einstein, 1993) dermatopathology; **Ira J. Bleiweiss** MD (St Georges Univ, 1984) breast pathology; **Edward J. Bottone** PhD (St Johns Univ, 1973) microbiology; **David Burstein** MD (Harvard Univ, 1977) cytopathology; **S. Yoon Choo** MD (Yonsei Univ, 1980) transfusion medicine; **Liane Deligdisch** MD (Bucharest Med Sch, 1957) obstetric and gynecologic pathology; **Steven H. Dikman** MD (SUNY Downstate, 1966) renal pathology; **Carol A. Eliasen** MD (Mount Sinai Schl Med, 1985) obstetric and gynecologic pathology; **Patrick Emanuel** MD (Otago, 1999) dermatopathology; **Adhan Fahmy** DDS (Columbia, 1995) oral pathology; **John T. Fallon** MD, PhD (Albany Med Col, 1974) cardiovascular pathology; **Thomas M. Fasy** MD, PhD (Univ Pennsylvania, 1968) research pathology; **M. Isabel Fiel** MD (Univ East, 1984) hepatopathology; **Daniel R. Foitl** MD (NYU, 1986) dermatopathology; **Mary Fowkes** MD, PhD (SUNY Upstate, 1999) neuropathology; **Alan H. Friedman** MD (NYU, 1963) ophthalmic pathology; **Marie A. Fusco-Ramer** DDS (NYU, 1984) oral and maxillofacial pathology; **Roberto A. Garcia** MD (INTEC Santo Domingo, 1989) orthopedic and soft tissue pathology; **Joan Gil** MD (Barcelona, 1964) pulmonary pathology; **Ronald E. Gordon** PhD (SUNY-Stony Brook, 1976) ultrastructural pathology; **Noam Harpaz** MD, PhD (Univ Miami, 1981) gastrointestinal pathology; **Shabnan Jaffer** MD (Mount Sinai Sch Med, 1992) breast pathology; **Tamara Kalir** MD (Univ Cal-San Diego, 1986) obstetric and gynecologic pathology; **George M. Kleinman** MD (SUNY Buffalo, 1974) neuropathology; **D. Stave Kohtz** PhD (Mount Sinai Sch Med, 1987) research pathology; **Vincent J. LaBombardi** PhD (St. John's Univ, 1978) microbiology; **Patrick A. Lento** MD (Georgetown Univ, 1993) autopsy pathology; **Harry Lumerman** DDS (NYU, 1961) oral and maxillofacial pathology; **Margaret S. Magid** MD (Cornell Univ, 1976) pediatric pathology; **Lorraine K. Miller** PhD (CUNY, 1970) immunopathology; **Susan Morgello** MD (Duke Univ, 1982) neuropathology; **Raffaella Morotti** MD (Univ di Milano, 1986) pediatric pathology; **Chandadeep Nagi** MD (Albany Medical Colleg, 1999) breast pathology; **Vesna Najfeld** PhD (Univ London, 1975) tumor cytogenetics; **Ellinor I Peerscke** PhD (NYU, 1980) hematology; **Daniel P. Perl** MD (SUNY-Downstate, 1967) neuropathology; **Melissa Pessin-Minsley** MD, PhD (Johns Hopkins, 1991) clinical pathology; **Bruce E. Petersen** MD (SUNY Downstate, 2001) hematopathology; **Robert G. Phelps** MD (Univ Pennsylvania, 1979) dermatopathology; **Alexandros D. Polydorides** MD, PhD (Cornell Univ, 2003, Rockefeller Univ 2002) gastrointestinal pathology; **Dushyant P. Purohit** MD (BJ Med Col, 1969) neuropathology; **Lihui Qin** MD, PhD (Beijing, 1986, Med Univ South Carolina, 1994) gastrointestinal pathology; **Libo Qiu** MD (Hengyang, 1985) surgical pathology; **Lakshmi Ramanathan** PhD (MIT, 1976) cliniical chemistry; **Michael Rivera** MD (SUNY Downstate, 2001) head and neck pathology; **Bruce A. Schainker** MD (Washington Univ, 1975) cytopathology; **William Scher** MD (Univ Virginia, 1961) research pathology; **Peter Schlosshauer** MD (Univ Heidelberg, 1987) obstetric and gynecologic pathology; **Helen Shim-Chang** MD (Hahnemann, 1991) dermatopathology; **Arnold H. Szporn** MD (Rutgers, 1979) cytopathology; **Swan N. Thung** MD (Univ Indonesia, 1970) hepatopathology; **Natalie Tulchin** PhD (NYU, 1966) research pathology; **Pamela D. Unger** MD (SUNY-Upstate, 1982) genitourinary pathology; **Stephen Ward** MD, PhD (Univ Maryland, 2003) hepatopathology; **Carolyn Whittsett** MD (Howard, 1970) transfusion medicine; **David E. Wolfe** MD (Columbia Col Physicians & Surgeons, 1960) neuropathology; **Hai-Shan Wu** PhD (Shanghai Univ, 1988) image analysis; **Maoxin Wu** MD, PhD (Shanxi Med Col, 1984) cytopathology; **Songyang Yuan** MD, PhD (Henan Med Univ, 1983) gastrointestinal pathology; **David Y. Zhang** MD, PhD (Norman Bethune Univ, 1982) molecular pathology,; **Wenyong Zhang** MD, PhD (Cornell Univ 2004, Rockefeller Univ 2002) molecular pathology; **Hongfa Zhu** MD, PhD (Soochow, 1985) gastrointestinal pathology.

Veterans Affairs Medical Center, Bronx, New York

Fiorenzo Paronetto MD (Univ Padua, 1952) Chief, Pathology; hepatopathology; **Ho-Soon H. Choi** MD (Korea Univ, 1961) neuropathology; **Azra Habib-Lemp** MD; **Giulia Orsatti** MD (Univ Rome, 1983); **Azra Shahidi** PhD (Univ Missouri, 1967) microbiology.

Elmhurst Hospital Center, Queens, New York

Valery Glezerov MD, PhD (Leningrad, 1963) Director, Pathology; immunopathology; **Ann Ester Chernys** MD (Duke Univ, 1973) cytopathology; **Svetlana Grinblat** MD (Ternopol Med Inst, 1978); **Lisa Lee** MD (Taishan Med Col, 1990); **Anatoly Leytin** MD (Moscow Med Inst, 1981) anatomic pathology; **Suneetha Natarajan** MD (Kasturba Med Col, 1989) neuropathology.

Englewood Hospital, Englewood, New Jersey

Miguel A. Sanchez MD (Univ Madrid, 1969) Chief, Pathology; cytopathology; **Ana Burga** MD (Univ Illinois, 1996); **Massoud Kashani** MD (Tehran, 1967); **Rosalyn E. Stahl** MD (Albert Einstein Col Med, 1976); **Mikhail Tismenetsky** MD; **Jausheng Tzeng** MD (UMDNJ, 1996).

APPLICATIONS

Applications are accepted through the ERAS. Applications for July 1 should be received by December 1. Appointments are made through the NRMP.

Address inquiries to:

James A. Strauchen, MD, Vice Chair
c/o Allene Carter, Residency Coordinator
Department of Pathology
Mount Sinai School of Medicine
New York, NY 10029
Phone: (212) 241-8014 • **Fax:** (212) 534-7491 • **E-mail:** allene.carter@mssm.edu
Web site: http://www.mssm.edu/path/

Mount Sinai School of Medicine, New York, New York

NEW YORK-PRESBYTERIAN HOSPITAL COLUMBIA UNIVERSITY MEDICAL CENTER

New York, New York

PROGRAMS OFFERED

The Department of Pathology and Cell Biology at the Columbia University Medical Center Campus of New York Presbyterian Hospital and the College of Physicians & Surgeons of Columbia University offers an extraordinary opportunity for graduate training in Pathology in a vibrant medical and cultural setting. The large volume of clinical material from all subspecialties of medicine and surgery and the full-time faculty:resident ratio of more than 4:1 provide unexcelled training in diagnostic pathology and laboratory medicine. Subspecialty expertise in the department and in the clinical services of the medical center assure state-of-the-art training and clinical research opportunities. All residents participate in medical student teaching in the College of Physicians & Surgeons. The department is also among the top recipients of NIH-sponsored research support among Departments of Pathology in the country; this provides outstanding research opportunities and excellent financial support for residents interested in experimental pathology. The department is proud of its long history of training men and women for careers in the clinical practice of pathology and leadership roles in diagnostic, academic, and research pathology.

The combined anatomic and clinical pathology training program integrates 24 months of anatomic pathology, 18 months of laboratory medicine, and 6 months in subspecialties or research of the resident's choice. The program in **anatomic pathology** includes 24 months of surgical, autopsy, pediatric, gynecologic, renal and molecular pathology, along with neuropathology, cytopathology, hematopathology and immunopathology. This is followed with 12 months of advanced training in surgical pathology with increased diagnostic and supervisory responsibilities or 12 months in an anatomic subspecialty or research of the resident's choice. This program is designed for the resident who wishes to practice in a large community hospital or group practice or in an academic setting with research, teaching and diagnostic responsibilities. The **laboratory medicine (clinical pathology)** program has an 18-month core program with rotations through the divisions of hematology and coagulation, transfusion medicine, clinical chemistry, microbiology, diagnostic immunology, immunogenetics and histocompatibility, cytogenetics, and medical informatics. The following 18 months of the program are devoted to advanced training in one of the subspecialty areas and includes a research project. This program is well suited to graduates of combined MD-PhD programs who are interested in practice or research in an academic or commercial setting. The program in **experimental pathology** is also particularly appropriate for graduates of MD-PhD programs. The resident completes either the 24-month anatomic pathology or the 24-month laboratory medicine core program. This is followed by 2 years of full-time research in one of the many research laboratories of the department or in collaboration with other departments at the medical center. **Fellowship training** is available in blood banking/transfusion medicine, surgical pathology, molecular pathology, neuropathology, hematopathology, and obstetric/gynecologic pathology.

TYPES AND NUMBERS OF APPOINTMENTS

The Pathology Residency Program has 21 ACGME-accredited positions in anatomic and clinical pathology.

FACILITIES

In 2008 the department had some 55,000 surgical accessions; 9,000 non-gyn cytology specimens; 41,000 Pap smears; and more than 4,000 frozen sections. A total of 249 autopsies was performed, including 157 adult and 92 pediatric cases. Combined with an active consultation service (which receives from other institutions approximately 3,700 general surgical pathology referrals, 2,600 renal biopsies, 200 gynecologic pathology cases, and 600 neuropathology cases each year) the department provides a wealth of clinical material for training and research purposes. The Center for Advanced Laboratory Medicine provides lab services for clinical trials and research at the medical center. The clinical laboratories perform approximately 6.0 million tests yearly.

Within the Department of Pathology and Cell Biology, each resident has dedicated desk space with microscope and computer, and has access to the Internet, Medline searches, word processing, and presentation software. The diagnostic activities of the department are on the Windows-based CoPath client/server. The hospital's Internet-based Clinical Information System ("WebCIS") provides patient information and search capabilities.

Presbyterian Hospital has approximately 1,100 patient care beds, including 745 at the Milstein Hospital Building and 300 at the Allen Pavilion. The medical center also includes the New York State Psychiatric Institute & Hospital, the Edward S. Harkness Eye Institute, the Neurological Institute, and Children's Hospital of New York. Other institutions at the medical center include the Columbia University School of Public Health, the School of Dental & Oral Surgery, and the School of Nursing. Affiliated centers on the campus include the Comprehensive Cancer Center and Institute for Cancer Research, the Center for Geriatrics and Gerontology and the Howard Hughes Medical Institute Program in Molecular Neurobiology.

STIPENDS AND MAINTENANCE

For 2009-10, salaries will range from $49,727 (PGY1) to $57,088 (PGY4) per year plus an additional supplement of $3,000. Residents are provided with: a flexible benefits package which provides malpractice insurance, life and disability insurance; paid sick leave; tax deferred annuities; a municipal credit union; uniforms and uniform laundry; medical and dental benefits; vision care discounts.

STAFF

Michael Shelanski MD, PhD Chairman (Univ Chicago, 1966, 1967) neurobiology; **Charles C. Marboe** MD, Vice Chairman and Director, Residency Training Program (Penn State Univ, 1976) cardiovascular pathology; **Steven Spitalnik** MD, Vice Chairman, Director, Clinical Pathology Training (Univ Chicago, 1978) clinical pathology; **Corinne Abate-Shen** PhD (Cornell Univ, 1988) cancer biology; **Asa Abeliovich** MD, PhD (Harvard Univ, 1996, MIT, 1994) neurobiology; **Rosanna G. Abellar** MD (Univ of the City of Manila, 1991) perinatal pathology; **Bachir Alobeid** MD (Damascus Univ, Syria 1984) hematopathology; **Ottavio Arancio** MD, PhD (Univ Pisa Sch Med, Italy, 1981, Univ Verona, Italy, 1991) neurobiology; **Richard Axel** MD (Johns Hopkins Sch Med, 1970) neurobiology; **Govind Bhagat** MBBS (Univ College of Med Sciences, Delhi Univ, India, 1992) hematopathology; **Eduardo Bonilla** MD (Javerina Med Sch, Bogota, Colombia, 1954) neurology and muscle pathology; **Alain C. Borczuk** MD (Cornell Univ, 1991) surgical pathology; **J. Chloe Bulinski** PhD (Univ Wisconsin, 1980) cell biology; **Peter Canoll** MD, PhD (NYU Sch Med 1998) neuropathology; **Xiaowei Chen** MD (Norman Bethune Univ of Med Sci, China, 1982) cytopathology, OB/GYN pathology; **Carlos Cordon-Cardo** MD (Autonomous Univ, Barcelona, 1980) PhD (Cornell Univ Medical College, 1985), genitourinary/translational pathology; **John Crapanzano** MD (Louisana State Univ, 1992) cytopathology, surgical pathology; **Vivette D'Agati** MD (NYU Sch Med, 1979) renal pathology; **Riccardo Dalla-Favera** MD (Univ Milan, Italy, 1976) Director, Institute Cancer Genetics; **Phyllis Della-Latta** PhD (NYU, 1978) Director, Clinical Microbiology Service; **Gilbert Di Paolo** PhD (Univ Lausanne, Switzerland, 1998) cell biology; **David Diuguid** MD Cornell Univ Med Col, 1979) hematology and coagulation; **Fiona Doetsch** PhD (Rockefeller Univ, 1999) neurobiology; **Karen Duff** PhD (Univ Cambridge, 1991) neurobiology; **Andrew Dwork** MD (Univ New Jersey Med Col, 1977) neuro; **Phyllis Faust** MD, PhD (Washington Univ Sch Med, 1989) neuropathology; **James Goldman** MD, PhD (NYU Sch Med, 1976) Director, Division Neuropathology; **Lloyd Greene** PhD (Univ California, 1970) neurobiology; **Ellen Greenebaum** MD (Col Physicians & Surgeons, Columbia Univ, 1977) cytopathology; **Wei Gu** PhD (Columbia Univ, 1995) cancer biology; **Diane Hamele-Bena** MD (New York Med Col, 1989) Director, cytopathology; **Lara Harik** MD (Amer Univ Beirut, Lebanon, 2000) genitourinary and surgical pathology; **Arthur Hays** MD (Univ Colorado Med Ctr, 1966) neuropathology; **Christopher Henderson** PhD (Cambridge Univ, 1979) Co-Director, Motor Neuron Center; **Hanina Hibshoosh** MD (New York Med Col, 1985) surgical pathology; **Sameera Husain** MD (Dow Med Col, Pakistan, 1985) dermatopathology; **Jeffrey Jhang** MD (Mount Sinai Sch Med, 1997) transfusion medicine; **Harold Kaplan** MD (Albert Einstein Col Med, 1962) Director, Transfusion Medicine; **Jan Kitajewski** PhD (Princeton Univ, 1987) cell biology; **Alexander Kratz** MD (Univ Vienna, Austria, 1989), MPH, PhD (Yale Univ, 1991, 1995) Assoc. Director, Core Laboratory; **Arnold Kriegstein** MD, PhD (NYU, 1977) neurobiology; **Brett Lauring** MD, PhD (NYU Sch Med, 1997) liver pathology; **Jay Lefkowitch** MD (Col Physicians & Surgeons, Columbia Univ, 1976) liver pathology; **Brynn Levy** PhD (Mount Sinai Sch Med, 1999) Director, Genetics Diagnostic Laboratory; **Ronald Liem** PhD (Cornell Univ, 1973) neurobiology; **Thomas Ludwig** PhD (EMBL Heidelberg, 1992) cancer genetics; **Mahesh Mansukhani** MD (Davao Med Sch, Philippines, 1985) Director, Molecular Diagnostics; surgical pathology; **Glen Markowitz** MD (Albert Einstein Col Med, 1994) renal pathology; **Thomas Martin** BVSc, PhD, (1971,1986, Univ Sydney, Australia) Director, Comparative Medicine; **Carol Mason** PhD (Univ California, 1973) neurobiology; **Roger Moreira** MD (Federal Univ of Rio Grande do Sul, 2002) surgical pathology; **Vundavalli V.V.S. Murty** PhD (Delhi Univ, India, 1986) cytogenetics; **Samih Nasr** MD (Damascus Univ Sch Med, Syria, 1996) renal pathology; **Kathleen O'Toole** MD (Albert Einstein Col Med, 1978) Director, Division Surgical Pathology; **Ramon Parsons** MD, PhD (SUNY at Stony Brook, 1992) Cancer Genetics; **Karl Perzin** MD (Col Physicians & Surgeons, Columbia Univ, 1958) surgical pathology; **Fabrizio Remotti** MD (Univ Rome, Italy 1983) surgical pathology; **Helen Remotti** MD (Northwestern Univ 1990) surgical pathology; **Ralph Richart** MD Vice Chairman (Univ Rochester Sch Med and Dent, 1958) OB/GYN pathology; **Heidrun Rotterdam** MD (Univ Munich, Germany, 1968) surgical pathology; **Anjali Saqi** MD (SUNY Downstate Col Med, 1996) cytopathology, surgical pathology; **Taka-Aki Sato** PhD (Univ Osaka Med Sch, Japan, 1990) cell biology; **Hermann Schubert** MD (Heinrick Heine Univ, Germany, 1974) ophthalmic pathology; **Joseph Schwartz** MD (Technion-Israel Inst Techno, 1989) Director, Special Hematology and Coagulation; **Deborah Sevilla** MD (Eastern Virginia Med Sch, 2004) hematopathology; **David Silvers** MD (Duke Univ, 1968) Director, dermatopathology; **Patrice Spitalnik** MD (Univ Chicago, 1978) medical education; **Michael B. Stokes** MB BCh (Univ Col, Dublin, Ireland, 1989) renal pathology; **Nicole Suciu-Foca** PhD (Univ Bucharest, Romania, 1965) Director, Immunogenetics; **Matthias Szabolcs** MD (Univ Vienna, Austria, 1989) surgical pathology; **Kurenai Tanji** MD, PhD (Kinki Univ, Japan, 1984, 1995) neuropathology; **Guo-Xia Tong** MD, PhD (Jiangx Med Col, Harbin Med Univ, China, 1986, 1992) cytopathology; **Benjamin Tycko** MD, PhD (NYU Sch Med, 1984) cell biology and neuropathology; **Richard B. Vallee** MPH, PhD (Yale Univ, 1974) cell biology; **Jean Paul Vonsattel** MD (Med Sch Lausanne, Switzerland 1978) neuropathology; **Dorothy Warburton** PhD (McGill Univ, 1961) Director, Genetics Diagnostic Laboratory; **Hynek Wichterle** PhD (Rockefeller Univ, 2000) neurobiology; **Thomas Wright** MD (Harvard Med Sch, 1977) Director, Gynecologic Pathology; **David Zegarelli** DDS (Columbia Univ Sch Dent and Oral Surg, 1969) Director, oral pathology; **Qi Zhang** MD (Harbin Med Univ, China, 1982), PhD (Rutgers Univ, 1994) AP/CP, Palisades Med Ctr.

APPLICATIONS

Address inquiries to:

Cheri Winston
Program Coordinator, Residency Training Program
Department of Pathology
Columbia University College of Physicians & Surgeons
630 West 168th Street
New York, NY 10032
Phone: (212) 305-5697
Web site: http://www.pathology.columbia.edu

Columbia-Presbyterian Medical Center adheres to affirmative action and equal opportunity principles.

NEW YORK-PRESBYTERIAN HOSPITAL WEILL CORNELL CAMPUS

New York, New York

PROGRAMS OFFERED

The Department of Pathology and Laboratory Medicine offers a flexible four year training program leading to Board certification in anatomic pathology, laboratory medicine, or combined anatomic pathology and laboratory medicine. These programs are individually tailored to be suitable for those individuals interested in an academic career in pathology, in the subspecialty practice of pathology, or in the practice of modern general pathology in the community. In addition, a training program in experimental pathology is available for those individuals who desire a career in scientific investigation. The experimental pathology training program is especially suited for graduates of combined MD/PhD programs. The core program in anatomic pathology consists of training in fetal, pediatric, adult and forensic autopsy pathology, pediatric and adult general surgical pathology, cytopathology, gastrointestinal pathology, gynecologic pathology, hematopathology and neuropathology. The core training program in laboratory medicine consists of rotations in chemistry, coagulation, hematology, microbiology and transfusion medicine. Rotations in molecular pathology and cytogenetics, are included in all the training programs. The residents are strongly encouraged to spend one year in an anatomic or laboratory medicine subspeciality of their choice in order to gain diagnostic expertise and/or research experience in a specific subspecialty area of pathology. All residents are actively encouraged to participate in the research programs of the department or the broader scientific community and to present the results of their research at appropriate national meetings. Experimental pathology trainees complete the core training program in either anatomic pathology or laboratory medicine in two years and spend the subsequent two years in full-time laboratory research. The research may be performed within the department, or with an appropriate preceptor within other departments of Weill Cornell Medical College or nearby Rockefeller University or Memorial Sloan-Kettering Cancer Center. These unrivaled research opportunities combined with excellent financial support for the trainees make the experimental pathology training program one of the most attractive in the United States. In addition, a fifth year of training leading to subspecialty certification is available by application. The interests, goals and performance of each resident are reviewed periodically by the Director and the Residency Committee, with guidance for residents in planning their advanced training years as well as in selecting specific laboratories in which to pursue their research. The residents participate in numerous teaching conferences concerning anatomic pathology, laboratory medicine, and clinical and basic science research. In addition, each resident engages in student teaching in the pathology courses of the Weill Cornell Medical College. All the residents receive training and instruction from a large full-time faculty devoted to the clinical practice of pathology, clinical and basic research, and teaching.

TYPES AND NUMBERS OF APPOINTMENTS

There is a total of 27 pathology residency and fellowship positions at the present time.

FACILITIES

New York-Presbyterian Hospital (NYPH) is the major clinical affiliate and teaching hospital of Weill Cornell Medical College. The NYPH-Cornell Campus, an 824-bed facility, is centrally located in a highly sophisticated medical community surrounded by the Hospital for Special Surgery, the Memorial-Sloan Kettering Cancer Center and the Rockefeller University. The number of specimens annually are as follows: autopsies, 112; surgical pathology specimens, 50,609; frozen sections, 4,082; cytopathology specimens, 54,291; laboratory procedures, 4,625,795.

COMMUNITY

The Medical Center is located in a beautiful residential neighborhood along the East River in Manhattan within walking distance of Central Park and the midtown entertainment and shopping areas. The major museums, concert halls and opera house are nearby.

STIPENDS AND MAINTENANCE

In 2009-2010, first-year residents receive $49,727 per year; second-year residents, $52,322. Apartments are available for single and married house staff in NYPH maintained apartment buildings adjacent to the Medical Center. All residents are covered under New York Presbyterian Hospital benefits program, which includes professional liability insurance, hospitalization and uniforms.

STAFF

Yashpal Agrawal MD, PhD (Baroda Med Col, India, 1983; Univ Kuopio, Finland, 1987) clinical chemistry; **Mohammad Akhtar** MD (King Edward Col, Pakistan, 1964) surgical pathology, renal pathology; **Rebecca Baergen** MD (Univ California, 1983) pediatric and perinatal pathology; **Debra Beneck** MD (SUNY Downstate Bklyn, 1981) pediatric pathology, surgical pathology; **M. Desmond Burke** MD (Nat Univ Ireland, 1959) professor emeritus pathology; **Andrea Cerutti** MD (Univ Med Sch of Padua, Italy, 1990) immunology, hematology; **Ethel Cesarman** MD, PhD (Univ Autonoma Metropolitana, Mexico, 1981; NYU, 1988) molecular pathology, hematopathology; **Yao-Tseng Chen** MD, PhD (Nat Taiwan Univ Sch Med, Taiwan, 1981; Cornell Univ, 1985) surgical pathology, molecular pathology; **Selina Chen-Kiang** PhD (Columbia Univ, 1979) molecular immunology; **Melissa Cushing** MD (Georgetown Univ Sch Med, 2001) transfusion medicine; **Francesca Demichelis** PhD (Univ of Trento, Italy, 2005) computational biology; **Lora Hedrick Ellenson** MD (Stanford Univ Sch Med, 1986) gynecologic pathology; **Scott A. Ely** MD, MPH (Tulane Univ Sch Med, 1991) hematopathology; **Domenick J. Falcone** PhD (Cornell Univ, 1981) cell biology, vascular biology; **David P. Hajjar** PhD (Univ New Hampshire, 1978) vascular biology; **Charles S. Hirsch** MD (Univ Illinois Col Med, 1962) Chief Medical Examiner City of New York, Consultant; forensic pathology; **Timothy Hla** PhD (George Washington Univ. 1988) vascular biology; **Rana Hoda** (Dow Med Col, India, 1983) cytopathology; **Syed A. Hoda** MD (Dow Med Col, Pakistan [MBBS], 1983) surgical pathology; **Stephen Jenkins** PhD (Univ of Vermont, 1979) clinical microbiology; **Joan G. Jones** MD (Albert Einstein Col Med, 1984) surgical pathology, gynecologic pathology; **Daniel M. Knowles** MD (Univ Chicago Pritzker Sch Med, 1973) hematopathology, immunopathology, molecular pathology; **June H. Koizumi** MD (Univ Illinois Col Med, 1976) cytopathology; **Ehud Lavi** MD (Technion-Israel Inst of Tech, 1978) neuropathology; **Jerry B Lefkowitz** MD (Med Col of Virginia, 1983) coagulation, hematology; **Debra G.B. Leonard** MD, PhD (Univ New York, 1988; New York Univ 1987) laboratory medicine; **Neil Lipman** VMD (Sch Vet Med, Univ Pennsylvania, 1984) laboratory animal and comparative medicine; **Cynthia M Magro** MD (Univ Manitoba, 1984) dermatopathology; **Susan Mathew** PhD (Andhra Univ, India, 1981) molecular pathology; **Charles R. Minick** (Cornell Univ Med Col, 1960) autopsy pathology; **Andrew Nicholson** PhD, DVM (Cornell Univ Med Col 1976) laboratory animal and comparative pathology; **Attilio Orazi** MD (Univ of Milan, Italy, 1979) hematopathology, immunopathology; **Edyta C. Pirog** MD (Warsaw Med Col, 1989) cytopathology, gynecologic pathology; **Venkat Pulijaal** PhD (Osmania Univ, India, 1978) cytogenetics; **Hanna Rennert** PhD (Technion-Israel Inst of Tech, 1989) molecular pathology; **David S Rickman** PhD (Mt Sinai Med Sch, 1997) molecular biology; **Juan Rosai** MD (Univ Buenos Aires Fac Med, Argentina, 1961) Consultant; dermatopathology, and surgical pathology; **Paul P. Rosen** MD (Columbia Univ Col Physicians & Surgeons, 1964) breast pathology; **Mark Rubin** MD (Mt Sinai Sch of Med, 1988) experimental pathology, genitourinary pathology; **Andrew Schreiner** MD (St. Louis Univ Sch of Med, 2000) cytopathology; **Audrey N Schuetz** MD, MPH (Emory Univ Sch Med, 2000; Rollins Sch of Public Med, 1999); **Theresa Scognamiglio** MD (MCP-Hahnemann Univ, 2001) surgical pathology; **Surya V. Seshan** MD (Government Med Col, India, 1974) renal pathology; **Rita Shaknovich** MD, PhD (Mt. Sinai Sch of Med, 1999; Mt Sinai Graduate Sch, 1997) hematopathology; **Maria Shevchuk** MD (Upstate Med Ctr NY, 1974) urologic pathology; **Sandra Shin** MD (Albany Med Col 1996) surgical pathology, breast pathology; **Donna L. Skerrett** MD (Temple Univ Sch Med, 1984) transfusion medicine; **Shivakumar Subramaniyam** PhD (Christian Med Col, India, 2003) cytogenetics; **Wayne Tam** MD, PhD (Joan and Sanford Weill Med Col Cornell Univ, 1996) hematopathology; **Julia Turbiner** MD (Universidad Nacional Autonoma de Mexico, 2002) hematopathology; **Rita Upmacis** PhD (Univ of Nottingham, England, 1986) vascular biology; **Y. Lynn Wang** MD, PhD (Beijing Med Univ, 1988; Brandeis Univ, 1996) molecular hematopathology; **Shu Yuan Xiao** MD (Hubei Med Univ, China, 1984) gastrointestinal pathology, hepatopathology; **Grace Yang** MD (UMDNJ-Robert Wood Johnson Sch Med, 1987) cytopathology; **Rhonda K. Yantiss** MD (Harvard Med Sch, 1996) gastrointestinal pathology, hepatopathology; **Pengbo Zhou** PhD (Univ Michigan, 1987) molecular and cell biology.

APPLICATIONS

Candidates must be graduates of approved medical schools in the United States or Canada or must have an ECFMG certificate. New York Presbyterian Hospital only supports J1 visas. July 1 is the start date for residents and fellows.

Address inquiries to:
Debra G.B. Leonard, MD, PhD
Residency Program Director
Donna M. Galvin, Senior Administrative Assistant
Department of Pathology & Laboratory Medicine
New York Presbyterian Hospital-Cornell Center
1300 York Avenue
New York, NY 10065
Phone: (212) 746-6464
Web site: http://www.nycornell.org/pathology/

NEW YORK UNIVERSITY MEDICAL CENTER

New York, New York

PROGRAMS OFFERED

Our pathology residency program is based at closely adjacent Bellevue, Tisch and Manhattan Veterans Hospitals staffed by NYU faculty. The NYU pathology residency program provides a broad and diversified curriculum to meet the ever-growing needs of contemporary residency education in pathology and is designed to satisfy the varied interests of the trainees in anatomic and clinical pathology. We offer residency training track programs in which individuals may choose a residency in Anatomic Pathology only (AP), Anatomic Pathology and Clinical Pathology (AP/CP), Anatomic Pathology and Research (AP/R), or Anatomic Pathology and Neuropathology (AP/NP). The pathology residency program training includes hands-on experience and responsibility in diagnostic surgical pathology and autopsy pathology, laboratory research, student teaching and progressive supervisory responsibilities up to the level of Junior Attending. Pathology residents are strongly encouraged to participate in investigative projects and present their work at scientific meetings. The long-standing goal of the Department of Pathology at New York University Medical Center to provide pathology training for careers in academic pathology was established in the 1950s by Dr. Lewis Thomas, then Chairman of the Department. Pathology residents from that and subsequent eras now chair or direct departments in medical centers throughout the country. For more information on our pathology residency programs see our residency program application section.

TYPES AND NUMBERS OF APPOINTMENTS

Six residencies are filled each year, with a total of 25 positions in the various program tracks.

FACILITIES

New York University Medical Center includes a 879-bed private university hospital, Tisch Hospital, the 1,100-bed municipally owned Bellevue Hospital, and the 576-bed Department of Veterans Affairs Medical Center. The anatomic pathology and clinical laboratory services of these hospitals are closely associated and provide a broad range of teaching material. Approximately 118,000 patients per year are admitted to the hospitals; about 200 post-mortem examinations are performed each year and approximately 42,500 surgical specimens and 50,000 cytology specimens, including 5,000 fine needle aspirates, are examined. The full-time anatomic and clinical teaching staff consists of more than 40 Board-certified pathologists, many of who conduct active investigative programs. An additional 25 faculty members are engaged in full-time research programs. Facilities for research and research training within the Department, the Skirball Institute, the various specialized Centers and the whole Medical School are exceptionally varied.

COMMUNITY

The exciting cultural, recreational, and educational opportunities of New York City and adjacent communities are without parallel.

STIPENDS AND MAINTENANCE

Stipends range from $56,073 per annum for house staff on the first postgraduate year level to $64,741 per annum for fourth-year residents. Malpractice coverage and a wide range of benefits including medical insurance are also provided. Tuition-free courses in New York University's many schools are available.

STAFF

David B. Roth MD, PhD, Professor and Chairman; **Joan F. Cangiarella** MD, Associate Professor and Vice Chair; cytopathology; **Luigia Abramovici** MD, Assistant Professor; bone & soft tissue; **Iannis Aifantis** PhD, Assistant Professor; hematopoietic stem cell differentiation; **E. Jane Albert Hubbard** PhD, Associate Professor; cell proliferation using C.elegans; **Constantin Aliferis** MD, PhD, Director Center for Health Informatics & Bioinformatics; **Edward Amorosi** MD, Associate Professor; hematology; **Michael Bannan** MD, Program Director, Assistant Professor; surgical pathology; **Laura M Barisoni** MD, Assistant Professor; renal pathology; **Ross S. Basch** MD, Professor; hematopoietic development; **Nina Bhardwaj** MD, PhD, Professor, Director Tumor Vaccine Program; immunobiology of antigen presenting cells; **Robert J. Boorstein** MD, PhD, Associate Professor; DNA repair, molecular pathology; **Silvia Buonamici** PhD, Research Associate; Notch1, chemokines, T-cell leukemia developm./progression, CNS infiltration; **Steven Burakoff** MD, Professor; immunology; **Norman Charles** MD, Clinical Professor; clinical correlation of external ocular disorders including lid, conjunctiva; **Dan Chen** PhD, Assistant Professor; clinical chemistry; **Fan Chen** MD, PhD, Clinical Assistant Professor; **Hearn J Cho** MD, PhD, Assistant Professor; medicine, oncology; **Maria Curotto de Lafaille** PhD, Research Assistant Professor, mouse models of allergic asthma; **Farbod Darvishian** MD, Assistant Professor; breast cancer pathology; **Kasturi Das** MD, Assistant Professor; Director of Cytopathology Bellevue; **Vittorio**

Defendi MD, Professor; viral oncogenesis; **Cesar DelRosario** MD, Clinical Assistant Professor; pathology of angiodysplasia of colon; **Sandra Demaria** MD, Assistant Professor; Immunotherapy of cancer; **Panna Desai** MD, Assistant Professor; non neoplastic and neoplastic bone and soft tissue lesions; **Cheryl DeScipio** PhD, Assistant Professor; cytogenetics; **Michael Dustin** PhD, Professor; Cell adhesion molecules; **Brian Dynlacht** PhD, Professor; Cancer, transcription, cell cycle, centrosome biology, genomics; **Adrian Erlebacher** MD, PhD, Assistant Professor, immunobiology of pregnancy; **Joel Ernst** MD, Professor; infectious diseases; **Stefan Feske** MD, Assistant Professor; T cell activation, immunity and development; **Blas Frangione** MD, PhD, Professor; Alzheimer's disease; dementia; stroke; **Hodaka Fuji** MD, PhD, Assistant Professor; signal transduction; **Jorge A. Ghiso** PhD, Associate Professor; Alzheimer's disease; neurodegeneration; **Miroslaw Gorny** MD, PhD, Professor; Human monoclonal antibodies, HIV-1 infection; **M. Alba Greco** MD, Professor and Director; perinatal pathology, congenital anomalie; **David Green** MD, PhD Assistant Professor; hematology; **Christina Hajdu** MD, Clinical Assistant Professor; gastrointestinal and liver pathology; **Bruce Hanna** PhD, Associate Professor; Isolation / Characterization of pathogenic microbes from human clinical material; **Osvaldo J Hernandez** MD, Assistant Professor; cytopathology and aspiration biopsy; **Eva Hernando** PhD, Assistant Professor; cell-of-origin, 'cancer stem cells'; **Avram Hershko** MD, PhD, Adjunct Professor of Pathology; **Timothy Hilbert** MD, PhD, JD, Assistant Professor; transfusion medicine; **Catarina Hioe** PhD, Assistant Professor; HIV vaccine, HIV-specific CD4 T cells; **Charles S. Hirsch** MD, Professor; sudden death due to natural causes, craniocerebral trauma; **Sherif Ibrahim** MD, PhD, Associate Professor; Leukemia, Lymphoma and Myeloproliferative disorders; **Ellis Jacobs** PhD, Associate Professor; lab medicine/automation; **Jessica Jacobson** MD, Assistant Professor, transfusion safety; **Hideko Kamino** MD, Associate Professor; dermatopathology, dermatology and pathology; **Margaret Karpatkin** MD, Professor; pediatrics; pediatric hematology; **Hannah Klein** PhD, Professor; DNA damage, genomic instability; **Michelle Krogsgaard** PhD, Assistant Professor; T-cell recognition, cancer immunology; **Suman Laal** PhD, Associate Professor; Immunol. and Mol. Biol. of Mycobacteria; **Juan J. LaFaille** PhD, Associate Professor; pathogenesis of autoimmune and allergic diseases; **Peng Lee** MD, PhD, Associate Professor, oncologic, GU & molecular pathology; **Pascale Levine** MD, Assistant Professor; GYN pathology, aspiration biopsy; **David E. Levy** PhD, Professor; signal transduction, gene expression; **Mark S. Lifshitz** MD, Clinical Professor and Director; laboratory automation; **Dan R. Littman** MD, PhD, Professor; T cell development; mechanisms of inflammation; **Cynthia Liu** MD, Assistant Professor; diagnostic hematopathology; **Cynthia Loomis** MD, PhD, Assistant Professor; developmental mechanisms in embryonic patterning; **Peter A. Lopez** BS, Research Assistant Professor; cytometry, fluorescence, cell biology; **Isabelle Marie** PhD, Assistant Professor; interferon, innate immune response; **Jonathan Melamed** MD, Associate Professor and Director Immunohistochemistry; Prostate cancer, tissue banking; **Daniel Meruelo** PhD, Professor; gene therapy, cancer, Alzheimer's disease; **Irina Mikolaenko** MD, Assistant Professor; surgical neuropathology; **Khush Mittal** MD, Associate Professor; Ob-Gyn pathology, oncogenesis; **Patricia K.A. Mongini** PhD, Associate Professor; B lymphocytes, COX-2, PGE2; **Michael Nardi** MS, Associate Professor; hematology; **Elizabeth W. Newcomb** PhD, Associate Professor; animal model of glioma, angiogenesis; **Diana Nimeh** MD, Assistant Professor; diagnostic cytopathology of the breast; **Daisuke Nonaka** MD, Assistant Professor; thoracic, endocrine, head & neck, and soft tissue tumors; **Ruth Nussenzweig** Doc en Med, PhD, Professor; immunology, vaccines, malaria, viral vectors; **Victor Nussenzweig** MD, PhD, Professor; Malaria biology and vaccine development; **Phillipe N. Nyambi** PhD, Assistant Professor; antigenic evol. of HIV-1 subtype B/ non B viruses; **David O'Neill** MD, Assistant Professor; immunotherapy, vaccine, dendritic cell; **Thaira Oweity** MD, Clinical Associate Professor; fine needle aspiration biopsy, GI and pancreas pathology; **Michele Pagano** MD Professor; Ubiquitin system, cell division cycle checkpoints, cancer; **Christine Pampeno** PhD, Assistant Professor; gene expression, virology; **Zhiheng Pei** MD, PhD, Assistant Professor; bacteria microbiome inflammation esophagus tonsils; **Angel G. Pellicer** MD, PhD, Professor; Ras, mouse models of cancer, oncogenes; **Mary Ann Perle** PhD, Assistant Professor tumor genetics, first trimester fetal loss; **Jennifer A. Philips** MD, PhD, tuberculosis, host pathogen interactions; **Julia M. Phillips-Quagliata** B.Sc, PhD, Professor; mucosal immunology; B cell migration and regulation; **David Polsky** MD, PhD, Associate Professor, melanoma, cell cycle, oncogenes; **Dorota Popiolek** MD, Assistant Professor; gynecological pathology; **Risha Ramdall** MD, Assistant Professor, cytopathology, surgical pathology; **Amy Rapkiewicz** MD, Assistant Professor, Director of Anatomic Pathology; **Karla S. Rosenman** MD, Clinical Assistant Professor, dermatopathology; hair disorders; **Agueda A. Rostagno** PhD, Assistant Professor; cerebrovascular amyloidosis; **Irma Sanchez** PhD, Assistant Professor; MAPK signal transduction and cell biology of the centrosome; **Susan R. Schwab** PhD, Assistant Professor, lymphocyte trafficking; **Filiz Sen** MD, Assistant Professor; molecular pathology of hematopoietic neoplasms; **Pratibha Shukla** MD, Assistant Professor, oncologic pathology; **Aylin Simsir** MD, Associate Professor, fine needle aspiration, breast and cervical cancer; **Baljit Singh** MD, Asssociate Professor; breast cancer, neo-adjuvant therapy; **Krishna Singh** PhD, Research Assistant Professor, pathogenesis of M. tuberculosis; **Jane A. Skok** PhD, Assistant Professor; nuclear organization of immunoglobulin genes; **Susan Smith** PhD, Associate Professor; telomeres, tankyrase, cohesion; **German C. Steiner** MD, Professor; orthopaedc pathology; **Wei Sun** MD, Assistant Professor; breast FNA and core biopsy; **George W. Teebor** MD, Professor; DNA base excision repair; **Philip M. Tierno** PhD, Clinical Professor, medical microbiology / ecology / human metagenomics; **E. Sergio Trombetta** PhD, Assistant Professor, dendritic cell function in innate and adaptive immunity; **Hui Tsou** MD, Clinical Associate Professor; dermatopathology; **Derya Unutmaz** MD, Assiociate Professor, immunology; **Jerry Waisman** MD, Professor; aspiration biopsy and cytology; **Beverly Y. Wang** MD, Associate Professor; risk factors of oral SCC; **Xiao-Jun Wei** MD, PhD, Assistant Professor; cytopathology; **Rosemary L. Wieczorek** MD, Adjunct Associate Professor; immunopathology; **Thomas**

Wisniewski MD, Professor; neuropathology, conformational disorders; **Ruliang Xu** MD, PhD, Associate Professor colorectal carcinogenesis; **Herman Yee** MD, PhD, CM, Associate Professor; hematopathology, surgical pathology, automation; **David Zagzag** MD, PhD, Associate Professor; neuropathology, angiogenesis; **Jiri Zavadil** PhD, Associate Professor; epithelial-mesenchymal transition; **Susan B. Zolla-Pazner** PhD, Professor; AIDS vaccines, HIV, antibodies.

APPLICATIONS

Applications should be submitted by December 1 for appointments beginning July 1 of the following year. Only ERAS applications will be considered.

Address inquiries to:

Michael Bannan, MD Director, Residency Training Program or
Adrienne Fabiano Coordinator, Residency Training Program
Department of Pathology
New York University Medical Center
522 First Avenue, SRB 301C
New York, NY 10016
Phone: (212) 263-5376 • **Fax:** (212) 263-8255 • **E-mail:** adrienne.fabiano@nyumc.org
Web site: http://pathology.med.nyu.edu/education/residency-programs

New York University Medical Center Photo: Gene Schultz

UNIVERSITY OF ROCHESTER MEDICAL CENTER

(Strong Memorial Hospital)

Rochester, New York

PROGRAMS OFFERED

A fully accredited training program offered in combined anatomic and clinical pathology, our program is structured to prepare residents for academic or community practice. Senior residents may apply for a departmentally sponsored resident year out research experience. AP and CP disciplines are integrated over the required four years. In keeping with the basic philosophy of the department, programs can be tailored to meet specific career objectives of the resident. These include programs with special emphasis on experimental pathology or one of several anatomic or clinical pathology disciplines. Participation in research endeavors is strongly encouraged during the training period. Three ACGME-accredited fellowships (Cytopathology, Hematopathology and Neuropathology) and one department fellowship (Genitourinary Pathology) are affiliated with our program.

FACILITIES

The University of Rochester Medical Center consists of the School of Medicine & Dentistry, School of Nursing and Strong Memorial Hospital. The faculty of the School of Medicine serves as the staff of Strong Memorial Hospital, a 750-bed facility and Level 3 trauma center. Our laboratories processes over 3.9 million laboratory examinations annually, including nearly 330 autopsies, 75,000 surgical specimens and greater than 85,000 gynecologic and non-gynecologic cytology specimens. Departmental research facilities and programs offer opportunities for applied and basic research. The medical center houses a modern library with 240,000 volumes and subscriptions to over 2,300 print and electronic journals.

COMMUNITY

Picture a city with miles of lakeshore, a central-city riverfront sprinkled with waterfalls, and a historic canal that flows through the heart of the small-town Americana. Now imagine that same city surrounded by glacier-carved lakes, one of the largest collections of cobblestone homes in the country, and world-class wine country. Welcome to the Rochester/Finger Lakes Region of Upstate New York. Monroe County, named after James Monroe, fifth president of the United States, is comprised of 19 towns, 10 villages and the City of Rochester, the third largest city in the state, with a combined population of approximately 750,000 residents and a land area of nearly 664 square miles. Monroe County has been a world leader in imaging technology. Today, we're not only on the cutting edge of imaging, but biotechnology, telecommunications, optics, photonics, and much more. We rank among the top three communities in the nation in the number of patents granted per capita. Monroe County and the City of Rochester are home to the University of Rochester, the county's largest employer, and Rochester Institute of Technology, two of the finest research institutions in the nation. We boast 39 golf courses, an extensive park system covering nearly 12,000 acres of land, and fresh water activities such as boating, fishing & swimming. Our sporting community includes professional baseball, hockey, lacrosse and soccer teams with our newest addition the Rochester Razor Sharks.

STIPENDS AND MAINTENANCE

Trainees receive a generous stipend with increases for the second through fourth years respectively. The university provides professional liability insurance and lab coats or scrubs, and the department equips each new resident with their own laptop. Twenty vacation days and five sick days are allowed each academic year, with trainees able to carry over ten vacation days into the next academic year.

STAFF

Daniel H. Ryan MD (Johns Hopkins Univ) Professor & Chair Pathology & Laboratory Medicine; research: B cell development and differentiation; **Scott A. Kirkley** MD (SUNY Upstate) Assoc Prof Pathology & Lab Medicine, Dir Residency Pgm, Assoc Dir Blood Bank & Transfusion Medicine; research: blood transfusion immunology; **John Bennett** MD Prof Hematology/Oncology; research: myelodysplastic syndromes; **Mark Berenson** MD (Chernovtsy State Med Sch) Asst Prof Clinical Pathology & Lab Medicine; research: tumor immunobiology; **Bradford C Berk** MD PhD (URSMD) Prof Medicine; research: cardiovascular; **Neil Blumberg** MD (Yale Univ) Prof Pathology & Lab Medicine, Dir URMC Clinical Laboratories, Dir Blood Bank & Transfusion Medicine; research: blood transfusion immunology; **Akiba Bokhari** MD Asst Prof Pathology & Lab Medicine; **Thomas A. Bonfiglio** MD (URSMD) Prof Pathology & Lab Medicine; research: new technologies in diagnostic cytopathology; **Brendan F. Boyce** MB ChB (Univ Glasgow) Prof Pathology & Lab Medicine and Orthopaedics; Dir Anatomic Pathology; research: bone cell biology; **W. Richard Burack** MD PhD (Univ Virginia Sch Med), Assoc Prof Pathology & Lab Medicine, Dir Hematology in Pathology Fellowship Pgm, Dir Resident Educ in Hematology; research: molecular mechanisms of lymphoma progression; **Chawnshang Chang** PhD (Univ Chicago) Whipple Prof Pathology & Lab Medicine, Prof Urology, Radiation Oncology; research: prostate cancer and molecular endocrinology; **LI-Sheng Chen** PhD (Univ of California), Asst Prof Pathology & Lab Medicine, Assoc Dir Automated Laboratory; research: translational molecular biology; **Myra Coppage** PhD (URSMD) Asst Prof Pathology & Lab Medicine, Dir, HLA/Tissue Typing Lab; research: tissue typing; **James P. Corsetti** PhD (Harvard Univ) MD (Brown Univ) Assoc Prof Pathology & Lab Medicine, Medical Dir Specimen Mgmt, Assoc Dir Protein Laboratory; research: lipid metabolism; **P. Anthony diSant'Agnese** MD (Columbia Univ) Prof Pathology & Lab Medicine; Dir GU Surgical Pathology department fellowship program; research: prostate cancer; **Julietta Fiscella** MD (SUNY Buffalo) Clinical Asst Prof Pathology & Lab Medicine, Assoc Dir HH Laboratories; research: non-neoplastic lung disease; **Charles W. Francis** MD (Univ Pittsburgh) Prof Medicine, Dir Pgm in Hemostasis & Thrombois; research: blood clotting disorders; **Ellen J. Giampoli** MD (SUNY Buffalo) Asst Prof Pathology & Lab Medicine, Dir Cytopathology Fellowship Pgm, Dir FNA biopsy service, Dir Resident Educ in Cytopath; research: fine needle aspirates; **Bruce I Goldman** MD (Northwestern Univ) Prof Pathology & Lab Medicine, Dir Autopsy Pathology, Dir Resident Educ in Autopsy Path, lead Pathologist for cardiac transplant service; research: cardiovascular disease; **Robert C. Griggs** MD (Univ Pennsylvania) Prof/Chair Neurology; research: muscle disease; **Dwight J. Hardy** PhD (Louisiana State Univ) Assoc Prof Microbiology & Immunology, Dir Clinical Microbiology Laboratory, Dir Resident Educ in Microbiology: research: antimicrobial susceptibility and resistance; **David Herrmann** MBBCh (Univ Witwatersrand) Assoc Prof Neurology, Pathology & Lab Medicine; research: neuromuscular disease; **David Hicks** MD (Univ of Rochester), Prof Pathology & Lab Medicine, Dir Surgical Pathology; research: bone, soft tissue and breast pathology; **M Anwar Iqbal** MD (Osmania Univ, India) Assoc Prof Pathology & Lab Medicine, Assoc Dir Cytogenetics Laboratory; research: molecular cytogenetics; **Mahlon D Johnson** MD PhD (Univ Tennessee) Prof Pathology & Lab Medicine and Neurosurgery, Dir Neuropathology Unit, Dir Neuropathology Fellowship Pgm; research: neurobiology; **Philip J. Katzman** MD (Univ Vermont) Assoc Prof Pathology & Lab Medicine; research: DiGeorge syndrome; **Tai C. Kwong** PhD (Univ Toronto) Prof Pathology & Lab Medicine, Dir Regional Toxicology Laboratory and Automated Laboratories, Dir Resident Educ in Chemistry; research: drug detection and monitoring; **Faqian Li** MD (Hubei Medical Univ) PhD (Univ of South Dakota), Asst Prof Pathology & Lab Medicine; research: pulmonary and cardiac pathology, cell signaling in myocardial hypertrophy; **Marilyn Menegus** PhD (Cornell Univ) Prof Microbiology & Immunology, Dir Immunology Laboratory; research: clinical virology; **Edward M. Messing** MD (NYU) Prof Urology, Pathology & Lab Medicine; research: urologic oncology; **Leon A. Metlay** MD (Univ Pittsburgh) Assoc Prof Pathology & Lab Medicine; research: placental and fetal pathology; **Richard K Miller** PhD (Dartmouth) Prof OB/Gyn, Pharmacology & Toxicology, Pathology & Lab Medicine; Dir PEDECS, Assoc Chair Research in OB/Gyn; research: teratogenesis and placental toxicology; **Hiroshi Miyamoto** MD PhD (Yokohama City Univ) Asst Prof Pathology & Lab Medicine; research: genitourinary pathology; **Robert A. Mooney** PhD (Johns Hopkins Univ) Prof Pathology & Lab Medicine, Dir Pathways of Human Disease Graduate Pgm, Dir Biochemical Genetics; research: diabetes and breast cancer; **Bernard J. Panner** MD (Case Western Reserve Univ) Prof Emeritus Pathology & Lab Medicine; research: renal disease; **Archibald Perkins** MD PhD (Columbia Univ) Prof Pathology & Lab Medicine; research: leukomogenesis; **Michael B Petzar** MD (Albany Med Col of Union Univ) Asst Prof Pathology & Lab Medicine; research: Shope papilloma virus; **Ming Qi** PhD (Univ Pittsburgh) Research Asst Prof Pathology & Lab Medicine, Cardiology; genetic and genomic medicine; **Zhenhong Qu** MD (Tongii Med Univ, China) PhD (Oregon Health Sciences Univ) Asst Prof Pathology & Lab Medicine; research: cell and molecular biology; medical informatics; **Paul G. Rothberg** PhD (SUNY Stony Brook) Prof Pathology & Lab Medicine, Dir Molecular Diagnostic Laboratory, Dir Resident Educ in Clinical Molecular Diagnostics; research: molecular genetics; **Charlotte K. Ryan** MD (Johns Hopkins Univ) Assoc Prof Pathology & Lab Medicine; research: gastrointestinal and hepatic pathology; **Linda M. Schiffhauer** MD (Albany Med Col) Asst Prof Pathology & Lab Medicine, Dean's Teaching Fellow, Co-Dir Resident Educ in SP; research: expression of C35 and HER-2 in breast cancer; **Glynis A. Scott** MD (Albany Med Col) Assoc Prof Dermatology, Pathology & Lab Medicine, Pediatrics; Dir Dermatopathology; research: melanocyte-extracellular matrix interactions; **Peter J Sims** MD PhD (Duke Univ) Prof Pathology & Lab Medicine; research: molecular phospholipid scramblases; **Harold C. Smith** PhD (SUNY Buffalo) Prof Biochemistry & Biophysics; research: molecular regulation of ApoB mRNA editing; **Mark Sowden** PhD (Oxford) Research Assoc Prof Biochemistry & Biophysics; **Charles E. Sparks** MD (Thomas Jefferson Univ) Prof Pathology & Lab Medicine, Dir URMC Central Labs for Clinical Trials; research: cardiovascular disease; **Janet D. Sparks** PhD (Univ Pennsylvania) Assoc Prof Pathology & Lab Medicine; research: protein metabolism; **Sherry L. Spinelli** PhD (Univ Rochester) Research Asst Prof Pathology & Lab Medicine; research: platelets as mediators of inflammation; **Ping Tang** MD (West China Univ Med Sci) PhD (Univ Texas MD Anderson) Asst Prof Pathology & Lab Medicine, Co-Dir Resident Educ in SP; research: early breast carcinogenesis; **Rabi Tawil** MD (American Univ Beirut) Prof Neurology, Pathology & Lab Medicine, Dir Muscle & Nerve Histopathology Laboratory, Co-Dir Neuromuscular Dis Clinic; research: neuromuscular disease; **Nancy Wang** PhD (Univ Minnesota) Prof Pathology, Pediatrics & Genetics, Dir Cytogenetics Lab, Dir Resident Educ in Cytogenetics; research: multiple approaches to genomic evolution in neoplasia; **Xi Wang** MD (Sun Yat-Sen Univ) Asst Prof Pathology & Lab Medicine; research: tumor cell origin and differentiation; **Therese Wiedmer** PhD (Univ of Bern, Switzerland) Assoc Prof Pathology & Lab Medicine; research: phospholipid scramblases; **Lianping Xing** PhD (Pennsylvania State Univ) Research Asst Prof Pathology & Lab

Medicine; research: bone biology; **Haodong Xu** MD PhD (Soowchow Univ Med Sch) Asst Prof Pathology & Lab Medicine; research: pulmonary and cardiovascular disease; **Jorge Yao** MD (Univ East Ramon Magsaysay Mem Med Ctr) Asst Prof Pathology & Lab Medicine; **Gabrielle A Yeaney** MD Asst Prof Pathology & Lab Medicine; research: neuroblastoma; **Shuyuan Yeh** PhD (Univ Wisconsin) Asst Prof Urology, Pathology & Lab Medicine; research: prostate cancer; **David Zhou** MD (Huabei Medical College) PhD (Shanghai Medical Univ) Asst Prof Pathology & Lab Medicine.

APPLICATIONS

Applications are accepted exclusively via ERAS (Electronic Residency Application Service). For additional information regarding our program, visit our website at http://www.urmc.rochester.edu/smd/gme/prospective/pathology/

STATE UNIVERSITY OF NEW YORK AT STONY BROOK

Stony Brook, New York

PROGRAMS OFFERED

The Department of Pathology of the School of Medicine at Stony Brook University provides training and experience in anatomic and clinical pathology that is oriented toward both community hospital and academic career goals. Residents devote much of the first year to developing a solid base in anatomic pathology with a strong emphasis on general surgical pathology. For most residents much of the second year is devoted to clinical pathology. Residents spend blocks of two months in at least three laboratories. In each, a formal, organized program of education focused on the scientific basis of tests done, the interpretation of the test results and the application of the results to clinical management. Clinical pathology rotations are viewed as an interlocking set of experiences with continuing attention to quality control, laboratory management, and the integration of laboratory services with clinical services in the hospital. The first set of rotations gives residents insight into the options available to pathologists. During the remainder of the second year and for the rest of the training program, the order and the length of rotations for each resident is based upon his or her then current interests and career goals. Care is taken to meet the requirements for Board qualification while structuring the schedules. Each rotation is discrete and is based upon a curriculum with delineated objectives. For those residents who have an interest in a particular anatomic or clinical pathology area, early rotation permits graded responsibilities during the residency program in this special area. For other residents, assignments are based upon logical sequences of exposure in a progressive education experience. Once all of the core rotations have been completed, advanced electives in a tutorial mode are available in many topics including research. With the exception of forensic pathology, all of the training usually takes place in University Medical Center. This arrangement facilitates integration into the hospital staff and eliminates transit time and the need to learn rules and practices peculiar to more than one facility. Special rotations at other sites or short courses are arranged for senior residents who will benefit from such enrichment. Throughout the four years of training, there are departmental lecture series and seminars which complement the rotations and provide continuing exposure in all core areas. In addition there are many multidisciplinary conferences in the hospital which are not mandatory but which offer substantial selective enrichment. An effort is made to tailor workloads so that residents have time for reading and personal life. All residents are mentored and guided to achieve a strong knowledge base and competence in use of the literature, in written and oral communication, in use of the laboratory and hospital information systems, and in participation in intradepartmental and interdepartmental conferences. There is an internet-based evaluation system which supplements continuing interactions between faculty and residents and is used by the faculty to provide information regarding progress and by the residents to give input regarding the quality of the training experiences. As competence is achieved, residents get increasing professional responsibilites so that they are capable of independent practice at the end of the program. Residents participate in teaching of medical students and residents in other disciplines. They also work with faculty on research projects that frequently result in presentations at national meetings or in publication in journals.

TYPES AND NUMBERS OF APPOINTMENTS

The program is approved for 14 residents.

FACILITIES

Stony Brook University Medical Center is the central teaching facility for the School of Medicine and is a regional referral center. Opened in 1980, the 570-bed hospital contains over 60,000 square feet of fully equipped laboratory space. Library and lecture halls are adjacent and the Department of Pathology's extensive research facilities and academic offices are easily accessible to laboratory staff and residents. The faculty of the Department regards the training of residents as an important aspect of their daily function. Physicians with special interests in each of the disciplines of anatomic and clinical pathology head the sections in the hospital laboratories and are responsible for the design and implementation of resident rotations in each area. Eighty autopsies, 17,500 surgicals and 2.2 million laboratory determinations are performed at University Medical Center annually. At nearby community hospitals, residents may gain service experience in a busy community hospital laboratory. The Suffolk County medical examiner's office provides experience in advanced methods of forensic medicine. An interface with medical jurisprudence is a strong feature of this affiliate, which performs toxicology examinations and collaborates with the police crime laboratory.

COMMUNITY

The State University of New York at Stony Brook offers academic programs in many subjects. Lectures, concerts, art and photography exhibits, films, theatrical performances and athletic events held on campus throughout the year complement Stony Brook's diverse academic programs. The campus is located on 1100 wooded acres on the North Shore of Long Island some 50 miles east of New York City in a region of coves, beaches and small historic villages which retains a distinctive New England flavor. Stony Brook therefore couples the charm of a rural setting minutes from the Long Island Sound and the Atlantic with the cultural, scientific, and industrial resources of the nation's largest city. New York City is easily reached by rail or car while jet service is available from nearby Islip, La Guardia, and J.F. Kennedy airports.

STIPENDS AND MAINTENANCE

Residents receive between $53,632 and $63,785 and are provided with professional liability insurance, hospitalization and medical care, uniforms and uniform laundry.

STAFF

Tahmeena Ahmed MBBS (Ahmadu Bello Univ, Nigeria) Assistant Professor; Transfusion Medicine and Hematopathology; **Jorge Benach** PhD (Rutgers Univ) Professor of Microbiology and Pathology; infectious organisms and immunology; **Ann-Leslie Berger-Zaslav** PhD, MS (St. John's Univ) Clinical Associate Professor, Cytogenetics; **Jay Lawrence Bock** MD, PhD (Albert Einstein Col Med) Professor, Director Clinical Pathology; chemical pathology; **Richard Bronson** MD (NYU) Professor of OB/GYN & Pathology; Reproductive Endocrinology; **John Chumas** MD (St Louis Univ) Clinical Associate Professor; surgical pathology (gynecologic pathology); **Thomas Cottrell** MD (Columbia Univ) Associate Professor Emeritus; pulmonary pathophysiology; **Stuart L. Dawson** MD (Univ Iowa) Assistant Professor and Deputy Chief Medical Examiner; forensic pathology; **William Engellenner** MD (SUNY at Stony Brook) Clinical Assistant Professor; surgical pathology; **Howard Fleit** PhD (NYU) Associate Professor; Fc receptors; granulocyte/macrophage growth and differentiation; **Martha Furie** PhD (Rockefeller Univ) Professor; Interactions of bacterial pathogens with host cells of innate immunity.; **Dennis Galanakis** MD (Univ Saskatchewan) Associate Professor and Director Blood Bank; coagulation, immunohematology and blood banking; **Berhane Ghebrehiwet** DVM, DSc (Univ Paris VII) Professor of Medicine and Pathology; C1q receptor mediated cellular responses; inflammation and microbial infection; **Marc Golightly** PhD (UCLA Sch Med) Professor; immunology; **Gail Habicht** PhD (Stanford) Professor; Immunobiology of aging; immunoparasitology; lymphokines; **Eli Hatchwell** MB BChir (Univ Cambridge); PhD (Oxford); Clinical Assistant Professor; Medical geneticist; **Alan Heimann** MD (Yale Univ) Associate Professor; surgical pathology, aspiration cytology; **Stephanie A. Horowitz** MD (SUNY-Downstate Brooklyn) Clinical Instructor and Deputy Medical Examiner; forensic pathology; **Youjun Hu** MD (Zhejiang Med Univ, China) Clinical Assistant Professor; clinical and anatomic pathology and hematopathology; **Mae Hultin** MD (Hahnemann) Clinical Professor of Medicine & Pathology; Coagulation proteins in hemostasis and thrombosis and vascular disease; **Sonya Hwang** MD (SUNY Brooklyn) Assistant Professor of Clinical Pathology; Surgical Pathology, aspiration cytology; **Jingfang Ju** PhD (Univ of Southern California) Visiting Associate Professor; Research focuses on elucidating the mechanism of translational control mediated by miRNAs in cancer and translating the new discovery to clinical diagnosis; **Philip B. Kane** MD (NYU Sch Med) Director of Anatomic Pathology; Associate Professor; environmental pathology; **Cynthia Kaplan** MD (NYU Sch Med) Professor; placental and pediatric pathology; **Richard Kew** PhD (SUNY at Stony Brook) Research Assistant Professor; Leukocyte chemotaxis; inflammation; pulmonary immunopathology; **Bernard P. Lane** MD (NYU Sch Med) Professor and Director of Residency Program; ultrastructural pathology and hepatic pathology; **Sharon Liang** MD, PhD (Hunan Med Sch) Assistant Professor; gynecological pathology; **Jingxuan Liu** MD, PhD (Peking Union Med Col) Clinical Assistant Professor; breast and surgical pathology; **James Magidson** MD (Chicago Sch Med) Clinical Assistant Professor; clinical and anatomic pathology and hematology; **Yvonne Milewski** MD (Feinberg School of Medicine) Assistant Professor; Chief Medical Examiner; **Frederick Miller** MD (NYU Sch Med) Professor; immunopathology and renal disease; **Ute Moll** MD (Univ Ulm, Germany) Professor; renal pathology; **Alexei Petrenko** PhD (Ukrainian Academy of Science - Kiev); Research Assistant Professor; Molecular biology of cancer; **Kanokporn Rithidech** PhD (Univ Texas Med Branch at Galveston) Research Associate Professor; Molecular cytogenetics; genomic instability and cancer; radiation biology; proteomics; **Roberta Seidman** MD (SUNY at Stony Brook) Clinical Associate Professor; neuropathology; **Lisa Senzel** MD, PhD (Albert Einstein Col Med) Assistant Professor of Clinical Pathology, Hematology and Blood Banking; **Kenneth R. Shroyer** MD, PhD (Univ of Colorado) Marvin Kuschner Professor and Chair; Surgical Pathology of tumors of the female genital tract; Gynecologic cytopathology; Fine Needle Aspiration cytopathology; **Sanford Simon** PhD (Rockefeller) Professor of Biochemistry & Pathology; Extracellular matrix degradation by proteases; design and evaluation of protease inhibitors; **Meenakshi Singh** MD (Panjab Univ, India) Vice Chair of Anatomic Pathology; surgical pathology, cytopathology, breast and GYN pathology; **Eric Spitzer** MD, PhD (Johns Hopkins Univ) Associate Professor; microbiology; **Silvia Spitzer** PhD (Univ Buenos Aires), Clinical Associate Professor, Molecular Genetics; **Roy Steigbigel** MD (Univ of Rochester) Professor of Medicine & Pathology; Mononuclear and polymorphonuclear phagocyte functions; macrophage function in human immunodeficiency virus (HIV) infection; **Carmen Tornos** MD (Univ Autonoma, Barcelona) Professor, GYN and Breast Pathology; **Denise Trochesset** DDS (Univ of Minn) Clinical Assistant Professor, Oral Pathology; **William VanNostrand** PhD (Univ Cal-Irvine) Associate Professor of Medicine & Pathology; Alzheimer's and neurodegenerative diseases; **James C. Wilson** MD (Univ Miami) Clinical Assistant Professor and Deputy Medical Examiner; forensic pathology; **Sui Zee** MD (Albert Einstein Col Med) Clinical Associate Professor, Director of Surgical Pathology; pancreatic pathology; **Gary Zieve** PhD (Massachusetts Inst Tech) Associate Professor; Synthesis and assembly of snRNP particles; autoimmunity.

APPLICATIONS

Address inquiries to:

Bernard P. Lane, MD
Director, Residency Training Program
University Hospital, Health Sciences Center
State University of New York at Stony Brook
Stony Brook, NY 11794-7025
Phone: (631) 444-2224
Web site: http://www.stonybrookmedicalcenter.org/body.cfm?id=1141

STATE UNIVERSITY OF NEW YORK UPSTATE MEDICAL UNIVERSITY AT SYRACUSE

Syracuse, New York

PROGRAMS OFFERED

The SUNY Upstate Medical University at Syracuse offers fully accredited training programs leading to American Board of Pathology certification in combined anatomic and clinical pathology (AP/CP), AP only, or CP only. AP/CP training consists of a 3-year core program, 18 months of structured training in anatomical pathology and 18 months of clinical pathology, as required by the American Board of Pathology, followed by 12 months of elective in the 4th year. During this last year, there is an optional track system of recommended rotations depending on the trainee's orientation toward general AP/CP practice, AP academic practice, or CP academic practice. For residents choosing AP only or CP only, up to 12 months of focused subspecialty training and/or related research is available in addition to the required 24 months of formal training in AP or CP. This latter track may be particularly attractive to individuals intent upon an academic career. Training at the Upstate Medical University and the affiliated Veterans Affairs Hospital is available in all aspects of anatomic and clinical pathology, including autopsy, clinical chemistry, cytogenetics, cytopathology, electron microscopy, environmental/occupational pathology, flow cytometry, forensic, general surgical pathology, hematopathology, microbiology, molecular diagnostics, neuropathology, ophthalmic, pulmonary and renal pathology and transfusion medicine. All residents receive training in both laboratory management and in laboratory information systems. Research opportunities abound, with particular emphasis on the application of molecular, biochemical, immunologic, and morphologic approaches to the study of disease processes.

REQUIREMENTS

Applications accepted through **ERAS** only (deadline for application submission is 10/15/09). No faxed or emailed applications are reviewed.

Applicants must be graduates of approved medical schools in the U.S. or Canada, or foreign graduates who hold required certification (**J-1 visas only**).

TYPES AND NUMBERS OF APPOINTMENTS

Medical school graduates may enter the program as first year residents on graduation from medical school. The program offers 16 positions, plus fellowships positions in surgical pathology, cytopathology, hematopathology and transfusion medicine. Applications for combined AP/CP, AP only or CP only are also welcome.

FACILITIES

Resources at the SUNY Upstate Medical University at Syracuse and the Affiliated VA Hospital provide ample volume and variety of material. A large and able staff at all levels insures a supervised, coordinated learning experience for each house officer according to the individual's needs and goals in service and research. The clinical and experimental laboratories are modern, well equipped and automated. The close proximity of the hospitals to each other promotes efficient and effective use of faculty and facilities so that residents have easy access among institutions to attend and participate in teaching and working interdepartmental conferences, while concentrating activities and responsibilities at a single institution during a specific rotation. There are approximately 70 autopsies, 20,000 surgical specimens, and 35,000 cytology specimens. Cytology includes an active fine needle aspiration (FNA) service with over 1,200 specimens and FNA clinic run by pathologists. In addition, residents are assigned to the Onondaga County Medical Examiner's Office, where 116 autopsies per year provide forensic and additional autopsy experience.

COMMUNITY

Syracuse, New York, has a greater metropolitan population of over 720,000 and is located in the central New York area adjacent to the Finger Lakes and the Adirondacks. Seasonal contrasts support a variety of year-round outdoor sports activities, and the Syracuse University Carrier Dome has brought an exciting new dimension to spectator sports. A first class symphony orchestra and professional theater, opera company, art museum, and a wide variety of superb social, cultural and recreational opportunities make Syracuse a highly desirable and rewarding community to live in.

STIPENDS AND MAINTENANCE

First-year residents in 2010 receive approximately $48,152 in salary. Modern, reasonably priced apartments are available within a few blocks of the medical center, as well as rental homes within Syracuse and nearby communities.

STAFF

University Hospital

Jerrold Abraham MD, Professor, environmental pathology and pulmonary pathology; **Katalin Banki** MD, hematopathology; **Ann Barker-Griffith** MD, ophthalmic pathology; **Sylva Bem** MD, hematopathology; **Kazim R Chohan** PhD, clinical pathology - andrology; **Robert Corona** DO, Professor, neuropathology; **Gustavo de la Roza** MD, Director, Residency Program; surgical pathology, cytopathology; **Ola El-Zammar** MD, surgical pathology, cyopathology; **Eileen Friedman** PhD, Endowed Research Professor; experimental pathology; **Nick Gonchoroff** DrPH, flow cytometry; **Gerald B. Gordon** MD, surgical pathology; **David Humphrey** MD; **Robert Hutchison** MD, Director, Clinical Pathology and Hematopathology; clinical pathology, hematopathology; **Anna-Luise Katzenstein** MD, Vice-Chair and Director, Anatomic Pathology; surgical pathology, pulmonary pathology; **Kamal Khurana** MD, Director of Cytopathology, cytopathology; **Deanna Kiska** PhD, microbiology; **Steve Landas** MD, surgical pathology, GI pathology and electron microscopy; **Sanjay Mukhopadhyay** MBBS, MD, surgical pathology, cytopathology; **Scott Riddell** PhD, microbiology; **Lazaro Rosales** MD, transfusion medicine, hemapheresis; **Paul Shanley** MD, renal pathology; **Antony Shrimpton** PhD, molecular pathology; **Zhanna Spektor** MD, transfusion medicine; **Constance Stein** PhD, cytogenetics and molecular pathology; **Arthur Tatum** MD, PhD renal pathology, immunology; **Gregory Threatte** MD, Chair Pathology; clinical chemistry; **Neerja Vajpayee** MD, hematopathology; **Alfredo Valente** MD, surgical pathology; **Jannie Woo** PhD, clinical chemistry; **Shengle Zhang** MD, surgical pathology and molecular diagnostics.

Veterans Affairs Medical Center

Margaret Kowalski MD, Director, Laboratory; **Yiran Dai** MD, surgical pathology; **Henry Friedman** MD, surgical pathology; **Seena Kumar** MD, surgical pathology.

Medical Examiner's Office, Onondaga County

Robert Stoppacher MD, Chief Medical Examiner; **Abraham Philip** MD, Staff ME.

APPLICATIONS

Applications should be received by October 15, 2009 for appointments beginning July 1, 2010.

Address inquiries to:

Gustavo de la Roza, MD, Residency Program Director
Department of Pathology
SUNY Upstate Medical University
750 E. Adams Street
Syracuse, NY 13210
Phone: (315) 464-4670 • **E-mail:** phillips@upstate.edu
Web site: www.upstate.edu/pathology

UNIVERSITY OF NORTH CAROLINA HOSPITALS UNIVERSITY OF NORTH CAROLINA

Chapel Hill, North Carolina

PROGRAMS OFFERED

The Department of Pathology and Laboratory Medicine at the University of North Carolina at Chapel Hill and the University of North Carolina Hospitals offers a flexible, four-year residency training program in anatomic and clinical pathology. Broad-based anatomic pathology training includes autopsy, surgical pathology, cytopathology and forensic pathology, with electives available in many of the subspecialty areas of anatomic pathology. Clinical pathology training includes hematopathology, blood coagulation, transfusion medicine, microbiology, clinical chemistry, molecular pathology, cytogenetics and toxicology. Fellowships are available in clinical microbiology, clinical chemistry, clinical molecular genetics, cytopathology, experimental pathology, forensic pathology, hematopathology, molecular genetic pathology, nephropathology, neuropathology, surgical pathology and transfusion medicine. The varied facilities at the University of North Carolina Hospitals enable the resident to arrange a number of special programs, including work in the various aspects of molecular pathology and laboratory medicine. Forensic pathology and toxicology training are available through the Office of the Chief Medical Examiner of the State of North Carolina, located in the same building as the Department of Pathology and Laboratory Medicine. Major departmental research programs include those in animal models of human disease, mechanisms of carcinogenesis and mutagenesis, molecular pathology and genetics, neuropathology, protease inhibitors, kidney pathobiology, infectious diseases, and vascular biology. Residents and fellows participate in conferences with other clinical departments and have an active role in teaching medical students. The Departmental web address is http://www.pathology.unc.edu.

TYPES AND NUMBERS OF APPOINTMENTS

The department offers 15 residency positions (3 to 4 first-year openings). In addition, fellowships are available in clinical microbiology, clinical chemistry, clinical molecular genetics, cytopathology, experimental pathology, forensic pathology, hematopathology, molecular genetic pathology, nephropathology, neuropathology, surgical pathology and transfusion medicine. Postdoctoral fellowships for MD's or PhD's also are available in clinical chemistry, clinical microbiology, and clinical molecular genetics.

FACILITIES

The faculty of the Medical School of the University of North Carolina at Chapel Hill staff the University of North Carolina Hospitals, a 726-bed facility. The State Medical Examiner's office is part of the medical center. The Schools of Dentistry, Nursing, Pharmacy, and Public Health are adjacent. A consulting service for community hospitals is available. The Department of Pathology and Laboratory Medicine performed approximately 175 autopsies, 22,800 surgical pathology accessions and 23,250 cytology examinations in 2007. The clinical laboratories performed approximately 5.5 million procedures, and the Medical Examiner's office performed approximately 1,500 autopsies. The Department of Pathology and Laboratory Medicine is housed in modern, well-equipped facilities.

COMMUNITY

Chapel Hill has a population of about 50,000, including approximately 25,000 students. The library, cultural and recreational facilities of the University are available to house staff members. They may also purchase staff tickets to the University intercollegiate athletic events. Both the University and nearby Duke and North Carolina State Universities have extensive programs of concerts, lectures, movies and special events. Several repertory theater groups are in the area. Local recreational facilities supplement nearby state parks, and several large man-made lakes offer water sports. Chapel Hill is nearly halfway between the mountains and the sea. Chapel Hill web address: http://www.chocvb.org/index.html.

STIPENDS AND MAINTENANCE

The stipend for the first year is $43,000. Malpractice insurance and disability insurance reimbursement are provided. Health insurance and parking costs may require an employee contribution. Salaries and benefits are reassessed annually and are subject to change.

STAFF

J. Charles Jennette MD (Univ North Carolina 1973) Brinkhous Distinguished Professor and Chair; immunopathology, renal pathology; **Araba N Afenyi-Annan** MD (Univ Michigan 1997) Assistant Professor; transfusion medicine; **C. Robert Bagnell, Jr.** PhD (Washington State Univ 1974) Professor; biotechnology, electron microscopy; **Peter M.**

Banks MD (Harvard Univ 1971) Clinical Professor; hematopathology; **Dwight A. Bellinger** DVM, PhD (Univ Georgia 1976, Wake Forest Univ 1981) Professor; comparative pathology; **Kirsten M. Boland** MHS (Duke Univ 2001) Instructor, Pathologists' Assistant; **Jessica K. Booker** PhD (Univ North Carolina 1994) Assistant Professor; clinical medical genetics, molecular pathology; **Thomas W. Bouldin** MD (Univ North Carolina 1974) Professor and Vice-Chair; neuropathology, ophthalmic pathology; **Jayne C. Boyer** MS, PhD (Drexel Univ 1983, Univ North Carolina 1990) Assistant Professor; molecular genetics; **John F. Bradfield** DVM, PhD (Ross Univ 1986, East Carolina Univ 2000) Professor and Director Div of Laboratory Animal Med; **Claudia M. Brady** BS, MT, MHS, PA (Quinnipiac Univ 1989, 1993) Pathologists' Assistant; **Harry R. Brashear, Jr** MD (Univ San Francisco 1945) Professor; orthopedics; **Debra N. Budwit** MD (Univ North Carolina 1986) Professor; surgical pathology); **John D. Butts** MD (Duke Univ 1972) Clinical Professor and Chief Medical Examiner State of North Carolina; forensic pathology, general pathology; **John F. Chapman** DrPH (Univ North Carolina 1978) Professor; clinical chemistry; **Frank C. Church** PhD (North Carolina State Univ 1982) Professor; protein chemistry, blood coagulation; **Thomas B. Clark III** MD (Med Univ South Carolina 1983) Clinical Associate Professor and Associate Chief Medical Examiner; forensic pathology; **William B. Coleman** PhD (Bowman Gray 1990) Professor; hepatic carcinogenesis; **Marila Cordeiro-Stone** PhD (Sao Paulo Univ 1976) Professor; molecular biology; **Georgette A. Dent** MD (Duke Univ 1981) Associate Professor; hematopathology; **Claire M. Doerschuk** MD (Rush Univ 1981) Professor; lung disease, particularly pneumonia, inflammation and innate immunity; **Cherie H. Dunphy** MD (Louisiana State Univ 1982) Professor and Director Hematopathology; hematopathology; **Ronald J. Falk** MD (Univ North Carolina 1977) Distinguished Professor; nephrology and hypertension; **Rosann A. Farber** PhD (Univ Washington 1973) Professor; human genetics, clinical chemistry; **George (Yuri) Fedoriw** MD (Medical College Ohio 2003) Assistant Professor and Associate Director Hematopathology; diagnostic hematopathology; **Thomas H. Fischer** PhD (Florida State Univ 1980) Associate Professor; clinical chemistry and molecular biophysics; **Susan A. Fiscus** PhD (Colorado State Univ 1986) Professor; retrovirus research; **William K. Funkhouser, Jr.** MD, PhD (Vanderbilt Univ 1979, CIT 1992) Professor and Director Surgical Pathology; surgical pathology, immunopathology; **Maryanne Gaffney-Kraft** DO (Philadelphia College Osteopathic Medicine 1992) Associate Chief Med Examiner, forensic pathology; **Peter H. Gilligan** PhD (Univ Kansas 1978) Professor; microbiology; **Virginia L. Godfrey** DVM, PhD (Auburn Univ 1982, Univ Tennessee 1990) Professor; immunopathology and toxicologic pathology of laboratory animals; **M. David Goodman** MD (UCLA 1969) Clinical Professor; anatomic pathology (autopsy); **Oleg Gorkun** PhD (Kiev State Univ, Ukraine 1987) Assistant Professor; biological science; **Thomas R. Griggs** MD (Univ North Carolina 1969) Professor; cardiology, blood coagulation; **Pamela A. Groben** MD (Tulane Univ 1977) Professor; dermatopathology, GYN pathology; **Margaret L. Gulley** MD (Univ North Carolina 1984) Professor and Director Molecular Pathology; molecular pathology; **Susan C. Hadler** MD, MS (UNC-Chapel Hill 1985, 1980) Associate Professor; **J. Edward Hall** PhD (Texas A&M Univ 1979) Associate Professor; epidemiology; **Catherine A. Hammett-Stabler** PhD (Univ Alabama at Birmingham 1987) Professor and Exec Director Core Labs, McLendon Clinical Labs; clinical chemistry, clinical toxicology; **Tracy M. Heenan** DVM (North Carolina State Univ 1989) Associate Professor: veterinary medicine; **Jonathon W. Homeister** BA, MD, PhD (Hope College 1985, Univ Michigan 1992, 1993) Assistant Professor; cardiovascular and autopsy pathology; **John P. Hunt** MD (Univ North Carolina 1997) Assistant Professor; surgical pathology, hematopathology; **Karou Inoue** PhD (Hokkaido Univ Japan 1992) Assistant Professor; biochemistry, blood coagulation factors; **H. Michael Jones** MD (Washington Univ 1966) Professor; autopsy pathology, history of medicine; **Kathleen Kaiser-Rogers** PhD (Univ North Carolina 1991) Associate Professor and Associate Director Cytogenetics Lab; genetics; **Masao Kakoki** MD, PhD (Univ Tokyo Med School 1991, 1999) Assistant Professor; medical science/genetics; **David G. Kaufman** MD, PhD (Washington Univ 1968, 1973) Professor and Vice-Chair; general pathology, DNA replication, carcinogenesis; **William K. Kaufmann** PhD (Univ North Carolina 1979) Professor; experimental pathology, DNA repair; **Hyung-S. Kim** PhD (Tohoku Univ, Japan 1982) Associate Professor; molecular genetics; **Suzanne L. Kirby** MD, PhD (Univ North Carolina 1988, 1994) Associate Professor; hematology/oncology; **Joe N. Kornegay** DVM, PhD (Texas A&M 1973, Univ of GA 1982) Professor; muscular dystrophy; **Ruth A. Lininger** MD, MPH (Univ North Carolina 1990, 1992) Associate Professor; breast/GYN pathology, cancer genetics, molecular epidemiology; **Chad A. Livasy** MD (Univ Iowa 1993) Associate Professor; cytopathology, breast and OB/GYN pathology; **Susan T. Lord** PhD (Cornell Univ 1977) Professor; structure-function analysis of human fibrinogen; **Christopher P. Mack** PhD (Univ Michigan 1995) Associate Professor; cardiovascular disease; **Nigel Mackman** PhD (Univ Leicester England 1985) Distinguished Professor and Co-Director Thrombosis & Hemostasis Program; genetics, tissue factor in hemostasis, thrombosis and ischemia-reperfusion injury; **Nobuyo N. Maeda** PhD (Tohoku Univ, Japan 1977) Wagoner Distinguished Professor; molecular genetics, molecular pathology; **Nadia N. Malouf** MD (American Univ, Beirut 1963) Professor; general pathology, pediatric pathology, muscle diseases; **Susan J. Maygarden** MD (Med Col Virginia 1983) Professor and Director Cytopathology Program; cytology; **Christopher R. McCudden** PhD (Univ Western Ontario 2003) Assistant Professor and Associate Director Core Labs, McLendon Clinical Labs; blood gas analysis, special chemistry; **C. Ryan Miller** MD, PhD (Univ of AL School of Medicine 2002) Assistant Professor; neuropathology; **Melissa B Miller** PhD (Princeton Univ 2002) Assistant Professor and Associate Director Microbiology-Immunology Lab, Dir Molecular Microbiology Lab; molecular biology; **Vincent Moylan, Jr.** BA (Univ Hawaii 1998) Instructor, Pathologists' Assistant; forensic pathology; **Valerie A. Murrah** DMD, MS (So Illinois Univ 1980, Univ Minnesota 1983) Professor; dentistry and oral pathology; **Timothy C. Nichols** MD (Med Col Virginia 1978) Professor; thrombosis; **Volker Nickeleit** MD, PhD (Univ Kiel Germany 1985, 1988) Professor; nephropathology, transplant pathology; **Judith N. Nielsen** DVM (Purdue Univ 1984) Associate Professor and Clinical Veterinarian; veterinary pathology and animal models of disease; **Yara Park** MD (Univ Alabama 2004) Assistant Professor and Associate Director Transfusion Medicine and Director Apheresis Services; transfusion medicine, therapeutic apheresis; **Charles M. Perou** PhD (Univ Utah 1996) Associate Professor; cancer genetics; **Gloria A Preston** PhD (Univ Tenn Biomedical Sci 1991) Associate Professor; pathogenesis of renal diseases; **Deborah L. Radisch** MD, MPH (Bowman Gray 1980, Univ North Carolina 1997) Clinical Associate Professor and Associate Chief Medical Examiner; forensic pathology; **Kathleen W. Rao** PhD (Univ North Carolina 1980) Professor and Director Clinical Cytogenetics Lab; cytogenetics; **Howard M. Reisner** PhD (Case Western Reserve Univ 1973) Professor; biology, immunogenetics; **Allen C. Rinas** MS SCT, (ASCP), CM(IAC) (State Univ New York Cortland 1983) Assistant Professor and Division Director Cytotechnology Program; cytology; **Harold R. Roberts** MD (Univ North Carolina 1955) Distinguished Professor; hematology; **Arlin B. Rogers** DVM, PhD (Univ Illinois 1990, Colorado State Univ 2001) Assistant Professor; comparative pathology, molecular carcinogenesis; **Tara Rubinas** MD (Loyola Univ Chicago 2001) Assistant Professor, gastrointestinal pathology, liver diseases, surgical pathology; **W. Eugene Sanders** MD (Univ North Carolina 1985) Adjunct Professor; cardiology; **John L. Schmitz** PhD (Univ Wisconsin-Madison 1991) Associate Professor; microbiology; **Dennis Simpson** PhD (Univ North Carolina 1996) Instructor; virology; **Harsharan Singh** MD (East Carolina Univ 1985) Associate Professor; nephropathology and electron microscopy, cytopathology; **Scott V. Smith** MD (Univ North Carolina 1992) Associate Professor; cardiovascular and pediatric pathology and hematopathology; **Oliver Smithies** DPhil (Oxford Univ, England 1951) Excellence Professor; genetics, molecular biology; **Darrel W. Stafford** PhD (Univ Miami 1964) Professor; blood coagulation; **James A. Swenberg** DVM, PhD (Univ Minnesota 1966, Ohio State 1970) Distinguished Professor; mechanisms of mutagenesis; **Nobuyuki Takahashi** MD, PhD (Tohoku Univ Japan 1989, 1995) Assistant Professor; hypertension; **Joan M. Taylor** PhD (Univ Michigan 1995) Associate Professor; cardiovascular disease; **Leigh Thorne** MD (Med Univ South Carolina 1995) Assistant Professor and Director Autopsy Service; molecular genetic pathology; **Richard R. Tidwell** PhD (Univ Tennessee 1974) Professor; medicinal chemistry, **Michael D. Topal** PhD (New York Univ 1973) Professor; physical biochemistry; **Heike Varnholt** MD (Hannover Med School 2000) Assistant Professor; surgical pathology; **Tracie L. Wagner** PA (ASCP) Instructor, Pathologists' Assistant; **Karen E. Weck** MD (Duke Univ 1988) Associate Professor and Director Molecular Genetics Lab; molecular genetic pathology; **Lisa Jacobs Weinstein** MD (Johns Hopkins Medicine 1993) Assistant Professor; surgical pathology and cytopathology; **Bernard E. Weissman** PhD (Univ California-Irvine 1980) Professor; microbiology, tumor suppressors; **Young E. Whang** MD, PhD (Univ Chicago 1989, 1988) Associate Professor; androgen receptor, prostate cancer; **Herbert C. Whinna** PhD, MD (Univ North Carolina 1992, 1994) Associate Professor and Interim Director McLendon Clinical Labs; blood coagulation; **Julia W Whitaker** DVM, MS (Univ Tennessee 1997, Mississippi State Univ 1999) Assistant Professor; laboratory animal medicine; **Monte S. Willis** MD, PhD (Univ Nebraska 2001, 2000) Assistant Professor; cardiovascular pathology; **Elizabeth M. Wilson** PhD (Vanderbilt Univ 1975) Professor; molecular endocrinology, prostate cancer, androgen receptor; **Ruth E. Winecker** PhD (Univ Florida 1996) Clinical Assistant Professor and Chief Toxicologist, Office of the Cheif Medical Examiner; toxicology; **Alisia S. Wolberg** PhD (Univ North Carolina 1996) Assistant Professor; thrombosis and hemostasis; **John T. Woosley** MD, PhD (Med Col Georgia 1984, 1976) Professor; surgical pathology, dermatopathology; **Hong Xiao** MD (Tongji Med College, Huazhong Univ Science and Tech 1983) Assistant Professor; immune-mediated glomerular disease, vasculitis; **Xianwen Yi** MD, PhD (Beijing Med & Pharm Univ China 1983, Rush Univ 1997) Assistant Professor; alpha lipoic acid and diabetes mellitus; **Maimoona A. Zariwala** PhD (Cancer Res Inst, Univ Bombay, India 1990) Assistant Professor; genetics.

APPLICATIONS

NONDISCRIMINATION POLICY The University is an Equal Opportunity Employer. The University reaffirms its commitment to equality of opportunity and pledges that it will not practice or permit discrimination in employment on the basis of race, color, religion, sex, national origin, or disability, or on the basis of sexual orientation as provided by University policy. The University complies with all applicable legislation prohibiting age discriminationin employment.

Address inquiries to:
Director, Residency Program
Department of Pathology and Laboratory Medicine
University of North Carolina at Chapel Hill
CB#7525, Brinkhous-Bullitt Bldg.
Chapel Hill, NC 27599-7525
Phone: (919) 966-4676
Web site: http://www.pathology.unc.edu/

DUKE UNIVERSITY MEDICAL CENTER

Durham, North Carolina

PROGRAMS OFFERED

Flexible, ACGME-accredited programs in anatomic and clinical pathology and anatomic pathology may be modified to fit individual goals and objectives. Anatomic pathology training is offered in autopsy and surgical pathology, forensic pathology, fine needle aspiration and cytopathology, ophthalmologic pathology, dermatopathology, neuropathology, molecular diagnostics,informatics and laboratory management.Clinical pathology training is offered in medical microbiology, transfusion medicine, clinical chemistry, cytogenetics, immunopathology, coagulation medicine, and hematopathology.There aredaily teaching conferences for residents and fellows and all residents in the departmentparticipate in medical student teaching activities with the faculty.

Fellowships are availablein cytopathology, dermatopathology, hematopathology and medical microbiology.

FACILITIES

The Duke University Health System (DUHS) is a regional provider of health care services. It currently comprises three (3) hospitals with over 1,500 beds. An affiliation with the Durham Veterans Affairs Hospital provides additional training opportunities. Duke laboratories perform more than 6 million laboratory tests per year; over 44,000 surgical pathology cases, 54,000 cytology cases, and over 330 autopsies. In addition, DUHS provides a significant level of molecular pathology testing including flow cytometry, image analysis, molecular diagnostics, cytogenetics, etc. The Pathology Department is fully equipped with the most modern technology for diagnosis and research. The Seeley Mudd Library is also available located centrally in the medical complex. In addition, residents have 24-hour access to the Forbus Reading Room, which houses essential textbooks and ample study materials. Within the department, the residents have personal carrels and are provided with laptop computers and microscopes. Our state-of-the-art media room allows for teaching and meetings in many configurations. Equipped with automated room controls, all computer and media functions, live-image microscope, and digital projector, the room is a versatile and comfortable space for departmental use.

COMMUNITY

The State of North Carolina is known for its great beauty, moderate climate and four "real" seasons. Durham is a city of over 470,000 located in the Piedmont region of North Carolina with easy access to both sea and mountains. It is positioned in the Research Triangle, within fifteen miles of North Carolina State Universityin Raleigh and eight miles from the University of North Carolina at Chapel Hill. The Research Triangle Park "RTP" is aworld-renowneduniversity-related research park composedof a large number of governmental and research institutes, which enrich our scientific community.

http://www.durham-nc.com http://www.ci.chapel-hill.nc.us http://www.raleigh-nc.org

STIPENDS AND MAINTENANCE

First year residents: $45,540 yearly (2008-2009 stipend), with annual increments. Duke provides each resident with health insuranceat no cost,and long-term disability insurance. Dental insurance is offered by the hospital at a reasonable rate. Residents and fellows are provided with professional liability insurance, uniforms and uniform laundry, and parking facilities. An exercise facility is located on-site and at no charge. The Pathology housestaff receive an annual $1,500 book/travel allowance from the department and additional travel allowance for presentations at scientific meetings.

STAFF

Professors

Salvatore V. Pizzo MD, PhD (Duke Univ 1973) Chairman; coagulation, fibrinolysis, proteinase regulation; **Soman N. Abraham** PhD (Univ Newcastle Upon Tyne, UK, 1981) clinical microbiology, mast cell biology; **Darell D. Bigner** MD, PhD (Duke Univ 1965, 1971) neuropathology; **Edward D Bossen** MD (Duke Univ 1965) surgical pathology, muscle pathology, ENT pathology; **William D. Bradford** MD (Case Western Reserve Univ 1958) medical education; **Patrick J. Buckley** MD, PhD (Washington Univ 1976, Univ Pennsylvania 1972) Director Residency Program & Hematopathology Fellowship; hematopathology; **Joseph Geradts** MD (Univ Chicago Pritzker 1987) surgical pathology, breast pathology; **Maureane R. Hoffman** MD, PhD (Univ Iowa 1982) coagulation; **David N. Howell** MD, PhD (Duke Univ 1984, 1982) immunopathology; **Christine M. Hulette** MD (Louisville Univ 1983) neuropathology; **Gordon K. Klintworth** MD, PhD (Univ Witwaterstrand 1957, 1966) ophthalmic pathology; **Roger E. McLendon** MD (Med Col Georgia 1982) neuropathology; **Sara E Miller** PhD (Univ Georgia 1972) electron microscopy; **Alan D. Proia** MD, PhD (Cornell Univ 1980) Chief of Autopsy Service; eye pathology; **L. Barth Reller** MD (Univ Virginia 1966) clinical microbiology; **Stanley J. Robboy** MD (Univ Michigan 1965) gynecologic pathology; **Victor L. Roggli** MD (Baylor Col Med 1976) pulmonary pathology; **Herman Staats** PhD (Univ South Alabama 1992) vaccine development; **Herman**

Staats MD PhD (Univ South Alabama 1992) vaccine development; **Mary E Sunday** MD, PhD (Harvard 1982) pulmonary pathology; **John G. Toffaletti** PhD (Univ North Carolina 1977) clinical chemistry.

Associate Professors

Nicholas Bandarenko MD PhD (Bowman Gray Medical School 1990) transfusion medicine; **Rex C. Bentley** MD (Harvard Univ 1986) surgical pathology, gynecologic pathology, obstetric pathology, electron microscopy of tumors, breast pathology; **Dongfeng Chen** PhD (Med Univ Hannover-Germany 1996) transplant immunology; **Thomas J. Cummings** MD (Univ Med and Dentistry New Jersey 1991) neuropathology, ophthalmic pathology, general surgical pathology; **Leslie Dodd** MD (Univ Nevada 1987) surgical pathology, cytopathology; **Richard M. Draffin** MD (Duke Univ 1975) surgical pathology, hematology; **Barbara Goodman** PhD (Univ of California 1994) cytogenetics; **Cynthia D. Guy** MD (Univ South Carolina 1993) surgical pathology, cytopathology; **Laura P. Hale** MD, PhD (Duke Univ 1990, 1991) inflammatory bowel disease research; **Claudia K. Jones** MD (Duke Univ 1985) surgical pathology, cytopathology; **Anand S. Lagoo** MD, PhD (BJ Med Col, Gujarat 1980, Univ Texas 1989) hematopathology; **Bruce Lobaugh** PhD (Pennsylvania State Univ 1981) coagulation; **John F. Madden** MD, PhD (Duke Univ 1989) surgical pathology, genitourinary pathology, infectious disease pathology; **Thomas L Ortel** MD (Indiana Univ 1985) PhD (Indiana Univ 1983); **Siby Sebastian** PhD (Univ of Pune, India 1996) molecular genetics; **Angelica Selim** MD (Univ Nacional de La Plata, Argentina 1990) dermatopathology; **Thomas A. Sporn** MD (George Washington Univ 1986) pulmonary pathology; **Robin T. Vollmer** MD (Duke Univ 1967) surgical pathology, dermatopathology; **Endi Wang** MD (China Med Univ 1982; PhD Univ of Southern California 1996) hematopathology; **Jogin Wu** PhD (Univ Sci & Technol-China 1982) clinical coagulation.

Assistant Professors

Robin Bachelder PhD (Harvard Med Sch 1995) oncology research; **Gansuvd Balgansuren** PhD (Tokai University, Kanagawa, Japan, 2001) clinical transplant immunology; **Maureen Bauer** MD (Univ of Texas Hlth Sci Ctr 1997) general surgical pathology; **Sarah M Bean** MD (Univ Rochester, 2002) surgical pathology, cytopathology, gynecologic and breast pathology; **Diana Cardona** (Univ Miami, 2004) liver and gastrointestinal pathology; **Rajesh C. Dash** MD (Univ Illinois 1995) cytopathology, breast pathology; medical informatics; **Michael B Datto** MD, PhD (Duke Univ 1999) molecular diagnostics; **Louis R. DiBernardo** MD (Duke Univ 1991) cardiovascular pathology; **Kenneth Ellington** MD (Bowman Gray Univ 1990) surgical pathology, cytopathology, clinical pathology; **Carol A Filomena** MD (Hahnemann Univ 1984) surgical pathology, cytopathology, chemical pathology; **Jane T. Gaede** MD (Duke Univ 1966) autopsy pathology; **Robert B. Kinney** MD (Duke Univ 1981) laboratory medicine; **Amy Lark** MD (Univ of North Carolina 2001) general surgical pathology; **Evelyn Lockhart** MD (UNC 2004) transfusion medicine; **Fred O'Dere** MD (George Washington Univ 1970) surgical pathology; **Puja Puri** (Eastern Virgina Medical School 2004) dermatopathology; **Catherine Rehder** PhD (Virginia Commonwealth Univ 2004); **Michael S Waugh** MD (Duke Univ 2001) general surgical pathology, cytopathology; **Hai Yan** MD (Beijing Med Univ 1991), PhD (Columbia Univ of Physician & Surgeons 1997) brain tumor research.

Professor Emeritus

Sandra H. Bigner MD (Univ Tennessee 1971) Emeritus; neuropathology, cytopathology, cytogenetics; **John M. Harrelson** MD (Duke Univ 1965) Emeritus; orthopaedic pathology; **John D Shelburne** MD (Duke Univ 1971), PhD (Duke Univ 1972) Emeritus; electron microscopy.

APPLICATIONS

Medical student candidates must be graduates of approved medical schools in the United States or Canada. Graduates of foreign medical schools must have ECFMG certification. All applicants must have USMLE scores of 85 or more.Applications must be submitted through ERAS (Electronic Residency Application Service) no later than November1.

Address inquiries to:

Patrick J. Buckley MD, PhD, Program Director
c/o Ms Debra S. Harris, Administrative Coordinator
Department of Pathology, DUMC 3712
Duke University Medical Center
Durham, NC 27710
Phone: (919) 684-2070 • **Fax:** (919) 681-7377 • **E-mail:** debra.harris@duke.edu
Web site: http://pathology.mc.duke.edu
Duke GME Web site: http://www.gme.duke.edu

PITT COUNTY MEMORIAL HOSPITAL
EAST CAROLINA UNIVERSITY
Greenville, North Carolina

PROGRAMS OFFERED

The program is approved for four years of training in anatomic and clinical pathology through the Department of Pathology and Laboratory Medicine of The Brody School of Medicine at East Carolina University and the Department of Pathology of Pitt County Memorial Hospital. Core experiences of 36 months (18 months of anatomic and 18 months of clinical pathology) and up to 12 months of residency training in specialized areas of pathology are available. Rotations provide experience in surgical, autopsy, and forensic pathology, cytopathology, fine needle aspiration, renal pathology and electron microscopy, dermatopathology, hematology, chemical pathology, microbiology, transfusion medicine, cytogenetics, histocompatibility testing, molecular diagnostics, informatics and laboratory administration and management. The program is designed to give the resident the knowledge, technical expertise, managerial and administrative skills through education, experience and research to competently handle issues commonly encountered in the routine practice of pathology. With the guidance of the faculty and the full-time staff, residents gradually assume greater responsibility for the pathology service. Opportunities for teaching and/or experimental (basic and clinical) pathology research exist. Strengths of the program include outstanding didactic conferences in pathology for the residents, a flexible program directed towards the needs and interests of the resident, opportunity for a dedicated research year, and a state-of-the-art modern laboratory. Fellowships in surgical pathology and cytopathology are also offered.

TYPES AND NUMBERS OF APPOINTMENTS

The department offers twelve residency positions-three positions at each level of training.

FACILITIES

Pathology residency training takes place predominantly at Pitt County Memorial Hospital, the teaching hospital of The Brody School of Medicine. This modern, 750-bed facility opened in April 1977 and is the center of tertiary medical care for the eastern portion of North Carolina. The department occupies 40,000 NSF of newly renovated laboratory space. Pathology personnel have full access to the extensive resources of the Health Sciences Library on the adjoining medical center campus with its more than 148,000 volumes and 2,100 journal subscriptions. The Department of Pathology performed 80 autopsies, 21,000 surgical pathology consultations, 9,000 cytology examinations (2,444 non-GYN procedures) in 2008. The clinical laboratories performed 5,184,225 procedures. The forensic pathology division of the department performed an additional 600 autopsies.

COMMUNITY

The city of Greenville is one of the fastest growing municipalities in North Carolina, yet it retains the historical charm and cultural appeal of this progressive southeastern state. With more than 76,000 residents, it is recognized as a focal point for cultural, industrial, educational and medical activities in eastern North Carolina. Greenville has been recognized as one of the best cities to live in in the U.S. It is also the home of a major university, the third largest in North Carolina, with a national reputation for its programs in the arts. Among its many advantages, Greenville has a lovely climate, and its geographic location provides access to many leisure activities. Water lovers enjoy fishing, kayaking, boating, skiing and surfing on nearby sounds and beaches. To the west, the scenic Blue Ridge and Great Smoky mountains offer additional recreational opportunities within a half-day's drive.

STIPENDS AND MAINTENANCE

The stipend for the first year is $42,687 (2007-2008). Hospitalization insurance, medical liability coverage, and group term life insurance are provided. First-year residents receive three weeks paid vacation annually and twelve days of sick leave. All house officers are issued an East Carolina University activity card entitling them to privileges at university libraries, theaters and sporting events. The state of North Carolina requires that all physicians and house staff trainees be licensed. Those who do not possess a permanent North Carolina medical license must have a North Carolina resident training license.

STAFF

Professors

Peter J. Kragel MD (Georgetown Univ Sch Med 1981) Professor and Chairman; **Arthur P. Bode** PhD (Univ North Carolina 1982) platelet research & coagulation; **Paul G. Catrou** MD (Tulane Univ 1974) clinical chemistry & informatics; **John D. Christie** MD, PhD (Univ Texas Med Branch 1982, Rutgers-State Univ New Jersey 1973) microbiology and pediatric pathology; **James L. Finley** MD (Med Col Pennsylvania 1978) surgical pathology, cytology, & FNA; **Mary G.F. Gilliland** MD (Loyola Univ Chicago 1969) forensic pathology; **Donald R. Hoffman** PhD

(California Inst Technol 1970) immunochemistry, allergies & insect venoms; **William R. Oliver** MD (Vanderbilt 1982) forensic pathology; **Robert H. Schosser** MD (Univ Louisville 1970) dermatopathology; **Paul H. Strausbauch** MD, PhD (Univ Miami 1974, Univ Washington 1969) electron microscopy; **R. Lee West** MD (Univ North Carolina 1959) surgical and autopsy pathology.

Associate Professors

Larry J. Dobbs Jr. MD, PhD (Univ Kansas Med Sch 1989, 1993) molecular & surgical pathology; **Gregory A. Gagnon** MD (LSU Med Sch 1982) hematology; **Karlene Hewan-Lowe** MD (Univ West Indies 1972) renal pathology & surgical pathology; **Anne E. Kellogg** MD (Univ Louisville 1980) transfusion medicine; **Karen Kelly** MD (University of Minnesota 1987) forensic and cardiovascular pathology; **Lorita Rebellato-Devente** PhD (East Carolina Univ Sch Med 1995) HLA-tissue transplantation; **John E. Wiley** PhD (North Carolina State Univ 1981) cytogenetics; **Jiaxi Wu** MD (Shanghai Med Univ 1987) chemistry.

Clinical Associate Professor

Lydia Franks MD (UNC-Chapel Hill, 1984) surgical and autopsy pathology.

Assistant Professors

Heng Hong MD (Shanghai Medical Univ 1982) surgical pathology, cytology & FNA.

Clinical Assistant Professors

Emmanuel Fadeyi MD (Ross University 1999) transfusion medicine; **Robert A Farrar** MD (University of Virginia 2003) surgical pathology and cytopathology; **Joseph D Jakowski** MD (Ohio State 2004) surgical pathology and cytopathology.

Clinical Instructors

Richard Hodges Pathologists' Assistant; **Rhonda Sakell** Pathologists' Assistant; **Sarah Spenser** Pathologists' Assistant; **Colleen Tetterton** Pathologists' Assistant.

Affiliate Faculty

William A Ballance MD surgical pathology.

Consulting Staff

H. Kim Park MD dermatopathology; **Donald L. Price** MD neuropathology.

APPLICATIONS

Appointments at Pitt County Memorial Hospital usually begin on July 1; however, special situations can be accommodated.

Address inquiries to:

Peter J. Kragel, MD Professor and Chair
Department of Pathology and Laboratory Medicine
The Brody School of Medicine at East Carolina University
Greenville, NC 27834
Phone: (252) 847-4951
Web site: http://www.pathology.ecu.edu

The Health Sciences Campus includes the Pitt County Memorial Hospital, Brody School of Medicine, East Carolina Heart Institute, Laupus Health Sciences Library, College of Nursing, College of Allied Health Sciences, and School of Dentistry.

WAKE FOREST UNIVERSITY BAPTIST MEDICAL CENTER

Winston-Salem, North Carolina

PROGRAMS OFFERED

House officer training for all four years of a combined program in anatomic and clinical pathology is available. In addition, training is available in comparative medicine and experimental pathology, which may lead to the MS or PhD degree, plus postdoctoral programs in atherosclerosis research, cancer research and clinical chemistry. House officers participate in the teaching of medical students, graduate students and students in the medical technology program.

TYPES AND NUMBERS OF APPOINTMENTS

There are 20 pathology house staff positions, 5 in each year.The availability of places in the graduate program depends on the interests of the person involved and admission to the graduate school. Fellowship programs in dermatopathology, cytopathology, surgical pathology, hematopathology and forensic pathology are available.

FACILITIES

The Department of Pathology of the University is also the pathology staff of the Wake Forest University Baptist Medical Center, to which the medical school is attached physically as well as in operation. At present, the hospital has 1,154 beds. During 2008 there were 28,521 surgical, 1,584 bone marrow, and 18,823 cytologic specimens examined, as well as 1,276 autopsies and 3,386 "billed procedures" in clinical pathology. There are approximately 300 people in the department at various levels. Our microscopy core facility is equipped with scanning and transmission electron microscopes, a laser-scanning confocal microscope, four fluorescence and phase contrast microscopes (including microinjection and time lapse microscopy) and a laser capture microdissection microscope. A full range of modern equipment supports the routine research and service activities of the department. Our department's Section on Comparative Medicine shares the graduate program and maintains a modern and well equipped primate facility.

COMMUNITY

Winston-Salem was founded in 1766. It began as a religious community of Moravians who emigrated first from Europe to Pennsylvania, and then to Salem. Their traditions are strong in the present industrial community and are particularly reflected in the considerable emphasis on the arts in community life. The city proper has 223,000 people, the county 326,000. There are four institutions of higher learning (Wake Forest University, Salem College, Winston-Salem State University and the North Carolina School of the Arts), a professional symphony orchestra, an opera company, Little Theater Company, three art galleries, and subscription series for symphonic, opera, choral and chamber music, as well as lectures and foreign films. The FM station of the university broadcasts classical music. The area offers golf (8 local public courses), water sports, hunting, fishing and skiing (five slopes). Wake Forest University provides major college sports events of all types.

STIPENDS AND MAINTENANCE

2008/2009 House staff salaries: First-year house officers receive $43,000 per year, with annual increases to $46,000 for a fourth-year resident. The chief resident receives an additional $1,000 per year. The house staff receives malpractice insurance coverage, life insurance, long-term disability insurance, and hospital insurance. There is a day-care center for staff children.

STAFF

Anatomic and Clinical Pathology Faculty

A. Julian Garvin MD, PhD Professor and Chairman; surgical pathology, cytopathology; **Constance A. Stanton** MD Program Director, Associate Professor neuropathology, ophthalmic pathology; **Michael W. Beaty** MD Associate Professor hematopathology, surgical pathology; **Simon Bergman** MD Associate Professor surgical pathology, cytopathology; **James O. Cappellari IV** MD Associate Professor cytopathology; **Kim R. Geisinger** MD Professor cytopathology, gastrointestinal pathology, gynecologic pathology; **Kathleen Gibson** MD Assistant Professor surgical pathology; **David D. Grier** MD Assistant Professor hematopathology, surgical pathology; **Michael G. Hitchcock** MB, ChB Clinical Assistant Professor dermatopathology, surgical pathology; **Samy S. Iskandar** MB, BCh, PhD Professor renal pathology; **Donald R. Jason** MD, JD Associate Professor autopsy and forensic pathology; **Scott E. Kilpatrick** MD Clinical Associate Professor soft tissue tumor pathology; **Patrick E. Lantz** MD Associate Professor autopsy and forensic pathology; **Jennifer Laudadio** MD Assistant Professor surgical pathology, molecular diagnostics; **Ryan T. Mott** MD Assistant Professor neuropathology; **John Owen** MD Professor coagulation; **E.L. Palavecino** MD Assistant Professor clinical microbiology; **Changlee S. Pang** MD Assistant Professor hematopathology; **Gregory J. Pomper**

MD Assistant Professor blood banking; **Shadi Qasem** MD Assistant Professor hematopathology, surgical pathology; **Omar P. Sangueza** MD Professor dermatopathology; **Zak K. Shihabi** PhD Professor clinical chemistry; **Marcus B. Simpson, Jr.** MD Associate Professor clinical pathology, blood banking; **S. Joseph Sirintrapun** MD Associate Professor GU pathology, informatics; **Mark C. Willingham** MD Professor and Director Research; molecular diagnostics.

Research Section on Comparative Medicine

Jay R. Kaplan PhD, Section Head (Friedberg Campus); **Michael R. Adams** DVM; **Susan Appt** DVM; **Jennifer Cann** DVM, PhD; **Thomas B. Clarkson** DVM; **J. Mark Cline** DVM, PhD; **Melaney Gee** DVM; **Kylie Kavanagh** VBS, MVB; **Nancy Kock** DVM, PhD; **Cynthia J. Lees** DVM, PhD; **Thomas C. Register** PhD; **Carol A. Shively** PhD; **Janice D. Wagner** DVM, PhD; **J. Koudy Williams** DVM; **Charles E. Wood** DVM, PhD; **Richard Young** DVM.

Research Section on Lipid Sciences

Lawrence L. Rudel PhD Section Head; **John S. Parks** PhD; **Gregory S. Shelness** PhD; **Mary Sorci-Thomas** PhD; **Richard W. St Clair** PhD; **Ryan E. Temel** PhD; **Liqing Yu** MD, PhD.

Research Section on Tumor Biology

Mark C. Willingham MD Section Head; **Zheng Cui** MD, PhD Associate Professor; **Purnima Dubey** PhD Assistant Professor; **Iris J. Edwards** PhD Associate Professor; **Kazushi Inoue** MD, PhD Assistant Professor; **Timothy E. Kute** PhD Associate Professor.

APPLICATIONS

Applicants who are medical school seniors follow the usual procedure of the matching plan. Applications must be submitted through ERAS (Electronic Residency Application Service). Those who have already completed a year or more of postmedical school training are handled individually by the department. Graduate school applicants are considered from January 1 to May 31. Federal fellowships are limited to U.S. citizens.

Address inquiries to:

Constance Stanton, MD
Department of Pathology
Wake Forest University School of Medicine
Winston-Salem, NC 27157-1072
Phone: (336) 716-2650
Web site: http://www.wfubmc.edu/pathology/

Wake Forest University Baptist Medical Center, Winston-Salem, NC

AKRON CITY HOSPITAL

Akron, Ohio

PROGRAMS OFFERED

The Department of Pathology offers a fully approved, closely supervised program of graduate medical education leading to Board eligibility in anatomic and clinical pathology. The combined anatomic/clinical pathology program is structured to conform to the guidelines set forth by the American Board of Pathology. The curriculum provides a minimum of 19 months of clinical pathology training interspersed amongst the remaining months of training in anatomic pathology with a strong emphasis on Hematopathology and Cytopathology. In anatomic pathology, the resident, under the direction of staff pathologists, is given graduated responsibilities in surgical pathology, frozen section consultation, necropsy, and exfoliative and aspiration cytology. Clinical pathology is taught with emphasis on test interpretation and clinical application, as well as test principles and methodology. Each section of the clinical laboratory is under the supervision of a staff pathologist or clinical scientist. The resident is again given graduated responsibility with opportunities for "hands on" experience, troubleshooting, and participation in quality control. The program is formally affiliated with Children's Hospital Medical Center of Akron where experience in pediatric pathology, electron microscopy, cytogenetics, molecular biology and neuropathology are provided for the resident. These rotations comprise approximately 4 months of the program. Conference presentations and teaching by residents are stressed heavily in this program. Formal didactic sessions and working conferences assure the resident ample opportunity to review the inpatient principles in anatomic and clinical pathology. Beginning in the second year, each resident is given the opportunity to function as a teaching assistant for the General Pathology course at Northeastern Ohio Universities College Medicine (NEOUCOM)

TYPES AND NUMBERS OF APPOINTMENTS

Eight residents are accepted, two each year.

FACILITIES

Akron City Hospital is part of the Summa Health System created by the merger with St Thomas Hospital (STH). Formally affiliated with NEOUCOM as one of the major teaching hospitals, Summa has a longstanding commitment to the education of health professionals and clinically related research. The residency program is housed and administered at Akron City Hospital and with the addition of STH, they provide a total census of 963 beds and a large volume of diversified surgical and clinical samples. Approximately 25,000 surgical and 15,000 cytology specimens were examined last year and 52 autopsies were performed. The local medical examiners office provides additional autopsy experience. The clinical laboratories perform 2.4 million billed procedures per year. Directed by clinical scientists in chemistry, microbiology and immunology, the laboratory provides a full complement of testing and training experience of a large tertiary hospital. Children's Hospital Medical Center Akron is a 253-bed regional pediatric facility. Admissions number about 9,600 per year and the total number of laboratory examinations approximates 400,000. Clinical virology, cytogenetics, molecular biology, and electron microscopy units are housed in a recently completed pathology research wing. Last year, 70 autopsies and 130 fetal evaluations were performed.

COMMUNITY

Akron, formerly known as the rubber capital, is a growing community. Serving as corporate headquarters for major tire, rubber, and chemical industries and home to an internationally renowned university program in polymer science, Akron is moving into the 21st century focused on high technology. Located in Northeast Ohio, Akron offers many cultural, educational, and recreational activities. It supports its own symphony orchestra, Institute of Art, and two major universities the University of Akron and Kent State University. A few miles north of the city is Blossom Music Center, the summer home of the Cleveland Orchestra and site of many pop-rock concerts as well. The Akron area boasts a wide selection of recreational facilities including snow and water-skiing, tennis, swimming, and golf. Much of Akron is surrounded by a beautiful and diversified Metropolitan Park System. Attractive, affordable housing is available in numerous areas located convenient to the hospital, as well as to shopping, business, and other facilities.

STIPENDS AND MAINTENANCE

The first-year stipend for 2009-2010 is approximately $46,383 and increases in increments of approximately $1,200 with each additional year of training. Benefits include hospitalization insurance, dental and eye care coverage, professional liability insurance, meals, uniforms, free parking, health club membership and allowances for professional meetings and workshops. The hospital also offers an on-site childcare center for a nominal fee.

STAFF

Raymond E. Clarke MD (Boston Univ 1974) Chairman, Department Pathology; AP/CP, Chief, Division Anatomic Pathology; Associate Professor Pathology; **Thomas S. Alexander** PhD (Kent State 1987) Head, Immunology; Associate Professor Clinical Immunology in Pathology; **Amy H. Deeken** MD (Northeastern Ohio Univ Col Med 2001) AP/CP,

Surgical Pathology, Assistant Professor Pathology; **Joseph R. DiPersio** PhD (Univ West Virginia Univ Med Ctr 1972) Head, Microbiology, Assistant Professor Pathology; **William Henthorne** MD (Ohio State Univ 1975) AP/CP, Cytopathology, Head Immunohematology; Assistant Professor Pathology; **Thomas J. Hlivko** MD (Med Col Virginia 1972) AP/CP, Surgical Pathology; Assistant Professor Pathology; **Harry C. Kellermier** MD (Northeastern Ohio Univ Col Med 2001) AP/CP, Surgical Pathology, Neuropathology; **Nickolas J. O'Donnell** PhD (Ohio State Univ 1980) Head, Chemistry and Toxicology; Assistant Professor Pathology; **Pars Ravichandran** MD (Thanjavur Medical College India 1985) AP/CP, Cytopathology, Surgical Pathology; **Nibha Saxena** MD (Jawaharlal Nehru Med Col India 1999) AP/CP, GI Pathology 2007, Surgical Pathology, Assistant Professor Pathology; **S. Mickey Thompson** MD (Northeastern Ohio Univ Col Med 2001) AP/CP, Surgical Pathology, Assistant Professor Pathology; **Silvia Verde de Peralta** MD (National Univ of Cordoba School of Medicine, Argentina 1980) Hematopathology.

Consulting Staff

Dimitris P. Agamanolis MD (Salonica 1962) neuropathology and electron microscopy (AP/NP); Professor Pathology; **William H. Herold** MD (Univ Colorado) pediatric anatomic pathology; Assistant Professor Pathology; **Robert W. Novak** MD (Duke Univ 1975) AP/CP, immunohematology; Professor Pathology; **Mark Steele** MD (Univ West Virginia 1994) AP/CP, pediatric pathology; Assistant Professor Pathology.

APPLICATIONS

Applicants should be graduates of approved medical schools in the United States or Canada. Specially qualified graduates of other international medical schools must have passed steps I and II of the USLME and must obtain an ECFMG certificate.

Address inquiries to:

Raymond E. Clarke, MD, Director
Pathology Residency Program
Akron City Hospital
525 East Market Street
Akron, OH 44304
E-mail: clarker@summa-health.org

UNIVERSITY OF CINCINNATI COLLEGE OF MEDICINE

Cincinnati, Ohio

PROGRAMS OFFERED

Approved training programs for residents and fellows are available in anatomic and clinical pathology. The usual program requires four years and includes autopsy, surgical and cytopathology, microbiology, hematopathology, toxicology, clinical chemistry, immunohematology, pediatric pathology, forensic pathology, molecular genetics, practical laboratory management and cytogenetics. Opportunities for participation in investigative pathology are also offered. Residents are encouraged to participate in clinical and basic research programs and present results of their investigations at national scientific meetings. All residents have responsibilities for teaching in the College of Medicine.

REQUIREMENTS

Candidancy requirements:
Graduation from medical school within the past 6 years.
Step I & II scores of 85 or better (the first time).
Applications only accepted through ERAS

TYPES AND NUMBERS OF APPOINTMENTS

A total of 12 pathology residents. The remainder of the house staff consists of 158 medicine, 33 OB/GYN, 42 psychiatry and 88 surgery residents as well as trainees in various subspecialties.

FACILITIES

The University Hospital Inc., Children's Hospital Medical Center (CHMC), Veteran's Administration Medical Center (VAMC), and the laboratories are contiguous to the University Medical Center, and are staffed by our faculty and residents in pathology. The University Hospital, Inc. (TUH), is part of the Health Alliance of Greater Cincinnati (HAGC) which consists of six hospitals totaling 2280 beds. CHMC provides 350 beds and the VAMC 420 beds. Core laboratory services are based at the Tri-State Laboratory Services, Inc., an off-site facility. The Immediate Response Laboratory is based at The University Hospital. Overall, the Department is responsible for the interpretation of approximately 27,000 surgical pathology cases, 20,000 cytologic specimens, and the performance of 300 autopsies annually. Alliance wide, there are over 200,000 cytology and 80,000 surgical pathology specimens. In clinical pathology, the Health Alliance Laboratory performs over 5 million tests per year. Within the department are laboratories for electron microscopy, immunopathology, tissue culture, chemical pathology, research coagulation, lipid chemistry and molecular genetics. Full access is extended to the College of Medicine's excellent library providing 226,775 volumes and journals. The department is located within a modern medical science building containing unique research and educational facilities as the heart of the University Medical Center.

COMMUNITY

Cincinnati, listed as one of America's most livable cities, has a population of 500,000. The metropolitan area has a population of more than 1.5 million. Cincinnati is an exciting blend of tradition and innovation, a location for corporate world headquarters and internationally respected symphony, opera and ballet. The birthplace of professional baseball is second only to San Francisco in its exquisite array of fine dining. There are many beautiful parks throughout the area offering a wide variety of attractions, including golf, tennis, biking, water recreations, hiking and fabulous scenery. The world-famous Cincinnati Zoo is located very close to the Medical Center. The Cincinnati River boasts many enticements, including river boat cruises, fine dining, boating and the renowned Riverfest fireworks extravaganza celebrating Labor Day. Housing is very affordable in the Cincinnati area where you may choose from one of the varied neighborhoods in numerous surrounding suburbs, or in the urban ambiance of our vital downtown.

STIPENDS AND MAINTENANCE

Postgraduate year I trainees salary will be $47,546 for 2009-10. Housing is not provided. Meals may be purchased at the hospital cafeteria at modest cost. All trainees are provided with hospitalization insurance, hospital parking, a yearly book fund and other benefits in accordance with the University Hospital Health Alliance.

STAFF

David Witte MD Professor; Chair, Pediatric Pathology, Molecular pathology; **Lois Arend** MD, PhD Assistant Professor; **Hai Bui** MD Associate Professor; **Cecilia M. Fenoglio-Preiser** MD Professor Emerita Gastrointestinal pathology, tumor marker; **Shagufta Khan** MD Assistant Professor; **Fred Lucas** MD; **Lili Miles** MD Assistant Professor; **Mohammad Nazek** MD; **Donna O'Black** PhD Associate Professor; **Kirby Reinhardt** MD Assistant Professor; **Judith**

Rhodes PhD Professor; **Saad Samaan** MD Associate Professor; **Jonathan Tobias** MD Assistant Professor; **Jiang Wang** MD, Assistant Professor; **Kathryn Wikenheiser-Brokamp** MD, PhD Assistant Professor; **Greg Retzinger** MD, PhD Professor, Program Director, Director Immediate Response Laboratory, Director Pathology Course; **Muhammad Ashraf** PhD Professor cardiovascular research, free radicals; **David Askew** PhD Assistant Professor molecular genetics of retrovirus-induced leukemia, regulation of apoptosis in hemopoiesis; **Edgar T. Ballard** MD Associate Professor pediatric pathology; **Kevin E. Bove** MD Professor pediatric pathology, neuromuscular disease, congenital heart disease; **Margaret Collins** MD Associate Professor Pediatric Pathology; **Saad Ghosn** MD Professor; Director, Clinical Laboratories, VAMC; **Philip Howles** PhD Assistant Professor lipid absorption, atherosclerosis, molecular biology, mouse models; **David Hui** PhD Professor atherosclerosis, molecular research; **Ady Kendler** MD, PhD Associate Professor, Director, Neuropathology; **Gabrielle deCourten Myers** MD Professor Emerita; Neuropathology; muscle pathology, experimental stroke; **R.D. Smith** MD Professor Emeritus nephropathology, experimental pathology, education; **Paul Steele** MD Associate Professor immunology, molecular genetics.

APPLICATIONS

Residency candidates must be graduates of approved medical schools in the United States or Canada and eligible for temporary licensure in Ohio. Graduates of foreign medical schools must have an ECFMG certificate. Satisfactory references and interview in Cincinnati are required. Applications must be received through ERAS by December 1 for appointments beginning July 1 of the following year. Selections will usually be announced in March in accordance with the Matching program. July 1 is the normal beginning date for residency but other times may be open for consideration. For advanced placement, applications should be made approximately one year prior to intended date of entry into the program.

Address inquiries to:

Pathology Education Office
Department of Pathology and Laboratory Medicine
University of Cincinnati Medical Center
231 Albert Sabin Way
Cincinnati, OH 45267 0529
Phone: (513) 558-7108 • **Fax:** (513) 558-2289 • **E-mail:** pathology@uc.edu
Web site: http://pathology.uc.edu/residents/index.asp

Cincinnati, Ohio — Downtown

THE CLEVELAND CLINIC
Cleveland, Ohio

PROGRAMS OFFERED

The Pathology and Laboratory Medicine Institute at the Cleveland Clinic consists of the Department of Anatomic Pathology, the Department of Clinical Pathology, the Department of Molecular Pathology, the Center for Pathology Informatics, and the Cleveland Clinic Medical Laboratory. Four types of full-time training programs are available in the Institute: 1) a combined four-year program in both anatomic and clinical pathology; 2) a single program, three years in anatomic pathology; 3) a single program, three years in clinical pathology; 4) subspecialty fellowships in anatomic and clinical pathology. The Institute provides instruction and training in surgical pathology, cytopathology, autopsy, molecular pathology, electron microscopy, immunohistochemistry, flow cytometry, morphometry, clinical automated chemistry analysis, microchemistry, applied clinical pharmacology, toxicology, therapeutic drug monitoring, hematology and coagulation, aerobic and anaerobic microbiology, parasitology, mycology, virology, immunopathology, blood banking & transfusion medicine, cytogenetics, plasmapheresis, and hemotherapy. All areas in anatomic and clinical pathology engage in extensive developmental and research activity.

TYPES AND NUMBERS OF APPOINTMENTS

The Institute is approved for 36 residency positions in anatomic and clinical pathology. Subspecialty fellowships are available at the fifth-year/sixth-year level in Cytopathology (1), Bone and Soft Tissue Pathology (1), Dermatopathology (2), Gastrointestinal/Hepatic Pathology (2), Genitourinary Pathology (1), Surgical Pathology (1), Clinical Chemistry (1), Clinical Microbiology (1) and Hematopathology (2).

FACILITIES

The Cleveland Clinic is composed of the 1,000-bed Cleveland Clinic Hospital and Outpatient facilities (including regional Family Health Centers and Ambulatory Surgery Centers), the Lerner Research Institute, the Lerner College of Medicine, and the Cleveland Clinic Educational Foundation. There are about 1,800 physicians and scientists on the professional staff. Annual statistics for the Cleveland Clinic include: 53,000 total admissions, 3.2 million outpatient visits, 73,986 surgical cases and 920 Residents and Fellows in Training in more than 52 training programs. The Pathology and Laboratory Medicine Institute is housed in a dedicated multistoried building of 185,000 square feet of floor space that is interconnected to all Cleveland Clinic facilities, in addition to a spacious surgical pathology desk and frozen section facility in the adjacent surgery pavilion. Overall, in excess of 8.7 million laboratory tests and procedures are performed each year. Annual accessions include approximately 97,000 surgical pathology cases, 74,000 cytopathology cases, and 210 autopsies. An adjacent five-story education building houses an auditorium, conference rooms, library, editorial offices and living quarters for residents assigned hospital duties. The Alumni Library contains 26,000 volumes and 850 subscriptions to periodicals and has electronic access to over 24,000 full-text journals in all subjects. The medical library has MEDLINE capabilities with connection to the National Library of Medicine bibliographic indexing services. All library services are provided at no charge.

COMMUNITY

Housing is available within a few minutes drive of the Cleveland Clinic in such suburban communities as Shaker Heights and Cleveland Heights. Within a short distance from the Cleveland Clinic are the Cleveland Museum of Art, Severance Hall- home of the Cleveland Orchestra, the Cleveland Playhouse, the Cleveland Museum of Natural History, Cleveland Botanical Gardens, and Case Western Reserve University. The city adjoins Lake Erie and is encircled by a system of metropolitan parks. Progressive Field, Cleveland Browns Stadium and Quicken Loans Arena are easily accessed via freeways or rapid transit for attendance at Indians (baseball), Browns (football), and Cavaliers (basketball) games.

STIPENDS AND MAINTENANCE

The resident stipend is $44,064 first year, $45,719 second year, $47,690 third year, $49,670 fourth year, $51,578 fifth year. Uniforms, laundry service, and on-call meals are furnished without charge. Each resident is eligible for $700 per academic year for educational materials. Residents are encouraged to attend regional and national meetings to present research projects. The Pathology and Laboratory Medicine Institute provides support for these meetings according to the following schedule: First, second and third-year residents: 1 meeting/year, $1,200 stipend/meeting; fourth-year residents: 2 meetings/year, $1,200 stipend/meeting. In addition to research meetings, each third and fourth-year resident is entitled to a $1,200 stipend and each 5th/6th-year fellow is entitled to a $1,200 stipend to attend an additional regional or national meeting.

STAFF

Kandice Kottke-Marchant MD, PhD Chair, Pathology and Laboratory Medicine Institute; Section Head, Hemostasis & Thrombosis; coagulation and hematopathology; **Carol F. Farver** MD MS Vice Chair for Education; pulmonary pathology; **Eric D. Hsi** MD Vice Chair for Research; Section Head, Hematopathology; hematopathology; lymph node pathology, flow cytometry, molecular hematology; **Raymond R. Tubbs** DO Vice Chair, Pathology and Laboratory Medicine Institute; Section Head, Molecular Genetic Pathology; molecular pathology, in situ hybridization, lymphoma; **John R. Goldblum** MD Chairman, Department of Anatomic Pathology; gastrointestinal and hepatic pathology; soft tissue tumors; **Gary W. Procop** MD Chairman, Department of Clinical Pathology; microbiology, molecular pathology, parasitology; **Andrea V. Arrossi** MD pulmonary pathology, gastrointestinal pathology; **Suzanne Bakdash** MD MPH transfusion medicine; **Thomas W. Bauer** MD, PhD orthopaedic pathology; **Ana Bennett** MD gastrointestinal and hepatic pathology; **Wilma F. Bergfeld** MD dermatopathology (Joint Appt); **Steven D. Billings** MD dermatopathology, soft tissue pathology; **Charles V. Biscotti** MD cytopathology, obstetrical and gynecologic pathology; **Christine N. Booth** MD Associate Residency Program Director; cytopathology and fine needle aspiration, breast pathology; **David Bosler** MD point of care testing, molecular pathology, hematopathology; **Jennifer A. Brainard** MD Section Head, Cytopathology; cytopathology and fine needle aspiration, obstetrical and gynecologic pathology; **Mary P. Bronner** MD Section Head, Morphologic Molecular Pathology, gastrointestinal and hepatic pathology; **Longwen Chen** MD, PhD cytopathology and fine needle aspiration, gynecologic and obstetrical pathology; **Andres Chiesa-Vottero** MD gynecologic and obstetrical pathology, genitourinary pathology; **Deborah Chute** MD cytopathology, head and neck pathology; **James R. Cook** MD, PhD Associate Residency Program Director; hematopathology, lymph node pathology, flow cytometry, molecular hematology; **Claudiu V. Cotta** MD, PhD hematopathology, molecular hematology; **Thomas Daly** MD Section Head, Immunopathology; immunopathology, test development; **Andrea E. Dawson** MD breast pathology, cytopathology; **Erinn Downs-Kelly** DO breast pathology, gastrointestinal pathology; **Priscilla I. Figueroa** MD Section Head, Transfusion Medicine; blood banking; **Andrew J. Fishleder** MD hematopathology (Joint Appt); **Manjula K. Gupta** PhD radioimmunoassay, endocrine immunology; **Geraldine S. Hall** PhD Section Head, Clinical Microbiology; mycology, mycobacteriology, anaerobes, parasitology, DNA probes; **Donna E. Hansel** MD, PhD genitourinary pathology; **Walter H. Henricks III** MD Director, Center for Pathology Informatics; medical informatics, gastrointestinal pathology; **Gerald A. Hoeltge** MD blood banking, cytogenetics; **Aaron P. Hoschar** MD ENT/endocrine pathology; **Carlos Isada** MD cytomegalovirus, molecular virology (Joint Appt); **Robert Kisabeth** MD Medical Director, Cleveland Clinic Medical Laboratory; **Anna Koo** MD plasmapheresis (Joint Appt); **Sucheta Kulkarni** PhD signal transduction; **Howard S. Levin** MD genitourinary pathology (Consultant); **Xiuli Liu** MD, PhD gastrointestinal pathology; **Cristina Magi-Galluzzi** MD, PhD genitourinary pathology; **James T. McMahon** PhD electron microscopy; **Gurunathan Murugesan** PhD phospholipids in endothelial injury and inflammation, endothelial-biomaterial interactions; **Jonathan L. Myles** MD cardiac pathology, breast pathology, medical nephropathology; **Marvin Natowicz** MD, PhD biochemical genetics; **Bettina G. Papouchado** MD breast pathology, cytopathology; **Melissa P. Piliang** MD dermatopathology (Joint Appt); **Thomas Plesec** MD gastrointestinal pathology; **Richard A. Prayson** MD Section Head, Neuropathology; neuropathology, placental pathology; **E. Rene Rodriguez** MD Section Head, Autopsy Pathology; cardiac pathology; **J. Jordi Rowe** MD breast pathology; **Brian P. Rubin** MD, PhD soft tissue pathology, orthopaedic pathology; **Andrew E. Schade** MD, PhD hemostasis and thrombosis, signal transduction; **Lynn Schoenfield** MD breast pathology, obstetrical and gynecologic pathology, gastrointestinal pathology, ophthalmic pathology; **Nabin Shrestha** MD infectious diseases (Joint Appt); **Kimia Sobhani** PhD clinical chemistry, core lab; **Susan M. Staugaitis** MD, PhD neuropathology (Joint Appt); **Carmela D. Tan** MD cardiac pathology; **Karl S. Theil** MD Residency Program Director; hematopathology, cytogenetics; **Ralph J. Tuthill** MD dermatopathology, hepatic pathology, cytopathology; **Sihe Wang** PhD Section Head, Clinical Biochemistry; clinical chemistry; **Ilka R. Warshawsky** MD, PhD molecular pathology, monoclonal protein analysis; **Bin Yang** MD, PhD cytopathology and fine needle aspiration, obstetrical and gynecologic pathology; **Belinda Yen-Lieberman** PhD retrovirology, molecular biology; **Lisa M. Yerian** MD Section Head Surgical Pathology; gastrointestinal and hepatic pathology; **Xiaoxian Zhao** PhD biomarkers; **Ming Zhou** MD, PhD genitourinary pathology.

APPLICATIONS

Residencies in pathology are granted by the Cleveland Clinic Educational Foundation. Candidates must have graduated from a medical school accredited by the American Medical Association or hold an equivalent degree. Satisfactory references and a personal interview are required. Residencies are renewable annually on the basis of satisfactory performance.

Pathology and Laboratory Medicine Institute Web site:
http://www.clevelandclinic.org/pathology/

Address inquiries to:

Director of Education
The Cleveland Clinic Foundation
9500 Euclid Avenue, NA23
Cleveland, OH 44195
Phone: (216) 444-9994 or 5690
Web site: http://www.clevelandclinic.org/education/gme

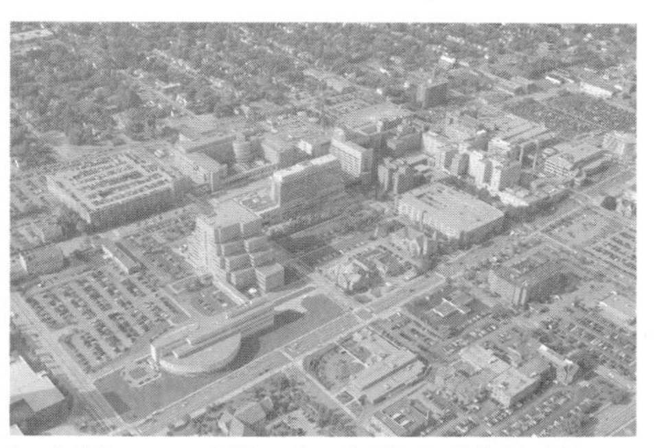

Aerial image of Cleveland Clinic Main Campus

METROHEALTH MEDICAL CENTER

(AN AFFILIATED HOSPITAL OF CASE WESTERN RESERVE UNIVERSITY SCHOOL OF MEDICINE)

Cleveland, Ohio

PROGRAMS OFFERED

Fully approved, four-year program in anatomic and clinical pathology. In anatomic pathology, training is offered in tissue diagnosis (autopsy and surgical specimens), cytopathology, cytogenetics, dermatopathology, electron microscopy, molecular pathology, immunopathology, immunocytochemistry, neuropathology and perinatal pathology. Appropriate training is also provided in forensic pathology and toxicology. The Clinical Pathology division offers training in clinical chemistry, hematopathology, (including gene molecular testing and flow cytometry), laboratory immunology (serology and cellular immunology), microbiology and transfusion medicine. Residents participate in the teaching of medical students from Case Western Reserve Medical School. Fellowships are available in surgical pathology and cytopathology.

TYPES AND NUMBERS OF APPOINTMENTS

There are 8 resident positions **including 2 categorical first-year positions**. The categorical first-year positions are offered through the National Resident Matching Program. One fellowship position in surgical pathology and one cytopathology fellowship are offered annually.

FACILITIES

MetroHealth Medical Center is a principal teaching hospital of Case Western Reserve University School of Medicine (CWRU). All members of the pathology faculty have appointments to the Faculty of Pathology at Case Western Reserve University. The hospital has 731 beds, and 89 bassinets, some 29,059 hospital admissions and 3,555 new-borns per year. The statistics for the past year are: 117 autopsies; over 7.5 million laboratory tests per year; 19,211 surgical specimens and 31,535 cytology cases. Staff and facilities are available for service and development in postmortem and surgical pathology, neuropathology, pediatric pathology, dermatopathology, immunopathology, immunohistochemistry, electron microscopy, hematopathology, cytochemistry, cytogenetics, cytopathology, microbiology, clinical immunology, blood bank, serology, and clinical chemistry. The Department has a dedicated staff and a laboratory computer with peripherals in all laboratories and nursing stations. The department maintains a working library of selected current pathology journals and textbooks. The hospital library subscribes to 425 journals, and has accessions of 9,000 books and 29,000 bound journals and an up to date collection of Pathology texts. The Cleveland Health Sciences Library and Allen Memorial Medical Library are available to all house officers.

COMMUNITY

Cleveland is the home of the internationally renowned Cleveland Orchestra, the Rock and Roll Hall of Fame, the Cleveland Museum of Art, the Cleveland Playhouse, the Karamu Theater, and the Cleveland Opera. Academic institutions in addition to Case Western Reserve University, in this locale are: Cleveland State University, John Carroll University, Kent State University, Baldwin Wallace College, and Cuyahoga Community College. Professional sports are represented by the Cleveland Indians (baseball), Cleveland Browns (football) the Cleveland Cavaliers (basketball), the Cleveland Lumberjacks (hockey), and the Cleveland Crunch (soccer). An extensive metropolitan park system surrounds the Cleveland area and offers boating, swimming, horseback riding, golfing, hiking, fishing, and camping facilities.

STIPENDS AND MAINTENANCE

Stipends begin at $44,600 (2009 figures) for the first year postgraduate level. Stipend levels are re-evaluated annually effective July 1. An additional stipend of $1,200 per annum is provided for chief resident(s). Residents are entitled to three weeks vacation during the year. All house officers are provided with uniforms and laundry service. They receive professional liability, and hospitalization insurance plans are available at low group rates.

STAFF

Joseph F. Tomashefski, Jr. MD Professor Pathology and Chairman (Anatomic Pathology, Pulmonary); **Timothy Beddow** MD Assistant Professor Pathology (Anatomic Pathology, Blood Bank/Transfusion Medicine); **Dan Cai** MD, PhD Assistant Professor Pathology (Anatomic Pathology and Neuropathology); **Ronald Cleveland** PhD Associate Professor Pathology (Clinical Immunology, Microbiology, and Flow Cytometry); **Santhi Ganesan** MD Assistant Professor (Anatomic Pathology, Cytopathology); **Michael Ip** PhD Associate Professor Pathology (Clinical Chemistry); **Lawrence Kass** MD Professor Medicine and Hematopathology (Hematopathology, Cytochemistry); **Amer Khiyami** MD Assistant Professor Pathology (Anatomic Pathology, Cytopathology); **Yao-Chang Liu** MD Associate Professor Pathology (Anatomic Pathology, Cytopathology); **Brenda Nicholes** PhD Assistant Professor Pathology (Clinical Chemistry, Toxicology); **Joram Sawady** MD Assistant Professor Pathology (Anatomic Pathology, Perinatal, OB/GYN Pathology and Cytopathology); **Michael Tyrkus** PhD Consultant, Cytogenetics.

APPLICATIONS

All candidates must be either graduates of U.S. or Canadian schools or Foreign graduates with a valid ECFMG certificate. All applicants are required to apply through ERAS by November 1 for appointments beginning July 1. **Applications will not be accepted through the mail.** Appointments will be announced at the time Matching Program results are released.

Address inquiries to:

Diane Gillihan, Program Coordinator, Department of Pathology
MetroHealth Medical Center
2500 MetroHealth Drive
Cleveland, OH 44109-1998
Phone: (216) 778-5181

The Twin Tower Building of MetroHealth Medical Center, Cleveland, Ohio

UNIVERSITY HOSPITALS CASE MEDICAL CENTER

Cleveland, Ohio

PROGRAMS OFFERED

Diversified, flexible educational programs are available in anatomic and clinical pathology. In anatomic pathology, residents gain a broad background in human disease by rotating in autopsy, surgical pathology, cytopathology, dermatopathology and forensic pathology. The clinical pathology program includes a core curriculum followed by rotation through chemistry, microbiology, hematopathology, transfusion medicine, immunology, molecular diagnostics, and cytogenetics. Forensic pathology training is provided at the Office of the Coroner of Cuyahoga County. Residents are encouraged to pursue professional interests in depth, and opportunities for experience in laboratory research can be arranged. Research areas include immunology and immunopathology, hematology, transfusion medicine, pediatric pathology, oncology, infectious disease, biomaterials and neuropathology. Residents and fellows participate in inter- and intradepartmental conferences, journal clubs and in the teaching of pathology to medical students and graduate students.

TYPES AND NUMBERS OF APPOINTMENTS

Residencies 24, including fellows (hematopathology, cytopathology, transfusion medicine)

FACILITIES

Facilities and clinical staff are those of the Department of Pathology of University Hospitals Case Medical Center, the flagship hospital of University Hospitals and the primary teaching hospital of Case Western Reserve University School of Medicine. The University Hospitals Case Medical Center complex includes two adult medical and surgical units, (Lerner Tower and Lakeside Hospital), as well as Rainbow Babies and Children's Hospital (240 beds) and MacDonald Hospital for Women (106 beds). The University Hospitals Ireland Cancer Center is the only National Comprehensive Cancer Center in Northern Ohio. In all, University Hospitals of Cleveland has 939 beds, 36,500 inpatient admissions and 210,000 outpatient visits per year. University Hospitals serves more than one hundred locations in forty-five Northeast Ohio communities and provides first-rate educational opportunities for residents in the form of tertiary patient referrals and reference laboratory accessions. The department handles 1.4 million laboratory examinations yearly in highly automated and computerized facilities. Anatomic specimens reflect the full spectrum of adult and pediatric disease and include 200 autopsies, 35,000 surgical specimens and 65,000 cytology specimens annually. Three experienced autopsy assistants permit efficient utilization of resident time. There is a departmental library with a 75 year collection of books and journals with current online pathology subscriptions. The Cleveland Health Sciences Library provides access to 380,000 volumes and 1,777 journal subscriptions at the Allen Memorial Medical Library (clinical science materials), the Case Western Reserve University Health Center Library (basic science materials) and the Dittrick Medical History Center (rare books and historical materials). A modern health and fitness club is available at moderate cost within one block of the hospital.

COMMUNITY

University Hospitals Case Medical Center and Case Western Reserve University, on their interwoven campuses, are the largest of 33 institutional members of University Circle, an extensive and unique concentration of educational, scientific, artistic and cultural organizations and open green spaces. Close neighbors of the Hospital are Severance Hall, home of the internationally renowned Cleveland Orchestra; the Cleveland Museum of Art, housing the country's third largest art collection; the Cleveland Institute of Art; the Cleveland Institute of Music; the Western Reserve Historical Society; the Cleveland Museum of Natural History; and the Cleveland Botanical Garden. Cleveland is a major science, industry, technology, sports, music, theatre and health center, circumscribed by a metropolitan park and recreational system. Downtown Cleveland is in the midst of a renaissance with recent addition of new baseball, basketball and football stadiums, a science center, and the Rock and Roll Hall of Fame. Access to downtown Cleveland, Cleveland Hopkins International Airport, and many suburbs is available from a surface rail transit station a few blocks from the hospital. Public and private schools in adjoining suburbs are excellent, and affordable housing is readily obtainable close to the hospital.

STIPENDS AND MAINTENANCE

Residents (first year post MD) begin at $46,276 effective July 1, 2009. Malpractice and group life insurance, book/travel allowance, hospitalization, medical care, vacation, sick leave, book/travel allowances, business cards, and uniforms/uniform laundry are provided.

STAFF

Clifford V Harding MD, PhD, Chair, immunology; **Joseph E. Willis** MD (Univ Col, Cork) Medical Director, Acting Director, Clinical Pathology; **Fadi W Abdul-Karim** MD (American Univ Beirut) Director Anatomic Pathology; surgical, cytopathology and orthopedic pathology.

Faculty on Staff, University Hospitals Case Medical Center

James M. Anderson MD, PhD (Case Western Reserve Univ, Oregon State Univ) biomaterials; **Rose C Beck** MD, PhD (Case Western Reserve Univ); **Mark L. Cohen** MD (Cornell Univ) neuropathology, surgical pathology; **Christine Curtis** PhD; **Beverly B. Dahms** MD (SUNY-Downstate) pediatric and gastrointestinal pathology; **Katharine A. Downes** MD (Case Western Reserve Univ) hematopathology, transfusion medicine; **Rosemary Farag** MD (Ain Shams Univ) surgical pathology and cytopathology; **Neil S. Greenspan** MD, PhD (Univ Pennsylvania) immunology; **Clifford V. Harding** MD, PhD, Chair, immunology; **Gretta H. Jacobs** MB, BCh (Univ Witwatersrand) electron microscopy, transplant and renal pathology; **Michael R. Jacobs** MB, BCh, PhD (Univ Witwatersrand) microbiology; **Catherine Listinsky** MD (Ohio State Univ) surgical pathology and cytopathology; **Gregory T. MacLennan** MD (Univ Manitoba) surgical and cytopathology; **Howard J. Meyerson** MD (Case Western Reserve Univ) hematopathology, immunology; **Raymond W. Redline** MD (Boston Univ) pediatric and perinatal pathology; **Mark Rodgers** MD (Thomas Jefferson Univ) surgical pathology; **Linda M. Sandhaus** MD (New York Univ) hematopathology, epidemiology; **Harry Taylor** MD (Med Col Georgia); **Jay K. Wasman** MD (Case Western Reserve Univ) surgical pathology, cytopathology; **Wei Xin** MD, PhD (Med Ctr Fudan Univ); **Lan Zhou** MD, PhD (Shanghai Med Univ).

Faculty on Staff, Office of the Coroner of Cuyahoga County

Elizabeth Balraj MD (Christian Med Col, India); **Joseph Felo** DO (Col Osteopath Med, Kansas City); **Dan Galita** MD (Carol Davila, Romania); **Andrea McCollum** MD (Colorado); **Frank Miller** MD (Case Western Reserve Univ) Coroner; **Stanley Seligman** MD (Univ the Andes, Venezuela).

Research Pathology Faculty, Case Western Reserve University Campus

Derek Abbott MD, PhD; **Shu Chen** PhD; **Brian Cobb** PhD; **Dawn Dawson** MD; **Laxminarayana Devireddy** DVM, PhD; **Xingjun Fan** MD; **Hisashi Fujioka** PhD; **Pierluigi Gambetti** MD; **Clive Hamlin** PhD; **Clifford Harding** MD, PhD; **Mark W Jackson** MD; **David Kaplan** MD, PhD; **Qingzhong Kong** PhD; **Lisa Kuttner-Kondo** PhD; **Michael Lamm** MD; **Paul Lehmann** MD, PhD; **Feng Lin** PhD; **Jinbo Liu** MD; **Edward Medof** MD, PhD; **Vincent Monnier** MD; **John Nedrud** PhD; **Robert Petersen** PhD; **Theresa Pretlow** PhD; **Thomas Pretlow** MD; **David Sell** PhD; **Neena Singh** MD, PhD; **Mark Smith** PhD; **Man-Sun Sy** PhD; **Alan Tartakoff** PhD; **Magdalena Tary-Lehmann** MD, PhD; **Xiongwei Zhu** PhD; **Nicholas Ziats** PhD; **Wen-Quan Zou** MD, PhD.

APPLICATIONS

Address inquiries to:

Director of Pathology Residency Program
University Hospitals Case Medical Center
Department of Pathology
11100 Euclid Avenue
Cleveland, OH 44106
Phone: (216) 844-6046 • **E-mail:** jeannie.stmarie@uhhospitals.org
Web site: http://path-www.path.cwru.edu/

University Hospitals Case Medical Center and Case Western Reserve University

THE OHIO STATE UNIVERSITY MEDICAL CENTER

Columbus, Ohio

PROGRAMS OFFERED

The department offers full residency training in all aspects of anatomic and clinical pathology as approved by the ACGME, leading to eligibility for the appropriate examination section of the American Board of Pathology. Post-residency fellowships in anatomical and clinical pathology are also offered. Individuals with strong academic interest and performance may be considered for the Master of Science degree in pathology or the Doctor of Philosophy degree in the OSU Integrated Biomedical Science Graduate Program (IBGP). Research fellowships provided by the university and national organization grants are available to residents who desire to become more familiar with research techniques.

TYPES AND NUMBERS OF APPOINTMENTS

There are 4 residency positions per year. The combined program consists of education in the divisions of autopsy pathology, surgical pathology and clinical pathology. Residents may elect to train only in anatomic or in clinical pathology. Fellowships are offered in transfusion medicine, hematopathology, cytopathology, renal and transplant pathology, gastrointestinal pathology, and dermatopathology. Pediatric pathology subspecialty training is provided at Nationwide Children's Hospital.

FACILITIES

The department is located on the main campus of the university with immediate access to the resources of all its constituent colleges and departments. Adjacent to the department, the College of Medicine operates within The Ohio State University Medical Center with 950 beds, including general medicine and surgery, a clinical research center, cardiac intensive care unit and special psychiatric and rehabilitation facilities. In addition, the medical center includes the James Cancer Hospital and Solove Research Institute, a 12-story, 160-bed facility and the Richard M. Ross Heart Hospital with 160 beds. The college is affiliated with Nationwide Children's Hospital of Columbus with 350 beds. The Department of Pathology provides service in anatomic and clinical pathology for the OSU Medical Center and Nationwide Children's Hospitals. The Department of Pathology has 40 clinical faculty members with subspecialty expertise. An experimental branch with 17 faculty members is also available for residents with research interest. Clinical services include approximately 250 autopsies annually for the OSU Medical Center and 115 autopsies annually at Nationwide Children's Hospital. Approximately 63,000 surgical specimens are examined by sub-specialty pathology diagnostic teams, including 7,700 intraoperative consultations. The specimens represent the whole spectrum of disease in all organ systems. Particular strengths include oncologic pathology, gastrointestinal and renal pathology. Forty-four thousand cytologic specimens are accessioned per year, twenty percent of which are extragenital in origin. Fine needle aspiration cytology is performed (approximately 1800 specimens). The clinical laboratories in the OSU Medical Center perform more than 8.5 million procedures annually and approximately 2 million procedures are performed at Nationwide Children's Hospital. The OSU Medical Center Gross Room laboratory has 9 grossing stations and is a state-of-the-art facility. Approximately 62,000 immunohistochemical stains are prepared annually in the clinical IHC laboratory. The clinical laboratories are computerized and extensively automated in the "core" areas. Research laboratories for immunology, molecular biology, cytogenetics, coagulation, protein chemistry, tissue culture, flow cytometry, image analysis, photography and immunohistology are in operation in addition to the service laboratories.

COMMUNITY

The Ohio State University is located two and one-half miles north of downtown Columbus, the capital of Ohio with a metropolitan area population of 1.75 million. Columbus has seven colleges and universities including The Ohio State University, 17 general and specialized hospitals, including The Ohio State University Medical Center, as well as many parks, art museums and galleries, and a wide variety of social, cultural and recreational opportunities.

STIPENDS AND MAINTENANCE

Annual stipends of at least $44,730 for first year trainees increasing in subsequent years. Housestaff are provided professional liability insurance and medical insurance for themselves and their immediate family. Additionally, they receive palm pilots, free parking and are given $1500 per year to use towards academic materials and travel to meetings. More benefit information may be viewed on the Graduate Medical Education website at http://medicine.osu.edu/gme/

STAFF

Sanford H. Barsky MD (Univ Pittsburgh 1974) Professor and Senhauser Endowed Chair of Pathology, investigative pathology; **Patricia Allenby** MD (Northwestern Univ 1983) Clinical Assistant Professor, autopsy; **Caroline Astbury** PhD (Medical Coll of Virginia 2000) Assistant Professor-Clinical, cytogenetics and molecular biology; **Leona Ayers**

MD (Duke Univ 1967) Professor, transfusion medicine, bacteriology; **Xue-Feng Bai** MD, PhD (Univ China 1988) Assistant Professor, immunological memory, tumor immunology and autoimmune diseases; **Peter Baker** MD (Ohio State Univ 1978) Clinical Professor, pediatric cardiac, transplant and renal pathology; **Joan-Miquel Balada-Llasat** PharmD, PhD (Tufts Univ 2006) Assistant Professor-Clinical, molecular biology, microbiology; **Gary Barnett** MD (Albany Med Col 1970) Clinical Associate Professor, frozen section; **Rolf Barth** MD (Columbia 1964) Professor, tumor immunobiology, autopsy; **Sujit Basu** MD, PhD (Nilratan Sircar Med Coll 1985, Chittaranjan National Cancer Instit 1996) Associate Professor, cancer, basic cell biology; **Michael Bissell** MD, PhD, MPH (Stanford Univ 1975) Professor, clinical chemistry; **Carl Boesel** MD (Univ Cincinnati 1966) Professor Emeritus, pediatric neuropathology; **Daniel Boué** MD, PhD (Univ Minnesota 1991) Associate Professor-Clinical, pediatric neuropathology; **Lawrence DeRenne** MD (Indiana Univ 1973) Clinical Assistant Professor, frozen section, community pathology; **Joan Durbin** MD, PhD (New Jersey 1989) Associate Professor, pediatric pathology, molecular genetics; **Wendy Frankel** MD (Univ Michigan 1988) Professor and Chief of Anatomic Pathology, gastrointestinal pathology; **Bonita Fung** MD (Univ Saskatchewan 1988) Clinical Assistant Professor, pediatric pathology; **Ramesh Ganju** PhD (Indian Inst of Sci, India 1986) Professor, translational research; **Jian-Xin Gao** PhD (Univ China 1989) Research Assistant Professor, immunology research; **Julie M. Gastier-Foster** PhD (Harvard Univ 1996) Assistant Professor-Clinical, clinical molecular genetics and cytogenetics; **Amy Gewirtz** MD (Univ Cincinnati 1990) Associate Professor-Clinical and Director of Clinical Pathology and Laboratory Services, hematopathology; **Sue Hammond** MD (Univ Cal-Davis 1982) Professor, pediatric and renal pathology, second malignancies; **Gang He** MD, PhD (Henan Med Univ China 1982) Assistant Professor-Clinical, head and neck, bone and soft tissue, breast and genitourinary, pulmonary pathology; **Nyla Heerema** PhD (Iowa Univ 1967) Professor, cytogenetics; **Charles Hitchcock** MD, PhD (Ohio State Univ 1983) Associate Professor - Clinical, autopsy, pulmonary pathology; **Iouri Ivanov** MD, PhD (Vitebsk State Med Schl, Belarus 1986) Assistant Professor-Clinical, gynecologic pathology; **O. Hans Iwenofu** MD (Univ of Nigeria 1995) Assistant Professor-Clinical, gynecologic, head and neck, bone and soft tissue pathology; **Scott Jewell** PhD (Ohio State Univ 1993) Research Associate Professor, experimental pathology; **Samir Kahwash** MD (Univ Damascus 1983) Associate Professor-Clinical, pediatric hematopathology; **Melanie Kennedy** MD (Ohio State Univ 1968) Associate Professor-Clinical, transfusion medicine; **Jeffrey Kneile** MD (Cincinnati 2002) Clinical Assistant Professor, community pathology; **Larry Lasky** MD (Univ Michigan 1976) Associate Professor, immunology research; **Marino Leon** MD (Peru 1990) Assistant Professor-Clinical, head and neck, bone and soft tissue pathology, pulmonary, cytopathology; **Nancy Lill** PhD (The Pennsylvania State Univ 1992) Associate Professor, cancer and basic cell biology; **James Liu** MD (Hebei Med Univ China 1983) Assistant Professor-Clinical, gastrointestinal, gynecologic pathology; **Gerard Lozanski** MD (Univ Med Sch Poland 1987) Assistant Professor, flow cytometry and hematopathology; **Mario Marcon** PhD (Bowman Gray 1978) Clinical Associate Professor, pediatric pathology and microbiology; **William Marsh** MD (Univ Virginia 1972) Professor-Clinical, gastrointestinal pathology; **Stephen Moore** MD (Ohio State Univ 1976) Clinical Assistant Professor, gynecologic, breast and genitourinary pathology; **Tibor Nadasdy** MD, PhD (Med Univ Hungary 1981) Professor, renal transplantation, ultrastructural pathology; **Kathleen Nicol** MD (Univ Louisville 1993) Associate Professor-Clinical, pediatric pathology and transfusion medicine; **Gerard Nuovo** MD (Univ Vermont 1983) Professor, molecular pathology; **Tatiana Oberys-zyn** PhD (Rutgers 1990) Associate Professor, wound healing research; **Preeti Pancholi** PhD (Postgrad Inst Med Ed Res, India 1988) Associate Professor-Clinical, microbiology; **Vijay Pancholi** PhD (Postgrad Inst Med Ed Res, India 1984) Associate Professor, research, Group A streptococcal disease; **Sara Peters** MD, PhD (SUNY 1991) Associate Professor-Clinical, dermatopathology; **Christopher Pierson** MD, PhD (Wayne State Univ 2002) Assistant Professor, pediatric neuropathology; **Vinay Prasad** MBBS (Univ Mysore 1990) Assistant Professor-Clinical, pediatric pathology; **Thomas Prior** PhD (Med Col Virginia 1987) Professor, diagnostic molecular genetics; **Daniela Proca** MD (Romania 1992) Clinical Assistant Professor, community pathology; **Robert Pyatt** PhD (Ohio State Univ 2001) Assistant Professor, molecular genetics; **Frederick Racke** MD, PhD (Case Western Reserve 1994) Associate Professor, hematopathology; **Nilsa Ramirez** MD (Univ of Puerto Rico 1981) Associate Professor-Clinical, pediatric surgical pathology; **Abhik Ray Chaudhury** MD (India 1979) Associate Professor-Clinical, neuropathology; **Anjali Satoskar** MD (India 1994) Assistant Professor-Clinical, renal transplantation; **Daniel Sedmak** MD (Ohio State 1980) Professor, renal and transplant pathol-ogy; **Arwa Shana'ah** MD (Univ Jordan 1989) Assistant Professor-Clinical, Director of Residency Training Program, hematopathology; **Rulong Shen** MD (Zhenjiang Med Col 1981) Assistant Professor-Clinical, gynecologic pathology; **Adrian Suarez** MD (Univ de Costa Rica 1994) Assistant Professor-Clinical, cytopathology and gyneclogic pathology; **Kenichi Tamama** MD, PhD (Gunma Univ Japan 1995) Assistant Professor, clinical chemistry; **David Thornton** PhD (Ohio State Univ 1986) Clinical Assistant Professor, pediatric pathology and chemistry; **Joanne Trgovcich** PhD (Univ North Carolina 1995) Research Assistant Professor, immunology and histology; **James VanBrocklyn** PhD (Ohio State Univ 1996) Research Assistant Professor, gangliosides research; **W. James Waldman** PhD (Ohio State Univ 1990) Associate Professor, cytomegalovirus research in transplantation; **Traci Wilgus** PhD (Ohio State Univ 2001) Assistant Professor, skin, wound healing and skin carcinogenesis; **JoAnna Williams** MD (Ohio State 2000) Assistant Professor-Clinical, community pathology; **Haifeng Wu** MD (China 1985) Assistant Professor, hematopathology, coagulation; **Martha Yearsley** MD (Colombia 1986) Assistant Professor-Clinical, gastrointestinal; **Weiqiang John Zhao** MD, PhD (Hunan Med Univ China 1982) Assistant Professor, hematopathology; **Xianghong Zou** PhD (Huazhong Agr Univ, China 1995) Assistant Professor, translational research.

APPLICATIONS

All applications must be submitted through ERAS. Residency candidates must be graduates of approved medical schools in the U.S. or Canada. Candidates of foreign medical schools must have an ECFMG certificate and have passed USMLE Parts I & II. All trainees must successfully complete USMLE Step III prior to completion of the PGY-2 training year. Satisfactory references are required. Applications must be received by November 1st for appointments beginning July 1st of the following year.

Address inquiries to:

Arwa Shana'ah, MD
Assistant Professor
Director, Pathology Residency Program
Department of Pathology
The Ohio State University
N-308 Doan Hall, 410 W 10th Ave
Columbus, OH 43210-1228
Phone: (614) 293-2458 • **Fax:** (614) 293-7273 • **E-mail:** jill.hostetler@osumc.edu
Web site: http://pathology.osumc.edu/ext/ and GME **Web site:** http://medicine.osu.edu/gme

Aerial photograph of Ohio State University Medical Center

UNIVERSITY OF TOLEDO UNIVERSITY MEDICAL CENTER

Toledo, Ohio

PROGRAMS OFFERED

The University of Toledo (formerly the Medical College of Ohio) Department of Pathology offers fully approved residencies in anatomicand combined anatomic and clinical pathologyare available. The Division of Anatomic Pathology provides training in autopsy and surgical pathology, cytology, dermatopathology, neuropathology, electron and fluorescence microscopy, histochemistry and immunopathology. Rotations in pediatric and forensic pathology are available through affiliated institutions. The Division of Clinical Pathology includes clinical chemistry, toxicology, hematology, blood banking, immunology, microbiology and virology, molecular diagnostics, cytogenetics, tissue typing, flow cytometry and coagulation. Administrative and managerial skills are included at all levels with the development of major responsibility in the final year. The program for each resident can be tailored to his or her interest and capabilities with special emphasis in any of the subspecialties desired. Active participation in research is encouraged. There are research opportunitics in tumor biology, molecular biology and neurosciences. The program is accredited by appropriate governmental and professional accrediting bodies.

REQUIREMENTS

Residency candidates must be graduates of approved medical schools in the USA or Canada. Alternatively, graduates of foreign medical schools must have an ECFMG certificate. Satisfactory references are required.

TYPES AND NUMBERS OF APPOINTMENTS

The University of Toledo Program provides opportunities for nine residents. Most residents are in the combined AP/CP program. However, AP only training is also available.

FACILITIES

TheUniversity of Toledo Medical Center is located on the UT Health Sciences Campus andhas a total of 319 beds. Also located on the UT Health Sciences Campus, adjacent to the Medical Center, are the regional blood distribution center for the American Red Cross and the Lucas County Coroner's Office. Affiliated institutions include the Pinkus Dermatopathology Laboratory in Monroe, Michigan (30 minutes away), Akron Children's Hopsital in Akron, Ohio; and Integrated Laboratories in Toledo. The program has access to 10-15,000 general surgical specimens, 10,000 cytopathology specimens, 100,000 dermatopathology specimens (through Pinkus Laboratories), more than 1,000,000 laboratory tests and procedures and, in combination with the Lucas County Coroner's Office, more than 1000 autopsies per year. The University Hospital emphasizes tertiary care and has an extensively modern facility and computerized laboratory services. Research opportunities and facilities are also available. Library and audiovisual facilities are extensive and include departmental libraries and the Health Science Campus' Mulford Library. The Main Campus Library at The University of Toledo is also available for residents. Residents are offered the opportunity to participate in the continuing education programs of the American Society of Clinical Pathologists, the College of American Pathologists and the United States and Canadian Academy of Pathology. The University of Toledo also offers the Morse Center, a state-of-the-art fitness and wellness center on the Health Science Campus. This is available to all students, staff, and faculty.

COMMUNITY

Toledo is the fourth largest city in Ohio and one of the top 60 metropolitan areas in the nation, with a metropolitan population of approximately 1,100,000 residents. There are excellent public and parochial schools and recreational and cultural facilities. Boating and fishing on Lake Erie is a major recreational resource. Toledo also has an exceptional art museum, as well as an outstanding zoo and many cultural attractions including opera, symphony, theater and the arts. There is an extensive system of Metroparks. The UT Health Science Campus is located in a residential area on the south side of the city that is within a few minutes driving time of the downtown area.

STIPENDS AND MAINTENANCE

Current stipends, 1st year, $41,566, 2nd year, $42,813, 3rd year, $44,097, 4th year, $45,420. All residents are provided with hospitalization insurance, professional liability insurance, uniforms, as well as, allowances and expenses for professional meetings and workshops. Other benefits include child care facilities for a nominal fee.

STAFF

University of Toledo Medical Center

Robert E Mrak MD, PhD (California Davis 1975. 1976) Professor and Chairman, Residency Program Director, Neuropathology; **Robert L. Booth** MD (Med Col Ohio 1985) Associate Professor, Chief of Clinical Pathology;

Hematopathology; **Peter J Goldblatt** Professor & Chairman Emeritus, Chief of Anatomic Pathology; GI Pathology; **Amira F. Gohara** MD (Univ Cairo, Egypt 1964) Professor and Dean Emerita, Clinical chemistry/flow cytometry/serology/immunology and tissue typing; **William T. Gunning** PhD (Med Col Ohio 1991) Professor, Diagnostic electron microscopy; **Mary R Smith** MD (Ottawa 1966) Professor, Hematology and coagulation; **Shaheda B Ahmed** MD (Gandhi Medical College) Assistant Professor, Surgical pathology & cytopathology; **Victor S Flauta** MD (Fatima College of Medicine) Assistant Professor, Microbiology; **Cara M. Gatto-Weis** MD (UMDNJ-Robert Wood Johnson Med Sch 1994) Assistant Professor, Surgical pathology & cytopathology; **Jill Zyrek-Betts** MD (Wayne State Univ) Assistant Professor, Surgical pathology & cytopathology.

Lucas County Coroner's Office (Forensic Pathology)

James R Patrick MD (Yale Univ 1956) Professor, Chairman Emeritus, and Lucas County Coroner; **Cynthia Beisser** MD (Univ Tenneessee) Associate Professor, Deputy Coroner; **Diane Scala-Burnett** MD (Univ Autonoma Guadalajara) Associate Professor, Deputy Coroner; **Maneesha Pandey** MBBS (Kottayam Medical College) Assistant Professor, Deputy Coroner.

Akron Children's Hospital (Pediatric Pathology)

Dimitri P Agamanolis MD (Aristotle Univ Thessaloniki 1962) Residency Program Director, Akron Children's Hospital.

Pinkus Laboratories (Dermatopathology)

David A Mehregan MD (Wayne State Univ) Dermatopathology; **Darius Mehregan** MD (Univ Michigan) Dermatopathology; **Jean Thomas** MD (Med College Ohio) Dermatopathology.

American Red Cross (Blood Banking and Transfusion Medicine)

NurJehan Quraishy MD (Dow Med Col, Pakistan 1975) Assistant Professor; Director, American Red Cross.

Integrated Laboratories (Molecular Pathology)

Gail D Wenger PhD. Associate Professor, Molecular pathology; **Dennis LeGolvan** MD (Univ Michigan 1969); **S. Strobel** MD (Ohio State Univ 1981).

Blanchard Valley Regional Health Center

H. Budke MD (Univ Cincinnati Col Med 1990); **D. Lai** MD (Natl Taiwan Univ 1965); **D. Praprotnik** MD (Univ Ljubljana, Slovenia 1988); **J. Sorrells** MD (Indiana Univ Med Sch 1976).

APPLICATIONS

Applications should be received by November 1 for appointments beginning July 1 of the following year. July 1 is the normal beginning date for residencies, but other times are open to consideration.

Address inquiries to:

Kim Mitchell
Residency Coordinator
Department of Pathology
The University of Toledo, University Medical Center
3000 Arlington Ave.
Toledo, OH 43614
Phone: (419) 383-3474 • **Fax:** (419) 383-6183
Web site: http://hsc.utoledo.edu/depts/path/residency.html

FORUM HEALTH
WESTERN RESERVE CARE SYSTEM

Youngstown, Ohio

PROGRAMS OFFERED

The Department of Pathology offers a fully approved combined four-year AP/CP training program. It consists of 18 months of anatomic pathology, 18 months of clinical pathology, and 12 months of elective sequence. The emphasis of this residency is on preparing trainees to function professionally in a community hospital setting. This is a relatively small program that utilizes size as a strength, therein providing both a cooperative, friendly environment and high accessibility of faculty to achieve its objectives. Residents are carefully and frequently evaluated and are offered the opportunity of frequent individualized conferences with faculty. Additionally, a "mentoring" program is in place to provide support to residents. Anatomic pathology rotations include surgical pathology, autopsy pathology and cytopathology. These rotations are supported by state-of-the-art immunohistochemistry,digitally enhanced electron microscopy, and molecular pathologytechniques. The residency takes advantage of a high-volume combined in-patient and out-patient surgical pathology and cytopathology practice and additionally provides access toon-siteforensic pathology. Advanced digital and computer technology training is provided. Clinical pathology training includes rotations in clinical chemistry, microbiology, virology, toxicology, hematology, coagulation, medical microscopy, blood banking, flow cytometry, immunology and molecular pathology. In clinical pathology, there is emphasis placed upon resident decision-making, clinical consultation, and increasing levels of responsibility. The residents are mentored in administrative and management subjects through lectures, conferences, participation in committee activities, and participation in the CAP accreditation process. Teaching opportunities are abundant. The residents conduct both interdepartmental and intradepartmental conferences and educate medical students in both an informal and formal manner.

TYPES AND NUMBERS OF APPOINTMENTS

There are eight residency positions available with two first-year residents appointed annually. This program participates in the National Resident Match.

FACILITIES

The main teaching campus is Northside Medical Center. The main laboratory is located at the Northside Medical Center (WRCS). It is comprehensively equipped and computerized. WRCS also maintains residency programs in Internal Medicine, General Surgery,Family Medicine, Dentistry and Podiatry. WRCS is one of the principal teaching campuses of the Northeastern Ohio Universities College of Medicine. This department processes approximately 10,000 surgicals, 100 autopsies, 7,000 cytopathology specimens,500 flow cytometry specimens, and 1.2 million clinical laboratory determinations annually. In addition, a closelyaffiliated out-patient laboratory provides regular on site resident rotations with access to an additional 16,000 surgical and 30,000 cytology specimens. Northside Medical Center is a teaching clinical affiliate of Youngstown State University School of Histotechnology. Histotechnology students interact daily with residents during their clinical rotations in Histology.

COMMUNITY

The Youngstown area provides abundant educational, recreational, athletic and cultural activities. Youngstown State University, which is well known for its modern facilities, athletic and community events, is located less than five minutes from Northside Hospital. The pathology faculty also maintain teaching appointments at Youngstown State University. One of the foremost collections of American art in the United States is at the Butler Museum of American Art. Mill Creek Park is a large urban wilderness with nature trails, golf course, Fellows Riverside Gardens, and is the site for winter cross-country skiing and ice skating. The International Peace Race for runners, the Youngstown-Warren Ladies Professional Golf Association Tournament and the Canfield Fair are very popular annual events. The Youngstown Symphony Orchestra provides excellent entertainment. Additionally, the community offers abundant residential, commercial and recreational areas. Youngstown is approximately one hour's drive from both downtown Pittsburgh and downtown Cleveland.

STIPENDS AND MAINTENANCE

First postgraduate year, $43,500; 2nd postgraduate year, $44,779; 3rd postgraduate year, $46,453; 4th postgraduate year, $47,959. There is financial support at any level for residents presenting material at national meetings. In addition, year 3 and 4 residents receive a generous allowance to attend national meetings. Parking for residents is free.

STAFF

Faculty and Specialty Interests

Geoffrey Mendelsohn MD, Program Director, Pathology Residency; Anatomic Pathology, Urologic, GI and Microbiology; **Shokat M. Fatteh** MD, Chairman; Dermatopathologist; **Kevin L. Scheetz** MD, Vice Chairman; Director,

Clinical Pathology; Urologic, Hematopathology, Flow Cytometry, Blood Bank; **Gary K. SeGall** MD, PhD, Assistant Program Director, Pathology Residency; Director, Anatomic Pathology and Research; Musculoskeletal, Breast, Electron Microscopy, Clinical Chemistry, Molecular Pathology and Toxicology; **Qing-Sheng Tian** MD, Associate Pathologist; Cytopathology, Breast; **Yuel D. Tom** MD, Associate Pathologist; Immunopathology, Hematopathology and Renal Pathology.

Consulting Staff

Dimitris P. Agamanolis MD, Neuropathology; **Surjit K. Bal** MD, Surgical Pathology; **Jean E. Blair** MD, Gastrointestinal and Pulmonary Pathology; **Robin S. Gautam** MD, Cytopathology; **Humphrey D. Germaniuk** MD, Forensic Pathologist; **Carmen J. Julius** MD, Blood Banking, Hematopathology; **Christine S. Marzich** MD, Cytopathology, Gastrointestinal Pathology; **Joseph S. Ohr** MD, Forensic Pathologist; **Gregory R. Roush** MD, Obstetrical and Gynecologic Pathology, Microbiology; **Carl R. Schaub** MD, Hematopathology, Cytopathology.

APPLICATIONS

Applications will only be accepted through the Electronic Residency Application Service (ERAS). Candidates must be graduates of approved medical schools in the United States or Canada. Graduates of foreign medical schools must have a current ECFMG certificate. Satisfactory references and a personal interview are required of all candidates.

Address inquiries to:

Geoffrey Mendelsohn, MD, Program Director or Pamela Carpenter, Program Coordinator
Western Reserve Care System
Department of Pathology & Laboratory Medicine
500 Gypsy Lane
Youngstown, OH 44501
Phone: (330) 884-3817 • **E-mail:** pcarpenter@forumhealth.org

UNIVERSITY OF OKLAHOMA HEALTH SCIENCES CENTER

Oklahoma City, Oklahoma

PROGRAMS OFFERED

Accredited residency training is offered in a combined anatomic/clinical program. The program provides four years of competency-based training to prepare residents for community or academic pathology practice. The program is designed to give residents a broad range of experiences. Included in the training is exposure to autopsy, surgical pathology, neuropathology, pediatric pathology, oral pathology, cytopathology (with fine needle aspiration), hematology, toxicology, clinical chemistry, clinical microbiology, clinical virology, immunopathology, immunohematlogy, immunocytochemistry, coagulation, forensic pathology, and dermatopathology. Residents have the opportunity to work with subspecialists in pathology covering such areas as breast pathology, pediatric/perinatal pathology, neuropathology, gynecologic pathology, urogenital pathology, and head and neck pathology. Residents participate in consultative pathology for muscle, nerve, bone marrow, and FNA biopsy cases and are exposed to such techniques as flow cytometry, electron microscopy, and nucleic acid-based testing. Research opportunities are available with major departmental emphasis on the application of molecular, immunologic, biochemical and morphologic approaches to the study of disease processes. Advanced training (fellowship) is offered in molecular genetic pathology

TYPES AND NUMBERS OF APPOINTMENTS

A total of 16 PGY1-4 positions are available in the program. The Department typically offers four first-year positions through the National Residents Matching Program (NRMP) each year.

FACILITIES

The primary site for resident training is the comprehensive, 200-acre OUHSC campus where the seven health-related colleges of the University of Oklahoma, including the College of Medicine, are located. At OUHSC, the largest group of physicians in Oklahoma come together on one campus to provide patients with cutting-edge medical care. Two adult care hospital facilities, Oklahoma Children's and Women's Hospital, a departmental molecular pathology laboratory, the Oklahoma Blood Institute, and the Chief Medical Examiners Office are all in close proximity and easily accessible for resident rotations. The campus is undergoing extensive expansion with many new facilities and programs, e.g. a comprehensive cancer institute, an adult outpatient clinic building, a pediatric outpatient clinic building, and an ambulatory surgical center.

OU Medical Center is composed of two hospitals - Presbyterian Tower for adult services and Oklahoma Children's and Women's Hospital for pediatric and obstetrical care. The pathology and laboratory annual workload is as follows: surgical pathology accessions approximately 17,000; cytology accessions approximately 60,000; and clinical laboratory tests approximately 3 million.

The Veterans Affairs Medical Center of Oklahoma is located adjacent to the campus and is physically connected to the Oklahoma Medical Center. The pathology and laboratory annual workload for this hospital is as follows: surgical pathology accessions approximately 6,000; cytology accessions approximately 4,000; and clinical laboratory tests approximately 1.5 million.

Oklahoma Blood Institute is a large non-profit regional blood center. The Chief Medical Examiners Office is the site where the majority of forensic autopsies in the state are performed. Both of these facilities provide residents with excellent training venues.

Residents also have the opportunity to train at off-campus locations. Rotation at the affiliated sites is an integral part of the training and provides exposure to additional practice settings. Integris-Baptist Medical Center is a large community hospital in Oklahoma City. Their annual surgical pathology workoad is approximately 12,000 accessions; the annual cytology workload is 180,000 accessions. By rotating at this hospital, residents obtain additional training in surgical pathology/cytopathology and hematopathology. Dermatopathology training is provided at St. John Medical Center in Tulsa, Oklahoma. Residents participate in pathology case sign-out and have patient contact through the dematology clinic.

COMMUNITY

The OUHSC campus is located in the thriving downtown area of Oklahoma City and is central to the surrounding suburbs. Oklahoma City is a growing, diverse community of approximately 600,000 with a metropolitan population in excess of one million. Its downtown area has been restored and transitioned into an exciting entertainment district with many restaurants, theaters, and sporting events. Oklahoma City is located in the center of the state and 20 miles north of the main campus of the University of Oklahoma in Norman. The relatively mild four-season climate, the affordable cost of living, and the many attractive parks, lakes, and recreational opportunities make the area an ideal place to live.

STIPENDS AND MAINTENANCE

Current first-year resident starting base salary is $45,666 plus benefits that include health, life and institutional malpractice insurance. Residents enjoy 15 days of vacation each year and are allowed 5 days professional leave to attend conferences. Residents are strongly encouraged and supported to present at local and national meetings.

STAFF

* Adjunct or Clinical Faculty Members

Professors

G.P. Altshuler MBBS* (Univ Sydney) pediatric path; **K.E. Blick** PhD (Univ Kentucky) computers; **L.E. DeBault** PhD (Univ Stockholm) flow cytometry, EM; **D.J. Flournoy** PhD (Univ Texas-Houston) microbiol; **J.H. Holliman** MD (Oklahoma Univ) Academic Programs; **G.D. Houston** DDS* (Baylor Col Med) Chairman, Oral Path; **R. A. Marlar** PhD (Wayne State) physiology, biochemistry; **D. M. Parham** MD (Univ Tenn HSC) pediatric path; **K.M. Parker** PhD (Univ Texas Southwestern Med Sch) toxicol; **J.V. Pitha** MD, PhD (Charles Univ, Australia Natl Univ) surg path, autopsy; Chief, VAMC; **M. L. Talbert** MD (UCLA) Chair, surg, GI path; **J. L. Waner** PhD* (Stritch Sch Med) microbiology; **G.L. White** DVM (Oklahoma State Univ) vet path; **S. K. Young** DDS* (Univ Michigan) oral path; **Z. J. Zhao** PhD (Oregon State Univ) biochemistry, biophysio; **R. E. Zuna** MD (Jefferson Med Col) cytopath.

Associate Professors

W. Aronson MD (Univ Pennsylvania) autopsy; **B. Bane** MD (Wayne State Univ) surg path, cytopath; **W. W. Brinkley** DVM (Oklahoma State Univ) vet medicine; **A. N. Crowson** MD* (Univ of Manitoba, Canada) anatomic path; **S.T. Dunn** PhD (The Queen's Univ, Belfast) molec biol; **K. Fung** MD, PhD (Taipei Med, Univ Pennsylvania) neuro, surg path; **L. A. Hassell** MD (Univ Utah Med) cytopathology; **W. F. Kern** MD (SUNY at Brooklyn) surg path, hematology; **S.D. Kosanke** DVM, PhD (Oklahoma State Univ, Texas A&M Univ) vet path; **D.M. Lewis** DDS* (Georgetown Univ) oral path; **S.A. Lightfoot** MD (Univ Texas Southwestern Med Sch) cytopath; **Y. Liu** PhD (Univ Miami) axonal growth and regeneration; **J.M. McCormack** PhD* (Univ of OK HSC) immuno, microbiology; **A. Pereira** PhD (Univ Melbourne, Australia) vasc biol; **J. J. Schnabel** MD, PhD* (Louisiana State Univ) chemical path.

Assistant Professors

L. Archer PhD (Oklahoma Univ) research; **G. L. Blakey** MD (UT Southwestern) anatomic, clinical, molec gen; **M. Cary** DVM, PhD* (Ohio State Univ,Kansas State Univ) vet path; **W. Ding** PhD (Shanghai Univ) molec onc; **B.C. Gehrs** MD (Univ of North Carolina) transf med; **E.M. Gillies** MD (Univ Santo Tomas, Manila) surg path, cytopath, autopsy; **C.Z. Liu** MD, PhD (Peking Med, Northwestern Univ) surg, molec, head and neck; **R. Sawh** MD (Univ West Indies, Jamaica) anatomic path; **Ethan D. Stolzenberg** MD, PhD (Univ Penn, Northwestern Univ) neuropath; **J.T. Yang** MD, PhD (Peking Med, Northwestern Univ) surg, molec; **X. Yang** MD, PhD (Luoyang Med Col, Finch Univ) research, breast mol biology, apoptosis; **Z. Yu** MD (Qingdao Med Coll) pediatric path; **R. R. Zhang** MD (Beijing Med Univ) cytopath, surg.

APPLICATIONS

Trainees must be graduates of approved medical schools in the U.S. or foreign countries. Satisfactory references and personal interviews are required. **Application, CV, copy of medical school transcript, letter from your Dean (indicating class rank and performance in your basic science course and clinical rotations)** and **three faculty members familiar with your work** (not necessarily pathologists) and **scores on certification examinations with copies of certificate (e.g., ECFMG, USMLE, etc.)** should be received by ERAS no later than November 30 for appointments beginning July 1 of the following year.

Address inquiries to:

Department of Pathology
Attention: Dianne Wright, Residency Coordinator
PO Box 26901, BMSB, Room 401
Oklahoma City, OK 73126-0901
Phone: (405) 271-2451
Web site: http://w3.ouhsc.edu/pathology

This modern 200-acre campus is located within a mile from downtown Oklahoma City and contains Women and Children's Hospital, Presbyterian Tower and Veterans Affairs Medical Center.

OREGON HEALTH & SCIENCE UNIVERSITY

Portland, Oregon

PROGRAMS OFFERED

The Oregon Health & Science University Department of Pathology offers a fully approved four year training program in clinical and anatomic pathology. The anatomic pathology program includes autopsy pathology, surgical pathology, and cytopathology. Subspecialty areas include cytopathology, electron microscopy, forensic pathology, immunohistochemistry, neuropathology, including nerve and muscle biopsies, hematopathology, and renal pathology. The clinical pathology training includes laboratory experience in blood banking, chemistry, hematology, toxicology, cytogenetics, molecular genetic pathology, and immunology. An AP & LM In-Service course of more than 100 instructional hours covers the breadth of the specialty. This course is given over two years, so residents experience two cycles prior to board examinations. Residents participate in many conferences in addition to assisting in teaching medical students and medical technology students. Approximately seven (7) months of electives are offered during the four year training program. Electives include advanced training in virtually all service and research laboratories, as well as laboratory management and informatics. For additional information, refer to our web page: www.ohsu.edu/pathology.

TYPES AND NUMBERS OF APPOINTMENTS

Three first-year positions are generally available for the four-year AP & LM training program.

FACILITIES

Training is provided by the Department of Pathology at Oregon Health & Science University (OHSU), the Portland Veterans Affairs Medical Center (VAMC), Kaiser Permanente NW and the Oregon Medical Examiner's Office. These medical centers have a combined bed capacity of more than 1,400. The anatomic laboratories process approximately 75,000 surgicals, 80,000 cytologies and in excess of 220 autopsies a year. The medical examiner performs about 1,000 examinations and 700 autopsies per year and has complete facilities and support personnel for all routine and special procedures including forensic toxicology.

COMMUNITY

The 116-acre campus of the Oregon Health & Science University overlooks the City of Portland and is 1.5 miles from the central business district. The Portland V.A. Medical Center is connected by a pedestrian footbridge, and is closely affiliated with the University. The Portland Metropolitan area has a population of more than 2 million and is one of the business and cultural centers of the Pacific Northwest. Portland borders the Willamette and Columbia Rivers. On the horizon to the east is the Cascade Mountain Range and to the west the Coast Range. Opportunities for winter sports, hunting, fishing, hiking, boating, skiing and beachcombing are all within a short distance.

STIPENDS AND MAINTENANCE

The salary for Training Level 1 residents is currently $41,700 with increments of up to $2,528 for each subsequent training level. Other benefits include professional liability insurance, medical insurance, gym membership, $1200 per year for books/travel, and use of a personal laptop computer. Residents receive three weeks of paid vacation annually. Time may be obtained for attending professional meetings and support is provided for attending those meetings in which the house officer presents peer reviewed research. No housing facilities are provided for residents; however, numerous apartments and homes are available within walking distance of the medical school.

STAFF

Anatomic Pathology

R. Braziel MD, Director Hematopathology; **C. Corless** MD, PhD, Shared Cancer Research, Director of Surgical Pathology; **D. Farrell** PhD, Associate Professor; **K. Gatter** MD, Hematopathology, Surgical Pathology; **M. Grafe** MD, PhD, Director of Neuropathology; **S. H. Gultekin** MD, Neuropathology; **D. C. Houghton** MD, Renal Pathology; **K. Kelemen** MD, PhD, Hematopathology; **J. Kihlstrum** MHS, surgical pathology; **F. Kratochvil** MD, oral pathology; **F. J. Kratochvil, DDS** Oral Pathology; **A. Mansoor** MD, surgical pathology; **T. Morgan** Director, Medical Director, Cytopatology; **N. Niles** MD, Emeritus professor; **R. Nixon** MD, PhD, neuropathology; **L. Picker** MD, Senior Scientist and Director Vaccine Development Center; **S. Poor** MHS, surgical pathology; **D. Sauer** MD, Cytopathology, Clinical Chemistry & Toxicology; **K. Schmidt** PhD, education; **W. Schmidt** PhD, MD, surgical pathology; **P. Stenzel** MD, PhD, Director Autopsy, surgical pathology; **M. Troxell** MD, PhD, Medical Director, Immunohistochemistry; **D. Weeks** MD, Chair, Department Pathology; **C. White** MD, dermatopathology; **R. Woltjer** MD, PhD, Neuropathology.

Laboratory Medicine

A. Bakke PhD, clinical immunology; **L. Boshkov** MD, Director Hemostasis and Thrombosis; **T. DeLoughery** MD, Director Anti-coagulation Clinic; **G. Fan** MD, PhD, Medical Director, Hematology Service; **S. Kazmierczak** PhD, DABCC, chemistry/toxicology; **J. Kujovich** MD, hematology, hemostasis; **J. MacLowry** MD, Medical Director Pathology and Laboratory Services; **R. Press** MD, PhD, molecular pathology; **R. Scanlan** MD, Director, Transfusion Medicine, Director, Pathology Residency Program; **K. Spackman** MD, PhD, transfusion medicine, informatics.

Kaiser

B. Armstrong MD, PhD; **E. Chinn** MD; **L. Dworkin** MD; **S. Guerin** MD; **K. Holahan** MD; **P. Jacky** PhD; **R. Krum** MD; **J. Liu** MD; **N. Olson** MD; **K. Oyama** MD; **J. Reiss** MD; **D. Runckel** MD; **D. Scott** MD; **J. Thompson** MD, Director of Laboratories; **S. Welch** PhD.

Medical Examiners

K. Gunson MD; **L. Lewman** MD; **C. Nelson** MD; **C. Young** MD, Forensic Pathology.

APPLICATIONS

Residency candidates from the USA or Canada must be graduates of LCME-accredited medical schools. Applications must have the MD degree from a school of medicine in the United States or Canada; or, if graduated from a foreign medical school, must be physicians with the qualifications required for admittance to a program in graduate medical education ith proper ECFMG Physicians may enter the program without prior graduate medical education. Applications will only be accepted through ERAS. Applications should be submitted by November 15th for appointments to begin July 1 of the following year.

Address inquiries to:

Anna Wedeking, Training Programs Coordinator
Richard Scanlan, MD, Residency Program Director
Oregon Health & Science University
Department of Pathology, L113
3181 S.W. Sam Jackson Park Road
Portland, OR 97239-3098
Phone: (503) 494-4110 • **E-mail:** ferencea@ohsu.edu
Web site: http://www.ohsu.edu/pathology

MILTON S. HERSHEY MEDICAL CENTER PENN STATE COLLEGE OF MEDICINE

Hershey, Pennsylvania

PROGRAMS OFFERED

Residencies are offered in anatomic and/or clinical pathology. Education is provided through residents' participation in anatomic and clinical pathology services, as well as through didactic lectures and conferences, and patient care-oriented interdisciplinary conferences. The combined anatomic/clinical pathology residency consists of 24 months each of required and elective rotations in both anatomic and clinical pathology. Anatomic pathology training includes rotations in surgical pathology, autopsy pathology, cytopathology, neuropathology, hematopathology, dermatopathology, forensic pathology, and other specialized areas. The resident plays a central role in each of these services, with abundant opportunities for review and signout of a very broad spectrum of common and uncommon disorders, presented in surgical and autopsy specimens, and exfoliative and aspiration cytology specimens. Immunohistochemistry and electron microscopy techniques are incorporated into other rotations or can be studied during elective time devoted to these areas. Clinical pathology training encompasses all areas of clinical pathology including chemistry, hematology, microbiology, virology, blood bank and transfusion medicine, immunology, HLA and cytogenetics. Approaches emphasize skills that lead to expertise in the ordering and interpretation of clinical laboratory tests, the analysis of laboratory use by individual and groups of physicians for effectiveness and cost, the use of computers for machine interface, communication with clinicians and the analysis of a wide range of laboratory programs and problems. Rotations are also provided in diagnostic molecular pathology and laboratory management, and additional formal and informal training in management skills addresses aspects of QA/QC/QI, and regulatory and inspection issues. Research elective time is also available. Efforts are also made to develop residents' teaching skills through mentored educational roles in conferences.

Three ACGME-accredited fellowship programs are offered by the department: Blood Banking/Transfusion Medicine, Dermatopathology, and Selective (Surgical/General) Pathology. See individual listings for additional information.

TYPES AND NUMBERS OF APPOINTMENTS

The program includes twelve resident positions. Approximately three PGY-1 positions are offered per year.

FACILITIES

The faculty, residents, hospital and research laboratories, conference rooms, and administrative offices are housed in the Penn State Milton S. Hershey Medical Center. The hospital has a capacity of approximately 500 beds. Facilities include a full spectrum of modern anatomic, clinical and molecular pathology laboratories that support clinical and research operations. Technologies available include light microscopy, fluorescence microscopy, electron microscopy, histochemistry, immunohistochemistry, in situ hybridization, tissue microarray preparation, cDNA microarray, PCR, autoradiography, tissue culture, flow cytometry, hematology, immunohematology, microbiology, radioimmunoassays, immunochemistry, enzymology, high pressure liquid chromatography, other molecular assays, and computerization. A system of institutional Core Laboratories offers a wide variety of additional technologies to support research. The 2008-2009 projected service volumes are 2,200,000 clinical laboratory tests; 85 autopsies; 42,000 surgical specimens; 22,000 cytology specimens; 1,200 bone marrow specimens; 2,200 fine needle aspiration specimens; 950 therapeutic apheresis procedures; and 150 peripheral blood hematopoietic stem cell collections.

COMMUNITY

Hershey, in the foothills of the Blue Ridge Mountains, is a community of approximately 20,000 people located approxiimately 12 miles away from Harrisburg, the state capital. Over one million people live within a fifty-mile radius of the medical center. Surrounded by rich farm lands and close to urban centers of the eastern seaboard, Hershey and environs have excellent educational and recreational programs and facilities, outstanding musical and stage performances, and numerous fine arts and cultural opportunities. Outdoor activities are readily available and include golf, swimming, fishing, hunting, mountain climbing, skiing, and ready access to the Appalachian Trail. Philadelphia, Baltimore, Washington, New York City, and the Pennsylvania Dutch country are just short distances by automobile or train. The Harrisburg International Airport (MDT) is 15 minutes away from Hershey, and airports in both Baltimore and Philadelphia are about 1.5 - 2.0 hours away by car.

STIPENDS AND MAINTENANCE

Salaries are comparable with salaries in the northeast as well as the rest of the United States, and residents are provided with professional liability insurance, health insurance, disability insurance, uniforms, laundry, and four weeks paid vacation per year. The Department also provides yearly stipends that can be used for support of continuing medical education expenses, dues and membership, books, and subscriptions.

STAFF

Dani S. Zander Chair and Residency Program Director; pulmonary pathology, cytopathology.

Anatomic Pathology

Catherine S. Abendroth MD (Director of Anatomic Pathology), fine needle aspiration cytology, nephropathology, surgical pathology; **Arthur B. Abt** MD nephropathology, surgical pathology; **Michael G. Bayerl** MD hematopathology, surgical pathology; **Loren E. Clarke** MD dermatopathology, surgical pathology; **Henry S. Crist** MD surgical pathology; **Elizabeth E. Frauenhoffer** MD orthopaedic pathology, surgical pathology, cytopathology; **Saralee Funke** MD forensic pathology (adjunct); **Bing Han** MD, PhD breast pathology, surgical pathology; **Klaus F. Helm** MD dermatopathology, dermatology; **Michael D. Iofredda** MD dermatopathology, dermatology; **John Liang** MD surgical pathology, gastrointestinal, liver, and pancreatic pathology; **Jozef Malysz** MD hematopathology; **Wayne Ross** MD forensic pathology (adjunct); **Francesca M. Ruggiero** MD gastrointestinal pathology, surgical pathology; **Joseph Sassani** MD ophthalmic pathology; **Charles S. Specht** MD neuropathology, opthalmic pathology; **Richard J. Zaino** MD gynecologic pathology, surgical pathology; **Shaobo Zhu** MD surgical pathology, cytopathology.

Clinical Pathology

Michael B. Bongiovanni MD (Director of Clinical Pathology), clinical pathology, therapeutic apheresis; **Peter C. Appelbaum** MD, PhD clinical microbiology, anaerobic microbiology; **William J. Castellani** MD clinical chemistry; **Laurence M. Demers** PhD endocrinology; **Ronald E. Domen** MD blood banking, transfusion medicine, therapeutic apheresis, histocompatibility, bioethics, medical education; **M. Elaine Eyster** MD hematology, flow cytometry; **Wallace H. Greene** PhD virology; **Roger Ladda** MD cytogenetics; **Thomas P. Nifong** MD hematology, coagulation, molecular diagnostics, therapeutic apheresis; **Witold Rybka** MD hematopoietic stem cell laboratory; **Hiroko Shike** MD histocompatibility.

Experimental Pathology

Keith C. Cheng MD, PhD (Division Chief of Experimental Pathology) genomic instability, tumor progression, zebrafish, melanogenesis; **Neil D. Christensen** PhD papilloma-virus immunology; **Gary Clawson** MD, PhD nuclear scaffold, HPV, HBV, ribozymes; **Kristin A. Eckert** PhD enzymology of DNA synthesis, DNA repair mechanisms, human cell mutagenesis; **Jan McAllister** PhD polycystic ovary syndrome; **David Mu** PhD cancer genomics.

APPLICATIONS

All applicants should apply through ERAS; applications will not be accepted through the mail. Additional information can be obtained on the Internet at www.hmc.psu.edu/pathology. Foreign medical graduates must be certified by the ECFMG. All applicants must be eligible for a Pennsylvania medical training license. An interview is required and is by invitation only.

Address inquiries to:

Dani S. Zander, MD, Chair of Pathology and Residency Program Director
Department of Pathology - H083, Penn State Milton S. Hershey Medical Center
500 University Drive, PO Box 850
Hershey, PA 17033-0850
Phone: (717) 531-8351 • **Web site:** http://www.hmc.psu.edu/pathology

The Penn State Milton S. Hershey Medical Center and College of Medicine of The Pennsylvania State University, Hershey, Pennsylvania

CONEMAUGH HEALTH SYSTEM

Johnstown, Pennsylvania

PROGRAMS OFFERED

The Pathology Residency Program is a four year accredited program that consists of combined training in Anatomic and Clinical Pathology. The program has been in place for more than 40 years and combines the sophistication of a university pathology experience with the service orientation of a community-based hospital. The collaborative design of our program enables us to achieve our primary objective: prepare graduates for competitive fellowships and productive careers in their chosen field.

Residents spend four years in the study of Anatomic Pathology and Clinical Pathology disciplines. Training is primarily at Conemaugh's Memorial Medical Center. University-based affiliate rotations include Pediatric Pathology, Dermatopathology, Renal Pathology/Electron Microscopy, Cytogenetics, Molecular Diagnostics, Transplant and Histocompatability. Research opportunities are available at a nearby research institute.

The Anatomic Pathology program includes training in Surgical Pathology, Forensic Pathology, Cytopathology, Neuropathology, Pediatric Pathology, Dermatopathology, Transplant Pathology and Renal Pathology/Electron Microscopy. In addition, senior residents are required to spend 30 weeks as a Junior Surgical Pathologist.

The Clinical Pathology program consists of closely supervised, self-paced studies in each division of the Clinical Laboratory. Residents act as Clinical Pathology consultants, and their responsibility for laboratory management and problem solving increases as their competence develops. A detailed curriculum, study guide and study materials are provided for each assignment. The training in Clinical Pathology consists of: Blood Bank/Transfusion Medicine, Clinical Chemistry, Cytogenetics, Hematopathology (including Flow Cytometry), Histocompatibility, Immunopathology (Including Serology), Microbiology, Molecular Diagnostics, Laboratory Information Systems, Laboratory Management. Senior residents are required to spend 22 weeks as a Clinical Pathologist.

Each resident is expected to have no fewer than four patient care-related projects in Anatomic and/or Clinical Pathology. At least two of these will be suitable for submission for publication in a peer review journal.

Pathology residents are required to attend at least 80% of all teaching conferences, including daily conferences, each on a different topic related to the residency, conferences to review interesting surgical cases, gross pathology reviews, formal clinicopathologic conference with the department of medicine; and many other interdepartmental and interdisciplinary conferences.

TYPES AND NUMBERS OF APPOINTMENTS

The Pathology Residency Program has 8 ACGME accredited positions in Anatomic and Clinical Pathology. Generally two PGY-1 positions are offered each year.

FACILITIES

Conemaugh Health System is the largest health care provider in west central Pennsylvania, serving families across 11 counties through our network of hospitals, physician offices, specialty clinics and other patient-focused programs. Through its members, the Conemaugh Health System offers a continuum of care and highly specialized services, including the Regional Heartcare Network; Regional Vascular Center; Regional Cancer Network; Regional Neuroscience Center; minimally invasive surgery; Regional Trauma Center; high-risk obstetrical care; Regional Intensive Care Nursery; and centers for breast care and cancer research. Over 4,500 employees of the Conemaugh Health System serve more than a half-million patients each year.

HealthGrades, the nation's leading healthcare ratings company, has ranked Conemaugh's Memorial Medical Center in the top five percent of all hospitals in the nation for clinical excellence for the past three years.

The Department of Laboratory Medicine is a recognized leader in pathology and laboratory computer science. Our staff pioneered the development of Sunquest Information Systems, a laboratory information system in use in hospitals around the globe. The clinical laboratory completes more than 2,000,000 tests each year, processes 18,000 Surgical specimens, 28,000 Cytologic specimens and 250 Autopsies annually.

COMMUNITY

Nestled in the spectacular Laurel Highlands region of the Allegheny Mountains, Johnstown's metropolitan area has a population of 232,621 and is a national leader in technology. There is a hometown feeling and quality of life in west central Pennsylvania that makes working, living and raising a family here special. With short commutes and one of the nation's lowest crime rates, most people live a comfortable life in affordable communities.

STIPENDS AND MAINTENANCE

All incoming PGY1 residents receive a total benefit package of $49,900. The benefit package for first year residents consists of an annual salary of $44,400, a one-time $5000 relocation stipend, and an educational allowance of $500. PGY2 residents receive $48,400; PGY3 residents receive $50,350; PGY4 residents receive $50,530. An annual $2000 educational allowance is provided in the second through fourth year of resident training. Chief Resident(s) receives up to $2,000 in addition to their annual educational allowance.

STAFF

Expertise of more than 425 active and courtesy physicians, represent 22 of the 24 American Boards of Medical Specialties. Faculty members bring extensive experience to their positions, often gained through clinical and research fellowships at some of the most renowned medical facilities in the country. Backed by the resources of the Conemaugh Health System, Memorial Medical Center and its residency programs provide today's physicians with the competitive skills and experience needed for a long, productive medical career.

Medical staff continuing education programs are open to resident physicians and offer a new schedule of rounds, seminars, conferences and visiting professorships each month, many of which are approved for continuing medical education credit.

Curtis Goldblatt MD, Director, Pathology Residency Program, Associate Medical Director Department of Laboratory Medicine; **Sidney A. Goldblatt** MD, Assistant Director, Pathology Residency Program, Medical Director, Department Laboratory Medicine; **Harold Ashcraft** MD, Chairman, Department of Laboratory Medicine; **Waheeb Rizkalla** MD, Associate Pathologist; **Manjunath Heggere** MD, Associate Pathologist; **Lian Qian** MD, PhD, Associate Pathologist.

APPLICATIONS

Residency candidates must be either a graduate of U.S. or Canadian schools or ECFMG certified foreign medical graduate. All applications must be submitted through ERAS (Electronic Residency Application Service) by December 1.

Address inquiries to:

Cindy Gregorich
Residency Training Program Coordinator
Department of Pathology
Conemaugh Valley Memorial Hospital
1086 Franklin Street, GS1252
Johnstown, PA 15905-4398
Phone: (814) 534-1624 • **E-mail:** cgregori@conemaugh.org
Web site: www.conemaugh.org

DREXEL UNIVERSITY COLLEGE OF MEDICINE

Philadelphia, Pennsylvania

PROGRAMS OFFERED

Drexel University College of Medicine offers an integrated four-year training program in anatomic and clinical pathology. The anatomic pathology section offers training in autopsy pathology, surgical pathology, cytopathology and neuropathology. Rotations at affiliated institutions include pediatric pathology and forensic pathology. The laboratory medicine section offers training in clinical chemistry including toxicology, hematology, transfusion medicine, coagulation pathology, cytogenetics and microbiology. Specialized training includes molecular pathology, electron microscopy, laboratory management, immunopathology, flow cytometry and informatics. Training in anatomic and clinical pathology are integrated throughout the program. Rotations in forensic pathology are conducted at the Office of the Medical Examiner of the City of Philadelphia. Rotations in Pediatric Pathology take place at St. Christopher's Hospital for Children. The primary research emphasis is on neoplasia, vascular biology and the biology of aging. Residents participate in teaching of pathology to medical students. In addition to departmental seminars and conferences, trainees also participate in clinical conferences. The training program will be structured according to individual need and may be oriented towards hospital service or academic pathology. The residency program is a flexible one organized around a basic core of rotations followed by elective research and/or clinical rotations. Research and elective programs are tailored to individual interests that develop during the core rotations. Career planning and preparation are stressed during all phases of the residency.

TYPES AND NUMBERS OF APPOINTMENTS

Twenty residency positions are available. Preference is given to applicants for the combined AP and CP program. There are two fellowship positions available in Cytopathology and one fellowship position available in Hematopathology.

FACILITIES

Drexel University College of Medicine has two clinical campuses with 700 beds and over 27,000 admissions per year, and an education/research campus. The laboratories are well equipped and the laboratory medicine section is highly automated. A computerized laboratory information system allows instantaneous data interchange between the various campuses. Research facilities include fully equipped laboratories for molecular biology, cell biology, electron microscopy, immunology and biochemistry. The departmental libraries contain commonly needed journals and books. The university library system, which has facilities on all campuses, has over 88,000 medical books and receives over 2,800 journals. A university-wide library information system links users on all campuses.

COMMUNITY

Hahnemann University Hospital is located in downtown Philadelphia (Center City). Philadelphia is a large metropolitan center with a wide variety of cultural and recreational facilities including museums, theaters, the Philadelphia Orchestra and numerous historical sites. Philadelphia is close to both seashore and mountain recreational areas. The Hahnemann Campus is easily accessible by public transportation from the Philadelphia suburbs. A variety of housing options for residents can found both downtown and in the adjacent suburbs.

STIPENDS AND MAINTENANCE

The salary (2008-2009) for first-year trainees is $44,280; second year $45,825; third year $47,312; fourth year $48,982; fifth year $50,721; sixth year $52,331 plus any increases that may be awarded by the administration. All residents are provided with professional liability insurance, uniforms, laundry service, parking and hospitalization insurance.

STAFF

Cheryl Hanau MD Chair, Director, Residency Program; cytopathology; **Xiaoli Chen** MD anatomic pathology, clinical pathology, cytopathology; **Gary Collins** MD forensic pathology, Medical Examiner's Office of Philadelphia; **J.P. deChadarevian** PhD pediatric pathology; **Christopher Emery** MD clinical microbiology; **James M. England** MD, PhD Autopsy Pathology; **Lorenzo Galindo** MD cytopathology, surgical pathology, fine needle aspiration; **Fernando Garcia** MD surgical pathology, cytopathology, breast and urologic pathology; **Sam Gulino** MD forensic pathology, Medical Examiner's Office of Philadelphia; **Marian Haber** MD surgical pathology, gastrointestinal pathology; **Ian Hood** MD forensic pathology, Medical Examiner's Office of Philadelphia; **J. Steve Hou** MD anatomic pathology, flow cytometry; **Gregg Johannes** PhD tumor biology; **Christos Katsetos** MD, PhD Neuropathology; **Frederick Kayne** PhD clinical chemistry, enzyme kinetics; **Cathy Litty** MD transfusion medicine; **Robert McAlack** PhD transplantation pathology; **Gregory McDonald** DO forensic pathology, Medical Examiner's Office of Philadelphia;

Jennifer Morrissette PhD cytogenetics and molecular genetics; **Robert Ownbey** MD surgical and autopsy pathology; **Judy M. Pascasio** MD pediatric pathology; **Prabha Patel** MD surgical pathology; **Nikolay Popnikolov** MD, PhD surgical pathology; **Hope Punnett** PhD cytogenetics; **Christian Sell** PhD Aging and signal transduction; **Suganthi Soundararajan** MD surgical pathology; **Mark Stearns** PhD tumor biology; **Vanlila K. Swami** MD hematopathology, transfusion medicine; **Min Wang** PhD tumor biology.

APPLICATIONS

Candidates must be graduates of U.S. or Canadian schools or eligible graduates of foreign medical schools. Candidates take part in the National Resident Matching Program. Applications are via ERAS.

Address inquiries to:

Cheryl A. Hanau, MD, Program Director
Department of Pathology and Laboratory Medicine
Drexel University College of Medicine
245 N. 15th Street, Mail Stop 435
Philadelphia, PA 19102
Phone: (215) 762-8375 • **Fax:** (215) 762-3274 • **E-mail:** chanau@drexelmed.edu

Hahnemann University Hospital

JEFFERSON MEDICAL COLLEGE AND THOMAS JEFFERSON UNIVERSITY HOSPITAL

Philadelphia, Pennsylvania

PROGRAMS OFFERED

The Department of Pathology, Anatomy and Cell Biology at Jefferson Medical College and Thomas Jefferson University Hospital offers a combined training program in anatomic pathology and clinical pathology. The program is designed with sufficient flexibility to provide suitable training for residents planning careers in academic medicine, in community practice, or for those planning to pursue further training in one of the subspecialty areas of pathology. Rotation assignments include surgical pathology, autopsy pathology, cytopathology, immunopathology, diagnostic electron microscopy, neuropathology, molecular diagnostics, chemical pathology, hematopathology, diagnostic microbiology, and laboratory management and administration. Special resources include flow cytometry, quantitative image analysis, and gas chromatography/mass spectrometry, molecular diagnostics laboratory, and laser capture facility. A rotation at the Philadelphia Medical Examiner's Office is part of the anatomic pathology experience. Training in transfusion medicine, blood banking and immunohematology is provided within the department and at the American Red Cross Blood Center. Throughout the program, residents are given increasing responsibilities including participation in various teaching programs and graded service responsibilities (see the departmental **Web site:** http://www.jefferson.edu/pathology/residency_training.cfm for details). The extensive translational research and educational programs and faculty investigators are described on the web site. The Department conducts a number of regularly scheduled intra-department conferences in all of the subspecialty areas of anatomic pathology and all areas of clinical pathology. In addition, elective rotations in areas such as informatics and laboratory management and administration are available. The program is designed around a 36-month core rotation that provides training and experience in all of the major areas of anatomic and clinical pathology. The fourth year is planned on an individual basis to assist each resident in selecting from the numerous educational activities in the Department, those most appropriate for his/her career objectives. Further experience in clinical medicine, research, or in-depth training in selected areas of pathology is available as elective rotations. A number of fellowships for specialized training are available including cytopathology and hematopathology, leading to sub-specialty Board eligibility. In addition, a joint surgical pathology fellowship is available at the Fox Chase Cancer Center. The Department is associated with Alfred I. DuPont Children's Hospital/Institute in Wilmington, Delaware and The Children's Hospital of Philadelphia and offers training in pediatric pathology. Thomas Jefferson's Department of Pathology is ranked eleventh nationally in NIH research funding.

TYPES AND NUMBERS OF APPOINTMENTS

The current staff consists of 15 residents in the AP/CP program and fellows in cytopathology and hematopathology. An affiliated surgical pathology fellowship program Fox Chase Cancer Center is available. Jefferson Medical College and Thomas Jefferson University Hospital offer residency and fellowship positions in 52 specialties and subspecialties.

FACILITIES

Thomas Jefferson University is situated on six square blocks in the Center City area of Philadelphia. Separate facilities have been provided for teaching, research, and patient care. A new Radiation Therapy Center, one of the most advanced of its kind in the country, is available. The Medical Center has a large Emergency Department facility, a new Outpatient Testing Center and an Ambulatory Practice facility that will be occupied in the near future. There is a fully equipped autopsy suite operated by the Department. Modern laboratories for surgical pathology and cytopathology were recently completed as well as new laboratories for immunopathology, cytogenetics, flow cytometry, and molecular pathology. The University Hospital has a total of 957 beds with 35,816 admissions in the most recent fiscal year, and had an average occupancy of 81.8%. Jefferson is affiliated with a number of hospitals in the Delaware Valley which constitute the Jefferson Health System, and maintains joint programs and special relationships with others. Pathology Department activities are housed in several buildings with a total of 70,000 square feet for laboratories and offices. Clinical Pathology Laboratories are located on three floors of the Foederer Pavilion. The Cytopathology and Surgical Pathology Laboratories are located on the second floor of two adjoining building. Teaching and research facilities are located in the College Building, Jefferson Alumni Hall, Pavilion, and the Kimmel Cancer Center. The Alcohol Research Center and other research laboratories occupy facilities in Jefferson Alumni Hall. Each resident is provided with a dedicated workstation and a PC with internet access. The department utilizes the CoPath plus information system and voice activated dictation. Last year, the number of autopsies performed was 123, surgical specimens 27,155, cytology cases 20,785, and over two million clinical laboratory tests. The Samuel Parsons Scott Memorial Library contains approximately 140,000 volumes and 1,800 journals and periodicals. Medical School enrollment for the current year is 1040.

COMMUNITY

Thomas Jefferson University Hospital is located in Center City Philadelphia, near a number of noted cultural institutions, scientific organizations, historic shrines, parks and recreation areas. These include the Philadelphia Orchestra, Pennsylvania Ballet, Independence National Historic Park (Independence Hall, the Liberty Bell, Betsy Ross House), first-run theatres, and major sport teams (Phillies, Eagles, Flyers, 76ers). The Center City area has undergone substantial renewal in the past 20 years and is the regional focus for shopping, theaters, restaurants, and entertainment. Philadelphia is within a short distance of seashore resorts and mountain recreation areas for activities such as swimming, boating, skiing, fishing, and hiking. Philadelphia is a center for prominent medical institutions; located nearby are four other teaching hospitals and medically-oriented commercial activities, and independent research institutes.

STIPENDS AND MAINTENANCE

First-year residents currently receive $45,500 per year with an increase for each subsequent year of training. Health insurance through Blue Cross/Blue Shield with major medical coverage is provided to house officers, spouses and dependent children at no charge. Alternatively, an approved HMO may be selected. Life insurance, travel insurance, and accident insurance are provided without charge. Laboratory coats and laundry service are provided as well. On-campus housing is available in the 20-story Orlowitz Residence Hall offering one, two, and three-bedroom apartments and in the Barringer Residence which provides efficiency one, two, or three-bedroom apartments. The Housing Information Service maintains information on non-university housing in the Philadelphia area.

STAFF

Stephen Peiper MD; Peter A. Herbut Professor and Chair,.

Professors

Fred Gorstein MD; **Marluce Bibbo** MD, Scd., Director, Cytopathology; **John L. Farber** MD, Pulmonary Pathology, Transplantation, Renal Pathology, Experimental Cell Injury; **Mark Feitelson** PhD, Molecular Microbiology; **Gene Gulati** PhD, Hematology, and Laboratory Automation; **Jay Herman** MD, Professor of Medicine and Pathology; **Renato V. Iozzo** MD, Director, Electron Microscopy; Connective Tissue and Proteoglycans; **Donald L. Jungkind** PhD, Director, Microbiology; Sexually Transmitted Diseases, Automation In Microbiology; **Peter A. McCue** MD, Director Anatomic Pathology/Surgical Pathology, Renal Pathology; **Juan Palazzo** MD, Breast and Gastrointestinal Pathology; **Emanuel Rubin** MD, Professor of Pathology; Hepatology, Alcohol Research, Biological Membranes; **Raphael Rubin** MD, Director, Liver and GI Pathology; **David S Strayer** MD, PhD, Experimental Pathology; **Richard R Schmidt** PhD, Gross Anatomy and Human Development; **Theodore F. Taraschi** PhD, Infectious Diseases, Malaria.

Associate Professors

Mary Cunnane MD, Surgical Pathology, Head and Neck Pathology; **Mark Curtis** MD, PhD, Neuropathology; **Lawrence Kenyon** MD, PhD, Neuropathology and Director, Autopsy Service; **Brian J. O'Hara** MD, Surgical Pathology; Soft Tissue and Bone Pathology.

Assistant Professors

Eric Behling MD, Hematopathology and Surgical Pathology; **Tina Edmonston** MD, Director, Molecular Pathology, Surgical Pathology; **Kocher D. William** MD, Director, Hematopathology/Immunopathology, Immunohistochemistry and Molecular Diagnosis; **Laura McCloskey** PhD, Immunopathology; **Agnieszka K. Witkiewicz** MD, Surgical Pathology, Dermatopathology and GYN; **Anthony Prestipino** MD, Surgical Pathology, GYN/GI Pathology; **Moira Wood** MD, Cytopathology,Immunocytochemistry; **Madalina Tuluc** MD, PhD, Surgical Pathology; **Sean Cote** DO, Director of Chemistry.

Voluntary Staff

Harvey J Bellin MD; **Katrina Conard** MD; **Harry Cooper** MD; **Ierachmiel Daskal** MD; **Hormoz Ehya** MD; **Benjamin Gerson** MD; **William V Harrer** MD; **Joseph P. Hostman** MD; **Albert A. Keshgegian** MD, PhD; **Geraldine Meny** MD; **Markku Miettinen** MD; **Scott Murphy** MD; **Arthur Patchefsky** MD; **Wayne K. Ross** MD; **Scott H. Saul** MD; **Nancy A. Young** MD.

APPLICATIONS

Residency candidates should be graduates of approved medical schools in the U.S. or Canada. Graduates of foreign medical school must have an ECFMG certificate. Satisfactory references are required. December 31st is the deadline for the submission of applications. The Department of Pathology participates in the National Resident Matching Program.

Address inquires to:

Fred Gorstein, MD, Director, Residency Training Program
Moira Wood, MD, Associate Director, Residency Training Program
c/o Mildred Figueroa, Coordinator, Residency Training Program
Thomas Jefferson University Hospital
125 S. 11th Street, Room 204 Pavilion Building
Philadelphia, PA 19107
Phone: (215) 503-3876 • **Fax:** (215) 955-2519
E-mail: mildred.figueroa@jeffersonhospital.org

Thomas Jefferson University Hamilton Education Building

PENNSYLVANIA HOSPITAL

Philadelphia, Pennsylvania

PROGRAMS OFFERED

A fully approved four-year training program in anatomic and clinical pathology and one-year fellowships in surgical pathology and soft tissue/bone pathology are available. The anatomic pathology training program provides basic instruction in autopsy and surgical pathology including the subspecialties of neuropathology, pediatric pathology, neonatal pathology, dermatopathology and cytology. In addition to the traditional methods of diagnosis, experience is provided in immunohistochemistry, flow cytometry, and in-situ hybridization that are related to diagnostic pathology. The clinical pathology program covers all the major disciplines including laboratory computers. The staff conducts the residency teaching program with emphasis on individual instruction. There are numerous hospital teaching conferences in which residents actively participate. Residents are encouraged to pursue investigative work. A flexible schedule of instruction accommodates the various individual needs of the residents. Completion of the training program prepares the resident for a career in either hospital or academic pathology.

This residency at Pennsylvania Hospital (PAH) is interactive with that at the Hospital of the University of Pennsylvania (HUP), with video connections for lectures and slide seminars, ability to attend lectures at HUP, and ability to complement training with rotations in special areas such as molecular diagnostics, neuropathology, hematopathology, gastrointestinal pathology and cytopathology. Both institutions are members of the same University of Pennsylvania Health System (UPHS).

TYPES AND NUMBERS OF APPOINTMENTS

Eight residencies are offered. Residents may enter the program in the first postgraduate year or after a year of clinical training. Well qualified residents with previous training in pathology are occasionally appointed at an advanced level. One-year fellowships in surgical pathology and soft tissue/bone pathology.

FACILITIES

The Pennsylvania Hospital is the nation's first hospital, founded in 1751. In 1997 Pennsylvania Hospital joined the University of Pennsylvania Health System to create a network of health care and clinical training unsurpassed in the region. Pennsylvania Hospital has 505 beds and 50 bassinets and over 19,000 annual admissions. All staff members hold faculty appointments at the School of Medicine. The Pathology Department conducts an approved school of medical technology. The laboratory has an annual volume of more than 1,000,000 clinical laboratory tests; 20 autopsies; 13,000 surgical and 2,000 cytology specimens. The technical and clerical staff numbers about 98. The laboratories are well equipped and highly automated. A new laboratory computer system employing the latest technology and encompassing both the anatomic and clinical laboratories has been installed. The pathology working library includes 300 volumes and current pathology journals. Additional texts and journals are available in the hospital library and through access to the libraries of the School of Medicine and the Philadelphia College of Physicians.

COMMUNITY

The hospital is situated in downtown Philadelphia. The city's medical schools, universities, historic sites and cultural centers are all easily accessible.

STIPENDS AND MAINTENANCE

At present (2008-2009), trainees receive $44,889.01for the first postgraduate year. Annual increments bring the stipend to $52,463.24at the fifth postgraduate year. Stipends are currently being reviewed and are increased from time to time in accordance with the cost of living. Professional liability insurance and health insurance are provided for the resident and immediate family. Meals are available at nominal charge.

STAFF

John S.J. Brooks MD (Jefferson Med Col 1974) Director; Professor of Pathology and Laboratory Medicine, Univ Pennsylvania Sch Med; general surgical pathology, soft tissue and bone pathology; **Julieta E Barroeta** MD (J.M. Vargas Sch Med 2000) Pathology; Clinical Associate of Pathology and Laboratory Medicine; surgical pathology, microbiology.; **Lisa Dwyer-Joyce** MD (Royal Col Surgeons, Ireland 1990) Pathologist; Clinical Associate of Pathology and Laboratory Medicine; cytopathology, surgical pathology; **Tunde A Farkas** MD (Univ Med Sch Debrecen, Hungary 1985) Pathologist Clinical Associate of Pathology and Laboratory Medicine; surgical pathology, cytopathology; **Jui-Han Huang** MD,PhD (Case Western Reserve Univ 1996) Pathologist; Clinical Associate of Pathology and Laboratory Medicine; surgical pathology, hematology; **Michael A. Husson** MD (Boston Univ 1976) Pathologist; Clinical Associate of Pathology and Laboratory Medicine; anatomic pathology, clinical chemistry, transfusion medicine.

APPLICATIONS

Candidates must be graduates of approved medical schools of the U.S. or Canada, or must hold an ECFMG certificate. Satisfactory references are required.

Address inquiries to:

Tunde A Farkas, MD
Director, Residency Training Program
Ayer Clinical Laboratory
Pennsylvania Hospital
8th and Spruce Streets
Philadelphia, PA 19107
Phone: (215) 829-6992 • **Fax:** (215) 829-7564 • **E-mail:** anmccl@pahosp.com
Anna Marie McClain, Residency Coordinator

The Historic Pine Building of Pennsylvania Hospital, the nation's first.

TEMPLE UNIVERSITY HOSPITAL

Philadelphia, Pennsylvania

PROGRAMS OFFERED

The Department of Pathology offers fully approved a four year program in combined anatomic and clinical pathology. The program is designed for the training of academic or community hospital-based pathologists. It recognizes the need for a graded increase in resident responsibility over the course of training in anatomic and clinical pathology, and has the flexibility to meet individual needs and special interests. Core rotations in anatomic pathology include those in surgical pathology, autopsy pathology, cytopathology, neuropathology, diagnostic electron microscopy, pediatric pathology and forensic pathology. Elective rotations in oral pathology and dermatopathology are also available. Core rotations in clinical pathology include those in chemistry, hematology, immunology, microbiology, transfusion medicine, and cytogenetics. Residents are encouraged to take advantage of opportunities in the Department for clinical or basic research. In addition to service activities, residents actively participate in the teaching of medical students, both in and outside of the classroom. The Department also offers a graduate program leading to PhD degree in Pathology.

TYPES AND NUMBERS OF APPOINTMENTS

There are 12 pathology residency positions funded by the hospital and available to qualified medical school graduates. The Temple University Hospital offers a total of 490 residency and fellowship positions in 37 specialties.

FACILITIES

Temple University Hospital is located on the University's Health Sciences campus, which also includes the Medical School, the Fels Institute for Cancer Research, the Thrombosis Research Center, the Cancer Center, and the Schools of Dentistry and Allied Health Professions. Also, the New Ambulatory Care Center. The 122,000-square-foot building will dramatically increase the amount of space available for Temple's rapidly expanding radiation oncology program. Other programs that are expected to occupy some of the space include Temple's surgery programs, Emergency Dept., and other ambulatory-based programs. The hospital has 635 beds with over 26,560 admissions yearly. It serves both as a primary care facility and as a tertiary referral center, and is a recognized center for heart, kidney, and bone marrow transplantation. The Department of Pathology received over 25,000 surgical specimens, (including nearly 1,600 cardiac specimens and 11,000 oral specimens), 9,800 cytology specimens, 140 autopsies (including pediatric cases), and performed 2,000,000 laboratory tests. Temple East also accessioned 6,000 surgical specimens. Special diagnostic laboratories include those for electron microscopy, immunohistochemistry in/situ hybridization, cytogenetics/molecular diagnosis, flow cytometry, and digital image analysis. Research laboratories are equipped for tissue culture and for research at the molecular level, including the use of recombinant DNA techniques. The department library contains specialized texts and journals as well as an on-line computerized literature search workstations; residents also have full privileges in the Medical School Library. Temple is now in the process of building a New Medical School. Temple also has a new lung facility.

COMMUNITY

Philadelphia combines the cultural amenities and atmosphere of a major urban center with the "livability" typical of smaller cities. It is home to a major symphony orchestra, a major ballet company, several theater companies, and four professional sports teams. With four major medical schools, Philadelphia is also known as a center for medical research and education.

STIPENDS AND MAINTENANCE

Salaries generally increase yearly and have been set at the following levels for fiscal year 2006- 2007; PGY1: $45,358; PGY2:$46,719; PGY3:$47,967; PGY4:$49,679; PGY5:$51,537. Residents are provided with professional liability insurance, health insurance, and other fringe benefits. PGY 1 residents receive 2 weeks vacation per year; all other house staff receive 3 weeks vacation/year.

STAFF

Professors

Yuri Persidsky MD (Kiev State Medical Institute 1978) PhD (Pathology, Kiev Research Institute of Urology and Nephrology 1984) Chairperson, Department of Pathology and Laboratory Medicine; Surgical Pathology, Nephropathology, Microbiology; research: Blood-brain barrier protection in HIv-1 infection of th brain and its associated neurodegeneration, Peroxisome Prolifertor-Activated Receptor (PPAR) y-mediated neuroprotection against HIV-1 and alcohol injury of central nervous system (CNS), Alcohol Abuse and HIV-1: Mechanisms of Combined CNS injury and Interventions, Neural progenitor cell migration across blood brain barrier and Combined effects of HIV-1 and methamphetamine in the CNS; **Rebecca M. Thomas** MBBS (Christian Med Col, Vellore, India, 1982) Vice Chairperson of Clinical

Services, Department of Pathology and Laboratory Medicine; Director of Surgical Pathology. gastrointestinal pathology, hepatopathology; research:hepatitis C.; **Raghbir S. Athwal** PhD (Univ Missouri 1971) analysis of human genome, transacting host genes for viral infections; research: tumor suppressor genes and mechanisms of neoplastic tumor progression; **Sow-Yeh Chen** DMD (Univ Taiwan 1965) PhD (Univ Illinois 1972) surgical oral pathology, electron microscopy; research: pathobiology of oral epithelium; **Nahum J. Duker** MD (Univ Illinois 1966) autopsy pathology; research: DNA repair; **Stephen H. Leech** MB, ChB, PhD (Univ Edinburgh, UK 1965, (Univ Col London 1976) Directot of clinical immunology; research: immunocytogenetics, flow cytometry; **Gordon Pringle** DDS, PhD (Univ Alberta, Canada 1976, 1985) oral pathology; research: immunohistochemistry, connective tissue biochemistry; **Carmen Sapienza** PhD (Dalhousie Univ, Canola 1982) research: genetic imprinting and human carcinogenesis; **Allan L. Truant** PhD (Univ Oregon 1977) Director of clinical microbiology, immunology, virology; research: antibiotics and chemotherapy, rapid diagnostic tests, persistent viral infection.

Associate Professors

Mark P. Birkenbach MD (Columbia Univ Col Physicians and Surgeons 1982) Renal Pathology; **Jasvir Khurana** MBBS (All India Inst Med Sci 1982) surgical pathology, bone diseases; **Hemant Parekh** PhD (Bombay Univ 1990) Director of molecular diagnostics; research: Resistance to taxol chemotherapy; **Charalambos Solomides** MD, DMSci (Friedrich Wilhelm Bonn, Germany 1988, 1991) surgical and cytopathology; research: lung pathology in COPD; **John Wurzel** MD (Univ Pennsylvania 1978) Director of autopsy pathology, endocrine pathology, cytogenetics; research: cardiac myocyte proliferation and differentiation.

Assistant Professors

Ruth C. Birbe MD (Central Univ of Venezuela 1995) surgical and cytopathology; **Andrew Czulewicz** MD (Harvard Med Sch 1974) Jeanes Hospital-blood bank, surgical pathology; **Heba Durra** MD (Univ of Jordon/Faculty of Medicine 1997) surgical; **Yajue Huang** MD, PhD (Shanghai Second Med Univ 1992, Univ of Sciences, Philadelphia 1996) surgical and cytopathology; **Matthew Hurford** MD (Indiana Univ 1995) hematopathology, flow cytometry; **Susan A. Inniss** MD (UMDNJ 1986) Director Pathology, Northeastern Hospital; surgical pathology, cytopathology, pediatric pathology; **Ming Jin** PhD (City University of New York 2002) Director of Clinical Chemistry. Clinical laboratory methods for the diagnosis oif endocrine diseases; **Adil I. Khan** PhD (Imperial Col Sch of Med 2000) Clinical Chemistry; **Irma Palazzo** MD (Univ Nacionan de Cordoba 1982) Chairperson, Jeanes Hospital-Pathology; surgical pathology, hematopathology; **Raghava Potula** MHA (Kasturba Medical College, Manipal, India 1995) PhD (Jawaharial Nehru Institute of Postgraduate Medical Education and Research, Pondicherry, India 2001)clinical microbiology and infectious disease; **Servio H Ramirez** MS, PhD, (University of Rochester School of Medicine and Dentistry 2004) research:Cerebral vascular biology, Molecular/signaling mechanisms leading to the Blood Brain Barrier and HIV-1 neuropathogenesis; **Hina A Sheikh** MBBS(The Aga Khan Univ Medical College1998) surgical and dermpathology; **Xinmin Zhang** MD (Sun Yat-sen Univ Med Sci 1982) surgical and cytopathology.

APPLICATIONS

Applications are received through the Electronic Residency Application Service (ERAS). Applications should be submitted by September 1, prior to the July 1 starting date. Applications for other starting dates also will be considered. Candidates must be graduates of LCGME-approved medical schools in the U.S. or Canada, or hold a valid ECFMG certificate.

Address inquiries to:

Matthew T. Hurford, MD, Resident Director
Department of Pathology and Laboratory Medicine
3401 North Broad Street
Philadelphia, PA 19140
Phone: (215) 707-7740 • **Fax:** (215) 707-2053

UNIVERSITY OF PENNSYLVANIA MEDICAL CENTER

Philadelphia, Pennsylvania

PROGRAMS OFFERED

The Department of Pathology and Laboratory Medicine offers a three year training program in anatomic pathology only and clinical pathology only, and a four year training program in combined anatomic and clinical pathology. Residents are encouraged to spend at least one additional year working in the area of clinical or basic research. The programs are individually tailored for those interested in an investigative and academic career as well as those primarily interested in some aspect of the clinical practice of pathology. The core program for anatomic pathology includes medical pathology (autopsy), surgical pathology and cytopathology while clinical pathology includes chemistry, microbiology, hematology/hematopathology, coagulation, transfusion medicine, molecular diagnosis and immunology. The research work may be performed within the department, with an appropriate preceptor in another department, or in one of our affiliated institutions such as the Wistar Institute. The Resident Education and Advisory Committee/HUP (REACH) review each resident's goals and performance periodically. This Committee will help define a plan for advanced training years which best meet the individual goals and talents of the resident. This program has been designed to prepare each individual for the clinical practice of anatomic or clinical pathology in a given subspecialty area and to provide the foundation in experimental approaches for future career development. The research activities of the department cover all areas of morphology, cell biology, biochemistry, and immunology with specifics in immunobiology, neurobiology, membrane biology, surface receptors, nucleic acid metabolism, cancer, hormone action, enzymology, plasma proteins, immunopathology, gynecologic, gastrointestinal, pulmonary and dermatopathology. Each resident will engage in a supervised program of graduate teaching opportunities at the medical school that will involve primarily small group teaching experience. The residents are involved in weekly teaching conferences covering such topics as laboratory medicine aspects of case material, surgical pathology, medical pathology (autopsy) and cytology. Approximately one and one-half hours a day are spent in formal or informal conferences. Fellowship positions are available in surgical pathology, neuropathology, cytopathology, blood banking/transfusion medicine, GI/Liver pathology, hematology/hematopathology, microbiology, chemistry, coagulation and molecular genetic pathology.

TYPES AND NUMBERS OF APPOINTMENTS

A total of 30 positions from the first to fourth year are available which may be entered either from medical school or after training in another medical specialty. Additional fellowship positions are available in many areas of study.

FACILITIES

A voluntary, nonprofit general hospital, the University Hospital is one of six in the University of Pennsylvania Medical Center. It has763 beds and 57 bassinets. There were approximately 38,213 admissions for the fiscal year 2008. The Medical School library contains nearly 180,000 volumes, subscribes to over 2,950 journals, and is at the disposal of the residents. Complete interlibrary loan and bibliographic services are available. In addition, the Department's Residents Room contains computers with modems for rapid literature searches. During 2007, over 7,250,000 clinical pathology procedures, approximately 32,460 (33,000) surgical pathology specimen examinations, 288 (280) autopsies, and 350 (320) electron microscopy examinations, and 34,186 (37,000 Total Cytology Specimen) (including 9,446 non-GYN and 2,214FNAs) cytology examinations were performed.

COMMUNITY

The Hospital of the University of Pennsylvania is 5 minutes from center city Philadelphia by car or public transportation. The Philadelphia Museum of Art, Academy of Music, Academy of Natural Sciences, Independence Hall, Franklin Institute and the 4,000-acre Fairmount Park are some of the historical and cultural attractions of the city.

STIPENDS AND MAINTENANCE

The salary for the first year of postgraduate training during 2007-08 was approximately $46,235 with increases with progression through the residency. There is a generous benefits package, including maternity/paternity leave and professional liability insurance. Two weeks vacation is provided the first year, and four weeks for subsequent years.

STAFF

Besides the full-time staff, approximately 100 additional affiliated or part-time staff participate in teaching and provide training and research opportunities in such areas as forensic, community hospital, and pediatric pathology.

J.E. Tomaszewski MD Interim Chair, Co-Vice Chair Anatomic Pathology; surgical pathology, renal and genitourinary pathology; **N.K. Gonatas** MD Vice Chair Academics; endocytosis and transport of macromolecules in the nervous system; **D.E. Elder** MB, ChB Vice Chair Anatomic Pathology; surgical pathology, dermatopathology, melanocytic neoplasms; **D.S. Young** MD, PhD Vice Chair Laboratory Medicine; development of diagnostic tests; **D.B. Cines** MD Co-Vice Chair, Laboratory Medicine; hematopathology, plasminogen activators, endothelial cell biology; **M. Greene** MD, PhD Vice Chair Immunobiology and Experimental Pathology; cell surface receptors and the immune response; **D.L. Siegel** MD, PhD Vice Chair, Transfusion Medicine; recombinant expression of human auto- and alloantibodies using phage display; **A. Bagg** MD hematopathology; **D. Baldwin** PhD Director, Microarray Facility; **Z. Baloch** MD, PhD cytopathology; **F.G. Barr** MD, PhD genetic basis of neoplasia; **L. Bekeris** MD Director Phoenixville Hospital & Community Pathology; laboratory management; **C. Cambor** MD Education Coordinator; medical pathology; **M. Cancro** PhD immunobiology of B cells; **D. Carlow** MD, PhD clinical chemistry; **J.K. Choi** MD, PhD hematopathology; **P.F. Davies** PhD Institute Medicine and Engineering; experimental pathology, molecular mechanisms of atherogenesis; **Kimberly Dumoff** MD GYN pathology; **P.H. Edelstein** MD clinical microbiology, infectious diseases, legionella; **L. Ernst** MD pediatric pathology; **M.D. Feldman** MD, PhD surgical pathology, informatics; **F. Fogt** MD, PhD Co-director, Presbyterian Hospital; GI pathology; **D. Frank** MD surgical pathology and hematopathology; **E.E. Furth** MD surgical pathology, GI pathology; **G. Gaulton** PhD lymphocyte membrane receptors and growth regulation; **J. Golden** MD pediatric neuropathology; **P. Gupta** MD cytopathology, cytometry and biomarkers; **M. Guttenberg** MD pediatric pathology; **D. Huff** MD pediatric pathology; **L. Jarett** MD mechanisms of insulin action and membrane receptors; **Bo Jian** MD Cytology/Surgical pathology. Presbyterian Hospital; **B. Johnson** MD, PhD immunology; **A. Judkins** MD pediatric neuropathology; **C. June** MD Director of Translational Research, Abramson Family Cancer Research Institute; **M. Kamoun** MD, PhD immunology, biology of T-lymphocyte growth and differentiation; **G. Koretzky** MD, PhD Director of Signal Transduction, Abramson Family Cancer Research Institute; **L. Kricka** PhD clinical chemistry, analytical techniques and instrumentation; **P. Lal** MD renal pathology; **J. Lambris** PhD protein biosynthesis; **F. Lee** MD, PhD signal transduction in activation of NF-kB and JNK pathways; **V.M. Lee** PhD cell biology of neuronal cytoskeleton monoclonal antibodies and protein biochemistry; **L.A. Litzky** MD medical pathology, surgical pathology; **V.A. LiVolsi** MD surgical pathology, endocrine and thyroid pathology; **N. Luning Prak** MD, PhD regulation of mobile DNA in somatic cells; **M.S. Marks** PhD immunology of B cells; **S. Master** MD, PhD clinical chemistry and proteomics; **C. McGrath** MD cytopathology; **C. Mies** MD breast pathology; **Michael Milone** MD, PhD Clinical Chemistry; **K. Montone** MD surgical pathology; **J. Moore** PhD B-cell neoplasia, autoimmunity and receptors; **Z. Mourelatos** MD, Vice Chair - neuropathology; **I. Nachamkin** MPH, DrPH clinical microbiology, molecular diagnosis, pathogenesis of campylobacter infections; **P.C. Nowell** MD tumor chromosomes, biology of normal and neoplastic lymphocytes; **U. O'Doherty** MD, PhD transfusion medicine; **M. Paessler** DO hematopathology; **B. Pawel** MD pediatric pathology; **W.S. Pear** MD, PhD molecular mechanisms involved in leukemogenesis; **Heather Peterman** MD gastrointestinal/hepatic pathology; **E. Pollak** MD coagulation, transcriptional regulation of vitamin K-dependent clotting factors; **L.B. Rorke-Adams** MD pediatric neuropathology; **E. Ruchelli** MD pediatric pathology; **P. Russo** MD pediatric pathology; **B. Sachais** MD, PhD biology and structure of platelet factor 4; **W.E. Schlaepfer** MD biochemistry and neuropathobiology of neuofilaments; **Antonia R Sepulveda** MD, PhD, Director Of Surgical Pathology/ GI Path; **D. Sesok-Pizzini** MD Associate Director, Blood Bank and Transfusion Medicine; **L.M. Shaw** PhD clinical toxicology, drug/protein interactions, sulfhydryl metabolism; **S. Shelat** MD, PhD hematology; **J.Q. Trojanowski** MD, PhD adsorptive endocytosis of toxins in the CNS and neuronal connectivity; **V. Van Deerlin** MD, PhD Associate Director, Molecular Pathology; **M. A. Wasik** MD hematopathology; **D. Weiner** PhD biology of HIV; **R.B. Wilson** MD, PhD transcription factors in hematopoiesis; **G.X. Xu** MD, PhD melanoma progression and skin stem cell biology; **G.H. Yu** MD cytopathology, fine needle aspiration, director of residency program; **P.J.L. Zhang** MD surgical pathology, soft tissue pathology; **X. Long Zheng** MD, PhD coagulation.

APPLICATIONS

Residency candidates must be graduates of approved medical schools in the U.S. or Canada, or graduates of foreign medical schools with ECFMG, VQE, or USMLE certificates with one full year of rigorous full-time in-hospital clinical experience in the U.S. Satisfactory references are required. Appointments are for a one-year period with automatic continuation of the appointment if the resident's work is satisfactory. Applications must be received via ERAS prior to November 15. The residency year starts approximately June 18th, with rare exceptions.

Address inquiries to:

Gordon Yu, MD, Director, Residency Training Program
c/o Mary Ann Broda
Department of Pathology and Laboratory Medicine
University of Pennsylvania Medical Center
3400 Spruce Street
Philadelphia, PA 19104-4283
Phone: (215) 662-6523 • **E-mail:** brodam@uphs.upenn.edu
Web site: http://pathology.uphs.upenn.edu

ALLEGHENY GENERAL HOSPITAL

Pittsburgh, Pennsylvania

PROGRAMS OFFERED

A fully approved four-year training program for residents is available in anatomic and clinical pathology. The Department of Pathology and Laboratory Medicine includes the divisions of anatomic and clinical pathology. The program in anatomic pathology includes training in surgical pathology, autopsy pathology, renal pathology, neuropathology, fine needle aspiration and general cytology, electron microscopy and immunohistochemistry. A rotation at the Allegheny County Medical Examiner's Office provides training in forensic pathology. Pediatric surgical and autopsy pathology experience is acquired through a rotation at a children's hospital. Clinical chemistry, hematology, endocrinology, molecular diagnostics, blood banking/transfusion medicine, microbiology, virology, cytogenetics and immunology are areas of training in clinical pathology. The programs in anatomic and clinical pathology are integrated throughout the training period. Residents actively participate in regularly scheduled interdepartmental clinicopathologic correlation conferences with internal medicine, surgery, radiology, pediatrics and obstetrics/gynecology. A didactic lecture series, as well as morning and afternoon conferences, cover a broad range of topics in anatomic and clinical pathology, including laboratory management, computerization and quality assurance. Research is encouraged. The residents may participate in teaching medical students who rotate to Allegheny General Hospital from various medical schools. Fellowships are available in cytopathology, and surgical pathology.

TYPES AND NUMBERS OF APPOINTMENTS

A total of 10 residency positions and 3 fellowship positions (surgical pathology and cytopathology) are offered.

FACILITIES

The Allegheny General Hospital is an 698-bed teaching hospital and a referral-oriented, tertiary institution with active general surgical, breast, urologic, GI/liver, gynecologic, neurosurgical, oncology, neurology and pulmonary disease services. In 2007, approximately 85 autopsies were performed, not including the over 1,000 autopsies performed at the Medical Examiner's Office. Over 18,000 surgical specimens and 20,000 cytology specimens were processed. The clinical laboratories are modern and automated with over 3 million laboratory tests performed annually and a staff which includes over 200 technical and nontechnical personnel. The clinical laboratory is the core lab for the six-hospital system where all specialized and non-time dependent testing is performed. In addition to numerous clinicopathologic conferences, the department has didactic lecture series in clinical pathology and daily surgical pathology and weekly cytology conferences. Research facilities include fully equipped laboratories for electron microscopy, flow cytometry, laser cytometry, histocompatibility, immunohistochemistry, cytogenetics, and molecular diagnostics.

COMMUNITY

Pittsburgh is a modern, dynamic city with a metropolitan population of approximately 1.4 million. The city provides excellent educational and cultural opportunities, including museums, art galleries, the world renowned Pittsburgh Symphony, Pittsburgh Ballet, and regional professional theater companies. Heinz Field is home to the Pittsburgh Steelers and PNC Park for the Pittsburgh Pirates and the Pittsburgh Penguins play hockey at the Mellon Arena. Downhill skiing is within a short driving distance and opportunities for water sports abound with the Allegheny, Monongahela, and Ohio Rivers which define the ''Golden Triangle'' of the downtown area. Pittsburgh has received many awards and recognitions for its accomplishments and achieved the ''most livable city' recognition, being the only city to place among the top five communities in the past three editions of Places Rated Almanac. Factored into these ratings are the city's low housing cost, strong cultural community, stable neighborhoods, diversified economy, moderate climate, low crime rate and strong educational and medical communities.

STIPENDS AND MAINTENANCE

The first-year resident receives $43,043 with annual increments to $46,336 for fifth-year resident. Also provided free of charge are parking, meal vouchers, lab coats, and a variety of insurances. A yearly $1,000 fund is provided for each resident for books, tuition and expenses for national meetings during the residency. The department also funds residents who are first authors on abstracts and presentations accepted at national meetings. Benefits also include an annual three-week vacation.

STAFF

Jan F. Silverman MD (Med Col Virginia 1970) Chairman and Director of Anatomic Pathology, Department Pathology and Laboratory Medicine; surgical pathology, fine needle aspiration biopsy, cytopathology; **Ali Darabi** PhD (Southern Illinois Univ Sch Med 1992) Director Microbiology and Molecular Diagnostics; **Sydney Finkelstein** MD (McGill Univ, Montreal 1977) Adjunct Faculty, Professor; molecular diagnostics; **Katherine M. Jasnosz** MD (SUNY at Buffalo 1980) Director Autopsy Pathology; surgical pathology, perinatal pathology, ob/gyn pathology, renal pathology, forensic pathology; **Mark Kranc** PhD (Memphis State Univ 1976) Director Clinical Chemistry; chemistry, toxicology; **Yulin Liu** MD, PhD (Hunan Med Univ, China) cytology, fine needle aspiration, surgical pathology, pulmonary pathology; **Girija Nathan** MD (Stanley Med Col 1969) surgical pathology, breast pathology, gastrointestinal pathology; **Peter R. Olson** MD (Univ Minnesota 1969) Director Clinical Pathology; surgical pathology, urologic pathology, transfusion medicine; **Telma Pereira** MD (Univ Brasilia 1997) cytopathology, surgical pathology, pulmonary pathology, molecular diagnostics; **Cunfeng (Frank) Pu** MD, PhD (Xuzhou Med Col 1984) Director of Neuropathology, surgical pathology; **Kun Ru** MD, PhD (Shandong Med Univ, China 1992) Director Hematology and Flow Cytometry, surgical pathology; **Darrell Triulzi** MD (Albany Med Col 1985) transfusion medicine.

APPLICATIONS

Residency candidates must be graduates of either an approved medical or osteopathic school in the United States or Canada. Graduates of foreign medical schools must have an ECFMG certificate. Satisfactory references are required. Our hospital participates in the matching program so that applications must be received by December 1. July 1 is the beginning date for the residency program although other dates will deserve consideration.

Address inquiries to:

Katherine M. Jasnosz, MD
Director of Pathology Residency Program
Allegheny General Hospital
320 East North Avenue
Pittsburgh, PA 15212
Phone: (412) 359-6037 • **Fax:** (412) 359-3598
Web site: http://www.wpahs.org/education/graduate/fellowships.html

Allegheny General Hospital, Pittsburgh, Pennsylvania

UNIVERSITY OF PITTSBURGH

Pittsburgh, Pennsylvania

PROGRAMS OFFERED

A four year training program is offered in combined Anatomic and Clinical Pathology, and three year programs in straight Anatomic Pathology (AP) or straight Clinical Pathology (CP). AP or CP may be combined with selected subspecialty fellowship areas as designated by the American Board of Pathology to allow training adequate for Board certification in both areas in a four year training program. Single track certification training in straight AP or straight CP is considered for in-depth academic focus including mentorship, clinical research training opportunities and elective time structured to promote the pursuit of an academic career. Combined anatomic and clinical pathology (AP/CP) is the core training component of the program committed to training across a broad base of pathology. In-depth training in Anatomic Pathology covers autopsy pathology, cytopathology and general plus subspecialty surgical pathology to include bone and soft tissue pathology, dermatopathology, forensic pathology, gastrointestinal pathology, genitourinary pathology, gynecologic and breast pathology, perinatal pathology, head and neck pathology, hematopathology, neuropathology, ophthalmic pathology, pediatric pathology, pulmonary pathology, renal pathology and electron microscopy, molecular anatomical pathology, and transplant pathology. In-depth training in Clinical Pathology covers blood banking, general and special chemistry, hemostasis, hematopathology and laboratory hematology, clinical immunology and tissue typing, clinical microbiology and virology, and transfusion medicine. All residents receive broad-based training in molecular diagnostics and cytogenetics, pathology informatics and principles of laboratory management. Training rotations are based on a Center of Excellence format. A wide range of elective experiences are available including molecular anatomic pathology, applied and basic research, in-depth experiences in selected areas of general and subspecialty pathology toward enabling the resident to be more competitive for fellowship training and administrative experiences. Senior electives are a component of progressive responsibility that is structured to serve the individual needs of a resident within applicable guidelines. An additional year of supported research time is offered on a competitive basis for residents interested in pursuing an independently funded research career. The Department offers formal fellowship training in at least a dozen subspecialty areas of pathology. MD PhD candidates may qualify for an extra one-year research opportunity. A full range of opportunities in the Department and at UPMC can be found in the Department's Web site http://path.upmc.edu

TYPES AND NUMBERS OF APPOINTMENTS

Currently we are accredited by the ACGME for thirty-three positions. Over the past few years we have on average been staffed with thirty residents. The vast majority of residents enter at the PGY1 level; higher-level resident positions are occasionally available.

FACILITIES

The University of Pittsburgh Medical Center (UPMC), located adjacent to the University of Pittsburgh in the Oakland section of Pittsburgh, is the major academic medical center serving central and western Pennsylvania, northern West Virginia and eastern Ohio. An outstanding volume and breadth of experience is obtained through training in five core general and subspecialty hospitals with a total bed capacity of 2,045. UPMC Presbyterian University Hospital, the home of many national and internationally recognized programs, is the major academic hospital and houses many subspecialty areas and research programs in the Department. UPMC Shadyside Hospital, adjacent to the NCI-funded comprehensive Hillman Cancer Center offers excellent exposure to the diversity of material and demands associated with a hospital combining academic medicine and premier community practice as well as outstanding subspecialty training in several areas. Magee-Womens Hospital of UPMC offers an unparalleled experience in cytopathology, gynecologic, breast and perinatal pathology. The Veterans Affairs Medical Center and the Children's Hospital of Pittsburgh provide excellent exposure to geriatric and pediatric pathology. Over 100 faculty at these sites are members of the Department. UPMC has been repeatedly judged among the 'best of the best' hospitals in America in U.S. News and World Report. The University and Medical Center as well as the Department rank among the top seven sites for NIH-funded research with active programs in basic and transplant immunology, cardiovascular biology, neurosciences, cancer biology and genetics, gene therapy, and many other fields. Over 100,000 surgical specimens, 160,000 cytology specimens, 400 autopsies, and 8,000,000 clinical tests were evaluated in primary residency training sites during 2008. Residents receive training in forensic pathology at the Allegheny County Medical Examiner's Office.

COMMUNITY

Hailed repeatedly in surveys as one of America's most livable cities, Pittsburgh no longer produces steel but has transitioned into a center with a diverse service economy featuring a large number of major corporate headquarters. Western Pennsylvanians are gracious and friendly, even when cheering professional sports franchises in baseball, football and hockey or college teams. Among the most beautiful cities in the United States, Pittsburgh offers an interesting blend of rivers, bridges, skyscrapers, hills, tunnels, distinctive public buildings, and affordable and safe neighborhoods. Recreational opportunities lie close by including excellent skiing, hiking, fishing, camping, boating, kayaking and white-water rafting; very few areas can boast as interesting or challenging a diversity of private and public golf courses. A rich array of cultural opportunities includes the Carnegie Museums and Library, vigorous theater programs, and the world-class Pittsburgh Symphony and Pops Orchestras.

STIPENDS AND MAINTENANCE

The 2009-2010 schedule of remuneration for graduate medical trainees at UPMC is anticipated to be: PGY1-$46,716, PGY2-$47,985, PGY3-$48,900, PGY4-$49,982. Health, life, disability, and professional liability insurance are provided along with parking, surgical scrub outfits, and lab coats. All residents receive a laptop computer, which they take with them upon graduation. A $1,000 fund is provided annually to each resident for books, dues, conference travel, and other purposes. Attendance at national meetings is also supported for residents presenting investigative results. Trainees are reimbursed for application fees to take the American Board of Pathology Certification examinations following the final year. Maternity leave is covered under short-term disability.

STAFF

A complete roster of Department of Pathology faculty, listed alphabetically or by Division, can be found at http://path.upmc.edu/people.html.

Professors

George Michalopoulos MD, PhD Chairman; hepatic and transplant pathology, growth factors and liver regeneration; **R. Marshall Austin** MD gynecologic pathology, cytopathology; **E. Leon Barnes** MD head and neck pathology; **Michael Becich** MD, PhD informatics; **Harry Blair** MD bone physiology/pathology; **David Dabbs** MD breast pathology, cytopathology; **Anthony Demetris** MD transplant, liver pathology; **Rene Duquesnoy** PhD immunopathology; **Ronald Jaffe** MD pediatric pathology; **Mirka Jones** MD gynecologic pathology; **Anisa L. Kanbour** MD, ChB cytology, obstetrical/gynecological pathology; **Amal Kanbour-Shakir** MD, PhD obstetrical/gynecologic pathology; **Jeffrey Kant** MD, PhD molecular diagnostics, genetics; **Trevor Macpherson** MD perinatal pathology; **Mona Melhem** MD hematopathology; **Michael Nalesnik** MD transplant pathology, lymphoproliferative disorders; **Yuri Nikiforov** MD, PhD molecular anatomic pathology; **N. Paul Ohori** MD cytopathology, fine needle aspiration; **Bruce Rabin** MD, PhD immunopathology; **Parmjeet Randhawa** MD transplant pathology; **Uma Rao** MD bone, soft tissue pathology, melanoma; **Miguel Reyes-Mugica** MD pediatric pathology; **Charles R. Rinaldo, Jr.** PhD viral immunology, AIDS; **Stephen Strom** PhD liver biology; **Steven Swerdlow** MD hematopathology; **Darrell Triulzi** MD transfusion medicine, coagulation; **Guiliana Trucco** MD gynecologic pathology; **Mohamed A. Virji** MD, PhD clinical chemistry; **Robert Wadowsky** ScD microbiology; **Alan Wells** MD, DMS clinical pathology, cell motility, cancer biology; **Clayton Wiley** MD, PhD neuropathology; **Cary Wu** PhD extracellular matrix; **Xiao-Ming Yin** MD, PhD molecular diagnostics, programmed cell death; **Samuel Yousem** MD pulmonary, mediastinal pathology; **Abdolreza Zarnegar** PhD cellular and molecular pathology; **Adriana Zeevi** PhD immunopathology.

Associate Professors

Sheldon Bastacky MD nephropathology, genitourinary pathology; **Gary Blank** PhD biochemical structural analysis, informatics; **Robert Bowser** PhD brain development, neurodegenerative diseases; **Gloria Carter** MD gynecologic pathology, cytopathology; **Charleen Chu** MD, PhD neuropathology, ophthalmic pathology; **Lydia Contis** MD hematopathology; **Fiona Craig** MD hematopathology; **Rajiv Dhir** MD genitourinary pathology, tissue banking; **Raymond Felgar** MD hematopathology; **Roy Frye** MD, PhD cellular and molecular pathology; **Dmitriy Gutkin** MD immunopathology, anatomic pathology; **Ronald Hamilton** MD neuropathology; **Sikandar Katyal** PhD biochemical pathology, pulmonary biology; **Walid Khalbuss** MD genitourinary pathology; **Alyssa Krasinskas** MD gastrointestinal pathology; **Shih-Fan Kuan** MD, PhD gastrointestinal pathology; **William LaFramboise** PhD genitourinary pathology, molecular diagnostics, genetics; **Geoffrey Murdoch** MD, PhD neuropathology; **Zoltan Oltvai** MD molecular diagnostics; **Tim Oury** MD, PhD molecular diagnostics, oxidative injury; **Alka Palekar** MD surgical, cytopathology; **William Parks** MD perinatal pathology; **Anil Parwani** MD, PhD anatomic pathology, pathology informatics; **A. William Pasculle** ScD medical microbiology; **Robert Peel** MD endocrine pathology; **Karen Schoedel** MD bone and soft tissue pathology; **Michael Shurin** PhD, immunopathology; **Urvashi Surti** PhD cytogenetics; **Lisa Teot** MD cytopathology; **Tong Wu** MD transplant pathology; **Chengquan Zhao** MD gynecologic pathology.

Assistant Professors

Evan Baker MD community hospital pathology; **Rohit Bhargava** MBBS gynecologic pathology; **Irina Chibisov** MD transfusion medicine; **Simion Chiosea** MD head and neck pathology; **Mamatha Chivukula** MD gynecologic pathology, cytopathology; **Rebecca Crowley** MD informatics; **Sanja Dacic** MD, PhD pulmonary, molecular anatomic pathology; **Amy Davis** MD pediatric pathology; **Jon Davison** MD gastrointestinal pathology; **Marie DeFrances** MD, PhD hepatic, molecular pathology; **Miroslav Djokic** MD hematopathology; **Esther Elishaev** MD gynecologic pathology; **Jeffrey Fine** MD gynecologic pathology, informatics; **Csaba Galambos** MD pediatric pathology; **Christine Garcia** MD hematopathology; **Drazen Jukic** MD, PhD dermatopathology; **Donald Kelley** MD transfusion pathology; **Larry Kiss** MD gastrointestinal pathology; **Matthew Krasowski** MD clinical chemistry; **Scott Kulich** MD, PhD, transfusion medicine, neuropathology; **Kathryn McFadden** MD neuropathology; **Sara Monaco** MD cytopathology; **Sara Monaghan** MD hematopathology; **Sarah Navina** MD cytopathology, gastrointestinal pathology; **Olga Navolotskaia** MD gynecologic pathology; **Larry Nichols** MD autopsy pathology, infectious diseases; **Marina Nikiforova** MD molecular anatomic pathology; **Erin Ochoa** MD transplant pathology; **Scott Owens** MD gastrointestinal pathology; **John Ozolek** MD pediatric pathology; **Octavia Palmer** PhD chemistry; **Aleksandr Perepletchikov** MD, PhD community hospital pathology; **Lirong Qu** MD transfusion medicine, coagulation; **Sarangarajan Ranganathan** MD pediatric pathology; **Lisa Robinson** MD hematopathology, molecular pathology; **Eizaburo Sasatomi** MD, PhD transplant pathology; **Raja Seethala** MD head and neck pathology; **Jagjit Singh** MD community hospital pathology; **Mark Yazer** MD transfusion medicine, coagulation; **Jing Yu** MD, PhD gynecologic pathology, cytopathology.

APPLICATIONS

Positions are offered to graduates of medical or osteopathic schools in the United States or Canada or international medical graduates with an ECFMG certificate holding permanent resident status or eligible for a J-1 visa in the USA. General application materials for the program year beginning in 2010 should be submitted through the AAMC Electronic Residency Application Service (ERAS). These are reviewed beginning in September. We prefer to receive applications through ERAS for upper level positions or from American applicants not required to participate in the National Resident Matching Program (NRMP). Applications to start training in July of 2010 should be received by October 15, 2009; earlier application is strongly recommended. Interviews are by invitation in the fall or early winter and are mandatory. First year or transfer residents begin orientation July 1st.

Address inquiries to:

Trevor Macpherson, MD
Professor of Pathology
Director, Pathology Residency Program
University of Pittsburgh Department of Pathology
A711 Scaife Hall
3550 Terrace Street
Pittsburgh, PA 15261
Phone: (412) 802-6013 • **Fax:** (412) 802-6079 • **E-mail:** training_path@upmc.edu
Web site: http://path.upmc.edu

UNIVERSITY OF PUERTO RICO

San Juan, Puerto Rico

PROGRAMS OFFERED

The Department of Pathology and Laboratory Medicine at the School of Medicine of the University of Puerto Rico offers a fully accredited four-year program in anatomic and clinical pathology. A three-year anatomic pathology program is also offered in selected cases. Training in anatomic pathology includes surgical and autopsy pathology, neuropathology, dermatopathology, pediatric pathology, forensic pathology, cytopathology, immunopathology, immunohistochemistry and electron microscopy. The laboratory medicine program includes training in transfusion medicine, clinical chemistry, microbiology, hematology and hematopathology including flow cytometry. Residents actively participate in departmental and interdepartmental conferences. They also have the opportunity to participate in the research and teaching activities of the department.

TYPES AND NUMBERS OF APPOINTMENTS

Eleven resident positions are available for the first to fourth year.

FACILITIES

The School of Medicine of the University of Puerto Rico is located in a large medical complex which includes the University District Hospital (for adults), the University Pediatric Hospital, the San Juan City Hospital, the Industrial Hospital, the Oncologic Hospital, the Veterans Affairs Hospital, the Puerto Rico and the Caribbean Cardiovascular Center, ASEM Blood Center, and the centralized services facilities which include Clinical Laboratories, Outpatient Clinics and Operating Rooms. Approximately 160 autopsies, 10,700 surgical specimens, and 4,800 cytology specimens are examined annually. Library facilities are extensive. The Central Laboratory (ASEM) performs approximately 5,000,000 tests per year. Special and research laboratories are localized within the School of Medicine and hospitals of the Medical Center.

COMMUNITY

The greater metropolitan area of San Juan has a population near of 500,000. The School of Medicine is near the Rio Piedras campus of the University of Puerto Rico and actually constitutes the medical campus of the University of Puerto Rico. The weather in the area varies from the lower 70's (F) in the winter months to the lower 90's (F) in the summer. The trade winds make the temperature more comfortable. Beautiful public beaches, sports and recreational facilities are available at distances of not more than 30 minutes by car. The Medical Center is surrounded by numerous residential areas and a network of highways which provide ready access to other parts of the city.

STIPENDS AND MAINTENANCE

Salaries are $29, 773.08 for PGY-I increasing to $32, 891.28 for PGY-IV.

STAFF

María J. Marcos-Martínez MD, Acting Chairman, Department of Pathology and Laboratory Medicine; **Angel A. Roman-Franco** MD, AP, Immunopathology; **Consuelo Climent** MD, AP /CP /BB, Director of Laboratories, Transfusion Medicine, Breast Pathology; **Roman Vélez-Rosario** MD, AP /CP /BB/H, Surgical Pathology, Transfusion Medicine, Hematopathology,; **Carmen GonzáleZ-Keelan** MD, AP, Surgical Pathology, Gastropathology; **Anarda GonzáleZ** MD, AP, CP, Surgical Pathology, Electron Microscopy, Clinical Chemistry; **Lillian Colón** MD, AP, Surgical Pathology, Neuropathology; **María I. Santé** MD, AP/CP, Surgical Pathology, Microbiology; **Maria S. Correa** MD, AP /CP, Surgical Pathology, Pediatric Pathology; **Julio I. Colón** PhD, Virology; **George V. Hillyer** PhD, Parasitology, Clinical Immunology; **Wilma V. Santana** Surgical Pathology, Blood Banking; **Jorge L. Sanchez** MD, Dermatopathology; **Irma Rivera** MD, Forensic Pathology.

Collaborators

Cristina Nery MD, Oncologic Pathology; **María de Lourdes Marín** MD, Oncologic Pathology.

APPLICATIONS

All candidates must be either graduate of U.S. or Canadian schools. Foreign graduates must have an ECFMG (Educational Commission for Foreign Medical Graduates) certificate. Applications must be received by November 30 for appointments beginning July I. Applications will not be considered at any other time except for special circumstances; a reading and writing knowledge and ability to communicate in both Spanish and English are required. All acceptable candidates will be given a personal interview.

Address inquiries to:

Roman Velez-Rosario, MD
Department of Pathology and Laboratory Medicine
University of Puerto Rico
School of Medicine, Medical Sciences Campus
P.O. Box 365067
San Juan, PR 00936-5067
Phone: (787) 758-2525 ext. 1331 • **Fax:** (787) 754-0710

BROWN UNIVERSITY WARREN ALPERT MEDICAL SCHOOL

Providence, Rhode Island

PROGRAMS OFFERED

The Department of Pathology and Laboratory Medicine offers a comprehensive training program for medical school graduates planning careers in hospital or academic pathology in four affiliated hospitals and on the campus of the Brown Medical School. Individual courses of study meet certification requirements of the American Board of Pathology for anatomic and clinical pathology. Training opportunities in anatomic pathology include dermatopathology, neuropathology, pediatric pathology, autopsy pathology cytopathology, immunopathology, gastrointestinal pathology, gynecologic pathology, renal pathology and surgical pathology. Training opportunities in clinical pathology include hematopathology, clinical chemistry, molecular/cytogenetics, immunology, microbiology, transfusion and laboratory informatics and management. Research in investigative pathology including diagnostic, molecular and experimental pathology is encouraged in campus and hospital laboratories. Training in forensic pathology is conducted at the Office of the State Medical Examiners. Clinicopathologic conferences, departmental teaching conferences, slide seminars and university seminars are all utilized. Residents and fellows participate in teaching Brown medical students.

TYPES AND NUMBERS OF APPOINTMENTS

The total number of appointments is 12 with three first-year appointments.

FACILITIES

Pathology training sites include the following hospitals: Memorial, Miriam, Rhode Island, and Women and Infants. These hospitals have a total of 1,500 beds and 150 bassinets, and annually process 400 autopsies, more than 60,000 surgical specimens, 6,000 frozen sections, 150,000 vaginal and cervical and extravaginal cytologic specimens, 5 million clinical chemistry tests, more than 375,000 bacteriology and viral exams, 2 million hematology tests and 35,000 blood transfusions. Rotations in the laboratories of the participating hospitals, the Brown Medical School, the Medical Examiner's Office, and the Rhode Island Blood Center include autopsy pathology, surgical pathology, cytopathology, flow cytometry, gynecologic pathology, hematopathology, dermatopathology, neuropathology, perinatal pathology, GI pathology, blood banking, clinical chemistry, microbiology, virology, molecular diagnosis, radioimmunoassay, immunohistochemistry, electron microscopy, research techniques, and laboratory administration.

COMMUNITY

Providence and surrounding metropolitan area have a population of about 500,000. Rhode Island offers the benefits of both urban life and quiet suburban and rural New England. The affiliated hospitals are all located within 10 minutes of each other and the Brown University campus. The city provides excellent and varied cultural and social facilities. It is located on Narragansett Bay near ocean beaches, ski resorts, and major and minor league athletic events.

STIPENDS AND MAINTENANCE

Current stipends as of July 2008 are: first year $49,738, second year $51,124, third year $54,193, fourth year $56,865. Stipends are adjusted on July 1st of each year.

STAFF

Chair

Agnes Kane MD, PhD Brown Univ, Department Pathology and Laboratory Medicine; asbestos toxicity and carcinogenesis.

Hospital Pathologists-in-Chief

Ronald A. DeLellis MD Rhode Island Hospital and The Miriam Hospital; Associate Chair, Brown Univ, Department Pathology; endocrine pathology; **Noubar Kessimian** MD Memorial Hospital; GI pathology; **W. Dwayne Lawrence** MD Women and Infants Hospital; gynecologic pathology.

Professors

Kim Boekelheide MD, PhD toxicology and testicular pathology; **Jacob Canick** PhD prenatal testing, endocrinology; **Kimberly Chapin** MD, microbiology; **Ronald A. DeLellis** MD endocrine pathology; **Douglas R. Gnepp** MD surgical pathology and head and neck tumors; **Judith S. Heelan** PhD microbiology; **Douglas Hixson** PhD hepatic carcinogenesis, tumor markers; **Agnes Kane** MD, PhD toxicology; **W. Dwayne Lawrence** MD gynecologic pathology; **David J. Morris** PhD endocrine metabolism; **M. Halit Pinar** MD perinatal and pediatric pathology; **Murray Resnick** MD surgical pathology, GI pathology; **Margaret Steinhoff** MD gynecologic and breast pathology; **Edward Stopa**

MD neuropathology; **C. James Sung** MD gynecologic and breast pathology, cytopathology; **Joseph Sweeney** MD transfusion medicine and coagulation; **Nancy H. Thompson** PhD liver differentiation, membrane markers; **Herman Vandenburgh** PhD molecular pharmacology, physiology, biotechnology research.

Associate Professors

Barbara E. Barker PhD hematopathology, lymphocyte biology; **Elaine L. Bearer** MD, PhD cytoskeleton, rel-oncogenes, teratology; **Lundy Braun** PhD human papillomaviruses and cervical cancer; **Suzanne de la Monte** MD neuropathology research; **Monique DePaepe** MD perinatal and pediatric pathology; **Alfredo R. Esparza** MD surgical and renal pathology; **Rogers Griffith** MD surgical pathology, hematopathology; **Cynthia L. Jackson** PhD molecular biology; **John Kasznica** MD perinatal, gynecologic and breast pathology; **Noubar Kessimian** MD GI pathology; **Jonathan Kurtis** MD, PhD transfusion molecular parasitology; **Geralyn Lambert-Messerlian** PhD prenatal testing, endocrinology; **Syed A. Latif** PhD endocrine metabolism; **Calvin E. Oyer** MD perinatal and pediatric pathology; **McMillan Paul** PhD, electron microscopy; **Latha Pisharodi** MD cytopathology; **M. Ruhul Quddus** MD gynecologic and breast pathology, cytopathology; **Abdalla Rifai** PhD immunopathology, IgA nephropathy; **Leslie Robinson-Bostom** MD dermatopathology; **Umadevi Tantravahi** PhD molecular and cytogenetics; **Gladys Telang** MD dermatopathology; **Cunxian Zhang** MD, PhD gynecologic and breast pathology, cytopathology.

Assistant Professors

Bassam Aswad MD surgical pathology; **James R Carlsten** MD surgical pathology; **John E. Donahue** MD neuropathology; **Lisa J. Goldstein** MD anatomic pathology; **Fusun Gundogan** MD, perinatal pediatric pathology; **Katrine Hanson** MD GYN Pathology; **Mai He** MD, PhD perinatal pathology; **Stefan Kostadinov** MD, perinatal pediatric pathology; **Michele Lomme** MD gynecologic pathology; **Shamlal Mangray** MD pedi pathology, autopsy services; **Jayasimha Murthy** PhD clinical chemistry; **Stanley Schwartz** MD anatomic pathology, hematopathology; **Dariusz Stachurski** MD surgical pathology / hematopathology; **Janusz Starakiewicz** MD surgical pathology, transfusion medicine; **Diana Treaba** MD surgical and hematopathology; **Li Juan Wang** MD renal pathology; **Jinjun Xiong** MD GYN / breaast pathology; **Evgeny Yakirevich** MD surgical pathology; **Carolyn Te Young** MD transfusion medicine.

Medical Examiner's Office, State of Rhode Island

Alexander Chirkov MD Assistant Medical Examiner; **Thomas Gilson** MD Chief Medical Examiner.

APPLICATIONS

Candidates for PGY-1 are selected through the National Resident Matching Program. Personal interviews are required of all candidates. All applications should be received by December 1st of the previous year. We will participate in ERAS 2009.

Address inquiries to:

Angel Crouse, Pathology Residency Coordinator
Department of Pathology
Rhode Island Hospital
593 Eddy Street
Providence, RI 02903
Phone: (401) 444-5981 • **Fax:** (401) 444-8514
E-mail: acrouse@lifespan.org

MEDICAL UNIVERSITY OF SOUTH CAROLINA

Charleston, South Carolina

PROGRAMS OFFERED

The Department of Pathology and Laboratory Medicine of the Medical University of South Carolina offers a fully accredited training program in anatomic and clinical pathology (AP/CP). The AP/CP program consists of a 39 month core curriculum with 9 months of elective. Anatomic Pathology core rotations include autopsy pathology, forensic pathology, surgical pathology, cytopathology, and dermatopathology. Clinical Pathology core rotations include hematopathology, immunopathology, serology, clinical chemistry, microbiology, tranfusion medicine, apharesis, histocompatibility laboratory, molecular pathology, cytogenetics, laboratory management and informatics. Nine months elective time is available for more in-depth studies in areas of special interest and/or research. Training programs for certification eligibility in anatomic pathology or clinical pathology are available and structured on an individual basis. A graduate (PhD) program in experimental pathology is available and may be coordinated with the residency training program. Fellowships are offered at the discretion of the Chair in forensic pathology, dermatopathology, cytopathology, surgical pathology and hematopathology.

TYPES AND NUMBERS OF APPOINTMENTS

The institution is accredited for twenty-two residency positions in anatomic pathology and clinical pathology, with an even distribution of residents at all levels. Persons seeking the PhD degree in experimental pathology must meet the requirements of the College of Graduate Studies, Medical University of South Carolina. The department participates in the electronic residency application service (ERAS). The deadline for residency application is by November 1st the year prior to entrance.

FACILITIES

The MUSC Teaching Hospital System and the Charleston VA provide the pathology training program with an abundance of clinical material. Yearly figures (2008) are: 147 medical autopsies; 715 forensic autopsies; 26,351 surgical pathology (including neuropathology and dermatopathology specimens); 25,865 cytology specimens (19,703 pap smears, 3,489 exfoliative cytology, 2,673 fine needle aspirations); 292 diagnostic electron microscopic procedures; and 440 tissue immunofluorescent procedures (kidney, heart and skin). The Division of Laboratory Medicine performs approximately 3,019,1957 clinical pathology tests, including transfusion medicine 112,612; HLA 19,875; chemistry/hematology 2,730,413; cytogenetics 1,766, with karyotypes, 1538, and an additional 520 FISH tests; and microbiological 155,291. In addition, an active apheresis unit is located in the Department of Nephrology. In Hemapheresis Services, 1,157 procedures were performed in 2008, including therapeutic plasma exchange, red blood cell exchange, hematopoietic progenitor cell collection from autologous and allogeneic donors, cell depletion, and therapeutic phlebotomy. The Divisions of Anatomic Pathology and Laboratory Medicine are housed primarily on the second and third floors of the Children's Hospital, with additional space located in Hollings Cancer Center, Rutledge Tower (outpatient facility), Ashley River Tower (GI and Cardiovascular) facility, and the Medical University Hospital. In excess of 55,000 square feet are dedicated to the two divisions.

COMMUNITY

Besides the Colleges of Medicine, Pharmacy, Dentistry, Nursing, Health Related Professions, and Graduate Studies of the Medical University of South Carolina, educational institutions in Charleston include the College of Charleston, Charleston Southern University, The Citadel Military College, Trident Technical College and several business colleges. This progressive historic seaport city offers its own symphony orchestra and ballet companies, choral and theater groups and outstanding recreational areas to 552,803 persons in the metropolitan area. Historic homes, plantations, gardens, access to the intracoastal waterway, beaches and year-round fresh and salt-water fishing, sailing, surfing, golfing, etc, which draws thousands of tourists yearly, are within minutes of the medical center.

STIPENDS AND MAINTENANCE

Annual stipends are from $43,947 upward. Interns and residents are provided individual office space, computer and equipment. Malpractice insurance is provided.

STAFF

Mariam Alsharif MD, cytopathology, fine needle aspirates, surgical pathology; **Maria Gallego Attis** MD, cytopathology, fine needle aspirates, surgical pathology; **Nicholas Batalis** MD, forensic pathology and medical autopsy; **Masha H Bilic** MD, surgical pathology, forensic pathology, immunopathology; **Robert A Bray** PhD Co-Director,

HLA; **Erika T. Brown** PhD, breast cancer, DNA damage and repair; **Christina Carrick** MD, surgical pathology; **Lisa L. Cunningham** PhD, molecular mechanisms of sensory hair cell; **Vincent Dammai** M.Phil, PhD, FGF receptor biology and novel approaches for targeting renal cell carcinomas; **Haytham Dimashkieh** MD, surgical pathology, cytopathology; **Weimin Fan** MD, molecular tumor biology; **Victoria J Findlay** PhD, role of microRNAs during cancer progression; **Howard M Gebel** PhD Co-Director, HLA; **Yong-Zhong Gong** MD, xenograft facility; **Debra Hazen-Martin** PhD, electron microscopy and freeze fracture; **Tien Hsu** PhD, developmental genetics and tumor metastasis; **Toshihiko Kawamori** MD, PhD, MIAC experimental pathology, chemoprevention of colon cancer; **Janice M. Lage** MD, Chair, Pathology and Laboratory Medicine; obstetrics/gynecologic, perinatal, breast pathology; **Hainan Lang** MD, PhD, auditory physiology, cell biology of hearing and deafness; **Amanda C LaRue** PhD, tissue reconstitution potential of hematopoietic stems cells; **John Lazarchick** MD, Director, Hematology; hematology and coagulation; **David N. Lewin** MD, surgical pathology, gastrointestinal pathology, hepatopathology, cytopathology; **Becky Madory** MD, surgical pathology, cytopathology, VA lab services; **James E. Madory** DO, surgical pathology, pathology informatics, and gynecologic pathology; **John S. Metcalf** MD, Vice Chair, Pathology and Laboratory Medicine; surgical pathology and dermatopathology; **Omar Moussa** PhD, molecular genetics of cancer, molecular pathology; **Frederick S Nolte** Ph.D. Director, Clinical Laboratories; medical microbiology, molecular diagnostics, laboratory management; **S. Erin Presnell** MD, Director, Forensic Pathology; **Gian G. Re** PhD, molecular biology; **Mary S. Richardson** MD, DDS, Director, Surgical Pathology; gynecologic and ENT pathology, cytopathology; **Ellen Riemer** MD, JD, pulmonary pathology and medical autopsy; **Tihana Rumboldt** MD, surgical pathology, breast pathology, head and neck pathology; **Cynthia A. Schandl** MD, PhD forensic pathology and molecular pathology; **Bradley A. Schulte** PhD, Director, Research; experimental pathology; **Sally E. Self** MD, Director, Diagnostic Immunology; immunopathology, renal pathology; **Amy Sheil** MD, forensic pathology and medical autopsy; **Avtar K. Singh** MD, hematopathology, VA lab services; **M. Timothy Smith** MD, Director, Anatomic Pathology; surgical pathology, neuropathology, dermatopathology, cytopathology; **Demetri D. Spryropoulous** PhD, hox and ets transcription factors in development and cancer; **Jerry E Squires** MD, PhD Director of Transfusion Services; **Lisa L. Steed** PhD, Director, Diagnostic Microbiology; **David P Turner** PhD, aberrant expression of cancer associated genes in transcriptional regulatory networks; **Dennis Watson** PhD, molecular biology of gene regulation, molecular genetics of cancer; **Cynthia T. Welsh** MD, surgical pathology, neuropathology, pediatric pathology, cytopathology; **Daynna J. Wolff** PhD, Director, Cytogenetics and Molecular Pathology; **Je-Song Won** PhD, neuroinflammation, neurodegenerative disease; **Jack Yang** MD, Director, Cytopathology, fine needle aspirates, surgical pathology; **Daohong Zhou** MD, hematopoietic toxicity of radiotherapy; **Yusheng Zhu** PhD, clinical chemistry, toxicology.

APPLICATIONS

Address inquiries to:

David N. Lewin, MD, Professor and Director
Department of Pathology and Laboratory Medicine
Residency Training Program
Suite 309 Children's Hospital
Medical University of South Carolina
165 Ashley Avenue, MSC 908
Charleston, SC 29425
Phone: (843) 792-3121 • **Fax:** (843) 792-0555
Web site: http://www.musc.edu/pathology/resident/index.htm

Medical University of South Carolina, and a nearby beach.

EAST TENNESSEE STATE UNIVERSITY COLLEGE OF MEDICINE AND AFFILIATED HOSPITALS

Johnson City, Tennessee

PROGRAMS OFFERED

A fully accredited four-year training program for residents is available in anatomic and clinical pathology. The integrated program provides the opportunity for training with the faculty of the Department of Pathology at the James H. Quillen College of Medicine, the Veterans Affairs Medical Center, and the Johnson City Medical Center. Training in anatomic pathology includes autopsy and surgical pathology, cytopathology, neuropathology, forensic pathology, dermatopathology, renal pathology, and electron microscopy. Training in clinical pathology includes clinical chemistry, transfusion medicine, hematopathology, and microbiology. Specialized training is also provided to residents in cytogenetics, molecular pathology, flow cytometry, and toxicology. The educational objectives of the program include the acquisition of fundamental knowledge in anatomic and clinical pathology that will prepare the resident for the general practice of pathology or for further training in special fields of pathology; the progressive development of diagnostic, interpretive, technical, and consultative skills; the development of skills necessary for laboratory management and administration; and the opportunity to gain experience in teaching and research.

TYPES AND NUMBERS OF APPOINTMENTS

The institution is accredited for 8 residents. Four years of training are available. Appointments are made on an annual basis.

FACILITIES

The James H. Quillen College of Medicine of East Tennessee State University is located on the historic, 220-acre grounds of the Veterans Affairs Medical Center which includes not only an acute care hospital, but also an intermediate care unit, nursing home care unit, and domiciliary. Johnson City Medical Center, a major tertiary referral center for the region, has 443 beds distributed between the JCMC adult hospital and the Niswonger Children's Hospital. This JCMC complex is the central facility of a twelve-hospital healthcare system and provides a Level I trauma center and a 32-bed neonatal intensive care unit. In a recent year, there were 29,391 admissions at these hospitals and the combined workload of the clinical laboratories included 2,722,054 laboratory tests, 32,212 surgical specimens, 37,600 cytology specimens, and 38 autopsies. Also, the medical school provides histopathology and clinical laboratory services to an expanding group of outpatients. The forensic division of the medical school pathology department performs up to 350 autopsies per year for eight counties in northeast Tennessee; it has recently moved to a newly renovated building providing more than 20,000 square feet of space. The ETSU Department of Pathology and each hospital maintain libraries of books and journals most frequently used by pathologists. Full access is provided to the medical library of the College of Medicine with over 35,000 books and over 1500 periodicals (most available online and including a comprehensive set of pathology journals). Pathology residents have recently been granted use of a suite of rooms that provides several offices, a multiheaded microscope, desks, and a computer linked to a digital camera-equipped microscope. Pathology resident research is strongly supported. Some of the equipment and resources especially pertinent to research that might be undertaken by our residents includes an Arcturus laser capture microdissection system, a digital transmission electron microscope, a confocal laser scanning microscope, a molecular biology core facility, a flow cytometer, histology laboratories performing both conventional and immunohistochemistry stains, and general-purpose research laboratories within the department.

COMMUNITY

Metropolitan Johnson City (#10 on the 2007 Forbes list of best smaller metro areas) has a population of about 200,000 and is located in the Tri Cities Tennessee/Virginia region, which has a population of more than 600,000. In addition to a major university and all it has to offer, the city also has parks, golf courses, pools, community theater groups, a symphony orchestra, and many art groups. State and national parks, as well as proximity to lakes, the highest mountains in the East, the Blue Ridge Parkway, the Appalachian Trail, and the Great Smoky Mountains National Park, provide for ample opportunities to enjoy outdoor recreational activities such as hiking, camping, boating, water and snow skiing, swimming, fishing, and hunting.

STIPENDS AND MAINTENANCE

Stipends are adjusted annually to reflect cost-of-living increases, and the 2008-2009 stipends were: first-year residents, $44,050; second-year, $45,365; third-year, $46,989 and fourth-year, $48,785. Chief Residents receive an additional $200 monthly. ETSU pays a large portion of the cost of residents' health insurance. All residents are granted

15 days of annual leave every year. The exercise facilities of the University are available to our residents at no charge. The cost of living and housing in Johnson City is low, and Tennessee does not tax personal income. Pathology residents have also been provided with an annual book fund of $650 and support for travel to meetings and courses.

STAFF

John B. Schweitzer MD (Washington Univ 1978) Chairman; anatomic pathology, neuropathology; **Mousa A. Al-Abbadi** MD (Univ Jordan 1986) Chief, Pathology and Laboratory Medicine Service, VA Med Ctr; surgical pathology, cytopathology; **Kevin F. Breuel** PhD, MS, HCLD (West Virginia Univ 1991) reproductive physiology, clinical chemistry; **Sandra K. Brooks** MD (East Tennessee State Univ 1988) anatomic and clinical pathology, cytopathology; **Earl J. Brown** MD (Louisiana State Univ 1981) surgical pathology, hematopathology; **Teresa Campbell** MD (Med Univ South Carolina 1984) anatomic and clinical pathology, forensic pathology; **Humera B. Chaudhary** MD (Fatima Jinnah Med Col for Women 1987) surgical pathology, cytopathology; **Patrick N. Costello** MD (University Col, Dublin 1992) anatomic and clinical pathology, gastrointestinal pathology; **Michelle M. Duffourc** PhD (Univ South Alabama 1993) molecular biology; **Theresa S. Emory** MD (Eastern Virginia Med Sch 1989) anatomic and clinical pathology, gastrointestinal pathology; **Donald A. Ferguson, Jr.** PhD (Syracuse Univ 1974) microbiology; **Kenneth E. Ferslew** PhD (Louisiana State Univ 1982) toxicology; **Andrew Fletcher** MD (Mercer Univ 2002) anatomic and clinical pathology, cytopathology; **Charles Ganote** MD (Vanderbilt Univ 1965) anatomic pathology, cardiac pathology; **J. Chadwick King** MD (Univ Virginia, 1987) anatomic and clinical pathology, hematopathology, coagulation; **Jerald E. Mullersman** MD, PhD (Univ Florida 1986) clinical pathology, transfusion medicine, molecular genetics; **Jack Rary** PhD (Univ Tennessee 1968) cytogenetics; **Julie S. Robertson** MD (Univ Louisville 1997) anatomic pathology; **Robert V. Schoborg** PhD (Univ Missouri 1991) virology, molecular biology; **M. Salah Shurbaji** MD (American Univ Beirut 1984) Director, ETSU Pathology Laboratory; anatomic pathology, genitourinary pathology, cytopathology; **David Sibley** MD (Univ Virginia 1984) anatomic and clinical pathology, transfusion medicine; **David R. Soike** MD (Med Col Ohio at Toledo 1979) Director of Laboratories, Johnson City Med Ctr; anatomic and clinical pathology; **Rowena Velilla** MD (Univ Santo Tomas 1990) anatomic and clinical pathology, hematopathology; **Yurong Wheeler** MD, PhD (Tianjin Med Univ 1996) anatomic and clinical pathology, cytopathology; **George A. Youngberg** MD (Northwestern Univ 1977) anatomic pathology, dermatopathology, nephropathology, immunopathology.

APPLICATIONS

Applicants for the first year of residency should apply via the Electronic Residency Application Service (ERAS). For further details, refer to our department's website at http://www.etsu.edu/com/pathology or contact us at the e-mail address below.

Address inquiries to:

Jerald E. Mullersman, MD, PhD
Program Director, Pathology Residency
James H. Quillen College of Medicine
Box 70568, East Tennessee State University
Johnson City, TN 37614-1707
Phone: (423) 439-6210 • **Fax:** (423) 439-8060 • **E-mail:** path@etsu.edu

UNIVERSITY OF TENNESSEE MEDICAL CENTER AT KNOXVILLE

Knoxville, Tennessee

PROGRAMS OFFERED

The Department of Pathology of the University of Tennessee Medical Center at Knoxville offers a four-year training program leading to qualification for Board certification in anatomic and clinical pathology. Training in anatomic pathology includes autopsy and surgical pathology, forensic pathology, neuropathology, pediatric pathology, and cytopathology including fine needle aspiration. Training in clinical pathology includes clinical chemistry/toxicology, endocrinology, hematology, transfusion medicine, microbiology, (general, parasitology, virology, bacteriology, mycology) instrumentation, and molecular pathology. Specialized training is also offered in research methodology, electron microscopy, and immunopathology. The program is experiential and didactic; the didactic clinical pathology and anatomical pathology lecture series runs on a two-year cycle, thus the ordinary resident will experience it twice. In both anatomic and clinical pathology, residents are accorded opportunities for independent activity commensurate with their degree of development. Yearly in-service, board type examinations, are given. Residents participate in teaching programs of the Graduate School of Medicine. All educational programs and evaluations correspond to the six competency based initiatives of the ACGME. Fellowships are offered in surgical pathology and cytopathology.

TYPES AND NUMBERS OF APPOINTMENTS

There are 10 pathology residency positions comprising the integrated four-year program. Post residency fellowships are available in cytopathology and surgical pathology. The total medical center residency staff includes approximately 140 interns/residents: 24 medicine, 18 surgical, 12 ob/gyn, 24 family practice, 21 anesthesia, 8 dentistry and oral surgery, and 20 radiology and nuclear medicine, and 7 transitional.

FACILITIES

University Hospital is a 602-bed acute care, general and teaching hospital, and is designated by the State as a Level I Trauma Center. In addition to customary medical services, the hospital has a full complement of specialty units. It is the largest medical facility in upper East Tennessee. Approximate statistics include 30,000 annual admissions, 4.0 million lab examinations, 23,000 surgicals, and 450 autopsies. The clinical laboratories are all newly constructed or renovated. The computer facilities are Cerner Powerchart and Cerner DHT. All residents have their personal computers, with system, internet and telepathology connection. The Knox County Forensic Unit is located at the Medical Center. The present staff includes 200 technical and nontechnical personnel. Extensive facilities are available for research programs in the adjacent research center. Full access is provided to the UT/Knoxville campus library which supports 113 undergraduate programs, 129 master programs, and 44 PhD programs with more than 5,000,000 items including more than 1,400,000 volumes and 21,000 journals. The hospital library currently has approximately 25,000 volumes with greater than 380 journals. A complete department resident library is maintained. A book stipend is offered. Telepathology facilities are available.

COMMUNITY

The Greater Knoxville area has a population of 335,749. The catchment area of the university is approximately 600,000. The largest campus of the UT system is located here with approximately 26,000 students. A broad range of cultural events are available. Participatory and spectator sports opportunities abound. Adjacent areas of interest include the Tennessee Valley Authority lake system and the Great Smoky Mountains National Park. The hospital is located in a pastoral setting at the edge of the city limits with convenient highway access to all parts of the city. Recent polls and studies have suggested Knoxville as one of the most desirable cities in the United States in which to reside.

STIPENDS AND MAINTENANCE

First year residents receive approximately $43,860 with life insurance provided, annual increments, major medical insurance, and three-weeks paid vacation per year. Opportunities for additional approved residency related employment are available to residents.

STAFF

Professors

John C Neff MD (St Louis Univ 1963); immunology/immunopathology; **Wahid Hanna** MD (Ain-Shams Univ, Egypt 1969) oncology/coagulation; **Karla J Matteson** PhD molecular pathology; **Michael J McCoy** DDS (West Virginia Sch Dent 1973) oral pathology.

Associate Professors

Lisa D Duncan MD (East Tennessee State Univ 1996) surgical pathology; cytopathology; **David Gerard** PhD (Univ Tennessee, Knoxville) electron microscopy; **Elizabeth W. Hubbard** MD (Med Univ South Carolina 1986) surgical pathology, cytopathology; **Murray K Marks** PhD (Univ Tennessee, Memphis, 1993) anthropology; **Darinka Mileusnic** MD, PhD (Univ Rijeka, Croatia 1986) forensic pathology; **Stuart E Van Meter** MD (Med Univ South Carolina 1986) Chairman; surgical pathology; cytopathology; **D Douglas Wilson** MD (Univ Tennessee, Memphis 1973) surgical pathology; hematopathology.

Assistant Professors

Leon F Baltrucki MD (Albany Medical College, New York, 1983) hematology; **Izabela Burja** MD (Pomeranian Med Academy, 1982)surgical pathology, cytopathology; **Christopher T Clark** MD (East Carolina Univ School of Med, 1991) blood bank, cytology; **Alan D Grindstaff** MD (East Tennessee State Univ 1994) surgical pathology/GIpathology; **Robert Page** MD (Univ Arkansas 1996) dermatopathology; **Neil Quigley** PhD (Univ Auckland, New Zealand 1984) molecular pathology.

Clinical Professor

Paul Googe MD (Univ Tennessee Memphis 1983) dermatopathology; **Mahlon Johnson** MD, PhD (Univ Tennessee, Memphis 1981) neuropathology.

Clinical Associate Professor

Roger Hubbard PhD (Univ Tennessee, Knoxville, 1978) molecular biology; **Roy King** MD (Univ Witwatersrand Med Sch, South Africa 1990) molecular pathology; **Rosalynn Miltenberger** PhD (Univ Wisconsin-Madison 1994), molecular pathology; **Nicholas Potter** PhD (Duke Univ 1986) molecular pathology.

Clinical Assistant Professor

Robyn M Atkinson PhD (Univ Tennessee, Memphis 2002) medical microbiology; **David A Birdwell** MD (Univ Tennessee, Memphis 1969) pediatric pathology; **Lynn F Blake** MD (Univ Tennessee, Memphis 1958) blood bank; **Timothy Powers** MD (East Tennessee State Univ 1988) ocular pathology.

Professor Emeritus

William M Bass PhD (Univ Pennsylvania 1961) forensic anthropology; **Jones S Francis** MD (Univ Boston 1946) emeritus; **Pennell C Painter** PhD (Univ Tennessee-Knoxville 1976) clinical chemistry.

APPLICATIONS

Completed applications must be received by December 31 for appointments through the NRMP beginning July 1 of the following year. Applications will be considered after the deadline if space is available. International medical graduates must have ECFMG certification, and US experience which we can evaluate is required. All residents must successfully complete Step III before entering into PGY3 year. All residents must apply for, and receive in state licenses by the end of the PGY3 year. Applications will only be accepted through the Electronic Resident Application Service (ERAS).

Address inquiries to:

John C. Neff, MD
Pathology Resident Education Director
University of Tennessee Graduate School of Medicine
1924 Alcoa Highway, Drawer U-108
Knoxville, TN 37920
Phone: (865) 305-8994
Web site: http://www.utmedicalcenter.org

Photograph of medical center complex

UNIVERSITY OF TENNESSEE AND AFFILIATED HOSPITALS

Memphis, Tennessee

PROGRAMS OFFERED

The University of Tennessee College of Medicine, Department of Pathology and Laboratory Medicine offers an ACGME approved training program for residents in Anatomic and Clinical Pathology. Training in Anatomic Pathology includes rotations in surgical pathology, neuropathology, forensic pathology, oral pathology, electron microscopy, cytology, dermatopathology, pediatric pathology, pediatric oncological pathology and autopsies. Training in Clinical Pathology includes clinical chemistry, hematopathology, hematology, blood bank/transfusion medicine, microbiology, cytogenetics, immunology, laboratory management and informatics. The more than 50 pathologists who are involved in this residency program provide a great depth and breadth to the residency experience. In addition to a variety of clinical research efforts, the University Department also has a strong basic research program with emphases in cancer patholobiology, cytokine biology, and vascular biology. There is also a PhD program in pathology operated co-jointly with departments at St Jude Children's Research Hospital.

TYPES AND NUMBERS OF APPOINTMENTS

Three or four residents are accepted each year for a total of 12-16 residents in the first four years of training. Fellowships are currently offered in dermatopathology, pediatric pathology, hematopathology, and anatomic pathology. The educational goals and objectives of our fellowship programs are to prepare the trainees for a career in academic or private practice.

FACILITIES

The University of Tennessee Health Science Center is one of the largest in the country. Within the medical center, rotations are taken at the University of Tennessee Health Science Center, Department of Pathology and Laboratory Medicine; Baptist Memorial Hospital - Memphis, Trumbull Laboratory - Pathology Group of the Mid South; the Regional Medical Center at Memphis; the Veterans' Affairs Medical Center (VAMC); St. Jude Children's Research Hospital (the world's leading children's cancer center); Memphis Pathology Laboratory (MPL); LeBonheur Children's Medical Center; G.I Pathology Partners, PLLC; Methodist University Hospital and Duckworth Pathology Group. Approximate numbers of autopsies and specimens are: 200 hospital autopsies, 500 forensic autopsies, 500,000 surgical pathology cases, 6,000 frozen sections, 400,000 cytopathology specimens, 5,000 bone marrows and 10,000,000 clinical laboratory determinations. Facilities available are complete in every detail including a library of 183,000 volumes with 1,325 current subscriptions to scientific journals, a comprehensive medical illustration service, computer centers and medical instrumentation division. Within the Pathology Department, there are many well equipped research laboratories and a variety of core laboratory facilities.

COMMUNITY

Memphis, situated in the southwestern corner of picturesque Tennessee, is a thriving community of about one million perched on bluffs that overlook the Mississippi River. The moderate climate affords nearly year-around opportunities for one to enjoy any of the city's many parks, public golf courses, tennis courts, or other recreational facilities. For the lover of the arts, there are museums and galleries, a symphony orchestra, a ballet company, and numerous community theater groups. When it's time to relax, one can enjoy fine restaurants representing cuisines from around the world or live spectator sports of virtually any kind. Memphis is renowned as the birthplace of the blues, and this musical tradition lives on in the clubs and cafes of Beale Street. While there are plenty of big city attractions, the forests and streams of the Ozark Mountains are only a short drive away. The Gulf Coast beaches of Florida and the festival atmosphere of New Orleans are also within driving distance.

STIPENDS AND MAINTENANCE

First year residents receive approximately $43,000 with a $1,500 dollar increase each year thereafter. All residents are provided with subsidized hospitalization, life, and disability insurance, liability protection, and parking. The program also provides time off for courses to prepare for board examinations and offers some financial assistance in the purchase of books.

STAFF

University of Tennesee Health Science Center

Charles Handorf MD, PhD Professor and Chair; **Vickie S. Baselski** PhD Professor, Clinical Microbiology; **Doug R. Shanklin** MD Professor, Neonatal Pathology, Electron Microscopy; **Toni Clinton** PhD Assistant Professor,

Administrative Director, Memphis Pathology Laboratory; **Ed Raines** Medical Director of MPL; **F. Curtis Dohan, Jr** MD Associate Professor, Neuropathology; **Pamela Osborne** MD Associate Professor, Surgical Pathology; **Andrzej Slominski** MD, PhD Professor, Dermatopathology; **Louisa Balazs** MD, PhD Associate Professor, Surgical Pathology and Autopsy; **Anne Jordan** MD Instructor, Surgical Pathology and Cytology; **Karen Chancellor** MD Clinical Faculty, Forensic Pathology; **Cameila Johns** MD Instructor, Pathology Informatics; Director, PathConnection; **Anand Kulkarni** MD Assistant Professor, Pathology; Director, Tissue Services Core; **Antonio Martinez** MD Professor and Vice Chair of Education; **Marco Ross** MD, Clinical Faculty, Forensic Pathology; **Nadeem Zafar** MD Associate Professor, Cytopathology.

Veterans Administration Medical Center, Memphis

Ilya Stone MD Chief VA Pathology and Laboratory Medicine Service, Hepatic Pathology; **Ted Strom** MD VA Director, Blood Bank Hematology.

Baptist Memorial Hospitals and Trumbull Laboratories

Thomas McC. Chesney MD Professor; Director, Trumbull Laboratories, Surgical Pathology and Dermatopathology; **Carolyn M. Chesney** MD Professor, Hematology and Coagulation; **Michael F. Bugg** MD Director, Rapid Service Clinical Labs and Associate Director, Clinical Pathology; **Bruce Webber** MBBS, CHFF Director, Surgical Pathology; **Allen Berry III** MD Staff Pathologist, Dermatopathology, Cytopathology and Neuropathology; **Thomas Callihan** MD Staff Pathologst, Hematopathology and Surgical Pathology; **Kenneth Groshart** MD Staff Pathologist; Medical Director, Blood Bank, Surgical Pathology; **J. Cameron Hall** MD Staff Pathologist; Associate Director, Clinical Pathology, Surgical Pathology; **Shamin Moinuddin** MD Staff Pathologist, Cytopathology; **G. David Spencer, Jr** MD Staff Pathologist, Surgical Pathology.

St. Jude Children's Research Hospital

James Downing MD Professor, Chairman, Department Pathology; Director, Molecular Pathology Laboratory; **Jesse Jenkins III** MD Associate Professor, UT Department Pathology, St. Jude; **Christine Fuller** MD Associate Professor, UT Department Pathology, St. Jude; **Susana Raimondi** PhD Associate Professor; Director, Cytogenetics Laboratory; **Mihaela Onciu** MD Associate Professor, UT Department Pathology, St. Jude.

Methodist University Hospital

Robert M Bradley MD Assistant Professor, Blood Banking and Surgical Pathology; **Noel T Florendo** MD Associate Professor, Microbiology; **Royce Joyner** MD Assistant Professor, Pediatric Pathology; **Olga Lasater** MD Associate Professor, Pediatric Pathology; **David McGregor** MD Associate Professor, Flow Cytometry; **Barry Randall** MD Associate Professor, Dermatopathology; **David Robbins** MD Associate Professor, Cytopathology; **Jeffrey J Roux** MD Assistant Professor, Cytopathology; **Frank White** MD Associate Professor, Hematology, Flow Cytometry.

APPLICATIONS

Residency candidates must be graduates of United States or Canadian medical schools or have received an ECFMG certification. Applications will only be accepted through ERAS. Three letters of recommendation and a personal interview are required.

Address inquiries to:

John K. Duckworth, MD
Director, Professor
930 Madison Avenue, 5th Floor
Memhis, Tennessee 38163
Phone: (901) 448-7027
E-mail: Jduckwo1@utmem.edu

Chasse Green, BS
Coordinator
930 Madison Avenue, 5th Floor
Memphis, Tennessee 38163
Phone: (901) 448-6344
E-mail: clgreen@utmem.edu

VANDERBILT UNIVERSITY AFFILIATED HOSPITALS

Nashville, Tennessee

PROGRAMS OFFERED

A fully approved training program in combined anatomic and clinical pathology is offered and includes: surgical pathology, autopsy pathology, cytopathology, renal pathology, pediatric pathology, neuropathology, forensic pathology, diagnostic electron microscopy, clinical chemistry, hematology, blood banking, microbiology, parasitology, immunopathology and flow cytometry, molecular pathology, cytogenetics, and laboratory administration. Additionally, training is offered in combined anatomic pathology and neuropathology. To meet the American Board of Pathology requirements, the AP/CP residency program consists of a three-year core curriculum and a flexible fourth year. A limited number of positions in either anatomic or clinical pathology only are allocated based on individual merit and interest. Fellowships in anatomic pathology, hematopathology, neuropathology, renal pathology, molecular genetic and GI pathology are also available.

REQUIREMENTS

Consideration for a residency position requires a completed application via ERAS, a personal statement, three letters of recommendation, a transcript of medical school grades, a Dean's letter, USMLE scores (80 or above, no failed attempts), and, where applicable, EFCMG certificate with J-1 visa. Candidates with appropriate academic and professional credentials and strong letters of recommendation are invited for a personal interview. The Department will arrange and pay for one night's hotel accommodation at the Hampton Inn Vanderbilt, adjacent to the campus. Selection is based on career goals, communication skills as demonstrated during the interview process, academic and professional performance, and letters of recommendation. There is no cut-off date for graduation. No previous US clinical or research experience is required.

TYPES AND NUMBERS OF APPOINTMENTS

Currently, 25 pathology residency positions are available in years 1-4. Usually six first-year positions are offered each year. Residents typically enter the program at the PGY1 level, although some residents enter after one or more years of training in other specialties.

FACILITIES

Vanderbilt University Hospital, Monroe Carell Jr. Children's Hospital at Vanderbilt, and the adjacent Nashville VA Medical Center comprise a total of 1,070 licensed beds. There are approximately 46,785 admissions per year with an average length of stay at 5.4 days. Ambulatory visits (including off-site) are 1,019,715 and emergency room visits 90,870. Vanderbilt University Hospital and Vanderbilt Clinic consistently rank among the premier health care facilities in the United States. U.S. News & World Report has ranked Vanderbilt University Medical Center among the foremost programs in the nation. Constructed in 2004, The Monroe Carell Jr. Children's Hospital at Vanderbilt is a leading provider of pediatric care and ranked as one of the 10 best children's hospitals in the country and among the top 10 in the nation for pediatric cancer services by Child magazine. It is ranked 23rd in the nation by U.S. News & World Report. Vanderbilt ranked 15th in the nation in the 2008 issue of America's Best Hospitals. Only 19 hospitals made the honor roll. U.S. News & World Report is listing Vanderbilt Medical Center on its ''Honor Roll'' of hospitals — an honor reserved for a select group of institutions labeled by the magazine as the ''best of the best.'' For the first time Vanderbilt was named one of the top 100 best places to work in 2009 in the United States in FORTUNE magazine's annual survey. Vanderbilt was the first university to ever be named to the list.

COMMUNITY

Nashville with Davidson County has a population of one million and is located in the rolling hills of central Tennessee. It is the site of numerous colleges and universities, two medical schools, and several large teaching hospitals. The city has an extensive parks system, a symphony orchestra, opera, ballet, a performing arts center, several museums, and the Grand Ole Opry. The city offers a wide variety of cultural, educational, and recreational opportunities, including professional football and hockey teams.

STIPENDS AND MAINTENANCE

Currently, first-year residents receive approximately $45,660 (2008-2009). Living arrangements are available nearby at moderate cost. All pathology residents are provided with professional liability insurance, health insurance, and computer equipment for personal and professional use. Additional funds are provided for books and travel to national meetings.

STAFF

Samuel Santoro MD, PhD (Vanderbilt Univ 1979) Chair; laboratory medicine, investigative pathology; **Sarki Abdulkadir** MD, PhD (Ahmadu Bello Univ, Nigeria, 1990, Johns Hopkins Univ 1995) prostate cancer; **Ty Abel** MD, PhD

(Univ Arizona 1999, 2001) neuropathology; **James Atkinson** MD, PhD (Vanderbilt Univ 1981) autopsy, surgical and cardiac pathology; **Mark W. Becher** (Univ of Nebraska Col Med 1988) neuropathology; **Paul Bock** PhD (Washington 1976) hemostasis and thrombosis; **Debra Callahan** MD (Ohio State 1996) transfusion medicine; **Justin Cates** MD, PhD (Tufts Univ 1997) anatomic pathology, bone and soft tissue pathology; **James Chappell** MD, PhD (Vanderbilt Univ 2001) microbiology; **William Chopp** MD (Michigan State Univ 2004) surgical pathology, cytopathology, autopsy; **Cheryl Coffin** MD (Univ of Vermont 1980) surgical pathology, pediatric pathology, molecular pathology; **Robert Collins** MD (Vanderbilt Univ 1951) hematopathology; **Alice Coogan** MD (Vanderbilt Univ 1988) anatomic pathology, cytopathology; **Hernan Correa** MD (Univ del Valle 1983) pediatric pathology; **Jeffrey Davidson** PhD (Stanford Univ 1975) investigative pathology; **Sheila Dawling** PhD (Univ London 1981) toxicology; **Thomas Deering** MD (Univ Iowa 1988) forensic pathology; **Christine Eischen** PhD (Mayo Clinic 1997) investigative pathology and lymphoma; **Rosana Eisenberg** MD (Universidade Federal, Brazil 1981) surgical pathology, cytopathology, autopsy; **Kim Ely** MD (Tulane Univ 1989) surgical pathology, cytology, head and neck pathology; **Oluwole Fadare** MD (Howard University 2000) anatomic pathology; **Agnes Fogo** MD (Vanderbilt Univ 1981) electron microscopy, renal pathology; **David Gailani** MD (Univ Illinois 1984) hematology and coagulation; **Adriana Gonzalez** MD (Louisiana State Univ 1994) surgical pathology, cytopathology, lung pathology; **David Head** MD (Univ Texas Med Branch-Galveston 1968) hematopathology; **Robert Hoffman** MD, PhD (Johns Hopkins Univ 1984) anatomic pathology; **Juan Iturregui** MD (Univ Puerto Rico 1999) renal, genitourinary and surgical pathology; **Joyce Johnson** MD (Vanderbilt Univ 1986) anatomic pathology; **Michael Laposata** MD, PhD (Johns Hopkins Univ 1978) coagulation; **Thomas McCurley** MD (Vanderbilt Univ 1974) immunopathology, hematopathology; **William Mitchell** MD, PhD (Vanderbilt Univ 1960, Johns Hopkins Univ 1966) investigative pathology; **Claudio Mosse** MD, PhD (Univ Virginia 2001) hematopathology; **David Page** MD (Johns Hopkins Univ 1966) surgical pathology, dermatopathology; **Fritz Parl** MD, PhD (Univ Goettingen 1968, New York Med Col 1978) clinical chemistry; **Paisit Paueksakon** MD (Mahidol Univ, Thailand 1987) renal pathology; **Melinda Sanders** MD (Jefferson Med Col 1995) breast, thyroid, oral pathology; **Stephen Schultenover** MD (Univ Minnesota 1972) surgical pathology, cytopathology; **Adam Seegmiller** MD, PhD (Univ of Texas 2004) hematopathology; **Gregory Sephel** PhD (Univ Utah 1986) clinical chemistry; **Jean Simpson** MD (Med Col Georgia 1983) general anatomic and breast pathology; **Charles Stratton** MD (Univ Vermont 1971) microbiology; **Larry Swift** PhD (Vanderbilt Univ 1971) investigative pathology; **Yi-Wei Tang** MD,PhD (Shanghai Med Univ 1982, Vanderbilt Univ 1995) molecular microbiology, infectious disease; **Mary Ann Thompson-Arildsen** MD, PhD (Univ Pennsylvania 1983) hematopathology; **Cindy Vnencak-Jones** PhD (Univ Virginia 1985) molecular genetics; **Mary Kay Washington** MD, PhD (Univ North Carolina 1986) anatomic and GI pathology; **Marcia Wills** (Dartmouth Med Sch 1992) pediatric pathology, GI pathology; **Alison Woodworth** PhD (Washington Univ 2003) Clinical Chemistry; **Pampee Young** MD, PhD (Univ Texas SW Med Sch Dallas 1998, 1996) vascular biology, transfusion medicine; **Tania Zuluaga Toro** MD (Universidade del Valle, Columbia 2002) surgical pathology, autopsy; **Mary Zutter** MD (Tulane Univ Sch Med 1981) hematopathology.

APPLICATIONS

Applications and satisfactory references must be received by December 1 for July appointments. Foreign graduates must have a valid ECFMG certificate and a J-1 visa or permanent resident status to be employed by Vanderbilt Hospital.

Vanderbilt University is an equal opportunity, affirmative action university.

Address inquiries to:

Robert Hoffman, M.D., Ph.D.
Director, Residency Training Program
Department of Pathology
Vanderbilt University School of Medicine
CC3322 Medical Center North, 1161 21st Avenue South
Nashville, TN 37232-2561
Phone: (615) 343-4882 • **Fax:** (615) 343-7023 • **E-mail:** pathres.prog@vanderbilt.edu
Web site: http://medschool.mc.vanderbilt.edu/pathology/

Vanderbilt University Pathology Residents, Nashville, Tennessee

UNIVERSITY OF TEXAS SOUTHWESTERN MEDICAL SCHOOL HOSPITALS

Dallas, Texas

PROGRAMS OFFERED

The University of Texas Southwestern Medical School with its affiliated institutions offers fully accredited programs in anatomic (AP) and clinical pathology (CP), including AP/CP-4, AP-3, and CP-3 programs. Also offered are fellowships in surgical pathology, pediatric pathology, cytopathology, neuropathology, dermatopathology, forensic pathology, hematopathology, transfusion medicine, clinical chemistry, clinical microbiology, clinical cytogenetics, and molecular genetic pathology, which speak to the broad range of available material and the large faculty committed to teaching. The program is well balanced, providing the resident with a solid foundation for a career in either academic pathology or clinical practice. Knowledge and expertise are gained through a structured schedule of didactic and interactive conferences, service work with graduated responsibility, and instruction of medical students. Participation in the strong basic and translational research programs of the department is encouraged but not required. The AP/CP-4 program consists of core rotations through each of the basic AP and CP disciplines, supplemented by advanced rotations and electives, including molecular and translational pathology, flow cytometry, electron microscopy, fine needle aspiration cytology, pediatric and perinatal pathology, cytogenetics, informatics and laboratory management. There is ample protected time for electives and/or research. Flexible programs can be constructed to meet the needs of those residents seeking opportunities in basic research, including the opportunity to apply to a funded Physician Scientist Training Program. Rotations for AP-3 or CP-3 residents are focused accordingly, with a two-year core and a flexible year of electives and/or research. Residents participate as discussion leaders in the sophomore pathology course at Southwestern Medical School.

REQUIREMENTS

All candidates for residency must be eligible for a Postgraduate Resident Training Permit from the State of Texas.Candidates from the United States and Canada must be graduates of accredited medical schools. International candidates must have graduated from a medical school with a comparable curriculum acceptable to the Texas Medical Board and must have scores on USMLE Step 1 and both parts of Step 2 available in order to be considered. In order to be competitive, scores should be above 82 (200) on the first attempt. UT-Southwestern sponsors J1 visas but not H1b visas for residents.

FACILITIES

Participating institutions include the University of Texas Southwestern Medical School, the contiguous facilities of Parkland Memorial Hospital, Children's Medical Center, and the UT-Southwestern University Hospitals, all located on the main campus three miles from downtown, as well as the Dallas Veterans Affairs Medical Center, located in south Dallas. These facilities serve both publicly funded and private patient populations. The main campus of the medical school, the University Hospitals, and Children's are all involved in major expansion projects. Parkland has recently opened a new ambulatory surgery building, and a bond proposal for the replacement of the main building of Parkland was passed by Dallas County in 2008, with planning now underway. The five hospitals together contain over 2100 beds with 75,000 admissions. There are 260 autopsies (excluding forensic cases), 47,000 surgicals and bone marrows, 2,500 fine needle aspirates, 69,000 cytology examinations, and over 7,100,000 clinical laboratory determinations per year.Additionally, the Southwestern Institute of Forensic Sciences, which is associated with the Department and is located in the Medical Center complex, performs 3,000 medicolegal autopsies and 28,000 toxicologic examinations per year.

COMMUNITY

"Where the West begins" according to Will Rogers, the Dallas metroplex is now home not only to the Mesquite Rodeo and the Texas State Fair, but also to professional football, baseball, basketball, soccer, hockey, NASCAR and horse racing. A downtown Arts District supports theater, art and history museums, a sculpture garden, and a variety of musical organizations including the Dallas Symphony Orchestra, while the more eclectic nightlife of the nearby Deep Ellum neighborhood hosts jazz and popular musical fare. As the home of Neiman-Marcus, Dallas of course offers world-class shopping, and we boast more restaurants per capita than New York City. Affordable housing is both suburban and urban, including university-owned apartments adjacent to the medical center. The city is ringed by recreational lakes, parks and trails. Our central geography provides ready access to the Gulf of Mexico, both coasts and the world.

STIPENDS AND MAINTENANCE

Annual salary for PGY-1 during 2009-2010 is approximately $46,878. Benefits include health insurance, malpractice insurance, life insurance, three weeks (15 work days) paid vacation per year,a book/travel fund, and a personal laptop computer for the duration of the residency. It should be noted that Texas has no state income tax.

STAFF

Professors

Errol C. Friedberg MD Chair; cancer biology; **Francisco R. Velazquez** MD, SM Associate Vice President for Health System Diagnostic Services; Vice Chair for Clinical Affairs; **Charles F. Timmons** MD, PhD Residency Director; pediatric pathology; **M. Qasim Ansari** MD immunopathology and laboratory management; **Raheela Ashfaq** MD cytopathology and translational pathology; **Jeffrey J. Barnard** MD autopsy and forensic pathology; **Michael Bennett** MD immunobiology; **Dennis K. Burns** MD neuropathology and muscle pathology; **Rita M. Gander** PhD medical microbiology; **Adi F. Gazdar** MD cancer biology; **Robert Genta** MD surgical pathology and gastrointestinal pathology; **Herbert K. Hagler** PhD informatics, bioengineering and electron microscopy; **Yue-Shoung Lu** DVM, PhD comparative medicine; **Linda R. Margraf** MD pediatric pathology and electron microscopy; **Thomas McConnell** MD allied health sciences; **Sara Milchgrub** MD surgical pathology; **Kyle H. Molberg** MD surgical pathology; **Steven P. Pakes** DVM, PhD comparative pathology; **James Richardson** DVM, PhD comparative pathology; **Beverly B. Rogers** MD pediatric pathology and molecular pathology; **Thomas Rogers** MD surgical pathology, kidney and liver pathology; **Ravindra Sarode** MD transfusion medicine and coagulation; **Merlyn Sayers** MD transfusion medicine; **Richard H. Scheuermann** PhD cancer biology; **Alice L. Smith** MD cytopathology and cancer biology; **Paul M. Southern, Jr.** MD medical microbiology; **Arthur G. Weinberg** MD pediatric pathology; **Charles L. White III** MD neuropathology and muscle pathology; **Frank H. Wians, Jr.** PhD clinical chemistry; **Dorothy C. Yuan** PhD immunobiology; **Xin Jin (Joseph) Zhou** MD renal pathology.

Associate Professors

Robin H. Amirkhan MD surgical pathology; **Arnaldo Arbini** MD hematopathology and flow cytometry; **Kelley Carrick** MD surgical pathology and cytopathology; **Tak-Shun Choi** MD transfusion medicine; **James H. Clark III** MD pediatric clinical pathology; **Gene Ewing** MD surgical pathology; **Ibrahim Hashim** PhD clinical chemistry; **Lindsey R. Inman** PhD immunology; **Patricia Jones** PhD pediatric clinical chemistry; **Nitin Karandikar** MD, PhD hematopathology, immunopathology and flow cytometry; **Makoto Kuro-o** MD, PhD molecular pathology; **Joni McClain** MD forensic pathology; **Deborah A Payne** PhD molecular pathology; **Jack Raisanen** MD neuropathology; **Venetia Sarode** MD surgical pathology and cytopathology; **John Schatzle** PhD molecular pathology; **Mark H. Siegelman** MD, PhD cancer biology; **Timothy Sliter** PhD forensic pathology; **Estelle Sontag** PhD neuropathology research; **Laurie J. Sutor** MD transfusion medicine; **Elizabeth L. Todd** PhD toxicology and forensic science.

Assistant Professors

Jyoti Balani MD surgical pathology and cytopathology; **Bradford Barker** MD surgical pathology; **James D Burner** MD transfusion medicine and coagulation; **Laurie Campagna** MD surgical pathology; **Diego Castrillon** MD, PhD translational pathology; **Dominick Cavuoti** DO surgical pathology, cytopathology and medical microbiology; **Weina Chen** MD, PhD hematopathology and flow cytometry; **Sandy Cope-Yokoyama** MD pediatric pathology; **Terri Crook** MD surgical pathology and gastro-intestinal pathology; **Tracy Dyer** MD autopsy and forensic pathology; **Pila Estess** PhD cancer biology; **Yisheng V Fang** MD, PhD surgical and clinical pathology; **Michael N Feliciano** MD surgical pathology; **Erika Fong** MD surgical pathology; **Franklin S. Fuda** DO hematopathology and flow cytometry; **Rene Galindo** MD, PhD molecular pathology; **Ana M Gomez** MD, PhD pediatric pathology; **Toby Gray** MD surgical pathology; **Amy Gruszecki** DO autopsy and forensic pathology; **Caixia Guo** PhD molecular pathology; **Chester Gwin III** MD forensic pathology; **Kimmo Hatanpaa** MD, PhD neuropathology; **Emily Herndon** MD neuropathology and muscle pathology; **R. Nick Hogan** MD, PhD ophthalmology and ophthalmic pathology; **Sarah Johnson-Welch** MD pediatric pathology; **Wareef Kabbani** MD surgical pathology and cytopathology; **Payal Kapur** MD surgical pathology and cytopathology; **Yuri Lemeshev** MD, PhD surgical pathology; **Karén Matevosyan** MD transfusion medicine; **Daniel Noland** MD pediatric clinical pathology; **Daniel Nussenzveig** MD, PhD surgical pathology; **Dwight Oliver** MD surgical pathology and molecular pathology; **Yan Peng** MD surgical pathology and cytopathology; **J. Keith Pinckard** MD, PhD autopsy and forensic pathology; **Reade Quinton** MD Assistant Residency Director; autopsy and forensic pathology; **Dinesh Rakheja** MD pediatric pathology; **Joseph L. Sailors** MD surgical pathology and cytopathology; **Lynn Salzberger** MD autopsy and forensic pathology; **Narayan Shivapurkar** PhD cancer biology; **Carlos Tirado** PhD cytogenetics; **Janis Townsend-Parchman** MD autopsy and forensic pathology; **Jill Urban** MD autopsy and forensic pathology; **Keith Wharton** MD, PhD molecular pathology; **An Zhu** MD surgical pathology.

Instructors

George John PhD molecular pathology; **Stacy McDonald** PhD forensic pathology; **Suwan Sinha** PhD molecular pathology; **Erin Spargo** MD forensic pathology.

Faculty Associates

Chan Choy Foong neuropathology.

APPLICATIONS

Applications must be submitted through the Electronic Residency Application Service (ERAS). Invitations to interview are extended to the most qualified candidates following evaluation of the completed application. Preference for interviews will be given to applications completed before December 1, 2009, for appointment July 1, 2010.

Address inquiries to:

Charles Timmons, MD, PhD
Director of Resident Training, Department of Pathology
University of Texas Southwestern Medical Center at Dallas
5323 Harry Hines Boulevard
Dallas, TX 75390-9073
Phone: (214) 648-2466 • **Fax:** (214) 648-6323 • **E-mail:** pathresprogdir@utsouthwestern.edu
Web site: http://pathcuric1.swmed.edu

UT Southwestern is an equal opportunity institution.

North Campus with University apartment housing in the background.

BAYLOR COLLEGE OF MEDICINE

Houston, Texas

PROGRAMS OFFERED

Accreditation Council for Graduate Medical Education (ACGME) approved training in both anatomical and clinical pathology exists. Trainees may pursue a combined AP-CP program or elect AP or CP tracks. Investigative opportunities are provided for all and emphasized for those inclined toward an academic career. Progressive responsibility is delegated as a motivation in developing competence and independence. Residents assist in teaching medical students and residents from other specialties. Daily teaching conferences are conducted in anatomical and clinical pathology. Subspecialty training in blood banking, cytopathology, dermatopathology, hematopathology, molecular pathology, and pediatric pathology is available.

TYPES AND NUMBERS OF APPOINTMENTS

Thirty-three residency and fellowship positions are offered and 4-6 first-year trainees are selected annually.

FACILITIES

The Baylor Affiliated Hospitals include St. Luke's Episcopal Hospital (625 beds), Ben Taub General Hospital (650 beds), Texas Children's Hospital (715 beds), The Michael E. DeBakey Veterans Affairs Medical Center (1,037 beds) and The Methodist Hospital (1000 beds). These hospitals, as well as the Baylor Department of Pathology Laboratories, provide a diverse spectrum of all types of clinical material. Annually they yield approximately 650 autopsies; 72,766 surgical accessions; 39,000 cytopathology specimens and 9,000,000 clinical tests. All hospitals are located on the campus of the Texas Medical Center except the Veterans Affairs Medical Center. The main campus is also the site of the renowned Texas Medical Center Library which is housed in its own building. Each hospital and laboratory service has its own working library. The facilities of the Baylor Affiliated Hospitals include on-line computer reporting of clinical laboratory results, apheresis, cryopreservation, flow cytometry, image cytometry, immunocytochemistry, electron microscopy and molecular diagnostics, as well as conventional equipment and techniques. Schools of medical technology are an integral part of the laboratory environment.

COMMUNITY

Houston is the fourth largest city in the country and the largest city in the Southwest. It is an active community with numerous productions in opera, symphony and theater. Major league sports are present and Gulf Coast recreation is nearby.

STIPENDS AND MAINTENANCE

The annual stipend for a first-year resident in 2009-10 was $43,221 with subsequent annual increases of approximately $1,000. Hospitalization; life insurance, and malpractice insurance are provided. Proximate parking is provided at nominal cost. There are affordable housing opportunities available near the Medical Center.

STAFF

Professor and Chairman

Thomas M. Wheeler MD urologic pathology, surgical pathology, and cytopathology.

Professors

Gustavo Ayala MD surgical and urologic pathology; **Gregory Buffone** PhD chemistry; **Thomas Cooper** MD molecular biology; **Gretchen Darlington** PhD molecular pathology; **Milton Finegold** MD Associate Chairman, Director Laboratories, Texas Children's Hospital; pediatric pathology; **Ramon Font** MD ocular pathology; **Francis Gannon** MD anatomic and bone pathology; **J. Clay Goodman** MD neuropathology; **Linda Green** MD anatomic pathology and cytopathology; **Mary V. Gresik** MD hematopathology; **M. John Hicks** MD, PhD, DDS electron microscopy, pediatric pathology; **Michael Ittmann** MD, PhD Chief, Service Veterans Affairs Medical Center; prostate/urologic and surgical pathology; **Han-Seob Kim** MD anatomic pathology and cytopathology; **Graeme Marden** PhD developmental biology; **Martin Matzuk** MD, PhD clinical pathology; **Ching-Nan Ou** PhD chemistry; **Perumal Thiagarajan** MD anatomic pathology; **James Versalovic** MD, PhD microbiology, molecular pathology; **David H. Yawn** MD transfusion medicine; **Mamoun Younes** MD tumor markers, GI pathology, immunohistochemistry.

Associate Professors

Adekunle Adesina MD neuropathology and molecular pathology; **Eugenio I. Banez** MD hematology; **Deborah Citron** MD surgical pathology and cytopathology; **Chris Finch** MD cytopathology, surgical pathology; **Carolina Gutierrez** MD surgical pathology; **Debra Kearney** MD cardiovascular pathology; **Bhuvaneswari Krishnan** MD surgical pathology and cytopathology; **Rodolfo Laucirica** MD surgical pathology and cytopathology; **Dolores Lopez-**

Terrada MD, PhD molecular and pediatric pathology; **Mary Ostrowski** MD surgical pathology; **Edwina J. Popek** DO placenta and perinatal pathology; **Richard Sifers** PhD molecular and cellular biology; **Charles Stager** PhD microbiology; **Jun Teruya** MD blood banking and transfusion medicine; **Gordona Verstovsek** MD surgical pathology and cytopathology; **Jochewed Werch** MD transfusion medicine.

Assistant Professors

Meena Bhattacharjee MD neuropathology; **Joiner Cartwright, Jr.** PhD electron microscopy; **Lisa Cohen** MD anatomic and clinical pathology; **Richard Davis** PhD development biology; **Hanna El-Sahly** MD tuberculosis research; **Karen Eldin** MD surgical pathology and cytopathology; **James Fletes** MD surgical pathology; **Scott Goode** PhD developmental genetics; **Michelle Hebert** MD surgical pathology and hematopathology; **Bharati Helekar** MD surgical pathology; **Yve T Huttenbach** MD dermatopatholgy and surgical pathology; **Armand Martel** MD anatomic pathology; **Janine Mawad** MD anatomic pathology and dermatopathology; **Jacqueline Monheit** MD anatomic and clinical pathology; **Thuy Phung** MD, PhD dermatopathology; **Peter Powaser** MD, PhD surgical pathology; **Emilie Rouah** MD surgical pathology and neuropathology; **Andrea Sheehan** MD hematopathology; **Norbert Sule** MD transfusion medicine, surgical pathology; **Ying Ye** MD, PhD cytopathology; **Pamela Younes** MHS, HTL(ASCP) Instructor; **Hong Zhang** MD anatomic pathology.

APPLICATIONS

Graduates of U.S. and Canadian medical schools seeking their first postdoctoral appointment are selected through the National Residency Matching Program. Candidates who have completed their first year of postdoctoral training are appointed directly. Applications will come through ERAS. All applications and accompanying documentation must be received before December 31.

Address inquiries to:

Francis H. Gannon, MD
Director, Residency Program
Department of Pathology
Baylor College of Medicine
One Baylor Plaza
Houston, TX 77030
Phone: (713) 798-4083
Fax: (713) 798-3665 • **E-mail:** yboney@bcm.tmc.edu
Web site: http://www.bcm.tmc.edu/pathology

Texas Medical Center

THE METHODIST HOSPITAL

Houston, Texas

PROGRAMS OFFERED

The Methodist Hospital in Houston, Texas, an affiliate of Weill Medical College of Cornell University, offers ACGME-accredited training in combined anatomic and clinical pathology (AP/CP), in anatomic pathology (AP only) and in clinical pathology (CP only). Residents are encouraged through graduated responsibility under supervision to develop skills that will allow them to practice competently and independently upon completion of their training. The training program is centered at the largest private academic tertiary care hospital in the Texas Medical Center (TMC). Rotations in other institutions at TMC supplement the educational experience (UT-Houston, UT M.D. Anderson Cancer Center and the Harris County Medical Examiner's Office) with elective opportunities as available at the Univeristy of Texas Medical Branch (UTMB) in Galveston, TX. Investigative opportunities are provided and encouraged, with residents expected to participate in scholarly activities leading to publication. A formal Methodist Pathology Resident Research Program (MPRRP) is also available. The primary goal of the program is to prepare clinician-scientists for highly productive careers in academic medicine through an intensely mentored research experience. Support is available for up to 3 years after core residency requirements are complete.

The teaching faculty is internationally renowned with expertise in major subspecialty areas of both anatomic pathology and clinical pathology. Anatomic pathology areas of expertise include multi-organ transplantation, soft tissue and bone pathology, gastrointestinal pathology, dermatopathology, head and neck pathology, cytopathology, renal pathology, genitourinary pathology, pulmonary pathology, ophthalmic pathology, neuropathology (neurodegenerative, forensic and neoplastic), placental and fetal pathology, cardiovascular pathology, autopsy pathology, forensic pathology (Harris County Medical Examiner's Office) and immunohistochemistry. Expertise in clinical pathology subspecialties includes clinical chemistry, core laboratory services, immunology, serology, hematopathology (bone marrow and lymph node interpretation and including flow cytometry), molecular diagnostics, microbiology (bacteriology, mycology, virology, mycobacteriology and parasitology), specialized ophthalmic microbiology service; transfusion medicine (donor services, transfusion service, therapeutic apheresis, peripheral blood progenitor cell harvesting), coagulation, and transplant immunology (HLA). Management training is provided during all rotations and focuses on economic, regulatory, operational and administrative aspects of pathology practice. Clinical pathology consultation is provided within each rotation and on-call 24/7 under the supervision of faculty. Subspecialty area rotations include cytogenetics, HLA, flow cytometry, and molecular diagnostics.

Senior residents are expected to mentor and teach junior residents in pathology. Residents are expected to participate in intradepartmental conferences, tumor boards, and hospital and citywide interdisciplinary conferences. Didactic teaching conferences in both anatomic and clinical pathology are provided as well as microscopic tutorials. Subspecialty training in ACGME-accredited fellowship programs in cytopathology, hematopathology, neuropathology (in conjunction with M.D. Anderson Cancer Center), ophthalmic pathology, surgical pathology and transfusion medicine are currently offered.

TYPES AND NUMBERS OF APPOINTMENTS

Twenty (20) residency positions are offered, and an average of five (5) PGY1 positions are offered annually through the NRMP Matching Program. Fifteen (15) subspecialty fellowship positions in ACGME-accredited programs in Surgical Pathology (5), Hematopathology (2), Selective Hematopathology (2), Cytopathology (2), Neuropathology (2), Ophthalmic Pathology (1), and Transfusion Medicine (1) are also offered (see subspecialty descriptions).

FACILITIES

The Methodist Hospital, a 1,000 bed academic tertiary care hospital, listed as one of the top 50 hospitals in seventeen (17) specialties by U.S. News and World Report, is the primary training site for the pathology residency programs. The following are affiliated hospitals and training sites: University of Texas — Houston (Memorial Hermann Hospital and Lyndon Baines Johnson General Hospital (Adult and Pediatric), UT M.D. Anderson Cancer Center, Harris County Medical Examiner's Office, and UTMB-Galveston.

A diverse case load and case volume of approximately 32,000 surgical pathology accessions, 40,000 cytopathology specimens, 125 autopsies, and 2,500,000 clinical pathology accessions are performed at The Methodist Hospital annually. Facilities include state of the art microscopes, an 18-headed teaching microscope with video setup, telepathology, on-line medical records and radiologic studies, internet access, molecular diagnostics, flow cytometry, apheresis, HLA, cryopreservation, immunocytochemistry, SurePath and ThinPrep techniques in cytopathology, and a fine needle aspiration clinic. A school of Medical Technology is also an integral part of the Department of Pathology.

COMMUNITY

Houston is the fourth largest city in the country and the largest city in the Southwest. Major league sports (baseball, basketball, football, soccer, and minor league hockey) as well as international renowned museums, symphony, opera, ballet, and theatre are an active part of the community. Restaurants featuring multicultural cuisines are available and affordable, and Galveston Island and the Gulf Coast are only 45 minutes away. The International Festival and Bayou City Art Festival are annual events. The George Bush International Airport (IAH) and Hobby Airport serve the city. (http://www.houston-guide.com/)

STIPENDS AND MAINTENANCE

The annual stipend for a PGY-1 resident for year 2008-09 is $45,702. Hospitalization, life, and malpractice insurances, and parking are provided free of cost to residents/fellows. Tuition forgiveness ($2,000 per year for up to 3 years) is paid at graduation to residents who have completed their entire residency training program at Methodist. Affordable housing is available near the Texas Medical Center.

The department of Pathology provides selected text books for PGY-1 residents, an annual book fund is available to PGY-2 residents and above, and membership in state and national organizations/societies for all residents and fellows. The department also provides funding to residents and fellows to attend three in-state meetings each year, and a sponsored meeting of individual choice is provided to PGY-4 residents. Also platform and/or poster presentations by residents/fellows at state and national meetings are financially completely supported by the department. Additional funds for educational activities of up to five days ($1,600 annually for PGY-2 and above, and $2,000 for all graduating residents and fellows) are provided by the Graduate Medical Education Department.

STAFF

Michael W. Lieberman MD, PhD Chairman, neoplasia; **Mojghan Amrikachi** MD surgical pathology and cytopathology; **Rose Anton** MD surgical pathology and cytopathology; **Hazel Awalt** MD surgical pathology; **Alberto Ayala** MD surgical pathology; **Ashok Balsaver** MD surgical pathology; **Roberto Barrios** MD, PhD pulmonary and renal pathology; **David W. Bernard** MD, PhD clinical chemistry; **Philip Cagle** MD pulmonary pathology; **Subhendu Chakraborty** MS flow cytometry and imaging in cancer cell biology; **Chung-Che (Jeff) Chang** MD, PhD hematology and coagulation; **Patricia Chevez-Barrios** MD ophthalmic and surgical pathology; **Donna Coffey** MD surgical pathology and cytopathology; **Richard Davey** MD blood banking; **James Davis** PhD microbiology and virology; **Smaroula Dilioglou** PhD HLA Lab histocompatibility; **April Ewton** MD surgical pathology and hematopathology; **Lillian Gaber** MD surgical pathology; **Yimin Ge** MD surgical pathology and cytopathology; **Enrique Gomez** MD surgical pathology; **Pablo Gomez** MD surgical pathology; **Abida Haque** MD surgical pathology; **Geoffrey Land** PhD HLA Lab histocompatibility; **Christopher Leveque** MD blood banking; **Joyce Maldonado** MD surgical pathology and cytopathology; **Dina R. Mody** MD surgical pathology and cytopathology; **Claudia Molina** MD surgical pathology and microbiology; **Federico Monzon-Bordonaba** MD molecular diagnostics; **Seema Mullick** MD surgical pathology; **James M. Musser** MD, PhD human bacterial pathogenesis; **Thu Ngo** MD surgical pathology; **Randall Olsen** MD, PhD microbiology and bacterial pathogenesis; **Suzanne Powell** MD surgical pathology and neuropathology; **Jae Ro** MD, PhD surgical pathology; **Megan Rust** MD surgical pathology; **Abdus Saleem** MD hematology and coagulation; **Mary R. Schwartz** MD surgical pathology and cytopathology; **Steven Shen** MD, PhD surgical pathology; **Hidehiro Takei** MD cytopathology and neuropathology; **Luan Truong** MD nephropathology; **Ping Wang** PhD clinical chemistry; **Donald Weilbaecher** MD cardiovascular pathology; **Qihui (Jim) Zhai** MD surgical pathology; **Youli Zu** MD, PhD hematology and coagulation.

APPLICATIONS

Graduates of Texas Medical Board (TMB) approved medical schools seeking their first postdoctoral appointment, are selected through the National Residency Matching Program (NRMP). All candidates must be eligible for a TMB physician-in-training permit. Applications will be accepted via ERAS through December 31st of the previous academic year, and all necessary documentation (including ECFMG status) must be received by that date. Transfer candidates may apply directly. For applicants interested in the Methodist Pathology Resident Research Program (MPRRP) please contact us for more information on the application process.

Address inquiries to:

Suzanne Z. Powell, MD
Director, Residency Program
Department of Pathology
6565 Fannin, M227
Houston, TX 77030
Phone: (713) 441-3496 • **Fax:** (713) 441-3489 • **E-mail:** ljozwiak@tmhs.org
Web site: http://www.methodisthealth.com

"The Methodist Hospital"

"The Methodist Hospital Research Institute
(Architect's rendering of the new TMHRI now under construction)"

"The Texas Medical Center with architect's rendering of the new Methodist Outpatient Center (left) now under construction"

THE UNIVERSITY OF TEXAS MEDICAL SCHOOL AT HOUSTON

Houston, Texas

PROGRAMS OFFERED

Fully approved programs are offered in anatomic and clinical pathology (combined or individually), including structured experiences in surgical and autopsy pathology, cytopathology, forensics, pediatric pathology, clinical chemistry, medical microbiology, immunopathology, hematopathology, blood banking, cytogenetics, and molecular diagnostics. Laboratory management training and a wide variety of subspecialty rotations are offered. Residents gain considerable experience in procedures (bone marrow biopsy, fine needle aspiration, and plasmapheresis) and participate in the undergraduate teaching programs of the UTMSH, as well as in the teaching conferences of other clinical departments of the UTMSH hospitals. Daily intradepartmental conferences are given in didactic, unknown, case discussion, and grand rounds formats.

TYPES AND NUMBERS OF APPOINTMENTS

The program is accredited for 28 resident positions, and 5-8 residents are accepted annually.

FACILITIES

Memorial Hermann Hospital (MHH), the primary teaching hospital of UTMSH, has over 750 adult and pediatric beds and is physically contiguous with the Medical School Main Building (where departmental offices, conference rooms, and research labs are located). Residents also rotate through Lyndon B. Johnson General Hospital, which is a UT-staffed county hospital. Between these 2 hospitals and our own Outreach Lab, the department annually performs between 125-150 autopsies, 22,000 surgical pathology examinations, 27,000 cytopathology examinations, and over 3 million laboratory analyses. The MHH clinical pathology laboratory, histology laboratory, and autopsy suite have been rebuilt or renovated since 2001. Other rotations, both elective and core, take place at MD Anderson Cancer Center (a separate unit of the University of Texas), St. Luke's Episcopal Hospital, and The Methodist Hospital; approximately 100,000 surgical pathology cases are accessioned annually at these 3 institutions combined. Thus, residents receive a very broad training experience through rotations at a university hospital, a county hospital, a cancer center, and 2 private hospitals. Residents also spend one month at the Harris County Medical Examiners Office to gain forensic pathology experience. The department maintains an extensive collection of reference textbooks, glass slides, and audiovisual self-study sets. Resident physicians are granted full library privileges at the Jesse Jones Library of the Houston Academy of Medicine, one of the nation's largest biomedical libraries, which is located across a courtyard from the department.

COMMUNITY

The University of Texas Medical School at Houston is located in the Texas Medical Center (TMC), Houston, Texas. Home to over 40 member institutions, the TMC is one of the nation's finest comprehensive centers for patient care, education, and research. Houston, the fourth largest city in the US, offers tremendous civic amenities including theater, opera, symphony, museums, university and professional sports, theaters, night life and excellent restaurants.

STIPENDS AND MAINTENANCE

Residents stipends are listed on the UTMSH Graduate Medical Education website at http://www.med.uth.tmc.edu/administration/gme/benefits.html. Professional liability and health insurance, uniforms, and uniform laundry are all provided. Each resident is given a $800 per year educational stipend, and additional funds are available to residents presenting a poster or platform presentation at national meetings. Health insurance for dependents is available on a contributory basis. Moderately-priced apartments, some owned by UTMSH, are located in the vicinity of the medical center.

STAFF

Robert Hunter Jr. MD, PhD (Univ Chicago 1965) department chairman; microbiology; **Jeffrey Actor** PhD (Univ Massachusetts 1991) microbiology; **Yu Bai** MD, PhD (Beijing Medical Univ 1987) blood banking, molecular diagnostics; **Diane Bick** PhD (Baylor Col Med 1993) biophysics/biochemistry; **Roger Bick** FAHA, CBiol, MIBiol (Univ London 1986) cellular & biochemical pathology; **Robert E. Brown** MD (Med Col Virginia 1966) vice chair; surgical pathology, morphoproteomics; **L. Maximilian Buja** MD (Tulane Univ 1967) cardiovascular and autopsy pathology; **Lei Chen** MD (Tongji Med Univ 1983) hematopathology, surgical pathology; **Michael Covinsky** MD, PhD (Baylor Col Med 1997) pediatric pathology; **Amitava Dasgupta** PhD (Stanford Univ 1986) chemistry; **Xiuzhen Duan** MD (Harbin Med Univ 1982) surgical pathology, cytopathology; **Diane Edmondson** PhD (Univ Texas Houston 1994) Lyme disease; **Rhonda Ghorbani** MD (Albany Med Col 1993) surgical pathology, cytopathology; **Orieji Illoh** MD (Ahmadu Bello

Univ 1991) blood banking; **Chinnaswamy Jagannath** PhD (Univ India 1984) microbiology; **Laura Jimenez-Quintero** MD (Univ Autonoma de Nuevo Leon 1985) surgical pathology; **Marylee Kott** MD (Univ Texas-Houston 1977) surgical pathology, cytopathology; **Gerhard Krueger** MD, PhD (Univ Berlin 1962) autopsy pathology, research; **Wei Li** MD, PhD (Guangxi Med Univ 1983) surgical pathology, cytopathology; **Tao Lin** MD, PhD (Beijing Med Univ, Inst Epidemiology & Microbiology 1986/93) microbiology, immunology; **Jing Liu** MD, PhD (Univ Beijing 1982) surgical pathology, cytopathology; **Jun Liu** PhD (Chinese Acad Science Beijing 1998) cryoelectronmicroscopy; **John Milam** MD (Louisiana State Univ New Orleans 1960) surgical pathology, blood banking; **Andy N.D. Nguyen** MD (Univ Texas Med Branch 1989) coagulation, hematopathology; **Yasuhiro Nishiyama** PhD (Kobe-Gakuin Univ 1995) chemistry; **Steven Norris** PhD (UCLA 1980) physiology and immunopathology of bacterial pathogens; **Sozos Papasozomenos** MD (Univ Greece 1971) neuropathology, neurobiology; **Angel Paredes** PhD (Univ Texas Austin 1993) cryoelectronmicroscopy; **Sudhir Paul** PhD (Univ India 1980) immunology; **Yingchao Piao** MD, PhD (Yanbian Med School 1985) cytopathology, hematopathology, surgical pathology; **Semyon Risin** MD, PhD (Minsk State Med Inst 1964) immunology; **Barry Rittman** PhD (Univ Iowa 1986) histology; **Harvey Rosenberg** MD (Baylor Col Med 1949) pediatric pathology; **Keri Smith** PhD (Montana State Univ 2001) cellular immunology, mucosal immunology; **James Stoops** PhD (Northwestern Univ 1966) structure & function of macromolecules; **Hiroaki Taguchi** PhD (Kobe-Gakuin Univ 1997) chemistry; **Nina Tatevian** MD, PhD (Second Moscow Med Sch 1973) pediatric pathology; **Margaret Uthman** MD (Univ Arkansas 1982) hematopathology; **Regina Verani** MD (Fed Univ Rio de Janeiro 1969) renal pathology; **Min Wang** MD, PhD (Bengbu Med Col 1982) surgical pathology, neuropathology; **Audrey Wanger** PhD (Cornell Univ 1986) microbiology; **Priya Weerasinghe** MD, PhD (Vitebsk State Med Univ, Belarus/Mem Univ Newfoundland 1990/2002) cancer biology oncosis; **Peisha Yan** MD (Third Military Med Col, China 1981) surgical pathology, cytopathology; **Rongzhen Zhang** MD, PhD (China Med Univ, Chinese Univ of Hong Kong 1994/2004) therapy of shock trauma; **Bihong Zhao** MD, PhD (Xiangya Med Sch 1982) surgical pathology.

APPLICATIONS

Applicants should be graduates of medical schools accredited by the ACGME. Foreign medical graduates must have an ECFMG Certificate. Satisfactory references are required. Residents are renewable annually on the basis of satisfactory performance.

Address inquiries to:

Director of Resident Training
Department of Pathology and Laboratory Medicine
University of Texas Medical School at Houston
6431 Fannin, MSB 2.262
Houston, TX 77030
Phone: (713) 500-5402
Web site: http://www.uth.tmc.edu/pathology/

The University of Texas Medical School at Houston is an equal opportunity/affirmative action employer.

TEXAS TECH UNIVERSITY HEALTH SCIENCES CENTER

Lubbock, Texas

PROGRAMS OFFERED

Texas Tech University Health Sciences Center (TTUHSC) Department of Pathology is a fully approved training program in combined anatomic and clinical pathology. The program is designed to provide a strong foundation of basic and current knowledge upon which to build a career in the general practice of pathology or any of its subdisciplines. TTUHSC Department of Pathology intends to meet the educational needs of those who wish to pursue academic careers as well as those who plan to enter the practice of pathology in a community hospital setting. Areas of training include: autopsy and surgical pathology, cytopathology, dermatopathology, diagnostic electron microscopy, forensic pathology, neuropathology, pediatric pathology, clinical chemistry and toxicology, hematopathology and flow cytometry, immunopathology, microbiology (including parasitology and virology), molecular biology and cytogenetics, transfusion medicine, medical informatics, and laboratory administration.

TYPES AND NUMBERS OF APPOINTMENTS

Currently, eight pathology residency positions are available. Two first-year positions are offered each year. In addition to Pathology, there are approved residency training programs in Anesthesiology, Dermatology, Family Practice, Internal Medicine, Obstetrics/Gynecology, Ophthalmology, Orthopaedic Surgery, Pediatrics, Psychiatry and Surgery.

FACILITIES

The Texas Tech University Health Sciences Center is contiguous with University Medical Center and Children's Hospital, which provide comprehensive medical care to the people of West Texas and Eastern New Mexico. Combined, these hospitals contain 365 beds and 40 bassinets, admit over 16,000 patients annually, and have been designated as regional perinatal, burn and trauma centers. There is an annual combined total of over 900 autopsies (including forensic examinations), 12,000 surgical pathology specimens, 15,000 cytologies, 290 bone marrow examinations and peripheral smear consultations, and 2,500,000 clinical laboratory determinations. Special service laboratories provide support for active bone marrow and renal transplant programs. The training program also includes rotations in pathology at the affiliated Covenant Health Care System. In addition to the library of the Health Sciences Center, residents have access to the extensive pathology reference materials of the department's own collection.

COMMUNITY

Lubbock has a population of 250,000 and is the hub city of the South Plains region of West Texas. The city and University offer numerous cultural, educational and recreational opportunities without "big city" hassles. The proximity to the main campus offers easy access to shared facilities such as the Student Recreational and Aquatic Centers. The climate is typical of the desert Southwest with mild winters and dry, warm summers.

STIPENDS AND MAINTENANCE

The current salary for first-year residents is $42,044 (2008-2009). Affordable housing is available nearby. Pathology residents are provided with professional liability insurance, uniforms, office space, and a microscope for their personal usage. Medical and dental insurance is provided for the resident and his/her family. Disability insurance is provided for the resident. A $2000/per year special augmentation (less taxes) depending on Dean's approval and departmental funding is provided for purchase of books. Leave is approved for 20 working days per year. Leave is in addition to holidays. Residents also receive 5 paid working days for attendance at outside educational activities.

STAFF

Dale Dunn MD (Univ Western Ontario 1979) Chairman and Director, Residency Program; transfusion medicine, histocompatability; **Charles Bradley** PhD (Univ Kentucky 1975) clinical chemistry, toxicology, medical informatics; **Chwan-LiShen** PhD (Purdue Univ 1995) physiopathology; **Suzanne Graham** MD (Duke Univ 1975) orthopedic pathology, surgical pathology; **Safaa Labib** MD (Ain Sham Univ 1986) hematopathology; **Viviane Mamlok** MD (Univ Brussels 1983) pediatric pathology; **Ruc Manh Tran** MD (Saigon Med Ctr 1970) renal and transplantation pathology, surgical pathology, electron microscopy; **Elizabeth Miller** MD (Texas Tech Univ 1998) hospital autopsies; **Jeffrey Oliver** MD (Texas Tech Univ 1995) microbiology, immunology, cytopathology, surgical pathology, hematopathology, flow cytometry; **Barbara Pence** PhD (Texas Tech Univ 1984) experimental pathology; **Christina Samathanam** MD (Albert Einstein 1997) gastro pathology; **Afzal Siddiqui** PhD(Univ Western Ontario 1986) parasitology; **Tootie Tatum** PhD (Univ of New Mexico SOM) Molecular Diagnostic Pathology; **Vijay Tonk** PhD (Southwestern Univ 1992) cytogenetics; **Mitchell Wachtel** MD (Univ Miami 1985) surgical pathology, cytopathology; **Irfan Warraich** MD (Punjab Medical College 1993) hematology, cytopathology.

APPLICATIONS

All required application materials must be received no later than November 30 for appointments beginning July 1 of the following year. All applicants will participate in the National Resident Matching Program.

Address inquiries to:

Anna Rodriguez, Residency Coordinator
TTUHSC, Department of Pathology
3601 4th Street
Lubbock, TX 79430
Phone: (806) 743-2533 • **Fax:** (806) 743-2111 • **E-mail:** Anna.Rodriguez@ttuhsc.edu
Web site: http://www.ttuhsc.edu/som/pathology/

THE UNIVERSITY OF TEXAS HEALTH SCIENCE CENTER AT SAN ANTONIO

San Antonio, Texas

PROGRAMS OFFERED

The Department of Pathology at The University of Texas Health Science Center in San Antonio offers a complete residency training program with a variety of options to be chosen by the trainee. Training is available for individuals wishing to pursue a combined AP/CP program or only anatomic pathology or clinical pathology. The program consists of three to four years of core training in AP and/or CP. Up to nine months of electives are available in the 4-year program. Core rotations are divided between University Hospital and Audie Murphy Veterans Affairs Hospital. Anatomic pathology rotations include surgical pathology, cytology, and autopsy with advanced training in electron microscopy, immuno cytochemistry, renal biopsy, neuropathology, breast pathology, and oral, head and neck pathology. Clinical pathology rotations include hematology, blood banking, clinical chemistry, and microbiology with advanced training in hematology, molecular diagnosis, coagulation, apheresis, cytogenetics, and special mycology techniques. Besides the usual duties expected of each rotation, residents prepare and participate in formal and informal presentations for departmental and interdepartmental conferences, journal clubs and research conferences. Residents participate in medical student teaching for second- and fourth-year students and monthly city-wide pathology conferences. The program requires participation in ongoing clinical or basic research projects and provides support for residency research experiences and presentations at state and national meetings.

TYPES AND NUMBERS OF APPOINTMENTS

The residency program is fully accredited for 16 AP/CP positions; clinical and research fellowships are also offered. Three to four first-year resident positions are routinely available each year.

FACILITIES

The 604-bed University Hospital opened in 1968 as the principal teaching hospital of The University of Texas Medical School at San Antonio. The Chairman and faculty members form the professional pathology staff of the hospital. The Audie Murphy Veterans Affairs Hospital, adjacent to the University Hospital, has more than 700 beds and is also staffed by full-time departmental faculty. The combined teaching material includes 25,000 surgicals; 100 autopsies; 28,000 cytologic specimens and more than four million clinical laboratory examinations per year. The Department of Pathology of the 900-bed Christus Santa Rosa Medical Center and Children's Hospital is affiliated with the residency program and provides special training in pediatric pathology. Other affiliated institutions offering electives in anatomic and clinical pathology for our residents include the South Texas Dermatopathology Lab and the Bexar County Medical Examiner's Office where additional autopsy experience is achieved.

Research: Most of the faculty actively pursue research ranging from clinically oriented studies to the basic sciences. The Medical School adjoins the University Hospital and the Department of Pathology provides special diagnostic and research facilities which include cell and molecular biology, cytogenetics, flow cytometry, virology, bacteriology, mycology laboratories, and biochemical research laboratories conducting research on the pathogenesis of disease. Departmental research is funded annually by over 4 million dollars from extramural sources. Core facilities in allied programs support nucleic acids synthesis and sequencing, peptide synthesis and sequencing, and transgenic mouse generation, as well as proteomics. The Department has a close association with Southwest Biomedical Foundation, a research facility with internationally recognized programs in atherosclerosis and neonatal pathology.

COMMUNITY

San Antonio, in South Central Texas, is a city of more than 1,000,000, eighth largest in the United States. It combines the cultural advantages of a large city, such as an outstanding symphony, art museum and theaters, with the charm of its Spanish heritage. The climate is warm and dry and ideal for year-round outdoor sports. San Antonio is a three-hour drive from Mexico and also from boating and fishing on the Gulf of Mexico. Several of the high schools in San Antonio have received awards of excellence from the US Department of Education. The cost of living in San Antonio is relatively low, and excellent housing is available near the hospital.

STIPENDS AND MAINTENANCE

Salary for the first year post-MD training is $42,675.78 per year with an approximate $1,000 increase for each subsequent year. Meals and quarters are not provided; however, meals are provided when residents are on call. Professional liability insurance and two weeks vacation with pay are provided for PG-1 level residents. All other residents are allowed three weeks vacation.

STAFF

Professor and Chair

Robert L. Reddick MD (Univ North Carolina Chapel Hill 1973) oncologic pathology and atherosclerosis.

Professors

C.N. Clare MD (Univ Texas Hlth Sci Ctr at San Antonio 1975) hematology, cytogenetics; **V.J.M. DiMaio** MD (SUNY Downstate 1965) County Medical Examiner; forensic pathology; **L.J. Fowler** MD (Wayne State Univ 1976) fine needle aspiration, endocrine; **C. R. Harrison** MD (Univ Florida 1971) immunohematology, blood banking; **J. Henry** MD (Univ Wuerzburg, Germany 1964) neuropathology; **J. Jagirdar** MD (Calcutta Med Col 1976) anatomic pathology, pulmonary pathology; **A.C. Jones** DDS (Med Col Virginia 1986) oral and maxillofacial pathology; **J.H. Jorgensen** PhD (Univ Texas Med Branch 1973) microbiology; **M.C. Kinney** MD (Univ Texas Southwestern Med 1981) hematopathology; **H.S. McGuff** DDS (Univ Texas Hlth Sci Ctr at San Antonio 1977) oral pathology; **C.A. McMahan** PhD (Rice Univ 1970) biostatistics,atherosclerosis; **L.M. McManus** PhD (Univ Colorado 1978) general pathology, immunology; **G.E. Mott** PhD (Texas A&M Univ 1970) biochemical pathology; **J.D. Olson** MD, PhD (Georgetown Univ 1970) hematopathology, thrombosis, hemostasis; **R.N. Pinckard** PhD (Univ Edinburgh, Scotland 1967) immunology; **M.S. Pollack** PhD (Rutgers Univ 1968) histocompatibility, immunogenetics; **M.G. Rinaldi** PhD (Univ Cal-Davis 1980) mycology; **F.E. Sharkey** MD (Cornell Univ 1970) surgical pathology; **J. Smith** PhD (Yale Univ 1970) molecular biophysics, cellular aging; **F. Tio** MD (Cebu Inst Med, Philippines 1964) surgical pathology, electron microscopy; **P.T. Valente** MD (Columbia Univ 1977) cytopathology, gynecologic pathology; **M.A. Venkatachalam** MD (Calcutta Med Col, India 1962) anatomic pathology, experimental renal pathology; **S.L. Werner** MD (Univ Maryland Sch Med 1976) surgical pathology, nephropathology; **I. Yeh** MD (Univ Arkansas 1982) breast and gynecologic pathology, cytopathology.

Associate Professors

S. Adhvaryu PhD (Gujarat Univ, India 1979) cytogenetics; **E. Bryan** MD (Univ Mississippi Sch Med 1978) transfusion medicine; **A. Ehsan** MD (Dow Med Col 1989) hematopathology; **K. Fiebelkorn** MD (Johns Hopkins Univ Sch Med 1996) microbiology, virology; **N. Ghosh-Choudhury** PhD (McMaster Univ 1987) bone cell differentiation, gene transcription; **J. Heim-Hall** MD (Univ degli Studi Siena 1986) surgical pathology; **M. Naski** MD, PhD (Univ Michigan 1991) experimental and anatomic pathology; **T. J. Prihoda** PhD (Texas A&M Univ 1981) biostatistics; **P. Saikumar** PhD (Indian Inst Sci 1985) molecular pathology.

Assistant Professors

H. Fan MD (Wenshou Medical College, China 1982) hematopathology; **M. Fernandez** MD (Instituto Tecnologico de Monterrey, Mexico 1995) surgical pathology; **A. Fothergill** MA, MBA (Webster Univ 1996) mycology; **W. Furmaga** MD (Col Med, Jagiellonian Univ Poland 1984) clinical chemistry; **S. Gunn** MD, PhD (Univ Texas Hlth Sci Ctr at San Antonio 2002) molecular pathology; **R. Higgins** MD (Univ NM Sch of Med 2002) hematopathology; **M. Reinhold** PhD (Univ Washington 1997) immunology, experimental pathology; **R. Robetorye** MD, PhD (Baylor Col Med 1997) hematopathology, lymphomagenesis; **D. Sutton** PhD (Univ Oregon Hlth Sci Ctr 1964) mycology.

Instructors

Y. Patel MSC,MS (Gujarat Univ, India 1967) experimental renal pathology, biochemical analysis; **A. Siddiqi** PhD (Karolinska Inst, Sweden 1992) cell death mechanisms; **H. Siddiqui** MBBS (King Edward Medical College, Pakistan 1990) transfusion medicine.

Associated Faculty

G.A. Bannayan MD (American Univ, Beirut 1957) renal pathology, surgical pathology; **T. L. Davis** MD (Univ Texas Hlth Sci Ctr at San Antonio 1983) dermatopathology; **R. Frost** MD (Texas Tech Univ 1983) forensic pathology; **L. F. Libow** MD (George Washington Univ Sch of Med 1980) dermatopathology; **D. K. Molina** MD (Univ Texas Hlth Sci Ctr at San Antonio 1998) forensics; **J. Rulon** MD (Univ Washington 1991) forensics; **V.A. Saldivar** MD (Univ Nacional Mexico 1966) pediatric pathology.

APPLICATIONS

Graduates of U.S. or Canada and of foreign medical schools will be considered who meet all Texas licensing requirements (must have passed each USLME exam in 3 or less attempts). Applicants for our residency must clear a screening process to ensure that they are not listed by a federal agency as excluded, suspended, or otherwise ineligible for participation in federal programs. The UTHSCSA will perform the screening for you at no cost. Graduates of foreign medical schools must have a valid ECFMG certificate, as well as J-1, green card or permanent citizenship. References are required. Applications must be submitted by November 26 through ERAS only for PGY-1 positions. Personal interviews will be granted to selected candidates meeting the qualifications, after review of completed application and references.

Address Inquires to:

Larry J. Fowler, MD, Director of Pathology Residency Program
The University of Texas Health Science Center at San Antonio
7703 Floyd Curl Drive
San Antonio, TX 78229-3900
Phone: (210) 567-6731
Web site: http://pathology.uthscsa.edu/residency/

The University of Texas Health Science Center at San Antonio including University Hospital and Audie Murphy VA Hospital

SCOTT & WHITE MEMORIAL HOSPITAL SCOTT, SHERWOOD AND BRINDLEY FOUNDATION

Temple, Texas

PROGRAMS OFFERED

A fully approved four-year program in anatomic and clinical pathology is offered. Emphasis is given to one-on-one teaching with residents at all levels working closely with the staff. In the anatomic pathology rotations, diagnostic skills in surgical pathology are emphasized. The exposure to large numbers of frozen sections instills an attitude of confidence that will be more than adequate preparation for future dealings with surgical colleagues. Residents have a great deal of input in the development of their curriculum in the fourth year. Opportunities for experience in administration, computerization (with internet access for each residentat his/her owndesk), molecular pathology (including FISH and PCR), reference laboratory programs, cytogenetics, immunohistochemistry, fine needle aspirations, and medical student teaching broaden considerably the scope of the program. Research is encouraged in molecular and molecular research rotations are available at the Division of Investigative Pathology on the VA Campus. There is also a carefully planned two-year core curriculum teaching conference schedule for both disciplines given by both staff and residents. A broad range of conferences, including a daily diagnostic Surgical Pathology conference is available for resident attendance.

TYPES AND NUMBERS OF APPOINTMENTS

Positions are available fortwelve residents. Fellowship positions in Hematopathologyand Cytopathology are also available.

FACILITIES

The Scott and White Memorial Hospital has approximately 687 beds and 40 bassinets. Housed within the same physical facilities is the Scott and White Clinic, one of the nation's largest multi-specialty clinics with 667 full-time permanent staff. The institution is concerned with both primary and tertiary care and is the major teaching facility for the Texas A&M University College of Medicine. There are a total of 29 satellite clinics in the Scott and White System. The anatomic and clinical pathology laboratory is extensively automated and performs approximately 3.5 million tests annually. The anatomic pathology laboratory examines over 40,000 surgical specimens per year of which approximately 1,600 are submitted for frozen section analysis. There are over 2,500 fine needle aspirations per year, both aspirates of superficial lesions performed by the pathology staff as well as deep-seated lesions aspirated by interventional clinicians. There are over 50,000 other cytology specimens (including over 3,000 non-GYN)and approximately 60 post-mortem examinations per year. One electron microscope is utilized within the department. The library has a print collection of about 6500 book titles and 490 journal titles. The library has 4600 electronic books and 1844 electronic journal subscriptions with access to about 15,000 more journal through our membership in TEXSHARE. All electronic databases, books and journal titles are IP address authenticated, making it possible to access them from anywhere on the S&W network. There is also access to the Texas A &M library.

COMMUNITY

Temple is a Central Texas city of approximately 50,000 population located between Dallas and San Antonio on Interstate 35. It is a transportation center, getting its start as a division center for the Santa Fe Railroad. A large variety of light industry is present in the city. In addition there is Temple College, The University of Mary-Hardin Baylor, Baylor University, Cultural Activities Center, civic theater, numerous parks and two large nearby lakes. The climate is moderate with average January temperatures ranging from 37 to 60 and average August temperatures ranging from 72 to 96.

STIPENDS AND MAINTENANCE

The annual stipend range for all house staff is $43,057 to $50,877 increasing at approximately $1,000 increments per year. Benefits include vacation, sick leave, funding for research presentations, free parking, uniforms and their laundering as well as medical and life insurance at low rates.

STAFF

John F. Greene, Jr. MD (Loma Linda Univ, Letterman) Chairman Dept Pathology; subspecialty boards dermatopathology; subspecialty interest malignant melanoma; **H. Ray Adams** PhD (Texas Southwestern Univ) pharmacology, clinical pathology in chemistry and toxicology; **Alexzander Asea** PhD (Gothenburg Univ) Chief Division of Investigative Pathology; Director of Proteonomics Laboratories and Cain Chair in Clinical Pathology; **Robert W. Astarita** MD

(Univ Rochester Sch Med) Chief, Pathology and Laboratory Medicine Service, Central Texas Veterans Hlth Care System; subspecialty interest hematopathology, lymphoproliferative disorders; **Robert S. Beissner** MD, PhD (Univ Texas Hlth Sci Ctr at San Antonio, Scott and White) subspecialty interests pulmonary pathology, fine needle aspiration; **Sheila Dobin** PhD (Univ Texas Grad Sch Biomed Sci, Houston) cytogenetics and genetics; **Ludvik R. Donner** MD, PhD (Charles Univ, Prague; George Washington Univ Med Ctr; MD Anderson) pathology; subspecialty interest lymphoproliferative disorders; **Robert Fader** PhD (Univ Texas Med Branch, Galveston) Section Chief, microbiology and virology; special interest applied clinical microbiology; **Shanthi Gopal** MD (Bangalore Med Col, Clinical Pathology, Stanford Health Services,) Staff Pathologist; subspecialty boards Hematopathology, Central Texas Veterans Hlth Care System; **Thomas W. Huber** PhD (Univ Texas at Austin) Staff Microbiologist, Central Texas Veterans Hlth Care System; **Edwin H. Johnson** MD (Baylor Col Med) Chief Anatomic Pathology, Central Texas Veterans Hlth Care System; **Kathleen A. Jones** MD (Texas A&M Univ, Scott & White) anatomic pathology; subspecialty interest renal pathology; **William Koss** MD (Buenos Aires, Argentina; Univ Pittsburgh Hlth Ctr) Director Division Clinical Pathology; subspecialty boards hematopathology; **Walter Linz** MD, Bowman Gray Sch Med, Wake Forest Univ, Blood Bank; **Lisa Lopez** MD (Texas A&M Univ., Scott and White) anatomic pathology; subspeciality interest dermatopathology; **Eric R. Rachut** MD (Univ Iowa) Staff Pathologist, Central Texas Veterans Hlth Care System; **Arundhati Rao** MD, PhD (Mysore Med Col, India; Univ Texas at Austin, Scott & White) anatomic and clinical pathology; subspecialty interest molecular pathology, renal pathology; **Edward S. Rappaport** MD (Loyola Univ, Stritch Sch Med) clinical pathology; subspecialty boards hematopathology; **Lubna H. Sayage-Rabié** MD (Univ Kuwait Fac Med, MD Anderson Cancer Ctr) cytopathology. anatomic pathology, fine needle aspirations; **V.O. Speights, Jr.** DO (Texas Col Osteopathic Med, Cleveland Clinic, Scott & White) anatomic pathology; subspecialty interest genitourinary pathology; **A. Michael Spiekerman** PhD (Univ Texas) biochemistry, clinical pathology in special chemistry, endocrine testing and immunochemistry.

APPLICATIONS

Residencies are open to graduates of approved medical schools. All applicants must pass USMLE Steps 1 and 2 before entering any Scott and White Residency program. Foreign medical graduates are required to have the ECFMG certificate. If on a Visa must have J-1. All applicants are received through ERAS.

Address inquiries to:

V. O. Speights, DO
Director, Pathology Residency Program
Scott& White Clinic
2401 S 31st
Temple, TX 76508
Phone: (254) 724-7354 • **Fax:** (254) 724-6329 • **E-mail:** cdixon@swmail.sw.org
Web site: http://www.sw.org

UNIVERSITY OF UTAH MEDICAL CENTER

Salt Lake City, Utah

PROGRAMS OFFERED

The pathology department offers approved postgraduate training programs in both anatomic and clinical pathology leading to board certification. The residency mission is to train exceptional board certified pathologists through flexible programs individually tailored for subsequent careers ranging from combined AP/CP community pathology service to specialized, academic research. The program uses an annually revised core curriculum emphasizing interdisciplinary education, and equal excellence in anatomic and clinical pathology. It incorporates graduated levels of responsibility and authority in the traditional service realm with training in molecular biology, medical informatics, quality assurance, and business and hospital management. With a faculty of over 90 committed academic and clinical practitioners at multiple facilities, including university, children's and Veterans Affairs hospitals, three major community hospitals, the state medical examiner, and a national reference laboratory, the residency provides exposure to and experience in a full complement of autopsy, surgical and clinical pathology cases and medical problems, as well as eminent basic science and clinical research. A complete program description can be found at http://www.path.utah.edu.

REQUIREMENTS

The program is accredited for 19 positions. We offer four AP/CP first year positions each year. CP-only and AP-only positions vary year to year. Also available are subspecialty fellowships in clinical chemistry, hematopathology, immunology, microbiology, molecular genetics, pediatric pathology, surgical pathology and cytopathology.

FACILITIES

Clinical facilities of the University of Utah Department of Pathology are comprised of the University Hospital, Huntsman Cancer Institute, Veterans Affairs Medical Center, St. Mark's Hospital, LDS Hospital, Primary Children's Medical Center, State Medical Examiner's Office, and a major clinical reference laboratory, the 290,000 square foot Associated Regional and University Pathologists (ARUP) facility.

The University Hospital and affiliated hospitals have a bed capacity of 1,700 that generate approximately 260 autopsies, 53,000 surgicals, 61,000 cytologies, 800 bone marrows and 8,800,000 clinical laboratory procedures each year. Since the University Hospital is the only academic hospital in the geographically vast intermountain area, a wide variety of sophisticated medical problems is available for study and the department provides pathology consultative services to many hospitals in the area. The Huntsman Cancer Institute is the only National Cancer Institute-designated cancer center in the Intermountain West. The Institute is a nonprofit research and treatment center that combines research, education and patient care programs and facilities, including the Huntsman Cancer Hospital.

ARUP Laboratories was created in 1984 to support the academic mission of the University of Utah and is located in the 320 acre Research Park adjacent to campus. ARUP is a wholly owned private enterprise of the University of Utah, managed by the Department of Pathology, and is recognized for excellence as a leading national reference laboratory. ARUP has over 2,200 employees and has one of the largest laboratory test menus in the United States offering more than 2,000 tests and test combinations in clinical laboratory testing and anatomic pathology services. ARUP has clients in all 50 states, and more than 85% of the 25,000 daily patient specimens come from outside the University Hospital. Pathology Residents rotate through ARUP for major portions of their clinical training and are thus exposed to the full spectrum of routine and esoteric laboratory testing as well as new test development, sales and marketing, and lab management. Laboratory Medical Directors are full-time faculty of the University of Utah. Residents also have the opportunity to perform research with various faculty members at ARUP as well as through the ARUP Institute for Clinical and Experimental Pathology.Research collaborations occur with faculty in multiple departments and organizations from within and beyond the University.

Website: www.aruplab.com.
www.arupconsult.com.

COMMUNITY

Salt Lake City, bounded on the west by the million-acre Great Salt Lake and on the east by the sharply rising Wasatch Mountains, is one of North America's most beautiful cities. Midway between Denver and San Francisco, it is the gateway to the Intermountain West. With a population approaching one and one-half million, greater Salt Lake blends the virtues of a small town with the advantages of a large city. The Utah Symphony Orchestra, Ballet West, Repertory Dance Theatre, Utah Opera Company, Tabernacle Choir, and a growing number of theatre groups and art galleries are assets unusual in a city its size. Major sporting events are provided by several colleges and professional basketball, baseball, soccer and hockey teams. In spite of recent growth, Salt Lake City remains a livable, compact city. The downtown area and the University are surrounded by attractive, well-maintained residential neighborhoods.

University of Utah pathology residents have full access to the University facilities for such activities as swimming and aquatic sports, tennis, golf and racquetball. Salt Lake City is in a valley surrounded by mountains which offer diverse outdoor sports such as skiing, kayaking, fishing, hiking and mountain climbing. The skiing is the most consistent in North America. At an elevation of some 4,300 feet, Salt Lake City enjoys a mild climate with four distinct seasons. Rainfall is limited in the valley but ample snowfall in the neighboring mountains provides some of the finest skiing in the world.

STIPENDS AND MAINTENANCE

Stipends vary between $47,625 and $58,935 for 2009/2010, depending on level of training. Funding is available for four years of pathology residency education. All residents are covered by professional liability insurance. Other benefits for the residents include three weeks paid vacation and a book/travel fund. The housestaff have a choice of health insurance plans that cover both the housestaff and their family with premium costs shared between the University Hospital and the housestaff. As a University employee, the houseofficer and family are eligible for reduced tuition, use of university recreation facilities on campus, reduced admission to entertainment, sports and cultural activities, bookstore discounts, and library and credit union privileges.

STAFF

University Hospital/ARUP Laboratories, Inc. - Anatomic Pathology

Lester J. Layfield MD, Division Head, Surgical Pathology and FNAs; **Xinjian Chen** MD, PhD, GI Pathology; **Steven S. Chin** MD, PhD, Neuropathology; **Frederic C. Clayton** MD, Autopsy and Renal Pathology; **Brian T. Collins** MD, Cytopathology; **Gary L. Ellis** DDS, Head and Neck Pathology; **Lyska L. Emerson** MD, Surgical and GI Pathology; **Evelyn V. Gopez** MD, Cytopathology; **Ronald M. Harris** MD, Dermatopathology; **Albert Ho** MD, PhD, Hematopathology; **Joseph A. Holden** MD, PhD, Surgical Pathology; **Elke A. Jarboe** MD, Surgical, GYN and Cytopathology; **Todd Kelley** MD, Flow Cytometry, Hematopathology; **Carl R. Kjeldsberg** MD, Hematopathology; **Ting Liu** MD, Surgical Pathology; **Rodney Miles** MD, PhD, Hematopathology; **Sherrie L. Perkins** MD, PhD, Hematopathology; **M Patricia Revelo** MD, PhD, Renal Pathology; **Mohamed E. Salama** MD, Hematopathology; **Wade S. Samowitz** MD, GI Pathology; **Harsh Thaker** MD, PhD, Placental and Surgical Pathology.

University Hospital/ARUP Laboratories, Inc. - Clinical Pathology

Peter E. Jensen MD Chair, Immunology; **Edward R. Ashwood** MD, CEO of ARUP; **David W. Bahler** MD, PhD, Flow Cytometry; **Pinar Bayrak-Toydemir** MD, PhD, Molecular Genetics; **Philip S. Bernard** MD, Molecular Pathology; **Robert C. Blaylock** MD, Transfusion Medicine; **Arthur Brothman** PhD, Cytogenetics; **Julio Delgado** MD, Immunology; **David D. Eckels** PhD, H&I; **Mark A. Fisher** PhD, Bacteriology; **Elizabeth Frank** PhD, Chemistry; **David G. Grenache** PhD, Chemistry; **Kimberly E Hanson** MD, Mycology; **Patrice K. Held** PhD, Biochemical Genetics; **Harry R. Hill** MD, Division Head, Immunology; **David R. Hillyard** MD, Molecular Pathology; **Brian R. Jackson** MD, Informatics; **Christopher M. Lehman** MD, Chemistry; **Christine M. Litwin** MD, Immunology; **Nicola Longo** MD, PhD, Biochemicl Genetics; **Elaine Lyon** PhD, Molecular Pathology; **Rong Mao** MD, Molecular Genetics; **Gwendolyn McMillin** PhD, Clinical Toxicology; **A. Wayne Meikle** MD, Endocrinology; **Marzia Pasquali** PhD, Biochemical Genetics; **Josef T. Prchal** MD, Special Genetics; **Larry G. Reimer** MD, Infectious Diseases; **William L. Roberts** MD, PhD, Chemistry; **Alan L. Rockwood** PhD, Mass Spectrometry; **George M. Rodgers, III** MD, PhD, Coagulation; **Rosemary She** MD, Microbiology; **Ila Singh** MD, PhD, Hepatitis/Retrovirus; **Patricia R. Slev** PhD, Serologic Hepatitis/Retrovirus; **Kristi J. Smock** MD, Hemostasis/Thrombosis; **Sarah South** PhD, Cytogenetics; **Anne E. Tebo** PhD, Immunology; **Karl V. Volkerding** MD, Molecular Genetics; **Ronald L. Weiss** MD, MBA, COO of ARUP, Lab Administration, Hematopathology; **Carl T. Wittwer** MD, PhD, Molecular Pathology; **Lily Wu** PhD, Chemistry; **Jia Xu** MD, Cytogenetics.

Primary Children's Medical Center

Theodore J. Pysher MD, Division Head; **Phillip R. Bach** PhD; **Judy A. Daly** PhD; **Amy Lowichik** MD, PhD; **Angelica Putnam** MD; **Holly Zhou** MD.

St. Mark's Hospital

Thomas M. Abbott MD, Head of Pathology; **Catherine A. Bowles** MD; **David P. Knight** MD; **Gregory P. Smith** MD.

Intermountain Medical Center

George H. Cannon MD, Head of Pathology; **James Albro** MD; **James Avent** MD; **Sterling T. Bennett** MD; **Jason Blaser** MD; **Mary Brieske** MD; **Chris Campana** MD; **Melissa H. Cessna** MD; **Landon W. Coleman** MD; **Rick Farnsworth** MD; **Elizabeth M. Hammond** MD; **Sarah J. Ilstrup** MD; **Jorge Isaac** MD; **Ryan Lundell** MD; **Todd Randolph** MD; **James Seaman** MD; **Ann Taylor** MD; **Michael Wright** MD.

Office of the Medical Examiner

Todd C. Grey MD, Chief Medical Examiner; **Erik D. Christensen** MD; **Edward A. Leis** MD.

VA Medical Center

Elizabeth M. Jensen MD, Head of Pathology; **Dan Nightingale** MD; **Jiahua Wu** MD, PhD.

APPLICATIONS

Medical School graduates seeking their first year of postdoctoral training are selected through the National Resident Matching Program.

Address inquiries to:

Evelyn V. Gopez, MD
Residency Program Director
Department of Pathology
University of Utah Health Sciences Center
50 North Medical Drive
Salt Lake City, UT 84132 -2501
Phone: (801) 587-4330 • **E-mail:** evelyn.gopez@hsc.utah.edu
Web site: www.path.utah.edu

Amy L. Motta
Residency Coordinator
Department of Pathology
University of Utah Health Sciences Center
50 North Medical Drive
Salt Lake City, UT 84132 -2501
Phone: (801) 587-4281 • **E-mail:** mottaa@aruplab.com

Huntsman Cancer Hospital and University Hospital (top)
ARUP Laboratories (bottom)

FLETCHER ALLEN HEALTH CARE AND UNIVERSITY OF VERMONT COLLEGE OF MEDICINE

Burlington, Vermont

PROGRAMS OFFERED

Fletcher Allen Health Care, Vermont's academic medical center, offers a combined training program in anatomic and clinical pathology that is designed to provide an integrated exposure to anatomic pathology and clinical laboratory medicine but is also sufficiently flexible to permit time for the resident to pursue areas of individual interest and research. Residents gain experience in autopsy pathology, surgical pathology, cytology, neuropathology, forensic pathology, cytogenetics, clinical chemistry, hematology, coagulation, blood banking, microbiology, clinical immunology, molecular genetics and medical informatics in the setting of a centralized, full-service laboratory. Active research programs are currently in progress in most major areas of experimental pathology. Weekly seminars and conferences systematically cover the theory and practice of laboratory medicine and anatomic pathology. A variety of research opportunities provides for a well-rounded exposure to the field of pathology. The training program is approved by the Accreditation Council for Graduate Medical Education and meets the requirements of the American Board of Pathology for certification in anatomical and clinical pathology.

TYPES AND NUMBERS OF APPOINTMENTS

There are 15 resident positions in pathology. In general, 3 first-year positions are available each year. Fellowship positions in cytopathology, dermatopathology, surgical pathology and environmental pathology are available.

FACILITIES

Fletcher Allen Health Care is an organization created by the merger of the Medical Center Hospital of Vermont, the Fanny Allen Hospital, and the University Health Center representing the teaching faculty of the University of Vermont. Fletcher Allen's new laboratory, located on Levels 1 and 2 in the East Pavilion of the Ambulatory Care Center, consolidates labs that were previously spread out in five different locations on two campuses. The combined bed capacity of Fletcher Allen Health Care is 500, which makes this one of the larger and more comprehensive general hospitals in New England. Approximately 400 autopsies are carried out annually on hospital and forensic cases; approximately 35,000 surgical pathology specimens and over 67,000 cytopathology examinations (62,000 gyn, 3,300 non-gyn, 2,000 fine needle aspirations) are performed each year. In addition, all clinical laboratories in Fletcher Allen Health Care are directed by members of the Pathology Department. Over 1.5 million tests are performed in these laboratories annually. Fletcher Allen Health Care is the teaching hospital for the University of Vermont College of Medicine. This affords complete access to all university facilities including the general library and the medical library. Space and excellent facilities are available for a variety of clinical or fundamental pathology research projects. The laboratory is fully computerized for the recording, storage, retrieval, and analysis of data. In addition, we have an alliance with Mayo Medical Laboratories. A full range of information services is available through the Department and the Dana Medical Library.

COMMUNITY

Burlington is Vermont's largest city, with a population of approximately 150,000 in the metropolitan area. The countryside consists of suburbs, farms, and woodlands, affording beautiful views of Lake Champlain and the Adirondack and Green Mountains, while the city itself has a cosmopolitan, university oriented population. There are several collegiate artist series sponsored by the University of Vermont or one of the three local colleges. As the largest city in the State of Vermont, the community attracts outstanding musical and stage performances. In addition, there are chamber arts series, summer concerts and plays, and several active local theater groups. Nearby outdoor activities include skiing, swimming, boating, fishing, hunting and mountain climbing. Burlington is served by an international airport which provides ready access to other major cities in the country.

STIPENDS AND MAINTENANCE

For 2009-2010 the stipend for trainees at the postgraduate year one level is $46,604, PG-2 trainees receive $48,462, PG-3 trainees receive $51,186, PG-4 trainees receive $53,501 and PG-5 trainees $56,299. Several options for healthcare coverage are provided. Attendance at national meetings is encouraged and financially supported by the Department.

STAFF

Abiy Ambaye MD Assistant Professor; surgical pathology, cytology; **Scott Anderson** MD Assistant Professor; surgical pathology, cytology; **Edwin G. Bovill** MD Professor and Chairman; coagulation; **Ronald J. Bryant** MD

Associate Professor; Director of Clinical Pathology, hematopathology; **Kelly Butnor** MD Associate Professor; surgical pathology; **Armando Ciampa** MD Assistant Professor, surgical pathology; **Deborah Cook** MD Associate Professor; dermatopathology, surgical pathology; **Kumarasen Cooper** MBChB, PhD Professor; Director Anatomic Pathology; **Abdelmonem Elhosseiny** MD Professor; surgical pathology, cytology; **Mark Evans** PhD Research Assistant Professor; research; **Mark Fung** PhD, MD Assistant Professor; Transfusion Medicine; **Pamela C. Gibson** MD Associate Professor; Med Director Sch Cytotechnology; Quality Assurance Officier; cytology, surgical pathology; **Andrew J Goodwin** Assistant Professor, Medical Director, Northeastern VT Regional Hospital & Cottage Hospital, surgical pathology, breast pathology; **Laura Greene** MD Assistant Professor, dermatopathology, surgical pathology; **Nicholas J. Hardin** MD Professor Emeritus; cardiovascular disease, autopsy pathology; **Maureen Harmon** MD Associate Professor; Med Director Porter Hospital Laboratory; cytology, surgical pathology; **Nicholas Heintz** PhD Professor; cell cycle, control in cancer; **Sally A. Huber** PhD Professor; immunology; **Anita S. Iyer** MD Assistant Professor, surgical pathology, GI; **Yvonne Janssen-Heininger** PhD Associate Professor; environmental lung diseases; **Alexandra Kalof** MD Assistant Professor, surgical pathology, soft tissue, neoplastic neuropathology; **Masatoshi Kida** MD Professor; surgical pathology; **Gladwyn Leiman** MBBCh Professor; Director, Cytopathology; **Michael Lewis** MD Assistant Professor, hematopathology; **John H. Lunde** MD Associate Professor; hematopathology; **Brooke T. Mossman** PhD Professor Emeritus; carcinogenesis; **Sharon L. Mount** MD Professor; surgical pathology electron microscopy, cytology; **William W. Pendlebury** MD Professor; neuropathology; **Mario Ramos** PhD Research Assistant Professor; environmental pathology; **Steven Shapiro** MD Clinical Assistant Professor; forensic pathology; **Gregory Sharp** MD Associate Professor; clinical chemistry; **Arti Shukla** PhD Research Assistant Professor; research; **Nancy Swords Jenny** PhD Research Assistant Professor; cardiovascular; **Douglas J. Taatjes** PhD Research Professor; immunohistochemistry; **Mary E. Tang** MD Associate Professor; cytogenetics; **Russell Tracy** PhD Professor; cardiovascular; **Albert van derVliet** PhD Professor; oxidant biology; environmental lung diseases.; **Brenda L. Waters** MD Associate Professor; autopsy, pediatric/perinatal pathology; **Donald L. Weaver** MD Professor; flow cytometry, surgical pathology; **Washington C. Winn, Jr.** MD Professor; microbiology, infectious disease; **David W. Yandell** PhD, Professor; cancer genetics; inherited diseases.

APPLICATIONS

Address inquiries to:

Abdelmonem Elhosseiny, MD
Director, Residency Program
Department of Pathology & Laboratory Medicine
Fletcher Allen Health Care
111 Colchester Ave.
ACC Bldg., EP1-178
Burlington, VT 05401
Phone: (802) 847-0392 • **E-mail:** jane.murray@vtmednet.org
Web site: http://www.fahc.org/pathology

UNIVERSITY OF VIRGINIA SCHOOL OF MEDICINE

Charlottesville, Virginia

PROGRAMS OFFERED

The Department of Pathology offers an ACGME-accredited training program in anatomic and clinical pathology, with options for straight AP and CP training. Our program provides intense training in the various disciplines of pathology, emphasizing resident responsibility and teaching at all levels. Numerous basic science and clinical research opportunities are available. A special program combining research and residency training is available for MD/PhD and MD applicants planning an academic research career. Our graduates are eligible to sit for the American Board of Pathology examination and are well prepared to assume leadership positions in academic and community practice.

TYPES AND NUMBERS OF APPOINTMENTS

Five positions are typically listed with the National Residency Matching Program. Twenty positions are active within the training program at any time. Accredited fellowships in Cytopathology, Neuropathology, Hematopathology, Dermatopathology and Transfusion Medicine are available. Non-accredited fellowships in Gynecologic Pathology and Surgical Pathology research are offered, as is a post-sophomore fellowship program.

FACILITIES

The Department of Pathology provides pathology and laboratory medicine support for the University of Virginia Hospital, a modern, 573-bed tertiary care hospital which draws its patients from central and southwestern Virginia. Additional material is provided by surrounding community hospitals and an active national referral base. In 2005 the Department performed approximately 200 autopsies; 27,915 surgicals; 3,247 medical cytologies; 25,775 gynecological cytologies; 1,479 fine needle aspirates; 2,624,705 laboratory examinations and provided 47,877 transfused products. A four-week forensic experience is conducted at the Chief Medical Examiner's Office in Richmond. A newly renovated resident learning center and state-of-the-art facilities and equipment are available, including access to various electronic media. The Claude Moore Health Sciences Library has 192,013 books and journals (45,000 monographs), 2,187 current journal subscriptions, on-line access to numerous medical databases, and 1,188 current electronic journals.

COMMUNITY

The historic charm of Jefferson's Virginia and the natural beauty of the Blue Ridge combine to make Charlottesville and the surrounding Albemarle county one of America's most desirable places to live. Employment and educational opportunities for spouses are available within and outside the University. Charlottesville is served by the Charlottesville-Albemarle Airport and is located 110 miles southwest of Washington, DC and 70 miles west of Richmond.

STIPENDS AND MAINTENANCE

As of July 2008, the PGY-1 stipend is $47,749 with 3-5% annual increases thereafter. Professional liability, disability and life insurance are provided by the medical center. Major medical insurance is provided at a nominal charge with reasonable family rates. Parking is convenient and affordable. Athletic facilities are available at a substantial discount. Funds are provided by the Department for books and meetings. Housing is conveniently located and affordable.

STAFF

Dennis J. Templeton MD, PhD (Univ Cal-San Diego 1984) Chair; signal transduction in neoplasia; **Kristen A. Atkins** MD (Univ of Vermont 1996) surgical pathology, cytopathology and gynecologic pathology; **James C. Boyd** MD (Washington Univ St. Louis 1973) clinical chemistry, computer-aided data interpretation, lipids, robotics; **Thomas J. Braciale** MD, PhD (Univ Pennsylvania 1975) T lymphocyte function, antigen presentation; **David E. Bruns** MD (St Louis Univ 1973) clinical chemistry, calciotropic hormones; **Timothy N J Bullock** PhD Use of dendritic cells (DC) as immunotherapeutic vaccines against tumors.; **Helen P. Cathro** MBChB, MPH (Univ Dundee, Scotland 1984) surgical pathology, cytopathology and renal pathology; **Pamela Clark** MD, JD (Univ Virginia 1982) blood banking and transfusion medicine; **John B. Cousar, Jr.** MD (Univ Virginia 1973) hematopathology, hematology; **Jamie L. Covell** BS (Tulane Univ 1968) cytology; **Robin A. Felder** PhD (Georgetown Univ 1983) clinical chemistry, renal hypertension, medical robotics; **Henry F. Frierson, Jr.** MD (Med Univ South Carolina 1981) surgical pathology, cytology; **Wendy L Golden** PhD (Med Col Virginia 1980) cytogenetics, molecular cytogenetics; **Adam N. Goldfarb** MD (Tufts Univ 1986) hematopathology; **Doris M. Haverstick** PhD (St Louis Univ 1982) clinical toxicology, T lymphocyte structure/function; **Frederick G. Hayden** MD (Stanford Univ 1973) clinical microbiology, virology, antiviral chemotherapy; **Kevin C. Hazen** PhD (Montana State Univ 1982) clinical microbiology, mycology; **Isa M. Hussaini** PhD (King's Col, England 1987) neuropathology, brain tumor invasive growth; **Julia C. Iezzoni** MD (Washington Univ St. Louis 1989) surgical pathology, liver and liver transplantation pathology; **Donald J. Innes**

MD (Univ Connecticut 1977) hematopathology; **Andrei Khokhlatchev** PhD (Univ Texas Southwestern 1997) signal transduction in oncology; **James P Landers** PhD (Univ Guelph, Canada, 1988); **Robin D LeGallo** MD (Univ of Virginia 1997) Molecular genetics of pediatric malignancies; **M. Beatriz S. Lopes** MD (Sao Paulo Univ 1982) neuropathology/pituitary pathology; **Mani S. Mahadevan** MD (Univ Ottawa 1986) human molecular genetics, molecular diagnostics, muscular dystrophy; **James W. Mandell** MD, PhD (Cornell Univ 1992) neuropathology; **Stacey E. Mills** MD (Univ Virginia 1977) surgical pathology, immunohistochemistry; **Paul D. Mintz** MD (Univ Rochester 1974) clinical pathology, blood bank and transfusion medicine; **Christopher A. Moskaluk** MD, PhD (Duke Univ 1990) surgical pathology, gastrointestinal pathology, molecular biology; **James W. Patterson** MD (Med Col Virginia 1972) dermatopathology, dermatology; **Richard D. Pearson** MD (Univ Michigan 1973) immunoparasitology, mononuclear phagocyte function; **William A. Petri, Jr.** MD, PhD (Univ Virginia 1982) molecular parasitology, infectious diseases; **Melinda D Poulter** PhD (Univ North Texas 1999) clinical microbiology, molecular diagnostics; **P. Prabhakara Reddi** PhD (National Inst of Immunology, New Dehli 1992) transcriptional regulation; male germ cell differentiation; **Lawrence M. Silverman** PhD (Ohio State Univ 1975) diagnostic molecular pathology, cystic fibrosis, breast cancer; **Avril V. Somlyo** PhD (Univ Pennsylvania 1976) muscle physiology; **Edward S. Stelow** MD (Med Col Wisconsin 1998) surgical pathology, cytopathology, gastrointestinal/pancreatobiliary pathology, head and neck pathology; **Mark H. Stoler** MD (Univ Rochester 1980) surgical pathology, cytopathology, molecular diagnostics; **Thomas W. Tillack** MD (Yale Univ 1963) Chair Emeritus; anatomic pathology; **Kenneth S.K. Tung** MD (Univ Melbourne 1959) tolerance and autoimmunity, renal immunopathology; **Scott B. Vande Pol** MD, PhD (Univ Cal San Diego 1985) oncogenes, cancer, papilloma viruses; **Gay Wehrli** MD, MS.Ed (USC) Transfusion Medicine; **Gail Wertz** PhD (Univ of Pittsburgh, 1970) Molecular mechanisms of repliaction and transcription of non-segmented negative strand RNA viruses.; **Mark R. Wick** MD (Univ Wisconsin 1978) surgical pathology, protein chemistry of human neoplasms.

APPLICATIONS

Applications must be submitted through the Electronic Residency Application Service (ERAS). An MSPE, medical school transcript, USMLE scores, and three letters of recommendation are required. An interview is required for acceptance into the program. Applications should be submitted by December 1 for positions beginning on or about July 1 of the following year.

Address inquiries to:

Mark R. Wick, MD
Director, Residency Training Program
Department of Pathology, Box 800214
University of Virginia Health Sciences Center
Charlottesville, VA 22908
Phone: (434) 982-1018 • **Fax:** (434) 982-6130 • **E-mail:** bun4n@virginia.edu
Web site: http://www.healthsystem.virginia.edu/internet/pathology/resident/intro.cfm

University of Virginia Medical Center, Charlottesville, Virginia

VIRGINIA COMMONWEALTH UNIVERSITY MEDICAL CENTER

Richmond, Virginia

PROGRAMS OFFERED

The Department of Pathology offers structured, yet flexible, training programs designed to prepare physicians for careers in the academic and private practice of pathology. Fully approved training programs are available in both anatomic and clinical pathology. In addition to autopsy and surgical pathology, the Anatomic service offers training in cytopathology, neuropathology, immunohistochemistry, forensic pathology, oral pathology and electron microscopy. The Clinical service offers extensive training in laboratory and morphologic hematology, immunology, blood banking and transfusion medicine, coagulation, chemistry, informatics, toxicology and therapeutic drug monitoring and forensic drug testing, microbiology, medical microscopy and human genetics. The laboratory of Molecular Diagnostics provides a core facility for research and clinical applications of molecular pathologic techniques. Fellowship programs, leading to appropriate specialty Board eligibility, are available in neuropathology, molecular genetic pathology, forensic pathology, hematopathology, cytopathology and surgical pathology (see Specialized Areas section in this directory). Special research, investigative, and/or developmental projects are available in all areas of the department. In addition to regular departmental and interdepartmental conferences, frequent resident "problem-solving" teaching conferences are given by the pathology staff. Pathology residents take an active part in student teaching conducted by the department.

TYPES AND NUMBERS OF APPOINTMENTS

A total of 22 positions is currently available with three to four being filled annually at the PGY-1 level. Positions are available for fellowship training in pathology subspecialties (see Specialized Areas section of this directory).

FACILITIES

The Medical College of Virginia (MCV) had its beginning in 1838. In 1968 MCV merged with the Richmond Professional Institute and formed a new state university—Virginia Commonwealth University. The VCU Medical Center is among the top five most complex and influential health centers in the United States. VCUMC has over 700 beds and admits over 30,000 patients annually. The HH McGuire Veterans Affairs Medical Center has over 700 additional beds. Continued growth of VCUMC is reflected by its current program of modernization and building. The Massey Cancer Center offers a multidisciplinary approach to the care of cancer patients. The MCV campus medical library contains over 175,000 bound journals. Approximately 110 autopsies are performed annually by MCVH and the VA Medical Center Hospital. An additional 700 medico-legal necropsies are performed by the Division of Forensic Pathology at the Office of the Chief Medical Examiner. Neuropathology examines over 300 brains per year in addition to histochemical and electron microscopic studies of muscle and brain biopsies. Approximately 16,000 surgical specimens are received of which 25 to 30% are neoplastic. The section of Cytopathology performs over 1,500 fine needle aspiration biopsies yearly. The clinical pathology laboratories occupy more than 40,000 square feet in a modern facility that is linked to the hospitals, clinics, and emergency rooms by a pneumatic tube transport system. The laboratories perform over 10 million procedures on approximately one million specimens annually using a wide array of automated instruments. Clinical pathology resident training and duties entail performance and interpretation of bone marrow aspirations and biopsies, medical interpretation of laboratory test abnormalities, participation in quality control, quality assurance, and method validation analyses, and review of utilization patterns. Word processing, database, spreadsheet, graphics, and communication software are available for resident use on PCs equipped with peripherals including laser printers, scanners and modems.

COMMUNITY

The historic city of Richmond is the state capital and main cultural center of Virginia with a symphony orchestra, ballet corps, several theatrical groups, and the Virginia Museum of Fine Arts. Richmond is one of the most conveniently located cities in the mid-Atlantic area, just 90 miles south of Washington, DC; 45 minutes away from Colonial Williamsburg, Jamestown and James River Plantations; 90 miles from Virginia Beach, Monticello, the Blue Ridge Mountains and Skyline Drive. Richmond recreational facilities include 5 large city parks, abundant tennis courts, gardens, wooded nature trails, a large coliseum, children's zoo, science museum, James River rapids and many public as well as private golf courses. Other major educational institutions within the city are the University of Richmond and Virginia Union University.

STIPENDS AND MAINTENANCE

Stipends start at approximately $44,776 a year for PGY-1 and range to $48,581 for fourth year positions for the 2007-2008 academic year. Uniforms and laundry of uniforms are provided. Health and malpractice insurance is paid for by the Hospital.

STAFF

S. Roseff MD (Albany Med Col 1986) Director Resident Program; Director transfusion medicine; **D. Wilkinson** MD, PhD (Univ Miami 1978) Department Chair; Director of Molecular Genetic Pathology; **L. Bachmann** PhD (UVA 2004) Molecular Med and Microbiology; **J. Ben-Ezra** MD (Boston Univ Sch Med 1979) Director hematopathology; **N. Brinster** MD (Univ Pennsylvania 1996) dermatopathology; **M. Contos** MD (VCU 1988) surgical pathology; **P. Coudron** PhD (Med Col Wisconsin 1982) microbiology; **E. Dragoescu** MD (Univ of Medicine, Romania 1997) surgical pathology and cytopathology; **C. Dumur** PhD (Univ Nacional Cordoba 1997) molecular diagnostics; **L. Elmore** PhD (VCU 1993) cellular and molecular pathogenesis; **S. Elshowaia** MD, (Fac of Med, Univ of Khartoum, Sudan 1986) cytopathology; **A. Ferreira-Gonzalez** PhD (George Washington Univ 1994) molecular diagnostics; **B. Forbes** PhD (Univ Oklahoma 1979) clinical microbiology; **W. Frable** MD (Northwestern Univ 1959) surgical pathology and cytopathology; **C. E. Fuller** MD (State Univ of NY Upstate Med Uni 1995) Director of Neuropathology; **C. Garrett** MD, PhD (Johns Hopkins Univ 1966) Director molecular diagnostics fellowship program; **E. Gerszten** MD (Buenos Aires Univ 1958) anatomic pathology and paleopathology; **N. Ghatak** MD (Univ Calcutta 1958) Director neuropathology; **M. Grimes** MD (New York Med Col 1975) surgical pathology; **S. Holt** PhD (Texas A&M Univ, 1994) cellular and molecular pathogenesis; **M. Idowu** MD (Univ of Ibadan, Nigeria 1995) surgical and cytopathology; **C. Jackson-Cook** PhD (VCU 1985) Director cytogenetics; **R. Jain** MD (Lady Hardinge Med Col 1989) cytopathology and surgical pathology; **R. Lippman** MD (NYU 1975) clinical chemistry; **MJ. Martin** MD (VCU 2003) Neuropathology; **D. Massey** MD, PhD (VCU 1996) surgical pathology; **R. McPherson** MD (Univ Cal-San Diego 1973) Director clinical pathology; **G. Miller** PhD (Univ Arizona 1973) Co-director clinical chemistry; Director pathology information systems; **S. Mills** MD (VCU 1977) surgical pathology; **Y. Oh** PhD (Stanford Univ 1993) oncogenomics and proteomics; **A. Poklis** PhD (Univ Maryland 1974) Director clinical toxicology; **C. Powers** MD, PhD (Univ Texas, Houston, 1985) Director anatomic pathology; **R. Riley** MD (Univ West Virginia 1978) hematopathology; **W. Rosenblum** MD (NYU 1961) neuropathology; **K. Sanford** MD (Virginia Commonwealth Univ Sch of Med 2006) Associate Director of transfusion medicine; **A. Sirica** PhD (Univ Connecticut 1976) cellular and molecular pathogenesis; **W. M. Todd** MD (UTCHS 1978) hematology; **J. Ware** PhD (UNC Chapel Hill 1979) functional genomics; **P. Weisz-Carrington** MD (Univ Nacional Autonoma Mexico 1971) immunohematology; **D. Williams, Jr.** MD, PhD (Univ Virginia 1998) hematopathology.

APPLICATIONS

Applicants must be graduates of an approved school of medicine or hold ECFMG certification.
All applications are received through ERAS.

Address inquiries to:

Ms. Violet R. Brown
Coordinator, Pathology Resident Training Program
Virginia Commonwealth University Medical Center
PO Box 980662
Richmond, VA 23298-0662
Phone: (804) 827-0561 • **E-mail:** vbrown3@mcvh-vcu.edu
Web site: http://www.pathology.vcu.edu

UNIVERSITY OF WASHINGTON

Seattle, Washington

PROGRAMS OFFERED

Candidates may take a four-year combined anatomic and clinical pathology track or three-year anatomic or clinical pathology track. Residents learn a core foundation of skills that becomes the basis for increased responsibility as the resident progresses through the program. In Anatomic Pathology, residents focus on surgical, cytological, neuro-, pediatric, and autopsy pathology with training in the most current diagnostic techniques, including immunohistochemistry and molecular diagnostics. In Laboratory Medicine, clinical pathology residents start with a core curriculum that encompasses the disciplines of clinical chemistry, coagulation, genetics, hematology, immunology, microbiology, transfusion medicine and blood banking, and virology. Beyond the first year, residents work with their faculty advisors to develop a program of elective studies tailored to their unique subspecialty interests. Residents are encouraged to explore research interests with faculty members for which there are diverse opportunities. Departmental research training programs are available for residents in aging, cardiovascular disease, developmental biology, DNA replication and repair, environmental pathology, gastrointestinal pathology, genetic pathology, hematopathology, neuropathology, renal disease, somatic cell genetics and tumor biology. Our combined research assets include over 68,000 square feet of research facilities. We are one of the largest recipients of NIH funding. Approximately a third of our graduates now staff community hospitals and clinics across the nation, 40% combine clinical practice with academic commitments, and 25% are faculty members in major medical schools.

TYPES AND NUMBERS OF APPOINTMENTS

Usually 6-7 first-year residency positions are available each year. Clinical fellowships are available for individuals interested in advanced training including bone and soft tissue pathology, breast and gynecological pathology, clinical chemistry, cytopathology, dermatopathology, gastrointestinal pathology, hematopathology, clinical microbiology, neuropathology, pediatric pathology, renal pathology, surgical pathology, and virology.

FACILITIES

The program is based at University of Washington Medical Center with rotations at affiliated hospitals: Harborview Medical Center, VA Puget Sound Health Services, Children's Hospital and Regional Medical Center, Seattle Cancer Care Alliance, and Puget Sound Blood Center. Elective studies are also available at Fred Hutchinson Cancer Research Center, Swedish Medical Center and King County Medical Examiner's Office. UWMC and its affiliates provide tertiary medical care to the five-state region of Washington, Wyoming, Alaska, Montana and Idaho. A total of over 1,500 beds provide 1,600 autopsies (including 1,300 forensic), 54,000 surgical, and 29,000 cytology specimens each year. More than 7 million clinical laboratory tests are done yearly.

COMMUNITY

Seattle, a tri-county metropolitan center of 3.3 million people, is beautifully situated on the shores of Puget Sound between two major mountain ranges: the coastal Olympic Range and the eastern Cascade Range. Abundant outdoor recreational opportunities are available within an hour's drive from the hospitals. Seattle enjoys all the cultural opportunities of a major metropolitan area.

STIPENDS AND MAINTENANCE

Stipends (changes effective 7/1/08 pending) are: 1st year $45,984, 2nd year $46,908, 3rd year $48,144, 4th year $50,750 and 5th year $53,328. Residents receive insurance benefits, including medical, dental, basic life, basic disability and professional liability plans; as well as retirement benefits. Departmental benefits include education and travel funds. Vacation is three weeks per year.

STAFF

K. Bornfeldt; **D. Bowen-Pope**; **T. Brentnall**; **P. Byers**; **M. Horwitz**; **M. Kaeberlein**; **L. Loeb**; **G. Martin**; **R. Monnat**; **S. Narayanan**; **B. Preston**; **M. Reidy**; **S. Schwartz**; **U. Schwarze**; **T. Wight**; **C. Wilson**; **N. Wolf**.

University of Washington Medical Center - Anatomic Pathology

N. Fausto Chair; **R. Garcia** Residency Director; **P.E. Swanson** Director; **K. Allison**; **C. Alpers**; **Z. Argenyi**; **S. Dintzis**; **C. Disteche**; **G. Finkel**; **C. Fligner**; **E. George**; **J. Haas**; **B. Hoch**; **D. Jordan**; **J. Kowalewska**; **M. Laflamme**; **T. Lawton**; **C. Murry**; **T. Norwood**; **P. Rabinovitch**; **D. Reichenbach**; **C. Rubin**; **R. Schmidt**; **K. Smith**; **K. Tham**; **L. True**; **M. Upton**; **M. Yeh**.

University of Washington Medical Center - Laboratory Medicine

J. Fine Chair; **P. Rainey** CP Director; **M. Astion**; **G. Baird**; **W. Chandler**; **S. Cherian**; **D. Chou**; **B. Cookson**; **R. Coombs**; **F. Fang**; **J. Fromm**; **H. Greisman**; **N. Hoffman**; **A. Hoofnagle**; **A. LaSpada**; **A. Limaye**; **M. Reyes**; **D. Sabath**; **K. Stephens**; **J. Tait**; **M. Wener**; **B. Wood**.

Children's Hospital and Regional Medical Center

J. Rutledge Director; **R. Ashley-Morrow**; **L. Finn**; **R. Hevner**; **R. Jack**; **R. Kapur**; **K. Opheim**; **K. Patterson**; **X. Qin**; **J Seibert**; **K. Tsuchiya**; **M. Xu**.

Fred Hutchinson Cancer Research Center/Seattle Cancer Care Alliance

L. Cook; **L. Corey**; **S. DeRosa**; **R. Hackman**; **K. Jerome**; **K. Loeb**; **D. Miller**; **D. Myerson**; **P. Porter**; **C. Posavad**; **G. Sale**; **H. Shulman**; **D. Sloan**; **S. Tapscott**.

Harborview Medical Center - Pathology

N. Kiviat Director; **H. Deubner**; **V. Grieco**; **A. Peck-Sabath**; **F. Vakar-Lopez**.

Harborview Medical Center/UWMC - Neuropathology

T. Montine Director; **E.C. Alvord** Emeritus; **D. Born**; **C-M. Shaw** Emeritus; **J. Sonnen**; **J. Zhang**.

King County Medical Examiner's Office

R. Harruff Chief Medical Examiner; **A. Fusaro**; **M. Lacy**.

Puget Sound Blood Center

T. Gernsheimer Director; **T. Nester**.

Swedish Medical Center - CellNetix Pathology LLC

D. Corwin Director; **A. Boudousquie**; **K.M. Chae**; **M. Horton**; **D. Howard**; **C. Hunter**; **C. Kitchell**; **R. Knierim**; **B. Kulander**; **D. McDonagh**; **N. Perez-Reyes**; **E. Pizer**; **R. Ranguelov**; **J. Rank**; **S. Rostad**; **S. Thornton**; **R. Tickman**; **NP Wang**; **D. Wolinsky**.

VA Puget Sound Health Care System

R. Nicosia Director; **D. Bankson**; **J Clarridge**; **D. Dong**; **R. Garcia**; **D. Thorning**; **J. Virgin**.

APPLICATIONS

The Pathology Residency Committee reviews applications and makes selections on the basis of academic excellence in medicine and interest in the specialty. All application materials should be received no later than November 15. All candidates must apply through ERAS. Applicants with previous residency experience must apply through ERAS, register with the NRMP Match, and provide a reference from the current residency director.

Address inquiries to:

Rochelle Garcia, MD, Director, or Michelle Rickard, Academic Programs Manager
Pathology Residency Program
University of Washington, Box 356100, 1959 NE Pacific, NE140J
Seattle, WA 98195-6100
Phone: (206) 598-4933 • **Fax:** (206) 598-7321 • **E-mail:** residency@pathology.washington.edu
Web site: http://www.pathology.washington.edu/academics/residency

Medical Center and Health Sciences facilities on the south campus of the University of Washington

WEST VIRGINIA UNIVERSITY HEALTH SCIENCES CENTER

Morgantown, West Virginia

PROGRAMS OFFERED

The Department of Pathology offers fully approved training programs for residents in anatomic pathology and clinical pathology as a combined AP/CP 4 year program. Training in anatomic pathology encompasses autopsy and surgical pathology, neuropathology, pediatric pathology, dermatopathology, nephropathology, cytopathology, immunopathology and forensic pathology. Clinical pathology training includes hematology, blood banking, coagulation, clinical chemistry, medical microbiology, parasitology, virology, tissue typing, immunology, flow cytometry, computer application to laboratory medicine, cytogenetics and instrumentation. Opportunities are available for specialized training in various techniques including tissue culture, immunohistochemistry and molecular pathology. Research opportunities are available, with emphasis on clinically-related topics. Residents participate in the department's teaching programs.

TYPES AND NUMBERS OF APPOINTMENTS

Two positions are normally available through the match. The department has ACGME approval to train 12 residents. Post sophomore or upper level fellowships can be arranged.

FACILITIES

There are a total of 520 beds in the West Virginia University Hospitals, consisting of 445 medical/surgical beds in Ruby Memorial Hospital, and 75 psychiatric beds are at Chestnut Ridge Hospital. Ruby Memorial is the University's main teaching hospital and tertiary referral center. Most of the medical and surgical specialties are represented here, and there is a level 1 trauma center. Several other facilities are present on the same campus. Outpatient clinics are located in the Physicians' Office Center, which is connected to Ruby Memorial Hospital. The Health Sciences Center contains the Mary Babb Randolph Cancer Center and the Betty Puskar Breast Cancer Center. The Health Sciences Center also contains schools of medicine and dentistry, medical and dental technology, nursing, pharmacy, and physical therapy. Mountain View Regional Rehabilitation Hospital is used by the University hospital and County hospital for patients requiring long-term recovery from trauma and other illnesses. NIOSH (National Institute for Occupational Safety and Health) has a major research establishment adjacent to the hospitals. In addition, each resident will do rotations at two affilitated hospitals, Charleston Area Medical Center in Charleston, West Virginia and the Louis A. Johnson VA Medical Center in Clarksburg, West Virginia.

The department examines approximately 19,000 surgical and 16,000 cytologic specimens per year. The number of autopsies is approximately 50 per year. Anatomic pathology utilizes a COPATH computer system. The clinical laboratory currently performs more than 2,000,000 examinations per year and uses the MISYS computer system. The laboratories are well equipped in all areas including special laboratories for coagulation and platelet studies, enzymology, immunology and histocompatibility antigen testing. The Health Sciences Center contains 190,000 volumes and receives 2,400 periodicals.

COMMUNITY

Morgantown, with a population of 35,000, is located on the Monongahela River 75 miles south of Pittsburgh. Elevation varies from 850 to about 2,000 feet above sea level. West Virginia University, the principal institution for higher education in the state, has a student enrollment of 25,000 on its three Morgantown campuses. Educational, cultural, and recreational facilities of the university, as well as tickets for intercollegiate athletic events, are available to house staff. The Center for Creative Arts has several series of repertory groups. Many outdoor recreational facilities (fishing, boating, skiing, golfing, etc.) are nearby.

STIPENDS AND MAINTENANCE

Stipends are determined by the candidate's previous training and experience. For 2008-2009, the stipend for trainees at the postgraduate year one PGY1 level is approximately $46,814 with yearly increases thereafter. Professional liability insurance, uniforms, uniform laundry, health insurance, a book allowance and a travel allowance for residents in their second and subsequent years in the program are furnished.

STAFF

Barbara S. Ducatman MD (Albany Med Col 1979) Professor and Chair. AP, CP, Cytopathology. FNA and GYN pathology; **Patrick Bacaj** (Univ Virginia 1987) Assistant Professor AP, CP; **William W. L. Chang** MD, PhD (Natl Taiwan Univ 1958, McGill Univ 1970) Professor Emeritus. AP. Surgical pathology, gastrointestinal pathology; **James E. Coad** MD (Univ Minnesota 1993) Professor. AP, CP, Hematopathology; **Kenneth B Fallon** MD (Louisiana State Univ 1989) Assistant Professor, AP, CP, Neuropathology. Surgical pathology and neuropathology; **Melina Flanagan**

(Univ Pittsburgh 2007) Assistant Professor, AP, CP, Cytopathology; **Maurice R Grant** (Univ Pittsburgh 2004; Univ of Michigan 2006) Assistant Professor; AP, CP, Hematopathology; **Kymberly A. Gyure** MD (Med Col Ohio Toledo 1992), Associate Professor. Director Anatomic Pathology. Residency Program Director. AP, CP, Neuropathology. Surgical pathology and neuropathology; **Tiffany Harper** (West Virginia University 2004) Assistant Professor, AP, CP; **Peter Perrotta** MD (Penn State Univ 1989) Associate Professor, Director Clinical Pathology, AP, CP, Blood Banking and Transfusion Medicine; **Matrina Schmidt** MD (Medical College of Ohio 2001) Assistant Professor, Forensic Pathology; **Kathryn Skitarelic** MD (Univ Maryland 1969), Assistant Professor. AP, CP. Surgical pathology, cytopathology, and gastrointestinal pathology; **Jeffrey A. Stead** MD (Hahnemann Med Col 1978) Associate Professor. AP, CP, Cytopathology. Surgical pathology, orthopedic pathology, outreach; **John G. Thomas** PhD (Syracuse Univ 1969) Professor. Clinical microbiology and virology; **Jeffrey Vos** (Univ Minnesota 1997) Associate Professor, AP, CP, Hematopathology; **Sharon Wenger** PhD (Univ Pittsburgh 1976) Professor. Cytogenetics; **H. James Williams** MD (Univ Mississippi 1985) Professor. AP, CP. Gynecologic oncology.

APPLICATIONS

First year resident candidates applying directly from medical schools in the United States or Canada should register with the National Resident Matching Program unless there is specific reason for applying outside the match. July 1 is the usual beginning date for appointments. Upper level candidates or those interested in fellowships may apply directly.

Address inquiries to:

Kymberly A. Gyure, MD
Director, Pathology Residency Program
Robert C. Byrd Health Sciences Center of West Virginia University
PO Box 9203
Morgantown, WV 26506-9203
Phone: (304) 293-3212 • **Fax:** (304) 293-2717

Medical Center, West Virginia University, Morgantown, West Virginia

UNIVERSITY OF WISCONSIN CENTER FOR HEALTH SCIENCES

Madison, Wisconsin

PROGRAMS OFFERED

The pathology training program is a fully accredited AP/CP 4-year, or AP only 3-year program that offers training in anatomic, clinical, and experimental pathology. AP instruction is given in autopsy, surgical and forensic pathology, and in the subspecialties cardiovascular, oncologic, pulmonary, hepatic, renal, endocrine and neuropathology. Also included is training in electron microscopy, immunohistochemistry and cytology. CP training concentrates on hematopathology, blood banking, molecular diagnostics, toxicology, immunology, cytogenetics, microbiology, clinical chemistry, chemical and electronic instrumentation, laboratory management, automation and informatics. Curriculum flexibility is provided to accommodate special interests of residents. Residents are strongly encouraged to engage in research projects, which are funded by the department. The residents actively participate in teaching of medical students and allied health students.

TYPES AND NUMBERS OF APPOINTMENTS

Eighteen residency positions and four subspecialty fellowships (transfusion medicine, cytopathology, hematopathology, and surgical pathology) are available. Typically, four to six residents are recruited through the NRMP Match process each year.

FACILITIES

Pathology training is offered in the University of Wisconsin Hospital and Clinics (471 beds), the connecting William S. Middleton Veterans Affairs Hospital (150 beds), St. Mary's Hospital (332 beds), and Meriter Hospital (500 beds). These hospitals annually provide over 500 autopsies, 73,000 surgicals, 10,000 cytologics, and more than 4,700,000 laboratory examinations. UWHC's Clinical Labs offers a wide range of highly complex testing including molecular diagnostics and histocompatibility and are staffed with experienced technologists. UWHC is affiliated with an NCI designated Comprehensive Cancer Center, and a major university medical school. UWHC is a leading transplant center in the U.S.

COMMUNITY

Madison is the capital of the state with a metropolitan population of approximately 300,000. Madison is situated on four picturesque lakes 150 miles northwest of Chicago. The major industries of Wisconsin are manufacturing, agriculture and recreation. The high percentage of academic professional personnel in the population has been a stimulus for the city and the university to offer a wide variety of educational, cultural and recreational opportunities. The public education system is excellent. Superb university and city facilities are available for summer and winter sports.

STIPENDS AND MAINTENANCE

First year to Board eligibility, $ 48,172; second, $ 49,977; third, $ 51,833; fourth, $ 53,855; (2008-09). Benefits include: health insurance, disability, social security and liability insurance. The department provides a $750 book allowance, 15 days of vacation and funding available for presentation of a paper at a national meeting. Residents may apply for housing in the University-owned apartments or may obtain private housing.

STAFF

M. N. Hart MD (Marquette Univ) Chair; neuropathology; **R Agni** MD (Maulana Azad Med Col) surgical pathology; **B. L. Allen-Hoffmann** PhD (Cornell Univ) epithelial differentiation; **A. J. Bridges** MD (Univ Illinois) immunology; **C. K. Chang** MD (Natl Taiwan Univ) hematopathology; **R. F. Corliss** MD (Univ Wisconsin) forensic pathology; **T. Darcy** MD (Univ Iowa) clinical pathology; **A. A. Eggert** PhD (Univ Wisconsin) computers/data management; **Z. Fabry** PhD (Eotvos Univ Sci, Budapest) neuroimmunology; **A. Friedl** MD (Friedrich-Alexander-Univ Erlangen, Germany) surgical pathology and renal pathology; **M. K. Fritsch** MD, PhD (Univ Wisconsin-Madison) pediatric pathology; **D. Greenspan** PhD (NYU) molecular biology; **G. R. Hafez** MD (Univ Ferdowsi, Iran) surgical pathology; **Josephine Harter** MD (Univ Michigan) cytopathology; **A. J. Hibbard** MD (Univ Illinois) transfusion medicine; **W. Huang** MD (Third Military Med Univ, China) GU pathology; **R. W. Huntington III** MD (Univ Rochester) forensic pathology; **D. F. Iyama-Kurtycz** MD (Univ Michigan) cytopathology; **C. P. Leith** MB, BChir (Kings Col Hosp, London) hematopathology; **A. Loeffler** MD, PhD (Dartmouth-Hitchcock) surgical pathology, autopsy; **J. S. Malter** MD (Washington Univ) transfusion medicine; **D. O'Connor** PhD (Univ Wisconsin) HIV/AIDS pathogenesis; **T. D. Oberley** MD, PhD (Northwestern Univ) renal pathology; **D. Peters** PhD (Rutgers Univ) connective tissue biology; **H. C. Pitot** MD, PhD (Tulane Univ) biochemical pathology and oncology; **G. Raca** MD, cytogenetics; **E. Ranheim** MD, PhD (Univ Minnesota) hematopathology; **A. Rapraeger** PhD (Univ Cal-Berkeley) connective tissue biology; **W.**

Rehrauer PhD (Northwestern) molecular diagnostics; **S. Salamat** MD, PhD (St George's Univ, Univ Michigan) neuropathology; **M. Sandor** PhD (Eotvos Univ Sci, Budapest) immunology; **S. Selvaggi** MD (Albert Einstein) cytopathology; **I. Slukvin** MD, PhD (Kiev, Ukraine) surgical pathology; **C. Spiegel** PhD (Univ Maryland) microbiology; **J. Stewart III** MD (Univ Arkansas) informatics, cytopathology; **M. Stier** MD (Univ Wisconsin-Madison) forensic pathology; **J. Torrealba** MD (Central Univ of Venezuela) renal pathology; **T. F. C. S. Warner** MD (Natl Univ Ireland) EM, surgical pathology, dermatopathology; **D. I. Watkins** PhD (Univ Rochester) immunology; **J. Weiss** MD, PhD (Univ Wisconsin) transfusion medicine; **D. A. Wiebe** PhD (Univ Iowa) clinical chemistry; **E. Williams** MD, PhD (Univ Indiana) coagulation; **David Yang** MD (The University of Utah), hematopathology, cancer medicine; **K. Young** MD, PhD (Zhejiang Univ, China) hematopathology; **W. Zhong** MD, PhD (Sun Yat-Sen) renal pathology; **G. M. ZuRhein** MD (Ludwigs-Maximilian Univ, Munich) neuropathology.

APPLICATIONS

All applications must be submitted through ERAS (Electronic Residency Application Service). We give priority to applicants with a minimum score of 200 (82) on parts 1 and 2 of the USMLE. Non-citizen candidates **must** have resident alien status or have a J1 clinical visa. Completed applications and three letters of reference should be received via ERAS by October 1. Deadline: October 15. Please visit our Web site at www.pathology.wisc.edu

Address inquiries to:

Erik Ranheim, MD, PhD
Director, Pathology Residency Program
c/o Amanda Paus
B4/243 Clinical Science Center
600 Highland Avenue
Madison, WI 53792-2472
Phone: (608) 262-7158 • **E-mail:** pathresidency@uwhealth.org
Web sites: http://www.pathology.wisc.edu/residency http://www.uwgme.org

University of Wisconsin Hospital & Clinics (right) connecting with the Health Science Learning Center (left)

MEDICAL COLLEGE OF WISCONSIN AFFILIATED HOSPITALS

Milwaukee, Wisconsin

PROGRAMS OFFERED

The Department of Pathology offers a four-year training program in anatomic and clinical pathology in addition to several fellowships including cytopathology, forensic pathology, hematopathology, pediatric pathology and transfusion medicine. All subspecialty areas of pathology are included in the training program which is designed to provide residents with a broad experience in pathology and is divided equally between anatomic and clinical pathology. Elective time is available for residents to pursue particular areas of interest in greater depth. Rotations in anatomic pathology include autopsy, surgical and pediatric pathology, neuropathology, electron microscopy, immunopathology, cytology and forensic pathology. Clinical pathology rotations include general and endocrine chemistry, microbiology, radioimmunoassay, toxicology, immunology, immunohematology, molecular pathology, hematology, coagulation, virology, serology, management, and computer science. A number of electives are available including clinical rotations, clinical research and extended experiences in molecular biology, chemistry, microbiology, virology, hematology, surgical pathology, cytology, and pediatric pathology. In addition, the department offers a Doctor of Philosophy in Pathology.

TYPES AND NUMBERS OF APPOINTMENTS

There are a total of sixteen pathology resident positions in the integrated program of the Medical College of Wisconsin.

FACILITIES

The Medical College of Wisconsin pathology program includes several institutions. Froedtert Memorial Lutheran Hospital is the primary teaching facility of the Medical College. It is a 469-bed facility which includes surgical, medical, neonatal, cardiovascular and coronary intensive care units, as well as Southeastern Wisconsin's only Level 1 Trauma Center. The Children's Hospital of Wisconsin is a 294-bed regional referral hospital for pediatric problems of diverse nature including pediatric oncology, pediatric cardiovascular surgery, metabolic disorders and pediatric neurology. The Medical College of Wisconsin, Froedtert Hospital and the Children's Hospital of Wisconsin are located on the 248-acre, park-like campus of the Milwaukee Regional Medical Center. Residents also rotate at the Zablocki VA Medical Center which is located just four miles from the Medical College. Several excellent libraries are available including the medical library of the College, several in the individual hospitals, and two department libraries. Rotations in forensic pathology take place in the facilities of the Waukesha County Medical Examiner's Office. Rotations in transfusion medicine are supplemented by experience provided at the Blood Center of Wisconsin. Some of the outstanding medical complex and community facilities include leukemia research, dialysis, cytogenetics, major trauma services, multidisciplinary oncology center, neuroscience center and organ transplantation (including heart, liver, bone marrow, pancreas, kidney and lung).

COMMUNITY

Milwaukee is a vibrant city located 90 miles north of Chicago on the shores of Lake Michigan. The Greater Milwaukee Area has a population of more than 1,500,000 and offers exceptional advantages for people with diverse interests including symphony orchestras, fine arts theaters, museum, great restaurants, beautiful parks and zoo. Major league sports, including baseball, hockey, basketball and soccer, and the Pettit Olympic speed skating training center supplement the unique variety of outdoor summer and winter sports and the many lakefront festivals.

STIPENDS AND MAINTENANCE

Residents' salaries range from $50,200 in the first year to $53,500 in the fourth year. Stipends are adjusted on July 1st of each year. Funds are available for local, state and national meetings. Professional liability insurance and group term life insurance are fully provided at no charge. Group health and dental insurance is available. There is a Working Condition/Fitness benefit of $1,500 paid at the end of the year. Campus child care is also available.

STAFF

Froedtert Memorial Lutheran Hospital

Saul M. Suster MD, Professor and Chairman; **Zainab Basir** MD, cytopathology, breast pathology; **Behnaz Behmaram** MD, gynecologic pathology, cytopathology; **Alexandra M. Harrington** MD, hematopathology; **Chun He** MD, PhD, renal pathology; **Khang-cheng Ho** MD, PhD, neuropathology; **Paul J. Jannetto** PhD, toxicology, chemistry; **Susan M. Koethe** PhD, immunology, chemistry; **Richard A. Komorowski** MD, Vice Chairman, Director, Anatomic Pathology, Pathology Program Director, gastrointestinal pathology, transplant pathology; **Steven H. Kroft** MD, hematopathology; **Nathan A. Ledeboer** PhD, microbiology, molecular biology; **Rongshan Li** MD, PhD, genitourinary pathology; **Jennifer D. Lorek** MD, breast pathology; **Natalia Markelova** MD, PhD, cytopathology, head and neck, endocrine pathology; **Rayasam K.S. (Arjun) Nagarjun Rao** MD, MRCPath pulmonary pathology, cytopathology; **Horatiu Olteanu** MD, PhD, hematopathology; **Vladimir Osipov** MD, orthopedic pathology, gastrointestinal pathology; **Jose A. Plaza** MD, dermatopathology; **Vinod B. Shidham** MD, MRCPath cytopathology, gastrointestinal pathology; **Peter vanTuinen** PhD, cytogenetics; **Paul E. Wakely** MD, cytopathology, head and neck pathology; **Steven H. Wong** PhD, toxicology.

Clement J. Zablocki Veterans Affairs Medical Center

Bruce E. Dunn MD, Chief, Laboratory Service; Vice Chairman, Dept Pathology; **Hongyung Choi** MD, anatomic pathology; **Catherine Hida** MD, surgical pathology, cytopathology; **Minerva Kryniak** MD, surgical pathology; **Suhas Phadnis** PhD, molecular pathology; **Elena Roukhadze** MD, surgical pathology.

Children's Hospital of Wisconsin

Paula E. North MD, PhD, Chief, Pediatric Pathology; **Jason A. Jarzembowski** MD, PhD, pediatric pathology, neonatal pathology; **Karen S. Kehl** PhD, microbiology, molecular biology; **Stanley F. Lo** PhD, clinical chemistry; **Tara Sander** PhD, molecular pathology; **Annette D. Segura** MD, pediatric pathology; **James F. Southern** MD, pediatric pathology, cardiovascular pathology; **Mariko Suchi** MD, PhD pediatric pathology; **Sara Szabo** MD, PhD, pediatric pathology; **Beth A. Trost** MD, pediatric pathology.

The Blood Center of Southeastern Wisconsin

Jerome L. Gottschall MD, Vice President, Medical Services; **Kenneth D. Friedman** MD, transfusion medicine; **Michael W. Lankiewicz** MD, transfusion medicine; **Alan Mast** MD, PhD, transfusion medicine; **Janice G. McFarland** MD, transfusion medicine; **Kathleen E. Puca** MD, transfusion medicine; **Rowena Punzalan** MD, transfusion medicine.

Waukesha County Medical Examiner's Office

Lynda M. Biedrzycki MD, forensic pathology.

APPLICATIONS

Applicants must be graduates of an approved medical school in the United States or Canada, or be in possession of the ECFMG certificate. July 1st is the usual starting date for our program. Applications should be received through ERAS no later than December 1st for appointments beginning July 1st of the following year.

Address inquiries to:

Richard A. Komorowski, MD
Director, Pathology Residency Program
Medical College of Wisconsin
9200 W. Wisconsin Avenue
Milwaukee, WI 53226
Phone: (414) 805-8443

42nd Edition

Canadian Residency Training Programs 2010–2011

All postgraduate specialty programs will be found in the section headed "Training in Specialized Areas of Pathology."

The Intersociety Council for Pathology Information, Inc.

UNIVERSITY OF CALGARY

Calgary, Alberta

PROGRAMS OFFERED

The Department of Pathology and Laboratory Medicine, University of Calgary, offers fully accredited five year training in **Anatomical Pathology** fulfilling the requirements of the Royal College of Physicians and Surgeons of Canada

The PGY-1 year is designed to provide exposure to most of the medical and surgical services that rely heavily on the pathology laboratory and to prepare the resident for the MCC qualifying examination part II. The PGY-2 and PGY-3 years constitute the core training with integrated rotations of autopsy and surgical pathology. In the PGY-4 year, the resident embarks upon mandatory (Pediatric Pathology, Forensic Pathology, Cytopathology and Electron Microscopy) and elective rotations (Neuropathology, Dermatopathology, Hematopathology, Flow Cytometry, Molecular Pathology, Research). The PGY-5 year may be spent in a variety of electives, which may include any one of the clinical laboratory subspecialties, a clinical rotation, a research rotation or one or more rotations in subspecialty pathology. Involvement in research activities is an integral part of the program and starting in the PGY-3 year, the residents are expected to present their research findings at the annual pathology residents' research day. Funding is available to present their papers at national or international meetings. The program is designed to give graded responsibility to the resident so that in the final year of training, the resident will be expected to perform to the level of a junior faculty member, recognizing that faculty resident supervision is always occurring. In addition to one-on-one teaching, clinical pathological conferences, and subspecialty rounds, there are coordinated didactic teaching sessions held in a weekly academic half-day (protected time). The residents write the yearly ASCP exam and participate in regular in-training evaluations that mimic the Royal College of Physicians and Surgeons of Canada exams. A philosophy of independent self-directed learning underlies the program. It is expected that by the end of the program the residents will have learned and developed skills which allow them to adopt a pattern of self-directed learning, which will continue beyond the completion of the program.

The Department also has a residency training program in Neuropathology and offers fellowship training in Surgical Pathology, Cytopathology, Neuropathology, Histocompatibility and Cytogenetics.

FACILITIES

The Department of Pathology & Laboratory Medicine (Calgary Laboratory Services) performs more than 20 million laboratory tests per year. In Anatomical Pathology, we examine approximately 115,000 surgical cases and 210,000 gynecologic/10,000 non-gynecologic cytology cases per year, and perform approximately 210 adult and 350 pediatric/fetal autopsies per year. The residency program is based in the university and teaching hospitals of the Calgary Health Region. The major teaching hospital, Foothills Hospital (700 beds), is located in the Foothills Medical Centre, which is also comprised of the University of Calgary Faculty of Medicine and the Tom Baker Cancer Centre. The other affiliated teaching institutions are the Rockyview General Hospital (500 beds), Peter Lougheed Hospital (500 beds), Alberta Children's Hospital (146 beds), Diagnostic & Scientific Centre and the Province of Alberta Chief Medical Examiner's Office. Calgary Health Region is the tertiary referral center for Southern Alberta, Eastern British Columbia and parts of Saskatchewan. Its catchment area population is over 1.5 million. This association provides the resident with a unique opportunity for training in Anatomical Pathology as well as subspecialty areas. The medical library, situated in the adjacent Health Sciences Center, contains up-to-date bound volumes and subscribes to numerous publications in the Health Sciences field. Online access to journals is also available.

The University of Calgary, Department of Pathology & Laboratory Medicine co-hosts (along with the University of Alberta) an annual Banff Pathology Update Course, which features world-renowned speakers. Residents are encouraged to attend these conferences.

COMMUNITY

Calgary has a population of over one million and boasts the second largest number of corporate head offices in the country. The city houses the Calgary Philharmonic Orchestra, both professional and amateur theatre groups, the Alberta Ballet Company, the Calgary Opera, and professional sports. There is a world-class zoological garden with a prehistoric dinosaur park, heritage park and science center. The world famous Calgary Stampede is held every July. The city has an extensive system of parks, golf courses and bicycle paths. Calgary, host of the 1988 Winter Olympics, has outstanding facilities for most winter sport activities. Calgary is within an hour's drive of world-class ski resorts, and in the summer the ski hills give way to backpackers and naturalists and the rivers and streams to whitewater rafters, kayakers, and fishermen. The nearby scenic resorts of Banff and Lake Louise draw visitors from around the world. The sunny climate and Calgary's proximity to the Rockies make the city a wonderful place in which to live.

STIPENDS AND MAINTENANCE

The annual stipend is in the range of $50,957 - $70,896 Canadian. These scales are negotiated by the Professional Association of Residents of Alberta (PARA).

STAFF

James R. Wright, Jr. MD, PhD, Professor and Department Head, pediatric-perinatal pathology, experimental transplantation; **Lisa DiFrancesco** MD, Director, Anatomic Pathology Residency, soft tissue and bone pathology; **Arthur Clark** MD, Director, Neuropathology Residency, neuropathology.

Professors (GFT and Clinical):

Roland Auer MD neuropathology, neurosciences; **Hallgrimur Benediktsson** MD renal pathology, transplantation pathology; **Deirdre Church** MD microbiology; **Arthur Clark** MD neuropathology; **Bernadette Curry** MD neuropathology (emeritus); **Maire Duggan** MD cytopathology, gynecological pathology; **James Gough** MD renal pathology, cytopathology; **Francis Green** MB, ChB pulmonary pathology, autopsy, experimental pathology; **Jeffrey Joseph** MD, PhD neuropathology; **Walid Mourad** MD cytopathology, hematopathology; **Johann Pitout** MB, ChB microbiology; **Hossein Sadrzadeh** PhD Clinical Chemistry (Division Head); **Harvey Sarnat** MD pediatric neuropathology (major cross-apt); **Anna Sienko** MD surgical pathology, cytology; **Stefan Urbanski** MD gastrointestinal/hepatic pathology, pulmonary neoplasia.

Associate Professors (GFT and Clinical):

Iwona Auer-Grzesiak MD lymphoma, flow cytometry; **Leland Baskin** MD chemical pathology, general pathology (Division Head); **Tarek Bismar** MD genitourinary pathology; **Valerie Boras** MD anatomical pathology; **Andrea Bruecks** MD dermatopathology; **Douglas Demetrick** MD molecular pathology; **Valerian Dias** PhD clinical chemistry (adjunct); **Les Eidus** MD gastrointestinal pathology; **Vincent Falck** MB, ChB gastrointestinal pathology, ENT pathology; **Zu-hua Gao** MD gastrointestinal/hepatic pathology, experimental transplantation; **Daniel Gregson** MD microbiology (Division Head); **Andrew Lyon** PhD clinical chemistry; **Martha Lyon** PhD pediatric clinical chemistry; **Anthony Magliocco** MD breast and gynecological pathology (major cross-apt); **Adnan Mansoor** MD hematopathology (Division Head); **Shaun Medlicott** MD gastointestinal pathology; **Allan Oryschak** MD breast pathology, genitourinary pathology, ophthalmic pathology; **Alfredo Pinto-Rojas** MD pediatric pathology, pediatric hematopathology; **Steve Rasmussen** MD ophthalmic pathology; **Birgitte Roland** MD cytogenetics; **M. Omar Shokeir** MD general pathology, VP Medical Operations CLS; **Gary D. Sinclair** PhD molecular hematology (adjunct, major cross-apt); **Cynthia Trevenen** MD pediatric-perinatal pathology; **Martin Trotter** MD dermatopathology; **Kiril Trpkov** MD genitourinary pathology, soft tissue and bone pathology; **Weiming Yu** MD pediatric pathology, cardiac pathology, experimental transplantation; **Kunyan Zhang** MD, PhD molecular microbiology.

Assistant Professors (GFT and Clinical):

Amid Abdullah MD general pathology; **Pauline Alakija** MD, cardiac pathology, forensic pathology; **Sam Andrews** MD forensic pathology; **Duane Barber** MD dermatopathology; **Noureddine Berka** PhD tissue typing (adjunct); **Holly Brown** MD dermatopathology, surgical pathology; **Julie Carson** MD Microbiology; **Jennifer Chan** MD neuropathology, brain tumor; **Vivien Chang-Poon** MD cytopathology, sugical pathology; **Ivan Chebib** MD cytopathology, surgical pathology; **Lisa DiFrancesco** MD soft tissue and bone pathology; **Wei-Feng Dong** MD, PhD breast pathology, molecular oncology; **Marc Dupre** MD gastrointestinal pathology; **Thomas Fourie** MD hematopathology; **Margaret Gorecki** MD cytopathology, surgical pathology; **Steve Gorombey** MD general pathology; **Kelly Guggisberg** MD dermatopathology, ENT pathology; **Clinton Ho** MD general pathology, cytopathology; **Xiu Yan Jiang** MD hematopathology; **Margaret Kelly** MD, PhD pulmonary pathology; **Moosa Khalil** MD cytopathology, endocrine pathology, surgical pathology; **Martin Koebel** MD autopsy, gynecological pathology; **Richard Krause** PhD clinical chemistry (adjunct); **Andrew Kulaga** MD genitourinary pathology; **Erik Larsen** MD general pathology, ENT pathology; **Lucja Meier** MD cytopathology, surgical pathology; **Travis Ogilvie** MD breast and gynecological pathology; **Doreen Paslawski** MD breast pathology, genitourinary pathology; **Andrew Schell** MD gastrointestinal pathology; **Taher Meer Shabani-Rad** MD hematopathology; **Janette van den Berghe** PhD cytogenetics; **Ranjit Waghray** MD cytopathology, surgical pathology; **Hua Yang** MD surgical pathology, experimental transplantation; **Asli Yilmaz** MD urological pathology, ultra-structural pathology.

APPLICATIONS

All Canadian, American and International candidates must apply through the Canadian Resident Matching Service (www.carms.ca)

Address inquires to:

Residency Training Program Assistant
Department of Pathology & Laboratory Medicine
Foothills Medical Center
1403-29th Street N.W.
Calgary, Alberta, Canada T2N 2T9
Phone: (403) 944-1692 • **Fax:** (403) 944-4748
E-mail: sandra.skrober@cls.ab.ca or lisa.difrancesco @cls.ab.ca

UNIVERSITY OF BRITISH COLUMBIA

Vancouver, British Columbia

PROGRAMS OFFERED

The UBC Laboratory Medicine program includes seven separate residencies in Anatomical Pathology, General pathology, Medical Microbiology, Medical Biochemistry, Neuropathology and Hematological Pathology and Transfusion Medicine.

The common PGY-1 year comprises standard medical and surgical rotations in the style of rotating internship. The content of of PGY-2 to 5 will reflect and fulfill the applicable training requirements of the Royal College of Physicians and Surgeons of Canada. In addition, each of the residencies offers blocks of elective time to support individual career plans.

For more information, please visit the Pathology Residency Program website, as follows:
http://www.pathology.ubc.ca/html/index.html

REQUIREMENTS

1. An acceptable academic record.
2. A proven interest and motivation in our specialty, demonstrated by electives or research in Pathology and Laboratory Medicine is preferable.
3. Candidates should have acceptable letters of recommendation, preferably from specialists in any of the areas of Pathology and Laboratory Medicine.
4. Candidates must have skills in communication and be able to work with a wide variety of people.

For more information on how to apply, please visit the following
Website: http://www.med.ubc.ca/education/postgrad_programs.htm

UNIVERSITY OF MANITOBA

Winnipeg, Manitoba

PROGRAMS OFFERED

The Department of Pathology currently offers programs in anatomic pathology approved by the Royal College of Physicians and Surgeons of Canada and the American Board of Pathology. Residents select the program that will equip them for their career goals, usually either the hospital practice of pathology, with special competence in one or more of the branches of anatomic pathology, or an academic career including teaching and research. The faculty members have a wide variety of sub-specialty interests and experience, and they are actively involved in all aspects of the training program. In addition to the main divisions of anatomic pathology, which are organized as an Autopsy Teaching Unit and Surgical Pathology Service, the Department includes specialty units with expertise in cytology, electron microscopy, neuropathology and forensic science. Training is offered in these areas at both the general and advanced level. Opportunity to gain expertise in other branches of pathology is afforded by elective periods in the Microbiology, Clinical Chemistry, and Hematology Laboratories, and also experience in the Clinical Units of the Faculty of Medicine. The training of research pathologists and medical scientists is an important concern. Residents may spend an extended period in full-time research and/or basic medical science.

TYPES AND NUMBERS OF APPOINTMENTS

Eleven pathology residents.

FACILITIES

The Department of Pathology is administered under the direction of the University of Manitoba (www.umanitoba.ca) and Diagnostic Services of Manitoba (www.wrha.mb.ca/dsm), which is responsible for the majority of laboratories in the province. It is also affiliated with CancerCare Manitoba, and is accredited by the Canadian Council on Health Services Accreditation. The major University of Manitoba affiliated teaching hospitals are the Health Sciences Centre and the St Boniface General Hospital. The Health Sciences Centre (www.hsc.mb.ca) including the Children's Hospital, is designated as the Trauma Centre for Manitoba, and is the centre for neurosurgery, transplants and for most hospital based pediatric care in the Province. With over 1,100 beds, it admits more than 35,000 patients per year. The St Boniface General Hospital, with over 850 beds, also has a major teaching and research role. Both hospitals have fully accredited laboratories and research facilities that allow for in-depth study and investigation and provide optimum teaching and study facilities. The Medico legal autopsy cases are done within the hospital setting in agreement with the Office of the Chief Medical Examiner. Training in community based pathology is available at the Grace Hospital. The Critical Services Redevelopment Project at the HSC opened in 2007; it includes state-of-the-art operating theatres, intensive care and emergency facilities. Linked to the new Critical Services Building will be the Siemens Institute for Advanced Medicine, a world-class research centre that will focus on neurosciences, infectious diseases and imaging technology. The National Microbiology Laboratory (www.nml.ca) located less than 1 km away is one of the world's leading infectious disease research facilities. The Institute for Biodiagnostics (http://ibd.nrc-cnrc.gc.ca/index.html), a division of the National Research Council, located 2 km from HSC, is a world class facility for research in magnetic resonance imaging, spectroscopy and bioinformatics.

COMMUNITY

The City of Winnipeg, the capital of the province Manitoba, is in the "heart of the Red River Valley" and has a population of approximately 1,000,000. The city has a broad ethnic diversity. One of its most appealing aspects is that the city provides all of the amenities of a larger centre in a small-town atmosphere. ART: In addition to the Winnipeg Art Gallery, which features the largest Inuit sculpture collection in the world, there are numerous private and specialized galleries. The Museum of Man and Nature is one of the finest interpretive museums in Canada, and there are a number of special interest museums as well. DANCE: Home of the internationally renowned Royal Winnipeg Ballet, there are also numerous contemporary and ethnic dance groups. MUSIC: There is a full symphony orchestra, a chamber orchestra, an opera company, jazz society, a nationally known competitive music festival. THEATRE: Canada's oldest consistently performing theatre company, Le Cercle Moliere, is an innovative French language group situated in historic St. Boniface. In addition to traditional mainstage theatre, experimental works are also presented at any one of the city's five permanent theatres. There is also a permanent open air summer musical theatre. SPORT: There is professional CFL football, and professional hockey. The city is the home of numerous annual festivals. Winnipeg has 2,964 hectares of parkland within its boundaries and 33 km of riverbank and its proximity to lake country provides ready access to other recreational and sporting facilities.

STIPENDS AND MAINTENANCE

Stipends depend on experience and level of training, and are in the range of $46,707-$63,690. A precise salary figure will be determined when an application is received and evaluated.

STAFF

S. Ahing DDS oral pathology; **A. Ahsanuddin** MD hematopathology; **I. Aljada** MD anatomic pathology; **P. Baker** MD gynecologic pathology; **T. Balachandra** MD forensic pathology; Chief Medical Examiner, Province of Manitoba; **C. Batangan Santos** MD surgical, cytopathology; **S. Battistuzzi** MD Anatomic Pathology; **R. Buksak** MD anatomic pathology; **M. Curtis** MD anatomic, cytopathology; **M.R. Del Bigio** MD, PhD neuropathology; **C. Ellison** PhD immunology; **G. Fischer** MD, PhD surgical, cytopathology; **E. E. Frost** PhD neurobiology; **J.G. Gartner** MD department head, surgical & pediatric pathology, immunology; **R. Gheorghe** MD Anatomic Pathology; **I. Gibson** MBChB, MD renal pathology; **D. Grynspan** MD pediatric, surgical pathology; **S. Hamza** MD dermatopathology; **N. Hussain** MBBS pediatric, surgical pathology; **J. Klein** MD anatomic pathology; **S. Krawitz** MD, PhD neuropathology; **C.D. Littman** MD anatomic pathology, forensic pathology; **L. Lucman** MD anatomic & pediatric pathology; **C. Ludwick** MD gynecologic pathology; **C. Morales** MD hematopathology; **C. Musuka** MD hematopathology; **Y. Myal** PhD molecular pathology; **C. Penner** DDS oral pathology; **Susan Phillips** MD pediatric pathology; **G. Qing** MD anatomic & pulmonary pathology; **H. Qiu** MD Anatomic Pathology; **G.E. Quinonez-Salmon** MD surgical pathology, diagnostic electron microscopy; **E. Ravinsky** MD cytology, surgical and gynecologic pathology; **K. Roland** MD hematopathology; **R.G. Stark** MB anatomic pathology; **K. Von Kuster** MD surgical pathology; **R. Wightman** MD urologic, surgical pathology; **G. Williams** MD, PhD hematopathology, cytogenetics; **J. Younes** MD anatomic pathology, forensic pathology.

APPLICATIONS

Application is made through the Canadian Resident Matching Service, 151 Slater Street, Suite 802, Ottawa, Ontario, Canada, K1P 5H3. www.carms.ca

Address inquiries to:

Dr. Michael Curtis
Pathology Residency Program
The University of Manitoba
c/o Department of Pathology, MS459
Health Sciences Center
820 Sherbrook Street,
Winnipeg, Manitoba
Canada R3A 1R9
Phone: (204) 787-2829 • **Fax:** (204) 787-4942 • **E-mail:** mcurtis2@exchange.hsc.mb.ca

MEMORIAL UNIVERSITY OF NEWFOUNDLAND

St. John's, Newfoundland

PROGRAMS OFFERED

Memorial University offers approved residency training in Anatomic Pathology, accredited by the Royal College of Physicians and Surgeons of Canada. The General Pathology residency training program is currently inactive. The first year (i.e. PGY-2) provides residents with a range of experience including rotations to all affiliated hospitals and initial instruction in the disciplines of laboratory medicine; a series of didactic seminars specifically designed for first-year residents runs throughout the academic year. In the second, third and fourth years, the general pathology and anatomic pathology programs are differentiated with respect to structure and content, each being designed to meet Royal College requirements in the respective specialty. Residents in the general pathology program (currently inactive)-participate in rotations in anatomic pathology, medical microbiology, medical biochemistry, cytology and hematology/ blood banking. There is also specific instruction in laboratory administration. There are rotations available in immunology and in the Public Health Laboratory. All of these are designed to equip the resident to practice as a well-rounded pathologist in a general hospital laboratory. Residents in the anatomic pathology program embark on a series of short rotations in the subspecialties including neuropathology, cytopathology and molecular pathology throughout the second year. Following a six-month elective period in the third year, experience as hot seat resident in surgical pathology at each of the affiliated adult hospitals follows a second cycle of subspecialty experiences together with some elective time prior to eligibility for the Royal College specialty examinations. Residents participate in the Residents Academic Half Day in Pathology, a weekly series of teaching sessions held throughout the year. Responsibility and involvement in decision making increase throughout the four years of training as skills and knowledge are applied to clinical problems and professional attitudes are further developed. Entering trainees are therefore expected to be well grounded in general medicine and to have all the attributes of a physician. Each of the two programs is under the charge of a Residency Director and has a Pathology Residency Committee on which there is elected resident representation.

TYPES AND NUMBERS OF APPOINTMENTS

Generally, eight funded positions are available. Appointments to the program are usually made at the PGY-1 level, which provides a year of broad based clinical training. Applicants who consider that they have had significant previous training in laboratory medicine are requested to have this validated by the Royal College of Physicians and Surgeons before submitting their application. The number of residents in each of the four years of training remains flexible. A fifth year of specifically designated training may be made available to trainees in good standing at the discretion of the appropriate Residency Committee. Because of the design of the programs and the need to certify competence to examining bodies, appointments to the fourth year of the program will rarely, if ever, be made from outside the program. All residents are registered as postgraduate students of Memorial University.

FACILITIES

The programs are University based and utilize the resources of the Health Care Corporation of St John's, namely St Clare's Mercy Hospital, the Janeway Child Health Centre and The General Hospital which shares the Health Sciences Centre with the Faculty of Medicine of Memorial University. In addition to general medicine and surgery, each of these hospitals has well-developed subspecialty programs which are reflected in their laboratory medicine practice. Departments of Laboratory Medicine of the affiliated hospitals are fully computerized and integrated with their hospital information systems. The office of the Chief Medical Examiner is in the Health Sciences Centre where much of the forensic pathology for the Province is conducted. The Health Sciences Library, physically incorporated in the Health Sciences Centre, offers complete library service including computerized literature search and reference service; its holdings include 82,000 books and 1,798 periodical titles.

COMMUNITY

St John's, the provincial capital, is the oldest city in North America. It inherits a unique and deeply rooted cultural tradition extending back to the arrival of Sir Humphrey Gilbert in 1583. The Province of Newfoundland and Labrador has a history quite distinct from the rest of Canada; the old seafaring traditions are now gradually blending with an increasingly active offshore oil endeavor yet the warm, relaxed and friendly attitudes engendered by centuries of mutual support in a potentially hostile environment still endure. A small city with a population of about 110,000, St John's has a symphony orchestra and an active artistic and cultural life. There is ready access to the countryside and large wilderness areas with legendary hunting and fishing.

STIPENDS AND MAINTENANCE

The resident salary scale under the collective agreement with the Professional Association of Interns and Residents of Newfoundland is PGYI-$42,781, PGYII-$46,854, PGYIII-$50,924, PGYIV-$55,001, PGYV-$59,073, PGYVI-

$63,150 and Fellow - $67,223. Fringe benefits under the agreement include 4 weeks vacation, 7 days conference leave, travel expenses for call back, and a contribution towards malpractice insurance coverage. A designated administrative resident receives an addtional allowance of $3,307.50 per annum. CMPA is reimbursed. Participating hospitals do not provide accommodation.

STAFF

M. Afrouzian MD; **K. Aljerian** MD, MBBS, MHSc, FRCPC; **S. Anwar** MD; **S.P. Avis** MD, FRCPC, Chairman & Chief Medical Examiner; **J. Barron** MD, MSc, FRCPC; **D. Cook** MD, FRCPC; **N. Denic** MD, MSc, PhD, FRCPC, Clinical Chief; **F. Elms** MD, FRCPC; **D. Fontaine** MD, FRCPC, Director, Cytopathology; **M. Hamodat** MD; **F. Han** MD, Cytogenetics; **J. Hutchinson** MD, FRCPC, Med Microbiology; **N. Makretsov** MD; **C. Morris-Larkin** MD, FRCPC; **A. Pirzada** MB, BS, DABP, Director, Anatomic Pathology Program; **C. Pushpanathan** MB, BS, FRCPC; **E. Randell** PhD, DCC, FCACB; **P.M. Wadden** MD, FRCPC; **L.A. Whitman** MD, FRCPC; **Y. Xie** MD, PhD, Molecular Genetics.

APPLICATIONS

Candidates must be graduates of approved medical schools and apply through the Canadian Resident Matching Service (CaRMS) at 171 Nepean St., Suite 300, Ottawa, Ontario, Canada, K2B 0B4. Graduates of international medical schools must be eligible for educational licensure in the Province of Newfoundland. For information write to: College of Physicians and Surgeons of Newfoundland and Labrador, Suite 603, 139 Water Street, St John's, NL, A1C 1B2.

Address inquiries to:

Dr Amrah Pirzada, Director, Anatomic Pathology
Postgraduate Medical Studies Office
Health Sciences Centre
St John's, Newfoundland,
Canada A1B 3V6
Phone: (709) 777-6680
Web site: http://www.med.mun.ca/pgme/

Health Sciences Centre in Memorial University campus, St John's, Newfoundland.

DALHOUSIE UNIVERSITY MEDICAL SCHOOL

Halifax, Nova Scotia

PROGRAMS OFFERED

The Department of Pathology provides residency training programs which are approved by the Royal College of Physicians and Surgeons of Canada and the American Board of Pathology. These programs include general pathology, anatomical pathology, hematological pathology transfusion medicine and medical microbiology. Each program is supervised by a coordinating residency committee with the objectives being to provide the training recommended by the Specialty Committee of the Royal College in each discipline. Inter- and intradepartmental conferences, including courses in pathobiology, medical biochemistry, immunology and medical microbiology, are held. Interested residents are encouraged to enroll for the MSc degree and to participate in the experimental research programs of the Department.

TYPES AND NUMBERS OF APPOINTMENTS

There are 21 existing residents in pathology with 3 new vacancies on a yearly basis.

FACILITIES

While the University has the overall responsibility for resident training, the total residency program represents a combined and coordinated effort of 3 institutions whose laboratory staff are members of the Departments of Pathology and Microbiology, located in the Sir Charles Tupper Medical Building on the Dalhousie University campus. The Halifax teaching hospitals and laboratories are within walking distance of each other and close to the Sir Charles Tupper Medical Building where the major experimental research activities of the Departments are based. The larger teaching hospital complex, the Queen Elizabeth II Health Sciences Centre, is located on two main sites within the Capital Health District, namely the Halifax Infirmary and the Victoria General Hospital. This complex includes a total of 1,125 inpatient beds, with outpatient services at both sites and an emergency room at the Halifax Infirmary. A blood transfusion service and emergency laboratory services are provided at the Infirmary site, while most laboratory services are centralized to the Dr DJ Mackenzie Building at the Victoria General Hospital. Pediatric and maternity care is provided at the adjacent IWK Health Centre for Children, Women & Families, (121 pediatric beds, 52 bassinets, 58 special care nursery beds, 78 antepartum/obstetrical beds, 23 gynaecology beds = 332 beds), which is primarily served by its in-house laboratories. The Department of Laboratory Medicine at the Saint John Regional Hospital, Saint John, New Brunswick also provides training for residents. Total tests (2008) for these institutions are: Queen Elizabeth II Health Sciences Centre: autopsies 135; surgicals 35,094; immunopathology 104,014; cytology 104,611, clinical chemistry 7,558,986; hematology 1,229,711; blood bank 466,328; microbiology 500,000; IWK Health Centre for Children, Women & Families: autopsies 115; surgicals 4,227; immunohematology 107,362; microbiology 64,486; cytogenetics 2,686; Core Lab 653,104; Shared Instrumentation Lab 224,080; Molecular Biology 1,434; Saint John Regional Hospital: autopsies 279; surgicals 19,544; electron microscopy 1,049; cytology 31,878; clinical chemistry 2,257,356; hematology 446,668; microbiology 185,813; transfusion medicine 37,001; cytogenetics 350.

COMMUNITY

Halifax, the capital city of Nova Scotia, has a population of approximately 220,000 and the Capital District Health Authority has a population of approximately 400,000. Nearly all of the teaching hospitals are located within a few minutes walking distance of each other and the medical school. The city has a very good public school system, five universities and colleges, and a number of cultural facilities including museums, a symphony orchestra, libraries and live theater. The local geography provides extensive recreational opportunities for water sports, hiking, camping and skiing.

STIPENDS AND MAINTENANCE

Residents are employed by the hospitals. Annual salaries range from $46,358.55 (first year) to $63,080.67 (chief resident). Four weeks vacation with pay is provided during each year of residency. Living quarters are not provided. Residents planning an academic career in pathology or affiliation with a teaching hospital on completion of residency can apply to Dalhousie University for a Killam Fund Fellowship which provides an additional stipend during one of the resident years. Research fellowships for suitable candidates are granted by Dalhousie University or are available from the Medical Research Council of Canada.

STAFF

Queen Elizabeth II Health Sciences Centre

P.J. Barnes MD; **M.J. Bullock** MD; **C. Cheng** MD; **A. Covert** MD; **A. Easton** MD; **K. R. Forward** MD; **A. Foyle** MD; **L. Geldenhuys** MD; **W. Greer** PhD; **A. Guha** MD; **R. Gupta** MD; **D. Haldane** MD; **T. Hatchette** MD;

J.G. Heathcote MB, PhD, Head of Department; **W. Huang** MD; **T. Issekutz** MD; **R. Juskevicius** MD; **M. Lamoureux** PhD; **R. Liwski** MD; **R.J.B. Macaulay** MD; **R.F. MacIntosh** MD; **J. Merrimen** MD; **S. Murray** MD; **A. Nanji** MB, ChB,; **B.A. Nassar** MD, PhD; **S. Pasternak** MD; **I. Sadek** MD; **H. Sapp** MD; **A. Shawwa** MD; **A. Thoni** MD; **N. Walsh** MD; **I. Wanless** MD; **Z. Xu** MD; **L. Yang** MD, PhD.

IWK Health Centre for Children, Women & Families

R.B. Fraser MD; **D.A. Gaskin** MD; **R.A. Koupaei** PhD; **J.F. Magee** MD; **T.L. Mailman** MD; **E.R. McBride** MD; **E.M. McKay** MD; **B.A. Morash** PhD; **C. Riddell** PhD.

Department of Laboratory Medicine, Saint John Regional Hospital, Saint John, New Brunswick

J. Flick MD; **A. Fraser** PhD; **M. Godlewski** MD; **G. Hardy** MD; **M. Hossain** MD; **I. Morava-Protzner** MD; **A. O'Brien** MD; **K. Obenson** MD; **K. Protzner** MD; **T. Rahmeh** MD; **L. Rajappannair** MD; **I. Umar** MD.

Sir Charles Tupper Medical Building

G. Dellaire PhD; **D. Guernsey** PhD; **D. Hoskin** PhD; **P. Lee** PhD.

APPLICATIONS

Candidates must be graduates of approved medical schools and apply through the Canadian Resident Matching Service at 151 Slayter Street, Suite 802, Ottawa, Ontario, Canada K1P 5H3. Graduates of medical schools outside of Canada must have an MCCEE certificate (Medical Council of Canada Evaluation Examination). For more information regarding the MCCEE, inquiries can be directed to: The Medical Council of Canada, PO Box 8234, Ottawa, Ontario, Canada K1G 3H7. Appointments begin on July 1 and are made on a yearly basis. Applications may be submitted at any time but most appointments are made by January.

Address inquiries to:

Mrs Debby Caldwell
Residency Training Program
Department of Pathology
Dr D. J. Mackenzie Building
5788 University Avenue
Halifax, Nova Scotia, Canada B3H 1V8
E-mail: caldwelld@cdha.nshealth.ca

Halifax, Nova Scotia

UNIVERSITY OF TORONTO

Toronto, Ontario

PROGRAMS OFFERED

The Department of Laboratory Medicine and Pathobiology offers intensive, integrated training programs in anatomic pathology, general pathology, hematopathology, medical biochemistry, medical microbiology, and neuropathology. The programs fulfill requirements of the Royal College and are fully accredited. Training is also accepted by the American Board of Pathology. In addition, students may also be accepted for MSc or PhD degrees in a new combined residency/graduate student program accredited by the Royal College. The training programs may be used to embark upon a career in either academic or community hospital setting. The Department sits at the crossroads of basic science and clinical medicine. Thus, all of our programs offer a wide variety of clinical experiences and opportunities for basic, translational and clinical research. Eligible students may combine training and graduate school leading to an MSc or PhD degree. An important priority of the Department is the study of the molecular mechanisms of human disease. Residents are expected to conduct regular seminars and prepare posters or platform presentations for national or international scientific meetings. Funds to assist presentation of data at meetings are available through Dutkevich Traveling Scholarships administered by the Department. All programs require FIVE years of training, except Hematopathology which requires four years. The first postgraduate year (PGY1) is a general clinical year similar to a rotating internship but biased towards laboratory medicine. PGY1 is considered a common year for the programs except for medical microbiology and hematopathology; trainees will be allowed to transfer from one laboratory specialty to another within that year. Entry is directly from medical school through the Canadian Resident Matching Service (CaRMS).

a) **Anatomic Pathology** The program is flexible to accommodate the training needs of individual residents. All complete an initial core training in adult anatomic pathology involving autopsy and surgical pathology. Subsequently, they train in cytopathology, neuropathology, pediatric, molecular, and forensic pathology. One year of elective time is available with choice of electives depending upon career goals. Core training may be limited to only some University affiliated hospitals, but elective training may occur anywhere within the University system. The program recognizes two broad streams. Residents planning a career in academic pathology may train exclusively in anatomic pathology and related disciplines. Residents planning a career in a community setting may choose to train in general pathology or, during electives, in one other clinical pathology discipline (hematopathology, microbiology or biochemistry) in addition to anatomic pathology. The latter training qualifies for anatomic pathology certification only.

b) **General Pathology** General Pathology is a four-year integrated program, after PGY1, to consist of an equivalent of two years of anatomic pathology, which includes neuropathology, forensic pathology, a 3-month rotation at a community hospital, and a 3-month rotation in pediatric pathology. There will be a 6-month rotation each in clinical chemistry, hematopathology, medical microbiology plus 6 months of electives to enhance career goals. The program offers core knowledge, skills and training in each laboratory discipline with emphasis on laboratory management, continuing quality improvement, informatics, and other necessary skills as a laboratory medical consultant and director.

c) **Hematopathology** The hematopathology program trains physicians in laboratory hematology as practiced in Canada. During the four-year residency following PGY1, experience is gained in the morphological and quantitative aspects of hematology, coagulation, transfusion medicine and lymph node pathology. Exposure to modern diagnostic techniques is provided and research is encouraged, particularly during elective rotations.

d) **Medical Biochemistry** The Medical Biochemistry Program is a four-year integrated program after PGY1. Two years of laboratory training focus upon analytical methods, interpretation, clinical liaison and management issues. The next year is devoted entirely to clinical medicine and spent in internal medicine exclusively or combined with a 3-6 month period in pediatrics and/or obstetrics. The final year during which the Royal College examination will be taken begins with 6 months at the Hospital for Sick Children followed by a period of monthly rotations to various specialized laboratories or services, typically, the Women's College Campus, the Lipid Core Laboratory at St Michael's Hospital, clinical nutrition, biochemical genetics, clinical pharmacology and oncology. Exposure to modern diagnostic techniques is provided, and research during training in hospital laboratories is highly encouraged.

e) **Medical Microbiology** The discipline of medical microbiology is a hybrid of clinical and laboratory activities. This Royal College program is designed to offer training in medical microbiology, with flexibility for those interested in a career in academic medicine. Following the PGY1, the four years of training include experience in infectious diseases, bacteriology, mycobacteriology, mycology, virology, parasitology, serology, diagnostic laboratory medicine, laboratory management and infection control. The trainee is expected to become familiar with laboratory operation and proficient as a consultant in all aspects of clinical microbiology and infection control. Opportunities to participate in research activities are provided and strongly encouraged.

f) **Neuropathology** Neuropathology is a four-year program following PGY1. One year is spent in anatomic pathology, two in neuropathology and one year in electives. During the elective year options are many, although a clinical rotation (6 months) and/or research is recommended. The clinical rotation may be in neurology, neurosurgery or neuroradiology. Facilities, technology and clinical material are outstanding. Neuropathology residents may rotate through any of four teaching hospitals accredited by The Royal College of Physicians and Surgeons of Canada.

TYPES AND NUMBERS OF APPOINTMENTS

Eight entry positions are available through the match. The number of residency positions are currently distributed as follows: Anatomic Pathology: 43; General Pathology: 2; Hematopathology: 3; Medical Microbiology: 2; Neuropathology: 0. Research fellowships for graduate students are also available.

FACILITIES

The Department of Laboratory Medicine and Pathobiology is one of the largest departments in the Faculty of Medicine and has staff and facilities in several institutions, teaching and community hospitals. The training program operates as a single educational unit. Facilities include the Banting Institute and Medical Sciences Building (basic research) on the University campus, the Forensic Sciences Building, and the following hospitals: Hospital for Sick Children, Sunnybrook and Women's College Health Sciences Centre, Sunnybrook and Women's College campuses, University Health Network (Toronto General Hospital, Toronto Western Hospital and Princess Margaret Hospital), Mount Sinai Hospital, St Michael's Hospital, North York General Hospital, Lakeridge Health Oshawa, and St Joseph's Health Centre. Basic research laboratories also exist in some hospital research institutes. At the Hospital for Sick Children pediatric laboratory medicine is practiced exclusively; most other hospital departments deal with a wide variety of adult material. All use multiple investigative techniques. Each hospital has particular strengths in some area or technique.

COMMUNITY

Toronto, a city of over two million, has a rich and dynamic cultural, entertainment and sporting life. Its multicultural character provides interesting diversions and attractions. The University and its hospitals are in the center of the city, adjacent to business and residential areas. Job, career and educational opportunities for residents' spouses are varied.

STIPENDS AND MAINTENANCE

The salary range for 2008 is from $47,172 for PGY1 to $66,506 for PGY5.

STAFF

Professor and Chairman

R.G. Hegele MD.

Professors

K. Adeli PhD; **O. A. Adeyi** MBBS; **S. Asa** MD, PhD; **A.D. Baines** MD, PhD; **B. Bapat** PhD; **M. Bendeck** PhD; **C. Bergeron** MD; **J.M. Boggs** PhD; **J. Butany** MBBS; **W. Chapman** MD; **R. Chetty** MBBCh, PhD; **L. Chiang** PhD; **D.E.C. Cole** MD, PhD; **T.J. Colgan** MD; **S. E. Croul** MD; **E. Cutz** MD; **M. Cybulsky** MD; **E.P. Diamandis** PhD,MD Head, Division of Clinical Biochemistry; **B. Fernandes** MBChB; **P.A. Gordon** MBChB; **A.I. Gotlieb** MDCM; **M.D. Grynpas** PhD; **W. Halliday** MD; **P. Hamel** PhD; **W. Hanna** MBChB; **A. Hinek** MD, PhD; **J. Hu** PhD; **D. Irwin** PhD; **M.G. Johnston** PhD; **S. Jothy** MD, PhD; **H.J. Kahn** MBChB; **S. Kamel-Reid** PhD; **R. Kandel** MD; **B. Kapur** PhD; **M. Khalifa** MBBCh, PhD; **K. Kovacs** MD, PhD; **C.C. Liew** PhD; **C.A. Lingwood** PhD; **D.E. Low** MD Head, Division of Medical Microbiology; **D.J. Mahuran** PhD; **T. Mazzulli** MD; **A.J. McGeer** MD; **J. McLaurin** PhD; **D. Munoz** MD, MSc; **S. Nag** MD, PhD; **F. O'Malley** MBBCh; **M. Opas** PhD; **D. Pantalony** MD; **M.J. Phillips** MD; **P.H. Pinkerton** MBChB, MD; **K. Pritzker** MD; **G. Prud'homme** MD; **S. Rajalakshmi** PhD; **M. Rand** PhD; **R. Riddell** MBBS; **R. Saad** MBChB, PhD; **D.S.R. Sarma** PhD; **A. Seth** PhD; **P.N. Shek** PhD; **A.E.M. Simor** MD; **L. Sugar** MD; **D.M. Templeton** PhD, MD; **P. Thorner** MD, PhD; **M.S. Tsao** MD; **T. van der Kwast** MD, PhD; **R. Vieth** PhD; **G. Wilson** MDCM; **P.Y. Wong** PhD; **B. Yang** PhD; **H. Yeger** PhD; **L. Zhang** MD, PhD.

Associate Professors

M. Abdelhaleem MBBCh, PhD; **L.C. Allen** PhD; **J.M. Bilbao** MD; **S. Boerner** MD; **W. Brien** MD; **J. Callum** MD; **H. Chang** MD, PhD; **M. Cheung** MD; **I. Crandall** PhD; **N. Crowcroft** MBBS; **G. Denomme** PhD; **H.P. Elsholtz** PhD; **A. Evans** MD, PhD; **D. Ghazarian** MBChB, PhD; **M. Guindi** MBChB; **C. Hawkins** MD, PhD; **V. Leytin** PhD; **D.F. Macdonald** MBChB; **M. McGavin** PhD; **C. McKerlie** DVM, DVSc; **J.O. Minta** PhD; **J. Mogridge** PhD; **J.B. Mullen** MD; **H. Ni** PhD; **M. Ohh** PhD; **H. Özçelik** PhD; **B. Perez-Ordonez** MD; **M.S. Pollanen** MD, PhD; **S. Raphael** MD; **M.D.O. Reis** MD; **R. Renlund** DVM; **S.E. Richardson** MDCM; **A.D. Romaschin** PhD; **M. Rozakis-Adcock** PhD; **G. Santos** MD, PhD; **P.A. Shaw** MD; **G. Taylor** MD; **R. Tellier** MD; **D. Tkachuk** MD; **M. Vearncombe** MD; **C. Wang** MD, PhD; **S. Wasan** MD; **E.J.T. Winsor** PhD; **J. Young** MD; **I. Zbieranowski** MD; **M. Zielenska** PhD.

Assistant Professors

I. Aubert PhD; **D.J. Bailey** MD, PhD; **M. Barnard** MD; **C.D. Bell** MD; **I.L. Bromberg** MD; **P.C. Chan** PhD; **A. Chesney** MD; **D. Chiasson** MD; **K. Chun** PhD; **B. Clarke** MBBCh; **C. Cserti-Gazdewich** MD; **S.S. Deodhare** MD, MBBS; **R.H. Devlin** MD; **S. Done** MBBCh, PhD; **S. Drews** PhD; **V. Dube** MD; **M. Fearon** MD; **S.E. Fischer** MD; **G. Gardiner** MD; **W. Geddie** MD; **Z. Ghorab** MD; **S. Girardin** PhD; **C. Guyard** PhD; **A. Herzenberg** MD, PhD; **B. Hoffman** PhD; **M. Hough** PhD; **D. Howarth** MD; **E. Hsieh** MD; **A. Huang** MD, PhD; **D.M. Hwang** MD,

PhD; **M. Irwin** MD; **N. Ismiil** MBChB; **F. Jamieson** MD; **L. Kapusta** MD; **K. Katz** MD, MSc; **S. Keating** MD; **T.-R. Kiehl** MD; **R. Kirsch** MBBS; **E. Kolomietz** PhD; **S. Krajden** MDCM; **G. Lajoie** MDCM; **W. Lau** MBBS; **Y. Lin** MD; **V. Lustig** PhD; **C. MacMillan** MD; **A.R. MacRae** PhD; **R. Melano** PhD; **N.A. Miller** MD; **A.M. Mulligan** MBBS; **B.Y. Ngan** MD, PhD; **S. Nofech-Mozes** MD; **N. Palaniyar** PhD; **B. Patterson** MDCM; **D. Pillai** MD; **S. Poutanen** MD, MPH; **G. Rasty** MD; **A. Rebbapragada** PhD; **J. Robertson** PhD; **T.H. Rose** MD; **D. Rowe-Magnus** PhD; **C. Rowsell** MD; **G. Schmitt-Ulms** PhD; **M. Shago** PhD; **N.A. Shaikh** PhD; **P. Shannon** MD; **B.L. Sheridan** MBBS; **C. Sherman** MD; **G. Somers** MBBS, PhD; **T. Stockley** PhD; **C. Streutker** MD; **J.M. Sweet** MD; **K. J. Tinckam** MB; **T. Treger** MD; **Z.H. Verjee** PhD; **S. Viero** MD; **I. Weinreb** MD; **J. Wong** MD; **Y. Yau** PhD; **P.M. Yip** PhD; **B. Youngson** MD; **G. Yousef** MD, PhD; **S. Zhang** PhD; **J. Zubovits** MD.

Lecturers

A. Al Habeeb MBBS; **S. Al-Haddad** MBChB; **N. Ali-Ridha** MBBCh; **V.G. Allen** MD; **A. Azad** PhD; **Z. Aziz** MD; **A. Blumenthal** MD; **S. Boss** PhD; **G. Brouckhanski** PhD; **D. Chan** MBBS; **I. Davis** MD; **J. Fiser** MD; **L. Fu** PhD; **W. Hammouda** MD; **W. Hu** MD, PhD; **L.S. Hung** MBBS; **V. Iakovlev** MD; **R. Jong** MD; **M.J. Khosravi** PhD; **L. Kyriakopoulou** PhD; **E. Latta** MD; **C.S. Leung** MBBS; **L. Matukas** MD; **F. Moid** MBBS; **S. Nanji** MBBCh; **S. Newbigging** DVM; **J. Pendergrast** MD; **A. Pollett** MD; **M. Quantz** MD; **M. Rouzbahman** MD; **M. Sapp** MD; **I. Seiden-Long** PhD; **W. Sirkin** MBBCh; **E. Szentgyorgyi** MD; **J. Tong** PhD; **M. Treloar** MD; **R. Vajpeyi** MD; **H. Vandenberghe** PhD; **L. Velsher** MDCM; **C. Wei** PhD.

APPLICATIONS

Candidates for residency training must be eligible for registration on the educational register of the College of Physicians and Surgeons of Ontario, 80 College Street, Toronto. It is the responsibility of the applicant to ensure that he or she is eligible for such registration.

Address inquiries to:

Residency Training Program
Department of Laboratory Medicine and Pathobiology
Faculty of Medicine, University of Toronto
Banting Institute
100 College Street, Room 110
Toronto, Ontario, Canada M5G 1L5
Phone: (416) 978-7535 • **Fax:** (416) 978-7361 • **E-mail:** pathology.residency@utoronto.ca
Web site: http://lmp.facmed.utoronto.ca

McGILL UNIVERSITY HOSPITALS

Montreal, Quebec

PROGRAMS OFFERED

McGill University offers postgraduate training for medical graduates interested in a career in anatomic pathology. This five-year program is fully approved and meets the requirements of the boards in anatomic pathology in Canada and the United States. The first year is in clinical medicine. It is followed by two years of core training designed to provide all trainees with both basic and specialized knowledge and experience in most fields of anatomic pathology. This includes "hands on" training in the adult and pediatric autopsy, surgical pathology and rotations in various subspecialties. Subspecialty training is available in most areas of anatomic pathology, including immunopathology, molecular pathology, electron microscopy, flow cytometry, ENT, dermatopathology, gynecologic pathology, respiratory pathology, gastrointestinal and liver pathology, renal pathology, breast pathology, transplantation pathology, hematopathology, ophthalmic pathology, genitourinary pathology, endocrine pathology, and bone and soft tissue pathology. The fourth year includes more specialized training in cytopathology, neuropathology, pediatric pathology, cytogenetics, emerging techniques and forensic pathology. The fifth year is tailored to the resident's needs and/or goals. Mentorship is the mode of teaching. The teaching is complemented by academic half-days, research seminars, Journal Club and surgical/autopsy/subspecialty conferences. The resident participates in medical teaching and is expected to participate in research activities. The program is flexible allowing, on an individual basis, time to pursue research training, including degree-oriented research (MSc, PhD). Fellowship positions are available.

TYPES AND NUMBERS OF APPOINTMENTS

There are approximately three entry level positions yearly reserved for participants in the Canadian Resident Matching Service (CaRMS); additional separate positions, variable in number, are appropriated to US citizens, Quebec graduates returning from general practice, and transfers from other provinces, depending upon conditions. In accordance with provincial licensing requirements, applicants for funded positions must be either Canadian or US citizens who are graduates of LCME-approved medical schools, who conform otherwise to eligibility requirements set by the McGill University Faculty of Medicine Post-Graduate Medical Education Office, which should be contacted first for further instructions in case of doubt regarding eligibility for training.

FACILITIES

Trainees rotate to the McGill University Health Centre (MUHC) and affiliated hospitals. The MUHC includes the following four major sites, the Royal Victoria Hospital (500 beds), the Montreal General Hospital (417 beds), the Montreal Children's Hospital (180 beds), and the Montreal Neurological Hospital (96 beds). The two other teaching hospitals are the Jewish General Hospital (571 beds) and St. Mary's Hospital (251 beds).

COMMUNITY

Montreal, a city with a metropolitan area population of 3.7 million, is located on the island of Montreal in the St Lawrence River. It is predominantly a French-speaking city with about 80 per cent of the inhabitants being of French-Canadian descent. There are excellent public and private schools, both French and English, and also four universities and a number of colleges. It is a lively, multicultural city with a flavor of its own, unique on the North American continent.

STIPENDS AND MAINTENANCE

Residents receive four weeks vacation per year with remuneration of $41,355-$58,397, depending upon the year of training.

STAFF

D. Haegert MD Professor and Chair, hematopathology, immunopathology; **S. Albrecht** MD neuropathology; **R. D. Amre** MD hematopathology; **J. Arseneau** MD GYN-pathology; **M. Auger** MD cytopathology; **K. Bakdounes** MD anatomic pathology; **C. Bernard** MD pediatric pathology; **M. Blumenkrantz** MD pediatric pathology, cytogenetics; **G. A. Brandao** MD cytopathology, pulmonary pathology; **M.-L. Brisson** MD nephropathology, hematopathology; **M. N. Burnier, Jr.** MD, PhD ophthalmic pathology; **D. Cagler** MD surgical pathology, cytopathology; **B. Case** MD occupational and environmental pathology; **P. Chauvin** DDS oral pathology; **M. F. Chen** MD perinatal and pediatric pathology; **A. Duncan** PhD cytogenetics; **A. Ferenczy** MD GYN-pathology; **R. Fraser** MD pulmonary pathology; **A. Gologan** MD gastrointestinal and liver pathology; **O. Gologan** MD cytopathology, ENT pathology; **M.-C. Guiot** MD neuropathology; **T. Haliotis** MD, PhD hematopathology; **Q. Hamid** MD, PhD molecular biology; **S. M. Jung** MD dermatopathology; **Y. Kanber** MD cytopathology; **E. Lamoureux** MD gastrointestinal and liver pathology; **J. Lavoie** PhD cytogenetics; **A. T. Marcus** MD anatomic pathology; **V. Marcus** MD gastrointestinal and liver pathology; **R. P. Michel** MD pulmonary pathology; **A. Nahal** MD bone and soft tissue pathology, cytopathology; **V. H. Nguyen** MD pediatric pathology; **A. Omeroglu** MD breast pathology, GYN-pathology, cardiovascular pathology; **G. Omeroglu-Altinel** MD breast pathology; **R. Onerheim** MD anatomic pathology; **D. Pilavdzic** MD anatomic pathology; **J. B. Richardson** MD, PhD neuropathology; **L. Rochon** MD prostate, thyroid, ENT and perinatal pathology; **I. Roy** MD anatomic pathology; **S. Sandhu** MD anatomic pathology; **A. Sauvageau** MD forensic pathology; **A. Spatz** MD dermatopathology; **H. Srolovitz** MD dermatopathology; **J. St. Cyr** MD medical biochemistry; **A. K. Watters** MD dermatopathology; **N. Zaklama** MD anatomic pathology; **E. Zorychta** PhD neurophysiology.

APPLICATIONS

Applicants must be graduates of approved medical schools in Canada or the United States.

Address inquiries to:

Dr. Chantal Bernard
Program Director
Pathology Residency Training Program
Department of Pathology
McGill University
3775 University Street
Montréal, Québec, Canada H3A 2B4
Phone: (514) 412-4495; (514) 398-7192 Ext. 00481
Fax: (514) 412-4258; (514) 398-7446

42nd Edition

Training in Specialized Areas of Pathology 2010–2011

The following pages describe fellowships and other postgraduate opportunities for training in the certifiable subspecialties and other specialized areas of pathology. There are pathology specialties concerned with every category of disease.

The Intersociety Council for Pathology Information, Inc.

UNIVERSITY OF ALABAMA MEDICAL CENTER, BIRMINGHAM
UNIVERSITY OF ALABAMA HOSPITAL
AMERICAN RED CROSS ALABAMA REGION

Blood Banking/Transfusion Medicine Fellowship

Description: This one-year jointly sponsored program provides experience in an academic hospital transfusion medicine service and a large blood center. Clinical experience at the University of Alabama Hospital includes: pre-transfusion testing, investigation of antibody problems and transfusion reactions, component therapy, therapeutic apheresis, including photopheresis, transplantation immunogenetics, HLA and paternity testing. Clinical experience at American Red Cross Blood Services includes: donor recruitment, collection, processing, component preparation, donor apheresis, distribution, quality control, and reference laboratory consultation. Teaching and research opportunities available.

Requirements: Candidates should be Board-eligible or Board-certified in Clinical Pathology or other major specialty board such as Anesthesiology, Medicine or Pediatrics. Candidates should have an unrestricted Alabama license prior to starting fellowship. For info on obtaining a license, go to the Alabama Board of Medical Examiners website (http://www.albme.org/). Other contact information for ALBME: **Phone:** (334) 242-4153 **Fax:** (334) 242-4155

Types and Numbers of Appointments: One position available each year.

Facilities: The University of Alabama at Birmingham (UAB) is a major research institution, ranking among the nation's top universities in terms of NIH funding. UAB Hospital is a nationally recognized tertiary care facility, with more than 900 inpatient beds. Nestled within the lush green foothills of the Appalachian Mountains in the modern city of Birmingham, UAB offers an opportunity to gain detailed knowledge and extensive experience in all aspects of transfusion medicine, while enjoying true Southern hospitality in a beautiful setting. The Division of Laboratory Medicine in the Department of Pathology at UAB, in cooperation with the American Red Cross, offers a one-year fellowship in blood banking and transfusion medicine to prepare you fully for a career in this field.

Community: Named "the Magic City " because of its explosive growth, today's Birmingham is an exciting and progressive city. Nearly a million people live in the greater metropolitan area. The warm hospitality of the people complements the temperate climate and the beautiful setting.
Birmingham 's economy continues to grow in the areas of engineering, finance, telecommunications, and biomedical research. Health care and education have replaced other industries as Birmingham 's economic base, and UAB is the state's largest employer. Birmingham also boasts exceptional museums, parks, historical landmarks, family attractions, concerts, festivals, and sporting events.

Stipends: Commensurate with the year of postgraduate training.

Applications: Should be sent to Marisa B. Marques, Director, Transfusion Medicine Services, University of Alabama Hospital, The University of Alabama at Birmingham, 619 South 19th Street, Birmingham, AL 35249-7331.

Phone: (205) 934-7774 (Ms. Morgan Burke) • **Fax:** (205) 975-4468

AMERICAN RED CROSS, NORTHERN OHIO REGION
CLEVELAND CLINIC
UNIVERSITY HOSPITALS CASE MEDICAL CENTER

Cleveland City-Wide Blood Banking/Transfusion Medicine Fellowship

Description: This ACGME-accredited fellowship program combines the strengths of the American Red Cross, the Cleveland Clinic, and University Hospitals Case Medical Center. The fellow rotates for four months at each institution. The program provides training in blood center operations and clinical transfusion medicine, including perioperative autotransfusion. Approximately 220,000 units of blood components are drawn annually to support adult and pediatric services, including stem cell and solid organ transplantation and neonatal intensive care. Over 2,000 therapeutic apheresis procedures and stem cell collections are performed every year. Specialized training in immunohematology consultation is provided through an AABB-accredited Immunohematology Reference Laboratory.

Requirements: Applicants must have satisfactorily completed an approved residency in anatomic and clinical pathology, clinical pathology, pediatrics, internal medicine, anesthesiology, or appropriate specialty by the starting date (July 1) and must be eligible for Ohio licensure.

Stipends: Commensurate with the applicant's level of training.

Staff: Gerald Hoeltge MD, Interim Director Fellowship Program; **Priscilla I. Figueroa** MD; **Harry Taylor** MD.

Applications: Letter of inquiry and curriculum vitae should be sent to Irene Walton, Fellowship Coordinator, 3747 Euclid Avenue, Cleveland, OH 44115-2501.

Phone: (216) 431-3285 • **Fax:** (216) 391-3505

UNIVERSITY OF ARKANSAS FOR MEDICAL SCIENCES

Blood Banking Fellowship

Description: The University of Arkansas for Medical Sciences (UAMS) is offering a one-year ACGME-accredited fellowship program in Blood Banking/Transfusion Medicine. Participating institutions include the UAMS University Hospital, Arkansas Children's Hospital and the American Red Cross. University Hospital has an extremely active cancer research and treatment program supported by the medical center's Blood Bank and Transfusion Service and Cell Therapy Laboratory. An active apheresis program performs therapeutic procedures and collects peripheral blood progenitor cells. Arkansas Children's Hospital has a busy transfusion service providing the fellow with exposure to the focused field of pediatric transfusion medicine. This lab is also engaged in serologically-based infectious disease testing and intraoperative blood salvage. The American Red Cross is the provider of blood products and services to much of Arkansas. This will provide the fellow with extensive experience in the medical, operational and regulatory aspects of blood collection. In addition to clinical rotations, the fellow will be engaged in research and development activities and educational efforts. For more information, please visit our webpage at: http://www.uams.edu/pathology/fellowships/felblood.asp

Requirements: Candidates must be Board-eligible or Board-certified in clinical pathology or a relevant clinical specialty.

Types and Numbers of Appointments: 1 Fellow per year

Stipends: $47,470 per year

Staff: Douglas Blackall MD Blood Bank Medical Director at Arkansas Children's Hospital and Fellowship Program Director; **Michele Fox** MD Director of Cell Therapy and Transfusion Medicine at UAMS; **Terry Harville** MD, PhD Director of the HLA Laboratory at UAMS and Arkansas Children's Hospital; **Krishna Oza** MD Director of the Blood Bank and Transfusion Service at UAMS; **John Theus** MD Medical Director of the American Red Cross Blood Services; **Mayumi Nakagawa** MD Transfusion Medicine Staff Physician at UAMS.

Applications: Send curriculum vitae, a personal statement concerning career goals and the names of three references to Dr. Douglas Blackall, Department of Pathology, Arkansas Children's Hospital, 1 Children's Way, Little Rock, Arkansas 72202. Dr. Blackall may also be contacted at blackalldouglasp@uams.edu. Contact: Ms. Renee' Gordon, Fellowship Program Manager.

Phone: (501) 603-1508 • **E-mail:** gordonreneen@uams.edu.

BAYLOR COLLEGE OF MEDICINE

Blood Banking/Transfusion Medicine Fellowship

Description: This is a one-year ACGME accredited fellowship program in Blood Banking /Transfusion Medicine. After completion of this program, the fellow will be eligible for subspecialty board certification by the American Board of Pathology. The fellow will rotate through St. Luke's Episcopal Hospital, Texas Children's Hospital, Ben Taub General Hospital, the Gulf Coast Regional Blood Center, and The Methodist Hospital. St. Luke's Episcopal Hospital is a tertiary care adult hospital internationally recognized for groundbreaking work in complex cardiovascular surgery procedures, including cardiac transplantation and ventricular assist devices. St. Luke's Hospital also has a blood donor center with on-site and mobile drive collections. Texas Children's Hospital provides specialized training in neonatal and pediatric transfusion therapy including intrauterine transfusion and fetal surgery, in addition to providing an active coagulation sign-out and consultation service. Ben Taub General Hospital, the major trauma center in Houston, provides experience in emergency and massive transfusion therapy. The fellow will learn of the blood bank requirements of the obstetric patient through both St. Luke's and Ben Taub, and may encounter complex obstetric cases, often with follow-up of the neonate at Texas Children's. A rotation at the Gulf Coast Regional Blood Center, one of the largest regional blood centers in the United States and an AABB accredited Immunohematology Reference Lab, will be an extensive experience in donor collection and testing, as well as complex serology. A rotation in histocompatibility (HLA) is done at The Methodist Hospital. The basics of parentage testing will be covered. Regulatory and compliance issues will be stressed at each rotation. Many local and at least one national teaching conferences are integrated into this program. All faculty involved in this program are experienced transfusion medicine specialists who are strongly committed to teaching.

Requirements: Candidates must be Board-certified or Board-eligible in Anatomic Pathology and Clinical Pathology, Clinical Pathology only, Hematology (subspecialty), or Anesthesiology.

Stipends: Commensurate with experience level.

Applications: Inquiries are to be directed to Jun Teruya, MD, DSc, Director of Blood Bank and Coagulation, Texas Children's Hospital, Department of Pathology, Baylor College of Medicine, 6621 Fannin Street, MC 1-2261, Houston, TX 77030.

Phone: (832) 824-1879 • **Fax:** (832) 825-1032 • **E-mail:** jteruya@bcm.edu
Web site: http://www.bcm.tmc.edu/pathology

BAYSTATE MEDICAL CENTER/ TUFTS UNIVERSITY SCHOOL OF MEDICINE

Department of Pathology

Blood Banking/Transfusion Medicine Fellowship

Description: This one-year ACGME-accredited fellowship provides comprehensive training with a broad range of clinical/consultative experiences in blood banking and transfusion medicine at a large academic community hospital transfusion medicine service/blood bank. Baystate Medical Center (BMC) is the largest hospital of the three-member Baystate Health complex and serves as a major clinical training site of the Tufts University School of Medicine. On-site services include donor facilities, therapeutic hemapheresis, and comprehensive immunohematologic diagnostic services. Active clinical consultation addresses routine/complex immunoserologic evaluations, component therapy issues, apheresis medicine and centralized transfusion medicine service problems. Cooperative programs with regional American Red Cross blood centers complement TMS hospital-based training environment. Quality improvement projects, research and teaching opportunities are available.

Requirements: Candidates should be Board-eligible/Board-certified in CP, AP/CP or other major specialty board.

Stipends: Commensurate with year of training.

Applications: Applications must be received by April 1 of the year prior to the start of the fellowship and include a curriculum vitae and 3 letters of recommendation. Submit applications to Chester Andrzejewski, PhD, MD, Transfusion Medicine Service, Baystate Medical Center, 759 Chestnut Street, Springfield, MA 01199.

Phone: (413) 794-5085 • **Fax:** (413) 794-5893
Web site: http://www.baystatehealth.com/pathresidency

EOE

BLOODCENTER OF WISCONSIN
MEDICAL COLLEGE OF WISCONSIN

Blood Banking/Transfusion Medicine Fellowship

Description: The BloodCenter of Wisconsin in association with The Medical College of Wisconsin, offers an ACGME-accredited one or two-year approved program leading to Board eligibility in blood banking/transfusion medicine. This program offers extensive experience in all aspects of transfusion medicine. The first year offers training in Blood Center operations including blood bank administration, donor room procedures, manufacturing and infectious disease testing, stem cell processing laboratory, and therapeutic apheresis. The fellow has the opportunity to train in the BloodCenter's national specialty reference laboratories including immunohematology, platelet immunology, hemostasis, histocompatibility/transplantation, and molecular diagnostics. The fellow will receive transfusion service experience through the two major teaching hospitals of the Medical College of Wisconsin including Children's Hospital of Wisconsin. Additional experience will be obtained through five community hospitals for which the Blood Center also provides medical direction for the transfusion services. The fellow will become involved in a clinically oriented research project in the first year. The fellow has an option for a second year with emphasis on either a clinical research program or a basic research project at the BloodCenter's Blood Research Institute. This institute is devoted to basic science research in hematopoiesis/stem cell biology, hemostasis, immunogenetics, transfusion medicine, and vascular cell biology. Training in this program provides a sound background for a future in any area of blood banking including the regional blood center, hospital transfusion service or an academic career in transfusion medicine.

Requirements: Candidates must be certified or eligible for certification in clinical pathology or hematology/oncology (adult or pediatric) or other major specialty board.

Stipends: Commensurate with level of relevant postgraduate training and experience.

Applications: Send letter of interest to Jerome L. Gottschall, MD, Vice President, Medical Services, The BloodCenter of Wisconsin, PO Box 2178, Milwaukee, WI 53201-2178.

Phone: (414) 937-6231 • **Fax:** (414) 933-6803 • **E-mail:** jerry.gottschall@bcw.edu

---

BONFILS BLOOD CENTER

Blood Banking/Transfusion Medicine Fellowship

Description: Bonfils Blood Center (BBC) is accepting applications for a one-year fellowship in Transfusion Medicine/Blood Banking. BBC is a regional community blood center in Denver, Colorado which collects 212,000 units per year and tests >225,000 units per year. This ACGME-approved program includes experience in various departments and services including donor services, phlebotomy at mobile and fixed sites, apheresis, donor testing, reference laboratory, quality resources and systems, Colorado Marrow Donor Program, Bonfils Cord Blood Services, and HLA and immunology testing at LABS, Inc. Additional rotations are offered in transfusion services at our affiliated institutions, Denver Health Medical Center, Exempla Saint Joseph's Hospital, Health-ONE Presbyterian/St. Luke's Medical Center, and Denver VA Medical Center. Elective time is included for research/scholarly activities or additional rotations in coagulation, stem cell transplantation and other areas.

Requirements: Applicants should be Board-eligible or Board-certified CP/AP or CP, Internal Medicine or Pediatric Hematology. Other specialties may apply. An interview is required.

Stipends: Commensurate with level of postgraduate training.

Applications: Applications and program information can be obtained on the website at www.bonfils.org. Submit applications online or mail to: Daniel R. Ambruso, MD, Bonfils Blood Center, 717 Yosemite Street, Denver, CO 80230.

Phone: (303) 363-2241 • **Fax:** (303) 340-2616 • **E-mail:** daniel_ambruso@bonfils.org
Web site: http://www.bonfils.org

UNIVERSITY OF CALIFORNIA, LOS ANGELES

Transfusion Medicine Fellowship

Description: The UCLA Department of Pathology and Laboratory Medicine offers an ACGME-approved one-year fellowship program with training in all areas of Transfusion Medicine and Blood Banking. The UCLA Blood Bank transfuses 75,000 blood products per year and provides specialized clinical consultation services in support of the many complex medical and surgical services at the UCLA Medical Center. Experience in blood center administration will be gained at the UCLA Blood & Platelet Center, which collects approximately 30,000 donations per year. Iin addition, trainees participate in Transfusion Medicine-based research and develop expertise in evaluating and implementing new techniques and laboratory procedures. The program includes integrated rotations in the Transfusion Service, UCLA Blood & Platelet Center, and therapeutic hemapheresis as well as elective rotations designed to meet the needs and interests of individual fellows and which generally include the American Red Cross Reference Laboratory, UCLA Immunogenetics (HLA) Center and UCLA's hematopoietic stem cell units. Clinical interaction, management decisions and teaching occur throughout the training period.

Requirements: Candidate must qualify for California medical licensure and be Board-certified/eligible in clinical pathology, or other qualifying clinical field.

Stipends: Support is commensurate with the candidate's level of training.

Applications: Please contact the Fellowship Coordinator for a list of material required for fellowship, in addition submit a curriculum vitae and the names of three references to:

Alyssa Ziman, MD, Program Director, Department of Pathology and Laboratory Medicine, David Geffen School of Medicine at UCLA, 10833 Le Conte Avenue, Room A7-149 CHS, Los Angeles, CA 90095-1732.
Fellowship Coordinator: Ms. Annetta Pierro

Phone: (310) 825-5719 • **Fax:** (310) 267-2058
Web site: www.pathology.ucla.edu

CEDARS-SINAI MEDICAL CENTER

Department of Pathology and Laboratory Medicine

Transfusion Medicine Fellowship

Description: The Rita and Taft Schreiber Division of Transfusion Medicine at Cedars-Sinai Medical Center offers an accredited one-year fellowship in transfusion medicine. Cedars-Sinai is a 969-bed tertiary care center with a Level 1 trauma service, a Comprehensive Cancer Center, and an active multi-organ transplant program including peripheral blood stem cell transplantation. The fellow will gain expertise in all aspects of clinical transfusion medicine through experience with our busy transfusion service, our therapeutic apheresis center, community and autologous donor services, and component processing immunohematology laboratories. Our teaching program relies heavily on direct patient and medical staff interaction via daily ward rounds and clinical consultation. Fellows will participate in clinical research projects. Training will include rotations at regional blood centers, HLA laboratories, and donor testing sites.

Requirements: Board eligibility in AP/CP, CP, or other board eligbility as outlined in the ABP information booklet. Fellow must have a California medical license at the time of appointment.

Stipends: Commensurate with applicant's level of training.

Staff: Ellen B Klapper MD; **Samuel H Pepkowitz** MD; **Eleftherios Vamvakas** MD.

Applications: For an application, information and correspondence, contact the program coordinator: Jean Havercroft, Department of Pathology, Cedars-Sinai Medical Center, 8700 Beverly Blvd., S. Tower Room 1670, Los Angeles, CA 90048

Phone: (310) 423-8981 • **Fax:** (310) 423-0175 • **E-mail:** havecroft@cshs.org

UNIVERSITY OF CHICAGO

Department of Pathology

ACGME-Accredited Transfusion Medicine Fellowship

Description: This one-year ACGME-Accredited Transfusion Medicine Fellowship offers extensive clinical and laboratory experience in a busy state-of-the-art center. The Blood Bank supports liver, renal, cardiac, lung, and bone marrow transplantation, stem cell collection, high risk neonatal and obstetrical programs, and cardiovascular surgery. Donor room/apheresis activities include donor recruitment, blood collection, therapeutic apheresis, autologous blood collection, therapeutic phlebotomy, and pediatric peripheral stem cell collection. Ample opportunities for research and teaching are provided. Trainees who complete the program are eligible for Transfusion Medicine Boards after one year.

Requirements: Position is open to physicians with current licensure trained in CP or AP/CP Pathology or other appropriate postgraduate medical training.

Stipends: Support is commensurate with the applicant's level of training.

Applications: Send inquiries to B. W. Baron, MD, Director, Blood Bank, University of Chicago Hospitals, MC 0007, 5841 South Maryland Avenue, Chicago, IL 60637.

Phone: (773) 702-1439 • **Fax:** (773) 702-4543 • **E-mail:** beverly.baron@uchospitals.edu

---

UNIVERSITY OF COLORADO DENVER SCHOOL OF MEDICINE

Blood Banking/Transfusion Medicine Fellowship

Description: The 12-month fellowship is designed to prepare individuals for a career in blood banking/transfusion medicine at an academic medical center, a community blood center, or a private practice setting where the individual will be responsible for managing a transfusion service or donor center. This fellowship provides primary training at The Children's Hospital and the University of Colorado Hospital, two large referral centers for pediatric and adult medicine. Additionally, training at the Veterans' Administration Medical Center and Denver Health Medical Center is available. Training encompasses all aspects of blood banking and transfusion medicine including donor testing, blood product processing, transfusion consultation, therapeutic and donor apheresis, coagulation, tissue typing, peripheral blood stem cell collection and blood bank management. More than 25,000 blood products are transfused at the primary fellowship institutions (including 14,000 red blood cells and 3,500 platelets). The fellow is encouraged to participate in research projects leading to presentation at national meetings and publication. The fellow will also be responsible for education of residents and medical students. An optional second year for in-depth research and additional studies may be available.

Requirements: Applicants should be AP/CP or CP Board-eligible or Board-certified, other specialties may also be considered; interview is required.

Stipends: Commensurate with level of postgraduate training.

Applications: Application and information can be found on our website. Applications accepted until December of the year before the fellowship begins.

Please address all inquiries to: Patricia Braund, Residency/Fellowship Coordinator, University of Colorado Denver School of Medicine, Dept of Pathology, 12631 E. 17th Avenue, Box B216, Mail Stop 6511, Aurora, CO, 80045. patricia.braund@ucdenver.edu.

Phone: (303) 724-3483 • **Fax:** (303) 724-1105
Web site: www.uchsc.edu/pathology

DARTMOUTH-HITCHCOCK MEDICAL CENTER
DARTMOUTH MEDICAL SCHOOL

Department of Pathology

Transfusion Medicine Fellowship

Description: One year fellowship based at the Dartmouth-Hitchcock Medical Center. The hospital is a tertiary 380-bed teaching facility with solid organ, stem cell and bone marrow transplantation programs, pediatric and neonatal services, cardiovascular surgery, a Level I trauma center, and hematology-oncology services. The fellowship is designed to provide a wide scope of experience in transfusion medicine including hospital transfusion service with trauma level 1 support, blood donor program, therapeutic apheresis, cellular therapy, HLA typing and infectious disease testing. The HLA typing training is provided in collaboration with American Red Cross New England Region (Dedham, MA), while training at a large blood donor operation with infectious disease testing is provided via a two-week rotation at Florida Blood Services (St. Petersburg, FL). Opportunities for clinical and laboratory research are part of the training. In addition, successful candidates may apply to combine their fellowship with the Dartmouth-Hitchcock Leadership Preventive Medicine Residency (DHLPMR) leading to a Masters in Public Health (see at www.dhmc.org for more details). The Cell Labeling Laboratory, directed by Dr. Larry J. Dumont, provides unique opportunities in clinical and laboratory research in applied transfusion medicine. The Cellular Therapy Center, directed by Dr. Szczepiorkowski, participates in the cell-based immunotherapy program and supports a FACT accredited bone marrow transplant program.

Requirements: Board certified/eligible in clinical pathology, internal medicine, pediatrics or another clinical specialty. Medical licensure in the State of New Hampshire required.

Stipends: Commensurate with the number of relevant years of postgraduate training. There is a book allowance and funding available for presentation at a national meeting.

Applications: Address inquiries to Zbigniew (Ziggy) M. Szczepiorkowski, MD, PhD, Medical Director, Transfusion Medicine Service, Dartmouth-Hitchcock Medical Center, 1 Medical Center Drive, Lebanon, NH 03756-0001. Application form and supporting document requirements are found on the program's web site.

Phone: (603) 653-9907 • **Fax:** (603) 650-4845 • **E-mail:** ziggy@dartmouth.edu
Web site: http://www.dhmc.org/goto/Transfusion_Med_Fellowship

---

DeGOWIN BLOOD CENTER
UNIVERSITY OF IOWA HOSPITALS AND CLINICS

Transfusion Medicine Fellowship

Description: One-year ACGME-accredited blood banking fellowship for physicians interested in transfusion medicine. The DeGowin Blood Center provides transfusion (red cell and platelet compatibility), donor center (whole blood and cytapheresis at central and mobile sites), therapeutic hemapheresis (plasma exchange, phlebotomy, photopheresis), hematopoietic progenitor collection and processing services, and tissue bank services to a large university tertiary care hospital. Daily exposure is provided in donor selection, blood banking serology, compatibility testing, autologous donation, and preparation of special products (leukocyte-poor, irradiated, cryopreserved and selected progenitor cells). The program features special emphasis on all aspects of therapeutic and preparative hemapheresis, platelet immunology, neonatal transfusions, and organ and bone marrow transplantation and tissue banking. An additional year of mentored research in several disciplines is an option for qualified candidates.

Requirements: Applicants eligible for certification in pathology or hematology (medicine or pediatrics).

Stipends: Applicants eligible for certification in pathology or hematology (medicine or pediatrics), and diplomates of the American Boards of Anesthesiology, Internal Medicine, Obstetrics/Gynecology, Pediatrics, Surgery, Orthopedic Surgery, Plastic Surgery, Colon and Rectal Surgery, Neurological Surgery, and Thoracic Surgery.

Staff: Yasuko Erickson MD; **C. Michael Knudson** MD, PhD; **Thomas Raife** MD; **Annette Schlueter** MD, PhD.

Applications: Thomas Raife MD, Medical Director, DeGowin Blood Center, University of Iowa Hospitals and Clinics, 200 Hawkins Drive, Iowa City, IA 52242.

Phone: (319) 356-0369 • **E-mail:** thomas-raife@uiowa.edu

EMORY UNIVERSITY HOSPITAL

Department of Pathology and Laboratory Medicine

Blood Banking/Transfusion Medicine Fellowship

Description: The Center for Transfusion and Cellular Therapies (CTCT) within the Department of Pathology and Laboratory Medicine at Emory University School of Medicine offers a one-to-two-year ACGME accredited fellowship program in blood banking/ transfusion medicine. The CTCT is organized as 4 integrated units (Division of Patient &Donor Services, Division of Research, Division of Training & Education, and Division of Biotechnology) that serve all clinical, research and teaching/training activities in blood banking, transfusion medicine, and many aspects of cellular therapies at Emory, and was ranked as the 5th largest transfusion system in the world. The Emory CTCT is dedicated to the optimal transfusion/transplantation of patients and the advancement of the field through outstanding clinical service, research, and education of the next generation of leaders in transfusion medicine. In addition to the 1 year clinical fellowship, which includes pediatric and adult transfusion services, donor services, cellular therapy, and therapeutic and donor apheresis, an optional additional 1 year of research training is available. The areas of research opportunity include transfusion-transmitted CMV, adoptive immunotherapy and novel vaccine strategies, investigations into the cellular and molecular mechanisms of alloimmunization to RBC antigens, understanding the pathogenic mechanisms of transfusion-related acute lung injury, and stem cell plasticity and regenerative medicine.

Requirements: Applicants are required to be eligible for USMLE Step 3 and Georgia medical licensure, and board eligible or certified in clinical pathology, anesthesiology, internal medicine or pediatrics.

Stipends: Support is usually at the level of PGY-5 and is commensurate with the candidate's level of training and experience.

Staff: Christopher D. Hillyer MD, Director Transfusion Medicine Fellowship; **Robert A. Bray** PhD; **Alexander Duncan** MD, ChB; **Howard M Gebel** PhD; **Alfred J. Grindon** MD; **Jeanne Hendrickson** MD; **Krista L Hillyer** MD; **Cassandra D. Josephson** MD; **Lennart E. Logdberg** MD, PhD; **John D. Roback** MD, PhD; **Beth H. Shaz** MD; **James C. Zimring** MD, PhD.

Applications:

Phone: (404) 727-4283 • **Fax:** (404) 727-2519 • **E-mail:** mmojonn@emory.edu
Web site: www.emory.edu/PATHOLOGY/

MEDICAL COLLEGE OF GEORGIA HOSPITAL AND CLINICS

Blood Banking Fellowship

Description: A one-year ACGME-accredited blood bank and transfusion medicine fellowship provides a broad range of experiences in a large medical center setting. Institutional services include a regional trauma center and extensive tertiary care in pediatrics, medicine, surgery and obstetrics/gynecology. Fellowship experience will include donor room, therapeutic apheresis, photopheresis, cytopheresis, pre-transfusion testing, transfusion medicine consultation, reference service antibody problems, HLA testing, frozen red cell inventory, autologous peripheral blood stem cell transplant program, autologous/allogenic bone marrow transplantation, and blood center operations. Teaching assignments, along with a research project, are a central part of the program. Candidates should gain the skills necessary to function as medical directors of hospital-based blood banks or as directors of community-based blood centers.

Requirements: Applicants must be Board-eligible or Board-certified in AP/CP or CP, Internal Medicine, or Pediatrics.

Stipends: Commensurate with PGY5 pay level or candidate's level of training.

Applications: Inquiries and requests for application should be addressed to
Shannon Williford, Fellowship Coordinator, Department of Pathology, Medical College of Georgia, 1120 15th Street BA-2576, Augusta, GA, 30912.

Phone: (706) 721-5118 • **Fax:** (706) 721-7781 • **E-mail:** swillifo@mcg.edu
Web site: http://www.mcg.edu/som/pathology

UNIVERSITY OF ILLINOIS COLLEGE OF MEDICINE

Transfusion Medicine Fellowship

Description: A one-year, ACGME-accredited fellowship in Blood Banking / Transfusion Medicine is offered at the University of Illinois Medical Center at Chicago. The Medical Center is a 441 bed tertiary care university hospital which supports an active solid organ and bone marrow transplantation service. Comprehensive donor, transfusion and hemapheresis services stress clinical transfusion medicine and consultation, allowing development of technical and administrative skills. The fellow will gain extensive experience in donor recruitment and blood procurement, immunohematology, transplantation immunology (bone marrow, stem cell, liver, kidney, pancreas and small bowel transplantation), therapeutic hemapheresis, stem cell collection and processing, outpatient transfusion, histocompatibility testing, and coagulation. A rotation at a regional blood center is also offered. Research experiences are strongly encouraged.

Requirements: Applicants must have completed training in an approved residency in Anatomic and Clinical Pathology or Clinical Pathology by July 1. Applicants completing training in Internal Medicine or Pediatrics who either are completing, have completed, or plan to complete a fellowship in Hematology will also be considered.

Stipends: Commensurate with level of training. The website of the Graduate Medical Education Office (http://www.uic.edu/com/gme/) contains specific information regarding stipends and benefits.

Applications: A letter of interest with attached curriculum vitae should be sent to:
Sally A. Campbell-Lee, MD
Medical Director, Transfusion Medicine
Department of Pathology
University of Illinois at Chicago
MC 847, Room 130 CSN
840 South Wood St.
Chicago, IL 60612

Phone: (312) 996-1350
Web site: pathology.uic.edu

JOHNS HOPKINS MEDICAL INSTITUTIONS

Transfusion Medicine Fellowship

Description: This fellowship is a one- or two-year program leading to Board eligibility in blood banking/transfusion medicine. The program is offered by the Johns Hopkins Medical Institutions Department of Pathology Transfusion Medicine Division and the Hemapheresis and Transfusion Support Service. In the first year of ACGME approved training, the fellow rotates through the Blood Bank, Hemapheresis Center, and specialty laboratories to provide theoretical concepts and practical exposure to blood bank administration, donor room procedures, reference immunohematology, platelet serology, donor testing, transfusion consultations, cytapheresis, bone marrow processing, and therapeutic apheresis. A clinically oriented research project is performed in the first year. At the end of the first year, the fellow is Board eligible and has the background to pursue a career in a hospital transfusion service or blood center. An optional second year is devoted to in-depth study of a clinical-immunohematologic area. The two-year program provides a sound background for a career in academic transfusion medicine.

Requirements: Board eligibility in clinical pathology or hematology (adult or pediatric).

Stipends: Commensurate with level of relevant postgraduate training and experience.

Applications: Karen E. King, MD, Transfusion Medicine Division, Department of Pathology, The Johns Hopkins Hospital, 600 N Wolfe Street, Baltimore, MD 21287-6417.

Phone: (410) 955-6583 • **E-mail:** kking@jhmi.edu
Web site: http://pathology.jhu.edu

The Johns Hopkins University does not discriminate on the basis of race, color, sex, religion, national or ethnic origin, age, handicapped or veteran status in any student program or activity administered by the University or with regard to admission or employment.

UNIVERSITY OF LOUISVILLE HEALTH SCIENCES CENTER

Div. of Lab. Med., Department of Pathology & Laboratory Medicine

Blood Banking/Transfusion Medicine Fellowship

Description: The Marie M. Keeling Blood Banking/Transfusion Medicine Fellowship at the University of Louisville Health Sciences Center is a one-year program integrating academic and community medical centers with one blood center. The teaching hospitals support cardiopulmonary surgery, solid organ and bone marrow transplantation, trauma service, neonatal and pediatric programs, and an HLA laboratory. Approximately 50,000 blood components are transfused in the affiliated teaching hospitals each year. The first two months are spent at the American Red Cross Blood Services, River Valley Region, in each of the blood component manufacturing areas as well as the compliance areas. This blood center collects over 120,000 whole blood and 8,000 apheresis donations, and maintains an accredited immunohematology reference laboratory. The remaining time is divided in the specialized areas of peripheral stem cell/bone marrow transplantation, HLA laboratory, and transfusion services of the affiliated hospitals. Research opportunities are available. The training program provides necessary experience to develop expertise in transfusion medicine required for medical director duties in a community blood center or hospital transfusion service.

Requirements: Certified, or certification eligible by the American Board of Pathology in clinical pathology or other appropriate major clinical specialty Board; completion of Step 3 of the USMLE.

Stipends: Commensurate with the year five (5) of postgraduate training.

Applications: Send application, CV, documentation of USMLE scores and two or more letters of recommendation to William B. Lockwood, PhD, MD, Transfusion Service Director, Dept. of Pathology & Lab. Med., Univ. of Louisville Hlth. Sci. Ctr., 530 South Jackson St., Suite C1R06, Louisville, KY 40202. Program begins July 1; applications due September 30 of the previous year.

Phone: (502) 852-5857 • **Fax:** (502) 852-1771 • **E-mail:** wblock01@gwise.louisville.edu

---

MAYO SCHOOL OF GRADUATE MEDICAL EDUCATION

Blood Banking Transfusion Medicine Fellowship

Description: This program offers extensive experience in an active, clinically-oriented blood bank and transfusion service which is part of a large medical practice annually using 130,000 units of blood and components. It encompasses the full range of blood center and transfusion medicine activities which include donor recruitment and donation (30,000 whole blood and 3,000 apheresis donations annually), compatibility testing, advanced red cell serology, component production, progenitor cell and cellular therapy laboratory, therapeutic apheresis unit (3,000 procedures annually), Hepatitis and HIV laboratory, and histocompatibility laboratory. Bone marrow, peripheral blood progenitor cell transplantation, liver, pancreas, heart, lung, and renal transplantation programs are supported. Transfusion Medicine provides clinical consultation, transfusion, and preoperative and intraoperative autologous transfusion programs (8,000 units processed annually) for patients at Mayo Clinic's Rochester hospitals (approximately 1,900 beds). Fellows will be involved in educational, investigative, medical, and administrative aspects of transfusion medicine, under the direction of four physicians. Experience in nucleic acid testing and regional blood banking is offered.

Requirements: Physicians who are U.S. citizens or hold permanent visas and who are certified or will be eligible for certification in pathology, internal medicine, surgery, anesthesiology or pediatrics will be considered for the program.

Applications: www.mayo.edu/msgme/application.html
Address inquiries to Jeffrey L. Winters, MD, Director, Educational Program, Division of Transfusion Medicine, Hilton 2-52B, Mayo Clinic, 200 SW First Street, Rochester, MN 55905. The program begins each July and applications must be completed by June 1 of the previous year.

Phone: (507) 284-2404 • **E-mail:** pathologyeducation@mayo.edu
Web site: www.mayo.edu/msgme/lm-transfusionmed-rch.html

Mayo is an equal opportunity affirmative action institution.

THE METHODIST HOSPITAL

Department of Pathology

Blood Banking/Transfusion Medicine Fellowship

Description: This program is a one year, ACGME accredited fellowship in blood banking/transfusion medicine. The primary hospital (The Methodist Hospital) is an adult, tertiary-care hospital known internationally for its cardiovascular surgery department. The fellow will have ample opportunities to respond to complex transfusion problems presented by this service in the pre-op, intra-op, and post-op theaters. The Methodist Hospital also has very active surgical services for orthopedic, organ transplant, neurosurgical, ENT, urologic, and general surgery. In addition, the hospital has hematology/oncology services with associated complex transfusion situations, as well as a busy bone marrow/stem cell transplant service. The program will introduce the fellow to the HLA service and parentage testing. The hospital has a blood donor center with both in-house and mobile blood collection facilities. The blood donor center also houses a very busy apheresis center that performs over 1000 therapeutic procedures annually as well as performing many stem cell collections for in-house transplants and the National Marrow Donor Program. The fellow will also rotate at The University of Texas, which has a Level I trauma center, where the fellow will be exposed to transfusion problems unique to trauma care. The fellow will, in addition, be introduced to the demanding problems of neonatal/pediatric transfusion therapy at The University of Texas. To round out the fellow's education, the program includes a rotation at The Gulf Coast Regional Blood Center, a very large and renowned blood center, where the fellow will be instructed in the blood center's very critical role in regional, national, and international management of the blood supply. The faculty is all transfusion medicine experts, most with many years of experience in transfusion medicine and teaching.

Requirements: Candidates must be Board-certified or Board-eligible in Clinical Pathology, Anatomic/Clinical Pathology or Clinical Hematology. Must hold or be eligible for a Texas Physician In Training Permit or Licensure.

Stipends: Commensurate with level of training.

Applications: Send to Richard Davey, MD, Department of Pathology, The Methodist Hospital, 6565 Fannin, M227, Houston, Texas, 77030.

Phone: (713) 441-3496 • **Fax:** (713) 441-3489 • **E-mail:** ljozwiak@tmhs.org
Web site: www.methodisthealth.com

UNIVERSITY OF MICHIGAN HOSPITALS

Blood Banking Fellowship

Description: This training program provides experience in all aspects of blood banking in a tertiary care hospital which houses a multi-organ transplant center, including bone marrow transplantation, a large hematology/oncology service and an extensive surgical program. The blood bank provides over 100,000 units of blood and components annually, and includes an AABB-accredited Reference Laboratory. The Apheresis Procedures Unit affords the candidate excellent experience in therapeutic apheresis, HPC collection and LDL apheresis. The program also provides for experience in perinatal transfusion, coagulation, histocompatibility testing, and HPC processing. Exposure to all aspects of blood procurement is provided through the cooperative participation of the American Red Cross Southeastern Michigan Blood Services. Graded assumption of responsibility for medical, administrative and instructional activities by the fellow is encouraged. Research opportunities are provided commensurate with the fellow's interest and experience.

Requirements: Candidates must be certified or eligible for certification by the American Board of Pathology or other major specialty board, meet the eligibility requirements of the Department of Pathology and be licensed or eligible for licensure, to practice medicine in the State of Michigan.

Applications: Inquiries should be sent to: Robertson D. Davenport, MD, Director, Blood Bank and Transfusion Service, University of Michigan Hospital, 2G332/5054, 1500 East Medical Center Drive, Ann Arbor, MI 48109-5054.

Phone: (734) 936-6776 • **E-mail:** rddvnprt@umich.edu
Web site: http://www.pathology.med.umich/residency/fellowships.html

MILTON S. HERSHEY MEDICAL CENTER
PENN STATE COLLEGE OF MEDICINE

Blood Banking/Transfusion Medicine Fellowship

Description: The Blood Banking/Transfusion Medicine fellowship is a fully-funded one year ACGME-accredited position that includes training in all aspects of clinical adult and pediatric transfusion medicine, immunohematology, on-site donor administration and blood collection, therapeutic apheresis, allogeneic and autologous hematopoietic stem cell collection and processing, coagulation, and HLA/Histocompatibility testing. The fellow will work closely with the Medical Director and 4 other clinical pathologists to provide clinical consultation to the medical staff in areas of apheresis, immunohematology, and clinical transfusion medicine. The fellow will have opportunities for teaching medical students, technologists, residents, and fellows from other services. This program will provide the fellow with a rich educational experience leading to expertise in Blood Banking/Transfusion Medicine and the qualifications for eligibility for specialty certification in Blood Banking/Transfusion Medicine. It will form a basis for a career in the academic or community practice setting.

Requirements: Applicants should be board-certified or board-eligible in combined Clinical/Anatomic Pathology, Clinical Pathology only, Hematology, Pediatrics, Internal Medicine, Obstetrics/Gynecology, Anesthesiology, Surgery, Colon and Rectal Surgery, Orthopaedic Surgery, Neurological Surgery, Plastic Surgery, or Thoracic Surgery.

Types and Numbers of Appointments: The Blood Banking/Transfusion Medicine program offers one position per academic year.

Facilities: The faculty, residents, and main laboratory facilities are housed in the Penn State Milton S. Hershey Medical Center. The hospital has a capacity of approximately 500 beds. It is a both an adult and pediatric tertiary care hospital and the main teaching hospital of the Pennsylvania State University College of Medicine. It includes a Level I trauma center, a Level III neonatal intensive care unit, and is a major referral center for complicated adult and pediatric hematology/oncology cases. The Division of Clinical Pathology has abundant clinical opportunities for training a fellow in Blood Banking/Transfusion Medicine. The Transfusion Service of the Hershey Medical Center is a full service operation providing allogeneic and autologous whole blood and hematopoietic stem cell collections, plateletpheresis collection, therapeutic phlebotomy, and therapeutic apheresis. Annually, over 20,000 units of allogeneic red blood cells (~50,000 total blood components) are transfused, and ~1200 therapeutic apheresis procedures are performed (including plasma exchange, red cell exchange, cytoreduction, and peripheral blood stem cell collections). The Blood Bank/ Transfusion Service is accredited by FACT and the AABB.

Community: Hershey, in the foothills of the Blue Ridge Mountains, is a community of approximately 20,000 people. Harrisburg, the state capital, is 12 miles away. There are over one million people within a fifty-mile radius. Surrounded by rich farm lands and close to urban centers of the eastern seaboard, Hershey can be described as a suburban community in a rural setting. It has excellent educational and recreational programs and facilities, outstanding musical and stage performances, and numerous fine arts and cultural opportunities. Outdoor activities are readily available and include golf, swimming, fishing, hunting, mountain climbing, skiing, and ready access to the Appalachian Trail. Philadelphia, Baltimore, Washington, New York City, and the Pennsylvania Dutch country are just short distances by automobile or train. The Harrisburg International Airport (MDT) is 15 minutes away from Hershey, and airports in both Baltimore and Philadelphia are about 1.5 - 2.0 hours away by car.

Stipends: Salaries are comparable with salaries in the northeast as well as the rest of the United States, and residents are provided with professional liability insurance, health insurance, disability insurance, uniforms, laundry, and four weeks paid vacation per year. The Department also provides yearly stipends that can be used for support of continuing medical education expenses, dues and membership, books, and subscriptions.

Staff: Ronald E. Domen MD, Professor of Pathology, Medicine, and Humanities; Program Director, Blood Banking/ Transfusion Medicine Fellowship; Medical Director, Histocompatibility Laboratory; Associate Dean for Graduate Medical Education; **Michael B. Bongiovanni** MD, Professor & Chief of Clinical Pathology; Director, Clinical Laboratory; **William J. Castellani** MD, Associate Professor; Medical Director, Clinical Chemistry; **Thomas P. Nifong** MD, Associate Professor; Medical Director, Hematology and Coagulation Laboratory; Medical Director, Molecular Diagnostics Laboratory; **Hiroko Shike** MD, Assistant Professor; Associate Director, Histocompatibility Laboratory.

Applications: The Milton S. Hershey Medical Center and College of Medicine of the Pennsylvania State University are currently soliciting applications for academic year 2010-2011. This is a fully-funded, one-year, ACGME-accredited position. Applications are evaluated on an on-going basis and will be accepted beginning 12-18 months prior to the anticipated start date. Applications will be accepted until the position is filled. Applications should include a cover letter with a personal statement, curriculum vitae, a letter from the current/most recent program director, and the names of three additional individuals who could provide letters of reference.

Address applications and/or inquiries to:

Ronald E. Domen, MD, Program Director, Blood Banking/Transfusion Medicine Fellowship, Department of Pathology - H160, Penn State M.S. Hershey Medical Center, 500 University Drive, PO Box 850, Hershey, PA 17033-0850.

Phone: (717) 531-5116 • **E-mail**: rdomen@hmc.psu.edu • **Web site:** http://www.hmc.psu.edu/pathology

UNIVERSITY OF MINNESOTA AFFILIATED HOSPITALS

Blood Banking/Transfusion Medicine Fellowship

Description: This program involves the University of Minnesota Medical School, Fairview- University Medical Center (FUMC), the Memorial Blood Centers of Minnesota (MBCM), the American Red Cross North Central Blood Services of St Paul (ARC), Hennepin County Medical Center (HCMC), and the Veterans' Affairs Medical Center (VAMC). This fellowship integrates the outstanding aspects of these transfusion services and blood centers into an exceptionally balanced, yet diversified transfusion medicine experience. While rotations vary with individual trainee interests, the standard program includes: 6 months at FUMC, 1 month MBCM, 2 months ARC, 6 weeks VAMC and 6 weeks HCMC. The fellowship is designed to prepare physicians for a career in either a hospital transfusion service or in a regional blood center. Substantial clinical experience with both laboratory problem solving and clinical consultation is provided. Complete laboratory training in immunology and coagulation is available. As fellows gain experience, more clinical duties and special projects are assigned. A second year of predominantly research is available for exceptional trainees.

Requirements: See Program Web site at http://residency.pathology.umn.edu for specific training program requirements.

Facilities: UMMC is a world leader in solid organ and hematologic stem cell processing/ transplantation and the treatment of hematological malignancies. The hospital has a broad range of active clinical services that extensively interact with the transfusion service, including cardiovascular surgery, obstetrics, neonatology, gynecology, and others. The Donor Center and Apheresis Unit provide peripheral blood stem cell collections, a busy therapeutic apheresis service, and carry out many developmental projects. MBCM is an American Association of Blood Banks (AABB) Rare Donor Reference Laboratory, conducts parentage testing, performs transfusiontransmitted disease and clinical diagnostic tests for viral markers, serves as a local immunohematology reference laboratory, and provides expertise in the legal aspects of blood banking. ARC is a large, multiservice blood center that collects about 240,000 units of whole blood annually. The departments of hospital services and blood donor collections provide the fellow with insight into the regional management of blood resources. The blood center operates a large apheresis unit that collects products for both transfusion and research. The Blood Center also houses the ARC national neutrophil serology reference laboratory, a platelet crossmatch and platelet serology laboratory, a red cell serology laboratory, a cord blood bank, and a donor registry for the National Marrow Donor Program. VAMC provides a range of clinical services including general and cardiovascular surgery, cancer therapy, and hematology. The fellow learns laboratory techniques directly at the bench under supervision, participates in the operation of a hospital-based blood donor program, and consults on clinical problems of transfusion medicine. HCMCprovides advanced proficiency in trauma/massive transfusion practices, obstetric-associated transfusion practices, and the principles of a hospital transfusion service.

Stipends: Commensurate with the applicant's level of training.

Staff: **Jeffrey McCullough** MD Program Director, Variety Club Chair and Director, Center for Molecular and Cellular Therapy; **Nicole Zantec** MD Coagulation Director; **Robert Bowman** MD Chief Executive Officer; **Scott Burger** MD Director, Cell Processing Center; **Jed Gorlin** MD Medical Director; **Zena Khalil** MD Blood Bank; **Deb Kim** MD Associate Medical Director; **David Mair** MD Assistant Medical Director; **Elizabeth Perry** MD Associate Medical Director.

Applications: Dr. Jeffrey McCullough, Blood Banking/Tranfusion Medicine Fellowship Director, Dept of Lab Med and Pathology, University of Minnesota, 420 Delaware St SE / MMC 609, Minneapolis, MN 55455. Application forms are available on the program Web site.

Fax: (612) 625-3976
Web site: http://residency.pathology.umn.edu

NATIONAL INSTITUTES OF HEALTH/CLINICAL CENTER

Blood Banking/Transfusion Medicine Fellowship

Description: The Department of Transfusion Medicine at the National Institutes of Health (NIH) offers a comprehensive, ACGME accredited two-year fellowship program in blood banking and immunohematology. The Department is located in the Warren Grant Magnuson Clinical Center, the research hospital of the NIH. The program prepares the trainee in the clinical, technical, investigational and administrative aspects of transfusion medicine. During the first year the fellow is trained in clinical and laboratory immunohematology, apheresis techniques, tissue typing, donor recruitment, blood component preparation and therapy, and specialized procedures such as bone marrow processing and gene therapy. During the second year, a wide variety of research opportunities are available in such areas as transfusion-transmitted viral disease, development of innovative techniques for stem cell and bone marrow collection and separation, gene therapy and cell culture techniques, applications of cellular radiolabeling techniques to red cell and leukocyte kinetics and transfusion compatibility, molecular-level tissue typing, flow cytometry, advanced immunohematology and reference laboratory studies. The fellow has access to a state-of-the-art facility with ample laboratory space and equipment, a large biomedical library, and a well-trained technical and nursing staff. The National Institutes of Health is the nation's largest biomedical research facility. The Department of Transfusion Medicine provides a unique opportunity for primary or collaborative research with the various institutes at the National Institutes of Health. Graduates of the program occupy positions of leadership in transfusion medicine and related fields.

Requirements: Qualified candidates should be physicians, U.S. citizens or resident aliens, Board-certified/eligible in pathology, internal medicine and /or hematology.

Types and Numbers of Appointments: The NIH Transfsuion Medicne fellowship appoints at least 2 fellows per year who must qulaify for clinical staff privileges.

Facilities: The Clinical Center at the National Institutes of Health (NIH) in Bethesda, Maryland, is the nation's largest hospital devoted entirely to clinical research. It is a national resource that makes it possible to rapidly translate scientific observations and laboratory discoveries into new approaches for diagnosing, treating, and preventing disease. Approximately 1,500 studies are in progress at the NIH Clinical Center. Most are Phase I and Phase II clinical trials. Most important, patients and families in the Clinical Center benefit from the cutting-edge technologies and research and the compassionate care that are the signature of NIH. The 27,000 sq. ft. Department of Transfusion Medicine supports all the blood banking and transfusion medicine needs of the patients at the Mark O. Hatfield Clinical Research Center which opened in 2005.

Community: The NIH is located in Bethesda, Maryland, in close proximity to Washington DC. It is rich in cultural and governmental events with has school systems that are among the best in the nation.

Stipends: Stipends range from $53,000 to $65,000 USD per year depending upon prior years of training.

Applications: Please contact Cathy Cantilena, MD or David Stroncek MD.

Phone: (301) 496-4506 • **E-mail:** ccantilena@mail.cc.nih.gov or dstroncek@cc.nih.gov

NEW YORK BLOOD CENTER

Transfusion Medicine Fellowship

Description: The New York Blood Center (NYBC) is the largest independent blood services organization in the United States, providing blood products and clinical services for 20 million people in the New York/New Jersey metropolitan area. As home to the Lindsley F. Kimball Research Institute, NYBC is also a world leader in hematology and transfusion science research. The Transfusion Medicine Fellowship Program has trained specialists in transfusion medicine for more than 30 years. The core one-year program is ACGME-accredited and designed to train physicians who are interested in acquiring the competence necessary for ABP sub-specialty certification in blood banking/transfusion medicine and subsequent practice. The fellow spends the year both at NYBC and at four participating tertiary care medical centers. The one-year core program consists of the following formal rotations: Blood services, collections,component and testing labs and Core operations; Quality assurance; Immunohematology reference laboratory; Hospital transfusion service and Therepeutic apheresis operations; Coagulation; Immunogenetics and Cord blood; Cellular therapy and time for a research project. A two year research/clinical track is available for selected candidates interested in pursuing an academic career in transfusion medicine. The additional research track is jointly sponsored with the Department of Pathology of Columbia University at New York Presbytarian Hospital.

Requirements: Candidates must pocess an unrestricted active license to practice medicine in New York State and must be board eligible/certified in one of the following areas: Anatomic and Clinical Pathology or Clinical Pathology/ Internal Medicine/ Hematology/ Pediatrics/ Anesthesiology or Surgery.

Types and Numbers of Appointments: Up to six positions per year.

Stipends: Commensurate with postgraduate training level with excellent benefit package.

Applications: Direct to:
Visalam Chandrasekaran MD, Director of Professional Education, New York Blood Center, 310 East 67th Street, New York, NY 10065. Obtain application from Education Department.

Phone: (212) 570-3175
E-mail: vkuhlemann@nybloodcenter.org or education@nybloodcenter.org
Web site: http://www.nybloodcenter.org

NEW YORK-PRESBYTERIAN HOSPITAL
COLUMBIA UNIVERSITY MEDICAL CENTER
NEW YORK BLOOD CENTER

Blood Banking/Transfusion Medicine Fellowship

Description: The Columbia University Department of Pathology and Cell Biology and the New York Blood Center together offer a jointly-sponsored, three-year, ACGME-accredited fellowship in transfusion medicine, which is designed to provide in-depth experience leading to a research-oriented academic career.

The clinical training provides experience in all areas of transfusion medicine, including blood collection and processing, transfusion therapy in inpatient and outpatient settings, therapeutic apheresis, stem cell processing and transplantation including cord blood collection, and HLA testing.

In addition, at least 24 months of intensive research training is expected, with a mentor chosen from either Columbia University Medical Center or the New York Blood Center. Research projects will typically focus on issues related to blood transfusion, stem cell biology, hematology, or immunology. There are extensive research opportunities at the New York Blood Center and in various divisions of the Columbia University Medical Center (e.g. the College of Physicians & Surgeons, the Mailman School of Public Health, the Columbia Genome Center, etc.).

Requirements: At the start of fellowship training, applicants should have completed pathology residency training and be Board eligible/certified in CP or AP/CP, or have completed residency training in internal medicine, anesthesiology, or pediatrics and be Board eligible/certified in one of those fields.

Stipends: Stipends are commensurate with the applicant's level of postgraduate training.

Applications: Applications (cover letter, personal statement, curriculum vitae, and the names of three references) should be received by September 1st (9 months prior to the start of the position) and addressed to: Joseph Schwartz, MD, Department of Pathology and Cell Biology, Columbia University, HP4-419 - 4th floor, Room 419, New York NY 10032.

Phone: (212) 305-3749 • **E-mail:** js2745@columbia.edu

SUNY SCHOOL OF MEDICINE

Transfusion Medicine Fellowship

Description: The Department of Pathology offers a one-year training program in transfusion medicine. An additional year with research emphasis will be considered if interest is demonstrated. The fellow attends a 3-4 week formal instruction in the field physician rotation program at the New York Blood Center. For the remaining 11 months, training is at University Medical Center Blood Services at Stony Brook. This includes rotations at Coagulation, Stem Cell and HLA Laboratories. Our approximate annual totals are: 30,000 blood product transfusions, 800,000 transfusion-related serologic tests, 4,000 blood donors, 1,200 hemapheresis procedures (1/3 therapeutic), approximately 50 stem cell harvesting and a lesser number of allogeneic/autologous (bone marrow) stem cell transplantations. Our transfusion laboratory is a reference laboratory for NY State Department of Health. The fellow supervises rotating clinical pathology residents and clinical hematology fellows, 6-8/year, participates in several weekly clinical pathology and clinical hematology conferences, and instructs in School of Medicine courses. Our service has a strong commitment to clinical and basic research, and the fellow is encouraged to develop a research project within our service or in any of numerous faculty research laboratories.

Requirements: MD degree and three years of training in pathology or completion of clinical hematology (medicine) fellowship. Must be Board-eligible or Board-certified. NY State license/eligibility is needed.

Stipends: Commensurate with level of training.

Applications: Submit a letter indicating long-term interests, curriculum vitae, and three letters of reference, one of which must be from the program director of prior training. All should be sent before May 1, to Dr. Dennis Galanakis, Blood Bank, L5, School of Medicine and University Hospital, HSC, SUNY, Stony Brook, NY 11794-7530.

UNIVERSITY OF NORTH CAROLINA AT CHAPEL HILL

Department of Pathology and Laboratory Medicine

Transfusion Medicine Fellowship

Description: This one-year ACGME-approved fellowship program includes didactic and practical training in advanced immunohematology, therapeutic and donor apheresis, blood donation, viral and bacterial testing, component processing and storage, coagulation, histocompatibility and stem cell collection and processing. This fellowship includes training in the clinical support of academic tertiary care hospitals (UNC Hospitals) and the operation of a small and large donor collection (Carolina ARC). Supported clinical programs include transplant programs in marrow/stem cells, liver, heart, lung and kidney. Ample opportunities for research, development, and collaborative projects are available. If mutually agreed upon, the program may be extended for a second year of research.

Requirements: MD degree and Board certified (or eligible) in clinical pathology, internal medicine, pediatrics, anesthesia or surgery.

Stipends: Commensurate with level of training.

Applications: Candidates should submit a curriculum vitae, three letters of recommendation, and a completed application which can be found on our website (http://www.pathology.unc.edu/fellowsp/transfus.htm). Applications should be submitted between March 1 and October 31 in the year preceding the proposed appointment.

For further information please contact: Ms. Janice Badstein, McLendon Clinical Laboratories, Room 1106, UNC Hospitals, Chapel Hill, NC 27514.

Phone: (919) 966-2318 • **E-mail:** jbadstei@unch.unc.edu

THE OHIO STATE UNIVERSITY MEDICAL CENTER

Department of Pathology

Blood Banking/Transfusion Medicine Fellowship

Description: This one-year ACGME approved program provides instruction and experience in hospital and blood center transfusion medicine. The trainee actively participates in routine and complex serological evaluations, perinatal testing, component collection and therapy, therapeutic apheresis, hematopoietic progenitor cell collection, quality processes, HLA, bone marrow transplant, flow cytometry, and information management at The Ohio State University Medical Center (950 beds), The James Cancer Hospital (160 beds), Columbus Children's Hospital (350 beds), Ross Heart Hospital (160 beds) and the Central Ohio Red Cross Blood Services. Protected research time is included. Proteomics and molecular pathology are available.

Requirements: Candidates must successfully complete USMLE Step III prior to their Medical Staff appointment at The Ohio State University Medical Center. They must also be Board-eligible or Board-certified in clinical pathology, anesthesiology, internal medicine, obstetrics/gynecology, pediatrics, surgery, orthopedic surgery, plastic surgery, colon and rectal surgery, neurological surgery, or thoracic surgery, or a primary certificate plus a subspecialty certificate in hematology.

Stipends: Commensurate with the year of postgraduate training.

Applications: Applications and supporting documentation should be sent to Gretchen Staschiak, Pathology Education Manager, N-308 Doan Hall, 410 W. 10th Ave., Columbus, OH 43210.

Phone: (614) 293-3055 • **Fax:** (614) 293-7273 • **E-mail:** Gretchen.Staschiak@osumc.edu
Web site: http://pathology.osumc.edu/ext

UNIVERSITY OF PENNSYLVANIA MEDICAL CENTER

Academic Transfusion Medicine Fellowship

Description: The Hospital of the University of Pennsylvania, Philadelphia, PA, is located on the campus of the University of Pennsylvania in close proximity to many research centers, all of which create a stimulating clinical and research environment. This program is designed to offer the fellow exposure to all areas of clinical transfusion medicine and to provide opportunities for investigational (basic and applied) studies. The Blood Bank at the Hospital of the University of Pennsylvania (725-bed facility) is clinically active in both adult and neonatal transfusion practices. The activities of the department include an accredited reference laboratory, compatibility testing, component preparation, histocompatibility testing, infectious diseases serology, hematopoietic stem cell processing for transplantation (peripheral blood, autologous and allogeneic bone marrow, umbilical cord blood), therapeutic hemapheresis including LDL-pheresis, therapeutic phlebotomy, medication (natural and recombinant) infusion service, and a cell and vaccine cGMP production facility. Transfusion Medicine is a multidisciplinary field and as such our program offers research opportunities in molecular and structural immunology, genetics, coagulation, stem cell biology and microbiology. The program is approved by Accreditation Council of Graduate Medical Education and supported by an NIH T32 Training Grant.

Requirements: Candidates must be certified, or eligible for certification, by the American Board of Pathology or other major specialty board. They must also be licensed or eligible for Pennsylvania licensure.

Applications: Inquiries should be sent to: Don L. Siegel, MD, PhD, Vice Chair & Professor of Pathology & Laboratory Medicine, Hospital of the University of Pennsylvania, 3400 Spruce Street, Philadelphia, PA 19104-4283.

Phone: (215) 662-3427
Web site: http://pathology.uphs.upenn.edu/Education/FellowshipPrograms/edu_fellow_prog_bb.aspx; http://pathology.uphs.upenn.edu/ClinicalServices/cs_transmed.aspx

UNIVERSITY OF PITTSBURGH MEDICAL CENTER AND THE INSTITUTE FOR TRANSFUSION MEDICINE

Transfusion Medicine Fellowship

Description: This joint program offers an ACGME-accredited one-year fellowship providing in-depth training in all aspects of transfusion medicine including blood center operations, patient transfusion services, hemophilia, therapeutic and donor apheresis, as well as HLA, viral, molecular diagnostic, and coagulation laboratory services. The fellow will receive extensive experience in a large centralized transfusion service which serves four teaching hospitals and 12 community hospitals, transfusing more than 125K red cells and 100K platelets annually. Active areas of research currently include: hematopoietic stem cell collection and transplantation, coagulation disorders and hypercoagulable states, transfusion support for adult and pediatric organ transplantation, transfusion immunomodulation, TRALI (Transfusion related acute lung injury) and donor safety studies and molecular-based testing.

Requirements: Applicants must be certified or eligible for certification in Clinical Pathology, Hematology, or other clinical specialty.

Stipends: Salary is commensurate with year of postgraduate training.

Staff: **Lirong Qu** MD, Fellowship Director; **Darrell Triulzi** MD; **Frank Bontempo** MD; **Irina Chibisov** MD; **Donald Kelley** MD; **Joseph Kiss** MD; **Mark Yazer** MD.

Applications: Submit application online at http://path.upmc.edu/fellowship. Send letter of interest to Lirong Qu, MD, PhD, lqu@itxm.org, The Institute for Transfusion Medicine, 3636 Blvd of the Allies, Pittsburgh, PA 15213.

PUGET SOUND BLOOD CENTER UNIVERSITY OF WASHINGTON

Blood Banking/Transfusion Medicine Fellowship

Description: Puget Sound Blood Center and the University of Washington offer fellowships in Transfusion Medicine/ Blood Banking. One-year ACGME-accredited clinical fellowship program includes extensive training in adult and pediatric transfusion medicine including immunohematology, virology, hemostasis, platelet immunology, HLA/immunogenetics, apheresis, solid organ, bone marrow and stem cell transplantation, trauma and blood center administration. Additional 1-2 years research training is available.

Requirements: Candidates must be Board-certified/eligible in hematology/oncology, internal medicine, clinical pathology, or pediatrics and must be eligible to obtain a Washington state medical license.

Applications: For applicants completing internal medicine residency, combined fellowship in hematology/transfusion medicine is available in conjunction with the University of Washington Division of Hematology. Please send letter of interest and CV to:

Terry Gernsheimer, MD, Director, Medical Education, Puget Sound Blood Center, 921 Terry Ave, Seattle, WA 98104-1256.

Phone: (206) 292-6521 • **Fax:** (206) 343-1774 • **E-mail:** bldbuddy@u.washington.edu
Web site: http://www.psbc.org/fellowship/index.htm

STANFORD UNIVERSITY MEDICAL CENTER

Department of Pathology

Transfusion Medicine Fellowship

Description: This one-year ACGME-accredited training program offers physicians career development training enabling them to assume the responsibilities of Medical Director of a transfusion service, either hospital-based or at a regional blood center. Two hospital-based transfusion services provides full exposure to adult, pediatric, and neonatal patients. Thus, practical experience is gained through daily exposure to red cell type and screen procedures, antibody identification and complex serologic evaluations; transfusion reaction reports; daily blood component inventory analysis; special needs consultations (CMV specific, leukoreduced, irradiated, washed, fresh, HLA-matched platelets, etc.); massive transfusion protocol support; outpatient services such as antenatal screens; and reference lab cases. An important component of the transfusion medicine training program, both in practical experience and in core curriculum, occurs at the Stanford Blood Center and through its medical and technical staff. During the Transfusion Service rotations, trainees also take first call for issues relevant to donor screening and testing.

Requirements: Candidates should be Board-eligible or Board-certified in Clinical Pathology, or an applicable clinical specialty, and be eligible for California licensure.

Stipends: Commensurate with experience, plus additional $8,400 per year housing allowance.

Applications: Send inquiries to Lawrence Tim Goodnough, MD, Director, Transfusion Medicine Fellowship Program, Department of Pathology, Stanford University Medical Center, 300 Pasteur Drive, Room H1402, Stanford, CA 94305-5626.

Phone: (650) 723-5848 • **E-mail:** ltgoodno@stanford.edu

THE UNIVERSITY OF TEXAS HEALTH SCIENCE CENTER AT SAN ANTONIO

Blood Banking/Transfusion Medicine Fellowship

Description: This fully accredited fellowship program in transfusion medicine is based in a tertiary care teaching hospital with active solid organ and bone marrow transplantation programs, cardio vascular surgery, Level I trauma center and a neonatal intensive care unit. During the year, the fellow will receive training in immunohematology, HLA, paternity testing, donor center supervision, therapeutic apheresis, transfusion therapy, coagulation, flow cytometry and molecular pathology. The program emphasizes investigational aspects, clinical and laboratory, of transfusion medicine. Training will consist of a mixture of day-to-day consultations and a didactic program in immunohematology in conjunction with an accredited school for Specialists in Blood Banking. The fellow will be expected to complete a research project during the year.

Requirements: Board eligibility or certification in clinical pathology, internal medicine, pediatrics or other related fields.

Stipends: Stipend will be appropriate for the training level of the applicant.

Applications: Should be sent before December 1, 2009 to: Chantal R. Harrison, MD, Department of Pathology, The University of Texas Health Science Center, 7703 Floyd Curl Drive, San Antonio, TX 78229-3900.

Phone: (210) 567-4090 • **Fax:** (210) 567-2367 • **E-mail:** harrisonc@uthscsa.edu

UNIVERSITY OF TEXAS SOUTHWESTERN MEDICAL SCHOOL

Blood Banking/Transfusion Medicine Fellowship

Description: One-year ACGME accredited fellowship position intended for physicians wishing to acquire special expertise in all aspects of transfusion medicine. The fellow is integrally involved in the activities of both the blood collection center and three hospital transfusion services. Hospitals are conveniently located on one campus and include a major county hospital (Parkland Memorial Hospital) with regional trauma and burn center, a children's hospital (Children's Medical Center), and University Medical Center Hospitals with surgical emphasis and both solid organ and hematopoietic progenitor cell transplantation. Therapeutic apheresis service is very active, performing >1100 procedures a year. The blood donation center collects more than 225,000 donations per year and is involved in peripheral blood progenitor cell harvesting and cryopreservation as well as bone marrow processing. Emphasis of the fellowship will be on clinical consultation with physicians, patient care and donor issues, with excellent laboratory exposure to serologic techniques and blood component processing. Training in the management of hemostasis problems and the reference hemostasis laboratory is an additional feature that allows the fellow to become a well rounded transfusion medicine expert. Responsibilities include participation in resident education and attendance at policy-making and utilization review organizations. Opportunities for research are available and encouraged. There is the possibility of an optional second year focusing on hemostasis and clinical research to prepare the individual for an academic career.

Requirements: Must be a physician Board-eligible or certified by a major specialty board (Pathology, Internal Medicine, Anesthesia, Pediatrics and Surgery). Candidate must be eligible for a Texas Institutional Permit.

Stipends: Support will be commensurate with the applicant's level of training.

Staff: Ravindra Sarode MD, Director; **James D Burner** MD, Assoc Director; **Laurie J. Sutor** MD; **Geeta Paranjape** MD; **Karen Matevosyan** MD.

Applications: Send no later than October 1. Address to Ravindra Sarode, MD, Department of Pathology, Univ. of Texas Southwestern Medical Center at Dallas, 5323 Harry Hines Blvd, Dallas, TX 75390-9073.

Phone: (214) 648-7887 • **E-mail:** ravi.sarode@utsouthwestern.edu
Web site: http://pathcuric1.swmed.edu

THOMAS JEFFERSON UNIVERSITY HOSPITAL
AMERICAN RED CROSS PENN-JERSEY REGION

Blood Banking/Transfusion Medicine Fellowship

Description: The Fellowship is a joint program supported by the Thomas Jefferson University Hospital and the American Red Cross Blood Services, Penn-Jersey Region. The fellowship is approved for one year of training in blood banking.

The concentration of study includes compatibility testing, resolution of antibody problems, therapeutic apheresis, transplantation and administration of blood and blood products to various patient populations, donor apheresis, whole blood collection, pediatric and neonatal transfusion, component processing and distribution, methodologies used in a large consultation reference laboratory, and HLA testing. Teaching opportunities to the resident and technical staff are provided.

The first two months are spent at TJUH with the exception of a selected orientation at ARC. The remaining ten months are spent at both TJUH and ARC, including the National Reference Lab.

The Transfusion Medicine Department includes the Transfusion Unit and Apheresis/ Blood Donor Center. There are opportunities for collaboration with the Divisions of Hematology, Oncology, Obstetrics, Pediatrics and other clinical areas (Dialysis, Transplantation). Hematology Fellows and Pathology residents rotate through the Blood Bank on a regular basis. The operational responsibilities of the Blood Bank are covered either by the Blood Bank Fellow, Pathology Residents and Hematology Fellows.

The Fellow is the principal liaison between the various clinical services and the Blood Bank regarding transfusion problems. There are abundant opportunities for clinical and basic research interaction within Thomas Jefferson University Hospital as well as the ARC. Academic pursuits or research projects are required of the Fellow. The program can be modified to provide individualized attention to relevant areas.

Requirements: Candidates should be Board-eligible or Board-certified in clinical pathology, board-certified in hematology, or another clinical specialty.

Stipends: Commensurate with the year of postgraduate training.

Applications: Should be made to Jay H. Herman, MD, Director, Transfusion Medicine, 111 S. 11th Street, Room 8220 Gibbon Building, Philadelphia, PA 19107.

Contact Information: Carole Ayling, Program Coordinator

Phone: (215) 955-8244 • **E-mail:** carole.ayling@jeffersonhospital.org

WASHINGTON UNIVERSITY SCHOOL OF MEDICINE

Transfusion Medicine Fellowship

Description: A one-year clinical fellowship in transfusion medicine is available. This Washington University School of Medicine program, accredited for subspecialty training, is centered at Barnes-Jewish Hospital, a 1,000 bed teaching hospital serving as both a general hospital and a major regional referral center. The blood bank collaborates closely in management of patients within the renal, heart, heart-lung, liver, and bone marrow transplantation services. Approximately 70,000 units of blood and blood components are transfused annually. Fellows receive training in all facets of modern blood banking, including apheresis, peripheral blood stem cell collection and cryopreservation, transfusion support of bone marrow and solid organ transplants, infectious disease testing, coagulation work-ups, HLA, and immunohematology. Direct clinical intervention in patient care is emphasized through daily rounds. Experience in blood center operations comes from on-site collection of whole blood (2,000 per year) and single donor platelets (7,000 per year) as well as rotations at the American Red Cross. Opportunities for participation in basic or clinical research in transfusion medicine are available.

Requirements: Applicants must be Board certified or eligible in clinical pathology, internal medicine, pediatrics, surgery, anesthesiology, or other relevant specialty.

Stipends: Support will be commensurate with the applicant's level of training.

Applications: Applicants should send a letter of interest, curriculum vitae, and the names of three references to: Douglas M. Lublin, MD, PhD, Department of Pathology, Washington University School of Medicine, 660 South Euclid Avenue, Box 8118, St Louis, MO 63110.

Phone: (314) 747-0687
Web site: http://pathology.wustl.edu/divisions/labmed/index/php

WILLIAM BEAUMONT HOSPITAL

Blood Banking Fellowship

Description: This program is designed to give the fellow the necessary training to become a director of a diversified hospital blood transfusion service or a regional blood center. William Beaumont Hospital is a 1061 bed, private, community teaching hospital with busy hematology and oncology services and a Level I Trauma Service. Rotations are included at the regional American Red Cross Blood Center and a university-based stem cell transplant service. The educational program includes graduated practical experience, didactic lectures, conferences, teaching and investigative activities. Upon completion of this program the fellow will be eligible to take the subspecialty examination in blood banking/transfusion medicine of the American Board of Pathology. See entry for William Beaumont Hospital, Royal Oak, MI, for more details about the institution.

Requirements: Candidates for this program must be certified, or eligible for certification, by the American Board of Pathology or hold subspecialty certification in hematology from another board of the ABMS. Candidates must also hold a license (or eligibility) to practice medicine in the State of Michigan.

Stipends: Salary is appropriate for the year of postgraduate training at Beaumont Hospital.

Applications: Should be made to Peter Millward, MD, Medical Director, William Beaumont Hospital, Transfusion Medicine, 3601 W Thirteen Mile Road, Royal Oak, MI 48073-6769.

Phone: (248) 898-8013 • **Fax:** (248) 898-3398 • **E-mail:** peter.millward@beaumont.edu
Web site: http://www.beaumonthospitals.com/gme

UNIVERSITY OF WISCONSIN HOSPITAL AND CLINICS MADISON AMERICAN RED CROSS BADGER REGION

Transfusion Medicine Fellowship

Description: One-year ACGME accredited fellowship providing comprehensive training in contemporary transfusion medicine. Training occurs in a large research institution with major transplant, surgical, trauma, and regional cancer programs and in a regional blood donor facility. A major goal of the program is a thorough understanding of scientific concepts underlying each aspect of transfusion medicine. Opportunities for clinical and laboratory research are available with possibility of continuation after the fellowship. Completion of the program prepares candidates for careers in academic transfusion medicine, supervision of a major transfusion service and/or operation of a regional blood collection-processing facility, and provides an entree to research in transfusion medicine.

Requirements: Candidates for this program must be certified or eligible for certification by a major specialty board, such as pathology, medicine, pediatrics, etc. They must also hold a license or be eligible for licensure to practice medicine in the State of Wisconsin.

Stipends: Salary is commensurate with the year of postgraduate training. There is a $500 book allowance, 15 days vacation, and funding available for presentation of a paper at a national meeting.

Staff: James Malter MD; **A.J. Hibbard** MD, Director of Cytopathology Fellowship; **John Weiss** MD.

Applications: A.J. Hibbard, MD, Director, Transfusion Medicine Fellowship Program, C5/253 CSC, University of Wisconsin Hospital and Clinics, 600 Highland Avenue, Madison, WI 53792-2472.

Phone: (608) 262-7158 • **E-mail:** apaus @uwhealth.org
Web site: http://www.pathology.wisc.edu/clinfellowship/transfusion

---

YALE-NEW HAVEN HOSPITAL YALE UNIVERSITY SCHOOL OF MEDICINE

Transfusion Medicine Fellowship

Description: A one-year accredited fellowship program based at Yale-New Haven Hospital in conjunction with the Connecticut Red Cross Blood Services. The hospital is a tertiary care 900-bed teaching facility with solid organ, stem cell and bone marrow transplantation programs, pediatric and neonatal services, cardiovascular surgery, a Level I trauma center, and hematology-oncology services. The blood bank service provides over 50,000 blood components per year, compatibility testing, bone marrow and stem cell processing including donor lymphocyte infusion, tumor purging, and CD34 positive selection. Other transfusion services include the collection of autologous blood, therapeutic and research plasmapheresis and cytapheresis, therapeutic phlebotomy, and infusion therapy. Experience in donor procurement, processing, production, and distribution of blood components including apheresis products and histocompatibility testing is provided by the American Red Cross, Connecticut Region, as part of the joint program. Departmental research relevant to transfusion medicine include pathobiology of platelet storage, immunobiology of CD-8, B cell recognition and tolerance, generation of B cell memory, role of cytokines in transfusion reactions, and stem cell development, regulation, and plasticity. Arrangements to extend the fellowship may be made for a second year of research.

Requirements: Candidates must be Board-eligible or Board-certified in clinical pathology, internal medicine, pediatrics, or another clinical specialty.

Stipends: Commensurate with postgraduate training and experience.

Applications: Inquiries to

YanYun Wu, MD, PhD, Director of Transfusion Medicine Fellowship, Rm CB-459, Yale- New Haven Hospital, 20 York Street, New Haven, CT 06510-3202.

Phone: (203) 688-2441 • **Fax:** (203) 688-2748 • **E-mail:** yan.wu@yale.edu
Web site: http://info.med.yale.edu/labmed
Completed applications should be made prior to April 1 for the position commencing July 1, of the following year.

UNIVERSITY OF PENNSYLVANIA MEDICAL CENTER

Department of Pathology and Laboratory Medicine

Coagulation Medicine Fellowship

Description: This one-year program trains academic physicians interested in clinical coagulation as well as basic research. The applicant participates in all of the activities of the Coagulation Laboratory of the Hospital of the University of Pennsylvania including: evaluation of patients, test design and analysis, quality assurance, participation in research projects, laboratory administration, and teaching clinical pathology residents and hematology fellows.
This fellwoship is specifically designed to initiate exposure to coagulation for individuals interested in an academic career with a research component (basic or translational) who are eligible for support through a T32 training grant in Hemostasis and Thrombosis.

Requirements: Completion of an accredited residency program in clinical pathology or fellowship in hematology/internal medicine with demonstrated strong interest in research.

Types and Numbers of Appointments: The number of appointments is dependent on a concerted effort regarding either a basic science or clinical research project by the applicant(s) with guidance by departmental faculty.

Facilities: The Coagulation Laboratory serves as a regional referral laboratory for a wide range of complex coagulation problems. The faculty consists of three senior investigators with expertise in platelet physiology, vascular biology, fibrinolysis, autoimmunity and molecular biology of coagulation proteins. The programs of the Coagulation Laboratory are closely integrated with those of the Hematopathology and Molecular Diagnosis sections within the department, with programs in the Hematology Division, as well as with departments at the Children's Hospital of Philadelphia.

Stipends: Stipends are commensurate with year of postgraduate training.

Applications: Inquiries to
Eleanor S. Pollak, MD, Fellowship Director, Department of Pathology and Laboratory Medicine, 310B Abramson Research Center, 3615 Civic Center Blvd, Philadelphia, PA 19104.
Web site: http://www.uphs.upenn.edu/path/TOCbroch.html
Phone: (215) 590-6117

JOHNS HOPKINS MEDICAL INSTITUTIONS

Clinical Chemistry Fellowship

Description: The clinical chemistry fellowship is a one- or two-year program designed to provide MD pathologists and PhD scientists with clinical, technical, research and management experience in clinical chemistry. Fellows rotate through routine automated chemistry, point-of-care testing, critical care, special chemistry, immunoassay for endocrine and tumor markers, toxicology/TDM laboratories, and the biomarker discovery center. The program provides training in laboratory operation, quality assurance, analytical methodologies, test interpretation, research and development. The trainee participates in weekly clinical rounds and scientific conferences. Research projects could be conducted in any of the chemistry laboratories, especially in the areas of cancer proteomics, drug assay, cardiovascular disease, and bioinformatics. The structure of the program is flexible to afford individualized training based on previous experience.

Requirements: MD with relevant clinical training or PhD in a chemistry-related field.

Stipends: The stipend is commensurate with the number of years of relevant postgraduate training and experience.

Applications: Applications should be addressed to
Daniel W. Chan, PhD, DABCC, Director, Clinical Chemistry Division, Department of Pathology, The Johns Hopkins Hospital, 1550 Orleans St., Room 3M05, Baltimore, MD 21231.

Phone: (410) 955-2674 • **Web site:** http://pathology2.jhu.edu/clinchem/index.cfm

The Johns Hopkins University does not discriminate on the basis of race, color, sex, religion, national or ethnic origin, age, handicapped or veteran status in any student program or activity administered by the University or with regard to admission or employment.

MAYO SCHOOL OF GRADUATE MEDICAL EDUCATION

Clinical Chemistry Fellowship

Description: This Program trains individuals with a PhD in biochemistry or molecular biology, or MD with interest in laboratory medicine to become subspecialized in clinical chemistry or molecular biology, so that they may assume a position of major responsibility in a clinical laboratory. Individuals who complete the program will understand the clinical utility and interpretation of laboratory tests and outcome assessment. During training, individuals will be exposed to the latest research techniques and applications in the field of biochemical genetics, clinical chemistry, cardiovascular risk assessment, endocrinology, immunology, molecular biology, and toxicology.

Requirements: Applicants are expected to have a PhD degree in biochemistry, clinical chemistry, chemistry, or molecular biology; or an MD degree board eligible for CP or AP/CP. Candidates must have completed the undergraduate and graduate qualifications to take the Board examination of the American Board of Clinical Chemistry (ABCC) or subspecialty certification in Chemical Pathology offered by the American Board of Pathology. See those respective Board websites for certification requirements.

Applications: www.mayo.edu/msgme/application.html Applications should be submitted no later than October 1st the year prior to the academic year you are applying for.

Phone: (507) 293-3839 • **E-mail:** pathologyeducation@mayo.edu
Web site: www.mayo.edu/msgme/lm-clinchem-rch.html

NATIONAL INSTITUTES OF HEALTH

Department of Laboratory Medicine

Chemical Pathology/Clinical Chemistry Fellowship

Description: A two-year service- or research-oriented training is offered. *In the service pathway*, fellows receive in-depth experience in clinical chemistry, laboratory management and research/method development. First, fellows are rotated through various sections of the Clinical Chemistry Service, the depth and intensity being tailored to their background. They are integrated into the management team of the Service immediately, and then take calls and field clinical inquires or problems. The second phase of this training pathway stresses participation in research projects including evaluation of new methodologies and/or instrumentation intended for implementation under the mentoring of Senior Staff members. *In the research pathway*, fellows are assigned to ongoing or new basic science and/or technology-related projects (e.g., development and implementation of new technologies for diagnostic laboratory applications).

Requirements: MD and/or PhD. Preferences: 2 years beyond doctoral degree with training in clin. path., clin. chem., and/or experience in relevant sciences (e.g., biomed. eng., biochem., mol. biol.).

Stipends: Starting salary is $45,000 per year with increments based on previous training, experience and Board certificate(s).

Applications: Should be made prior to October 1 for the position commencing July 1, of the following year to Gyorgy Csako, MD, Clinical Chemistry Service, DLM, CC, NIH, Building 10, Room 2C-407, Bethesda, MD 20892-1508 and must include a current curriculum vitae with bibliography, three letters of recommendation and undergraduate and graduate transcripts.

Phone: (301) 496-1924 • **Fax:** (301) 402-1885 • **E-mail:** gcsako@nih.gov
Web site: http://www.cc.nih.gov/cp/chemistryfellowships.shtml

---

UNIVERSITY OF PENNSYLVANIA MEDICAL CENTER

Department of Pathology & Laboratory Medicine

Clinical Chemistry Fellowship

Description: The fellowship provides the fellow with sufficient interpretive, technical and administrative skills to be able to run a laboratory effectively, and helps develop the conceptual background and analytical ability to carry out meaningful research under the supervision of one or more of the laboratory directors. The first phase of the training consists of rotations through the Toxicology, Endocrinology, Stat and Routine Chemistry Sections. During these rotations, there is close interaction with the laboratory directors so that the fellow becomes familiar with the spectrum of analytical capabilities and research opportunities of the William Pepper Laboratory. Faculty interests include molecular and cellular endocrinology, detoxification of xenobiotics, pharmacokinetics, interaction of radiolabelled drugs with binding proteins, methods for monitoring transplant recipients, development of micro-scale systems for diagnostic assays, diagnostic applications of chemiluminescence and bioluminescence (*i.e.*, ultra-sensitive immunoassays), laboratory utilization, instrument and method evaluation. The laboratories are modern and well equipped with the overall setting conducive to a productive fellowship experience.

Requirements: Applicants must have completed at least two years of clinical pathology.

Stipends: Stipends are commensurate with year of postgraduate training.

Staff: Dean Carlow MD; **Larry J. Kricka** DPhil; **Stephen R Master** MD; **Michael C Milone** MD, PhD; **Les M. Shaw** PhD; **Peter Wilding** PhD; **Donald S. Young** MD.

Applications: Inquiries should be sent to:
Larry J Kricka, DPhil, Clinical Chemistry/ 7 Founders, Hospital of the University of Pennsylvania, Philadelphia, PA 19104-4283.

Phone: (215) 662-6575 • **Web site:** http://www.uphs.upenn.edu/path/residency.html

UNIVERSITY OF TEXAS SOUTHWESTERN MEDICAL SCHOOL

Department of Pathology

Clinical Chemistry Fellowship

Description: The Department of Pathology offers a Commission on Accreditation of Clinical Chemistry Fellowship Program (ComACC)-accredited one- or two-year fellowship program in clinical chemistry which begins on 1 July of the year in which a candidate is selected for this Fellowship. The individual will receive intensive training in both the analytical and clinical aspects of clinical chemistry. Laboratory management and organization is an integral part of the program. The Fellow is also expected to participate in a research project with supervision from a member of the faculty and publish the results of this research in an appropriate peer-reviewed scientific journal.

Requirements: PhD degree, preferably in biochemistry or clinical chemistry, and/or MD degree. Physician candidate must be eligible for a Texas Institutional Permit.

Stipends: Support is established by the Department of Pathology salary schedule for clinical fellows.

Staff: Ibrahim Hashim PhD DABCC, FACB Clinical Chemistry; **Frank H Wians, Jr.** PhD DABCC FACB Clinical Chemistry; **Patricia M Jones** PhD DABCC FACB Pediatric Clinical Chemistry; **Elizabeth L. Todd** PhD Clinical Chemistry.

Applications: Applications are accepted ONLY between 1 Jul and 31 Dec of the year preceding a 1 Jul start date of the following year and all applications MUST be submitted by following the instructions at The University of Texas Southwestern (UTSW) Medical Center web site indicated below. the selection of an applicant from the pool of all applicants is made between 1 Jan and 1 Mar of the year in which the Fellowship Program begins. Example: an applicant is interested in starting the UTSW Clinical Chemistry Program on 1 Jul 09. The applicant must apply between 1 Jul 08 and 31 Dec 08 and the accepted applicant will be notified of their acceptance some time between 1 Jan 09 and 1 Mar 09. Inquiries should be addressed to: Frank H. Wians, Jr., PhD, Division of Clinical Pathology, Department of Pathology. UT Southwestern Medical Center, 5323 Harry Hines Blvd, Dallas, TX 75390-9073.

Phone: (214) 648-7634
Web site: http://pathcuric1.swmed.edu/Teaching/fellowship/clinical_fellow

---

UNIVERSITY OF UTAH MEDICAL CENTER

Clinical Chemistry Fellowship

Description: This two-to-three year fellowship provides a broad experience in clinical chemistry for pathologists and scientists with appropriate prior training. Fellows rotate through clinical laboratories at ARUP Laboratories, The University Hospital, and Primary Children's Medical Center. Independent research, method development, laboratory management, and interaction with practicing clinicians are required. During the latter part of the fellowship, trainees may assume the duties of assistant medical director for one of the clinical chemistry laboratories.

Requirements: MD, PhD, or other doctoral degree in chemistry, biochemistry, medicine or closely related field from an accredited institution. Pathology residents who wish to specialize in clinical chemistry are encouraged to apply. Clinical laboratory experience is highly recommended.

Stipends: Commensurate with year of postgraduate training.

Staff: Edward R. Ashwood MD, ABP (CP and ChemP), Laboratory Director, ARUP Laboratories; **Phil Bach** PhD, Director, Pediatric Clinical Chemistry, Primary Children's Medical Center; **Elizabeth L. Frank** PhD, DABCC, FACB, Director, Analytic Biochemistry and Calculi; **David G. Grenache** PhD, DABCC, FACB, Director, Special Chemistry; **Charles Hawker** PhD, MBA, FACB, Scientific Director, Automation & Special Projects; **Chris Lehman** MD, ABP (CP, BB and Transfusion Medicine), Assistant Director, University Hospital Labs; **Gwen McMillin** PhD, DABCC, FACB, Director, Clinical Toxicology, Clinical Drug Abuse Testing, Co-Director, Pharmacogenomics, Trace Elements; **A. Wayne Meikle** MD, ABIM (Endo), Director, Endocrine/RIA; **Marzia Pasquali** PhD, Director, Biochemical Genetics; **William L. Roberts** MD, PhD, ABP (CP and ChemP), Director, Chemistry Group; **Alan L. Rockwood** PhD, Scientific Director, Mass Spectrometry, Co-Director, Trace Elements; **Lily L. Wu** PhD, Director, Reagent Production Lab.

Applications: Application should be made before October 15th of the year preceding the July start date.
Address inquires to: David G. Grenache, PhD, ARUP Laboratories, 500 Chipeta Way, Salt Lake City, UT 84108

Phone: (801) 583-2787 ext. 3547
E-mail: david.grenache@path.utah.edu

WASHINGTON UNIVERSITY SCHOOL OF MEDICINE

Division of Laboratory Medicine

Clinical Chemistry Fellowship

Description: This fellowship program in clinical chemistry combines training in the analytical, clinical and administrative aspects of clinical chemistry with basic and applied research experience. The training is designed to prepare the candidate for a career in academic medicine or clinical practice by providing a foundation to apply to future developments in clinical chemistry as well as current practice. The training program is organized in the laboratories of the two hospitals of the Washington University Medical Center: Barnes-Jewish Hospital and St Louis Children's Hospital. The clinical chemistry training faculty includes eight individuals of varied backgrounds and interest. The integrated research experience is generally in the laboratories of these faculty members, but can be arranged in the laboratory of other members of the Washington University faculty if circumstances warrant. The minimum period of the fellowship is two years.

Requirements: Applicants should have an MD or PhD degree.

Stipends: Based on each individual's level of postgraduate year training.

Applications: Inquiries should be addressed to: Mitchell G. Scott, PhD, Division of Laboratory Medicine, Box 8118, Washington University School of Medicine, St Louis, MO 63110.

Phone: (314) 362-2998
Web site: http://pathimm.wustl.edu/

UNIVERSITY OF WASHINGTON SCHOOL OF MEDICINE

Department of Laboratory Medicine

Clinical Chemistry Fellowship

Description: This two-year comprehensive clinical chemistry training program incorporates structured training in all working areas of the clinical chemistry laboratory, including general chemistry, toxicology, therapeutic drug monitoring, endocrinology, nutrition, molecular diagnostics, proteomics, pediatric clinical chemistry, and special chemistry. The fellowship includes formal and informal teaching from Chemistry Division faculty, participation in laboratory operations and consultations, and independent research. During the first year, fellows learn practical aspects of laboratory technology, operations, and administration by rotating through the clinical chemistry laboratories at four diverse medical centers: UW Medicine, Harborview (county hospital with Level I trauma center), Seattle Children's Hospital, and the VA Medical Center. In addition, fellows attend seminars and lectures and begin to develop their research program. During the second year, fellows pursue a basic, applied, or clinical research project and develop teaching skills. Fellows share laboratory management activities with the faculty director of a section in which they are especially interested (e.g., proteomics, toxicology, or endocrinology). The goal of the program is to develop the teaching, management, research and interpretive/clinical skills of trainees, so that they are well prepared to direct an academic clinical chemistry laboratory.

Requirements: Candidates must have a PhD in Chemistry or a related discipline, or an MD degree.

Stipends: Stipends are commensurate with the level of postgraduate training.

Applications: Apply by Oct. 1 for positions beginning in July of the following year to Rhona M. Jack, PhD, NRCC, A-6901 Children's Hospital and Regional Medical Center, 4800 Sand Point Way NE, Seattle, WA 98105. Application forms may be downloaded from the web site below.

E-mail: rhona.jack@seattlechildrens.org
Web site: http://depts.washington.edu/labweb/Education/Fellowship/index.htm

The University of Washington is an equal opportunity institution.

WILLIAM BEAUMONT HOSPITAL

Clinical Chemistry Fellowship

Description: William Beaumont Hospital is a 1061-bed tertiary care teaching hospital with busy inpatient, outpatient and outreach laboratory services. The chemical pathology sections perform over 4 million tests annually, are well equipped with state of the art automated instruments and are staffed by 2 pathologists and 3 PhD clinical chemists. The fellowship is a one-year training program (ACGME accredited) designed to provide the fellow with an intensive period of training in many aspects of clinical chemistry, laboratory automation, toxicology, therapeutic drug monitoring, endocrinology, immunology and urinalysis. Fellows will gain experience in laboratory management, quality control and assurance, method evaluation, principles of methods and instrumentation, equipment selection, use of laboratory tests in the evaluation of disease and prenatal screening for Down syndrome. The fellow is expected to participate in a research project. See entry for William Beaumont Hospital, Royal Oak, MI for more details about the institution.

Requirements: Candidates for this program must be Board-certified or Board-eligible for certification by the American Board of Pathology in AP/CP or CP. They must also hold a permanent license (or be eligible) to practice medicine in the State of Michigan.

Stipends: Salary is appropriate for the year of postgraduate training.

Applications: Should be addressed to
Elizabeth Sykes, MD, Medical Director, Clinical Chemistry, Department of Clinical Pathology, William Beaumont Hospital, 3601 W 13 Mile Rd, Royal Oak, MI 48073-6769.

Phone: (248) 551-2935
Web site: http://www.beaumonthospitals.com/gme
(click on Health Professionals, Graduate Medical Education, Accredited Fellowships)

THE CLEVELAND CLINIC

Division of Pathology and Laboratory Medicine

Clinical Microbiology Fellowship

Description: The Cleveland Clinic offers a one-year ACGME-approved fellowship in clinical microbiology. Training is provided in all aspects of clinical microbiology, including the isolation and identification of aerobic and anaerobic bacteria, mycobacteria, fungi, parasites, chlamydiae, mycoplasmas, and viruses including human retroviruses. Emphasis is placed on the practical aspects and clinical relevance of clinical microbiological procedures. Training is also provided in the area of molecular diagnostic techniques including the use of genetic probes, PCR, Real-time PCR, DNA sequencing, and epidemiological typing. Fellows are provided the opportunity to participate in developmental research and are expected to participate actively in the consultative activities of the Department and in the educational activities of the Infectious Diseases Department.

Requirements: Candidates must have completed training in Clinical Pathology or Infectious Diseases.

Stipends: Support is commensurate with the candidate's level of postgraduate training.

Applications: Inquiries should be addressed to
Nabin K. Shrestha, MD, Section of Clinical Microbiology, The Cleveland Clinic, 9500 Euclid Avenue, Cleveland, OH 44195.

EMORY UNIVERSITY HOSPITAL

Department of Pathology and Laboratory Medicine

Clinical Microbiology Fellowship

Description: This one-year ACGME-accredited program is designed to train academically oriented pathologists and infectious disease specialists for a career in clinical microbiology. The fellows rotate through the clinical microbiology laboratories serving Emory University, Crawford Long, and Grady Memorial Hospitals (approximately 2,000 beds and 500,000 microbiology procedures/year). The trainees gain hands-on experience in all aspects of clinical microbiology including bacteriology, mycobacteriology, mycology, parasitology, virology, antimicrobial susceptibility testing, and serology through a series of structured bench rotations. The program places special emphasis on molecular microbiology and has an active program of new test development and evaluation in this area. The fellow gains administrative experience through participation in laboratory management and hospital committee meetings and assumes increasing responsibility for interactions with clinicians, test interpretations, and presentations at conferences as the training progresses. A one-month rotation on the clinical infectious disease service and rounds with infection control practitioners provide training in these areas. Ample opportunity exists for interaction with the nearby Centers for Disease Control. The fellows will participate in test development and evaluation as well as applied clinical research.

Requirements: USMLE Step 3, completed training in clinical pathology or infectious diseases. Georgia medical licensure.

Stipends: Commensurate with the applicant's level of postgraduate training.

Staff: Angela Caliendo MD, PhD Fellowship Director; **Eileen Burd** PhD, Co-Director; **John E McGowan, Jr.** MD; **Yun Wang** MD, PhD.

Applications: Mary Lou Mojonnier, mmojonn@emory.edu and www.emory.edu/PATHOLOGY/

Phone: (404) 727-4283

INDIANA UNIVERSITY SCHOOL OF MEDICINE

Department of Pathology and Laboratory Medicine

Clinical Microbiology Fellowship

Description: This ACGME accredited program provides advanced training to pathologists who wish to subspecialize in clinical microbiology. Comprehensive training is provided in bacteriology, antimicrobial testing, anaerobic bacteriology, molecular diagnostics, mycobacteriology, mycology, parasitology, serology and virology. The trainee actively participates in the diagnostic activities of these sections and participates in rounds and teaching conferences of the Section and of the Infectious Diseases Service of the Department of Medicine. The trainee is an active participant in management of the laboratories and consults with clinicians relative to use of the laboratory and interpretation of results. During the one year fellowship (with an option for a second year) the trainee is expected to pursue a research project or projects. Research interests include enteric and anaerobic bacterial diseases, antimicrobial testing, infections in immunocompromised patients, fungi, Pneumocystis, free-living amoebae, rapid methods and instrumentation, and molecular diagnostics of infectious diseases. State-of-the-art diagnostic methods include: microbial identification by nucleic acid amplification including Real-Time PCR, molecular detection of antimicrobial resistance, bacterial strain typing, HPV DNA-typing and viral load testing and genotyping of HIV and HCV.

Requirements: Fellows will be selected by the Director and the Chair of the Department of Pathology and Laboratory Medicine. Candidates must have completed CP or AP-CP Pathology residency and must hold (or be eligible for) a regular license to practice medicine in the State of Indiana. If candidates are not citizens of the U.S., they must hold a valid visa.

Stipends: Commensurate with the year of postgraduate training in pathology.

Staff: **S. D. Allen** MD, Director; **D.E. Blue** MD; **T. E. Davis** MD, PhD; **G. A. Denys** PhD; **Mark Lasbury** PhD; **C H. Lee** PhD; **D. S. Leland** PhD; **L. M. Marler** MS, MT (ASCP) SM.

Applications: Apply to: Stephen D. Allen, MD, Clarian Pathology Laboratory, 350 West 11th Street, Indianapolis, IN 46202.

Phone: (317) 491-6643 • **Fax:** (317) 491-6649 • **E-mail:** sallen@iupui.edu

UNIVERSITY OF IOWA HOSPITALS AND CLINICS

Clinical Microbiology Fellowship

Description: The University of Iowa Hospitals and Clinics offers a one year ACGME accredited fellowship in clinical microbiology. The fellowship program combines training in the analytical, clinical, and administrative aspects of clinical microbiology with clinical research experience. The training is designed to prepare the candidate for a career in academic medicine. Exposure to infection control, molecular diagnostics, and molecular epidemiology is included. The clinical microbiology training faculty is comprised of three individuals of varied backgrounds and interests. The clinical research experience is generally in the laboratories of these faculty but can be arranged in the laboratories of other members of The University of Iowa faculty if desired. Most of the fellowship training occurs at the University of Iowa Hospitals within the Department of Pathology's Division of Medical Microbiology. Fellows also complete six weeks of rotations at the University Hygienic Laboratory (state public health laboratory): a two-week parasitology rotation and three one-week rotations in bacteriology/bioterrorism, virology/serology, and molecular diagnostics.

Requirements: Eligible for certification in clinical pathology or infectious diseases (successful completion of ACGME-accredited training program in CP, AP/CP, or infectious diseases).

Facilities: The Microbiology facilities consist of a state-of-the-art clinical laboratory which houses molecular diagnostics, virology, bacteriology, and the mycobacteriology/mycology lab. In addition, a diverse research area is established which includes the Anti-Infectives Research Center and Molecular Epidemiology Laboratories.

Stipends: Support is commensurate with the candidate's level of postgraduate training.

Staff: Teachingfaculty includes: **Sandra Richter** MD; **Dan Diekema** MD; **Aaron Bossler** MD, PhD.

Applications: Inquiries should be addressed to:

Sandra Richter, MD, University of Iowa Department of Pathology, C606-GH, Iowa City, IA 52242.

Phone: (319) 356-2990 • **Fax:** (319) 356-4916 • **E-mail:** sandra-richter@uiowa.edu

JOHNS HOPKINS MEDICAL INSTITUTIONS

Clinical Microbiology Fellowship

Description: The Medical Microbiology Fellowship program is designed to provide in-depth experience and consulting expertise in the laboratory-based diagnosis of infectious diseases and to prepare the individual for a career in academic microbiology. The program is ACGME accredited in all major areas of microbial identification and susceptibility testing. The fellow will be responsible for designing and completing a clinical or basic science research project that requires application of microbiologic skills under the direction of a Microbiology Division faculty member. Successful fellows may be certified by the American Board of Pathology examination in Medical Microbiology. The core program is one year; an optional second year of research may be available.

Requirements: MD applicants must have completed training in clinical pathology, or equivalent postgraduate training in an ACGME accredited Infectious Diseases Program.

Stipends: Support is commensurate with the candidate's background and previous training.

Applications: Should be made to
Karen C. Carroll, MD, Division of Medical Microbiology, Department of Pathology, The Johns Hopkins Hospital, Meyer B1-193, 600 N Wolfe Street, Baltimore, MD 21287-6417.

Phone: (410) 955-5077
Web site: http://pathology.jhu.edu

The Johns Hopkins University does not discriminate on the basis of race, color, sex, religion, national or ethnic origin, age, handicapped or veterans status in any student program or activity administered by the University or with regard to admission or employment.

MAYO SCHOOL OF GRADUATE MEDICAL EDUCATION

Department of Laboratory Medicine and Pathology

Clinical Microbiology Fellowship

Description: The Mayo Clinic Foundation offers a one-year ACGME-accredited fellowship for training in clinical microbiology, leading to eligibility for examination by the American Board of Pathology in Medical Microbiology and by the American Board of Medical Microbiology. Training is provided in all aspects of clinical microbiology, including the isolation, identification (molecular and non-molecular), and serology of bacteria, mycobacteria, fungi, viruses, and parasites. The Mayo Clinic Clinical Microbiology Laboratory performs in excess of one million analyses per year, allowing for training in the clinical interpretation and application of test results. Opportunity exists for fellows to participate in developmental research. Significant internal funding is available to support developmental research. There are active investigational programs using immunologic methods, molecular diagnostics, and automation to improve diagnostic testing. Fellows participate in quality control, leadership, infection control, teaching, and ''on-call'' consultative activities.

Requirements: Candidates must have completed training in clinical pathology or another recognized medical specialty with subspecialty training in infectious diseases within the U.S. or Canada.

Stipends: Support is commensurate with the candidate's level of postgraduate training and in accordance with the Mayo School of Graduate Medical Education guidelines.

Staff: M.J. Binnicker PhD; **F.R. Cockerill, III** MD; **R. Patel** MD, Program Director; **B.S. Pritt** MD; **G.D. Roberts** PhD; **J.E. Rosenblatt** MD; **T.F. Smith** PhD; **N.L. Wengenack** PhD; **J.D. Yao** MD.

Applications: www.mayo.edu/msgme/application.html Applications for each academic year, which begins in July, should be completed by January 1 of the previous year. Applicants are responsible for ensuring that all necessary materials are received by us prior to consideration for an interview. Positions will be offered beginning March 1 of the previous year.

Address inquiries to: Tasha Gilbertson, Education Program Coordinator, Mayo Clinic, 200 First Street SW, Stabile SL-16 Education, Rochester, MN, 55905.

Phone: (507) 538-6453 • **E-mail:** pathologyeducation@mayo.edu
Web site: www.mayo.edu/msgme/lm-clinmicrobio-rch.html

UNIVERSITY OF PENNSYLVANIA MEDICAL CENTER

Department of Pathology & Laboratory Medicine

Clinical Microbiology Fellowship

Description: The University of Pennsylvania School of Medicine offers a one to two-year fellowship for training in clinical microbiology. Training is provided in all aspects of clinical microbiology, including bacteriology, antimicrobial susceptibility testing, anaerobic bacteriology, mycology, mycobacteriology, parasitology, serology, virology and molecular infectious disease testing. The fellow interacts with other areas of Laboratory Medicine, is an active participant with the Infectious Diseases Division, and is involved in clinical research activities. The program is accredited by the American Academy of Microbiology and ACGME.

Requirements: Candidates must have completed training in clinical pathology, medical microbiology, or other specialty with training in infectious diseases. A doctoral degree including MD, PhD, or equivalent is required.

Stipends: Stipend is commensurate with year of postgraduate training.

Applications: Inquiries should be directed to:
Dr. Irving Nachamkin or Dr. Paul Edelstein, Department of Pathology & Laboratory Medicine, Clinical Microbiology Section, Hospital of the University of Pennsylvania, 3400 Spruce Street, 4th Floor Gates Bldg., Philadelphia, PA 19104-4283.

Phone: (215) 662-6651 • **Fax:** (215) 662-6655
Web site: http://pathology.uphs.upenn.edu/Education/FellowshipPrograms/edu_fellow_prog_clinical.aspx

---

UNIVERSITY OF TEXAS SOUTHWESTERN MEDICAL SCHOOL

Department of Pathology

Clinical Microbiology Fellowship

Description: The Department of Pathology offers a one-year fellowship program in clinical microbiology which begins in July each year. The individual will receive intensive training in aspects of clinical microbiology to include general bacteriology, anaerobic bacteriology, mycobacteriology, mycology, parasitology, virology, pediatric microbiology, susceptibility testing, molecular diagnostics, diagnostic immunology of infectious diseases, quality control, specimen processing and public health microbiology. The fellow will work closely with the Infectious Diseases fellows and staff correlating clinical findings. There is also close interaction with Infection Control during outbreak investigations and surveillance for multi-drug resistant organisms. Research projects of a clinical nature are strongly encouraged. The program is accredited with the ACGME.

Requirements: MD, DO, MBBS, or similar medical degree. Candidates must be eligible for a Texas Institutional Permit, and must have had an ACGME-accredited residency and have successfully passed the USMLE exams.

Stipends: Support will be commensurate with the applicant's level of training.

Staff: Dominick Cavuoti DO Clinical Microbiology; **Paul M Southern** MD Clinical Microbiology; **Rita M Gander** PhD Clinical Microbiology; **Paula Revell** PhD Clinical Microbiology; **Robin H Amirkhan** MD Clinical Microbiology.

Applications: Inquiries should be addressed to
Paul M. Southern, MD, Director of Microbiology, Department of Pathology, UT Southwestern Medical Center, 5323 Harry Hines Blvd, Dallas, TX 75390-9073.

Phone: (214) 648-3587
Web site: http://pathcuric.swmed.edu

UNIVERSITY OF UTAH MEDICAL CENTER

Department of Pathology

Medical Microbiology Fellowship

Description: This two-year program provides extensive experience in clinical microbiology aiming toward certification by the ABP or ABMM and a career in academic medicine or clinical practice. Clinical laboratory areas covered include bacteriology, anaerobic bacteriology, mycobacteriology, mycology, parasitology, virology, and immunology. Training rotations occur in three clinical settings: a pediatric hospital,a public health department, and University hospital laboratory which also serves as a large reference laboratory. Experience in clinical infectious diseases and infection control is also emphasized. Opportunities for limited clinical research projects are available with the understanding that any such project will result in publication of results.

Requirements: Candidates must have completed training in clinical pathology, specialty training in infectious diseases, or a PhD in relevant areas of microbiology.

Stipends: Stipend is commensurate with year of postgraduate training.

Applications: ABMM Program Director, Mark Fisher PhD, mark.fisher@aruplab.com - ABP Program Director, Kimberly Hanson MD, kim.hanson@hsc.utah.edu. Please send inquiries to Program Coordinator: Anna Peters, ARUP Laboratories, 500 Chipeta Way, Salt Lake City, Utah 84108

Phone: (801) 583-2787 ext.2110 The required application is on the following **Website:** http://www.path.utah.edu/education/fellowships/clinical-microbiology, complete and send to Anna Peters at the address above or anna.peters@aruplab.com

---

UNIVERSITY OF WASHINGTON SCHOOL OF MEDICINE

Department of Laboratory Medicine

Clinical Microbiology Fellowship

Description: This training program provides opportunities to acquire skills in clinical microbiology by participating in the activities of large clinical laboratories in tertiary care medical centers. Our affiliated hospitals provide additional opportunities for exposure to the practice of clinical microbiology in settings with varied patient populations. Training in this one-two year program includes exposure to all of the major laboratory sections including bacteriology, mycobacteriology, mycology, parasitology, virology, antibiotics, and molecular diagnosis. Additional training includes rotations in clinical infectious disease and hospital infection control. Participation in clinical or basic science research either within the Department or in cooperation with faculty in the Department or in cooperation with faculty in the Department of Microbiology or other units within the medical school is strongly encouraged. The program is approved by the American Academy of Microbiology.

Requirements: Candidates must have completed at least two years of clinical pathology or laboratory medicine, or training in medicine or pediatrics with experience in infectious diseases; or have earned doctorate in the microbiological sciences.

Stipends: Stipends or support will be commensurate with candidate's level of postgraduate training.

Staff: **Susan Butler-Wu** PhD; **Jill Clarridge** PhD D(ABMM); **Linda Cook** PhD; **B. T. Cookson** MD, PhD; **Ferric C. Fang** MD; **Amanda Harrington** PhD D(ABMM); **Steve Libby** PhD; **Ajit P. Limaye** MD; **Rhoda A. Morrow** PhD; **Xuan Qin** PhD D(ABMM).

Applications: Inquiries should be directed to:
Linda Norkool, Program Coordinator, Department of Laboratory Medicine, University of Washington, Seattle WA 98195-7110.
E-mail: norkool@u.washington.edu.
Applications are accepted July through September, with a deadline of October 1st for program entrance the following July 1st.

YALE-NEW HAVEN HOSPITAL
YALE UNIVERSITY SCHOOL OF MEDICINE
Department of Laboratory Medicine
Clinical Microbiology Fellowship

Description: This is a one-year ACGME-accredited fellowship in clinical microbiology based at the Yale-New Haven Hospital. The hospital is a tertiary 900-bed teaching facility with solid organ, stem cell and bone marrow transplantation programs, pediatric and neonatal services, cardiovascular surgery, a level I trauma center, and complete HIV care services. Training in bacteriology, mycology, mycobacteriology, parasitology, molecular diagnostic microbiology, virology, public health microbiology, hospital epidemiology and molecular epidemiology, and serodiagnosis of infectious disease are provided through the hospital laboratories and a public health laboratory. The fellowship has a special emphasis on mycobacterial disease. The fellow actively participates in laboratory operations, clinical consultation, and daily teaching and clinical problem-solving rounds with the Infectious Diseases staff. Developmental research and teaching experiences in Yale medical student courses are part of the fellowship, as are practical aspects of quality control, laboratory safety, laboratory information systems, and laboratory management and administration.

Requirements: Candidates should be physicians who are Board certified or eligible in clinical pathology or infectious disease.

Stipends: Commensurate with postgraduate training and experience.

Applications: Inquiries/applications should be sent to:

Sheldon Campbell, MD, PhD, Director, Dept. of Laboratory Medicine, Yale University School of Medicine, P.O. Box 208035, New Haven, CT 06520-8035.
E-mail: Sheldon.Campbell@yale.edu
Phone: (203) 688-2457 Program Coordinator • **Fax:** (203) 688-5736

JOHNS HOPKINS MEDICAL INSTITUTIONS

Clinical Pathology/Laboratory Medicine - Post-Residency Experience

Description: This is a one-year program (with an option for 2nd year) that allows the successful candidate to function as assistant/junior faculty member in the Immunology Laboratory. This service laboratory evaluates samples from patients with a variety of immune-mediated conditions, i.e. autoimmunity, monoclonal gammopathy, transplantation, and infectious diseases. The junior faculty member will participate with other pathology faculty in interpreting, reporting and signing-out cases addressing immunoglobulin abnormalities. This position is designed to provide advanced experience in clinical/diagnostic, laboratory and teaching aspects of immune diseases. Research is an important component and strongly encouraged at both the experimental and clinical level in cytokine biology, transplantation, autoimmunity and tumor immunology. There is also potential for interdivisional collaboration in molecular oncology, immunopathology, neuropathology and immunohematology. Participation in clinical conferences and immunology-related seminars is also encouraged.

Requirements: Board eligible in CP or in AP/CP. A Maryland medical license is required prior to starting date. Start date: July 1, 2010

Stipends: Commensurate with applicant's training and experience.

Applications: Letters of inquiry, CV, should be forwarded to: Barbara Detrick, PhD, Assoc Prof, Director, Immunology Laboratory, Department of Pathology, Meyer B-125, The Johns Hopkins Hospital, 600 N Wolfe St, Baltimore, MD 21287.

Phone: (410) 614-3286 • **E-mail:** bdetrick@jhmi.edu
Web site: http://pathology.jhu.edu

EOE

UNIVERSITY OF TORONTO

Department of Laboratory Medicine and Pathology

Laboratory Medicine Fellowship

Description: The University of Toronto Fellowship Training Program in Laboratory Medicine is a postgraduate program that provides unique professional subspecialty training in the Department of Laboratory Medicine and Pathobiology. The program is organized and funded by the affiliated teaching hospitals including the University Health Network, Mount Sinai Hospital, Sunnybrook and Women's College Health Sciences Centre, St Michael's Hospital, and The Hospital for Sick Children. Trainees are located in a clinical and/or research environment within teaching hospital settings. In addition to subspecialty training, trainees participate in applied laboratory research projects and/or basic research. Fellowships are available for 1 or 2 years in advanced electron microscopy, bone and joint, sarcoma, breast, cardiovascular, cytopathology, dermatopathology, endocrine, forensic, gynecologic, GI/hepatopathology, hematopathology, image analysis, medical biochemistry, medical microbiology, molecular diagnostics, nephropathology, neuropathology, oncologic pathology, pediatric molecular diagnostics, pediatric pathology, and surgical pathology.

Requirements: RCPSC/Board eligible or MDs certified in a laboratory medicine specialty.

Stipends: Commensurate with credentials and experience.

Applications: Send application form (on web site), curriculum vitae, and supporting documentation to: Fellowship Training Program in Laboratory Medicine, c/o Department of Laboratory Medicine and Pathobiology, Faculty of Medicine, University of Toronto, Banting Institute, Room 110, 100 College Street, Toronto ON, M5G IL5.

Phone: (416) 978-7535 • **Fax:** (416) 978-7361 • **E-mail:** pathology.residency@utoronto.ca
Web site: http://lmp.facmed.utoronto.ca

AKRON CITY HOSPITAL (SUMMA HEALTH SYSTEM)

Cytopathology Fellowship

Description: A one-year advanced training in cytopathology is provided. The Cytopathology Program offers the full resources of Cytology and Surgical Pathology from the member hospitals of Summa Health System—namely Akron City Hospital and St Thomas Hospital. These services have been consolidated at the Akron City Hospital campus. This campus also offers flow cytometry and immunohistochemistry. Specialty resources such as electron microscopy and molecular biology are provided by the regional Children's Hospital Medical Center. Approximately 20,000 cytology cases are processed and evaluated annually, including 4,200 non-GYN cases (of which fine needle aspirates total 1,200). The training experience includes daily sign-out of GYN and non- GYN specimens, including superficial and deep fine needle aspirates. The fellow will perform fine needle aspirations of superficial masses in an outpatient setting. Participation in teaching in an accredited Pathology Residency Program, conference participation, and involvement in quality assurance in Cytology are required. Research endeavors are encouraged.

Requirements: Applicants should preferably have completed a 4-year AP/CP residency.

Stipends: Stipends are commensurate with the year of postgraduate training in pathology.

Staff: Y. Chang MD, Cytopathologist; **W. Henthorne** MD, Cytopathologist; **Pars Ravichandran** MD, Director, Cytopathologist.

Applications: Inquiries are to be directed to P. Ravichandran, MD, Director of Cytopathology, Department of Pathology, Akron City Hospital, 525 East Market Street, Akron, OH 44304.

UNIVERSITY OF ALABAMA MEDICAL CENTER

Division of Anatomic Pathology

Cytopathology Fellowship

Description: The Division of Anatomic Pathology at the University of Alabama Medical Center, Birmingham, offers a one-year ACGME-approved fellowship experience in cytopathology. The University of Alabama Cytopathology Laboratory performs approximately 25,000 tests per year, with both conventional and liquid based gynecologic cases, including approximately 1,000 fluids, 1,200 FNAs and 300 EUS-FNAs and 1,000 pulmonary cases per year. Fellows participate in colposcopy, breast and endoscopic ultrasound clinics. Opportunities for elective rotation in subspecialty areas of surgical pathology are available. Participation in ongoing clinical studies and translational research is also encouraged. Rotations are entirely at the University of Alabama Hospital. This program is directed by Isam A. Eltoum, MD, MRCPath, MBA. ieltoum@uab.edu

Requirements: Applicants must be AP or AP/CP Board eligible, or Board certified. Graduates of medical schools approved by the Liaison Committee on Medical Education (LCME) and those who are Board certified will be given preference.

Stipends: Stipends are commensurate with the year of postgraduate training in pathology.

Applications: Applications should be submitted to: Gene P. Siegal, MD, PhD, Professor and Director, Division of Anatomic Pathology, 619 South 19th Street, KB506, Birmingham, AL 35294-7331. Applications should be made 12 to 18 months prior to initiation of training.

Phone: (205) 975-8880 • **Fax:** (205) 975-7284
Web site: http://cyto.path.uab.edu

ALBERT EINSTEIN COLLEGE OF MEDICINE MONTEFIORE MEDICAL CENTER

Cytopathology Fellowship

Description: The Cytopathology Division of the Department of Pathology offers two fully approved one-year fellowship positions in cytopathology. The 800-bed institution is the University Hospital for the Albert Einstein College of Medicine, with extensive clinical and research programs. The Cytopathology Division accessioned over 53,000 specimens last year. Approximately 85% of the specimens were in gynecologic cytology (with a high abnormal rate). Among the nongynecologic specimens there were approximately 1,800 aspiration biopsies from superficial and deep locations. The Division is staffed by five Board-certified cytopathologists. Fellows receive personal guidance and gain experience in diagnostic evaluation of all cytologic specimens with histologic correlations, hands-on performance of aspiration biopsies of palpable lesions and evaluation of deep aspirates. Fellows are expected to participate in the Division's strong research programs which include immunocytochemistry, in situ hybridization, and molecular genetics.

Requirements: MD degree or equivalent, and Certification or Board eligibility in anatomic pathology, or anatomic and clinical pathology.

Stipends: Dependent upon level of training.

Applications: Send requests for applications 19 months prior to fellowship beginning to
Mark J. Suhrland, MD, Professor and Chief of Service, Director of Cytopathology Training Program, Department of Pathology, Montefiore Medical Center, 111 East 210th Street, Bronx, NY 10467.
Web site: http://www.aecom.yu.edu

ALLEGHENY GENERAL HOSPITAL, PITTSBURGH

Department of Pathology and Laboratory Medicine

Cytopathology Fellowship

Description: A one-year fellowship in cytopathology offers advanced training with emphasis on fine needle aspiration biopsy and the application of ancillary techniques. Two positions are available. The fellows will have increasing levels of responsibility commensurate with level of performance. Emphasis is also placed on the integration of surgical pathology with cytology and the use of both air-dried Diff-Quik and alcohol-fixed Papanicolaou stains, as well as liquid-based monolayer preparations. The fellows will participate in the service, teaching and research activities of the laboratory. The laboratory accessions approximately 20,000 cytology specimens per year with an expanding fine needle aspiration biopsy service. The NSABP is located at AGH. Elective time is also available for the fellow to pursue other areas of interest in anatomic pathology. The fellows also review the numerous cytology consults sent to the faculty. Opportunities for regional and national teaching exist.

Requirements: Board certification or eligibility in AP or AP/CP.

Stipends: Support will be commensurate with the applicant's level of training.

Staff: Telma Pereira.

Applications: Applications should be submitted to Jan F. Silverman, MD, Director of Cytology and Cytopathology Fellowship, Allegheny General Hospital, Department of Pathology and Laboratory Medicine, 320 East North Avenue, Pittsburgh, PA 15212-4772

Phone: (412) 359-6886 • **Fax:** (412) 359-3598 • **E-mail:** jsilverm@wpahs.org

UNIVERSITY OF ARKANSAS FOR MEDICAL SCIENCES

Department of Pathology

Cytopathology Fellowship

Description: This one-year program is based on the cytopathology laboratories at the University of Arkansas for Medical Sciences and the contiguous John L. McClellan Veterans Affairs Medical Center. Opportunities to resolve diagnostic problems through interaction with the laboratories of electron microscopy, hematopathology and flow cytometry, as well as close cooperation with the division of surgical pathology enhance the fellow's experience. The material available for study and diagnosis includes 7,000 nongynecologic specimens, of which approximately 1,800 are fine needle aspirations. Almost half of fine needle aspirations are performed by the pathology department, including the cytopathology fellow. Proficiency in obtaining, preparing and interpreting aspirate samples is a major focus of our program, and close interaction with the clinical services is an essential part of the experience. Our 12,000 gynecologic specimens are predominatly thin preparation based and represent a high-risk population, and extensive interaction with our active gynecologic oncology service is an important part of the program. A rich teaching conference schedule for cytopathology and other areas of pathology, and comprehensive teaching sets complement training.

The fellow is given gradually increasing and supervised responsibility, and is expected to participate in the teaching of cytotechnology students in the Cytotechnology School of the College of Health Related Professions as well as pathology residents. He/she is also expected to participate in the research activities of the division, leading to presentations at the national/international meetings, and to publications. This program aims for training cytopathologists with well-rounded skills and the flexibility to pursue any goal they may have in their career.

Little Rock is the capitol city of Arkansas, with a variety of outdoor, indoor and cultural activities and is within driving distance to several larger metropolitan areas.

Requirements: Board certification or eligibility in AP or AP/CP.

Types and Numbers of Appointments: 1 Fellow per year

Stipends: $47,470 per year

Staff: Soheila Korourian MD; **Murat Gokden** MD Fellowship Director; **Michael Johnson** MD; **Chien Chen** MD, PhD; **Fengjuan Zhang** MD; **Anissa Hodges** MD.

Applications: Submitted to: Murat Gokden, MD, or Ms. Renee Gordon (Fellowship Program Manager) Department of Pathology, #517, University of Arkansas for Medical Sciences, 4301 W. Markham, Little Rock, AR 72205.

Phone: (501) 603-1508 • **Fax:** (501) 686-5959

BAYLOR COLLEGE OF MEDICINE

Department of Pathology

Cytopathology Fellowship

Description: The Department of Pathology at Baylor College of Medicine and its affiliated hospitals offers a one year Cytopathology Fellowship Program. The Program is designed to provide comprehensive training in diagnostic cytology including fine needle aspiration biopsy with surgical pathology and clinical correlation. The Fellow will rotate through Ben Taub General Hospital and the DeBakey VA Medical Center. Training will be provided in both gynecologic and non-gynecologic cases including performance and interpretation of fine needle aspiration biopsies. For 2008, the volume of cases generated by both hospitals included 28,256 cervicovaginal smears, 5,365 non-gynecologic cases and 1,901 FNA's. Incorporation of ancillary studies such as immunohistochemistry and flow cytometry will be an integral component of the fellows training. Research opportunities are available in cytopathology, immunocytochemistry, flow cytometry and other ancillary technologies. The fellows will also be responsible for the weekly cytology conferences, tumor boards and thyroid conferences.

Requirements: Candidates must be Board certified or eligible for certification in anatomic pathology or AP/CP and must be eligible for a training permit or license in the state of Texas.

Stipends: Commensurate with candidate's level of training.

Applications: Inquiries are to be directed to

Rodolfo Laucirica, MD, Department of Pathology, Baylor College of Medicine, One Baylor Plaza, Houston, TX 77030.

Phone: (713) 713-798-4083 • **Fax:** (713) 798-3665 • **E-mail:** yboney@bcm.tmc.edu

Web site: http://www.bcm.tmc.edu/pathology

BAYSTATE MEDICAL CENTER
TUFTS UNIVERSITY SCHOOL OF MEDICINE
Department of Pathology
Cytopathology Fellowship

Description: This one-year ACGME-approved fellowship program provides comprehensive training in all aspects of diagnostic cytopathology under the supervision of seven faculty cytopathologists, 2 hematopathologists, and a teaching cytotechnologist. The Cytopathology Laboratory of Baystate Medical Center evaluates in the order of 70,000 cases per year, of which approximately 8,000 are non-gynecologic, including 1,500 to 2,000 fine needle aspiration biopsies. The fellow will have exposure to ancillary techniques including flow cytometry, molecular diagnostics, image analysis, in-situ hybridization, and immunocytochemistry, with opportunity for training and performance of clinical fine needle aspiration biopsies and certification in monolayer Pap test evaluation. He/She will eventually assume junior staff sign-out responsibilities under faculty supervision, and will play an active role in teaching residents and medical students rotating through the Cytopathology Service. He/She will participate in weekly cytopathology review conferences and annual workshops/conferences given by the faculty at local, regional and national meetings. Fellows participate in research projects utilizing resources in the department as well as the affiliated institutions of Baystate Health.
Requirements: Applicants must be Board-certified or eligible in AP or AP/CP.
Stipends: Commensurate with the year of postgraduate training.
Staff: **Robert Goulart** MD — Program Director; **Q. Jackie Cao** MD; **Roxanne Florence** MD; **Katya Ford** MD; **Jonathan Freeman** MD, **Vandita Johari** MD; **Paula LaPolice** CT(ASCP); **Rukmini Modem** MD; **Luis Moral** MD; **Liron Pantanowitz** MD
Applications: Applications should be received by April 1 of the year prior to the start of the fellowship and must include a curriculum vitae, 3 letters of reference, and a letter of professional goals. Submit applications to Robert Goulart, MD, Director, Cytopathology Services, Department of Pathology, Baystate Medical Center, 759 Chestnut Street, Springfield, MA 01199.
Phone : (413) 794-5085 • **Fax:** (413) 794-5893
Web site : http://academics.bhs.org/Fellowships/Cytopathology_Fellowship/index.html

---

BETH ISRAEL DEACONESS MEDICAL CENTER
Department of Pathology
Cytopathology Fellowship

Description: This one-year fellowship is devoted to advanced training in diagnostic cytopathology with options to participate in clinical research. The cytology lab evaluates approximately 50,900 specimens a year, of which 7,900 are non-gynecologic, including 2,250 fine needle aspirations. Approximately 5.5% of the gynecologic specimens are abnormal. The teaching collection in the lab contains about 3,500 illustrative cytology cases with corresponding or follow-up surgical pathology slides. The fellows are expected to participate/present in conferences, teach residents, and attend immediate evaluations for fine needle aspirations in clinics, radiology suites and operating rooms. The fellows are also expected to perform fine needle aspirations. The fellows may assume sign-out responsibilities under supervision after a training period. The fellows are encouraged to initiate or participate in a research project. The hospital as well as the laboratory is fully computerized. Please see the full description of the department for additional information.
Requirements: At least three years of training in anatomic pathology or four years of combined training in AP/CP. Applicants must be eligible for a Massachusetts medical license.
Types and Numbers of Appointments: Two fellows per year.
Stipends: Commensurate with the level of training.
Applications: Direct inquiries to
Helen Wang, MD, Department of Pathology, Beth Israel Deaconess Medical Center, East Campus, 330 Brookline Avenue, Boston, MA 02215.
Applications should be received no later than February 1 the year before.

BRIGHAM AND WOMEN'S HOSPITAL

Department of Pathology

Cytopathology Fellowship

Description: This fellowship provides one full year of advanced training in diagnostic cytology and the performance of FNA's in a dedicated FNA clinic. The cytology service evaluates approximately 70,000 cases per year, of which 7,000 are nongynecologic specimens that include about 1,600 fine needle aspiration biopsies. After a training period, the fellow is expected to assume sign-out responsibilities under supervision. Participation in conferences and teaching of pathology residents is required. The fellow is encouraged to design and complete a research project, and resources include flow cytometry, image analysis, and molecular diagnostics. The laboratory is fully computerized, allowing easy retrieval of specimens by specimen type or diagnosis for teaching, research, and quality control purposes.
Requirements: Preference will be given to candidates who are Board certified or eligible for certification by the American Board of Pathology in anatomic pathology or anatomic and clinical pathology and who have demonstrated an interest in pursuing an academic career in cytopathology. Applicants must be eligible for a Massachusetts medical license.
Stipends: Commensurate with the level of training.
Staff: Edmund S. Cibas MD (Director of Cytology); **Christopher A. French** MD; **Eleonora G. Galvanek** MD; **David W. Kindelberger** MD; **Jeffrey F. Krane** MD, PhD; **Xiaohua Qian** MD, PhD; **Tad J. Wieczorek** MD.
Applications: Applications should be received no later than September 1 and should be sent to
Paula DelGrosso, Program Coordinator, Cytopathology Fellowship
Department of Pathology
Brigham and Women's Hospital
75 Francis Street
Boston, MA 02115
E-mail: pdelgrosso@partners.org.

UNIVERSITY OF CALIFORNIA, DAVIS

Cytopathology Fellowship

Description: The Department of Pathology offers a one-year fellowship which includes training in all aspects of diagnostic cytology, quality assurance and laboratory management. The fellow will participate in the FNA clinic at the UC Davis Cancer Center and in resident and medical student teaching. (In addition, the training program offers opportunities for elective rotation, training in Flow Cytometry and, Molecular Pathology. Performance of a research project during the fellowship year is encouraged. Annually, the Cytology Laboratory receives approximately 30,000 GYN specimens, 2,500 non-GYN specimens, and 1,200 FNAs.
Requirements: Candidates must be Board-eligible or Board-certified in anatomic pathology at the time she/he begins the fellowship program.
Stipends: Stipends are those of appropriate postgraduate levels established by the University of California Davis.
Staff: Alaa Afify MD Director of Cytopathology Fellowship; **Penny Young** Residency and Fellowship Physician Program Coordinator; **John Bishop** MD, Director, Surgical Pathology; **Lydia Howell** MD, Cytopathology and Acting Chair; **Malathy Kapali** MD, Breast and GYN Pathology; **Cindy Yu** MD, Cytopathology and Surgical Pathology.
Applications: Applications should be sent to: Penny Young, Residency and Fellowship Program Coordinator, University of California, Davis, Medical Center, 4400 V St PATH Building, Sacramento, CA 95817.
Web site: http://www.ucdmc.ucdavis.edu/pathology

UNIVERSITY OF CALIFORNIA, IRVINE

Cytopathology Fellowship

Description: The Department of Pathology at the University of California, Irvine offers a one-year Cytopathology Fellowship Program. The Program is designed to provide comprehensive training in diagnostic cytology including fine needle aspiration biopsy with surgical pathology and clinical correlation. Training will be provided in both gynecologic and non-gynecologic materials including performance and interpretation of fine needle aspiration biopsies. In addition to cytopathology responsibilities, Fellows will also rotate through flow cytometry and image analysis units which are parts of the pathology laboratory. They are expected to be involved in research opportunities that are available in cytopathology, immunocytochemistry and flow cytometry/image analysis. Fellows will also be responsible for the biweekly cytology conference and for actively participating in the cytopathology review courses and workshops given by the University of California, Irvine.
Requirements: Candidates must be Board-certified or eligible for certification in anatomic pathology or AP/CP and must possess a license to practice medicine in California at the beginning of their fellowship.
Stipends: The salary is comparable to that of residents of this institution with equivalent years of postdoctoral training.
Applications: Applications with curriculum vitae, three references, and a statement of professional goals are to be directed to Mai Gu, MD, PhD, Department of Pathology, University of California, Irvine, 101 The City Drive, Bldg. 10, Rm. 101, Orange, CA 92868.
Phone: (714) 456-6141 • **Fax:** (714) 456-5873 • **E-mail:** mgu@uci.edu
Web site: http://www.ucihs.uci.edu/com/pathology

UNIVERSITY OF CALIFORNIA, LOS ANGELES

Department of Pathology and Laboratory Medicine

Cytopathology Fellowship

Description: The Department of Pathology and Laboratory Medicine offers a one-year accredited fellowship in Cytopathology that provides an in-depth experience in both exfoliative cytology and fine needle aspiration for the fellow to attain a level of diagnostic autonomy, and become knowledgeable with the current technical and managerial aspects of operating an active cytology laboratory. The Cytology Laboratory at UCLA processes about 36,000 exfoliative specimens and 2,200 fine needle aspirations in a year. The fellow participates in the daily sign-out and teaching of all specimens. The fellow will have the opportunity to closely interact with all other pathology services including surgical pathology and flow cytometry, immunohistochemistry, molecular pathology and electromicroscopy laboratories. The fellow is expected to be involved in research projects, responsible for several interdepartmental conferences, and participate in teaching residents and both cytotechnology and medical students. Two fellowship positions are available.
Requirements: Candidates must be Board certified or eligible for certification in anatomic pathology. Candidates must hold or be eligible to hold a California Medical license, possession of which is necessary before beginning the fellowship.
Stipends: Support is commensurate with the candidate's level of training.
Applications: Please contact the Fellowship Coordinator for the list of requirements and application, submit a curriculum vitae and the names of three references to:
Jianyu Rao, MD, FCAP, Program Director, Cytopathology Fellowship, Department of Pathology and Laboratory Medicine, David Geffen School of Medicine at UCLA, 10833 Le Conte Avenue, Room A7-149 CHS, Los Angeles, CA 90095-1732.
Fellowship Coordinator: Ms. Annetta Pierro
Phone: (310) 825-5719 • **Fax:** (310) 267-2058
Web site: www.pathology.ucla.edu

UNIVERSITY OF CALIFORNIA, SAN FRANCISCO

Department of Pathology

Cytopathology Fellowship

Description: UCSF accepts two fellows per year into its ACGME-accredited program for training in all areas of cytology. A special emphasis is placed on fine needle aspiration (FNA) biopsy techniques, sample preparation, smear interpretation, and the application of ancillary studies to cytology specimens. During the course of training the fellow will learn the basic use of ultrasound in the FNA clinic setting. Annually, UCSF affiliated clinics have a caseload of 4,500 FNAs, 36,000 Pap tests and over 3,500 non-GYN specimens. Each fellow will spend six months of the year at UCSF Mt. Zion Comprehensive Cancer Center and Moffitt Long Hospital. Fellows participate in the daily service dedicated to patients at the FNAB clinic. The remaining six months include a rotation at San Francisco General Hospital where she/he will gain exposure to a highly diverse patient population with a disease spectrum somewhat different from the other campuses. Fellows participate in clinical patient conferences, daily cytopathology signouts, and in interdepartmental teaching conferences, Grand Rounds, and teaching of residents.

Requirements: Candidates must have three years of AP or AP/CP residency training and be Board eligible in pathology by starting date of the fellowship.

Stipends: As of 2008-09, $50,987 for PGY IV up to $60,017 for PGY IX

Staff: Frederick Baehner MD; **Anna Berry** MD; **Teresa Darragh** MD; **Douglas Hanks** MD; **Gioia Iezza** MD; **Kirk Jones** MD; **Elham Khanafshar** MD; **Zoltan Laszik** MD PhD; **Britt-Marie Ljung** MD Director, Cytopathology Fellowship Program; **Theodore R. Miller** MD Director, Cytology Service; **Annemieke Van Zante** MD.

Applications: Applications should be completed by 12/31/09 for fellowship beginning 07/01/11 Apply to: Britt-Marie E. Ljung MD, c/o Laurie Wagner, Department of Cyotopathology, Mt.Zion /UCSF, Box 1785, San Francisco, CA 94143-1785.

Phone: (415) 353-7320 • **Fax:** (415) 885 7588 • **E-mail:** britt-marie.ljung@ucsf.edu

Web site: http://pathology.ucsf.edu/education/fellowship/fs-cytology.html

---

UNIVERSITY OF CHICAGO

Department of Pathology

Cytopathology Fellowship

Description: The University of Chicago offers a one-year fellowship that provides comprehensive training in all aspects of Cytopathology, including traditional morphologic analysis, advanced diagnostic techniques such as flow cytometry, immunocytochemistry, and molecular diagnostics, as well as laboratory management. The University of Chicago is renowned for its oncology services that include a full range of cancer-related clinical and research programs. The hospitals, clinics, and the pathology department are fully computerized, facilitating data retrieval for diagnosis and research. The Section of Cytopathology processes about 15,000 Pap tests,predominantly liquid-based specimens, with a high abnormal rate, and more than 3,000 non-gynecologic specimens from diverse body sites. There is a pathologist-based fine needle aspiration biopsy service with a total of about 1,800 biopsies, including superficial and deep organs. The fellow will gain experience in performance and interpretation of FNA biopsies, and actively participates in conferences, teaching, research, and quality improvement activities.

Requirements: Candidates must be Board eligible or certified in anatomic pathology, or combined AP/CP, and must have or be eligible for an unrestricted license to practice medicine in Illinois.

Stipends: Stipends are commensurate to the year of postgraduate training.

Applications: Send a letter explaining your interest and background in Cytopathology, curriculum vitae, and three letters of recommendation to

Richard M. DeMay, MD, Director, Section of Cytopathology, The University of Chicago, MARP 212, MC 2050, 5841 South Maryland Avenue, Chicago, IL 60637.

Phone: (773) 702-6569 • **Fax:** (773) 702-6570

UNIVERSITY HOSPITALS CASE MEDICAL CENTER

Cytopathology Fellowship

Description: This one-year fellowship program provides extensive training in diagnostic cytopathology utilizing an annual volume of about 60,000 gynecologic and 5,000 nongynecologic specimens from the outpatient and inpatient clinical services of a 1,000-bed teaching hospital. The training involves active participation in signing out, teaching, fine needle aspiration, quality assurance, and research activities of the laboratory. It is complemented by a cytopathology lecture course given over a three-month period. Limited fellowship duties in surgical pathology are required, and an elective rotation is offered.
Requirements: Applicants must have completed requirements for primary certification in AP or AP/CP before the start of this fellowship. One fellowship is available per year.
Stipends: Commensurate with level of postgraduate training.
Applications: Applications should sent before June 30 of the year preceding the intended fellowship to: Fadi Abdul-Karim, MD, Director, Anatomic Pathology, c/o Jeannie St. Marie, University Hospitals Case Medical Center, Department of Pathology, 11100 Euclid Avenue, Cleveland, OH 44106-5077.
Phone: (216) 844-6046 • **Fax:** (216) 844-1810 • **E-mail:** jeannie.stmarie@uhhospitals.org
Web site: http://path-www.path.cwru.edu/

DARTMOUTH-HITCHCOCK MEDICAL CENTER DARTMOUTH MEDICAL SCHOOL

Department of Pathology

Cytopathology Fellowship

Description: This ACGME-accredited one-year fellowship program offers advanced training in diagnostic cytopathology. The Cytopathology Laboratory at DHMC processes a total of 36,000 specimens annually, of which 4200 are non-gynecologic including fine-needle aspirations. Teaching is provided through conferences, didactic sessions and daily sign-out of gynecologic and non-gynecologic specimens as well as training in performance and interpretation of fine needle aspiration biopsies. Emphasis is placed on integration of surgical pathology with cytology including cytology-histology correlation and in the use of ancillary techniques in cytology including molecular diagnostics, immunocyto/histochemistry and flow cytometry. Laboratory management and quality improvement issues are also included in the training. Fellows will gain experience in the use of air-dried Diff-Quick stains, alcohol-fixed Papanicolaou stains and monolayer preparations and will have graduated levels on increasing responsibility. Participation in conferences, teaching medical students, pathology residents and cytotechnologists is required. Fellows are encouraged to initiate or participate in a research project.
Requirements: Completed residency in Anatomic Pathology or Anatomic and Clinical Pathology and Board certified/eligible in AP or AP/CP. Medical licensure in the State of New Hampshire required.
Stipends: Commensurate with the number of relevant postgraduate years of training. There is a book allowance and funding available for presentation at a national meeting.
Staff: **Vijayalakshmi Padmanabhan** MD (Program Director); **Jorge L. Gonzalez** MD; **Edward J. Gutmann** MD; **Wendy A. Wells** MD.
Applications: To review application requirements and to download an application form go to the program's web site. Early application encouraged (no later than December, 18 months prior to July 1 start date). Send to Susan Hawk, Program Coordinator, Department of Pathology, Dartmouth-Hitchcock Medical Center, 1 Medical Center Drive, Lebanon, NH 03756-0001.
Phone: (603) 650-8623 • **Fax:** (603) 650-4845 • **E-mail:** Viju@Hitchcock.org; Susan.Hawk@Hitchcock.org
Web site: http://www.dhmc.org/goto/Cytopathology Fellowship

DREXEL UNIVERSITY COLLEGE OF MEDICINE

Department of Pathology & Laboratory Medicine

Cytopathology Fellowship

Description: This is a one-year program with an emphasis on diagnostic cytology with biopsy and clinical correlation. The program represents a merger of the previously existing programs at Medical College of Pennsylvania and Hahnemann. The laboratories process a complete spectrum of non-GYN cytologic specimens. The case load has a strong emphasis on gynecologic material and needle aspirations as well as numerous samples from bone marrow and cardiac transplant recipients. The fellow will participate in the performance and on-site evaluation of needle aspirations. The fellow will actively participate in all aspects of the Cytology Laboratory including administrative responsibilities, teaching of residents and medical students. Elective time is available in surgical pathology and subspecialty areas including immunoperoxidase studies, molecular studies, image analysis, and flow cytometry.
Requirements: Candidates must have completed a four-year AP/CP residency or three years of a straight AP residency.
Stipends: Are commensurate with the year of postgraduate training.
Staff: Xiaoli Chen MD, Director; **Lorenzo Galindo** MD; **Fernando Garcia** MD; **Cheryl A. Hanau** MD; **Suganthi Soundararajan** MD.
Applications: Must be completed by July 1 of the year preceding the intended fellowship which begins in July. Apply to Xiaoli Chen, MD, Cytopathology Fellowship Director, Department of Pathology, 245 N. 15th Street, Mail Stop 435, Philadelphia, PA 19102.
Phone: (215) 762-1179 • **Fax:** (215) 762-1051 • **E-mail:** xchen@drexelmed.edu

DUKE UNIVERSITY MEDICAL CENTER

Cytopathology Fellowship

Description: Duke offers a one-year ACGME accredited fellowship with extensive training in fine needle aspiration (FNA) and exfoliative cytology. The fellowship is primarily clinical service oriented with some research and elective time. The fellow alternates between the exfoliative and FNA services. Experience in laboratory management, QI, and teaching is included. Participation in national scientific meetings and clinical research projects is expected and supported. The Division of Cytopathology accessions over 45,000 gynecologic cytology cases and 9,000 non-gynecologic cases a year, approximately 1,800 of which are fine needle aspiration biopsies performed by our service.
Requirements: Applicant must be Board certified or eligible in AP/CP or AP.
Types and Numbers of Appointments: One position.
Stipends: Commensurate with the year of postgraduate training.
Staff: Rajesh C. Dash MD Program Director, Assistant Professor; **Sarah M. Bean** MD Assistant Professor; **Leslie Dodd** MD Associate Professor; **Cynthia D. Guy** MD Assistant Clinical Professor; **Claudia K. Jones** MD Associate Professor; **Michael S Waugh** Assistant Professor.
Applications: Send CAP standard fellowship application (photo optional), cover letter with personal statement, curriculum vitae, three letters of recommendation, and copies of USMLE (Steps 1-3) to: Raj C. Dash, MD Director, Cytopathology Fellowship, Duke University Medical Center, Box 3712, Durham.
Deadline for Application for 2011: January 1, 2010.
Phone: (919) 684-2533 • **Fax:** (919) 681-7634 • **E-mail:** bonnie.lynch@duke.edu
Web site: http://pathology.mc.duke.edu
Duke GME • **Web site:** http://gme.duke.edu

EMORY UNIVERSITY HOSPITAL

Department of Pathology and Laboratory Medicine

Cytopathology Fellowship

Description: A fellowship program of one-year duration in cytopathology with clinical and histopathologic correlation is offered. The fellowship training is centered at Emory University Hospital, The Emory Clinic, Emory Crawford Long Hospital and Grady Memorial Hospital with a combined annual volume of over 50,000 cytologic specimens. This figure includes approximately 4,000 fine needle aspirations of superficial and visceral lesions. The fellow works with the faculty and develops increasing independent diagnostic abilities. Both the interpretation and the performance of fine needle aspirations are included in the training program. Planning and participation in departmental and interdepartmental conferences are a part of the fellowship, as is the instruction of residents and medical students, and the planning and execution of a clinical or basic science research project.
Resources available for this research include laboratory facilities and faculty expertise in immunocytochemistry, in-situ hybridization, flow and image cytometry, polymerase chain reaction and FISH test. The fellowship is designed to develop special competence in individuals planning an academic career with emphasis on cytopathology.
Requirements: USMLE Step 3, Georgia medical licensure, and applicants must have completed the requirements of the American Board of Pathology for AP or AP/CP.
Stipends: Commensurate with level of training and experience.
Staff: Momin Siddiqui MD, Director of Cytopathology and Cytopathology Fellowship Training Program; **George Birdsong** MD; **Xin Gao** MD; **Melinda Lewis** MD; **Sanjay Logani** MD; **Marina Mosunjac** MD; **Gabriela M Oprea** MD; **Talaat S. Tadros** MD.
Applications:
Phone: (404) 727-4283 • **E-mail:** mmojonn@emory.edu
Web site: www.emory.edu/PATHOLOGY/

UNIVERSITY OF FLORIDA HEALTH SCIENCE CENTER

Cytopathology Fellowship

Description: The Department of Pathology at the University of Florida College of Medicine-Jacksonville Division offers two one-year cytopathology fellowship positions with emphasis on diagnostic cytology. The fellows evaluate and participate in the sign-out of all abnormal gynecologic preparations, as well as all non-gynecologic preparations. Training is provided in the performance, preparation and evaluation of fine needle aspiration biopsies and ductal lavage. Immunocytochemistry, electron microscopy, flow cytometry, image analysis and automated cytology are utilized for analysis of cytologic material. The fellow participates in training junior residents. Research activity is encouraged. Resources include all technical procedures performed in the Cytopathology Laboratory as well as the Tumor Analysis Laboratory.
Requirements: Candidates must have achieved Board eligibility in anatomic pathology and must have an interest in research activity.
Types and Numbers of Appointments: They cytopathology fellowship has two positions available each year.
Facilities: See residency program for details.
Community: See residency program for details.
Stipends: Each fellow will be started out as a PGY 5 level resident, in which the salary is $50,475.00
Staff: Shahla Masood MD (Shiraz Univ, Iran 1973) Professor and Chair; Chief Pathology; Director Pathology Residency and Fellowship Programs; Medical Director of Shands Jacksonville Breast Health Center; anatomic, clinical pathology, cytopathology; **Marilin Rosa** MD (Universidad Autonoma de Ciencias Medicas de centro America, Costa Rica 1999) Clinical Assistant Professor; Breast pathology and cytopathology; **Sania Shuja** MD, PhD (King Edward Med Col, Pakistan 1981) Clinical Associate Professor; anatomic pathology and cytopathology; Director of Neuropathology; **David J. Wolfson** MD (Univ Florida Col Med 1988) Clinical Assistant Professor, Director of Transfusion Medicine; anatomic & clinical pathology and cytopathology.
Applications: Applications should be addressed to:
Shahla Masood, MD, Director, Pathology Residency & Fellowship Programs, c/o Rebel Jones, GME Program Assistant/ Resident Coord. University of Florida College of Medicine - Jacksonville, 655 West 8th Street, Jacksonville, FL 32209.
Phone: (904) 244-4889 • **Fax:** (904) 244-4060 • **E-mail:** rebel.jones@jax.ufl.edu
Web site: www.hscj.ufl.edu

UNIVERSITY OF FLORIDA

Cytopathology Fellowship

Description: The ACGME-accredited cytopathology fellowship program is a one-year comprehensive program in cytopathology, offered by the Department of Pathology, beginning July 1. The fellowship provides the opportunity for advanced training and experience in all areas of cytopathology. The program includes medical and gynecological pathology, including fine-needle aspiration cytology and experience with ultrasound guided thyroid FNA. We currently review over 4,000 medical specimens, (including approximately 1,300 FNA's) and numerous thin layer and conventional Pap tests per year. Emphasis is placed on correlation of surgical and cytopathology findings. The program can be tailored to the fellow's individual interests to include an intensive overview of cytopathology and concentration in one or more specialty areas. The fellowship faculty include four pathologists with American Board of Pathology added qualification in Cytopathology. The fellow is expected to participate in related interdepartmental conferences. Opportunity and support are provided for research activity in the course of the fellowship program. Molecular biology, immunohistochemistry, cytometry, as well as other anatomic pathology facilities are available for the study of cytopathology related issues. Lecture series, comprehensive teaching conferences and computerized library and record retrieval are available for the fellowship program.
Requirements: Requirements of a successful candidate must include being Board eligible or certified in anatomic, or anatomic and clinical pathology, by the American Board of Pathology. Applicants are required to have passed USMLE Steps 1, 2 and 3.
Stipends: The stipend is related to years of training and experience, and is available upon request.
Applications: Applications and interviews must be completed by March 1 the year preceding the start of the fellowship, however, earlier application is preferred. The appointment will begin on July 1. Direct inquiries and requests for applications to
Edward J. Wilkinson, MD, Professor and Director of Cytopathology Fellowship, University of Florida College of Medicine, Department of Pathology, Immunology and Laboratory Medicine, PO Box 100275, Gainesville, FL 32610-0275.
Phone: (352) 265-0238 • **Fax:** (352) 265-0437
Web site: http://www.pathology.ufl.edu/fellowship.htm

GEISINGER MEDICAL CENTER

Cytopathology Fellowship

Description: This one-year, ACGME-approved fellowship program provides in-depth training in diagnostic cytopathology. The fellow's training is in a busy cytology laboratory, processing more than 79,000 gynecologic, 6,400 non-gynecologic and 1,800 FNA cases per year. The laboratory is fully automated and utilizes both Sure Path thin-layer technologies with computer-assisted primary screening as well as Thin Prep technologies for the cervical screening specimens.
The technique of fine needle aspiration biopsy is heavily emphasized and the fellow will gain significant experience in performance and on-site interpretation. The fellow will provide on site interpretation for endoscopic ultrasound guided biopsies as well as bronchoscopic ultrasound guided biopsies. Ancillary tests such as immunocytochemistry, flow cytometry, and molecular pathology are routinely a part of the evaluation of various cytology specimens and the fellow will be educated in these techniques. The fellow will be responsible for weakly tumor board conferences and will present the pathology materials at these conferences. A research project will be designed through staff collaboration with the intention of presentation at a national meeting. Sign-out occurs under direct staff supervision with graduated responsibilities assigned as competence is demonstrated
Requirements: Applicants must be Board certified or eligible for certification in AP/CP or AP, and have (be eligible for) a Pennsylvania Medical License.
Stipends: Stipends are commensurate with the level of training.
Applications: Universal Applications (available on the web site) should be sent to
Tammy J. Rodenhaver, Cytopathology Fellowship Coordinator,
Geisinger Medical Center, 100 North Academy Ave, Danville, PA 17822-1406
Phone: (570) 271-8071 • **E-mail:** smeschter@geisinger.edu or trodenhaver@geisinger.edu
Web site: www.geisinger.edu/cytofell

GEORGE WASHINGTON UNIVERSITY MEDICAL CENTER

Department of Pathology

Cytopathology Fellowship

Description: The Division of Anatomic Pathology offers a one-year ACGME-accredited fellowship position in cytopathology. The fellowship offers comprehensive training in all aspects of cytopathology, and provides the fellows with the necessary tools and skills for a successful transition to an attending pathologist. The fellow signs out cases with appropriate supervision and instruction by the senior faculty. Participation in quality assurance, intraoperative consultations, intra-and inter-departmental conferences and teaching is required. Two months of elective time in a specialized area is provided, and participation in research is encouraged. We also offer one month of the fellowship year at the National Institute of Health (NIH). The majority of fine needle aspiration procedures are performed by the pathologists in our FNA clinic, thus providing the fellows with a very good experience. The use of ThinPrep technology, ancillary techniques and the integration of surgical pathology with cytopathology are emphasized.
Requirements: Applicants for the program should have completed at least three years of straight AP or four years of combined AP/CP training and must be eligible for a District of Columbia medical license.
Stipends: Commensurate with level of training
Applications: Inquiries concerning the program should be received at the latest by December 31 one year before the anticipated starting date. Write to Sana O. Tabbara, MD, Director Division of Anatomic Pathology,The George Washington University Medical Center, Ross Hall #502, 2300 Eye Street, NW, Washington, DC 20037.
Phone: (202) 994-3391 • **Fax:** (202) 994-2618

HARTFORD HOSPITAL

Department of Pathology and Laboratory Medicine

Cytopathology Fellowship

Description: The Cytology Division offers a one-year fellowship program with emphasis on diagnostic cytology with tissue and clinical correlation. The laboratory processes approximately 70,000 gyn and 6,000 non-gyn cytology specimens per year including approximately 2,000 FNAs. The fellow will participate in cytology signout with faculty, resident training, performance of FNA, and rapid adequacy evaluation. The fellow will also gain exposure to immunocytochemistry, flow cytometry, molecular pathology, administration, and cytopreparatory techniques. Resources include an extensive collection of cross-indexed teaching cases, and a library of conference materials. Hartford Hospital is a tertiary care facility with over 37,500 surgical pathology accessions per year.
Requirements: Candidates must be Board-certified or eligible in AP or AP/CP and have passed USMLE Step 3.
Stipends: See the general description of programs offered at Hartford Hospital.
Applications: Addressed to
Theresa Voytek, MD, Department of Pathology, Hartford Hospital, 80 Seymour St, PO Box 5037, Hartford, CT 06102-5037.
Phone: (860) 545-6113 • **E-mail:** cdavids @clpct.com
Web site: http://www.harthosp.org/education

HENRY FORD HOSPITAL

Department of Pathology

Cytopathology Fellowship

Description: This fellowship is a one-year, ACGME-accredited program that offers advanced training in diagnostic cytopathology, including application of ancillary techniques such as immunohistochemistry, molecular diagnostics and electron microscopy to cytologic specimens. Considerable emphasis is placed on correlations between cytopathology and surgical pathologic diagnoses. The cytopathology laboratory in 2008 examined approximately 67,400 cytology specimens of which 7,314 were non-gyn and 2967 were fine needle aspiration biopsies (FNAs). The fellow also participates in interdepartmental conferences and in resident teaching. The fellow is expected to pursue a quality assurance project, as well as a scholarly project leading to publication in a peer-reviewed journal.
Requirements: Applicants should be Board eligible or certified in anatomic pathology or AP/CP.
Stipends: Stipends are commensurate with the year of postgraduate training in pathology.
Applications: Inquiries are to be directed to
Chad H. Stone, MD, Program Director, Cytopathology Fellowship. Department of Pathology, Henry Ford Hospital, 2799 West Grand Boulevard, Detroit, MI 48202.
Phone: (313) 916-2356 • **Fax:** (313) 916-2385

INDIANA UNIVERSITY SCHOOL OF MEDICINE

Department of Pathology and Laboratory Medicine

Cytopathology Fellowship

Description: This accredited fellowship program provides one year of advanced training in diagnostic cytopathology. The trainee will actively participate in all aspects of cytopathology, including the signout of routine gynecologic and non-gynecologic specimens and the procurement and analysis of fine needle aspiration biopsies. The program emphasizes a comprehensive cytologic approach to both superficial and deep-seated FNA diagnosis. There is a wide spectrum of material (approximately 50,000 cases) originating from the four hospitals (university, county, pediatric and tertiary adult) comprising our medical center. This includes approximately 3,200 fine needle aspiration cases per year and approximately one-third of these are collected by the cytopathology staff and fellows.
Requirements: Three fellows will be selected each year. Candidates must have completed an AP or AP/CP pathology residency and hold (or be eligible for) a medical license in the State of Indiana.
Stipends: Stipends are commensurate with the year of postgraduate training in pathology.
Staff: Harvey Cramer MD Director, Division of Cytopathology; **William Crabtree** PhD, SCT (ASCP) ProgramDirector, School of Cytotechnology; **Darrell Davidson** MD, PhD; **Rosen Dimitrov** MD; **Robert Emerson** MD; **Paul Musto** MD; **Xiaoyan Wang** MD, PhD.
Applications: Applications (CV + 3 letters of reference) should be submitted (preferably by email) by June 30 of the year prior to the intended fellowship. Apply to
Harvey Cramer MD, Division of Cytopathology, Department of Pathology and Laboratory Medicine, Clarian Pathology Laboratory, 350 West 11th Street, Indianapolis, IN 46202.
Phone: (317) 491-6353 • **Fax:** (317) 491-6334 • **E-mail:** hcramer@iupui.edu
Web site: http://www.pathology.iupui.edu

UNIVERSITY OF IOWA HOSPITALS AND CLINICS

Cytopathology Fellowship

Description: This accredited program is designed to train academically-oriented cytopathologists. Two positions are offered. Fellowships include both clinical and research training. Clinical training includes signing out gynecologic cytology smears (about 20,000 a year), aspirates (about 2,500) and other non-gyn specimens (about 6,000). An active pathology based FNAB clinic is present where fellows learn how to perform and interpret FNABs. Immunocytochemistry is routinely utilized on clinical specimens. Research interests of the faculty include fine needle aspiration biopsy, molecular techniques, G.I. pathology, urologic pathology and head and neck pathology.
Requirements: Applications will be accepted from residents who have had three years of straight anatomic pathology training, or four years of combined anatomic and clinical pathology training. Board-eligible applicants are preferred.
Stipends: Commensurate with level of training.
Staff: **Chris S. Jensen** MD; **Michael B. Cohen** MD; **Robert A. Robinson** MD, PhD; **Laila Dahmoush** MBChB.
Applications: Chris S. Jensen, MD, Director of Cytopathology Fellowship Program, Department of Pathology, University of Iowa, 200 Hawkins Drive, 5216 RCP, Iowa City, IA 52242.
Phone: (319) 356-4434 • **Fax:** (319) 384-8052 • **E-mail:** chris-jensen@uiowa.edu

---

JACKSON MEMORIAL HOSPITAL/JACKSON HEALTH SYSTEM UNIVERSITY OF MIAMI SCHOOL OF MEDICINE

Cytopathology Fellowship

Description: This one-year fellowship program is designed to provide comprehensive training in diagnostic cytology. Our laboratory is located at the University of Miami/Jackson Memorial Medical Center which provides service to over 65,000 in-patients and more than 300,000 out-patients, annually. We evaluate approximately 26,000 cases per year, of which 7,000 are non-gynecologic, including over 2,500 fine needle aspirations. The location of our laboratory within the Department of Pathology provides ready access to a wealth of teaching material and three large libraries which offer unique patient care perspectives and research-related services. The first six months of training includes review of the wealth of diagnostic material available in Cytology teaching files and practicing first hand screening of new cases. In addition the Fellows cover Breast Health Center, Thyroid, Head & Neck and Surgical Oncology Clinics with a total of 12,000 visits a year and participate by performing FNA and immediate FNA analyses of various anatomic sites performed at our medical center. During the following six months, the Fellows assume the daily sign-out responsibilities under faculty supervision. They take an active role in teaching medical students and pathology residents, present at departmental conferences, and participate in the cytology workshops given by faculty at local and national meetings.
Requirements: Candidates should be Board eligible or certified by the American Board of Pathology in Anatomic Pathology or AP/CP; licensed or eligible for Florida medical licensure.
Stipends: Commensurate with the level of training and experience.
Applications: Applications should be submitted by Jan 31st of the year preceding the intended fellowship appointment and addressed to
Parvin Ganjei-Azar, MD, Director of Cytology and Cytopathology Fellowship, Department of Pathology, University of Miami, PO Box 016960, Miami, FL 33101.
Phone: (305) 585-6055 • **Fax:** (305) 585-2598 • **E-mail:** pganjei@med.miami.edu
Web site: http://path.med.miami.edu/umpath/umpath.htm

JOHNS HOPKINS MEDICAL INSTITUTIONS

Cytopathology Fellowship

Description: This one- or two-year fellowship offers advanced, post-residency training in diagnostic cytopathology. The program is designed to provide experience in diagnosis, research and teaching in clinical cytopathology. Diagnostic material consists of a wide variety of gynecologic and non-gynecologic specimens, including deep and superficial fine needle aspirations from in-patient and out-patient services of The Johns Hopkins Hospital. Training includes performing superficial fine needle aspirations under senior faculty supervision and assisting radiologists to determine the adequacy of specimens in deep needle aspirations. The fellows are given increasing responsibility in cytopathology sign-out as they acquire experience. Fellows participate in teaching residents and medical students. Research opportunities include molecular pathology, computer-based education, flow cytometry, and immunocytochemistry. The second year provides an opportunity for independent diagnosis and is tailored to the trainee's career goals, allowing more time in research or diagnostic service.
Requirements: Candidates must be Board certified or eligible for certification in AP or AP/CP and have a Maryland license prior to starting the second year of the fellowship.
Stipends: Commensurate with the candidate's level of postgraduate training in pathology.
Applications: Applications must be submitted by April 1, 15 months prior to July 1 starting date. Apply with CV and four references to:
Syed Z. Ali, MD, Associate Professor of Pathology and Radiology, Division of Cytopathology, Dept. of Pathology, The Johns Hopkins Hospital, 600 N. Wolfe Street, PATH 406, Baltimore, MD 21287-6417.
Phone: (410) 955-1180 • **Fax:** (410) 614-9556 • **E-mail:** sali@jhmi.edu
Web site: http://pathology.jhu.edu

EOE

UNIVERSITY OF KANSAS MEDICAL CENTER

Cytopathology Fellowship

Description: This one-year accredited program is designed to train up to three well-rounded, academically oriented cytopathologists and provide advanced training in diagnostic cytopathology and the performance of FNAs. Over 15,000 patient cases are evaluated each year in our hospital-based laboratory, of which about 4,000 are nongynecologic specimens. FNAs comprise approximately one-third of the nongynecologic specimens. Particularly strong interdepartmental programs exist in cancer prevention and control, epidemiology and biostatistics; and fellows have the opportunity to evaluate research FNA material in addition to diagnostic cases. After an initial closely supervised training period, the fellow is expected to assume graded sign-out responsibilities under supervision. Participation in patient management conferences and teaching of pathology residents and cytotechnology students is required. The program is designed to provide the successful candidate with an in-depth experience that will include liquid based, thin layer cytology techniques, image analysis, flow cytometry, immunohistochemistry, molecular diagnostics and health services research. Fellows are encouraged to design and complete a research project.
Requirements: Candidates must be Board eligible or certified in anatomic pathology or anatomic and clinical pathology and must have or be eligible for an unrestricted license to practice medicine in Kansas. Preference will be given to candidates who have demonstrated an interest in pursuing an academic career in cytopathology.
Staff: Patricia A. Thomas MD, MA, Program Director; **Fang Fan** MD, PhD, Co-program Director; **Rashna Madan** MD; **Ossama W. Tawfik** MD, PhD; **Barbara Atkinson** MD.
Applications: Applications must be received by December 1 of the year prior to the intended fellowship. Please complete the standardized form and E-mail: Charla Tunget, Program Coordinator, University of Kansas School of Medicine, Department of Cytopathology; 3901 Rainbow Blvd, 2006 Wahl West, Mail Stop 3045, Kansas City, KS 66160-7410.
Phone: (913) 588-7076 • **Fax:** (913) 588-7073 • **E-mail:** ctunget@kumc.edu

UNIVERSITY OF KENTUCKY MEDICAL CENTER

Department of Pathology and Laboratory Medicine

Cytopathology Fellowship

Description: This program is a one-year clinically oriented program devoted to all areas of cytopathology. Extensive training and experience in gynecologic, nongynecologic, and fine needle aspiration biopsy cytology are provided, with the pathology service performing most of the aspirates. The fellow rotates through both the University and VA hospitals which are connected by a walkway. The total number of cytology specimens accessioned annually is about 21,000 with about 13% abnormal gynecologic specimens, and over 1,600 FNAs. Time is also devoted to laboratory management and quality assurance skills, teaching, and a research project in cytopathology. Training in immunocytochemistry and other ancillary techniques is included. Accredited by ACGME for 2 positions. A combined 2 year cytopathology / surgical pathology fellowhip leading to Cytopathology Board eligibility is offered.
Requirements: Applicants who are Board-eligible in AP or AP/CP at the start of the fellowship are preferred. Candidates should be eligible for a medical license in the state of Kentucky.
Stipends: Commensurate with year of postgraduate training in pathology plus $1,200 per year available for attending meetings and purchasing books.
Staff: **Luis Samayoa** MD; Director, Fellowship, Veterans Affairs Medical Center; **Kimberly J. Absher** MD; **Yolanda M Brill** MD; **Laura Crump** MD; **Rouzan Karabakhtsian** MD; **Bonnie Mitchell** MD, Veterans Affairs Medical Center.
Applications: Universal Application, including CV and letters of recommendation, should be sent to Luis M. Samayoa, MD, Director, Cytopathology Fellowship, Department of Pathology and Laboratory Medicine, University of Kentucky Medical Center, 800 Rose Street Ste MS117, Lexington, KY 40536-0298.
Phone: (859) 323-6183

LONG ISLAND JEWISH MEDICAL CENTER

Department of Pathology and Laboratory Medicine

Cytopathology Fellowship

Description: This one-year fellowship provides advanced training in diagnostic cytopathology. Training will be provided in both gynecologic and non-gynecologic cytology including hands-on performance and interpretation of fine needle aspiration biopsies. Fellows will gain experience with techniques such as immunohistochemistry, electron microscopy, flow cytometry and image analysis. They will participate in conferences, teach residents and attend immediate interpretations of fine needle aspirations in clinics, radiology suites and operating rooms. Active participation in clinical research is essential. The total number of cytology specimens accessioned annually in this growing laboratory is over 27,000 with about 9% abnormal gynecologic specimens and about 3,500 FNA's. The laboratory is equipped with a multiheaded microscope and video camera and monitor, flow cytometer, computerized image analyzer and a laboratory information system. The laboratory has implemented the use of the ThinPrep Imaging System for the screening of Pap tests. In addition, ThinPrep Processing is utilized in the routine of preparing gynecologic and non-gynecologic specimens. Long Island Jewish Medical Center is a tertiary care teaching facility. The Surgical Pathology Service has over 36,100 accessions per year. Completion of the program qualifies the candidate to take the cytopathology subspecialty Board exam.
Requirements: Candidates must be Board eligible or certified in anatomic pathology (AP) or anatomic pathology/ clinical pathology (AP/CP) by the American Board of Pathology. It is also required that the individual who is selected for the position obtains a New York State license prior to commencing the program on July 1, 2011 and holds a certificate in Basic Life Support.
Stipends: Commensurate with year of postgraduate training in pathology.
Applications: Address request to
Patricia G. Wasserman, MD, Chief, Div. of Cytopathology, Dept. of Pathology, Long Island Jewish Med. Ctr., 270-05 76th Ave., Rm. B-67, New Hyde Park, NY 11040. The program is filled for 2010. The standardized dates for applications and interviews for 2011 is December 1, 2009 (19 months before) and February 28, 2010 (16 months before).
Phone: (718) 470-7709 • **Web site:** http://www.northshorelij.com.

LOUISIANA STATE UNIVERSITY HEALTH SCIENCES CENTER SHREVEPORT

Cytopathology Fellowship

Description: The Department of Pathology offers a one-year ACGME-accredited fellowship in cytopathology with two positions under the supervision of Fleurette Abreo, MD. The fellow is expected to participate in the cytology service and teaching clinical and/or basic research activities. Completion of a research project is expected by the end of the fellowship year with a presentation to faculty, staff, and peers at the Annual Albert G. Smith Resident Research Forum. The fellowship program is designed to provide advanced training in the interpretation of gynecologic and non-gynecologic specimens. The training includes the use and interpretation of immunohistochemistry, ultrastructural and molecular pathology. Two months of electives are available which may be dedicated to research. Teaching activities include departmental and interdepartmental conferences.
Requirements: MD degree. Board eligibility or certification in Anatomic Pathology.
Stipends: Stipend is commensurate with level of postgraduate training: $50,720.05 for PGY-VI. A $2,200 allowance is provided for textbooks and professional fees. In addition, travel expenses are paid to present research accepted for presentation at national meetings.
Staff: Stephen M. Bonsib MD, AP/CP, Chairman of Pathology, renal pathology, male genitourinary, surgical pathology, electron microscopy; **Fleurette Abreo** MD, Cytopathology Fellowship Director, breast, renal pathology, and surgical pathology; **Jaiyeola Thomas-Ogunniyi** MD, cytopathology, surgical pathology, GI pathology, hematopathology; **Marie Beckner** MD, PhD, molecular pathology, neuoropathology; **Jim Cotelingam** MD, Hematopathology; **Diana Veillon** MD, flow cytometry, hematopathology; **Mary Nordberg** PhD, molecular pathology, flow cytometry; **Songlin Zhang** MD, cytopathology, surgical pathology, GYN pathology.
Applications: Mail application, three letters of recommendation (addressed to Dr. Fleurette Abreo), and a statement of interest to: Lisa LaChance BA, Program Coordinator, Department of Pathology, LSUHSC-Shreveport, PO Box 33932, 1501 Kings Highway, Shreveport, LA 71130
Phone: (318) 675-7822 • **Fax:** (318) 675-7966 • **E-mail:** llacha@lsuhsc.edu
Web site: http://www.sh.lsuhsc.edu/pathology/
Please see website for application and further details.

UNIVERSITY OF LOUISVILLE HEALTH SCIENCES CENTER

Division of Anatomic Pathology, Department of Pathology & Laboratory Medicine

Cytopathology Fellowship

Description: The cytopathology fellowship at the University of Louisville Health Sciences Center is a comprehensive one-year program integrating academic and community medical centers. Approximately 9,000 pap smears and 1,000 non-gyn specimens are reviewed each year. The training program is designed to provide the experience and training needed for successful community or academic cytology practice.
Requirements: Candidates must be certified, or eligible for certification, by the American Board of Pathology in anatomic pathology. Candidate must have completed Step 3 of the USMLE.
Stipends: Commensurate with that provided for physicians at year five (5) of postgraduate training.
Applications: Send application, CV, documentation of USMLE scores and two or more letters of recommendation to Sunati Sahoo, MD, Director of Cytopathology, Department of Pathology and Laboratory Medicine, University of Louisville Health Sciences Center, 530 South Jackson Street, Louisville, KY 40202. The program begins each July 1. The deadline for the receipt of applications is July 31 of the previous year.
Phone: (502) 852-1762 • **Fax:** (502) 852-1761 • **E-mail:** sunati.sahoo@louisville.edu

LOYOLA UNIVERSITY MEDICAL CENTER

Cytopathology Fellowship

Description: The Cytopathology fellowship is a one year comprehensive ACGME approved program designed to provide eligibility for the American Board of Pathology speciality examination in cytopathology. The state of the art cytology laboratory evaluates approximately 23,000 gynecologic and 3,000 non-gynecologic specimens and over 1,300 FNAs. The department has a strong academic mission with a wide range of translational research programs and a division of molecular pathology. The fellow will become proficient in laboratory management, quality assurance systems, diagnostics; including the performance and interpretation of FNAs, and new technologies; including the Thin Prep Pap test, image analysis, and laser scanning cytometry. Opportunities for cytology-based molecular research are provided. The fellow will participate in the instruction of residents and medical students rotating in cytology and in the departmental conferences. The fellow is expected to complete a research project with the goal of publication and/ or presentation at a national meeting. This fellowship will offer the full spectrum of cytopathology applications today as well as developing technologies of the future.
Requirements: Applicants should be AP or AP/CP Board eligible, or Board-certified.
Stipends: Commensurate with the year of postgraduate training.
Applications: Send cover letter, CV, and three letters of recommendation to: Vicki Baertschi, Fellowship Training Program, Loyola University Medical Center, Department of Pathology, Bldg #103, Rm #0177, 2160 S First Avenue, Maywood, IL 60153.
Letters of recommendation should be addressed to:
Eva Wojcik, MD, Director of Cytopathology Fellowship
Phone: (708) 216-5591 • **Fax:** (708) 216-8225
Web site: http://www.stritch.luc.edu/depts/path/index.htm

MASSACHUSETTS GENERAL HOSPITAL

Department of Pathology

Cytopathology Fellowship

Description: This one-year, ACGME-approved fellowship program provides advanced training in diagnostic cytopathology under the supervision of twelve staff pathologists. The Cytopathology Laboratory handles over 62,000 cases, of which nearly 14,000 are nongynecologic and nearly 4000 are fine needle aspirations, (25 % performed by the cytopathologists). Training includes supervised signout, use of ancillary tests, performance of superficial fine needle aspiration biopsies, immediate assessment and triage of needles aspirations and aspects of quality assurance and laboratory management. Additional rotations to the cytopathology lab at the Brigham and Women's Hospital, to the molecular pathology lab at MGH and in surgical pathology sign-out are included. Fellows are encouraged to design and complete a research project.
Requirements: Applicants must be Board-certified or eligible for certification in AP or AP/CP and have a Massachusetts license prior to starting the fellowship.
Stipends: Commensurate with the candidate's level of postgraduate training.
Applications: Candidates should submit a letter of interest,their curriculum vitae, USLME scores and three letters of recommendation by December 1st 18 months prior to the starting date of the fellowship (July 1) to:
Joan Ricker, Pathology Fellowship Administrator,
Department of Pathology, Warren 219, Massachusetts General Hospital, 55 Fruit Street, Boston, MA 02114 - 2696.
Phone: (617) 643-4482 • **Fax:** (617) 643-4045 • **E-mail:** jaricker@partners.org

UNIVERSITY OF MASSACHUSETTS MEDICAL SCHOOL

Cytopathology Fellowship

Description: The University of Massachusetts offers a one-year ACGME-accredited Cytopathology Fellowship position. Currently, the Fellowship is filled through June 2010. This highly structured Fellowship efficiently covers the skills required for Board certification and a successful Cytopathology practice, while allowing a motivated fellow the opportunity to participate research. Two major research areas include the molecular basis of diagnostic changes in cancer cell structure, and biotechnology related to improving the handling of micro-sized biopsies. The curriculum includes a strong foundation in classical morphologic diagnosis (54,000 GYN, Cytyc ThinPrep Imager-based, and 10,000 non-GYN per year), FNA performance, molecular diagnostic exposure relevant to Cytopathology, cytology preparation techniques, cell research techniques, and laboratory management. The program is described fully at http://www.umassmed.edu/pathology/fellowship/structure.cfm

Requirements: Candidates must be AP or AP/CP board certified/eligible and must have passed Step 3 of the USMLE. Preference will be given to academically-oriented candidates.
Facilities: The UMASS Memorial Health Care system is located in Worcester, about 40 miles west of Boston. The University of Massachusetts Medical School has a strong research base, an excellent graduate school and significant resources to support research in cell biology and live cell imaging. The central part of Massachusetts has exceptionally good public schools, historic and natural beauty, and abundant year-round cultural and outdoor activities. The Fellowship Faculty includes six cytopathologists and four molecular/hematopathologists (see web site above).
Stipends: Determined by years of postgraduate experience.
Applications: Send CV with names of three references and a letter describing career goals to Patti Davis, UMass Memorial Medical Center, Pathology Residency/Fellow Coordinator, Rm 220, One Innovation Dr., Three Biotech, Worcester, MA 01605
Phone: (508) 793-6156 • **E-mail:** Patricia.Davis@umassmemorial.org.

MAYO SCHOOL OF GRADUATE MEDICAL EDUCATION

Cytopathology Fellowship

Description: This new ACGME-accredited one-year fellowship is designed to develop expertise in the performance and interpretation of fine needle aspiration biopsies; interpretation of gynecologic and non-gynecologic exfoliative cytology; and application of ancillary techniques such as flow cytometry, molecular diagnostics, cytogenetics and immunocytochemistry.
The emphasis will be on reviewing and diagnosing clinical cytology specimens and interacting with the clinicians and radiologists involved with these patient specimens. The annual volume of cytology specimens at Mayo Clinic Rochester is: Gynecologic Cytology, 53,000; Non-gynecologic Cytology, 16,000; FNAs: Superficial, deep and endoscopic, 7,000. Diagnostic material consists of a wide variety of specimens including gynecologic (cervix, uterus, vagina), breast, thyroid, urine, pulmonary, body fluids, lymph node biliary tract and liver. Performance of superficial fine needle aspirations; and on-site assessment of superficial and image guided deep aspirates provides fellows with extensive expertise in this popular technique.
The fellow will be given increasing responsibility in cytopathology sign-out as they acquire experience. Research opportunities in immunocytochemistry, morphometry and applied molecular pathology are available.
Training in molecular cytopathology includes FISH for urine, biliary and bronchial brushings (more than 6,000 specimens per year); DIA (nearly 1,200 specimens per year); and CellSearch for circulating tumor cells. Training in the techniques of ultrasound-guided fine needle aspiration for thyroid FNAs will be given under the guidance of endocrinologists.
Requirements: Applicants should have completed an AP or AP/CP residency training program within the United States or Canada.
Types and Numbers of Appointments: One position is available each year on a competitive basis.
Applications: http://www.mayo.edu/msgme/application.html
Applications for each academic year, which begins in July, should be completed by January 1st (18 months before). Positions will be offered beginning March 1 the previous year.
Address inquiries to Aziza Nassar, MD, Program Director, Cytopathology Training Program, Mayo Clinic, 200 First Street SE, Rochester, MN 55905.
Phone: (507) 293-3839 • **E-mail:** pathologyeducation@mayo.edu
Web site: http:http://www.mayo.edu/msgme/cytopathology-rch.html

McGAW MEDICAL CENTER OF NORTHWESTERN UNIVERSITY

Cytopathology Fellowship

Description: The Department of Pathology offers an ACGME-accredited fellowship in cytopathology that emphasizes a comprehensive, multidisciplinary approach. The Division is headed by Dr Ritu Nayar and the faculty are actively involved in Cytopathology at the local, national and international level. The program offers the opportunity to learn the diagnostic and prognostic applications of cytopathology in a variety of specimens including gynecologic and non-gynecologic samples, as well as fine-needle aspirates of deep-seated organs and superficial masses. Northwestern University's Robert H. Lurie Cancer Center is an NCI-designated comprehensive facility for the treatment and research of neoplastic disorders. The Division of Cytopathology's annual volume is approximately 50,000 (37,000 gynecologic and 13,000 non-gynecologic including 4500 fine needle aspiration specimens). There is an active FNA clinic within the Division and the staff and trainees participate in performance of superficial FNAs as well as on site evaluations/ triage of specimens acquired in interventional Radiology and interventional Gastroenterology. Ancillary facilities in immunocytochemistry, flow cytometry, molecular diagnostics, liquid based and automated cytology, as well as other emerging technologies are available. A close working relationship exists with Surgical pathology and Hematopathology. Regular teaching conferences are held in cytopathology for residents and the fellow and there is significant involvement in departmental, inter-departmental and multidisciplinary conferences. The fellow participates in service, review of outside consultations, teaching, quality assurance activities and translational research.
Requirements: Applicants must have completed AP training or concluded the AP/CP requirements for Board eligibility, and hold a license to practice medicine in the State of Illinois. Recruitment interviews occur between January and February of the preceeding year.
Stipends: The stipend is commensurate with the PGY year of training.
Applications: Send a letter with a one-page summary of your cytopathology interest and background to:
Ritu Nayar, MD, MIAC, Associate Professor of Pathology, Northwestern University Feinberg School of Medicine and Director of Cytopathology, Northwestern Memorial Hospital, 251 East Huron Street, Feinberg 7-210, Chicago, IL 60611

MEMORIAL SLOAN-KETTERING CANCER CENTER NEW YORK

Cytopathology Fellowship

Description: This is a one-year program in diagnostic cytopathology offered by the Cytology Service of the Department. During this period, the fellow is engaged in the examination of the cytopathologic material submitted to the service, under the supervision of the Attending staff. The material comprises approximately 35,000 specimens per year (17,000 gynecologic, 14,000 nongynecologic, 4,000 FNAs). The program includes participation in the intraoperative cytology consultation service and interaction with the School of Cytotechnology run by the Cytology Service. Fellows are encouraged to participate in research projects with members of the Department and/or in cooperation with clinicians. There is a cytology-based Fine Needle Aspiration Service.
Facilities: Memorial Hospital for Cancer and Allied Diseases is a 425-bed hospital devoted to the care of patients with neoplastic diseases. The hospital is part of the Memorial Sloan-Kettering Cancer Center which also includes the Sloan-Kettering Institute for Cancer Research. There is an affiliation and close interaction between the clinical and research units of the Center and the Weill Medical College of Cornell University, as well as with Rockefeller University.
Stipends: The stipend is commensurate with the year of postgraduate training. Housing is available; professional liability insurance and health coverage are provided.
Staff: Marc K. Rosenblum MD Attending Pathologist and Chairman; **Maureen F. Zakowski** MD Attending Pathologist and Program Director; **Edi Brogi** MD, PhD Associate Attending Pathologist; **Oscar Lin** MD, PhD Associate Attending Pathologist; **Andre L. Moreira** MD, PhD Assistant Attending Pathologist; **Cristina Vallejo** MD Assistant Attending Pathologist; **Natasha Rekhtman** MD Assistant Attending Pathologist.
Applications: All fellowships are available to those who have completed their basic training in pathology, either AP or combined AP-CP, with at least two years of AP training in an accredited US or Canadian program. All qualified applicants are welcome, but preference will be given to those committed to an academic career in pathology. Application deadline: March 1st. Early application is encouraged.
Address inquiries to: Sophia Oreste, Department of Pathology
Memorial Sloan-Kettering Cancer Center, 1275 York Avenue, New York, NY 10065
Phone: (212) 639-6336 • **E-mail:** orestes@mskcc.org
Web site: http://www.mskcc.org/pathologyfellowships

THE METHODIST HOSPITAL

Department of Pathology

Cytopathology Fellowship

Description: The Methodist Hospital in Houston, Texas, an affiliate of Weill Medical College of Cornell University, offers an ACGME accredited cytopathology fellowship. The Methodist Hospital is a 1,000-bed hospital located in the heart of the Texas Medical Center, offering a full range of services from primary to tertiary care, including a multi-organ transplant center and cancer center. Two ACGME accredited cytopathology fellowship slots are available each academic year under the directorship of Dina R. Mody, MD. The fellows spend eight to nine months at The Methodist Hospital, two months at M.D. Anderson, and one to two months at The University of Texas. A large volume of gynecologic, non-gynecologic and fine needle aspiration materials is available for daily sign-out. Ample opportunities for performing and interpreting fine needle aspirations are available at all three sites. A short rotation is also available in the radiology section of The Methodist Hospital. In gynecologic cytology, The Methodist Hospital offers conventional, ThinPrep and SurePath training, as well as cytology-histology correlates on dysplasia clinic and low risk populations. Scholarly activity in the form of a research project to be completed under staff supervision for publication is a requirement. Fellows are responsible for the cytopathology conference at The Methodist Hospital and have the opportunity to attend various surgical pathology and clinical pathology conferences, along with other residents and fellows in the program. The fellowship is supervised by five board-certified cytopathologists and three additional experienced anatomic pathologists with special interest in cytopathology.
Requirements: The candidates must have completed four years of AP/CP residency or three years of AP residency, must hold or be eligible for a Texas Physician-In-Training Permit or Licensure.
Stipends: Commensurate with level of postgraduate training.
Applications: Deadline for applying is January 30th of the year prior to the intended fellowship year which begins July 1st. Application inquiries are to be directed to Dina R. Mody, MD, The Methodist Hospital Department of Pathology, 6565 Fannin, M227, Houston, TX 77030.
Phone: (713) 441-3496 • **Fax:** (713) 441-3489 • **E-mail:** ljozwiak@tmhs.org
Web site: www.methodisthealth.com

UNIVERSITY OF MICHIGAN MEDICAL CENTER

Department of Pathology

Cytopathology Fellowship

Description: This one-year advanced training in cytopathology is designed to provide comprehensive training in diagnostic cytology including both gynecologic and nongynecologic material with emphasis on performance and interpretation of fine needle aspiration biopsies (FNA) with surgical pathology and clinical correlation. The cytology lab evaluates approximately 43,000 Pap smears and 8,800 nongynecologic specimens including 2,000 FNAs per year. The University of Michigan has a strong oncologic service with a full range of cancer-related clinical and research programs. The fellow will be expected to participate fully in the FNA Clinic, daily cytologic signing out, conferences and teaching and will be required to initiate a research project. The fellow will also gain experience in utilization of new preparation techniques, e.g. the ThinPreps. Ancillary techniques such as flow cytometry, immunohistochemistry, image analysis and molecular biology are available. The laboratory is fully computerized which allows easy retrieval of specimens for teaching, research or quality control purposes.
Requirements: Candidates must be Board certified or eligible for certification in anatomic pathology or AP/CP and must be eligible for a license to practice in Michigan.
Stipends: Commensurate with the level of training.
Applications: Applications should be received no later than April 1 and should be sent to:
Claire W. Michael, MD, Director of Cytopathology, Department of Pathology, University of Michigan Medical Center, Room 2G332/Box 5054, 1500 E Medical Center Drive, Ann Arbor, MI 48109-5054.

UNIVERSITY OF MINNESOTA AFFILIATED HOSPITALS

Cytopathology Fellowship

Description: The Department of Lab Medicine and Pathology at the University of Minnesota offers a one-year ACGME accredited fellowship in cytopathology primarily based at the University, Hennepin County Medical Center and Abbott-Northwestern Hospital. The University Hospital is a state of the art general and subspecialty care facility with 743 beds and have a workload of 59,000 cytopathology cases annually. Hennepin County Medical Center with 360 beds has 18,000 cytopathology accessions and ABNW Hospital with 642 beds has 89,200 cytopathology accessions annually. The goals of the fellowship are to develop a strong foundation in diagnostic cytopathology and the fellow is encouraged to participate in national conferences, teach post-sophomore fellows and residents and be involved in clinical research. Completion of this program qualifies the candidate to take the cytopathology subspecialty Board exam.
Requirements: At least 3 years of AP or 4 years of AP/CP training.
Stipends: Commensurate with the level of postgraduate training.
Staff: Stefan Pambuccian MD Cytopathology Fellowship Program Director.
Applications: Mail applications to: Stefan Pambuccian, MD, Cytopathology Program Director, Department of Lab Medicine and Pathology, University of Minnesota, 420 Delaware St. SE, MMC 76, Minneapolis, MN 55455.
Fax: (612) 625-3976
Please see Web site for application and requirements.
Web site: http://residency.pathology.umn.edu

UNIVERSITY OF MISSISSIPPI MEDICAL CENTER

Department of Pathology

Cytopathology Fellowship

Description: The Department of Pathology at the University of Mississippi Medical Center/Jackson offers a one-year, ACGME approved fellowship program focusing on diagnostic cytology. The fellowship provides advanced training and experience in all areas of cytology including gyn, non-gyn, and fine needle aspiration biopsies. Our cytology laboratory processes 64,447 pap smears (liquid based), 2,657 cervical biopsies with cytohistologic correlation, 1,455 body fluids and 682 fine needle aspiration biopsies. Ancillary techniques such as immuncytochemistry, electron microscopy, and flow cytometry are available for more comprehensive evaluation of diagnostically challenging cases. The fellow also participates in intra and interdepartmental conferences, teaching pathology residents and medical students. Involvement in clinical research leading to publication in a peer-reviewed journal is encouraged and well supported. Completion of this program qualifies the candidate to take the cytopathology subspecialty boards.
Requirements: Board eligibility or certification in anatomic pathology or AP/CP.
Stipends: Commensurate with level of postgraduate training: $52,634.00 for PGY-6.
Applications: Mail, e-mail, or fax curriculum vitae and three letters of recommendation to:
Mithra Baliga, MD, Director of Cytopathology, University of Mississippi Medical Center, 2500 North State Street, Jackson, MS 39216-4505.
Phone: (601) 984-1897 • **Fax:** (601) 984-4967 • **E-mail:** mbaliga@pathology.umsmed.edu

The University of Mississippi Medical Center is an Equal Opportunity Employer, M/F/D/V.

H. LEE MOFFITT CANCER CENTER AND UNIVERSITY OF SOUTH FLORIDA COLLEGE OF MEDICINE

Cytopathology Fellowship

Description: The Department of Pathology and Laboratory Medicine at the University of South Florida offers a one-year fellowship in cytopathology, beginning July 1 and is based primarily at the NIH-designated comprehensive H. Lee Moffitt Cancer Center and Research Institute with additional 1-month long rotations at the University-affilated James A. Haley VA Hospital and Bayfront Medical Center, respectively. The ACGME-accredited program provides extensive training in all areas of cytopathology, including gynecologic and non-gynecologic specimens as well as performance and interpretation of fine needle aspiration biopsies. Training in intraoperative cytology for evaluation of lumpectomy margins and sentinel lymph nodes is also provided. The fellow is expected to participate in one of several programmatic multidisciplinary conferences at the Cancer Center and to bring to completion a research project. The Department accessions approximately 5,560 exfoliative, 1,789 fine needle aspiration biopsy specimens, and 722 reviews/consultations annually.

Requirements: At least three years of AP or four years of AP/CP training.

Stipends: Commensurate with level of postgraduate training.

Applications: Must be completed by November 30th of the year preceeding the intended fellowship which begins in July. Request application at sbeacham@health.usf.edu or snicosia@hsc.usf.edu.

Director: Barbara Centeno, MD, Director Cytopathology Fellowship, H. Lee Moffitt Cancer Center & Research Institute and the University of South Florida.

NATIONAL INSTITUTES OF HEALTH NATIONAL CANCER INSTITUTE

Cytopathology Fellowship

Description: The Cytopathology Section of the National Cancer Institute provides diagnostic cytology services for the National Institutes of Health (NIH) Clinical Center, a 280-bed research hospital, and the NIH Institutes. The relatively high frequency of pathologic findings combined with the diversity of types of exfoliative and FNA specimens seen in our section provide a broad experience in diagnostic cytopathology. The Cytopathology Section accessions approximately 3,300 specimens per year. Eighty percent of our caseload is extra-vaginal cytology including 23% FNA cases. There is an active immunocytochemistry service utilized for diagnostic and research purposes. The fellowship program is 12 months in duration. For the clinical training, fellows are assigned to the cytology diagnostic service approximately 75% of their time. While on the diagnostic service, the fellow is the pathologist of record on the majority of the accessioned cases and is responsible for performing FNAs. A staff pathologist is available for backup and consultation at all times. The goals of the fellowship are to develop a strong foundation in diagnostic cytopathology through progressive responsibilities and to introduce clinically oriented physicians to current research techniques. The fellowship is fully accredited by the ACGME.

Requirements: Board certification or eligibility in AP or AP/CP and medical license in the USA.

Stipends: Commensurate with level of postgraduate training.

Applications: Mail inquiries to

Armando Filie, MD, Director of Cytopathology Fellowship, Cytopathology Section, Laboratory of Pathology, NCI/NIH, Building 10, Room 2A19, 10 Center Drive, Bethesda, MD 20892.

Phone: (301) 496-6355 • **Fax:** (301) 402-2585 • **E-mail:** afilie@mail.nih.gov

UNIVERSITY OF NEW MEXICO SCHOOL OF MEDICINE

Cytopathology Fellowship

Description: This fully accredited cytopathology fellowship combines strong clinical experience with the opportunity for using molecular technology to pursue important diagnostic and prognostic questions in cytopathology. The year comprises nine months of clinical training in gynecologic and non-gynecologic cytology with three months optional for research. Clinical training occurs at the University of New Mexico Health Sciences Center, and TriCore Reference Laboratories, both located in Albuquerque. Research occurs at the UNM School of Medicine Department of Pathology. Annual combined clinical cases include: approximately 123,000 cervicovaginal specimens, 2700 fine needle aspiration biopsies, and 7850 other non-gynecologic specimens. The fellow works closely with seven faculty members, four of whom are subspecialty board-certified in cytopathology. The fellow also has the opportunity to teach residents and pathology student fellows as these trainees rotate onto the cytology service. Upon satisfactory completion of the fellowship, the fellow will be well prepared to serve as the cytology expert in a private practice group or join an academic department of cytopathology. (Please see our two page description about the UNM Pathology Residency Program for more details regarding the Department of Pathology and the city of Albuquerque.)
Requirements: MD and at least three years of anatomic pathology residency training or four years of combined anatomic/clinical pathology residency.
Stipends: Salary is commensurate with the candidate's training year level.
Applications: Please inquire regarding application forms to
Ms. Jeanne Lay, Cytopathology Fellowship and Pathology Residency Coordinator at: jlay@salud.unm.edu

NEW YORK UNIVERSITY MEDICAL CENTER

Cytopathology Fellowship

Description: Two positions are available for a one-year ACGME approved fellowship in cytopathology at New York University Hospitals Center including Bellevue Hospital, a 1100-bed city hospital and Tisch Hospital, a 700-bed tertiary care hospital, together comprising a nationally designated cancer center. The program includes training in the performance and interpretation of fine needle aspirations, in the interpretation of gynecologic and non-gynecologic exfoliative cytology and in specimen processing and lab management. The cytopathology laboratory processes over 50,000 cases annually including over 6000 aspiration biopsies performed by cytopathologists. There are nine cytopathologists, 10 cytotechnologists and 3 cytopreparatory technicians. The fellows participate in clinical conferences for the housestaff and pathology residents.
Requirements: Board eligibility in anatomic or anatomic/clinical pathology. USMLE III, and NY State license by the start date.
Stipends: Commensurate with candidate's level of training.
Applications: Applications for positions for July 1 should be received by December 15 two years prior to start date. Requests for information or applications should be addressed to
Dr. Pascale Levine, NYU Cancer Institute, 160 East 34th Street, New York NY 10016
Phone: (212) 731-5115 • **Fax:** (212) 731-5535 • **E-mail:** pascale.levine@med.nyu.edu

NEW YORK-PRESBYTERIAN HOSPITAL
WEILL CORNELL CAMPUS

Cytopathology Fellowship

Description: This one-year ACGME approved program includes training in diagnostic gynecologic and non-gynecological cytopathology, fine needle aspiration biopsy, laboratory management and specimen preparation. The Papanicolaou Cytopathology Laboratory had over 53,000 specimens accessioned last year, of which approximately 12,045 were non-gynecological specimens and of those, over 4,000 were fine needle aspirations, offering a broad range of specimens from which the trainee may learn. Training in fine needle aspirations includes participation in the performance and on-site interpretation of needle aspirations of palpable masses and in the on-site interpretation of specimens obtained under radiologic guidance. To augment training in fine-needle aspiration biopsy, the fellow will complete a one-month rotation at an outside institution in New York City that is devoted entirely to the performance of superficial, palpable fine-needle aspirations. The fellow will also participate in clinical management conferences with the clinical services and teaching conferences for the housestaff in anatomic pathology. The fellow will be expected to complete one project in cytopathology for presentation at the ASC or USCAP.
Requirements: Candidates must have completed a four-year AP/CP residency or three years of a straight AP residency.
Types and Numbers of Appointments: One position is available
Facilities: New York Presbyterian Hospital is the major clinical affiliate and teaching hospital of Weill Cornell Medical College. It's New York Weill Cornell Campus, an 824-bed facility, is centrally located in a highly sophisticated medical community surrounded by the Hospital for Special Surgery, Memorial-Sloan Kettering Cancer Center and Rockefeller University.
Community: The Medical Center is located in a beautiful residential neighborhood along the East River in Manhattan within walking distance of Central Park and the midtown entertainment and shopping areas.
Staff: **Rana Hoda** MD; **June Koizumi** MD; **Andrew Schreiner** MD; **Grace Yang** MD.
Applications: Please address inquiries to: Rana Hoda, MD c/o Jessica Pfeifer, Administrative Specialist, Dept of Pathology and Laboratory Medicine, New York Presbyterian Hospital-Weill Cornell Campus, 525 East 68 Street, Room C302, New York, NY 10065.
Phone: (212) 746-6464 • **Fax:** (212) 746-8192

SUNY UPSTATE MEDICAL UNIVERSITY AT SYRACUSE

Department of Pathology

Cytopathology Fellowship

Description: This fellowship is a one-year, ACGME-accredited program that offers advanced training in diagnostic cytopathology, with emphasis on fine needle aspiration. During this time, the fellow will have increasing levels of responsibility commensurate with level of performance. Substantial emphasis is also placed on the integration of surgical pathology with cytopathology. Currently the SUNY Upstate Medical University Cytopathology Laboratory examines approximately 18,000 specimens per year including approximately 2,500 non-gynecologic specimens. Both ThinPrep and Surepath technologies are utilized in the laboratory. In addition, the laboratory directs a pathology-based FNA Service with cytopathologist-staffed clinics and performs or assists with the vast majority of superficial and deep fine needle aspirations (approximately 1,100). Ancillary techniques such as immunocytochemistry, flow cytometry, molecular diagnostics and electron microscopy are available for more comprehensive evaluation of difficult cases. In addition, the Cytopathology Laboratory is closely associated with the Program of Cytotechnology - with access to extensive teaching collections. The fellowship offers opportunities for teaching cytotechnology students, residents and medical students as well as the opportunity to investigate any one of a number of research projects during the year. Diagnostic, research and teaching skills are emphasized in this academic environment.
Requirements: Applicants should be Board-eligible or Board-certified in anatomic pathology or AP/CP.
Stipends: Stipends are commensurate with the year of postgraduate training in Pathology.
Applications: Send letter with CV and three letters of recommendation to Kamal K. Khurana, MD (khuranak@upstate.edu), Director, Cytopathology Fellowship Program, Department of Pathology, SUNY Upstate Medical University, 750 E. Adams St, Syracuse, NY 13210.
Phone: (315) 464-4270 • **Fax:** (315) 464-7130

UNIVERSITY OF NORTH CAROLINA AT CHAPEL HILL

Department of Pathology and Laboratory Medicine

Cytopathology Fellowship

Description: This one-year program, under the direction of Dr. Susan Maygarden, consists primarily of service responsibilities in the division of cytopathology, with opportunities for study in surgical pathology and other specialized areas. The cytopathology laboratory accessions approximately 18,000 gyn specimens (over 95% of which are processed by Thin Prep), 4,500 nongynecologic fluids and 1,300 fine needle aspirations per year. The FNAs include specimens aspirated by the cytopathology service and specimens aspirated by radiology, GI medicine and bronchoscopy with on site pathologic immediate interpretation. The responsibilities of the fellow include supervision of the fine needle aspiration service, participation in cytopathology sign-out, and participation in teaching and conferences in cytopathology with residents and staff. Fellows are also expected to pursue a scholarly project during their fellowship year.
Requirements: Applicants must have at least two years of anatomic pathology training. Preference is given to applicants who are AP or AP/CP Board eligible at the time of the fellowship.
Types and Numbers of Appointments: There are two positions available per year.
Stipends: The stipend is that of a comparable-year resident at UNC Hospitals, and is competitive with others in the region.
Applications: Should be submitted between October 1 and March 31 in the academic year preceding the proposed appointment (between 15 and 21 months before the start date). Instructions for applications and forms may be found on our **Website:** http://www.pathology.unc.edu/fellowsp/cytopath.htm

THE OHIO STATE UNIVERSITY MEDICAL CENTER

Department of Pathology

Cytopathology Fellowship

Description: This is a one-year cytopathology training program at The Ohio State University Medical Center, which includes the Arthur G. James Cancer Hospital and Solove Research Institute and the Richard M. Ross Heart Hospital. The cytology laboratory performs approximately 45,000 tests per year. This includes more than 5,000 non-gynecologic, and about 3,000 FNA specimens. The cytopathology fellow will experience preliminary sign-out of non-gynecologic and gynecologic specimens, gynecologic Pap smear/cervical biopsy correlations. Our FNA services including superficial palpable masses and deep organs (endoscopic ultrasound guided pancreas, mediastinum, liver, kidney and bronchoscopic/CT lung et al.) The fellow will get personalized training in performing and interpreting FNA. Our lab has a large collection of cytology teaching sets and most of them have histology correlation. The fellow will participate in the cytopathology teaching of cytotechnologists, medical students and residents. He/she may also participate in the regular resident microscopic seminars, hospital tumor boards, cytopathology teleconferences, CAP proficiency tests and formal cytopathology lectures. Strengths of the program include the cytopathology faculty as well as their strengths in gynecologic and non-gynecologic cytology, and extensive fine needle aspiration cytology training.
Requirements: Candidates must successfully complete USMLE Step 3 prior to their Medical Staff appointment to The Ohio State University Medical Center. They must also be AP/CP Board eligible or Board certified.
Stipends: The stipend is commensurate with the number of years of postgraduate training.
Applications: Application and supporting documents should be addressed to Gretchen Staschiak, Pathology Education Manager, The Ohio State University Medical Center, N-308 Doan Hall, 410 W. 10th Avenue, Columbus, OH 43210.
Phone: (614) 293-3055 • **Fax:** (614) 293-7273 • **E-mail:** Gretchen.Staschiak@osumc.edu
Web site: http://pathology.osumc.edu/ext

OREGON HEALTH & SCIENCE UNIVERSITY

Cytopathology Fellowship

Description: The Oregon Health & Science University, Department of Pathology offers a one-year ACGME-approved fellowship in cytopathology. The program is designed to provide comprehensive training in cytopathology with emphasis on the performance and interpretation of fine needle aspiration biopsy, the integration of surgical pathology with cytology and the use of both air-dried Diff-Quick and alcohol-fixed Papanicolaou stains. Proficiency in obtaining, preparing and interpreting aspirate samples is a major focus of our program. The material available includes 12,000 gynecologic specimens and 950 fine needle aspirations, most of which are performed by the cytopathology service. The fellow will have increasing levels of responsibility commensurate with level of performance and will participate in the laboratory service, teaching and research activities. Ancillary facilities in electron microscopy, immunocytochemisty, flow cytometry, image analysis, molecular biology and other emerging technologies are available for research projects.

Requirements: Applicants must be AP or AP/CP Board eligible or Board-certified.

Stipends: The stipend is commensurate with the year of postgraduate training.

Applications: Applications will be accepted up to two-years in advance and will be reviewed as rolling admissions. Please submit your curriculum vitae, personal statement, an application form from our website, and three letters of recommendation to:

Anna Wedeking, Training Programs Coordinator, Department of Pathology, Oregon Health & Science University, 3181 SW Sam Jackson Park Rd., L113, Portland, Oregon 97239-3098.

E-mail: ferencea@ohsu.edu

Web site: http://www.ohsu.edu/pathology/win/Fellcyto.htm

UNIVERSITY OF PENNSYLVANIA MEDICAL CENTER

Department of Pathology & Laboratory Medicine

Cytopathology Fellowship

Description: This is a one-year fellowship program with an emphasis on diagnostic cytology with tissue and clinical correlation. The laboratory processes over 50,000 specimens per year, including 10,000 nongynecologic cases, of which over 2,600 are fine needle aspirations. The material is varied with a strong emphasis on on-site evaluation and performance of aspirates, as well as cytohistomorphologic correlation. Immunodiagnostic and flow cytometric studies are performed on appropriate specimens. The fellows will familiarize themselves with various cytopreparation and laboratory data management techniques and actively participate in fine needle aspiration service and teaching. Rotation in flow cytometry, and immunodiagnostic laboratories is available.

Requirements: Candidates must have completed a residency training or at least three years of straight anatomic pathology residency. (This fellowship can be used for Cytopathology Board certification provided all Board training requirements have been met prior to entry.) Three fellowships are available.

Stipends: Stipends are commensurate with the year of postgraduate training in pathology.

Staff: Zubair W. Baloch MD, PhD Associate Director; **Prabodh K. Gupta** MD Director; **Cindy M. McGrath** MD; **Gordon H. Yu** MD.

Applications: Must be made by January 31st of the year preceding the intended fellowships (begins July 1). Apply to Prabodh Gupta, MD, Director Cytopathology Section/6 Founders, Hospital of the University of Pennsylvania, 3400 Spruce Street, Philadelphia, PA 19104-4283.

Phone: (215) 662-3238 • **Fax:** (215) 662-6518

PITT COUNTY MEMORIAL HOSPITAL
BRODY SCHOOL OF MEDICINE
EAST CAROLINA UNIVERSITY

Department of Pathology & Laboratory Medicine

Cytopathology Fellowship

Description: The department offers an ACGME-accredited one-year fellowship in cytopathology. The fellowship provides extensive training in GYN and non-GYN cytology, including fine-needle aspiration biopsy. The cytology service manages over 9,000 cases per year, of apporximately 1,000 are fine-needle aspiration biopsies from multiple sites. Some of the superficial biopsies are performed by pathologists. The fellow assists and performs these FNA biopsies and reviews all consultation cases. Also included are approximately 7,000 GYN cases and more than 2,400 non-GYN cases. Contemporary techniques are utilized including liquid-based preparations, interpretation of rapid stains such as the Diff-Quik stain for preliminary diagnosis, immunocytochemistry, electron microscopy, molecular diagnosis and flow cytometry. Often the Diff-Quik stain is used to preliminarily evaluate difficult and/or interesting cases that may need ancillary studies on the cytologic material. Opportunities exist for participation in a number of conferences, teaching, and clinical research projects as well as national workshops.
Requirements: Completion of pathology residency requirements and full licensure to practice medicine in North Carolina required for this position.
Stipends: The stipend is that of a comparable year resident at Pitt County Memorial Hospital and competitive with others in the region. Benefit package includes institution and resident share Cost for major medical health insurance, major medical health insurance for dependents, outpatient mental health insurance, group life insurance, dental insurance, disability insurance and disability insurance for occupationally acquired HIV,
Applications: Should be made to Heng Hong, MD, PhD, Director of Cytopathology Fellowship, Department of Pathology & Laboratory Medicine, Room 7S-10, The Brody School of Medicine at East Carolina University, Greenville, NC 27834.
Phone: (252) 744-5911

UNIVERSITY OF PITTSBURGH MEDICAL CENTER

Cytopathology Fellowship

Description: Three positions are available. The objective of this one-year fellowship is to provide comprehensive and advanced training in all aspects of cytopathology. UPMC Presbyterian and Shadyside Hospitals process over 11,000 non-gynecologic specimens annually with a large volume of fine needle aspirations. The cytopathology laboratory at Magee-Womens' Hospital processes approximately 145,000 specimens annually including 141,500 gynecologic and 3,500 non-gynecologic cases. The fellow will be involved in review of atypical gynecological specimens, cytohistologic correlation, and diagnosis of non-gynecological specimens including fine needle aspiration. The fellowship includes experience in the administration of cytology services, teaching of residents, medical students and cytotechnology students, and opportunities for research with experienced cytopathologists. Flow cytometry, immunohistochemistry, in situ hybridization, and molecular techniques are available in the Department of Pathology. Completion of this program qualifies the candidate to take the Cytopathology subspecialty Board Examination by the American Board of Pathology.
Requirements: Completion of AP or AP/CP residency and all 3 steps of USMLE.
Stipends: Commensurate with the level of postgraduate training in Pathology.
Staff: Walid E. Khalbuss MD, PhD, FIAC, Fellowship Director; **R. Marshall Austin** MD, PhD; **Sheldon Bastacky** MD; **Gloria Carter** MD; **Mamatha Chivukula** MD; **David Dabbs** MD; **Esther Elishaev** MD; **Anisa Kanbour** MD; **Amal Kanbour-Shakir** MD, PhD; **Sara Monaco** MD; **Olga Navolotskaia** MD; **N. Paul Ohori** MD; **Alka Palekar** MD; **Robert Peel** MD; **Karen Schoedel** MD; **Lisa Teot** MD; **Giuliana Trucco** MD; **Jing Yu** MD, PhD; **Chengquan Zhao** MD.
Applications: Walid E. Khalbuss, MD, PhD, Director of Cytopathology Fellowship, UPMC, Department of Pathology, UPMC-Shadyside, 5150 Centre Avenue, POB2-Suite 201, Pittsburgh, PA 15232, USA. Submit application online at http://path.upmc.edu/fellowship
Phone: (412) 623-3765 • **Fax:** (412) 623-4779 • **E-mail:** delledonnej@upmc.edu; khalbussw2@upmc.edu

UNIVERSITY OF ROCHESTER MEDICAL CENTER

Department of Pathology and Laboratory Medicine

Cytopathology Fellowship

Description: This 12 month ACGME-accredited fellowship program commencing July 1st offers one position for advanced training in diagnostic cytopathology, including application of ancillary techniques such as immunocytochemistry, flow cytometry and molecular diagnostics to cytologic specimens. Considerable emphasis is placed on correlations between cytopathologic and surgical pathologic diagnoses. Our cytopathology laboratory examines approximately 85,000 gynecologic and non-gynecologic specimens annually. In addition, the laboratory provides an FNA service, with the cytopathologist performing superficial FNAs in both clinical and hospital settings, and consulting on image-guided FNAs. The fellow also participates in interdepartmental conferences and in teaching residents and medical students. The fellow is expected to pursue a quality assurance project, as well as a scholarly project leading to publication in a peer-reviewed journal.

Requirements: Applicants must have successfully completed a three-year AP or four-year AP/CP residency training program and be Board eligible.

Facilities: The University of Rochester Medical Center is a regional referral center and our Department of Pathology Cytopathology Unit accessions over 85,000 gynecologic and non-gynecologic specimens a year.

Community: Picture a city with miles of lakeshore, a central-city riverfront sprinkled with waterfalls, and a historic canal that flows through the heart of the small-town Americana. Now imagine that same city surrounded by glacier-carved lakes, one of the largest collections of cobblestone homes in the country, and world-class wine country. Welcome to the Rochester/Finger Lakes Region of Upstate New York. Monroe County, named after James Monroe, fifth president of the United States, is comprised of 19 towns, 10 villages and the City of Rochester, the third largest city in the state, with a combined population of approximately 750,000 residents and a land area of nearly 664 square miles. Monroe County has been a world leader in imaging technology. Today, we're not only on the cutting edge of imaging, but biotechnology, telecommunications, optics, photonics, and much more. We rank among the top three communities in the nation in the number of patents granted per capita. Monroe County and the City of Rochester are home to the University of Rochester, the county's largest employer, and Rochester Institute of Technology, two of the finest research institutions in the nation. We boast 39 golf courses, an extensive park system covering nearly 12,000 acres of land, and fresh water activities such as boating, fishing & swimming. Our sporting community includes professional baseball, hockey, lacrosse and soccer teams with our newest addition the Rochester Razor Sharks.

Stipends: Stipends are commensurate with the year of postgraduate training in Pathology. Trainees are provided with five sick days and 20 vacation days.

Staff: Ellen Giampoli MD (SUNY Buffalo); research interests include mechanisms for deriving maximum information from cellular samples so that the minimally-invasive technique of fine needle aspiration cytology can be used with a wider variety of tissue types.; **Thomas Bonfiglio** MD (University of Rochester); research interests include adaptation of new technologies to cytologic diagnosis.; **Julietta Fiscella** MD (SUNY Buffalo); research interests include effects of gamma interferon on pulmonary interstitial fibrosis and the effects of mifepristone on intrauterine leiomyomas.; **Jorge Yao** MD (University of the East - Ramon Magsaysay Memorial Medical Center); research: gu and prostatic cancer, tissue banking; **David Zhou** MD (Huabei Medical College) PhD (Shanghai Medical Univ) Asst Prof Pathology & Lab Medicine.

Applications: Send curriculum vitae, personal statement, a letter from your current residency program director and two letters of recommendation to Betsy McDonald, University of Rochester Medical Center, Pathology & Laboratory Medicine at 601 Elmwood Ave Box 626, Rochester NY 14642.

SAINT LOUIS UNIVERSITY SCHOOL OF MEDICINE

Department of Pathology

Cytopathology Fellowship

Description: A one-year ACGME-approved fellowship in cytopathology is offered and designed as a comprehensive training experience in diagnostic clinical cytopathology. Experience is provided at Saint Louis University Health Sciences Center and Quest Clinical Laboratories. Diagnostic material consists of gynecologic (450,000 cases), nongynecologic (3,800 cases), and fine needle aspiration (FNA) biopsy (2,200 cases). Fellows participate in all aspects of the service and are given progressive responsibilities. Emphasis is placed on the performance and interpretation of percutaneous FNA biopsies. Diagnostic and research facilities are available in molecular biology, immunohistochemistry, electron microscopy and flow cytometry. There is time devoted to specimen preparation, laboratory management, quality issues, and automated cytology. Fellows participate in medical student and pathology resident education, as well as in interdepartmental conferences. The overall goal of the fellowship is to provide strong, broad-based training in clinical cytopathology.
Requirements: Candidates must have completed AP or AP/CP pathology residency and be board-certified or board-eligible in AP or AP/CP.
Types and Numbers of Appointments: One per year.
Stipends: Stipends are commensurate with the level of training.
Staff: **Ritu Bhalla** MD, Program Director, Cytopathology Fellowship, Saint Louis University School of Medicine; **E. Stephen Bolesta** MD, Saint Louis University School of Medicine; **Norman Grossl** MD, Quest Clinical Laboratories; **Bisong Haupt** MD, Saint Louis University School of Medicine; **Necat Havlioglu** MD, Saint Louis University School of Medicine; **Thuy-Lieu Vo** MD, Quest Diagnostics Laboratories.
Applications: Inquiries should be sent to:ÂMaria Turnbough, Cytopathology Fellowship Program,ÂDepartment of Pathology, Saint Louis University School of Medicine, 1402 South Grand,ÂSt Louis, MO 63104.
E-mail: mturnbou@slu.edu
Web site: http://path.slu.edu

SCOTT & WHITE MEMORIAL HOSPITAL, TEMPLE

Department of Pathology

Cytopathology Fellowship

Description: A one-year fellowship, ACGME-accredited program offers advanced training in diagnostic clinical cytopathology. Experience is provided through daily signout of gynecologic and non-gynecologic specimens as well as training in performance and interpretation of fine needle aspiration biopsies. Scott& White cytology laboratory processes a total of 50,000 specimens annually, of which 3,000 are non-gyn and 3,000 are fine needle aspirations. Participation in conferences and teaching of pathology residents and cytotechnologists is required. Involvement in clinical research is also encouraged. Diagnostic and research facilities are available in molecular biology, immunocytochemistry, electron microscopy and flow cytometry. The fellow participates in all aspects of the service and is given progressive responsibilities. Devoted time to specimen preparation, laboratory management and quality issues is provided.
Requirements: Candidates must have completed AP or AP/CP pathology residency and be certified or eligible in AP or AP/CP.
Stipends: Stipends are commensurate with the level of training.
Applications: Inquiry should be sent to: Lubna Sayage-Rabie, MD, Director of Cytopathology, Scott& White Memorial Hospital, Pathology Department 2401 South 31st Street, Temple, TX 76508.
Phone: (254)724-7354 • **Fax:** (254) 724-6329 • **E-mail:** cdixon@swmail.sw.org
Web site: http://sw.org

MEDICAL UNIVERSITY OF SOUTH CAROLINA

Cytopathology Fellowship

Description: The Cytopathology Service of the Department of Pathology and Laboratory Medicine at the Medical University of South Carolina in Charleston offers three positions for a one-year program of subspecialty training in cytopathology. The Cytopathology Service at MUSC receives a wide spectrum of specimens. During 2007, the Cytopathology Service examined 19,789 gynecologic and 3,276 exfoliative specimens and 2,652 fine needle aspirates (FNA). The latter includes CT-guided and Ultrasound-guided (bronchoscopic and endoscopic) FNA performed by specialists and FNA on superficial lesions performed by the Cytopathology fellows. Ninety-nine percent of gynecological and exfoliative specimens are processed through liquid-based technology (ThinPrep). Immunocytochemical, ultrastructural, and flow cytometric analysis is available for pertinent cases. On-site adequacy assessment via Telecytopathology is also in use. The fellowship offers in-depth exposure to Cytopathology with emphasis on clinical and histologic correlation. The fellows will actively participate in inter-and intradepartmental conferences. There is ample opportunity for involvement in teaching pathology residents, medical students, and cytotechnology students. The fellows are encouraged to participate in research projects related to cytologic and molecular diagnosis. Successful completion of the Fellowship training qualifies the candidate for special certification examination of the American Board of Pathology.
Requirements: Candidates must have completed an AP or AP/CP residency. Candidates must hold or be eligible to hold a medical license in South Carolina. For the fellowship year beginning July 1, 2011, the deadline for application is December 31, 2009.
Stipends: Salary is at PGY 5 level.
Applications: Address inquiries to Jack Yang, MD, Director of Cytopathology, Department of Pathology and Laboratory Medicine, Medical University of South Carolina, 171 Ashley Avenue, Suite 309, MSC 908, Charleston, SC 29425.
Phone: (843) 792-3121 • **Fax:** (843) 792-0555 • **E-mail:** yanja@musc.edu

STANFORD UNIVERSITY MEDICAL CENTER

Department of Pathology

Cytopathology Fellowship

Description: This one-year, ACGME-accredited cytopathology fellowship provides advanced, in depth exposure to all aspects of diagnostic cytopathology, including performance and interpretation of fine needle aspiration biopsies, immediate evaluation of samples obtained under radiographic guidance, interpretation of conventional and thin-layer Pap smears, and application of ancillary diagnostic techniques. Approximately 70,000 specimens are evaluated annually, including over 2000 fine needle aspiration biopsies, 3500 other non-gynecologic specimens and 64,000 gynecologic specimens (ThinPrep, SurePath and conventional). The fellow is also exposed to state of the art ancillary diagnostic techniques including HPV testing, immunocytochemistry, flow cytometry, and molecular diagnostics. Research is encouraged, and departmental support for research is available.
Requirements: AP training and eligibility for California medical license are required.
Stipends: Commensurate with experience, plus additional $8,400 per year housing allowance.
Applications: Application deadline: January 31 of the year prior. Program starts July 1. Submit to: Christina Kong, MD, Program Director, Cytopathology Fellowship, Department of Pathology, Stanford University School of Medicine, 300 Pasteur Drive, Room L223, Stanford, CA 94305-5324
Phone: (650) 725-0405 • **Fax:** (650) 725-6902

THE UNIVERSITY OF TENNESSEE MEDICAL CENTER

Cytopathology Fellowship

Description: One, one-year fellowship in Cytopathology is available beginning each July 1. The program emphasizes the achievement of competence in interpreting cytopathologic preparations; Total accessions: 36,317; gynecologic: 29,893; non-gynecologic: 5,067; fine needle aspirations: 1,257. Approximately 99.5% of all gynecologic specimens are currently evaluated via one of two liquid based techniques. Approximately 70% of monolayer Paps are image guided. The fellow will have exposure to ancillary techniques such as flow cytometry, molecular biology, in-situ hybridization, and immunohistochemistry. Correlation with associated surgical pathology material is emphasized. There will be ample opportunity for training and performance of clinical fine needle aspiration and the fellow will assume junior staff sign-out responsibilities under faculty supervision; the fellow will play an active role in teaching residents and medical students rotating on the pathology service. The fellow will participate in the weekly cytology slide review conferences and departmental QA procedures. A research project is not a requirement during the fellowship year; however, it is strongly recommended and supported. The Department of Pathology, which includes over twenty faculty, has an excellent computer information technology base (Cerner, Powerchart, CoPath) and incorporates state of the art facilities.

Requirements: Candidates must have completed, prior to entering the fellowship, three years of AP or four years of AP/CP. USMLE Step III must be completed prior to beginning the fellowship. Those accepted into the fellowship must acquire their Tennessee medical license by the completion of the third month of their fellowship. The candidate must have completed requirements to sit for the ABP, AP examination, prior to starting the fellowship.

Stipends: Commensurate with postgraduate level of candidate.

Staff: Elizabeth W. Hubbard MD, Director.

Applications: Should be submitted by March 1 of the proceeding year to: Elizabeth W. Hubbard, MD, Fellowship Program Director. Application consists of cover letter, CV, and three letters of evaluation, including one from the candidate's program director.

Address Inquiries to:
Pamela C. Guider, Program Coordinator
Department of Pathology
The University of Tennessee Medical Center at Knoxville
1924 Alcoa Highway
Box 108
Knoxville, Tennessee 37920

Phone: (865) 305-8994 • **Fax:** (865) 305-8563 • **E-mail:** Pguider@mc.utmck.edu
Web site: www.utmedicalcenter.org/pathology/

THE UNIVERSITY OF TEXAS HEALTH SCIENCE CENTER AT SAN ANTONIO

Department of Pathology

Cytopathology Fellowship

Description: This fellowship provides for one full year of advanced training in diagnostic cytology. The experience includes daily sign-out of gynecologic and nongynecologic specimens as well as training in the performance and interpretation of fine needle aspiration biopsies. Participation in conferences and teaching of pathology residents and cytotechnology students is required. Involvement in clinical research is also encouraged. Specimens from the University Hospital and the South Texas Veterans Health Care System, Audie L. Murphy Division, total 20,000 annually, of which 5,000 are nongynecologic specimens. The latter group includes approximately 1,000 fine needle aspiration biopsies.

Requirements: Applicants must have completed a four-year AP/CP residency or a straight anatomic pathology residency.

Stipends: Stipends are commensurate with the year of postgraduate training in pathology.

Applications: Inquiries are to be directed to
Philip T. Valente, MD, Department of Pathology, The University of Texas Health Science Center at San Antonio, 7703 Floyd Curl Drive, San Antonio, TX 78229-3900.

Phone: (210) 567-6731 • **Fax:** (210) 567-2478

THE UNIVERSITY OF TEXAS M.D. ANDERSON CANCER CENTER

Cytopathology Fellowship

Description: This one-year fellowship provides a concentrated experience in diagnostic cytopathology that includes the interpretation of both aspiration and exfoliative cytologies and the performance of superficial needle aspirations. Immediate assessment of specimen adequacy is made for all aspirations (superficial andimage-guided- CT, ultrasound and endoscopic ultrasound). Interaction with surgical pathology and the submission/interpretation of ancillary tests, such as, flow cytometry, immunochemistry, molecular pathology and image analysis are part of the evaluation of many cytology specimens. Approximately 31,000 cases are processed annually with 75% representing non-gynecologic specimens, including 11,800 needle aspirations.Selected specimens (primarily urine) are evaluated for DNA content (image analysis) or chromosomal abnormalities (FISH) within the cytology laboratory. The fellow participates in a number of teaching cytology conferences, can attend a variety of surgical pathology conferences, and must complete a research project for publication under staff supervision. Supplementation of the gynecologic cytology portion of the program is achieved through a two week rotation at the Methodist Hospital and a mandatory 400-slide gynecologic cytology study set review. There are six funded full-time, ACGME accredited, fellowship positions available.

Requirements: Candidates must complete a four year AP/CP or three-year AP residency. Candidates must hold or be eligible to hold a Texas medical license.

Stipends: Commensurate with candidate's level of training.

Applications: Applications must be submitted using the Discover System, a web based application, at https://www2.mdanderson.org/sapp/discover/. The deadline to submit application is December 1st, nineteen (19) months prior to the intended fellowship year which begins July 1st. Correspondence should be addressed to Nancy P. Caraway, MD, Director, Cytopathology Fellowship, The University of Texas M.D. Anderson Cancer Center, 1515 Holcombe Blvd., Unit 53, Houston, Texas 77030. For inquiries and to request additional information, please contact Cheryl Conner.

Phone: (713) 792-2068 or (713) 794-5625 • **Fax:** (713) 792-2313 • **E-mail:** crconner@mdanderson.org
Web site: http://www.mdanderson.org/departments/pathology

UNIVERSITY OF TEXAS SOUTHWESTERN MEDICAL SCHOOL

Cytopathology Fellowship

Description: ACGME accredited one-year fellowship program in cytopathology at the University of Texas Southwestern Medical Center and Parkland Health & Hospital System offer intense training in all aspects of cytopathology through utilization of an annual volume of about 65,000 specimens of gynecologic and nongynecologic material from out-patient and in-patient clinical services of a 900-bed teaching hospital. Training involves direct participation in cytopathologic evaluation as well as teaching responsibilities and ongoing research activities. Teaching experience includes active participation in lectures and seminars as well as informal sessions with medical students, graduate students, and other pathology residents. Special emphasis is given to aspiration cytopathology through close cooperation between the Pathology Laboratory, Clinical Services and the Radiology Department. The fellow performs all superficial FNAs in FNA clinic and becomes proficient both in the techniques and in the interpretation of material so obtained. The Laboratory of Diagnostic Cytology is computerized and opportunities for experience in computer techniques related to cytopathology are part of the program. (For basic program description see main listing.)

Requirements: Applicants must have satisfactorily completed at least four years of approved training in anatomic pathology or four years in combined AP/CP and be eligible for a license to practice medicine in Texas.

Stipends: Support will be commensurate with the applicant's level of training.

Applications: Applications should be made no later than February 1 prior to the intended fellowship beginning the following July 1. Address inquiries to:
Wareef Kabbani, MD, Department of Pathology, University of Texas Southwestern Medical Center at Dallas, 5323 Harry Hines Boulevard, Dallas, TX 75390-9073.

Phone: (214) 590-8897 • **Web site:** http://pathcuric1.swmed.edu

---

THOMAS JEFFERSON UNIVERSITY HOSPITAL

Department of Pathology and Cell Biology

Cytopathology Fellowship

Description: This one-year Fellowship Program provides extensive training in diagnostic cytopathology. The laboratory processes 12,158 gynecologic and 6,808 non-gynecologic specimens per year, including 2,329 fine needle aspirations. The laboratory is staffed by two full-time cytopathologists and equipped with a modern computer system (COPATH), multiheaded microscope with video camera and monitor, and computerized image analyzer. The fellow participates in the service, teaching and research activities of the laboratory. There is ample opportunity to examine a large collection of transparencies and approximately 4,000 glass slide study sets on various cytologic specimens with histologic correlation. The fellow will also learn the application of immunocytochemistry, flow cytometry and image analysis to cytologic specimens. Qualified individuals will receive a faculty appointment as Instructor in Pathology at Jefferson Medical College and will participate in teaching medical students and cytotechnology students.

Requirements: Candidates must have completed an AP or combined AP/CP residency and must be eligible for a license to practice medicine in Pennsylvania.

Stipends: Commensurate with level of postgraduate training.

Staff: Moira D. Wood MD, Director, Cytopathology Fellowship Training Program, Cytopathology-Immunocytochemistry; **Marluce Bibbo** MD, Director of Cytopathology.

Applications: Applications should be sent before November 30 of the academic year preceding the intended fellowship to: Moira D. Wood, MD, Cytology, Thomas Jefferson Univ. Hospital, 132 S 10th Street, Rm 260 A Main, Philadelphia, PA 19107.

Phone: (215) 955-6437 • **E-mail:** moira.wood@jefferson.edu

TULANE UNIVERSITY HEALTH SCIENCES CENTER SCHOOL OF MEDICINE

Department of Pathology

Cytopathology Fellowship

Description: The Department of Pathology at Tulane University Health Sciences Center offers a one-year ACGME accredited fellowship in cytopathology. Training is conducted at the modern and expanding Tulane University Health Sciences Center and Ochsner Medical Center in New Orleans. The section of cytopathology accessions over 30,000 cytology specimens (gyn including liquid based Pap tests: 26,000; non-gyns: 2,700; aspiration cytologies: 1,200). The fellow participates in the FNA clinic, and in the service, teaching and research activities of the laboratory. The fellow assumes graded responsibility in the sign-out of cytology cases. Elective time is available outside the cytopathology core in cytogenetics, image analysis, flow cytometry and molecular diagnostics.

Requirements: Board eligibility or certification in AP or AP/CP. Eligibility for Louisiana Medical Licensure.

Stipends: Commensurate with the year of postgraduate training.

Staff: Krzysztof Moroz MD, TUHSC, Cytopathology Fellowship Director; **N. Dhurandhar** MD, TUHSC, Professor Emeritus Cytopathology; **R. Jetly** MD, TUHSC, Anatomical Pathology; **T. Smilari** MD, Ochsner, Cytopathology Director.

Applications: Application requirements can be found on our website http://www.som.tulane.edu/departments/pathology/fellows/cytopath.html.

Applications include curriculum vitae, personal statement, ECFMG certificate if applicable and three letters of references should be submitted 18 months prior to the year of the fellowship.

Submit application to:
Bea DeLucca
Program Coordinator
1430 Tulane Ave. SL-79
New Orleans, LA 70112

Phone: (504) 988-2436 • **Fax:** (504) 988-7389 • **E-mail:** bdelucc@tulane.edu

UNIVERSITY OF UTAH MEDICAL CENTER

Cytopathology Fellowship

Description: The Department of Pathology at The University of Utah School of Medicine offers an ACGME accredited one year Cytopathology Fellowship. Experience is provided at the University of Utah Hospital and Clinics, Huntsman Cancer Hospital and ARUP™ Laboratories. Diagnostic material covers the spectrum of cytopathology practice and includes utilization of specialized, ancillary tests. The fellow participates in all aspects of the service and is given progressive responsibilities. Emphasis is placed on the performance and interpretation of FNA biopsies. Diagnostic and research facilities are available in molecular biology, immunohistochemistry, immunofluorescence and flow cytometry. There is training time dedicated to specimen preparation, laboratory management, automated cytology, quality control and regulatory issues. The fellow participates in educational activities with involvement in interdisciplinary conferences. The overall goal of the fellowship training is to provide comprehensive, broad-based training in cytopathology.

Requirements: Applicants are accepted for a training period of one year and must be board eligible or board certified in anatomic pathology. A Utah medical license is required at the time of appointment.

Stipends: Commensurate with year of postgraduate training.

Staff: Brian T. Collins MD, Fellowship Program Director; **Joel S. Bentz** MD; **Evelyn Gopez** MD; **Elke Jarboe** MD; **Lester Layfield** MD.

Applications: Utilize the standard application form and it should be submitted by December 1
(19 months before matriculation) and directed to Brian T. Collins, MD, Cytopathology Fellowship Program Director, Huntsman Cancer Hospital, 1950 Circle of Hope, Room 3860, Salt Lake City, UT 84112. The fellowship follows the sub-specialty fellowship application process issued by the Association of Pathology Chairs.

E-mail: brian.collins@path.utah.edu.
Web site: http://www.path.utah.edu/education/fellowships/cytopathology-fellowship/

UNIVERSITY OF VERMONT COLLEGE OF MEDICINE

Department of Pathology and Laboratory Medicine

Cytopathology Fellowship

Description: The Department of Pathology and Laboratory Medicine at Fletcher Allen Health Care (FAHC) and the University of Vermont (UVM) offers a one-year ACGME-accredited Fellowship in Cytopathology. The primary site of Fellowship training is in the Ambulatory Care Center of the Medical Center Campus at FAHC, adjacent to the Radiology Department, Hematologic Oncology, Ambulatory Services and the Breast Care Center. The program provides extensive training in all aspects of cytopathology, including gynecologic specimens, performance of superficial fine needle aspirations, rapid interpretation of deep needle aspirations, quality control and regulatory issues. The Department utilizes developing technologies within Cytopathology, including thin layer, flow cytometric and immunocytochemical methodologies. Additionally, the Cytopathology Division sponsors a School of Cytotechnology. The Fellow is expected to participate actively in clinical and didactic teaching activities involving cytotechnology students, medical students, residents and clinical colleagues. Fellows are encouraged to complete a research project during the year under the supervision of the attending staff, with the assistance of the Research Laboratory of the Pathology Department at UVM. The Division of Cytopathology accessions 62,000 gynecologic cytology specimens and 5,700 non-gyn cases per year, approximately 1,800 of which are fine needle aspiration biopsies.

Requirements: Board certified or eligible in AP or AP/CP.

Community: Burlington is a New England university city situated on the shores of beautiful Lake Champlain, with easy access to both summer and winter outdoor activities/sports. Burlington is within driving distance of several major US and Canadian cities and was recently voted to be one of the top ten desirable cities in the USA to raise children.

Stipends: The appointment is for one year and the stipend is based upon the applicant's level of postgraduate training.

Applications: Applications should be received prior to February 1 of the year preceding the intended fellowship. Apply to: Scott Anderson, MD, Cytopathology Program Director, University of Vermont Department of Pathology, FAHC - ACC-EP2, 111 Colchester Avenue, Burlington, VT 05401.

Phone: (802) 847-5932 • **Fax:** (802) 847-9644

VIRGINIA COMMONWEALTH UNIVERSITY MEDICAL CENTER

Cytopathology Fellowship

Description: This program provides intensive training in **cytopathology** as well as substantial exposure to surgical pathology, with emphasis on the correlation between these two disciplines. It is aimed at those who have fulfilled a standard pathology residency and wish to specialize and become board eligible in cytopathology. In addition to training in both conventional and liquid based gynecologic, non-gynecologic, and aspiration specimens, training is provided in the technique of fine-needle aspiration biopsy. Fellows perform FNAs and provide immediate interpretations for both superficial and radiologic guided FNAs. The use of immunochemistry, flow cytometry and molecular and cytogenetic testing is stressed as well as appropriate clinical management as applied to surgical and cytopathology diagnoses. Fellows will also gain practical skills in laboratory management. Translational research as well as clinical research for presentation at national level is also encouraged.

Requirements: Candidates must have satisfactorily completed an accredited training program in AP or AP/CP.

Stipends: Salary and benefits are commensurate with level of training.

Applications: Interested individuals should contact the training program coordinator, Ms. Violet Brown, Department of Pathology, P.O. Box 980662, Richmond, VA 23298-0662 for additional information. The program accepts the CAP Standardized Application form. Completed applications should be sent to Celeste N. Powers, MD, PhD, Chair, Division of Anatomic Pathology, Virginia Commonwealth University Medical Center, Box 980139, Richmond, VA 23298-0139

Phone: (804) 827-0561 • **E-mail:** vbrown3@mcvh-vcu.edu

WAKE FOREST UNIVERSITY BAPTIST MEDICAL CENTER

Department of Pathology

Cytopathology Fellowship

Description: This program provides 1 year of advanced training in diagnostic cytopathology. The fellow will participate actively in all aspects of the service including the interpretation of gynecologic and non-gynecologic specimens, procurement and analysis of fine needle aspiration biopsies, interacting with clinicians and patients, teaching of house officers, and clinical research. We receive a wide spectrum of specimens, including approximately 10,500 gynecologic samples and 6,500 nongynecologic samples. The vast majority of the gynecologic specimens are thin layer Pap tests (SurePath) of which approximately 10% are abnormal. The non-gynecologic specimens include more than 2,500 fine needle aspiration biopsies (FNABs). The FNABs are quite diverse with regard to both target site and method of procurement, including a significant number of bone and soft tissue tumors, transbronchial needle aspirates and endoscopic ultrasound-guided aspirates. The fellow is expected to organize and present cytopathology unknown conferences and to present the pathology component of cases selected for the weekly Thoracic Oncology Program multidisciplinary conference.

Requirements: Applicants should be AP Board eligible or Board certified.

Stipends: Commensurate with year of postgraduate training.

Staff: James O. Cappellari, IV MD, Director, Cytopathology Fellowship; **Simon Bergman** MD, DDS; **A.J. Garvin** MD, PhD, Chair; **Kim R. Geisinger** MD, Director of Surgical Pathology and Cytopathology; **Kathleen Gibson** MD.

Applications: Please contact
James O. Cappellari, MD, Director, Cytopathology Fellowship, Department of Pathology, Wake Forest University School of Medicine, Medical Center Blvd., Winston-Salem, NC 27157-1072.

Phone: (336) 716-4311 • **Fax:** (336) 716-5795 • **E-mail:** jcappell@wfubmc.cdu

---

WASHINGTON UNIVERSITY MEDICAL CENTER

Department of Pathology

Cytopathology Fellowship

Description: The Department of Pathology at Washington University offers a one-year, ACGME accredited program with extensive exposure and experience in fine needle aspiration biopsy, gynecological and non-gynecological exfoliative cytopathology, application of a wide range of adjuvant technologies to cytological diagnosis, and correlations between cytopathologic and surgical pathologic interpretations. The cytopathology laboratory serves the Washington University campus institutions of Barnes-Jewish Hospital and the St Louis Children's Hospital. Approximately 25,000 cytologic cases are processed and examined annually, including 2,800 fine needle aspiration biopsies. Although emphasis is placed in diagnostic cytopathology, academic and research activities are encouraged and supported.

Requirements: Candidates must be ABP Board-eligible or Board-certified in anatomic or combined anatomic and clinical pathology. They must be able to apply successfully for medical licensure in the state of Missouri.

Stipends: Stipends are commensurate with the year of postgraduate training in pathology.

Applications: Lourdes Ylagan, MD, Department of Pathology, Washington University School of Medicine, Campus Box 8118, 660 South Euclid Ave, St Louis, MO 63110.

Phone: (314) 362-0115 • **Fax:** (314) 747-2663
E-mail: lylagan@path.wustl.edu

UNIVERSITY OF WASHINGTON
HARBORVIEW MEDICAL CENTER
Department of Pathology
Cytopathology Fellowship

Description: The ACGME-accredited program offers advanced subspecialty training in diagnostic cytopathology, including interpretation of gynecologic, non-gynecologic, and fine needle aspiration (FNA) specimens and experience in the performance of FNAs and assisting imaging-guided biopsies by clinicians. Fellows also participate in resident teaching and research. This program is certified by the American Board of Pathology.

Requirements: Applicants are selected for interview based on academic excellence and interest in the subspecialty. Applicants need to be board eligible for Anatomic Pathology certification by the American Board of Pathology and must be eligible for a Washington State license.

Facilities: The program is based at Harborview Medical Center which is affiliated with the University of Washington Medical Center. UW Medicine, among the most successful academic medical centers in the US, provides tertiary medical care and medical education to the five-state region of Washington, Wyoming, Alaska, Montana and Idaho.

Stipends: One-year appointment with salary and benefits based on the schedule for residents at an equivalent level (R4=$52,944). Fellows are encouraged to apply for extramural funding, if additional research training is desired. (1 position).

Staff: A. Peck-Sabath Director; **R. Garcia**; **V. Grieco**; **N. Kiviat**.

Applications: Inquiry: Annette Peck-Sabath, MD, Fellowship Director, at apeck@u.washington.edu. Available at the web site or contact Michelle Rickard, Academic Programs Manager, Cytopathology Fellowship Program, at the email address below. Application materials must be received by February 1 with selected interviews to follow until the position is filled.

Phone: (206) 598-4933 • **Fax:** (206) 598-7321 • **E-mail:** fellowship@pathology.washington.edu
Web site: www.pathology.washington.edu/academics/fellowship/

The University of Washington is an equal opportunity institution.

WAYNE STATE UNIVERSITY
DETROIT MEDICAL CENTER
Cytopathology Fellowship

Description: The Department of Pathology of Wayne State University School of Medicine, and the Detroit Medical Center, offers 2 one-year, ACGME-accredited fellowships in cytopathology, beginning July 1, annually. The program is offered at the central campus of the Detroit Medical Center - University Laboratories (DMCUL), which includes Harper University Hospital, Karmanos Cancer Center, and a large outreach Anatomic Pathology and Cytopathology lab based at Hutzel Hospital. The cytopathology annual workload includes approximately 90,000 GYN Pap tests, including 70 percent Thin Prep specimens, 700 image guided FNAs, 3000 non-GYN specimens of all varieties, 700 outpatient FNAs and NON-GYN specimens. The Outreach laboratory is unique in offering both cytopathology and GYN biopsy interpretations and is staffed by 5 FTE cytosurgical pathologists. The rotation includes in depth exposure to GYN cytology, including biopsy, HPV and colposcopy correlation, and abundant non-GYN specimens from tertiary care hospital and comprehensive cancer center. About 50 percent of time is spent in FNA performance and FNA adequacy valuation for radiology, EUS and intra-operative specimens. Participation in laboratory management, QA/QC, hospital conferences and medical and cytotechnology school student teaching is expected. Fellows are encouraged to participate in clinically related research and presenting at national meetings or writing one paper. In addition, elective rotation in Molecular Diagnostic or Cytogenetics laboratory or surgical pathology is available. Facilities for basic science research projects are available on campus.

Requirements: Applicants should be Board eligible or certified in anatomic or anatomic and clinical pathology and be eligible for Michigan license.

Stipends: Stipends are commensurate with the year of pathology postgraduate training as determined by the Wayne State University School of Medicine.

Applications: Applications should be completed by August 1 of the preceding year. Inquiries should be accompanied by a curriculum vitae and letter to: Mujtaba Husain, MD, Director Fellowship Program, Director of Cytopathology and Outreach Anatomic Pathology, DMC Univ Laboratories, 4707 St. Antoine, Detroit, MI 48201.

Phone: (313) 745-0831

WILLIAM BEAUMONT HOSPITAL

Cytopathology Fellowship

Description: This one-year ACGME-approved fellowship offers advanced training in diagnostic cytopathology. Approximately 86,951 specimens are processed in the Cytology Laboratory annually (74,672 GYN, 8,894 non-GYN, and 3,385 FNA). The fellow will participate in all aspects of cytopathology, including interpretation of gynecologic, nongynecologic and fine-needle aspiration specimens and procurement of superficial fine-needle aspiration specimens. The cytopathologists hold Fine-Needle Aspiration Clinic twice weekly. William Beaumont Hospital is a 1,061-bed tertiary care teaching hospital servicing several large suburban communities in Oakland County, 13 miles north of Detroit. The Department of Anatomic Pathology currently processes 72,436 surgical specimens per year. Sign-out responsibilities in cytopathology are graduated and based on the level of experience of the fellow. The fellow will be involved in the teaching of residents and rotating medical students. The fellow is required to participate in a research project. Ancillary techniques such as immunocytochemistry, flow cytometry, image analysis, and molecular pathology are available for such purposes.

Requirements: Candidates must have completed either a four-year combined AP/CP residency or a three-year residency in anatomic pathology. Candidates must hold, or be eligible to hold, a medical license in the State of Michigan.

Stipends: Commensurate with level of postgraduate training in pathology.

Staff: Edward G. Bernacki, Jr MD Chief of Cytopathology; **Tomi J. Kuntzman** DO Director of Cytopathology Fellowship; **Michele T. Rooney** MD Director Residency Training in Pathology, Cytopathologist; **Mariza dePeralta-Venturina** MD Cytopathologist.

Applications: Applications are available on the William Beaumont Hospital website (listed below) or you may contact Sandra Plumb, Cytopathology Fellowship Coordinator at splumb@beaumonthospitals.com or

Phone: (248) 898-1256.

Please submit an application, personal statement, curriculum vitae and three letters of recommendation to: Tomi J. Kuntzman, DO, Department of Anatomic Pathology, William Beaumont Hospital, 3601 West Thirteen Mile Road, Royal Oak, MI 48073-6769.

Phone: (248) 898-1256 • **Fax:** (248) 898-1257 • **E-mail:** tkuntzman@beaumont.edu
Web site: https://www.beaumonthospitals.com/gme

MEDICAL COLLEGE OF WISCONSIN

Department of Pathology and Laboratory Medicine

Cytopathology Fellowship

Description: One-year fellowship in cytopathology offers advanced training with emphasis on fine needle aspiration biopsy and the selective application of ancillary techniques. The fellow will have increasing levels of responsibility commensurate with the level of performance. Emphasis is also placed on the integration of surgical pathology with cytology and the use of both air-dried DiffQuik and Papanicolaou stains. The fellow will participate in the service, teaching and research activities of the laboratory. The laboratory processes more than 88,000 cytology specimens per year (2008) with an expanding fine needle aspiration biopsy service. Research opportunities are available in cytopathology, immunocytochemistry, flow cytometry and surgical pathology. The fellow will also be responsible for the cytology conference presentations to the residents with active participation in resident teaching in cytopathology.

Requirements: Board certification or eligibility including USMLE-III, in AP or AP/CP.

Stipends: Commensurate with the applicant's level of training.

Applications: To apply, submit the College of American Pathologists Standardized Application for Pathology Fellowships application with personal statement, curriculum vitae and three letters of recommendation to: Vinod B. Shidham, MD, FIAC, FRCPath, Cytopathology Fellowship Program Director; ATTN: Marie Hardy, Cytopathology Fellowship Coordinator, Department of Pathology, Medical College of Wisconsin, P. O. Box 26509, 9200 West Wisconsin Avenue, Milwaukee, WI 53226.

Phone: (414) 805-8452 or (414) 805-6987
E-mail: vshidham@mcw.edu or mhardy@mcw.edu
Web site: http//:www.mcw.edu/pathol/cytopath

UNIVERSITY OF WISCONSIN MADISON HOSPITAL AND CLINICS

Cytopathology Fellowship

Description: This one year ACGME-accredited program is designed to provide comprehensive training in diagnostic cytopathology, particularly the immediate evaluation, triage and final diagnosis of Fine Needle Aspirations (FNA's). The cytology laboratory evaluates approximately 12,000 gynecologic and 3,600 non-gynecologic specimens of which 1600 are FNA's per year. The fellow will become proficient in laboratory management, diagnostics; including the performance and interpretation of FNA's and new technologies; including the ThinPrep Pap Test, HPV- DNA testing, and medical informatics. The cytopathology section utilizes video streaming for immediate evaluation and static imaging for archival purposes. This cutting edge experience provides fellows with comprehensive training in the new technologies benefiting cytopathology today. The department has a strong academic mission, and provides opportunities for cytology-based research, including molecular diagnostics. The fellow will participate in the education of residents and medical students on cytology rotations. Educational opportunities exist for rotation at the Wisconsin State Laboratory of Hygiene (including its large volume of gynecologic specimens, Cytogenetics Laboratory, and School of Cytotechnology). The fellow is expected to complete a research project for publication. Upon completion, the fellow will be prepared to direct a university or community-based practice cytopathology laboratory.
Requirements: Applicants must be AP or AP/CP Board eligible or Board certified.
Stipends: Commensurate with the year of postgraduate training.
Staff: Suzanne Selvaggi, MD Medical School: Albert Einstein Medical College, New York, New York (1978); Pathology Residency: New York University Medical Center, New York, New York (1983); Research Fellow in clonal culture patterns and cytogenetics of lymphomas and leukemias: New York University Medical Center, New York (1982); **Jimmie Stewart III, MD** Medical School: University of Arkansas for Medical Sciences (1992); Pathology Residency: University of Kentucky, Lexington (2000); Cytopathology Fellowship: University of Wisconsin Hospital and Clinics, Madison (2001); Biomedical Informatics Fellowship: University of Pittsburgh (2002).
Applications: Send cover letter with application (download from website) personal statement, CV and three letters of recommendation to: Jimmie Stewart III, MD, Associate Director Cytopathology, University Hospital and Clinics, Cytology/Clinical Labs E5/488 CSC, 600 Highland Avenue, Madison, WI 53792-2472.
Phone: (608) 265-5264 • **Fax:** (608) 263-6453 • **E-mail:** jstewartIII@uwhealth.org
Web site: http://www.pathology.wisc.edu/clinfellowship/cytopathology

---

YALE UNIVERSITY SCHOOL OF MEDICINE

Department of Pathology

Cytopathology Fellowship

Description: This fellowship is a one-year intensive training in all aspects of cytopathology. The fellow will actively participate in review of GYN and non-GYN material and participate in both the performance and analysis of fine needle aspirations. Fellows will also attend and occasionally give teaching conferences related to cytopathology. A critical and unique part of this fellowship will be the understanding and application of advanced molecular techniques to cytodiagnostics. Each fellow is expected to begin personal research projects mentored by departmental faculty. A second year of funding may be available for continuation of research begun during the fellowship

Requirements: Three years of training in anatomic pathology or four years of training in combined anatomic and clinical pathology.

Stipends: Commensurate with hospital policy.

Applications: Apply to Diane P. Kowalski, MD, Cytology Fellowship Program Director, Department of Pathology, Yale School of Medicine, PO Box 208070, New Haven, CT 06520-8070.

Phone: (203) 785-2774 • **Fax:** (203) 785-3585 • **E-mail:** diane.kowalski@yale.edu

UNIVERSITY OF ALABAMA MEDICAL CENTER

Dermatopathology Fellowship

Description: This one-year Dermatopathology fellowship is sponsored jointly by the Departments of Pathology and Dermatology of the University of Alabama at Birmingham School of Medicine. It is designed to provide intensive training in Dermatopathology for Board-certified/eligible graduates of Pathology and Dermatology programs. Experience in the techniques of imunohistochemistry, immunoflouresence, and molecular techniques as it pertains to Dermatopathology will be provided, as well as appropriate training in Pathology for those with a Dermatology background and in Dermatology for Pathology graduates. The fellow will be expected to identify areas of interest in the specialty and pursue them through a clinical/basic research project. The fellowship program director is Aleodor Andea, MD. Two Dermatopathology funded fellowship positions are available each year.

Requirements: Candidates must be Board-certified or eligible for certification in Anatomic Pathology, AP/CP or Dermatology, and be eligible for Alabama Medical License.

Stipends: Salary levels are commensurate with the level of postgraduate training.

Staff: Andea A Aleodor Program Director, Dermatopathology.

Applications: Applications should be submitted to Aleodor Andea, MD, Assistant Professor Dermatology and Pathology, and Director, Dermatopathology Program, University of Alabama at Birmingham, 619 South 19th Street, PD6A, Room 149, Birmingham, AL 35249-4550. Applications should be made 12 to 18 months prior to initiation of training.
For further questions please contact
Regina Farmer, Fellowship Coordinator

Phone: (205) 975-6941
Web site: http://www.uab.edu/derm

ALBERT EINSTEIN COLLEGE OF MEDICINE

Dermatopathology Fellowship

Description: One year ACGME approved fellowship in dermatopathology, providing an outstanding clinical training experience with a faculty rich in experience in the clinical practice of dermatopathology, clinical dermatology and anatomic pathology and with a high volume of clinical material obtained both from hospital —based and practice- or outpatient-based dermatology. The fellow will rotate through the departments of dermatopathology and dermatology at Einstein/Montefiore and through our affiliated institution, Dermpath. Diagnostics. The combined volume of accessions seen in these institutions is in excess of 220,000 per annum. There is opportunity for extensive experience in all aspects of dermatopathology: clinical, academic research, immunofluorescence, immunoperoxidase and molecular pathology. Graduates of this program are trained to be excellent clinical dermatopathologists who should secure positions in either academic institutions or private practice dermatopathology laboratories.

Requirements: Eligible for AP or AP/CP Board certification or Dermatology Board certification.

Stipends: Appointment is for one year. Salary based on schedule for residents.

Staff: Mark Jacobson MD (Director of Dermatopathology, Montefiore Medical Center, Associate director, Dermpath. Diagnostics); **Paul Chu** MD (Executive Managing-Director, Dermpath Diagnostics); **Damian Di Costanzo** MD (Dermpath Diagnostics); **Kenneth Shulman** MD (Dermpath Diagnostics); **Greg Seidel** MD (Dermpath Diagnostics); **Michael Mlller** MD (Dermpath Diagnostics); **Jason Cohen** MD (Dermpath Diagnostics); **Steven Cohen** MD (Chairman, Dermatology, Albert Einstein College of Medicine); **Michael Fisher** MD (Past Chairman, Dermatology, Albert Einstein College of Medicine); **Ranon Mann** MD (Dermatology, Albert Einstein College of Medicine); **Michael Prystowsky** MD (Chairman, Pathology, Albert Einstein College of Medicine); **James Pullman** MD (Director of Surgical Pathology, Montefiore Medical Center); **Katherine Tanaka** (Attending Pathologist, Montefiore Medical Center); **Kathleen Whitney** (Attending Pathologist, Montefiore Medical Center).

Applications: Send curriculum vitae, three letters of recommendation, Dean's letter and transcript and a brief statement of career objectives to: Mark Jacobson MD, Director of Dermatopathology, Montefiore Medical Center, 111 East 210th Street, Bronx, NY 10467
E-mail: mjacobso@montefiore.org

BAYLOR COLLEGE OF MEDICINE

Department of Pathology

Dermatopathology Fellowship

Description: This one-year dermatopathology fellowship is sponsored jointly by the Departments of Pathology and Dermatology of the Baylor College of Medicine. It is designed to provide intensive training in dermatopathology for Board-certified/eligible graduates of Pathology and Dermatology programs. Experience in the techniques of immunohistochemistry, immunofluorescence, and electron microscopy as they pertain to dermatopathology will be provided. Appropriate training in pathology for those with a dermatology background and in dermatology for pathology graduates will be provided for Board eligibility. The fellow will be expected to identify areas of interest in the specialty and pursue them through a clinical/basic research project.

Requirements: Candidates must be Board-certified or eligible for certification in Anatomic Pathology, AP/CP or Dermatology.

Stipends: Commensurate with candidate's level of training.

Applications: Inquiries are to be directed to
Yvetter Boney, Coordinator of Dermatopathology Fellowship Program, Department of Pathology, One Baylor Plaza, MC 315, Houston, TX 77030.

Phone: (713) 798-4083 • **Fax:** (713) 798-3665 • **E-mail:** yboney@bcm.edu

---

UNIVERSITY OF CALIFORNIA, LOS ANGELES

Dermatopathology Fellowship

Description: The Department of Pathology and Laboratory Medicine offers one-year accredited fellowships that provide intensive training in all aspects of dermatopathology to prepare trainees for an academic or community career in the field. Fellows trained in dermatology do an ACGME-approved combination of months of dermatopatholgy and months of pathology with an emphasis on those fields most relevant to dermatopathology. Fellows trained in AP or AP/CP likewise do a combination of dermatopathology months and months at UCLA's prestigious Dermatology Clinic. All fellows are provided with the highest level of dermatopathology training including daily sign-out of many extremely challenging consult cases and a high volume of routine cases from community dermatologists and the hospital's inpatients. A broad range of ancillary studies including immunohistochemistry and molecular pathology are routinely employed by the service. Extensive opportunities for basic, translational, and clinical research are available including collaborations with UCLA professors studying a wide spectrum of clinical and basic science disciplines. Educational opportunities are limitless. Three fellowship positions are available beginning July 1, 2010.

Requirements: Board eligible in AP, AP/CP, or dermatology. A California Medical license is required.

Applications: Please contact Fellowship Coordinator to receive the requirements and application, submit a curriculum vitae and arrange to have three letters of recommendation sent to: Scott W. Binder, MD, Program Director, Dermatopathology Fellowship, Department of Pathology and Laboratory Medicine, David Geffen School of Medicine at UCLA, 10833 Le Conte Avenue, Room A7-149 CHS, Los Angeles, CA 90095-1732. Applications should be received by February 1 for the year preceding the fellowship.
Fellowship Coordinator: Ms. Annetta Pierro

Phone: (310) 825-5719 • **Fax:** (310) 267-2058
Web site: www.pathology.ucla.edu

UNIVERSITY OF CALIFORNIA, SAN FRANCISCO

Dermatopathology Fellowship

Description: The Dermatopathology Fellowship is planned as preparation for a career in dermatopathology, either in an academic setting or in practice with an academic orientation. Our philosophy is that a second year of training is desirable for almost all applicants. Training in diagnostic dermatopathology is founded on our volume of over 92,000 accessions per year, roughly 20,000 of which are consultations on previously prepared slides, and thus contain a high proportion of challenging material. Fellows see a proportion of cases prior to their being signed out by an attending. Ancillary diagnostic training is available in immunoperoxidase techniques and molecular biology. Research opportunities include clinicopathologic studies, immunoperoxidase, ultra structural and molecular biologic investigation of aspects of skin disease, in collaboration with laboratories in the departments of Pathology and Dermatology, and the UCSF Cancer Center. Special interests include molecular cytogenetics of melanoma, cutaneous lymphomas, vascular neoplasms, and inflammatory skin disease. The next available position begins July 1, 2011. The deadline to apply is October 15, 2009.

Requirements: Board eligible in AP, AP/CP, or Dermatology.

Stipends: Commensurate with PGY level. As of 2009, $49,347.00 for PGY IV up to $52,968.00 for PGY VI.

Applications: Inquiries should be addressed to: Philip E. LeBoit, MD, c/o Mary Kate Fitzsimon. University of California, San Francisco, 1701 Divisadero St, Rm 350, San Francisco, CA 94115

Phone: (415) 353-7550 (#6) **Fax:** (415) 353-7553 **E-mail:** mary-kate.fitzsimon@ucsf.edu

THE CLEVELAND CLINIC

Department of Anatomic Pathology

Dermatopathology Fellowship

Description: The Cleveland Clinic's Dermatopathology Fellowship is an ACGME approved fellowship, that includes a year of dermatopathology with concurrent training in clinical dermatology or anatomic pathology. Each fellow is exposed to a wide variety of dermatopathology diseases, including special studies and techniques. The major emphasis is placed on inflammatory disease, cutaneous tumors, lymphoma, pigmented lesions, laboratory procedures, immunopathology and molecular diagnostic techniques. Research projects, teaching, publications and local and national presentations are encouraged and expected. The Dermatopathology Fellowship emphasizes interaction between dermatology and pathology.

Requirements: Candidates for fellowship should be eligible or Board certified by either the American Board of Dermatology or the American Board of Pathology. Two positions are available annually.

Stipends: The fellows will be paid according to the scale listed in the general Cleveland Clinic program entry.

Applications: Should be made well before October for a July entry to
Wilma F. Bergfeld, MD, Head, Section of Dermatopathology, Department of Anatomic Pathology, The Cleveland Clinic, 9500 Euclid Avenue, Cleveland, OH 44195-5032.

Phone: (216) 444-2168 • **Fax:** (216) 445-6967

UNIVERSITY OF COLORADO DENVER SCHOOL OF MEDICINE

Dermatopathology Fellowship

Description: The 12-month fellowship is designed to prepare individuals with a background in pathology or dermatology for a career in dermatopathology. Training covers a broad range of subjects including immunopathology and laboratory management. Emphasis is placed on clinico-pathologic correlation. Formal teaching conferences and daily sign out of cases utilize 14-headed and 18-headed teaching microscopes. Over 90,000 specimens are accessioned each year. The fellow has graduated responsibility for signing out cases and for teaching dermatopathology to pathology and dermatology residents. Pathologists receive training in clinical dermatology and dermatologists receive training in general pathology as required for certification. Dermatopathology responsibility and training continues throughout the full 12 months. The fellow is expected to complete a project suitable for presentation at a national meeting and publication in a medical journal. Support is offered in identifying employment opportunities, which will utilize the fellow's dermatopathology experience. Two fellows are appointed each year. James E. Fitzpatrick, MD serves as Co-director. The staff includes five full-time and two part-time board certified dermatopathologists.

Requirements: Board certification or eligibility in pathology or dermatology; interview.

Stipends: Commensurate with level of postgraduate training.

Staff: Loren E. Golitz MD, Clinical Professor of Pathology and Dermatology.

Applications: Application and information can be found on our website. Send completed application by Nov 1, 2009 for July 1, 2011 position to: Patricia Braund, Residency/Fellowship Coordinator, University of Colorado Denver School of Medicine, Department of Pathology, 12631 E. 17th Avenue, Box B-216, Mail Stop 6511, Aurora, CO, 80045. patricia.braund@ucdenver.edu.

Phone: (303) 724-3483 • **Fax:** (303) 724-1105
Website: www.uchsc.edu/pathology

DARTMOUTH-HITCHCOCK MEDICAL CENTER DARTMOUTH MEDICAL SCHOOL

Department of Pathology

Dermatopathology Fellowship

Description: This accredited one-year fellowship is sponsored by the Department of Pathology and the Section of Dermatology at Dartmouth-Hitchcock Medical Center. Dermatopathology Training occurs each morning throughout the year, including a daily consensus conference with all four faculty members and all trainees. Concurrent cross-training in Dermatology or Pathology is emphasized as essential to the practice of dermatopathology, with a longitudinal experience each afternoon throughout the year. Participation in dermatopathology research and presentation at a national conference is supported and expected. Strong collegial interactions between the Dermatology Section and the Department of Pathology, and between the four faculty Dermatopathologists, are a hallmark of our program.

Requirements: Board eligibility in Anatomic Pathology or in Dermatology. Medical licensure in the State of New Hampshire required.

Stipends: Commensurate with the number of relevant postgraduate years of training. There is a book allowance and funding available for presentation at a national meeting.

Staff: Jeoffry B. Brennick MD (Program Director); **Ann E. Perry** MD; **Craig A. Storm** MD; **Shaofeng Yan** MD, PhD.

Applications: To review application requirements and to download an application form go to the program's web site. Completed applications accepted 30 months (January 1) in advance of July 1 start date. Send to Susan Hawk, Program Coordinator, Department of Pathology, Dartmouth-Hitchcock Medical Center, 1 Medical Center Drive, Lebanon, NH 03756-0001.

Phone: (603) 650-8623 • **Fax:** (603) 650-4845
E-mail: susan.hawk@hitchcock.org; jeoffry.b.brennick@hitchcock.org
Web site: http://www.dhmc.org/goto/Dermatopathology_Fellowship

UNIVERSITY OF FLORIDA

Dermatopathology Fellowship

Description: This is an ACGME accredited fellowship in dermatopathology. The dermatopathology unit interprets over 10,000 skin biopsies per year, including interesting cases from Shands University Hospital and the University of Florida Diagnostic Reference Laboratories. The latter receives specimens from all over the state of Florida and the whole southeast with an active outside consultation service. The dermatopathology service is closely coordinated with the Department of Dermatology and fellows actively participate in dermatology clinics and conferences. The dermatopathology unit performs a wide range of immunohistochemical staining, immunofluorescence and salt split skin testing. The dermatopathology laboratories have all the state-of-the-art molecular techniques, which are used in the diagnosis of cutaneous lymphoproliferative disorders. The fellow is expected to master these techniques that are performed on a daily basis. Appropriate training in pathology for those candidates with a dermatology background and in clinical dermatology for pathology graduates will be provided. The fellow will be expected to identify areas of interest and to pursue them through a clinical and/or basic research project.

Requirements: Applicants must be Board eligible or Board certified in anatomic pathology, anatomic and clinical pathology or clinical dermatology. Special consideration will be given to candidates interested in pursuing an academic career in dermatopathology.

Stipends: Stipends are commensurate with the year of postgraduate training.

Applications: Send a personal statement concerning career goals, CV, and three letters of recommendation to Vladimir Vincek, MD, PhD, University of Florida, College of Medicine, Department of Pathology, P O Box 100275, Gainesville, FL 32610-0275. Submit applications by February 1 for July of the next year.

Phone: (352) 265-9919 • **Fax:** (352) 265-9918 • **E-mail:** Vincek26@pathology.ufl.edu
Web site: http://www.pathology.ufl.edu/fellowship.htm

INDIANA UNIVERSITY SCHOOL OF MEDICINE

Dermatopathology Fellowship

Description: The intent of this one to two year fellowship is to prepare individuals for a career in academic dermatopathology. It is jointly sponsored by the Depts. of Pathology and Dermatology, at the Indiana Univ. Sch. of Medicine in Indianapolis. The Division of Dermatopathology is housed in a state of the art stand-alone pathology and lab medicine complex. Cutaneous biopsy material (over 40,000 accessions annually) is received from the four hospitals on campus (Indiana Univ Hosp, Wishard Memorial Hosp, Riley Children's Hosp, and Roudebush Veterans Affairs Hosp), and a private dermatology/dermatopathology practice. Consultation cases are received from physicians in Indiana and surrounding states. Training in immunohistochemical techniques, PCR, in situ hybridization, electron microscopy, and immunofluorescence is provided through the Pathology Dept. Abundant clinical material is available through the Dermatology Dept., which provides patient care at the four hospitals and at numerous outpatient clinics. Exposure to clinical and histopathologic material via daily sign-out, weekly teaching conferences, bimonthly Dermatology Grand Rounds and attendance at local and national meetings will extend throughout the fellowship, as will opportunities for research experience. Representative research opportunities include compilation of morphologic studies, evaluation of prospective clinical and histopathologic studies, involvement in molecular biology research, and participation in epidemiologic studies. Primary faculty includes a dermatologist/dermatopathologist, and a pathologist/dermatopathologist. Additional interactions occur with numerous faculty members in dermatology and pathology. The dermatopathology fellow will cross-train in either pathology or dermatology throughout the training period.

Requirements: Board eligibility in pathology or dermatology.

Stipends: Commensurate with level of postgraduate training within the School of Medicine.

Applications: Address inquiries to: William B. Moores, MD, Dir. Dermatopathol, Dept. of Pathol., Indiana Univ. Sch. of Med., Clarian Pathology Laboratory, 350 West 11th Street, Indianapolis, IN 46202. Application deadline is December 1, 2010 for the fellowship beginning July 1, 2011.

Phone: (317) 491-6000
Web site: http://www.pathology.iupui.edu

HARVARD MEDICAL SCHOOL HOSPITALS

Dermatopathology Fellowship

Description: The Harvard Dermatopathology Program is a fully approved fellowship training program that draws on the facilities of the Beth Israel Deaconess Medical Center, the Brigham and Women's Hospital, and Massachusetts General Hospital. The period of fellowship is one year. Fellows enter the program eligible for Board certification in Dermatology or Pathology and receive one-half of their training in the complementary fields of anatomic pathology or clinical dermatology, respectively. Additionally, fellows receive training in immunopathology, immunofluorescence, microbiology/mycology, tissue processing for both routine and specialized microscopy, molecular pathology, immunohistochemistry, and laboratory management. Fellows attend a wide variety of clinical and pathological diagnostic conferences, and participate in numerous venues teaching residents and medical students. In addition diverse research opportunities are available in all of the participating institutions.

Types and Numbers of Appointments: Three funded dermatopathology fellowship positions are available.

Facilities: The Beth Israel Deaconess Medical Center, Brigham &Women's Hospital, Children's Hospital Medical Center, and Massachusetts General Hospital provide total program resources of approximately 3000 beds and 300,000 surgical pathology specimens, of which approximately 75,000 are skin. In addition, a large number of cases are received from outside institutions for consultation. The dermatology clinics at the three institutions have a total yearly patient census of approximately 130,000. Research facilities available at each participating institution include laboratories for immunohistochemistry, immunofluorescence, molecular biologic studies including laser capture microdissection, genetic profiling using microarrays, specialized histology, and electron microscopy. There is a broad range of internet accessed library resources, as well as libraries at all participating Pathology and Dermatology departments at the individual institutions and Harvard Medical School. The Harvard Medical School's 500,000-volume collection, housed at the Countway Library, is adjacent to the Longwood area hospitals.

Community: Boston and its surrounding communities have a total population of over three million, the sixth largest metropolis in the nation. The city has many universities and cultural facilities, including the Boston Symphony, Boston Ballet, and several fine theater companies. The Beth Israel Deaconess Medical Center and Brigham and Women's Hospital are located in the Longwood Medical Area, on rapid transit, and close to the Museum of Fine Arts and the Isabella Stewart Gardner Museum. The Massachusetts General Hospital is situated in the center of Boston, at the foot of Beacon Hill on the Charles River, convenient to rapid transit, downtown, and the airport.

Stipends: Stipends range from $63,000 to $71,000, depending on PGY year.

Staff: Steven R. Tahan MD Program Director, Associate Professor of Pathology, Director, Dermatopathology, BIDMC; **Michael Atkins** MD Director, Cutaneous Oncology Program, BIDMC; **W. Stephen Black-Schaffer** MD, MA Director, Pathology Residency Training Program, MGH; **Susan Burgin** MD Dermatologist; **James L. Connolly** MD Director, Pathology Residency Training Program, BIDMC; **Christopher P. Crum** MD Pathologist; vulvar pathology; **Lyn M. Duncan** MD Associate Professor of Pathology, Dermatopathologist; melanoma and hyperplasia research; **Beverly Faulkner-Jones** MD, PhD Dermatopathologist; **Christopher D. M. Fletcher** MD Pathologist; cutaneous soft tissue tumors; **Scott R. Granter** MD Associate Professor of Pathology, Dermatopathologist; diagnostic dermatopathology, melanocytic nevi; melanoma and inflammatory dermatoses; **Harley A Haynes** MD Dermatologist; cutaneous oncology; **Mai P. Hoang** MD Dermatopathologist; **Mei-Yu Hsu** MD, PhD Dermatopathologist; **Richard A. Johnson** MD Dermatologist; HIV infection and epidemiology, Lyme borreliosis; **Caroline Kim, MD** MD Dermatologist; **Thomas S. Kupper** MD Dermatologist; molecular biology, cutaneous T-cell lymphoma; **Joseph Kvedar** MD Dermatologist; **Paul Levins** MD Dermatologist; **Janina A. Longtine** MD Pathologist; diagnostic molecular pathology; **Martin C. Mihm Jr.** MD Clinical Professor of Pathology; biology of melanoma, precursors and problematic lesions; delayed hypersensitivity response; pathogenesis of vasculitis; molecular biology of pigmentation; lymphoma; **George Murphy** MD Director, Dermatopathology Unit, BWH; epidermal stem cell research; **German Pihan** MD Hematopathologist; molecular pathologist; **Geraldine S. Pinkus** MD Pathologist; hematopathology, immunopathology; **Adriano Piris** MD Dermatopathologist; **Abrar Quereshi** MD Dermatologist; **Rachel Reynolds** MD Dermatologist; **Arturo Saavedra-Lauzon** MD, PhD Dermatologist; Dermatopathologist; **Brigitta Schmidt** MD Pediatric Dermatopathologist; **Stuart Schnitt** MD Director, Anatomic Pathology, BIDMC; **Su-Jean Seo** MD, PhD Dermatopathologist; **Alireza Sepehr** MD Dermatopathologist; **Arthur J. Sober** MD Dermatologist; melanoma and dysplastic nevi; **Robert Stern** MD Dermatologist; psoriasis; **Hensin Tsao** MD Dermatologist; melanoma; **Elsa Velazquez** MD Dermatopathologist; **Gayle Winters** MD Director, Pathology Residency Training Program, BWH; **Sook-Bin Woo** DMD Pathologist; oral pathology; **Mary Jane Zimerowski** MD Dermatopathologist.

Applications: Fellowship candidates must be graduates of approved medical schools in the United States or Canada. Graduates of foreign medical schools must have an ECFMG Certificate. Applicants must have completed a residency training program in either Pathology or Dermatology and be eligible for certification in either one to enter the program. Applications must be received by October 31, 2009 for appointments beginning on July 1, 2011.

Address inquiries to:
Joan Allin, Coordinator, Harvard Dermatopathology Fellowship Program,
Pathology Department
Beth Israel Deaconess Medical Center, 330 Brookline Avenue
Boston, MA 02215
Phone: (617) 667-7284 • **Fax:** (617) 667-7120 • **E-mail:** jallin@bidmc.harvard.edu

UNIVERSITY OF MASSACHUSETTS MEDICAL SCHOOL

Dermatopathology Fellowship

Description: This new ACGME-accredited fellowship program in Dermatopathology in the Department of Pathology at Univeristy of Massachusetts is a two-year program geared to prepare individuals for an academic career in dermatopathology. The fellow will be expected to actively participate in all clinical and teaching activities in both pathology and dermatology services.The Department of Pathology has an active dermatopathology service processing over 15,000 accessions of skin specimen from dermatology clinics at UMass, as well as in the community of central Massachusetts. We also provide immunohistochemistry and immunofluorescence studies, molecular and cytogenetic testing and electromicroscopy service. The dermatology clinic at UMass has over 28,000 annual patient visits, perform close to 3,000 biopsies, an active Moh's /Slow Moh's service /fellowship, and a pediatric dermatology service /fellowship. The second year in dermatopathology would offer the fellow opportunity to gain additional experience in dermatopathology while pursuing a research project in depth.

Requirements: Applicants must be board eligible/certified in anatomic pathology or in dermatology and must have passed Step 3 of the USMLE.

Stipends: The stipend is commensurate with candidate's training and experience.

Applications: Send CV with names of three references and a letter describing career goals to Patti Davis, Residency/ Fellowship Coordinator, Biotech Three, One Innovation Drive, Worcester, MA 01605

Phone: (508) 793-6156 • **Fax:** (508) 793-6145 • **E-mail:** Patricia.Davis@umassmemorial.org.

MAYO SCHOOL OF GRADUATE MEDICAL EDUCATION

Departments of Dermatology and Pathology

Dermatopathology Fellowship

Description: The Department of Dermatology offers a 12-month training program in dermatopathology to provide qualification toward certification by the American Boards of Dermatology and Pathology. The training program emphasizes direct experience in dermatopathology with clinical pathological correlation. The training program is designed to develop competence in special areas of tissue examination including cytology, histochemistry, immunocytochemistry, electron microscopy, immunofluorescence, and dermatopathological mycology. Experience is gained in the interpretation of molecular genetics studies. For the dermatologist in the program, there is six-months experience in surgical and anatomic pathology as well as dermatopathology. For the pathologist, the 12-month course is devoted primarily to dermatopathology with clinical correlation.

Requirements: Applicants must have completed the requirements for Board Examination by the American Board of Dermatology or the American Board of Pathology. Applications should be received by November 1, 19 months preceding the intended fellowship, which begins the end of June. Interviews will be accomplished and completed by January 31 for appointments commencing the end of June of the following year.

Staff: **L. E. Gibson** Program Director; **A. G. Bridges**; **M. J. Camilleri**; **N. I. Comfere**; **L. A. Erickson**; **T. J. Flotte**.

Applications: Mayo School of Graduate Medical Education is committed to equal opportunity and affirmative action in the appointment process.

Web site: http://www.mayo.edu/msgme/application.html

UNIVERSITY OF MICHIGAN MEDICAL CENTER

Dermatopathology Fellowship

Description: The Department of Pathology, in conjunction with the Department of Dermatology, offers an ACGME-accredited, one-year fellowship in dermatopathology with emphasis on diagnostic dermatopathology. The program is well balanced and provides broad exposure to all areas of dermatopathology, including inflammatory dermatoses and cutaneous oncology. Pathology-trained fellows spend a portion of their training rotating in the Dermatology Clinic. Dermatology-trained fellows rotate in surgical pathology, with emphasis in areas that overlap with dermatopathology. All fellows interact closely with residents, fellows and staff of the Dermatology Department and University of Michigan Multidisciplinary Melanoma Program. The dermatopathology service has approximately 20,000 accessions per year, including in house cases, outside consultative cases, and direct immunofluorescence specimens. The fellow is encouraged to participate in ongoing investigative projects in the area of dermatopathology.

Requirements: Applicants must be Board-certified or Board-eligible in anatomic pathology and/or dermatology.

Stipends: Support is commensurate with the candidate's level of training.

Applications: Inquiries should be sent to Douglas Fullen, MD, Associate Professor of Pathology and Dermatology, University of Michigan Hospital 3261C Medical Science 1, 1301 Catherine, Ann Arbor, MI 48109-5602.

Phone: (734) 764-4460
Interested applicants can find further instructions and an application at: http://www.pathology.med.umich.edu/education/ResidencyProgram/fellowships.html

Applications should be made by January 1st for fellowships beginning July 1st of the following year. Early applications are encouraged.

NEW YORK UNIVERSITY MEDICAL CENTER

Department of Dermatology

Dermatopathology Fellowship

Description: The objective of this one year ACGME accredited fellowship is to prepare dermatologists and pathologists for careers in academic dermatopathology. The fellow will receive extensive training in dermatopathology during the sign-out sessions and throughout many teaching conferences. The dermatologists will receive additional training in general pathology, and the pathologists will be trained in clinical dermatology. Additional training may include immunopathology, electron microscopy, molecular biology, and cytometric studies.The fellow will actively participate in teaching and signing out cases under faculty supervision. The fellow may pursue a research project suitable for publication. A second year devoted to research as a fellow is optional.

Requirements: Board certification or eligibility in dermatology or anatomic pathology.

Stipends: Commensurate with the level of postgraduate training.

Staff: Faculty members of the Dermatopathology Section and Departments of Dermatology and Pathology.

Applications: Should be sent at least 19 months in advance. The fellowship begins on July 1. Apply to:
Shane Meehan, MD, Program Director, Dermatopathology Section, Department of Dermatology, New York University Medical Center, 530 First Avenue, Suite 7J, New York, NY 10016.

MILTON S. HERSHEY MEDICAL CENTER
PENN STATE COLLEGE OF MEDICINE
Dermatopathology Fellowship

Description: The aim of the Penn State Dermatopathology Fellowship is to train physicians to excel in dermatopathology. This is accomplished by providing an environment that encourages personal growth and inquiry and scientific discovery. Critical and analytical skills necessary for the acquisition of new medical information are developed. Fellows will acquire a comprehensive fund of knowledge essential for the diagnosis and management of the wide variety of entities encountered in dermatopathology. The fellow will be exposed to the subject matter necessary for passing the certifying examination.
To accomplish this, a faculty dedicated to patient care, teaching, research, and intellectual curiosity will provide the infrastructure for the fellowship learning experience. The fellow will be expected to be self motivated, collegial, and exhibit the highest levels of personal integrity. Fellows must be responsive to guidance, invest the time and effort necessary for independent learning, and be dedicated to providing the highest quality patient care.

Requirements: Applicants should be board-certified or board-eligible in either Anatomic Pathology or Dermatology.

Types and Numbers of Appointments: The dermatopathology program offers one position per academic year.

Facilities: The faculty, residents/fellows, main laboratory facilities, and dermatology clinic are housed in the Penn State Milton S. Hershey Medical Center. The hospital has a capacity of approximately 500 beds. The dermatopathology service accessions approximately 20,000 cases per year, exposing the fellow to a variety of common and uncommon diseases. The dermatopathology specialty also receives about 400 consult cases per year from other pathologists and dermatopathologists.

Community: Hershey, in the foothills of the Blue Ridge Mountains, is a community of approximately 20,000 people. Harrisburg, the state capital, is 12 miles away. There are over one million people within a fifty-mile radius. Surrounded by rich farm lands and close to urban centers of the eastern seaboard, Hershey can be described as a suburban community in a rural setting. It has excellent educational and recreational programs and facilities, outstanding musical and stage performances, and numerous fine arts and cultural opportunities. Outdoor activities are readily available and include golf, swimming, fishing, hunting, mountain climbing, skiing, and ready access to the Appalachian Trail. Philadelphia, Baltimore, Washington, New York City, and the Pennsylvania Dutch country are just short distances by automobile or train. The Harrisburg International Airport (MDT) is 15 minutes away from Hershey, and airports in both Baltimore and Philadelphia are about 1.5 hours away by car.

Stipends: Salaries are comparable with salaries in the northeast as well as the rest of the United States, and residents are provided with professional liability insurance, health insurance, disability insurance, uniforms, laundry, and four weeks paid vacation per year. The Department also provides yearly stipends that can be used for support of continuing medical education expenses, dues and membership, books, and subscriptions.

Staff: Klaus F. Helm MD, Professor, Dermatology and Pathology; Director, Dermatopathology Laboratory; Program Director, Dermatopathology Fellowship; **Michael D. Ioffreda** MD, Associate Professor, Dermatology and Pathology; **Loren E. Clarke** MD, Assistant Professor, Pathology and Dermatology.

Applications: The Milton S. Hershey Medical Center and College of Medicine of the Pennsylvania State University are currently soliciting applications for academic year 2011-2012. This is a fully-funded, one-year, ACGME-accredited position. Applications are evaluated on an on-going basis and will be accepted through December 30, 2009. Applications should include a cover letter with a personal statement, the standardized application for pathology fellowships, curriculum vitae, examination scores, a letter from the current/most recent program director, and three letters of recommendation.
Application materials and/or inquiries should be directed to:
The Penn State Milton S. Hershey Medical Center/College of Medicine, Dermatopathology Fellowship Program, Klaus F. Helm, Program Director, ATTN: Mandi Smith, 500 University Drive, PO Box 850, MC H179, Hershey, PA 17033

Phone: (717) 531-8247 • **Fax:** (717) 531-7741 • **E-mail:** asmith5@hmc.psu.edu

STATE UNIVERSITY OF NEW YORK (SUNY) DOWNSTATE MEDICAL CENTER ACKERMAN ACADEMY OF DERMATOPATHOLOGY

Dermatopathology Fellowships

Description: The Academy in New York City offers seven PGY-5 fellowships in preparation for Board certification. This training year for dermatologists and pathologists consists of sign-out of over 100,000 dermatopathology accessions and 4,000 cases sent in consultation. Engagement of a clinical research project also is encouraged, and there are opportunities for intensive investigative work leading to publication in the largely in-house journal, Dermatopathology: Practical and Conceptual, as well as to presentation in other venues. Training includes extensive experience in either clinical dermatology or general pathology at Kings County Hospital Center and Downstate University Hospital. Fellows participate actively in periodic seminars and inter-hospital and regional conferences.

Requirements: Only board-eligible or board-certified physicians in dermatology or pathology are welcome to apply.

Types and Numbers of Appointments: Up to seven (7) funded positions are available each year.

Applications: Fellowship appointments are effective as of July 1 of each academic year. Applications must be received at least 18 months prior to the date of anticipated appointment as a fellow. Acceptances are communicated at least 15 months prior to the start of fellowship. Interviews are conducted between October through March.

To apply, please visit http://www.ackermanacademy.org and complete the online fellowship application.

Phone: 212-889-6225 • **E-mail:** admissions@ackermanacademy.org

---

THE OHIO STATE UNIVERSITY MEDICAL CENTER

Department of Pathology

Dermatopathology Fellowship

Description: The dermatopathology fellowship at The Ohio State University Medical Center is a 12-month program. Training in dermatopathology is done synchronously with dermatology. The pathology experience takes place in the Department of Pathology at OSUMC. Dermatology experience takes place in the Division of Dermatology at OSUMC. Dermatology experience is patient care oriented with the fellow assigned patients in a clinic setting. The dermatopathology portion of the fellowship involves service, teaching and clinical or basic research. The fellow is expected to work on a subject suitable for presentation at a national meeting and publication. Opportunities for basic research are available. Most techniques of molecular biology are online allowing for the development of individual research projects. The Department of Pathology has laboratory techniques and instrumentation expected at a tertiary care center.

Requirements: Candidates must successfully complete USMLE Step III prior to their Medical Staff appointment to The Ohio State University Medical Center. They must also be Board eligible in pathology or dermatology. If pathology-trained, applicants who have completed a Surgical or Oncologic Pathology Fellowship will be preferred.

Stipends: Commensurate with the year of postgraduate training. Funds are available to support a national meeting.

Applications: Application and supporting documentation should be addressed to: Gretchen Staschiak, Pathology Education Manager, The Ohio State University Medical Center, N-308 Doan Hall, 410 W. 10th Ave., Columbus, OH 43210.

Phone: (614) 293-3055 • **Fax:** (614) 293-7273
Web site: http://pathology.osumc.edu/ext

MEDICAL UNIVERSITY OF SOUTH CAROLINA

Dermatopathology Fellowship

Description: This is an accredited one-year training program offered by the Departments of Dermatology and Pathology. Emphasis is placed on morphology and correlation with clinical findings but there is also ample opportunity for research. A resident with a dermatology background receives six months of training in anatomic pathology with emphasis on surgical pathology, which is integrated through the year. For the resident with previous pathology training, participation in dermatology clinics, rounds and clinical conferences is expected in addition to the study of morphology and mechanisms of skin disease. The faculty includes Dr. John S. Metcalf, and other members of the faculties of the Departments of Dermatology and Pathology and Laboratory Medicine.

Requirements: Board certification or eligibility in anatomic pathology or dermatology. Applications should be received by January 1st of the year preceding the year of the fellowship (18 months prior to the beginning of the fellowship).

Stipends: Commensurate with the level of postgraduate training.

Applications: Address inquiries to: John S. Metcalf, MD, Director, Dermatopathology Training Program, Department of Pathology and Laboratory Medicine, Medical University of South Carolina, 171 Ashley Avenue, Suite 309, MSC 908, Charleston, SC 29425.

Phone: (843) 792-1086 • **Fax:** (843) 792-8974 • **E-mail:** metcalfj@musc.edu

---

STANFORD UNIVERSITY MEDICAL CENTER

Department of Pathology

Dermatopathology Fellowship

Description: This one-year, ACGME-accredited fellowship provides advanced training in diagnostic dermatopathology. The Dermatopathology Service of the Laboratory of Surgical Pathology accessions over 12,000 dermatopathology specimens annually (including consultation cases), representing a broad spectrum of dermatologic diseases. The fellow works closely with faculty and housestaff in the Departments of Dermatology and Pathology. Case signout is conducted over a multiheaded microscope each morning. Cross-training in either dermatology or pathology occurs each afternoon throughout the year. Participation in teaching conferences, medical student teaching and departmental activities is expected. Research activities are encouraged and are supported by the department.

Requirements: AP or Dermatology residency training and eligibility for California medical license.

Stipends: Commensurate with experience, plus additional $8,400 per year housing allowance.

Applications: Submit to:
Uma Sundram, MD, PhD, Director of Dermatopathology Fellowship Program, Room H2117, Stanford Health Services, 300 Pasteur Drive, Stanford, CA 94305.

Phone: (650) 498-4401 • **Fax:** (650) 725-7409 • **E-mail**: sundram@stanford.edu

UNIVERSITY OF TENNESSEE AND AFFILIATED HOSPITALS

Dermatopathology Fellowship

Description: The Dematopathology Fellowship is an eighteen month program that includes a six-month research block (basic research in skin molecular biology) and twelve mandatory months: six months devoted to rotation in pathology and six months of rotation in dermatology. The six month research block includes supervised dermatopathology sign-out combined with clinically relevant research, and basic research in molecular biology. In addition, the fellow is offered an additional six months of independent basic research in molecular neuroendocrinology of the skin under supervision of Dr. Andrzej Slominski, Program Director of the Dermatopathology Fellowship.

Requirements: Board eligibility or certification in AP, AP/CP, or Dermatology.

Stipends: Stipends are commensurate with the year of postgraduate training.

Applications: Inquiries should be addressed to Andrzej Slominski, MD, PhD, Program Director, Dermatopathology Fellowship, University of Tennessee Department of Pathology, 930 Madison Avenue 5th Floor, Memphis, Tennessee 38163.

Phone: (901) 448-6344 **Fax:** (901) 448-6979

THE UNIVERSITY OF TEXAS M.D. ANDERSON CANCER CENTER

Dermatopathology Fellowship

Description: The Dermatopathology Fellowship is a one-year Program accredited by the ACGME. This program also has an optional second-year primarily dedicated to diagnosis and research. Our specimens range from punch and shave biopsies to large surgical excisions and lymphadenectomies. There are approximately 8000 accessions (12,000 specimens) a year. A significant number of our cases represent diagnostic challenges, primarily in the oncologic area (carcinoma, melanoma, soft tissue tumors, and lymphoma involving the skin), as well as cancer and therapy-related processes, such as graft versus host disease. A very important and challenging part of the volume corresponds to cases, predominantly melanocytic lesions, coming from other institutions to be reviewed in our department prior to the patient's clinic appointment. In addition to our material, the fellows will have the opportunity of also reviewing Dermatopathology cases at Baylor College of Medicine and University of Houston Health Science Center.

Requirements: Candidates must be Board-certified or eligible for certification in Anatomic Pathology, AP/CP, or Dermatology.

Stipends: Commensurate with the candidate's level of training.

Applications: must be submitted using the Discover System, a web based application, at https://www2.mdanderson.org/sapp/discover/. The deadline to submit application is December 31st, eighteen (18) months prior to the intended fellowship year which begins July 1st. Correspondence should be addressed to Victor Prieto, MD, PhD, Director, Dermatopathology Fellowship, The University of Texas M.D. Anderson Cancer Center, 1515 Holcombe Blvd., Unit 085, Houston, Texas 77030. For inquiries and to request additional information, please contact Kareen Chin.

Phone: (713) 792-3108 • **Fax:** (713) 745-0789 • **E-mail:** kechin@mdanderson.org
Web site: http://www.mdanderson.org/departments/pathology

UNIVERSITY OF PENNSYLVANIA

Dermatopathology Fellowship Program

Description: The goal of this fully approved program is training and certification in dermatopathology that will produce future leaders in clinical or academic practice. One or two years are offered that encompass comprehensive exposure to diagnostic dermatopathology, immunodermatology, mycology, correlative clinical dermatology, and research. Physical and administrative location of the Dermatopathology Division in the Department of Dermatology affords routine clinical/ patient interaction. Opportunities to interface with members of the Pathology Department are integral to the program. The Division emphasizes application of specialized technology and expertise advantageous to both future academic pursuits and community practice. Exposure to immunofluorescence microscopy, immunohistochemistry, specialized microscopy and ultrastructure, and diagnostic molecular biology is offered. Fellows assume teaching responsibilities at the Medical School, residency, staff, and postgraduate levels. Areas of specialized faculty expertise include malignant melanoma, cutaneous lymphoma, psoriasis, bullous disorders, cutaneous manifestations of immunodeficiency states, and alopecia.

Requirements: Board-eligible/Board-certified in Dermatology or Pathology.

Types and Numbers of Appointments: Two ACGME accredited fellowship appointments are available. Training may be also offered or extended based upon postdoctoral collaborative research interactions at either the Hospital of the University of Pennsylvania or the University of Pennsylvania School of Medicine.

Facilities: The University of Pennsylvania, founded in 1740, gave rise to the nation's first medical school, and the Hospital of the University of Pennsylvania ("HUP") was the first teaching hospital in America. The Division of Dermatopathology has a very active primary and consultative practice for provision of specimens for fellowship training. The Pigmented Lesion Clinic generates one of the largest and most sophisticated computerized databases in existence for correlation of clinical and epidemiologic information with biopsy findings. The central laboratory and diagnostic suites are physically contiguous with the out-patient clinics, facilitating ongoing interaction with clinicians and patients. The Division's Diagnostic Immunodermatology Laboratories and morphology-oriented research laboratories assist actively in diagnostic evaluation and in teaching. Here are located resources for computer-assisted image analysis, immunofluorescence microscopy, immunohistochemistry for lymphocyte and tissue typing, tissue and skin organ culture. The Department's Duhring Research Laboratories are centralized in the adjacent Clinical Research Building, where investigations focused at mast cell biology, cutaneous immunity, T cell malignancy, cutaneous microbiology and aging are actively pursued by fellows and staff. The Medical School, Medical Library, and associated facilities such as the Wistar Institute are within one block. The Division is completely computerized, and equipped with Medline literature retrieval and Internet access. Frequent departmental lectures and visiting professorships foster interaction with clinicians and researchers of national and international repute.

Community: In addition to the proximity of the Hospital-Medical Center Complex to the undergraduate and graduate facilities of the University and to the cultural resources of Philadelphia, a number of major attractions are within two hours by land. These include Washington DC, New York City, shore points, and mountain ranges to the west.

Stipends: Fellowship stipends for PGY 5-6 level applicants range from approximately $50,850 to $55,600. A full fringe benefit package accompanies each yearly stipend.

Staff: Rosalie Elenitsas, MD Associate Professor Dermatology; Program Director; **Bernett L. Johnson, MD** Professor Dermatology; **John T. Seykora, MD, PhD** Assistant Professor Dermatology; **Carrie L. Kovarik, MD** Assistant Professor Dermatology; **Faizan Alawi, DDS** Assistant Professor Pathology, School of Dental Medicine; **Waine C. Johnson, MD** Clinical Professor Dermatology; **Adam I. Rubin, MD** Assistant Professor Dermatology; **Andras Schaffer, MD, PhD** Instructor Dermatology; **David E. Elder, MB, ChB** Professor Pathology; **George Xu, MD, PhD** Assistant Professor Pathology; **George Cotsarelis, MD** skin stem cell biology; **Joel Gelfand, MD, MSCE** clinical trials, psoriasis; **Meenhard Herlyn, DVM, PhD** molecular immunology (Wistar Institute); **Albert M. Kligman, MD, PhD** cutaneous aging; **Sarah Millar, PhD** wnt signaling, development & tumorigenesis; **Michael Ming, MD** melanocytic lesions, epidemiology; **Warren Pear, MD, PhD** notch signaling in hematopoiesis & neoplasia; **Alain Rook, MD** immunology, lymphoma; **John R. Stanley, MD** bullous disorders; **Victoria Werth, MD** connective tissue & bullous disorders.

Applications: Applications for the July 1, 2011 - June 30, 2012 fellowship will be accepted beginning July 15, 2009. Applications and requirements can be downloaded from http://www.uphs.upenn.edu/dermatol/education/dermpath.html and must be submitted on or before November 15, 2009.

Address Inquiries to:

Susan Lamey, Dermatopathology Coordinator
University of Pennsylvania School of Medicine
2 Maloney Building - 3600 Spruce Street
Philadelphia, PA 19104-4128

Phone: (215) 662-4497 • **Fax:** (215) 349-5615 • **E-mail:** susan.lamey@uphs.upenn.edu

Duhring Laboratories, Clinical Research Building

UNIVERSITY OF TEXAS SOUTHWESTERN MEDICAL SCHOOL

Departments of Dermatology and Pathology

Dermatopathology Fellowship

Description: The dermatopathology fellowship consists of one to two years training in diagnostic dermatopathology, clinical dermatology, general pathology, basic sciences and research. The program is designed to prepare the candidate for an academic career in dermatopathology. The program is approved for five positions per year. Abundant material and the most up-to-date facilities provide an excellent opportunity including clinical and laboratory service, teaching and research. The fellowship qualifies for special competence training in dermatopathology. (For basic program description see main listing.)

Requirements: Satisfactory completion of approved residency training in either pathology or dermatology. For candidates with a dermatology background, the training consists of (1) six months of basic dermatopathology training, (2) six months general pathology training concurrently with diagnostic dermatopathology, clinical dermatology, selected teaching conferences, and independent research projects. For candidates with a pathology background, the equivalent of six months clinical dermatology training is substituted for general pathology. Personal interviews and a visit to the institution on invitation are required. Candidates must be eligible for a license to practice medicine in Texas.

Stipends: PGY-5 salary + benefits.

Applications: Applications should be made no later than October 1 prior to the intended fellowship beginning the following July 1. Address inquiries to

Clay J. Cockerell, MD, 2330 Butler Street, Suite 115, Dallas, TX 75235

Phone: (214) 530-5200 • **Fax:** (214) 530-5232
Web site: http://www.utsouthwestern.edu/home_pages/derma/

TULANE UNIVERSITY HEALTH SCIENCES CENTER SCHOOL OF MEDICINE

Department of Pathology

Dermatopathology Fellowship

Description: The objective of this one-year fellowship is to prepare trainees for a career in academic dermatopathology. The fellowship consists of training in dermatopathology including immunopathology, dermatology, and surgical pathology. Fellows will be exposed to a high volume of cases during sign-out. Dermatologist will be trained in surgical pathology, and pathologists will be trained in dermatology through dermatology clinical rotation and conferences. Research activities are encouraged and expected. Trainees are also expected to participate in house staff teaching and helping day to day work of the dermatopathology lab.

Requirements: Applicants must be Board eligible or certified in anatomic/anatomic and clinical pathology or dermatology.

Stipends: Commensurate with the level of postgraduate training in pathology or dermatology. Support is available for one trainee per year.

Staff: A. Wang MD, PhD, Dermatopathology Fellowship Director.

Applications: Applications include curriculum vitae, personal statement, ECFMG certificate if applicable and three letters of references should be submitted 18 months prior to the year of the fellowship.
Submit application to:
Bea DeLucca
Program Coordinator
1430 Tulane Ave. SL-79
New Orleans, LA 70112

Phone: (504) 988-2436 • **Fax:** (504) 988-7389 • **E-mail:** bdelucc@tulane.edu

UNIVERSITY OF VERMONT COLLEGE OF MEDICINE

Dermatopathology Fellowship

Description: This is an accredited one-year fellowship training program sponsored by the Department of Pathology and Division of Dermatology at Fletcher Allen Health Care / University of Vermont College of Medicine. One position is available each year. The objective of the program is to provide individuals with training for a career in dermatopathology with an emphasis on morphologic diagnosis and clinicopathologic correlation. To achieve this objective, the fellow will attend daily case sign-out and participate in multidisciplinary clinical conferences and teaching sessions in both pathology and dermatology. Depending upon the individual's background training, the fellow will also receive training in either clinical dermatology or general pathology, as required for certification. There is ample opportunity for a broad range of research and scholarly activities.

The Dermatopathology Division is a division of Surgical Pathology within the Department of Pathology. There are two full-time dermatopathologists, Deborah L. Cook, MD and Laura A. Greene, MD. The Dermatopathology Division is responsible for approximately 9,000 accessions (averaging 2-3 specimens/accession) per year. The specimens represent a spectrum of diagnostic entities including inflammatory dermatoses, blistering disorders, infectious diseases, and neoplasms. Diagnostic services include a full panel of histochemical and immunohistochemical stains, molecular techniques, immunofluorescence, and electron microscopy.

Requirements: Board certification or eligibility in anatomic pathology/clinical pathology (AP/CP), anatomic pathology (AP), or dermatology.

Stipends: Based upon the applicant's level of postgraduate training.

Applications: Inquiries should be addressed to:
Deborah L. Cook, MD, Director, Dermatopathology Training Program
Department of Pathology and Laboratory Medicine
Fletcher Allen Health Care, MCHV Campus
111 Colchester Avenue, Burlington, VT 05401

Phone: (802) 847-5186 • **Fax:** (802) 847-4155 • **E-mail:** deborah.l.cook@vtmednet.org

---

WAKE FOREST UNIVERSITY BAPTIST MEDICAL CENTER

Department of Pathology

Dermatopathology Fellowship

Description: This one-year ACGME accredited fellowship program is designed to provide dermatopathology training to individuals with a background in pathology or dermatology. Dermatopathology training continues throughout the year, with pathologists receiving clinical dermatology training and dermatologists receiving anatomic pathology training. Biopsy materials from academic and private practice settings are analyzed, with an emphasis on clinical-pathologic correlation. State of the art ancillary techniques available include PCR and in situ hybridization as well as immunohistochemistry and immunofluorescence. Abundant research opportunities are available.

Requirements: Board certification or eligibility in anatomic pathology or dermatology.

Stipends: Commensurate with level of training.

Applications: Inquiries regarding applications should be addressed to
Omar P. Sangüeza, MD, Director of Dermatopathology, Wake Forest University Baptist Medical Center, Department of Pathology, Medical Center Blvd., Winston-Salem, NC 27157-1072.

Phone: (336) 716-4096 • **Fax:** (336) 716-7595 • **E-mail:** osanguez@wfubmc.edu

WASHINGTON UNIVERSITY MEDICAL CENTER

Dermatopathology Fellowship

Description: This one-year fellowship program is designed to prepare individuals to function independently as academic and non-academic dermatopathologists. The program provides intensive training in the morphologic evaluation of skin disease, including the use of immunofluorescence and immunoperoxidase methods and electron microscopy. Research programs in a wide range of fields are available, and participation is encouraged.

Requirements: Applicants must be Board-certified or Board-eligible in AP, AP/CP or Dermatology.

Stipends: Support is commensurate with applicant's level of postgraduate training.

Staff: Anne Lind MD, Director; **Louis Dehner** MD; **Dongsi Lu** MD, PhD.

Applications: The application period begins on July 1 of each year and should be sent to Mary Madden with the address, Washington University School of Medicine, 660 South Euclid Ave, Campus Box 8118, St Louis, MO 63110

Phone: (314) 747-0687 • **Fax:** (314) 747-2663

UNIVERSITY OF WASHINGTON

Department of Pathology

Dermatopathology Fellowship

Description: An ACGME accredited program that provides theoretical and practical educational experiences in dermatopathology. Fellows coming from a pathology residency will spend 50% of their time in clinical dermatology and those from dermatology will focus on pathology in a similar time frame to ensure a comprehensive knowledge base in both disciplines. Training will also include the use of special techniques and presentations at teaching conferences. Research is strongly encouraged through a variety of ongoing projects in both pathology and dermatology.

Requirements: Applicants are selected for interview based on academic excellence and interest in the subspecialty. Applicants are expected to have completed the training required for certification in Anatomic Pathology by the American Board of Pathology or Dermatology by the Dermatology Board. Must be eligible for a Washington State license.

Facilities: The program is based at University of Washington Medical Center in partnership with the Department of Dermatology. UW Medicine provides tertiary medical care and medical education to the five-state region of Washington, Wyoming, Alaska, Montana and Idaho.UW Medicine provides tertiary medical care and medical education to the five-state region of Washington, Wyoming, Alaska, Montana and Idaho.

Stipends: One-year appointment with salary and benefits based on the schedule for residents at an equivalent level (R5=$55,032). Fellows are encouraged to apply for extramural funding, if additional research training is desired. (1 position)

Staff: Z. Argenyi Director; **E. George**; **C. Alpers**; **P. Swanson**; **B. Wood**.

Applications: Inquiry: Zsolt B. Argenyi, MD, Fellowship Director, at zsolt@u.washington.edu
Available at the web site or contact Michelle Rickard, Academic Programs Manager, Dermatopathology Fellowship Program, at the email address below. Application materials must be received by February 1 with selected interviews to follow until the position is filled.

Phone: (206) 598-4933 • **Fax:** (206) 598-7321 • **E-mail:** fellowship@pathology.washington.edu
Web site: www.pathology.washington.edu/academics/fellowship/

The University of Washington is an equal opportunity institution.

UNIVERSITY OF ALABAMA AT BIRMINGHAM

Forensic Pathology Fellowship

Description: The Pathology Department of the University of Alabama at Birmingham and the Jefferson County Coroner/Medical Examiner Office offer a one-year accredited fellowship training program in forensic pathology. The office draws its caseload from Jefferson County, which includes the city of Birmingham, and has a population base of approximately 662,000. The office annually examines approximately 700 bodies including approximately 100 homicides and 230 accidental deaths. Complete scene investigations are routinely conducted by in-house investigators of homicidal, accidental, and suicidal deaths. All medical and police records are routinely obtained. The fellow acts as a functioning forensic pathologist and is responsible, under supervision by staff pathologists, for scene investigations, complete postmortem examinations, protocol preparations, conferences with interested parties, and actual court testimony. Consultation in all medical specialties is readily available if needed, as are opportunities for teaching. Two crime laboratories (representing two jurisdictions) serve the metropolitan area. The medical examiner office is well staffed and equipped, including complete photographic and x-ray facilities and computerization of all records. The database makes research feasible, and research with presentation at a national scientific meeting is encouraged.

Requirements: Successful completion of accredited pathology residency training program in either anatomic pathology or anatomic/clinical pathology.

Stipends: Commensurate with year of postgraduate training, plus fringe benefits.

Applications: Write or call
Dr. Gregory G. Davis, Jefferson County Coroner/Medical Examiner Office, 1515 Sixth Avenue South, Room 220, Birmingham, AL 35233-1601.

Phone: (205) 930-3603 • **Fax:** (205) 930-3595

UNIVERSITY OF COLORADO DENVER SCHOOL OF MEDICINE

Forensic Pathology Fellowship

Description: This 12-month training program is designed to prepare individuals for a career in forensic pathology. The fellowship provides primary training at the Denver Office of the Medical Examiner, a NAME accredited office with academic ties to the University Of Colorado School Of Medicine. Additional rotations at the Denver Police Department Crime Laboratory and The Veterans Affairs Medical Center /Chemistry and Molecular Laboratories provide training is DNA/serology, firearms, trace evidence, scene documentation and photography, latent prints, drug analysis and toxicology. The Denver Office of the Medical Examiner accepts primary jurisdiction on between 1050 and 1200 cases each year, and performs approximately 730-850 medicolegal autopsies and 250-300 visual examinations each year. Faculty includes 3 AP/CP/FP board certified pathologists. Support staff includes 7 medicolegal death investigators and 4 full time forensic autopsy technicians. The fellow will be expected to perform between 200 and 250 autopsies, and will be responsible for the final report and death certification. In addition, the fellow will communicate with families, law enforcement, attorneys, health professionals and other interested parties; participate in community emergency preparedness and various death review processes; provide testimony and expert opinions and participate in resident and medical student education. During the training period the fellow will develop skills in forensic photography, chain of custody and evidence collection, interpretation of postmortem laboratory testing, and identification of remains. The fellow is encouraged to present a paper or poster at a national forensic meeting.

Requirements: Applicants must have graduated from an accredited school of medicine or osteopathy, be eligible for medical licensure in the State of Colorado and be board eligible or board certified in AP or AP/CP by the start of the fellowship term. An interview is required.

Stipends: The fellow will be an employee of the City and County of Denver. The salary for this position is currently $72,322; pay grade 401-D. Benefits with the City and County of Denver meet the requirements of ACGME.

Applications:
Application and information can be found on the UCDSOM website. Applications for July 2010 will be accepted until April 1, 2010; for 2011, until April 1, 2011. Completed applications, along with a current CV, letter of interest and three references, should be sent to Amy Martin MD, Program Director, Denver Office of the Medical Examiner, 660 Bannock St., Denver CO, 80204; amy.martin@denvergov.org. Application also must be made to the City and County of Denver at www.denvergov.org/jobs.

Phone: (303) 436-7001 • **Fax:** (303) 436-7709
Web site: www.uchsc.edu/pathology

OFFICE OF THE MEDICAL EXAMINER OF ALLEGHENY COUNTY

Forensic Pathology Program

Description: The Allegheny County Medical Examiner"s Office (ACME) offers a one-year residency program in forensic pathology. Both the American Board of Pathology and the American Medical Association have accredited this program. Residents will participate in approximately fifteen hundred medical-legal examinations performed each year at the ACME. Toxicological and histological studies are also integral components of the program. In addition, opportunities to engage in forensic scientific research and medical-legal teaching will be available during the year.
Types and Numbers of Appointments: Each year, one fellow in forensic pathology is selected.
Facilities: The ACME is the main forensic facility in Western Pennsylvania. As such, the most modern and sophisticated equipment and facilities are generally available for conducting in-depth medical-legal investigations. This is also true with respect to the Toxicology Laboratory. The ACME has an excellent cooperative relationship with the Duquesne University School of Pharmacy (just two blocks away) and the University of Pittsburgh Schools of Medicine and Public Health. The extensive libraries and laboratories of these Institutions are available to ACME personnel, along with numerous opportunities for various research programs.
Community: Allegheny County (Pittsburgh), with a population of approximately 1,450,085, is the major metropolitan area of Southwestern Pennsylvania, Northeastern Ohio, and Northern West Virginia. The downtown area features a magnificent skyline set in the ''Golden Triangle'' formed by the meeting of the Allegheny and Monongahela Rivers to form the Ohio River. Once known as a ''smokey'' steel town, Pittsburgh is now the beneficiary of a massive and successful clean-up effort in the 1960's. Heinz Hall attracts cultural activities such as opera, ballet, theatre, and is the home for the world renowned Pittsburgh Symphony. The Scaife Art Gallery offers countless and varied exhibitions of Art. Major college and professional athletic events are offered in football, baseball, basketball, hockey, and soccer.
Stipends: Salaries for residents are $58,000-$61,500 per year, Accidental Insurance and medical benefits are available through group plans offered by the ACME.
Staff: Karl Williams MD, University of Pittsburgh, Medical School, 1969-1974; MPH, Masters in Public Health, University of Pittsburgh, 2003; Internship Veterans Administration Hospital, 1974 - 1975; Pathology Residency Program Allegheny General Hospital and Shadyside Hospital, 1979 - 1983; Forensic Pathology, Allegheny County Coroner's Office, 1983-1985; Director of Laboratories, 1985 - 2007; Medical Director Precision Therapeutics, Inc, 2005 - 2007; Medical Examiner of Allegheny County, 2007 to present; **Abdulrezak M. Shakir** MD, Baghdad University Medical School, 1965; FRCS Diploma (The Royal College of Surgeons of Edinburgh), 1977; Pathology Residency Program of the University Health Center of Pittsburgh, 1984-1988; Associate Pathologist, Allegheny County Coroner's Office, 1988-1990; Forensic Pathologist, Allegheny County Coroner's Office, 1990-Present; Clinical Associate Professor of Pathology, University of Pittsburgh, Medical School, 1989 Present; **Todd Luckasevic** DO, Lake Erie College of Osteopathic Medicine, 1996-2000; Residency in Pathology Allegheny General Hospital 2001-2004; Fellowship in Forensic Pathology Virginia Commonwealth University 2004-2005; Assistant Chief Medical Examiner, Virginia Office of Medical Examiner 2005-2007; Associate Medical Examiner, 2007-Present; **Baiyang Xu** MD, Harbin Medical University, 1982; Postdoctoral Fellow Training, Heshey Medical Center, Penn State University College of Medicine, 1992-1994; Anatomic and Clinical Pathology Residency Training, Hershey Medical Center, Penn State University College of Medicine in Pennsylvania and MetraHealth Medical Center, Case Western Reserve University in Cleveland Ohio, 2001-2006; Forensic Pathology Fellowship Training, Harris County Medical Examiner's Office in Houston, Texas, 2006-2007; Associate Medical Examiner, 2008-Present; **Jennifer Janssen** Bachelors in biology, Clarion University; Masters in Pharmacology/Toxiology, University of Duquesne, Assistant Chief Toxologist, Allegheny County Coroner's Office, 1980-2008, Chief Toxicologist, Allegheny County Medical Examiner's Office, 2008-Present.
Applications: Residents must be graduates of approved medical schools in the U.S. or Canada. Graduates of foreign medical schools must have an ECFMG certificate. Residents must have completed training in an accredited anatomic or anatomic/clinical pathology program.
Address inquiries to:
A. M. Shakir, MD
Director of Residency and Fellowship
Allegheny County Medical Examiner's Office
542 Fourth Avenue
Pittsburgh, PA 15219
Phone: (412) 350-4800

BEXAR COUNTY MEDICAL EXAMINER'S OFFICE

Forensic Pathology Fellowship

Description: The Bexar County Medical Examiner's Office offers an ACGME accredited one-year fellowship in forensic pathology at its office in San Antonio, Texas. The successful applicant will experience a comprehensive program with training in diverse types of death investigation cases, as well as experience in the administration of a successful medical examiner's office and courtroom testimony. The goal of the program is to produce physicians with an excellent understanding of the philosophical goals of death investigation, the ability to integrate all types of investigative data into a cogent conclusion, and a high degree of integrity and independence as an investigator. The Office is staffed by five forensic pathologists, nine investigators, nine toxicologists and approximately seventeen technical and clerical support personnel. A board-certified forensic odontologist has an office in the facility, and training and consultation in forensic anthropology is provided by a board-certified forensic anthropologist. Neuropathology, pediatric pathology and other subspecialty consultations are readily available. There are multiple scheduled didactic lectures for the fellow and rotating residents, and various types of case and topical conferences are held on a regular basis. In 2007, the Office investigated 9,304 deaths, accepting jurisdiction in 2,370 cases and conducting 1,507 autopsies. Case breakdown was 176 homicides, 182 suicides, 832 accidents, 838 naturals, and 157 undetermined/unclassified. Over 58,000 individual toxicology tests were performed, and a total of 648 scene investigations were conducted.
Requirements: Successful completion of training in anatomic or anatomic & clinical pathology.
Types and Numbers of Appointments: The program is accredited for two fellowship positions. However, only one position is currently funded.
Facilities: The Medical Examiner's Office is housed in a modern, spacious, and well-equipped building located in the South Texas Medical Center. The University of Texas Health Sciences Center at San Antonio Schools of Medicine, Dentistry and Nursing are adjacent to the office. A full service medical library, a fully stocked bookstore, and several large tertiary care teaching hospitals are in the complex.
Community: Bexar County has a diverse population of approximately 1.5 million. The largest city in the county is San Antonio, the seventh largest city in the United States. The city provides a full range of cultural activities, and the mild and sunny climate allows for year-round outdoor recreation. The scenic Texas Hill Country is just north of the city, and the Gulf Coast beaches are a short drive away.
Stipends: $65,000 + benefits.
Applications: For more information or to apply, contact Randall E. Frost, MD, Chief Medical Examiner, Bexar County Medical Examiner's Office, 7337 Louis Pasteur Drive, San Antonio, TX 78229. Applicants should submit a letter of interest, a current curriculm vitae, and two letters of professional recommendation.
Phone: (210) 335-4053 • **Fax:** (210) 335-4052 • **E-mail:** frostmd@bexar.org

BROWARD COUNTY OFFICE OF THE MEDICAL EXAMINER FORT LAUDERDALE

Forensic Pathology Program

Description: The Broward County Medical Examiner's Office (BCMEO) offers a one-year Fellowship program in forensic pathology. This program has been accredited through the Accreditation Council of Graduate Medical Education. Residents will participate in approximately 2,000 medical-legal examinations performed each year at the BCMEO. Toxicological and histological studies are also integral components of the program. In addition, opportunities to engage in forensic scientific research and medical-legal teaching will be available during the year. Each year, one Fellow in forensic pathology is selected.

Requirements: Completed training in an ACGME-accredited program for anatomic or anatomic/clinical pathology

Types and Numbers of Appointments: Each year, one fellow in forensic pathology will be funded. Another position is accredited but not funded

Facilities: In January 1998, the Broward County Medical Examiner's Office expanded into a new and spacious facility. The most modern and highly sophisticated equipment is available for conducting in-depth medical-legal investigations. This is also true with respect to the Toxicology Laboratory which is being completely renovated. The BCMEO has an excellent cooperative relationship with the University of Miami and NOVA Southeastern University. The extensive libraries and laboratories of these institutions are available to BCMEO personnel along with numerous opportunities for various research programs.

Community: The geographical area served by the Broward County Medical Examiner's Office covers the full 1,211 square miles of Broward County, bounded by Palm Beach County to the North and Miami-Dade County to the South. In 2007, the Broward County population was estimated to be 1,753,162. Included within Broward County are 31 municipalities including Fort Lauderdale, the county's largest city with a population of more than 175,000 residents. Also included within Broward County are a major international airport and the nation's second busiest cruise-ship seaport. In Broward County there are 19 major hospitals, including a trauma treatment network with three major trauma centers.

Stipends: Salaries for Fellows are $78,396 per year, and medical benefits are available through group plans offered by Broward County.

Staff: **Joshua A. Perper** MD, LLB, MSc Medical School of Hebrew University, 1960; Law School of Hebrew University, 1966; Postgraduate studies in forensic pathology, Johns Hopkins University, 1969; Associate Medical Examiner and Senior Research Fellow, Office of the Chief Medical Examiner, Baltimore, Maryland, 1969-71; Chief Forensic Pathologist, Allegheny County Coroner's Office, Pittsburgh, Pennsylvania, 1972-80; Acting Coroner, Allegheny Coroner's Office, Pittsburgh, Pennsylvania, 1980-81; Coroner, Allegheny County Coroner's Office, Pittsburgh, Pennsylvania, 1982-94; Chief Medical Examiner, Broward County Medical Examiner's Office, Ft. Lauderdale, Florida, 1994-Present; Clinical Professor of Pathology, Epidemiology and Public Health, University of Miami, 1994-Present; **Stephen J. Cina** MD Vanderbilt University, School of Medicine, 1992, Pathology Resident in Anatomic Pathology, Medical University of South Carolina, 1992-1995, Senior Clinical Fellow in Surgical Pathology, John Hopkins Hospital, 1995-1996, State of Maryland, Fellowship in Forensic Pathology, Office of the Chief Medical Examiner, 1996-1997, Major, USAF Medical Corps, 59th Wing, Wilford Hall Medical Center, Lackland Air Force Base, Texas, 1997-2001; Office of the Armed Forces Medical Examiner, Regional Medical Examiner, 1997-2001, Medical Examiner, Bexar County, San Antonio, Texas, 1998-2000, Deputy Coroner, Larimer County, Colorado, 2001-2006, Coroner/Medical Examiner, Weld County, Colorado, 2003-2006, Deputy Chief Medical Examiner, Director, Fellowship Program, Broward County Medical Examiner's Office 2007-Present.; **Lance G. Davis** MD American University of the Caribbean School of Medicine, 1987; Medical Internship Program, Chestnut Hill Hospital of Philadelphia, 1987-1988 (Instructor of Anatomy and Physiology, Montgomery County Community College, 1989); Pathology Residency Program, University of Medicine and Dentistry of New Jersey, New Jersey Medical School, 1989-1993, Staff Pathologist, East Orange Veterans Affairs Medical Center, 1992-1993, Forensic Pathology Fellowship, Dade County Medical Examiner's Office, Miami, Florida, 1993-1994; Associate Medical Examiner, Broward County Medical Examiner's Office, Ft Lauderdale, Florida, 1994-Presenet. Clinical Assistant Professor, NOVA Southeastern University; **Iouri V Boiko** MD Voroshilovgrad State Medical Institute, Ukraine, 1983, Resident in Pathology and Clinical Medicine Program, University of Texas Medical School, Houston, TX, 2000-2004, Fellow in Forensic Pathology Program, Office of the Medical Examiner of Harris County, Houston, TX, 2005; R.E. Kavetsky Institute for Oncology Problems, Ukranian Academy of the Sciences, Kiev, Ukraine, 1990, PhD, Deputy Chief Medical Examiner, Office of the Chief Medical Examiner, Charleston, WV, 2005-2007, Associate Medical Examiner, Broward County Medical Examiner's Office, 2008-present.; **Khalil Wardak** MD, Kabul University School of Medicine, Kabul, Afghanistan, 1990-1994; Ross University School of Medicine, 1995-1999;Pathology Residency, George Washington University Hospital, D.C., 2000-2004;Pathology Fellowship, Broward County Medical Examiner's Office, Ft. Lauderdale, Florida, 2007-2008; Associate Medical Examiner, Broward County Medical Examiner's Office, Ft. Lauderdale, Florida, 2008-Present.; **Harold E. Schueler** PhD University of Cincinnati, 1989; Chief Toxicologist, Hamilton County Coroner's Office, 1989-1991; Chief of Toxicology, Hamilton County Coroner's Office, 1991-1997; Chief Toxicologist, Broward County Medical Examiner's Office, 1997-present.

Applications: Joshua A. Perper, MD, LL.B., M.Sc.
Broward County Office of the Medical Examiner
5301 SW 31st Avenue
Ft Lauderdale, FL 33312
Phone: (954) 327 6511 • **E-mail:** sbaker@broward.org

COOK COUNTY OFFICE OF THE MEDICAL EXAMINER

Forensic Pathology Fellowship

Description: This program is designed to provide one year of training in the special field of forensic pathology to individuals previously trained in anatomic and clinical pathology or in anatomic pathology alone. All training is provided in the Office of the Medical Examiner of Cook County, Chicago, Illinois, under the supervision of fully qualified forensic pathologists. A fellow in forensic pathology would ordinarily perform approximately 300 medicolegal autopsies. In the majority of these cases, death would be due to the immediate and direct effects of physical and chemical injury. A fully equipped toxicology laboratory, supervised by qualified toxicologists, is present in the office and residents spend one month in this area for training. X-ray and fluoroscopy equipment are available in the autopsy area and all X-rays are taken by registered X-ray technicians.
Requirements: Applicants must be Board certified or eligible in anatomic pathology and eligible for licensure in the State of Illinois.
Stipends: The salary and benefits package is competitive with similar fellowship programs.
Applications: Inquiries should be addressed to:
Nancy L. Jones, MD, Residency Program Director and Chief Medical Examiner, 2121 West Harrison Street, Chicago, IL 60612.
Phone: (312) 997-4500

FULTON COUNTY MEDICAL EXAMINER
EMORY UNIVERSITY SCHOOL OF MEDICINE

Department of Pathology and Laboratory Medicine

Forensic Pathology Fellowship

Description: Fully accredited, this fellowship provides the necessary experience to meet the requirements set forth by the ACGME. Offered through the Emory University School of Medicine, training is based at the Fulton County Medical Examiner's Center. Approximately 2,200 deaths are reported to the office per year. A full-time staff of five Board-certified forensic pathologists and 12 death investigators conduct inquiries into approximately 160 homicides, 80 suicides, 200 accidental deaths, and 150 traffic fatalities per year, along with many sudden and unexplained natural deaths. In 2007, approximately 1000 autopsies, 300 external exams, and 900 scene investigations were conducted, with over 1,000 toxicologic examinations, performed by the Crime Laboratory. The fellow is expected to perform 200-250 autopsies during the year and participate in scene investigations. Adequate staff and teaching material are available to facilitate education without undue or excessive caseload and service work. Experience in toxicology, firearms, criminalistics, and rotations at the Georgia State Crime Laboratory. Other features include in-house digital photography and histology, office computerization, and access to Grady Memorial Hospital laboratory. The program is directed toward board certification in Forensic Pathology.
Requirements: USMLE Step 3; completion of AP training; Georgia medical licensure.
Stipends: Commensurate with PGY-5. Information: Mary Lou Mojonnier, Education Coordinator
Staff: **Randy Hanzlick** MD, Director and Chief Med Examiner; **Michele Stauffenberg** MD, Deputy Chief Medical Examiner and Assistant Director; **Michael Heninger** MD; **Geoffrey Smith** MD; **Karen Sullivan** MD.
Applications:
Phone: (404) 727-4283 • **E-mail:** mmojonn@emory.edu
Web site: www.emory.edu/PATHOLOGY/

CUYAHOGA COUNTY CORONER'S OFFICE

Forensic Pathology Fellowship

Description: The Cuyahoga County Coroner's Office is the medicolegal death investigation entity serving Cleveland and 58 surrounding suburban municipalities. Cuyahoga County has a population of 1.34 million people and comprises a geographic area of 458 square miles.

In 2006, the office investigated 5307 reported cases, assumed jurisdiction in 3564 cases, and performed complete autopsies on 1322 cases. Of the cases falling under the office's jurisdiction, 59.9% were naturals; 3.1% were vehicular fatalities; 4.0% were suicides; 4.1% were homicides; 27.8% were accidents; and 1.1% were undetermined. The office also performed 231 additional complete autopsies for several neighboring counties.

Training in forensic pathology will be a tutorial system under the direction of Dr. Joseph A. Felo, Director of the Fellowship Program, and associates. This program is designed to provide one year of training in the special field of forensic pathology to individuals previously trained in anatomic and clinical pathology or in anatomic pathology alone. All training is provided in the Office of the Cuyahoga County Coroner.

The main objective of this training program is to provide the trainee with a broad exposure to the practice of forensic pathology from which he or she may gain solid, wide, wholesome knowledge, with the necessary skills and attitudes for this discipline. Evaluation of the trainee with the purpose of achieving these objectives will be made continually.

During this year of fellowship, the trainee will be appointed as a junior Deputy Coroner, and will work with each of the on-duty professional staff, but will work most closely with the program director and senior Deputy Coroner, Dr. Joseph A. Felo. The fellow will conduct a substantial number of medicolegal autopsies on routine and unique cases, and will be given substantial control of cases at all levels (naturals, accidents, suicides, and homicides), commensurate with their increasing ability. Special emphasis will be placed on autopsy technique, photographic documentation, proper evidence and toxicologic specimen collection and handling, microscopic tissue analysis, and the written protocols used to document the autopsy. All of the fellow's cases will be reviewed with the fellow by a senior Deputy Coroner.

The fellow will gain experience in case analysis daily during morning viewing, and will participate in intradepartmental conferences that are held weekly. The fellow will participate in teaching of rotating pathology residents, medical students, and other groups as needed. The fellow is expected to answer death related inquires from families, treating physicians, law enforcement agencies, insurance agencies, attorneys, news media, and other interested parties to develop necessary communication skills and circumspection.

The trainee is encouraged to go to selected crime scenes in order to become acquainted with the type of information that needs to be accumulated, the preservation of evidence, and the importance of cooperation with law enforcement officials. Training during the year also includes toxicology experience, both on a day-to-day level and through dedicated time spent in the ABFT and ASCLD/LAB-accredited toxicology laboratory located in the same building. Dedicated time will be spent in the ASCLD/LAB-accredited forensic laboratories, also located in the same building, to survey forensic topics including serology, DNA, hair and fiber analysis, clothing and vehicle inspection, gunshot residue analysis, etc. The opportunity to work with anthropology, odontology, entomology, and radiology expert consultants is available on relevant cases.

The forensic pathology fellow will participate in the preparation of cases for court and will attend court proceedings where a pathologist is an expert witness. The fellow will be expected to testify in court regarding the cases in which he or she participated, with appropriate guidance and supervision.

The fellow will be encouraged to participate in ongoing research by the staff and to conduct his or her own investigative work where feasible within the office. The fellow will be expected to give occasional presentations on subjects of forensic interest to anatomic and clinical pathology residents at any of the three pathology residencies in Cleveland.

Requirements: Requirements include previous training in anatomic and clinical pathology or in anatomic pathology alone.

Stipends: Are commensurate with years of post graduate training plus governmental fringe benefits; currently $70,000 annual salary.

Applications: Address inquiries to:

Joseph A. Felo, DO, Deputy Coroner and Director of Fellowship Program
Cuyahoga County Coroner's Office
11001 Cedar Avenue
Cleveland, OH 44106
Phone: (216) 698-5491 • **Fax:** (216) 698-6649 • **E-mail:** jfelo@cuyahogacounty.us

HENNEPIN COUNTY MEDICAL EXAMINER

Forensic Pathology Fellowship

Description: The Hennepin County Medical Examiner (HCME) offers a one-year, ACGME-accredited fellowship in forensic pathology. The fellow participates in all aspects of medicolegal death investigation, from scene investigation through case review, autopsy, grand jury and trial. The fellow is given increasing responsibility as the year progresses with regard to handling of scenes, determination of depth of investigation and trial preparation. The fellow is expected to complete approximately 250 medicolegal autopsies during the year of training, including 40-50 homicides. Skill in prosection is expected and will be taught. Extramural rotations include the Hennepin County Sheriff's Office Crime Lab (ASCLD-certified), forensic anthropology and cardiovascular pathology. The fellow participates in the annual Minnesota Coroners' and Medical Examiners' Association meeting in October, and has expenses paid to the American Academy of Forensic Sciences Meeting in February. In addition to teaching in the autopsy room and at the microscope, the HCME physicians provide the fellow with a weekly series of didactic lectures throughout the year to assist in preparation for Forensic Pathology board certification. All HCME physicians are affiliated with the University of Minnesota Department of Laboratory Medicine and Pathology and the Hennepin County Medical Center Pathology Department. Pathology residents and medical students from the University of Minnesota regularly rotate through the office, and the fellow is an active participant in their education.
Requirements: Applicants must have completed training in AP or AP-CP prior to the beginning of the fellowship, and be eligible for Minnesota medical licensure.
Facilities: The HCME's office is a spacious, state-of-the art facility located in downtown Minneapolis within walking distance of shopping districts, theaters, sporting arenas and the courts. All photography, radiography and dictation is digital and accessible on computers throughout the facility. The fellow is provided his/her own office, laptop computer and parking space.
The office is staffed 24 hours a day, 7 days a week with in-house, trained medicolegal death investigators. Autopsy technicians prepare bodies for autopsy and assist with prosections as directed. Odontology, anthropology, and entomology support is provided by local experts in the Twin Cities metro area. The toxicology lab is located across the street in the Hennepin County Medical Center, and is directed by a PhD chemist who joins the ME staff weekly for our toxicology conference. Neuropathology expertise is available in house and through the University of Minnesota. Cardiovascular pathology support is provided by the nationally-renowned Jesse Edwards Cardiovascular Registry.
Community: Hennepin County, with a population of 1.1 million and an area of 600 square miles, includes the city of Minneapolis and the surrounding suburbs. The Twin Cities and Minnesota abound with cultural, artistic, outdoor and athletic activities. The Minneapolis-St. Paul International Airport is one of the largest airports in the country and is readily accessible via car or light rail.
Stipends: Current stipend for a PGY5 resident is $51,674 plus $18,900 deputy medical examiner pay.
Staff: Andrew M Baker MD (AP/CP/FP) Chief Medical Examiner; **Lorren W Jackson** MD Assistant Medical Examiner; **Owen L Middleton** MD (AP/CP/FP) Assistant Medical Examiner; **Mitchel K Morey** MD (AP/FP/NP) Assistant Medical Examiner.
Applications: Inquiries can be directed to David Eggen, Administrator, Hennepin County Medical Examiner's Office, 530 Chicago Avenue, Minneapolis, MN 55415.
Phone: (612) 215-6300 • **E-mail:** david.eggen@co.hennepin.mn.us

INDIANA UNIVERSITY SCHOOL OF MEDICINE

Department of Pathology

Forensic Pathology Fellowship

Description: The Indiana University provides an ACGME-accredited fellowship in forensic pathology with the IU Department of Pathology and the Marion County Coroner's office, which fulfills the eligibility requirements of Board certification. The university-based program provides forensic pathology services to the Indianapolis metropolitan area (population est. 1.5 million) and surrounding 23 counties. The forensic pathology division performs approximately 1,650 death investigations and 950 autopsies annually, encompassing a broad spectrum of both urban and rural cases. The faculty of three experienced Board certified forensic pathologists provide supervision, guidance, and support. The forensic fellow will perform approximately 250 autopsies of varying complexity. Consultation with neuro- and pediatric pathologists, forensic anthropologists and odontologists are available. The fellow will spend time at the Indianapolis/ Marion County Forensic Laboratory and the Indiana State Police Laboratory. The trainee will be allotted time and encouraged to perform a research project or write a paper for presentation at one of the two annual national forensic science meetings (NAME, AAFS). The fellow will also assist in teaching and giving lectures for medical students and pathology residents.
Requirements: Applicants must have completed an accredited residency in either anatomic or anatomic/clinical pathology prior to beginning the fellowship.
Stipends: Commensurate with the year of post graduate training in pathology.
Applications: Interested applicants should submit a curriculum vitae and 3 letters of recommendation to: Joye M. Carter, MD, Director of Forensic Pathology Program, 521 West McCarty Street, Indianapolis, IN 46225
Phone: (317) 327-5841 • **Fax:** (317) 327-5798 • **E-mail:** jcarter@indygov.org
Website: http://www.pathology.iupui.edu

KING COUNTY MEDICAL EXAMINER'S OFFICE

Affiliation with Univ of Washington Department of Pathology

Forensic Pathology Fellowship

Description: The office offers a year long ACGME accredited fellowship in forensic pathology. Located in Seattle, the office also serves all of King County which incorporates 39 smaller cities and towns, two major airports, several colleges and universities, and more than twenty hospitals including the regional level I trauma center for the Pacific Northwest. Our jurisdiction covers mountains, beaches, rivers, lakes, farms, national parks, as well as urban and suburban locales to provide a rich variety of forensic casework. Under the supervision of board certified forensic pathologists the fellow will assume the duties of Assistant Medical Examiner and complete 250-350 autopsies, 50-100 external examinations, death scene investigations, and court appearances. Fellows are expected to interact with and instruct medical students, residents, police, and attorneys as time and experience permit.
The NAME accredited office is professionally staffed by five full time forensic pathologists, a forensic anthropologist, and a fellow. Autopsy support is provided by four technicians and case investigations are carried out by 14 medicolegal death investigators. We are located in Harborview Medical Center and have ready access to a wide range of consultative services. The Washington State Patrol Toxicology and Crime Laboratory is a five minute drive from the office and all toxicology is performed there.
Requirements: Completed training in AP or AP/CP residency prior to beginning fellowship and eligible for Washington State licensure.
Stipends: Commensurate with level of training plus benefits.
Applications: Positions will be filled on a rolling basis. Interested residents are invited to submit a letter of interest well in advance of the July 1 start date. Address inquiries to:
Richard Harruff, MD, PhD, King County Medical Examiner's Office, Harborview Medical Center, Box 359792, 325 Ninth Avenue, Seattle, WA 98104-2499.
Phone: (206) 731-3505
Web site: www.kingcounty.gov/healthservices/health/examiner.aspx

OFFICE OF THE CHIEF MEDICAL EXAMINER
JOSEPH A. JACHIMCZYK FORENSIC SCIENCE CENTER

Forensic Pathology Fellowship

Description: The Office of the Medical Examiner of Harris County, fully accredited by the National Association of Medical Examiners (NAME), offers two positions for ACGME-accredited fellowship in forensic pathology. The training program fulfills the eligibility requirements for Board certification. Fellows participate in the functioning of a busy Medical Examiner's Office, which serves the metropolitan Houston area and 8 surrounding counties. Fellows perform approximately 250 autopsies, as well as external examinations, participate in death scene investigations, handle questions from family members, lawyers, police officers, and testify in court. Fellows are monitored by staff assistant medical examiners and ABFT certified toxicologists. On- site services include anthropology, toxicology, firearms, trace evidence, controlled substances, DNA, and photography. The crime laboratory disciplines are all accredited by the American Society of Crime Laboratory Directors/Laboratory Accreditation Board (ASCLD/LAB); the toxicology laboratory is additionally accredited by the American Board of Forensic Toxicology (ABFT). The Texas Medical Center, the University of Texas, Baylor College of Medicine and Methodist Hospital Houston provide consultation services in forensic odontology, neuropathology, pediatrics, and cardiology. Fellows may participate in the local trauma centers' regular morbidity and mortality conferences, as well as monthly child and elder fatality meetings. There is on-site access to the Internet, including Pubmed/Medline. The office actively participates in teaching medical students and residents. Research and publication activities are encouraged, and presentations at national meetings are facilitated.
Requirements: Applicants must be Board-certified or eligible in AP or AP/CP and have a Texas medical license. Board-eligible applicants may apply for a training permit from the Texas State Board of Medical Examiners. Residents pursuing an AP-FP track, and already enrolled in an ACGME-approved residency program, will also be considered.
Stipends: Approximately $100,000.00.
Applications: Address inquiries to:
Dwayne A. Wolf, MD, PhD, Deputy Chief Medical Examiner, Office of the Medical Examiner of Harris County, Joseph A. Jachimczyk Forensic Center, 1885 Old Spanish Trail, Houston, TX 77054.
Phone: (713) 796-9292 • **Fax:** (713) 795-8987 • **E-mail:** dwayne.wolf@meo.hctx.net
Web site: www.co.harris.tx.us/ME

LOS ANGELES COUNTY DEPARTMENT OF CORONER

Affiliation with UCLA & USC Schools of Medicine

Forensic Pathology Fellowship

Description: A one-year accredited fellowship program is available as preparation for taking the forensic pathology board exam. A total of approximately 19,000 cases are reported annually to the office and approximately 4,800 necropsies are performed of which 1,100 are investigated as homicides. Full microscopic and toxicology studies are performed. A full range of consultative services are available in the fields of neuropathology, odontology, anthropology, radiology, anesthesiology, surgery, pediatrics, ophthalmologic pathology, pulmonary pathology, and psychological autopsy. Fellows can attend the annual American Academy of Forensic Sciences Meeting or the National Association of Medical Examiners (NAME) Meeting. They receive toxicology and electron microscopy training at in-house laboratories, and train in firearms, trace evidence and serological analysis at the Los Angeles County Sheriff's Crime Lab, and Los Angeles Police Department Crime Lab. They also are exposed to at-scene investigations, gross/microscopic/lab pathology conferences, resident lectures, and court testimony. Hands-on training in odontology and neuropathology is also available. A week of anthropology training is offered. Continuing Medical Education guest lectures are also part of this unique fellowship program.

Requirements: Applicants should be permanent residents or citizens of the USA. They must have completed AP or AP/CP residency and be Board-eligible or certified. Applicants also need a State of California medical license and driver's license.

Stipends: $69,519.60

Staff: Chief Medical Examiner-Coroner; 20 Board-Certified Forensic Pathologists.

Applications: Send complete CV, proof of Board certification/eligibility, copy of California medical license, and three references to

Lakshmanan Sathyavagiswaran, MD, Chief Medical Examiner-Coroner, 1104 North Mission Road, Los Angeles, CA 90033.

Phone: (323) 343-0522 • **Fax:** (323) 225-2235

UNIVERSITY OF LOUISVILLE HEALTH SCIENCES CENTER

Forensic Pathology Fellowship

Description: The University of Louisville Division of Forensic Pathology, in conjunction with the Kentucky Office of the Chief Medical Examiner (KY OCME), offers a unique educational opportunity during a 12 month fellowship program in Forensic Pathology. The KY OCME is staffed by five full-time, board-qualified forensic pathologists, all of whom actively participate in the training of the forensic fellow. The office performs approximately 1200 cases per year, from both urban and rural areas. The fellow is thus afforded with the opportunity to participate in a wide variety of cases, including cases unique to rural settings, such as farming, hunting, and mining fatalities. Located in Louisville, KY, the KY OCME also conducts many cases associated with urban areas. Weekly neuropathology and monthly cardiovascular pathology conferences are scheduled, along with monthly journal club meetings, and other regularly scheduled academic meetings including Check Sample reviews. Specialty consultants who regularly participate in the fellow's academic experience include a full-time forensic anthropologist, a forensic odontologist, and pediatric pathologists who collaboratively participate in studies and cases at the KY OCME. The KY OCME has a Forensic Medicine Program which is staffed by forensic pathologists, a full-time forensic pediatric consultant, and three forensic nurses and conducts approximately 300 examinations each year on living victims of violence, including child physical abuse, elder abuse, domestic violence, and investigations of excessive use of force by police when consulted by law enforcement officers or social services workers. Fellows are provided private office space, and ample educational materials, including standard texts and microscopic glass slide teaching files. The fellow is given time and funds to attend a two week homicide seminar, a bloodstain pattern interpretation course, and one national meeting (either NAME or AAFS). Off-site rotations during the one-year fellowship include rotations at the Forensic Toxicology Laboratory, and the State Police Crime Laboratory. The fellow participates in the courtroom experience, first by accompanying the attending physician to court and later in the year, by giving sworn testimony in the cases that the fellow has participated.

Requirements: Successful completion of an ACGME-accredited residency in Anatomic Pathology or Anatomic and Clinical Pathology.

Stipends: Commensurate with the year (5) of postgraduate training.

Applications: Please address to: Tracey Corey MD, OCME, 810 Barret Ave., Louisville, KY 40204.

Phone: (502) 852-5587 • **E-mail:** tracey.corey@ky.gov

OFFICE OF THE CHIEF MEDICAL EXAMINER STATE OF MARYLAND

Forensic Pathology Fellowship

Description: The Office of the Chief Medical Examiner (OCME) for the State of Maryland provides a well-established, nationally recognized one-year program in Forensic Pathology. Maryland initiated one of the country's first medical examiner systems and the OCME continues that innovative history by maintaining one of the finest teaching programs. There is exceptional diversity through our statewide system, which provides exposure to a variety of both rural and urban cases with over 9,000 death investigations and 4,000 autopsies each year. The OCME utilizes the team approach to death investigation and teaching with an experienced staff of 15 forensic pathologists, forensic toxicologists, and forensic investigators. Fellows will accompany investigators to learn the basics of death scene investigation. Fellows are introduced to the intricacies of courtroom testimony by first observing and later testifying. A weekly lecture series covering a broad range of topics in forensic pathology is augmented by journal club, and regular conferences in neuropathology and cardiovascular pathology. The fellows will also attend weeklong courses in basic forensic pathology, forensic anthropology, criminalistics, toxicology, National Forensic Science Technology Center and rotate through the state crime lab (ballistics, serology, and trace evidence). The OCME provides excellent opportunities for research through our affiliations and consultations with the University of Maryland, Johns Hopkins University, the Armed Forces Institute of Pathology, and the Smithsonian Institution. The OCME is located in Baltimore which provides an eclectic blend of cultural activities, fine dining, historical sites and scenic tourist sites such as the Inner Harbor and professional baseball and football teams. Salary is $52,251 with vacation and seminar time allowance. Excellent health benefits are provided.
Requirements: Successful completion of an accredited pathology residency training program in either straight anatomic pathology or combined anatomic/clinical pathology.
Applications: Address inquiries to
David R. Fowler, MD, Office of the Chief Medical Examiner, 111 Penn Street, Baltimore, MD 21201.
Phone: (410) 333-3225

MILWAUKEE COUNTY MEDICAL EXAMINER'S OFFICE

Forensic Pathology Fellowship

Description: The Milwaukee County Medical Examiner's Office offers an excellent training opportunity for forensic pathology. Situated downtown in a major metropolitan area of over 1 million citizens, the office performs over 1000 autopsies annually, and investigates nearly 5500 cases. The variety of cases provides broad exposure to all aspects of forensic pathology, including scene investigation, autopsies, courtroom testimony, toxicology and ancillary forensic specialties such as neuropathology, cardiac pathology, forensic anthropology and forensic odontology. The one-year fellowship program is designed to prepare the fellow (s) for board certification in forensic pathology through the performance of 250-300 medicolegal autopsies, courtroom testimony, scene investigations, specialized training in the in-house forensic toxicology laboratory and affiliated crime laboratory work. Professional staff consists of three board-certified forensic pathologists, board-certified forensic toxicologist and numerous consulting specialists representing a full scope of forensic expertise. The affiliation with the Medical College of Wisconsin offers a focused approach to forensic pathology within the context of a multi-specialty medical school program, including teaching and learning opportunities from clinical conferences, resident and medical students training and clinical case presentations beyond the confines of the medical examiner function.
Requirements: Successful completion of an accredited residency program in either anatomic pathology or combined anatomic/clinical pathology prior to beginning fellowship, and eligible for Wisconsin medical license.
Stipends: The salary and benefits package is competitive with similar fellowship programs.
Applications: Inquiries should be addressed to Christopher Happy, MD, Medical Examiner, Milwaukee County Medical Examiner's Office, 933 West Highland Avenue, Milwaukee, WI 53233.
Phone: (414) 223-1200

NEW MEXICO STATE
OFFICE OF THE MEDICAL INVESTIGATOR

Forensic Pathology Fellowship

Description: The Office of the Medical Investigator for the State of New Mexico offers an excellent opportunity for training in the field of forensic pathology. This one-year program concentrates on preparing the fellow to successfully complete requirements for board certification. To this end, the fellow will participate in the examination of approximately 2,100 cases under OMI jurisdiction and will personally perform approximately 250 medicolegal autopsies. The fellow will also accompany deputy medical investigators to scenes to learn the essential techniques of scene investigation. After a period of observation of expert testimony provided by the eight forensic pathologists, the fellow will be given the opportunity to testify first-hand. The program also offers instruction regarding key components of forensic medicine, specifically forensic anthropology and odontology, toxicology, and radiology. The OMI is generally considered one of the finest medicolegal death investigation centers in the country. It has the added advantages of an extensive electronic database and a full-time epidemiologist offering unique possibilities for multivariant analysis and research.
Requirements: Successful completion of an accredited pathology residency training program in either straight anatomic pathology or combined anatomic/clinical pathology.
Facilities: The facility, situated on the campus of the University of New Mexico in the city of Albuquerque, is one element of the Health Sciences Center.
Stipends: The salary is set by University guidelines based on year of postgraduate training.
Applications: Should be addressed to:
Jeffrey Nine, MD, Office of the Medical Investigator, MSC 11 6030, 1 University of New Mexico, Albuquerque, NM 87131-0001.
Phone: (505) 272-4422

OFFICE OF THE CHIEF MEDICAL EXAMINER
STATE OF NORTH CAROLINA

Forensic Pathology Fellowship

Description: The North Carolina OCME is the central office for the NC state medical examiner system. Each year, the OCME performs approximately 1,500 autopsies and reviews approximately 10,000 death investigations. The OCME is located on the campus of the University of North Carolina and has a close affiliation with the UNC Department of Pathology and Laboratory Medicine. The state toxicology laboratory is part of the office and housed in the same building as the OCME. It is our philosophy that a training program in forensic pathology should prepare an individual for a career in forensic pathology. The goals of our training program include: 1) the acquisition of the knowledge, skills and experience to perform and interpret the findings of death investigations and medicolegal autopsy examinations; 2) the acquisition of the ability to effectively communicate the findings to other physicians, law enforcement officials, family members and the courts; and 3) to become a competent medicolegal death investigator, able to combine information gathered from medical history, scene investigation, forensic laboratory, autopsy and other sources in order to determine cause and manner of death. These objectives are met by allowing the trainee to perform approximately 200-250 medicolegal autopsies under the supervision of five board-certified forensic pathologists; providing learning opportunities in several specialized areas of forensic pathology (forensic anthropology, forensic neuropathology, forensic odontology and forensic toxicology) and participation in clinical conferences.
Requirements: Successful completion of an accredited pathology residency training program in either straight anatomic pathology or combined anatomic/clinical pathology.
Stipends: The salary and benefits package is competitive with similar fellowship programs.
Applications: Address inquiries to
John D. Butts MD Chief Medical Examiner, Office of Chief Medical Examiner, Campus Box 7580, Chapel Hill, NC 27599-7580.
Phone: (919) 966-225 • **E-mail:** jbutts@ocme.unc.edu

SAINT LOUIS UNIVERSITY SCHOOL OF MEDICINE

Forensic Pathology Fellowship

Description: The Saint Louis University Department of Pathology offers a 1 year accredited training program in forensic pathology directed towards board certification. The training is based at the City of St. Louis Medical Examiner's Office. Among the approximately 2600 deaths annually reported to the office there are approximately 125 homicides, 60 suicides and 330 accidents. The resident functions as a forensic pathologist under the supervision of a senior pathologist and conducts autopsies (up to 2 daily), attends scenes and interacts with families, treating physicians, police and attorneys. Case material supplemented by selected cases from surrounding jurisdictions. Dedicated rotations in toxicology and police laboratories;monthly clinicopathology conferences with trauma surgery service;attendance at Medicolegal Death Investigators' Course in addition to a national meeting.
Requirements: Successfully completed accredited pathology residency in AP or AP/CP.
Types and Numbers of Appointments: One fellow is trained per year as an assistant medical examiner/forensic pathologist.
Stipends: Commensurate with level of training.
Staff: **Michael Graham** MD Professor; St. Louis City Chief Medical Examiner; **Jane W Turner** MD, PhD Assoc. Professor, Assistant Medical Examiner, and Director, Forensic Pathology Residency Program; **Phillip Burch** MD Asst. Professor, St. Louis City Deputy Medical Examiner; **Mary Case** MD Professor; St. Louis County Chief Medical Examiner.
Applications: Inquiries should be sent to Jane Turner, MD, Department of Pathology, Saint Louis University School of Medicine, 1402 South Grand Blvd., St. Louis, MO 63104.
E-mail: turnerjw@slu.edu • **Web site:** http://path.slu.edu

MEDICAL UNIVERSITY OF SOUTH CAROLINA

Forensic Pathology Fellowship

Description: Prepare for a lifetime career in the field of Forensic Pathology at the Medical University of South Carolina in beautiful Charleston. The ACGME accredited one-year training is offered to one applicant each academic year. It is a full-time program that is located within an academic medical center where extensive pathology specialist support is available. Trainees are responsible under supervision for scene investigations, post-mortem external examinations, autopsies (approximately 250), microscopic evaluation of tissues, interpretation of toxicology, completion of anatomic protocols, appearances in court upon occasion, and conferences with attorneys and/or police officials. Approximately 800 selected autopsies, including a large percentage of homicides, are performed in a modern autopsy facility. The cases are varied as they come both from urban and rural counties both on the coast and inland. Experienced autopsy technicians help with the physical performance of the autopsies. Trainees have the opportunity to assist in teaching police, coroners, lawyers, medical students and residents and are expected to participate in weekly conferences. Time and funding are provided for study of forensic application of anthropology, toxicology, crime scene, odontology, DNA/serology and ballistics at nearby state or national centers. Computer and internet access are provided, and a complete medical library is on the Medical University premises. The fellow is expected to submit a forensic pathology-related article to a peer-reviewed journal for publication; ample faculty support is available for this endeavor.
Requirements: Three years of anatomic pathology or two years of anatomic and two years of clinical pathology are preferred prerequisites for applicants. Applications should be received by January 1st of the preceding year.
Stipends: Salary is set by the University guidelines for PGY5 level applicants, current salary is approximately $50,000. Benefits include: $2500 annual book fund; Three weeks vacation; educational leave; private office space; use of a laptop computer; microscope use; all expenses for authorized conferences; Travel fund for poster/platform presentations.
Staff: **Nicholas I Batalis** MD; **Russell Harley** MD; **S. Erin Presnell** MD; **Ellen C. Riemer** MD, JD; **Cynthia A. Schandl** MD, PhD; **Amy T. Sheil** MD; **William Brewer** PhD; **Demi Garvin** PharmD.
Applications: Address inquiries to: Cynthia A. Schandl, MD, PhD, Assistant Professor, Dept of Pathology and Lab Med, Med Univ of South Carolina, 171 Ashley Ave, Suite 309, MSC 908, Charleston, SC 29425.
Phone: (843) 792-3500 • **Fax:** (843) 792-3537 • **E-mail:** schandlc@musc.edu

UNIVERSITY OF SOUTH FLORIDA COLLEGE OF MEDICINE HILLSBOROUGH COUNTY MEDICAL EXAMINER DEPARTMENT

Forensic Pathology Fellowship

Description: The emphasis in this ACGME accredited program is on the acquisition of analytical and cognitive skills of a caliber to permit the graduate to function at the consultant level. The fellow performs approximately 35 scene investigations and 250 autopsies under graded supervision. As sole signatory to the autopsy reports, the fellow testifies in grand jury, depositions and trial, during and after the fellowship. The fellow spends two weeks in the toxicology laboratory, two weeks at the regional crime laboratory and attends an extra-mural week-long course in forensic anthropology. Three weekly teaching conferences are held; Ektachrome Review, Pending Case Review and a Neuro- and Cardiac Pathology working conference. The professional staff comprises four forensic pathologists. The special interests of the staff lie in the areas of ligamentous neck injuries caused by blunt impact to the head, wounds caused by motor vehicle crashes, cardiac pathology and neuropathology. The office performs 1,450 autopsies per year. The Hillsborough County Medical Examiner Department is a teaching affiliate of the University of South Florida College of Medicine.
Requirements: Completion of training in anatomic pathology.
Stipends: Commensurate with postgraduate training.
Applications: Send CV to
Vernard Adams, MD, Hillsborough County Medical Examiner Department, 11025 North 46th Street, Tampa, FL 33612.
Phone: (813) 914-4506 • **E-mail:** adamsv@hillsboroughcounty.org

---

OFFICE OF THE CHIEF MEDICAL EXAMINER VIRGINIA COMMONWEALTH UNIVERSITY MEDICAL CENTER

Forensic Pathology Fellowships

Description: The Office of the Chief Medical Examiner and the Department of Pathology, Virginia Commonwealth University (VCU) Medical Center, offer three one-year ACGME-accredited fellowships in forensic pathology - two in our Richmond district office and one in our Norfolk/Virginia Beach district office. The training program fulfills the eligibility requirements for Board certification. Fellows participate in the operations of a district office of one of the nation's first statewide medical examiner systems either in the historic city of Richmond or in the historic maritime city of Norfolk. Fellows investigate scenes, perform 200-250 complete medicolegal autopsies, sign out inspections, conference with interested parties and testify in courts. Fellows are mentored by six Board certified forensic pathologists. Co-location with the State Division of Forensic Science permits contemporaneous case consultation with firearms (IBUS) and tool marks, trace evidence, latent prints/imaging/AFIS, questioned documents, forensic biology (DNA) and other forensic scientists. VCU Medical Center provides forensic radiology, odontology, neuropathology and pathology subspecialty consultation. Trainees attend subspecialty courses and reference a medicolegal library, Medline, Internet, and case database. The office participates in the teaching of students and residents. Fellows work with staff to undertake a research project.
Requirements: Applicants must be Board certified or eligible in AP or AP/CP and be able to obtain an unrestricted medical license in the State of Virginia. A valid drivers license is also required.
Stipends: The University salary and benefits are competitive.
Applications: Deborah Kay, MD, Assistant Chief Medical Examiner, Office of the Chief Medical Examiner, 400 East Jackson Street, Richmond, VA 23219.
Phone: (804) 786-1033 • **Fax:** (804) 371-8595 • **E-mail:** betha.plutro@vdh.virginia.gov
Web site: www.vdh.virginia.gov/MedExam/vcu.htm

STATE OF TENNESSEE AND METROPOLITAN NASHVILLE-DAVIDSON COUNTY

Forensic Pathology Fellowship

Description: Forensic Medical Management, PLLC, a division of a large multispecialty pathology group, offers a one year fellowship in Forensic Pathology. It is accredited by the Accreditation Council for Graduate Medical Education. In addition, the office is accredited by the National Association of Medical Examiners (NAME). All investigators have passed certifying examinations given by the American Board of Medicolegal Death Investigators. Approximately 4500 deaths are reported annually, resulting in at least 1700 autopsies. About 100 of these cases are homicides and the remainder are divided among natural causes, accidents, and suicides. The result is a wide variety of autopsy material available for teaching and learning. Further, Forensic Medical has a close working relationship with Vanderbilt University Medical Center. Residents and students rotate regularly through the Office and the pathologists have appointments as Clinical Professors at the medical school where they are active teachers of students, residents, and attending staff. Pathologists from Vanderbilt regularly assist the office pathologists with neuropathology consultations and in other areas as needed. Other valuable resources which enhance the training program include the fully dedicated toxicology laboratory where specimens are sent. The laboratory has highly trained PhD toxicologists who work full time in the field. In addition, the office of the Director of the Tennessee Bureau of Investigation is located near Forensic Medical and training will be available there. A forensic anthropologist, a forensic odontologist, and a neuropathologist provide frequent consultation to Forensic Medical.
Requirements: Applicants must be board certified or eligible in AP or AP/CP and have or be eligible for a Tennessee license.
Facilities: A 20,000 square foot state-of-the-art medical examiner's facility has been constructed; the move to that site was in the summer of 2001. Individual office space for each Fellow was an integral part of the planning for the building.
Community: Nashville, Tennessee is located in the gently rolling mountains of Middle Tennessee. Many industries provide a strong economic climate and Vanderbilt is only one of a number of fine institutions of higher learning located in the area. Cultural opportunities, professional sporting teams, great music, and numerous lakes and parks make it a particularly enjoyable place to live.
Stipends: $65,000. yearly salary.
Staff: Forensic Medical has six board-certified forensic pathologists on staff; each one of these individuals have received their anatomic and clinical pathology training in large academic medical centers across the country.
Applications:
Staci Turner, MD
Center for Forensic Medicine
850 R.S. Gass Blvd.
Nashville, TN 37216-2640
Phone: (615) 743-1800 • **E-mail:** contact@forensicmed.com
Web site: www.forensicmed.com

WAYNE COUNTY MEDICAL EXAMINER'S OFFICE

Forensic Pathology Fellowship

Description: The Wayne County Medical Examiner's Office is a new, modern, fully equipped state-of-the-art facility. The office conducts approximately 2600 autopsies annually, approximately 500 of which are homicides. Toxicology, histology, fluoroscopy, anthropology, odontology, neuropathology and photography are readily available support services. Rotations through the in house toxicology laboratory as well as the Detroit and Michigan State crime laboratories compliment the forensic training. The fellows will assist in the forensic training of rotating Pathology residents and Wayne State University medical students.

The fellow will be exposed to a wide variety of interesting forensic case material, have the opportunity to visit crime scenes, have the opportunity to observe and ultimately testify in court in criminal cases, develop the art of writing the forensic opinion, and develop the skills, logic, thinking process and independence required to competently handle any forensic autopsy case. The fellow will be given the opportunity to communicate and work with the DPD homicide detectives, prosecutors and Michigan state police.

Seven board certified forensic pathologists, two forensic toxicologists, investigators, clerical and computer support personnel, a pathologist assistant, autopsy attendants, a photographer and a histotechnologist comprise the forensic team. The professional staff are faculty members at Wayne State University School of Medicine. The professional staff and guest speakers participate in a bi-annual Medicolegal Death Investigation Course.

Requirements: Applicants should have completed residency training in Anatomic Pathology, be Board-eligible or Board-certified in Anatomic Pathology and demonstrate a strong interest and enthusiasm for a future career in Forensic Pathology.

Stipends: A competitive salary and a generous benefit package, including complete medical insurance is included.

Applications: Inquiries should be addressed to or telefaxed to:

Cheryl L. Loewe, MD, Deputy Chief Medical Examiner/Forensic Pathology Program
Phone: (313) 833-2543 • **Fax:** (313) 833-2534 • **E-mail:** cloewe@co.wayne.mi.us
Carl Schmidt, MD, Chief Medical Examiner
Phone: (313) 833-2524
Wayne County
1300 East Warren Avenue
Detroit, MI 48207

WAKE FOREST UNIVERSITY BAPTIST MEDICAL CENTER

Forensic Pathology Fellowship

Description: This fellowship is one year in duration and provides the opportunity to perform about 6-8 autopsies per week, including scene investigation and trial testimony when possible. In addition to frequent opportunities to participate in in-house and local conferences and seminars, fellows will attend (at department expense) the annual meeting of the American Academy of Forensic Sciences, and are expected to author or co-author at least one presentation. Upon completion of the program, fellows will be able to perform a competent medicolegal investigation from start to finish on cases of homicide, suicide, accident, and natural causes. Cases come to us from about 25 counties in northwest North Carolina and are weighted towards the more complicated variety. The fellow is sent for one month to train at the Virginia State Division of Forensic Sciences in Richmond in criminalistics, ballistics, toxicology et cetera. In-house weekly neuropathology conferences are held and a local American Board of Forensic Odontology expert is on-hand for consultation and didactic training.

Requirements: Satisfactory completion of training in an approved anatomic pathology program.

Types and Numbers of Appointments: A single one-year forensic fellowship position is available each year.

Facilities: The autopsy facility is located within the Wake Forest University / Baptist Medical Center in Winston-Salem, North Carolina. The fellow will therefore have available all the amenities of a large medical center.

Stipends: The salary is set by the Hospital guidelines based on the year of postgraduate training.

Staff: Donald R. Jason MD, JD Program Director; **Patrick E. Lantz** MD; Third position to be filled in the near future.

Applications: An application form may be obtained at our Internet site at http://www1.wfubmc.edu/pathology/fellowships/forensic.htm and click on the link to "Forensic Pathology Fellowship Applications".

UNIVERSITY OF UTAH MEDICAL CENTER

Clinical Biochemical Genetics Fellowship

Description: The Division of Medical Genetics in collaboration with ARUP Laboratories offers a two-year fellowship program (with the possibility of an additional year of research) in clinical biochemical genetics. This fellowship provides training in laboratory testing for the diagnosis and follow-up of patients with inherited metabolic disorders. Physicians and PhD scientist fellows participate in the testing conducted by the Biochemical Genetics and Newborn Screening laboratories of ARUP Laboratories, learning chromatographic and mass-spectrometry techniques. Fellows rotate in clinical and laboratory departments to become familiar with medical genetics and inborn errors of metabolism. Research is directed toward the elucidation of the molecular bases/pathophysiology of inborn errors of metabolism and the development of new diagnostic tests for metabolic disorders. Fellows assume progressive independence in conducting and interpreting biochemical laboratory tests in the course of training and need to maintain a logbook of cases for certification. This training program satisfies the requirements for the American Board of Medical Genetics examination in Clinical Biochemical Genetics.
Requirements: Applicants must hold an MD or PhD or other doctoral degree in genetics, biochemistry, chemistry or closely related field from an accredited institution. Previous clinical laboratory experience or a postdoctoral fellowship in genetics or training in medical genetics (for physicians) is highly recommended. Individuals with an MD or PhD earned outside of the United States or Canada must have their degree reviewed by the ABMG Credentials Committee prior to entering this training program.
Stipends: Commensurate with year of postgraduate training.
Staff: Lorenzo Botto MD; **Arthur Brothman** PhD; **John Carey** MD; **Patrice Held** PhD; **Nicola Longo** MD, PhD, Co-director; **Elaine Lyon** PhD; **Rong Mao** MD; **Marzia Pasquali** PhD, Co-director; **Sarah South** PhD; **David Viskochil** MD, PhD.
Applications: Application should be made before December 1 for positions beginning in July. Address inquires to John Carey, MD, MPH, University of Utah Dept. of Pediatrics, 295 Chipeta Way, Salt Lake City, UT 84108.
Phone: (801) 587-7400 • **E-mail:** john.carey@hsc.utah.edu

The University of Utah does not discriminate on the on the basis of gender, sexual orientation, race, age, religion, color, national origin, disability, or veteran's status.

UNIVERSITY OF UTAH MEDICAL CENTER

Clinical Molecular Genetics Fellowship

Description: The clinical molecular genetics fellowship is a two-year program (with possible extra year of research and case review). The fellowship provides training for physicians and PhD scientists focusing on laboratory testing for genetic mutations underlying disease. Training includes: didactic lectures in clinical molecular genetics, rotations through genetics laboratories and clinics, performing molecular genetics testing, and active consultation on clinical problems related to these tests. Development of new assays and assay improvements incorporates a broad range of traditional and cutting-edge technologies; fellows participate in assay development and validation projects. Lab management and administrative responsibilities may also be assumed by the fellow, with formal training in laboratory management provided.
Requirements: Laboratory postdoctoral fellowship training programs in this specialty are accredited by the American Board of Medical Genetics and require a minimum of 24 months of training, with a significant amount of clinical interaction as related to human genetic abnormalities. Trainees entering this specialty must hold either an MD or PhD (or their equivalent); the PhD degree must either be in genetics, molecular biology, or a related field within the biological sciences. Individuals with an MD or PhD earned outside of the United States or Canada must have their degree reviewed by the ABMG Credentials Committee prior to entering a training program. For information on procedures for degree review, please visit http://www.abmg.org/pages/training_forcredential.shtml.
Facilities: The clinical molecular genetics laboratories are within Associated Regional and University Pathologists (ARUP) Laboratories, an enterprise of the Department of Pathology, University of Utah. ARUP is a national clinical and anatomic pathology reference laboratory, offering an extensive menu of highly complex and innovative genetic tests. The large variety and volume of samples tested at ARUP are drawn from around the nation, as well as from the University of Utah Health Sciences Center, the major medical center in the Intermountain West region. For more on ARUP, please go to www.aruplab.com.
Stipends: Commensurate with level of training and experience.
Staff: Rong Mao MD, Program Director; **Elaine Lyon** PhD, Co-Program Director; **Pinar Bayrak-Toydemir** MD, PhD.
Applications: Apply before December 1 for positions beginning in July. Forward current Curriculum Vitae, brief statement of personal goals and objectives, and three letters of recommendation to: Diane Meyer, Academic Coordinator/ Supervisor, Clinical Support, Dept. of Pediatrics/Medical Genetics Division, 2C412 SOM, 50 North Mario Capecchi Drive, Salt Lake City, UT 84132.

UNIVERSITY OF UTAH MEDICAL CENTER

Clinical Cytogenetics Fellowship

Description: The Division of Medical Genetics in collaboration with ARUP Laboratories offers a two-year fellowship program (with the possibility of an additional year of research) in clinical cytogenetics. This fellowship involves the processing and analysis of the chromosomes of various types of samples with the express purpose of detecting and interpreting chromosomal abnormalities. Fellows who train for certification in clinical cytogenetics will participate in all aspects of sample preparation, analysis, and reporting, with more than enough opportunities to acquire cases for their logbook. Fellows will be responsible for quarterly chromosome rounds held within the division to enhance their teaching skills and encourage publication of highly interesting cases. Fellows will also develop an individualized research project based on the ongoing research and development activities within the laboratory, which will be primarily translational in scope and will likely involve collaborations within our Division of Medical Genetics and within ARUP Laboratories. This training program satisfies the requirements for the American Board of Medical Genetics examination in Clinical Cytogenetics.
Requirements: Applicants must hold an MD or PhD (or equivalent); the PhD degree must be in genetics or a related field within the biological sciences. Individuals with an MD or PhD earned outside of the United States or Canada must have their degree reviewed by the ABMG Credentials Committee prior to entering this training program.
Stipends: Commensurate with year of postgraduate training.
Staff: Arthur Brothman PhD, Co-director; **Shashi Shetty** PhD; **Sarah South** PhD, Co-director; **Jia Xu** MD.
Applications: Application should be made before December 1 for positions beginning in July. Address inquires to John Carey, MD, MPH, University of Utah Dept. of Pediatrics, 295 Chipeta Way, Salt Lake City, UT 84108.
Phone: (801) 587-7400 • **E-mail:** john.carey@hsc.utah.edu

The University of Utah does not discriminate on the on the basis of gender, sexual orientation, race, age, religion, color, national origin, disability, or veteran's status.

UNIVERSITY OF ALABAMA HOSPITALS

Hematopathology Fellowship

Description: The Hematopathology Fellowship at the University of Alabama at Birmingham (UAB) is a one-year program which is fully accredited for subspecialty Board certification. The program includes experience in all major aspects of hematopathology, including morphology, immunocytochemistry, flow cytometry, coagulation and diagnostic molecular pathology approaches. There are an estimated 800 diagnostic lymph node workups and 1200 bone marrow biopsies per year, and additional material is received from outside institutions for flow cytometric analysis (~2400). Material is derived from the University of Alabama Hospitals and Clinics (which includes a Co mprehensive Cancer Center, an active organ transplantation program, and a major AIDS center), from the Birmingham VA Medical Center, from the Children's Hospital of Alabama, and from outside consultations. The fellow will be involved in research, either clinical or translational, during the fellowship year. The program is directed by Vishnu V. B. Reddy, MD.
Requirements: Applicants must be AP or AP/CP Board eligible, or Board certified. Graduates of medical schools approved by the Liaison Committee on Medical Education (LCME) and those who are Board certified will be given preference.
Stipends: Salary levels are commensurate with the level of postgraduate training.
Applications: Applications should be submitted to Gene P. Siegal, MD, PhD, Professor and Director, Division of Anatomic Pathology, University of Alabama at Birmingham, 619 South 19th Street, KB 506, Birmingham, AL 35294-7331. Applications should be made 12 to 18 months prior to initiation of training.
Web site: http://www.path.uab.edu

ALBANY MEDICAL COLLEGE

Department of Pathology and Laboratory Medicine

Hematopathology Fellowship

Description: The Albany Medical College Hematopathology Fellowship is offering a one- or two-year Hematopathology Fellowship Program directed toward subspecialty Board certification. The program will provide in-depth experience in morphologic hematopathology and liquid hematology as well as flow cytometry, immunohistochemistry and molecular diagnostic techniques. Case material is derived from the Albany Medical Center Hospital and the Veterans Affairs Medical Center as well as from consultation cases from regional hospitals. Fellows are encouraged to pursue investigative research.
Requirements: Applicants must be Board eligible in anatomic and clinical pathology.
Stipends: Salary levels are commensurate with the level of postgraduate training.
Applications: Address inquiries to
Tipu Nazeer, MD, Director of Hematopathology, Department of Pathology and Laboratory Medicine, Albany Medical College, (Mail Code 81), 47 New Scotland Avenue, Albany, NY 12208.

ALBERT EINSTEIN COLLEGE OF MEDICINE

Department of Pathology

Hematopathology Fellowship

Description: One-year ACGME-approved fellowship in hematopathology, providing excellent materials and instructors known for their highly personal, one-on-one teaching approach. Einstein/Montefiore are NIH-designated centers for oncology and sickle cell disease. We have a faculty of specialists with expertise in morphology, molecular diagnosis, immunohistochemistry, flow cytometry, hemoglobinopathies, coagulation, classical and molecular cytogenetics, lab management and other aspects of laboratory hematology. Mastery of diagnostic hematopathology and molecular pathology with research leading to publication is strongly encouraged, especially in the molecular pathology laboratory. Graduates are trained to secure positions as hematopathologists and as directors of hematology, flow cytometry or molecular pathology laboratories.

Requirements: Eligible for AP or AP/CP Board certification.

Stipends: Appointment is for one year. Salary based on the schedule for residents.

Staff: Howard Ratech MD, Director of Hematopathology and Flow Cytometry Laboratory; **Linda Cannizzaro** PhD, Director of Cytogenetics; **Christine McMahon** MD, Hematopathologist; **Quilu Pan** PhD, Director of Molecular Pathology; **Jacob Rand** MD, FACP, Director of Hematology Laboratory; **Ira Sussman** MD, ViceChairman of Pathology.

Applications: Send curriculum vitae, three letters of reference, and a brief statement of career objectives to:
Howard Ratech, MD, Director of Hematopathology, Montefiore Medical Center, Pathology, North 4, 111 East 210th Street, Bronx, NY 10467.

ARIZONA HEALTH SCIENCES CENTER

Hematopathology Fellowship

Description: The Department of Pathology offers a Fellowship in Hematopathology that starts on July 1. This is a 1-2 year, ACGME accredited fellowship with emphasis on both diagnostic skills and research. A first year of diagnostic, clinical service will be followed by a year of research experience. The clinical service year will include acquisition of diagnostic skills in bone marrow, lymph node, nonmalignant laboratory-based hematology and teaching of residents and medical students. This will include use of our extensive automated immunohistochemistry facility, flow cytometry laboratory, specialized coagulation laboratory and developing molecular diagnostics section. In addition, the Hematopathology section is actively involved in support of the adult and pediatric bone marrow transplant programs, regional Hemophilia Center, and Artificial Heart transplant program. The research year will consist of developing and executing a research project with emphasis on publication of data and initiation of a project with potential for independent funding. There is a strong tradition of excellence in Hematopathology at the University of Arizona. We are recognized as a regional Hematopathology referral center for the Southwest. We are an active participant in the Southwest Oncology Group including being the tissue repository for all lymphoma studies and head their Lymphoma Correlative Sciences Committee. Molecular testing, including a microarray core facility, is available.

Stipends: Salary and benefits are commensurate with the level of training of the individual.

Applications: Please send your letter of intent, a curriculum vitae, and three letters of recommendation to: Catherine M. Spier, MD, Fellowship Director, Department of Pathology, University of Arizona College of Medicine, 1501 N. Campbell Avenue, P.O. Box 245059, Tucson, AZ 85724-5059.

UNIVERSITY OF ARKANSAS FOR MEDICAL SCIENCES

Department of Pathology

Hematopathology Fellowship

Description: The Department of Pathology at the Arkansas for Medical Sciences offers a one-year ACGME-accredited fellowship in hematopathology. The fellowship provides comprehensive training in morphologic and immunologic hematopathology as well as subspecialty training in molecular diagnostics, flow cytometry, blood coagulation, laboratory hematology, pediatric hematopathology, and cytogenetics. The fellow will have increasing levels of responsibility commensurate with level of performance and will participate actively in diagnostic evaluations, clinical consultations, and teaching programs in the department. Opportunities for clinical and translational research are available, in which participation is strongly encouraged. An option exists for a second non-accredited research year for qualified individuals. The clinical material signed out by the UAMS Hematopathology Division includes nearly 6000 bone marrow biopsies and approximately 350 lymph node biopsies. The Division also provides consultation and leukemia immunophenotyping services for Arkansas Children's Hospital. Fellowship training is enhanced by a close interaction with the UAMS Myeloma Institute for Research & Therapy, an international center of excellence for research and treatment of plasma cell myeloma and with the Winthrop P. Rockefeller Cancer Institute, which is currently embarking on a major infrastructural and programmatic expansion.
Requirements: Applicants should be Board eligible in AP or AP/CP.
Stipends: $47,470 per year
Staff: Ila Bansal MD; **William T. Bellamy** RPh, PhD; **Emily Howard** MD, PhD; **Robert Lorsbach** MD, PhD; **Steven A. Schichman** MD, PhD; **Zeba N. Singh** MD; **Marwan Yared** MD.
Applications: Applications for positions beginning July 1 should be submitted as early as possible as fellowship candidates are typically selected by January 1 of the preceding year. Send curriculum vitae, a personal statement concerning career goals, and 3 letters of recommendation to: Renée Gordon, Residency & Fellowship Program Manager, University of Arkansas for Medical Sciences, Department of Pathology, 4301 W Markham, #517, Little Rock, AR 72205. UAMS is an *Equal Opportunity Employer*, Promoting Workplace Diversity.
Phone: (501) 603-1508 • **Fax:** (501) 686-5959

BAYLOR COLLEGE OF MEDICINE

Department of Pathology

Hematopathology Fellowship

Description: The Department of Pathology offers one year of approved training in hematopathology. The program is designed to provide competence in diagnosis, data interpretation and methodologies as they relate to the diseases of hemopoietic system. Areas of training include bone marrow examination and related immunohistochemistry, hemoglobinopathies, coagulopathies, lymph node and spleen pathology, cytogenetics, flow cytometry and molecular hematopathology. There is close interaction with the training programs in clinical hematology, anatomic pathology and immunohematology. The fellow will be encouraged to participate in supervised research.
Requirements: Candidates must have satisfactorily completed three or more years of an approved program in clinical and/or anatomical pathology by the American Board of Pathology. At the discretion of the Chairman of the Department and the Program Director, Board-certified or Board-eligible physicians in related specialties may be considered for appointment.
Stipends: Stipend will be commensurate with the level of the applicant's training.
Applications: Direct inquiries to Andrea Sheehan, MD, Assistant Professor of Pathology, Baylor College of Medicine, Department of Pathology, MC 315, One Baylor Plaza, Houston, TX 77030.
Phone: (832) 824-1864 • **Fax:** (832) 825-0164 • **E-mail:** rosariog@bcm.edu

BETH ISRAEL DEACONESS MEDICAL CENTER HARVARD MEDICAL SCHOOL

Hematopathology Fellowship

Description: The Department offers a one-year fellowship in hematopathology. Candidates may continue their fellowships beyond one year through sponsored research. The fellowship is approved by the Accreditation Council for Graduate Medical Education, and fellows are eligible to take the American Board of Pathology subspecialty examination in hematology. The fellowship emphasizes a multidisciplinary approach to the diagnosis of diseases of the lymphoid and hematopoietic systems. Cases are worked up routinely using morphology, immunohistochemistry, flow cytometry, cytogenetics and molecular diagnostic assays as needed. In addition there are rotations exclusively dedicated to cancer cytogenetics, molecular diagnostics, and pediatric hematology. Fellows participate daily in laboratory hematology, including coagulation, automated hematology and special hematology. Fellows steer interdisciplinary conferences and teach pathology residents, medical students and clinical fellows. Fellows are invited to participate in ongoing basic or translational research programs in hematopathology.
Requirements: Completion of residency training in AP, CP or AP/CP.
Facilities: Beth Israel Deaconess Medical Center is a large referral center with active bone marrow and solid organ transplantation programs. The center is equipped with state-of-the-art laboratory facilities.
Stipends: Salary is commensurate with postgraduate level of training.
Staff: **Parul Bhargava** MD; **Carlo Brugnara** MD; **Reed E. Drews** MD; **Gary Horowitz** MD; **Rajan Mariappan** MD, PhD; **Cynthia Morton** PhD; **German Pihan** MD, Program Director; **Lynne Uhl** MD.
Applications: Request application materials from Joan Allin, Residency & Fellowship Programs Coordinator (jallin@bidmc.harvard.edu) c/o German Pihan, MD Director, Hematopathology Fellowship Program, Department of Pathology, Beth Israel Deaconess Medical Center, 330 Brookline Ave, Boston, MA 02215. Completed applications should be received by February 1 of the year prior to fellowship training.
Phone: (617) 667-7284 • **Fax:** (617) 667-7120
Web site: http://www.bidmc.harvard.edu/pathology

UNIVERSITY OF CALIFORNIA, DAVIS

Hematopathology Fellowship

Description: This full accredited program is designed to give a broad experience in diagnostic and laboratory hematopathology. The 12 month program is divided as follows:
7 months of tissue diagnosis (bone marrow, lymph node, other tissues, and flow cytometry interpretation). 2 months of laboratory hematology (laboratory operations and instrumentation of the hematology, coagulation, flow cytometry, molecule and cytogenetics laboratories, and interpretation of peripheral blood smears, body fluid smears, coagulation tests, molecular/cytogenetics data, hemoglobin analysis, and protein electrophoresis). 1 month rotation at the Veterans Administration Hospital. 1 month of research or an elective rotation at an ACGME accredited institution. 1 month of vacation.
The fellow is also integrally involved in teaching pathology residents and medical students rotating through the hematopathology service, as well as being primarily responsible for presentations to clinical colleagues during interdisciplinary conferences. The fellow will be encouraged to develop research projects in one or more areas of interest to him/her.
Requirements: The Program Director will select from resident applicants, preferably who have had four or more years of training with two years anatomic pathology and two years clinical pathology experience. E.O.E.
Types and Numbers of Appointments: 1- Fully accredited 1 year program.
Stipends: Stipends are those of appropriate postgraduate levels established by the University of California, Davis.
Staff: **Jimmy Chen** MD, Hematopathology and Director LIS; **Penny Young** penny.young@ucdmc.ucdavis.edu; **Ralph Green** MD, Hematopathology and Research; **Denis Dwyre** MD, Director, Hematopathology Fellowship; **Carol Marshall** MD, Hematopathology and Transfusion Medicine; **Edward C Larkin** MD, Hematopathology, Emeritus.
Applications: Completed applications which consists of; CV or CAP Application, personal statement and, three letters of recommendation (one must be from your current Program Director) should be sent to: Penny Young, Residency and Fellowship Program Coordinator, Department of Pathology, University of California Davis, Medical Center, 4400 ''V'' Street, PATH Building, Sacramento, California 95817.
Web site: http://www.ucdmc.ucdavis.edu/pathology

UNIVERSITY OF CALIFORNIA, LOS ANGELES

Department of Pathology and Laboratory Medicine

Hematopathology Fellowship

Description: The Department of Pathology and Laboratory Medicine offers a one-year accredited fellowship in Hematopathology that provides intensive training in all aspects of hematopathology, including morphologic analysis of blood smears and peripheral fluids; morphologic analysis of bone marrow, lymph nodes and other tissues; performance of bone marrow biopsies; interpretation of flow cytometry and immunohistochemistry; coagulation and hemostasis; chromosomal and molecular cytogenetics; and molecular diagnostics. The fellow will learn diagnostic skills during exposure to internal cases as well as a large number of referral cases sent to UCLA for consultations. The fellow interacts with Pathology and Laboratory Medicnie residents, as well as residents, fellows and faculty in the adult and pediatric clinical services. The fellow participates in teaching, conferences and tumor boards, and fellows are encouraged to develop scholarly or research activities; additional years of training may be arranged to pursue research activities. Fellows spend the majority of their time at the Westwood campus, with some activities at affiliated hospitals in Santa Monica and the San Fernando Valley. Two fellowships positions are offered each year.
Requirements: Applicants must be BE/BC in anatomic and/or clinical pathology. A California medical license is required.
Stipends: Support is commensurate with the candidate's level of training.
Applications: Please contact Fellowship Coordinator for list of requirements and application, submit a curriculum vitae and the names of three references to: Sheeja Pullarkat, MD, Program Director, Hematopathology Fellowship, Department of Pathology and Laboratory Medicine, David Geffen School of Medicine at UCLA, 10833 Le Conte Avenue, Room A7-149 CHS, Los Angeles, CA 90095-1732. Applications should be received by February 1 of the year preceding the fellowship, although applications are considered on a rolling basis.
Fellowship Coordinator: Ms. Annetta Pierro
Phone: (310) 825-5719 • **Fax:** (310) 267-2058
Web site: www.pathology.ucla.edu

UNIVERSITY OF CALIFORNIA, SAN FRANCISCO

Hematopathology Fellowship

Description: The Department of Laboratory Medicine offers two one-year accredited fellowship positions with emphasis on diagnostic hematopathology and laboratory hematology. The program includes training in: peripheral smear interpretation, body fluid cytopathology, bone marrow and lymph node morphology interpretation; laboratory hematology; coagulation; flow cytometric immunophenotyping; immunohistochemistry; molecular diagnostics; and chromosomal and molecular cytogenetics. The fellow serves as the primary consultant for the Hematology Laboratory and interacts with Laboratory Medicine residents and Hematology-Oncology clinical fellows. The hematology laboratory performs approximately 600,000 hematology and coagulation tests per year and 1,300 bone marrows. The lymph node service comprising both internal cases and cases sent to UCSF for consultation is approximately 200 per year and is complemented by retrospective review of clinical study cases and a large set of teaching cases. The fellow participates with faculty mentors to gain experience in improving testing in the clinical laboratory, augmenting the teaching program, and pursuing an investigative project in the broad field of hematopathology.
Requirements: Applicants must be Board-certified or eligible in anatomic and/or clinical pathology and eligible for California medical licensure.
Stipends: Support is commensurate with the candidate's level of training.
Applications: Apply with curriculum vitae to: Joan E. Etzell, MD, Hematology Section, Clinical Laboratories, Department of Laboratory Medicine, Box 0100, University of California, San Francisco, 505 Parnassus Ave., San Francisco, CA 94143-0100. For priority consideration applications should be submitted by January 1 in the year preceding the fellowship.
Phone: Fellowship coordinator: (415) 353-7359
Hematology service: (415) 353-1672

CEDARS-SINAI MEDICAL CENTER

Hematopathology Fellowship

Description: The Department of Pathology and Laboratory Medicine offers a one-year fellowship in hematopathology. Cedars-Sinai is an 969 bed tertiary care center in which the Hematopathology Laboratory offers a large volume of tests including extensive special coagulation and special hematology procedures. There is abundant hematopathology material with over 1,500 bone marrows and lymphoma cases from adult and pediatric patients. Training includes experience in flow cytometry, immunophenotyping, immunoperoxidase techniques, molecular diagnostics, and coagulation. The fellow is expected to participate in clinical or translational research. The fellow also will engage in teaching pathology and hematology-oncology residents and participate in appropriate conferences. The program is accredited for two fellows.
Requirements: Candidates must be eligible to sit for AP/CP, AP or CP boards. California licensure is required at the time of appointment.
Stipends: Commensurate with the applicant's year of postgraduate training.
Staff: **Randa Alsabeh** MD; **Jerry Hussong** MD; **Stephen Lee** MD.
Applications: For an application, information and correspondence, contact the program coordinator: LeeTanya Marion-Murray, Department of Pathology, Cedars-Sinai Medical Center, 8700 Beverly Blvd., S. Tower Room 8709, Los Angeles, CA 90048
Phone: (310) 423-6941 • **Fax:** (310) 423-5881 • **E-mail:** marionl@cshs.org

---

UNIVERSITY OF CHICAGO

Hematopathology Fellowship

Description: The University of Chicago Department of Pathology offers a one year accredited hematopathology fellowship. The fellowship is designed to prepare individuals for a career in diagnostic hematopathology, by providing training in morphologic, flow cytometric, immunohistochemical and molecular techniques as well as in coagulation. During the first year, trainees will concentrate on diagnostic skills. Approximately 2,000 bone marrow specimens and lymph node biopsy specimens from pediatric and adult patients in the University Hospitals are submitted to the section each year for diagnosis. In addition, about 400 outside cases are received in consultation or for diagnosis for cooperative study groups. The fellows are encouraged to participate in research studies during their first year, and participation is required for those wishing to stay a second year.
Stipends: Commensurate with year of postgraduate training.
Staff: **J. Anastasi**; **J. Dickstein**; **E. Hyjek**; **J. Miller**; **J. Vardiman**.
Applications: Applications for positions beginning July 1 should be received by July 1 of thepreceding year. They should be sent to
Dr James Vardiman, Director, Hematology Laboratory, Department of Pathology, MC0008, University of Chicago, 5841 South Maryland Avenue, Chicago, IL 60637.

CITY OF HOPE NATIONAL MEDICAL CENTER

Hematopathology Fellowship

Description: This ACGME accredited Hematopathology Fellowship is a one year program that emphasizes diagnostic neoplastic hematopathology, for fellows interested in either academic or community practice careers. With one of the largest bone marrow transplantation programs in the United States and an active consultation service, the division evaluates over 3,000 diagnostic peripheral blood, bone marrow, lymph node and extranodal biopsy specimens for hematopathologic disorders, from City of Hope patients and as outside consultations. Multiparameter studies are stressed, including application of morphologic, immunologic, cytogenetic and molecular genetic studies. Fellows may participate in the clinical and basic research performed within the division.
Requirements: Candidates should have completed 3 years of AP or 2 years of AP and 2 years of CP, and be eligible for a California medical license.
Types and Numbers of Appointments: Up to 3 ACGME accredited fellowship positions are available each year.
Stipends: Commensurate with year of postgraduate training.
Staff: Karl Gaal Fellowship Program Director, Section Head Hematopathology; **Karen Chang** Chief, Clinical Pathology; **Qin Huang** Section Head, Molecular Diagnostics Lab; **Young Kim** Staff hematopathologist; **Marilyn Slovak** Section Head, Cytogenetics; **Lawrence Weiss** Department Chair.
Applications: For positions beginning in July, a brief cover letter stating interested date of matriculation, curriculum vitae and 3 reference letters should be sent a year and a half in advance (i.e. by Dec 2009 for July 2011 start) to: Karl Gaal, MD, Section Head Hematopathology, Fellowship Program Director, Division of Pathology, City of Hope National Medical Center, 1500 E. Duarte Road, Duarte, CA 91010.
Phone: (626) 359-8111 extension 65596 • **Fax:** (626) 301-8145 • **E-mail:** kgaal@coh.org

THE CLEVELAND CLINIC

Hematopathology Fellowship

Description: The Department of Clinical Pathology at the Cleveland Clinic offers two one-year ACGME-accredited hematopathology fellowships. The program is designed to provide the trainee a broad exposure to all facets of diagnostic hematopathology including blood and bone marrow morphology, lymph node pathology, body fluid interpretation, molecular pathology, flow cytometry, immunohistochemistry, in situ hybridization, coagulation, automated hematology, cytogenetics, bone marrow transplantation, hemoglobinopathics, red cell studies and laboratory management. In addition, there are several clinical conferences in which the fellow participates and there is close interaction with the clinical hematology service. Approximately 4000 bone marrow and lymph node biopsies are reviewed annually. The fellows are strongly encouraged to participate in ongoing clinical research projects in hematopathology that will result in publication in peer-reviewed journals. This fellowship can prepare the trainee for either academic or private practice positions.
Requirements: Applicants must be Board certified/eligible in anatomic and/or clinical pathology.
Stipends: The stipend is dependent on previous level of training.
Staff: Eric D. Hsi MD; **James R. Cook** MD, PhD; **Claudiu V. Cotta** MD, PhD; **Kandice Kottke-Marchant** MD, PhD; **Karl S. Theil** MD; **Raymond R. Tubbs** DO.
Applications: Address inquiries to: The Cleveland Clinic, Graduate Medical Education Department NA23, 9500 Euclid Avenue, Cleveland, OH 44195, (800) 323-9259.
Early application (no later than March 31 for positions the following year) is encouraged. Applicants may also contact Dr. Eric Hsi for additional details at the Department of Clinical Pathology, Cleveland Clinic, 9500 Euclid Avenue L11, Cleveland, OH 44195
Phone: (216) 444-5230 • **Fax:** (216) 444-4414 • **E-mail:** hsie@ccf.org

UNIVERSITY HOSPITALS CASE MEDICAL CENTER

Hematopathology Fellowship

Description: This ACGME-accredited fellowship consists of a clinically-oriented year in laboratory and morphologic hematology with an optional year of research, arranged by mutual agreement with investigators in the Department. Rotations are offered in bone marrow and lymph node pathology, coagulation, laboratory hematology, flow cytometry, blood banking and cytogenetics. Research projects are encouraged. Fellows assume responsibility for signing out bone marrows, lymph nodes, outside consultations, coagulation studies and special hematology tests under supervision. The fellowship services the Ireland Cancer Center of University Hospitals of Cleveland and Case Western Reserve University, a Comprehensive Cancer Center as designated by the National Cancer Institute, and provides extensive exposure, opportunities and challenges for solid, fundamental hematopathology training. University Hospitals of Cleveland is a 946-bed institution serving adult and pediatric patients and is part of the University Hospitals Health System. Approximately 1,500 bone marrow, lymph node and outside consultations are seen annually.
Requirements: Board eligible or certified in AP/CP, AP or CP
Stipends: The stipend is based on the applicant's postgraduate level.
Applications: Send to Howard J. Meyerson, MD, Director, Hematopathology, c/o Jeannie St. Marie, University Hospitals Case Medical Center, 11100 Euclid Avenue, Cleveland, OH 44106. Deadline: July 1 for fellowship beginning July 1 of the following year.
Phone: (216) 844-6046 • **Fax:** (216) 844-4668 • **E-mail:** jeannie.stmarie@uhhospitals.org

---

DARTMOUTH-HITCHCOCK MEDICAL CENTER DARTMOUTH MEDICAL SCHOOL

Department of Pathology

Hematopathology Fellowship

Description: The Department of Pathology of Dartmouth-Hitchcock Medical Center offers a one-year ACGME-accredited Hematopathology fellowship. The program is designed to provide the trainee broad exposure to all facets of diagnostic hematopathology including blood and bone marrow morphology, lymph node pathology, body fluid interpretation, molecular pathology, flow cytometry, cytogenetics/fluorescent in-situ hybridization, coagulation, automated hematology and laboratory management. Approximately 1300 bone marrow and lymph node biopsies are reviewed annually. In addition, there are several clinical conferences in which the fellow participates, and there is close interaction with the clinical hematology service. Trainees will participate in teaching medical students and pathology residents. The fellow is also strongly encouraged to participate in ongoing or original clinical research projects in Hematopathology that will result in publication in peer-reviewed journals.
Requirements: Board certified/eligible in anatomic and/or clinical pathology. Medical licensure in the State of New Hampshire required.
Stipends: Commensurate with the number of relevant postgraduate years of training. There is a book allowance and funding available for presentation at a national meeting.
Staff: Prabhjot Kaur MD (Program Director); **Norman B. Levy** MD; **T. K. Mohandas** PhD, FACMG; **Gregory J. Tsongalis** PhD.
Applications: To review application requirements and to download an application form go to the program's web site. Early application encouraged (no later than December, 18 months prior to July 1 start date). Send to Susan Hawk, Program Coordinator, Department of Pathology, Dartmouth-Hitchcock Medical Center, 1 Medical Center Drive, Lebanon, NH 03756-0001.
Phone: (603) 650-8623 • **Fax:** (603) 650-4845 • **E-mail:** Susan.Hawk@Hitchcock.org; Prabhjot.Kaur@Hitchcock.org
Web site: http://www.dhmc.org/goto/Hematopathology_Fellowship

DREXEL UNIVERSITY COLLEGE OF MEDICINE

Department of Pathology and Laboratory Medicine

Hematopathology Fellowship

Description: Drexel University College of Medicine, Department of Pathology and Laboratory Medicine offers a one year fellowship program in Hematopathology. The program is a comprehensive one designed to provide the Fellow with a balanced exposure to the evaluation of all aspects of adult and pediatric lymph node and bone marrow pathology including morphology, immunopathology, flow cytometry, and cytogenetics and molecular techniques. Training includes clinical and laboratory evaluation of coagulation disorders as well as other aspects of Laboratory Pathology including Quality Assurance, Quality Control, and Lab Management. The Fellow is encouraged to participate with a faculty member in an investigative project in the broad field of Hematopathology during the fellowship. The Fellow will be given progressive responsibility in signing out and participation in the teaching of medical students, residents and laboratory staff.

Requirements: Candidates must have completed their AP/CP, AP or CP residency program.

Stipends: Commensurate with level of training

Staff: **J Steve Hou** MD, Director; **Vanlila Swami** MD; **Frank Shafer** MD; **Jennifer Morrissette** PhD.

Applications: Please send a letter of application to: J. Steve Hou, MD, Director of Hematopathology Fellowship, Drexel University College of Medicine, Department of Pathology, 245 N. 15th Street, Mail Stop 435, Philadelphia, PA 19102.

Phone: (215) 762-1179 • **Fax:** (215) 762-1051 • **E-mail:** eregan@drexelmed.edu

---

EMORY UNIVERSITY HOSPITAL

Department of Pathology and Laboratory Medicine

Hematopathology Fellowship

Description: The Hematopathology Fellowship Program at Emory University School of Medicine is an academically-oriented one-year program emphasizing clinical experience and research activity. The year includes rotations in morphologic evaluation of bone marrows, lymph nodes, and other organs, flow cytometric and immunohistochemical immunophenotyping, cytogenetic and molecular genotyping, hemoglobinopathies, and coagulation, as well as elective time for research projects. Yearly volume includes approximately 2,500 cases for morphologic assessment, 5,000 cases for flow cytometric immunophenotyping, and 3,500 cases for cytogenetic and molecular evaluation. Active stem cell transplantation and fine needle aspiration services ensure variety and growth of the workload. Fellow assumes graduated responsibilities in signing out, and participates in teaching residents, medical students, and laboratory staff.

Requirements: USMLE Step 3, Georgia medical license; applicants must have completed the requirements of the American Board of Pathology for AP/CP, AP, or CP.

Stipends: Support is usually at the level of PGY-4 and 5, and is commensurate with the candidate's level of training and experience.

Staff: **Shiyong Li** MD, PhD, Program Director; **Alexander Duncan** MD, ChB; **Jeannine Holden** MD; **David L. Jaye** MD; **Karen Mann** MD, PhD.

Applications:

Phone: (404) 727-4283 • **Fax:** (404) 727-2519 • **E-mail:** mmojonn@emory.edu

Web site: www.emory.edu/PATHOLOGY/

UNIVERSITY OF FLORIDA

Hematopathology Fellowship

Description: The ACGME-accredited Hematopathology fellowship program at the University of Florida is designed to train academically oriented physicians in the practice of modern hematopathology with an emphasis on neoplastic hematologic diseases. Upon completion, the fellow should be able to interpret the results of a variety of diagnostic procedures including conventional morphology, immunohistology, flow cytometry, cytogenetics and molecular genetics. Rotations in laboratory hematology and coagulation are also provided. It would also be expected that the fellows engage in research activities. Our laboratory serves the needs of the local affiliated teaching hospitals and is one of the largest referral centers for hematological neoplasias in the Southeast. Facilities and staff are described in detail under Residency Program.
Requirements: This is one of three competitive subspeciality fellowship positions offered annually by the Department; only candidates with the highest qualification chosen. Physicians with a minimum of three years postdoctoral training in Pathology will be considered. A background in experimental biology is helpful. Candidates must meet the application requirements described in the main Directory entry of the University of Florida.
Stipends: The appointment is for one to two years. The fellow's salary will be comparable to those of the residents at this institution with equivalent years of postdoctoral training.
Applications: Send a personal statement concerning your career goals, CV, and three letters of recommendation to Ying Li, MD, PhD, Assistant Professor and Director of Hematopathology, Department of Pathology, The University of Florida, College of Medicine, P O Box 100275, Gainesville, FL 32610-0275. Submit applications by February 1 for July of the next year.
Phone: (352) 265-9919 • **Fax:** (352) 265-9918 • **E-mail:** liying@pathology.ufl.edu
Web site: http://www.pathology.ufl.edu/fellowship.htm

GEORGETOWN UNIVERSITY HOSPITAL

Department of Pathology

Hematopathology Fellowship

Description: The Department of Pathology of the Georgetown University Hospital sponsors a fellowship program in hematopathology. This is a balanced program in diagnostic anatomic and clinical hematopathology, as well as experimental hematopathology. Clinical material is from the Lombardi Cancer Center, a NIH-funded comprehensive cancer facility of Georgetown Hospital. In excess of 500 bone marrow biopsies and aspirations are performed annually. More than 250 adult and pediatric lymphoma patients are currently followed by the Lombardi Cancer Center. In the Molecular Diagnostic Laboratory, fellows are trained in the use and interpretation of monoclonal antibodies, flow cytometry, immunochemistry, gene rearrangement analysis, PCR and cytogenetics, in addition to conventional histopathology. Productive research opportunities are available which focus on the molecular genetics of human lymphoma and leukemia and utilize techniques such as gene expression studies. Programs are tailored to fit the needs and interests of the fellow.
Stipends: The range of salaries for fellows is approximately $46,920.00 to $54,958.80.
Staff: **Norio Azumi** MD, PhD; **Pedro deBrito** MD; **Mary A. Furlong** MD; **David F. Garvin** MD; **Dan-Paul Hartmann** PhD; **Bhaskar V. Kallakury** MD; **Craig Kessler** MD; **Metin Ozdemirli** MD, PhD; **Stephen Peters** PhD; **Gerald Sandler** MD; **C. Richard Schlegel** MD, PhD; **Mary K. Sidawy** MD.
Applications: Metin Ozdemirli MD, PhD, Director of Hematopathology
Georgetown University Hospital, Department of Pathology
3900 Reservoir Road, NW
Medical Dental Bldg. #SW209
Washington, DC 20007
Phone: (202) 687-6205

HARTFORD HOSPITAL

Department of Pathology and Laboratory Medicine

Hematology/Hematopathology Fellowship

Description: A 1-year ACGME-approved fellowship is offered. Hematology training includes: bone marrow, body fluid/CSF, and abnormal peripheral blood examinations; instrumentation; special hematology including cytochemistry and hemoglobin electrophoresis; and comprehensive coagulation. Hematopathology training includes lymph node examinations, fine needle aspiration biopsies, surface marker studies including immunohistochemistry techniques, flow cytometry, DNA ploidy analysis and molecular genetic applications. Fellows participate in the daily activities of the laboratory and are encouraged to participate in administrative, developmental and investigational projects in areas of interest. Participation in departmental conferences, clinical rounds, and teaching activities including residents and medical students is also encouraged. Staff includes five Board-certified hematopathologists in a department with 20 doctorate-level staff. Hartford Hospital is an 867-bed, university-affiliated, tertiary care community hospital serving primarily adult patients. Diagnostic hematology/hematopathology services are also provided for the Connecticut Children's Medical Center. Approximately 37,250 surgical specimens including 4,700 hematology/hematopathology cases are seen annually.
Requirements: Three or more years of training in AP and/or CP are required. Applicants must have passed USMLE Step 3.
Stipends: See the general description of programs offered at Hartford Hospital.
Applications: Addressed to
William N. Rezuke, MD, Director of Hematopathology Fellowship, Department of Pathology, Hartford Hospital, 80 Seymour St, PO Box 5037, Hartford, CT 06102-5037.
Phone: (860) 545-6113 • **E-mail:** cdavids@clpct.com
Web site: http://www.harthosp.org/education

UNIVERSITY OF ILLINOIS COLLEGE OF MEDICINE

Hematopathology Fellowship

Description: A one-year, ACGME-accredited fellowship in Hematopathology is offered at the University of Illinois Medical Center at Chicago. The Medical Center is a 441-bed, tertiary care, university hospital, which supports an active bone marrow/peripheral blood stem cell transplantation service. The fellowship is designed to provide a broad and intensive experience in all aspects of neoplastic and non-neoplastic Hematopathology. Training includes evaluation of bone marrow specimens, lymph nodes, and other tissues with hematologic disorders, interpretation of peripheral blood and body fluids, and hematology laboratory instrumentation. The fellow will also gain experience in immunohistochemical and flow cytometric phenotyping, cytogenetics, molecular pathology, hemoglobinopathies, and disorders of hemostasis and thrombosis. Presentation of cases at hospital-wide clinicopathologic conferences, supervision of residents, and teaching of medical students and residents is expected. Participation in a range of scholarly activities is required, and, depending on the fellow's interests and career goals, research experiences are strongly encouraged.
Requirements: Applicants should be Board eligible or certified in Anatomic and Clinical Pathology (preferred), Anatomic Pathology, or Clinical Pathology.
Stipends: Commensurate with level of training. The Web site of the Graduate Medical Education Office (http://www.uic.edu/com/gme/) contains specific information regarding stipends and benefits.
Applications: Address letter of interest with curriculum vitae to:
Frederick Behm, MD, Department of Pathology, University of Illinois at Chicago (MC 847), 840 S. Wood Street, Suite 130 CSN, Chicago, IL 60612.
Phone: (312) 996-7250 • **Web site:** pathology.uic.edu

INDIANA UNIVERSITY SCHOOL OF MEDICINE

Department of Pathology and Laboratory Medicine

Hematopathology Fellowship

Description: The ACGME-accredited hematopathology fellowship program at the Division of Hematopathology of Indiana University School of Medicine is a one-year program, which offers a broad based training experience in diagnostic hematopathology. Training involves a comprehensive training including adult and pediatric service with wide variety of specimens such as bone marrows, lymph nodes, spleens and other tissues. The fellowship also includes designated rotations in general laboratory hematology, flow cytometry, cytogenetics, molecular diagnostics and coagulation. Dedicaed elective months are provided for research and additional diagnostic exposure. The Division is actively involved in clinically oriented research particularly in the area of neoplastic hematopathology. Participation in departmental and clinical conferences is also encouraged. The case material is derived from a 1700 bed tertiary care academic medical center complex with active hematology/oncology and bone marrow transplant divisions.
Requirements: Fellows are accepted for a training period of one year and must be Board eligible or certified in anatomic and clinical pathology or anatomic pathology.
Stipends: Salary levels are commensurate with the candidate's training and experience.
Applications: A letter of application, curriculum vitae and three letters of reference should be sent to:
Magdalena Czader, MD, PhD, Director of Hematopathology Fellowship Program, Indiana University School of Medicine, Clarian Pathology Laboratory, 350 N. 11th Street, Room 5034, Indianapolis, IN 46202.
Phone: (317) 491-6510 • **Fax:** (317) 491-6509 • **E-mail:** mczader@iupui.edu
Web site: http://www.pathology.iupui.edu

UNIVERSITY OF IOWA HOSPITALS AND CLINICS

Hematopathology/Laboratory Hematology Fellowship

Description: Fellowships include one year of clinical training in the practice of hematopathology with the option for one or more additional years of research. One position is offered. Clinical training includes bone marrow pathology, lymph nodes, spleens, laboratory hematology/coagulation, immunopathology and molecular pathology. A variety of observational and clinical pathologic studies can be pursued during the clinical year. Research training involves basic research or application of basic research techniques either in immunologic or molecular aspects of hematology or in hemostasis/thrombosis.
Requirements: Applications will be accepted from residents who have had three years of straight anatomic or clinical pathology training, or four years of combined anatomic and clinical pathology training.
Facilities: See residency program for details. The University of Iowa Hospitals and Clinics is a quaternary care center with a large referral volume of leukemias and lymphomas, and a bone marrow transplantation unit.
Stipends: Commensurate with level of training.
Staff: Faculty includes three hematopathologists, two immunopathologists, and three molecular pathologists. **Aaron Bossler** MD, PhD Molecular Genetics; **Jonathan Heusel** MD, PhD Molecular Genetics; **Michael Icardi** MD, Immunopathology; **John Kemp** MD, Immunopathology; **Peter Nagy** MD, PhD Molecular Genetics; **Vishala Neppalli** MD, Hematopathology; **Nancy Rosenthal** MD, Hematopathology; **Sergei Syrbu** MD, PhD, Hematopathology & Immunopathology.
Applications: Nancy Rosenthal, MD, Director of Hematopathology, University of Iowa Hospitals and Clinics, Department of Pathology, 200 Hawkins Drive, 6233 RCP, Iowa City, IA 52242-1009.
Phone: (319) 384-8751 • **E-mail:** nancy-rosenthal@uiowa.edu

JACKSON MEMORIAL HOSPITAL/JACKSON HEALTH SYSTEM/ UNIVERSITY OF MIAMI MILLER SCHOOL OF MEDICINE

Hematopathology Fellowship

Description: This ACGME-accredited program is a one-year program that emphasizes diagnostic skills. The program is designed to provide the Fellow with exposure to the evaluation of pediatric and adult bone marrow and lymph node pathology amounting to 1,600 cases per year. The program also includes training in coagulation, flow cytometry, molecular biology including gene rearrangement analysis, PCR, and diagnostic interpretation, cytogenetics including FISH, immunohistochemistry and laboratory hematology.
Requirements: Applicants must be Board eligible or certified in Anatomic Pathology/Clinical Pathology or Anatomic Pathology.
Stipends: Commensurate with the applicant's year of postgraduate training.
Staff: **G.E. Byrne, Jr.** MD; **C.C. Whitcomb** MD; **M. Nadji** MD; **D. M. Andrews** MD; **P. Ruiz** PhD, MD; **Y-S Fan** MD.
Applications: Applications for a position beginning July 1st should be received by September 1st of the preceding year. They should be sent to Dr. Gerald E. Byrne, Jr, Director of Hematopathology, Jackson Memorial Hospital, Holtz Bldg, Room 2053, 1611 NW 12 Avenue, Miami, Florida, 33136-1094.
Phone: (305) 585-7242 • **Fax:** (305) 585-1064 • **E-mail:** gbyrne@med.miami.edu

JOHNS HOPKINS MEDICAL INSTITUTIONS

Hematopathology Fellowship

Description: The Department of Pathology offers two one-year ACGME approved fellowships in Hematopathology which emphasize diagnostic aspects of hematopathology. The fellows will be trained in morphologic examination of blood, bone marrow and lymph nodes, and particular emphasis will be given to the use of ancillary techniques in the work-up of diagnostic problems and their interpretation in the context of morphology. The fellows will have direct responsibility for certain ancillary procedures including flow cytometry and immunocytochemistry, and will also have opportunities to gain experience in cytogenetics and molecular pathology. The program also will include exposure to coagulation and other aspects of laboratory hematology, and significant flexibility exists to tailor the fellowship toward individual interests. For interested candidates, there is an opportunity for a one month elective at the NIH. The candidates will have a significant role interacting with the clinical staff in both adult and pediatric hematology and oncology, and with other physicians outside the Johns Hopkins Medical Institutions who provide material for consultation. The fellows are encouraged to participate in research projects, and the potential exists for pursuing significant research by extending the fellowship beyond a single year.
Requirements: The candidates must be Board eligible or certified in anatomic pathology, clinical pathology, or anatomic and clinical pathology; combined training is preferred.
Stipends: The stipend is commensurate with the number of years of relevant postgraduate training and experience.
Applications: Address correspondence to
Michael J. Borowitz MD, PhD, Department of Pathology, The Johns Hopkins Hospital, Weinberg Building, 2nd floor, Room 2335, 401 N Broadway, Baltimore, MD 21231. We do not anticipate offering any fellowship positions for the academic year 2011-2012.
Phone: (410) 614-2889 • **Web site:** http://pathology.jhu.edu

The Johns Hopkins University does not discriminate on the basis of race, color, sex, religion, national or ethnic origin, age, handicapped or veteran status in any student program or activity administered by the University or with regard to admission or employment.

LOYOLA UNIVERSITY MEDICAL CENTER

Hematopathology Fellowship

Description: This laboratory hematopathology fellowship is a one-year ACGME-accredited program which is designed to provide eligibility for the American Board of Pathology subspecialty examination in hematology. The full range of hematopathology is covered, including bone marrow biopsy and aspirate morphology, lymph node biopsy interpretation, body fluid and peripheral blood smear morphology, flow cytometric immunophenotyping, immunohistochemical staining, molecular pathology, coagulation evaluation, and cytogenetic analysis. Hematopathology fellows will become proficient not only in the laboratory evaluation of patients with hematologic disorders, but also in the evaluation of pathologic materials such as blood, bone marrow, lymph nodes and other tissues. The training includes a separate rotation to a coagulation laboratory with clinical exposure to get an excellent experience in coagulative disorders.An active role in teaching pathology residents and medical students is highly encouraged. Fellows are expected to participate in research projects in hematology that will lead to presentation at national meetings, and publishable data in leading journals. The laboratory routinely freezes viable tissue and cells from various hematologic neoplasms for in vitro investigations. Research opportunities particularly related to applied clinical science projects related to the biology of leukemia/lymphoma involving tissue culture, molecular techniques and protein analysis are available.
Requirements: Applicants should be AP, CP, or AP/CP Board eligible or Board certified.
Stipends: Commensurate with the year of postgraduate training.
Applications: Send cover letter, CV, and three letters of recommendation to: Vicki Baertschi, Fellowship Training Program, Loyola Univ Medical Center, Dept of Pathology, Bldg 103, Rm #0177, 2160 First Avenue, Maywood, IL 60153.
Phone: (708) 216-5591 • **Fax:** (708) 216-8225
Web site: http://www.stritch.luc.edu/depts/path/index.htm

UNIVERSITY OF MARYLAND MEDICAL CENTER

Hematopathology Fellowship

Description: The Department of Pathology at the University of Maryland Medical Center offers a one-year ACGME-approved Hematopathology Fellowship for the future competent hematopathologist. The program provides a comprehensive and highly integrated training in the discipline of hematopathology, including microscopic morphology, immunohistochemistry, cytochemistry, flow cytometry, cytogenetics, and molecular studies. The laboratory evaluates approximately 1,200 bone marrow biopsies and aspirates, 1252 lymph node biopsies, 200,000 blood specimens, 180,000 coagulation studies, 160 hemoglobin electrophoresis and 3,400 CSF and other body fluids. Candidates must be AP/CP board certified or eligible at the time they begin the fellowship program.
Community: UMMS is located in downtown Baltimore near the award-winning Inner Harbor of Chesapeake Bay, minutes from the Baltimore Orioles and Baltimore Raven's Stadiums.
Applications: Applications are reviewed on an on-going basis and may be submitted up to 24 months before the starting date (July 1).
Interested applicants may apply by sending a CV and three letters of reference to:
Frank Zhao, MD, PhD
Director, Hematopathology Fellowship
University of Maryland Medical Center
22 S. Greene Street, Room NBW78
Baltimore, MD 21201

UNIVERSITY OF MASSACHUSETTS MEDICAL SCHOOL

Hematopathology Fellowship

Description: The Department of Pathology at University of Massachusetts Medical School - UMass Memorial Medical Center offers a one-year ACGME-accredited fellowship program in Hematopathology. The UMass Memorial Medical Center is the clinical partner of the University of Massachusetts Medical School and the largest health care system in Central Massachusetts. We have an active hematology/oncology team and bone marrow transplant program. The Department of Pathology provides hematopathology consultation services to all of Central Massachusetts. We have a large volume of materials including over 1155 bone marrows, approximately 315 lymph node specimens and 1962 diagnostic flow cytometry cases annually, and the ancillary diagnostic laboratories are excellent. The program is designed to provide the trainee a broad exposure to all aspects of diagnostic hematopathology including bone marrow and lymph node pathology, peripheral blood and body fluid examination, general hematology and coagulation, flow cytometry, immunohistochemistry, molecular pathology and cytogenetics. The fellows are encouraged to work with the faculty, or independently, during their training to pursue a research project.
Requirements: Candidates should possess MD and be Board certified/eligible in anatomic pathology (AP), clinical pathology (CP) or anatomic pathology and clinical pathology (AP/CP) and must have passed USMLE Step 3.
Stipends: The stipend is commensurate with candidate's training and experience.
Applications: Interested candidates should submit their curriculum vitae, personal statement and three references to:
Patti Davis, Pathology Residency/Fellow Coordinator, UMass Memorial Medical Center, Biotech 3, One Innovation Drive, Worcester, MA 01605.
Phone: (508) 793-6156 • **E-mail:** Patricia.Davis@umassmemorial.org.

McGAW MEDICAL CENTER OF NORTHWESTERN UNIVERSITY

Department of Pathology

Hematopathology Fellowship

Description: The Department of Pathology offers a one to two year accredited fellowship program in hematopathology that includes both diagnostic and investigative hematopathology. The program is designed to give the fellow in depth experience in the broad spectrum of hematopathology including laboratory hematology, body fluid evaluation, detection and characterization of hemoglobinopathies, blood and bone marrow biopsy interpretation, and lymph node pathology. The fellow will gain experience in the techniques and application of flow cytometry, immunohistochemistry, and molecular diagnostic testing. The fellowship also includes exposure to coagulation and cytogenetics. The fellow is expected to participate in translational research projects in collaboration with the hematopathology staff. The research experience would be more in depth in a two-year program.
Requirements: The candidate must be Board eligible or certified in either clinical pathology or clinical and anatomic pathology; combined training is preferred.
Stipends: The stipend is determined by previous pathology training and experience.
Applications: Address correspondence to
LoAnn Peterson, MD, Division of Hematopathology, Northwestern Memorial Hospital, Feinberg Pavilion, Room 7-205, 251 E Huron Street, Chicago, IL 60611.
For inquiries and requests for applications contact the program coordinator, Irene Galace.
E-mail: i-galace@northwestern.edu

MAYO SCHOOL OF GRADUATE MEDICAL EDUCATION

Department of Laboratory Medicine and Pathology

Hematopathology Fellowship

Description: The Mayo Clinic offers a one- or two-year ACGME-accredited Hematopathology Fellowship Program that will prepare you for a career in the diagnostic and research aspects of hematopathology.

The Division of Hematopathology is a comprehensive diagnostic laboratory that serves the Mayo Clinic and many other institutions through the reference services of Mayo Medical Laboratories (MML). Hematopathology fellows receive training in all aspects of laboratory hematology including automated cell counting, reticulocyte counting, body fluid analysis and morphologic evaluation of peripheral blood smears. Both the Metabolic Laboratory (red blood cell disorders) and the Cell Kinetics Laboratory (flow cytometry) have large extramural volumes through MML. This includes annual volumes of approximately 21,000 hemoglobin electrophoresis evaluations, 5000 red blood cell enzyme determinations, 2200 osmotic fragility tests, 16,000 specimens for leukemia/lymphoma immunophenotyping and 2000 samples for evaluation of paroxysmal nocturnal hemoglobinuria.

The fellows are exposed to the entire spectrum of neoplastic and benign bone marrow (3800 in-house and 4000 extramural cases) and lymph node pathology (1000 in-house and 5500 extramural cases). During these rotations, fellows learn to interpret and incorporate the ancillary techniques of cytochemistry, immunohistochemistry, flow cytometry, cytogenetics and molecular genetics into the final pathology reports. There are also excellent opportunities to become proficient in the bone marrow biopsy procedure. The fellows spend a month each rotating through the Molecular Hematopathology, Special Coagulation and Cytogenetics Laboratories. The fellows also attend the Department of Laboratory Medicine and Pathology (DLMP's) Leadership and Management Training Course. Participation in research projects under the direction of the hematopathology staff is required, and dedicated off-service time is provided.

Requirements: Applicants must have completed four years of a combined anatomic and clinical pathology residency in an ACGME-accredited program in the U.S. or Canada.

Stipends: Support is commensurate with the candidate's level of postgraduate training and in accordance with the Mayo School of Graduate Medical Education guidelines.

Staff: **J.D. Hoyer** MD Program Director and Director, Metabolic Laboratory; **D. Chen** MD, PhD; **A. Dogan** MD, PhD Director, Immunohistochemistry Laboratory; **A.L. Feldman** MD; **K.L. Grogg** MD; **C.A. Hanson** MD; **J.A. Heit** MD Director, Special Coagulation Laboratory; **J.L. Herrick** MD; **D. Jevremovic** MD, PhD; **P.J. Kurtin** MD; **W.R. Macon** MD Head, Lymph Node Working Group; **R.F. McClure** MD Director, Molecular Hematopathology Laboratory; **W.G. Morice II** MD, PhD Chair, Division of Hematopathology and Director, Cell Kinetics Laboratory; **P.L. Nguyen** MD Director, Hematopathology Morphology Laboratory; **W.L. Nichols Jr.** MD; **R.K. Pruthi** MBBS; **E.D. Remstein** MD; **D.S. Viswanatha** MD.

Applications: www.mayo.edu/msgme/application.html

Applications for each academic year, which begins in July, should be completed by December 1 (19 months prior) with Letter of Recommendations being received by January 1. Applicants are responsible for ensuring that all necessary materials are received by us prior to consideration for an interview. Positions will be offered beginning February 1 of the previous year. Our next available positions (2) for candidates interested in the program will begin July 2, 2011.

Address inquiries to: Tasha Gilbertson, Education Program Coordinator, Mayo Clinic, 200 First Street SW, Stabile SL-16 Education, Rochester, MN 55905.

Phone: (507) 538-6453 • **E-mail:** pathologyeducation@mayo.edu

Web site: www.mayo.edu/msgme/lm-hematopath-rch.html

THE METHODIST HOSPITAL

Department of Pathology

Hematopathology Fellowship and Selective Hematopatholgy Fellowship

Description: The Methodist Hospital in Houston, Texas, an affiliate of Weill Medical College of Cornell University, offers two ACGME accredited hematopathology fellowship programs. The Methodist Hospital is a 1,000-bed hospital located in the heart of the Texas Medical Center, offering a full range of services from primary to tertiary care, including a multi-organ transplant center, cell and gene therapy and cancer center.

The Department offers a one-year fellowship in hematopathology to result for board eligibility. Fellows will have 2 months of rotation at MD Anderson Cancer Center. Training will include experience in bone marrow and lymph node pathology, immunophenotyping by flow cytometry and immunohistochemistry, molecular diagnostics, coagulation and other area of laboratory hematology. There are specific rotations in cytogenctics, molecular genetics, and pediatric hematology. Fellows present conferences and teach pathology residents, medical students, and clinical fellows.

The Department also offers a one-year fellowship in selective hematopathology. Training will focus on technical and research applications in the areas of immunophenotyping by flow cytometry, immunohistochemistry, molecular diagnostics, and cytogenetics. There are specific rotations in cytogenetics, molecular genetics, and flow cytometry. Near the end of the fellowship the fellow will also rotate through clinical service for review of bone marrow and lymph node histopathology. Note: This selective hematopathology fellowship does not confer board eligibility in Hematopathology.

For both fellowships it is anticipated that an area of research interest will be identified early in the fellowship and that one or more clinical research projects will be completed during the training. State-of-Art technologies, such as cDNA microarray, 8-color flow cytometry, and fluorescence-activated cell sorting are available for fellow interested in pursuing academic career.

Requirements: Completion of residency training in CP or AP/CP. Must hold or be eligible for a Texas Physician In Training Permit or Licensure.

Stipends: Commensurate with level of training.

Applications: Deadline for applying is January 31st of the year prior to the intended fellowship year which begins July 1st.

Application inquiries are to be directed to Chung-Che (Jeff) Chang, MD, PhD, The Methodist Hospital Department of Pathology, 6565 Fannin, M227, Houston, TX 77030

Phone: (713) 441-3496 • **Fax:** (713) 441-3489 • **E-mail:** ljozwiak@tmhs.org

Web site: www.methodisthealth.com

UNIVERSITY OF MICHIGAN

Hematopathology Fellowship

Description: The Department of Pathology offers an ACGME-accredited fellowship in hematopathology with emphasis on diagnostic hematopathology and laboratory hematology. The two-year program is designed to train academically oriented physicians to be subspecialists in the area of hematopathology. Program includes training in peripheral blood and bone marrow morphology/interpretation, lymph node pathology, laboratory hematology, coagulation, flow cytometric immunophenotyping, immunohistochemistry, cytogenetics, and molecular pathology. The fellow is the primary reviewer of cases submitted to the Hematology Laboratory and interacts closely with fellows and staff on the Hematology Service. The laboratory performs approximately 370,000 hematology tests/year and evaluates more than 3000 bone marrows and lymph nodes per year. The program consists of one year of diagnostic hematopathology with a second year which offers ample opportunities for dedicated basic and translational research. In addition, specialty electives and opportunities for independent case signout privileges will be available.
Requirements: Applicants must be Board-certified or eligible in anatomic and/or clinical pathology.
Stipends: Support is commensurate with the candidate's level of training.

Staff: **Megan S. Lim** MD, PhD Director; **Kojo S.J. Elenitoba-Johnson** MD molecular hematopathology; **William G. Finn** MD clinical and laboratory hematology, bone marrow and lymph node pathology; **Jay L. Hess** MD, PhD bone marrow and lymph node pathology; **Charles W. Ross** MD flow cytometry, bone marrow and lymph node pathology; **Bertram Schnitzer** MD lymph node pathology; **Lloyd M. Stoolman** MD flow cytometry; **Lauren Smith** MD lymph node and bone marrow pathology.
Applications: Apply with curriculum vitae and three letters of reference to:
Megan S. Lim, MD, PhD Department of Pathology, University of Michigan, M5242 Medical Science I, 1301 Catherine, Ann Arbor, MI 48109-5602. Applications should be made by January 1, 2009 for fellowships beginning July 1, 2010.
Phone: (734) 936-1874

UNIVERSITY OF MINNESOTA AFFILIATED HOSPITALS

Hematopathology Fellowship

Description: This program provides advanced training in the diagnosis of diseases affecting the blood, bone marrow, and lymph nodes, using morphology, cytochemistry, immunohistochemistry, and immunophenotyping by flow cytometry and correlation with ancillary studies: fluorescent in situ hybridization, cytogenetics, and molecular diagnostics. The one year program includes 7 to 9 months of integrated bone marrow, lymph node, and flow cytometry training and 4 to 6 weeks in each of the following areas: coagulation, cytogenetics, and molecular diagnostics. Under supervision, the trainee is responsible for the day to day management of the special hematology (bone marrow) laboratory and is a consultant to the acute care (routine hematology) and flow cytometry laboratories.
Requirements: Three years of approved CP or four years of ACGME approved combined AP/CP residency training, including experience in diagnostic bone marrow and lymph node pathology. See Program Web site for specific training program requirements.
Stipends: Support is commensurate with level of training.
Staff: **Vanessa Dayton** MD Hematopathology Fellowship Program Director.
Applications: Vanessa Dayton, MD, Hematopathology Program Director, Dept. of Laboratory Medicine and Pathology, 420 Delaware St SE / MMC 609, Minneapolis, MN 55455. Application forms are available on the program Web site.
Fax: (612) 625-3976
Web site: http://residency.pathology.umn.edu

H. LEE MOFFITT CANCER CENTER AT UNIVERSITY OF SOUTH FLORIDA

Hematopathology Fellowship

Description: The Department of Pathology and Laboratory Medicine at the University of South Florida College of Medicine offers a one-year combined clinical/research fellowship in Hematopathology. The Hematopathology Fellowship program is based solely within the Hematopathology Division of the Department of Interdisciplinary Oncology at Moffitt Cancer Center and Research Institute with rotations in cytogenetics and pediatrics pathology at All Children's Hospital in St. Petersburg. Hematopoietic specimens are obtained through inpatient and outpatient services as well as referral cases from affiliated and non-affiliated area health centers. Upwards of 3,000 to 4,000 new heme cases, heme reviews, flow cytometry, molecular, coagulation cases are seen annually. The Department of Pathology program handles approximately 9,000 complex surgical cases, 5,000 consultations/reviews, 6,000 cytology cases, and 1,300 fine needle aspirations. Many lymphoma cases are triaged initially as fine needle aspiration with flow cytometry and molecular test complement.
Requirements: The ideal candidate should have completed their Board eligibility requirements for anatomic pathology (AP) or anatomic and clinical pathology (AP/CP). Applicants must have completed two or more years of studies in an accredited U.S. or Canadian medical school.
Stipends: Commensurate with level of postgraduate training.
Applications: Hernani Cualing MD, Director of the Hematopathology Fellowship, Moffitt Cancer Center and Research Institute, University of South Florida. Interested applicants, please forward curriculum vitae to: Lorraine Barnett.
Fax: (813) 745-5618 • **E-mail:** lorraine.barnett@moffitt.org

NATIONAL INSTITUTES OF HEALTH NATIONAL CANCER INSTITUTE

Hematopathology Fellowship

Description: The Hematopathology Section of the Laboratory of Pathology, National Cancer Institute, in collaboration with the Department of Laboratory Medicine, Hematology, at the Warren G. Magnuson Clinical Center, offers an ACGME accredited fellowship in hematopathology. Material is derived principally from an active in-house treatment program for both adult and pediatric hematologic malignancies, autoimmune disorders, lymphoproliferative diseases, and acquired and congenital immunodeficiency diseases. In addition, approximately 1,900 challenging cases are submitted in consultation each year. The clinical rotations provide for training in specialized diagnostic techniques, including immunohistochemistry, flow cytometry, molecular and cytogenetics. Participation in research is an intrinsic component of our fellowship program. Fellows have an opportunity to pursue laboratory interests related to experimental hematopathology, immunology, and molecular oncology during the two-year program.
Requirements: Board eligible/certified in AP or AP/CP.
Facilities: The research complex of the NIH provides unique facilities for clinical and basic research.
Stipends: Stipends commensurate with training level (Title42 pay scale); moving expenses to Washington, DC provided.
Staff: **Elaine S. Jaffe** MD; **Diane Arthur** MD; **Louis DePalma** MD; **Donald Karcher** MD; **Irina Maric** MD; **Pierre Noel** MD; **Stefania Pittaluga** MD, PhD; **Mark Raffeld** MD; **Maryalice Stetler-Stevenson** MD, PhD; **Edward Wong** MD; **Liqiang Xi** MD; **Constance Yuan** MD.
Applications: Stefania Pittaluga, MD, PhD, Program Director, Hematopathology Section, Laboratory of Pathology, NCI, NIH, Bldg 10, Rm. 2N202, 10 Center Dr. MSC-1500, Bethesda, MD 20892-1500.
Phone: (301) 496-0183 • **Fax:** (301) 402-2415
Web site: http://www.training.nih.gov/clinical GME programs: TP-87

UNIVERSITY OF NEBRASKA MEDICAL CENTER

Department of Pathology and Microbiology

Hematopathology Fellowship

Description: This two-year program is designed to train academically-oriented physicians to be subspecialists in the area of hematopathology. The position consists of one year of diagnostic hematopathology (lymph nodes, spleen, bone marrow, wet hematology, etc.) and a second year which may include specialty electives, case signout privileges, and clinical and/or basic research. A large number of community-based cases are reviewed as part of the Nebraska Leukemia/Lymphoma Study Group Network. The Medical Center also has an active hematology/oncology service and hematopoietic stem cell transplantation program. A full range of morphologic, histochemical, immunologic, cytogenetic, and molecular biologic techniques are performed as diagnostic and investigative tools. The fellow may also elect to participate in basic research in the area of lymphomagenesis and oncogenes. This program is approved by the American Board of Pathology (ABP) for subspecialty training in Hematology.
Requirements: Board eligible or certified in both anatomic and clinical pathology.
Facilities: See residency program for details.
Stipends: The stipend is that of a fifth year resident, but may be adjusted appropriately for the level of post-residency training; see residency program for other benefits.
Applications: Apply with curriculum vitae before December 1st to
Dennis D. Weisenburger MD, Director of Hematopathology, Department of Pathology and Microbiology, 983135 Nebraska Medical Center, Omaha, NE 68198-3135.
Phone: (402) 559-7688 • **Fax:** (402) 559-6018 • **E-mail:** dweisenb@unmc.edu
Web site: http://www.unmc.edu/pathology

ROBERT WOOD JOHNSON MEDICAL SCHOOL

University of Medicine and Dentistry of New Jersey

Hematopathology Fellowship

Description: A one-year fellowship is offered in laboratory hematology and hematopathology. Training will focus on skills in laboratory methods including automation and instrumentation, interpretation of peripheral blood morphology, performance of bone marrow aspirations and biopsies and their interpretation, and lymph node and spleen pathology. Fellows are also trained in coagulation, immunohistochemistry, flow cytometry, cytogenetics and molecular biologic techniques related to the diagnosis of hematopoietic disorders. The program is affiliated with the Cancer Institute of New Jersey and supports allogeneic and autologous bone marrow transplant programs. Participation in independent research projects is encouraged. The fellow will be active in conferences and teaching of pathology residents and medical students.
Requirements: Completion of anatomic and clinical pathology with Board eligibility.
Stipends: Stipends are established by the University annually and are usually at the PGY-5/6 level.
Applications: Lauri A. Goodell, MD, Director of Hematopathology Fellowship Program, Department of Pathology, UMDNJ-Robert Wood Johnson Medical School, MEB212, One Robert Wood Johnson Place, New Brunswick, NJ 08903-0019.
Phone: (732) 235-8121

UNIVERSITY OF NEW MEXICO

Hematopathology Fellowship

Description: The University of New Mexico Department of Pathology offers a one-year fellowship program in hematopathology which is divided into clinical and research rotations. The purpose of this fellowship is to train candidates in a broad spectrum of pediatric and adult morphologic hematopathology, including disorders of the bone marrow, peripheral blood, lymph node and other solid tissues, and coagulation. The fellow will gain experience in laboratory management in hematology, flow cytometry, and molecular diagnostics laboratories and in consulting on hematology patients. Clinical material includes both UNM patient cases as well as hematopathology consult cases. The full breadth of routine and specialized hematologic testing is available;the fellow will become very facile with the integration of specialized testing into diagnostic decision-making. Numerous teaching conferences supplement our clinical workload. Fellows will learn a full range of techniques: flow cytometry, DNA content analysis, immunoperoxidase procedures, FISH, conventional karyotyping, and other molecular/genetic diagnostic studies including microarray techniques. Research opportunities in fundamental molecular and cellular hematology and basic and clinical problems in hematopathology are available. A Department of Pathology endowed training grant fund is available to support translational research projects and educational travel.
Requirements: Fellowship applicants must have completed a pathology residency training program and be Board eligible in AP/CP.
Stipends: Level V salary for 2008 is $48,155. A book fund allowance is provided. Additional travel and research funds may be available through the Department or through an endowment fund.
Staff: **K Foucar** MD, Director; **C Wilson** MD, PhD; **K Reichard** MD; **M Vasef** MD; **Q-Y Zhang** MD, PhD; **C Sever** MD; **J Hozier** PhD; **K Crookston** MD, PhD; **T Williams** MD; **B Masten** PhD; **C Willman** MD; **David Czuchlewski** MD; **James Gale** PhD; **Sheldon Robinett** PhD.
Applications: The UNM Hematopathology training program follows Society for Hematopathology/APC recommended time lines for interviewing candidates and offering fellowship positions. CV, personal statement, and 3 letters of reference to be received no later than Nov. 1 of each year for positions commencing July 1 two years later. Although late applications will be considered, we usually conduct interviews in Dec-Jan. Address inquiry to: Kathryn Foucar, MD, Hematopathology Fellowship, 1001 Woodward Place NE, Albuquerque, NM 87102-2705
Phone: (505) 938-8457
Web site: http://hsc.unm.edu/som/pathology/fellowships/hematopathology_fellowship.shtml

NEW YORK UNIVERSITY MEDICAL CENTER

Hematopathology Fellowship

Description: One fellowship. The Department of Pathology at New York University Medical Center offers a one-year ACGME accredited fellowship in hematopathology. This is designed to provide focused and in-depth experience in the diagnosis of hematopoietic diseases. Training is provided in all aspects of hematopathology, i.e., histology, immunohistochemistry, flow cytometry and molecular pathology. Approximately 1300 solid lymphoid tissue specimens and 1500 bone marrow specimens are accessioned every year in the Division. The close relations with the Hematology/ Oncology Section of the Department of Medicine provide access to additional material. The fellows are strongly encouraged to participate in research projects of the Division and to develop their own.
Requirements: Applicants should be Board eligible in AP or AP/CP. USMLE III, and NY State license by the start date.
Stipends: The salary level is commensurate with the level of training.
Applications: Applications for positions beginning July 1 should be received by December 1 of the preceding year. Interested candidates should email or send a copy of their Personal Statement and CV (Curriculum Vitae) to the address listed below. Additionally, candidates are required to submit at least three letters of recommendation, addressed and sent directly to the Hematopathology Fellowship Director. All requests for information or applications should be addressed to::
Dr. Sherif Ibrahim, NYU Medical Center, Department of Pathology, Tisch Hospital, 560 First Avenue, Room 375, New York, NY 10016.
Phone: (212) 263-5967 • **Fax:** (212) 263-7712 • **E-mail:** ibrahs01@nyumc.org

SUNY UPSTATE MEDICAL UNIVERSITY AT SYRACUSE

Hematopathology/Laboratory Hematology Fellowship

Description: In this fellowship, individuals devote varying amounts of time to bone marrow and lymph node interpretation, flow cytometry, immunohistochemistry, immunocytochemistry, special coagulation and platelet studies, general laboratory hematology, erythrocyte studies, cytogenetics and molecular diagnostic techniques. Research opportunities are available in: pathology and immunologic characterization of lymphomas and leukemias (Dr. R. E. Hutchison); and apoptotic signaling in T lymphocytes (Dr. K. Banki); possibility of collaborations in other areas. The fellow also participates in teaching residents and students. The fellowship is one year's duration.
Requirements: Applicants should have completed training in an approved residency program in AP/CP or in CP.
Facilities: SUNY Upstate Medical University is a tertiary care center with strong programs in the divisions of adult and pediatric hematology/oncology and active research-oriented departments in the basic sciences. Close working relationships exist and frequent joint conferences are held. Flow cytometry is integrated with morphologic Hematopathology and both Cytogenetics and Molecular Diagnostics are closely affiliated in the same division. The Coagulation and Hemostasis Laboratory serves as the principal referral center for a broad geographic region. A strong Anatomic Pathology division provides consultative support. The Hematopathology Division has a long tradition of supporting cooperative cancer treatment groups.
Stipends: Commensurate with the level of postgraduate medical training.
Applications: Send letter with CV, and three letters of recommendation to:
Katalin Banki, MD (bankik@upstate.edu), Department of Pathology, Division of Clinical Pathology, SUNY Upstate Medical University, 750 East Adams Street, Syracuse, NY 13210.
Phone: (315) 464-6790 • **Fax:** (315) 464-6721

NEW YORK-PRESBYTERIAN HOSPITAL
COLUMBIA UNIVERSITY MEDICAL CENTER

Hematopathology Fellowship

Description: The Department of Pathology at Columbia University Medical Center offers a one-year ACGME-accredited fellowship in hematopathology.
Goal of the Program: To provide a broad and in-depth experience in adult and pediatric hematopathology, including (1) morphologic evaluation of lymphoid tissues, bone marrow biopsies and aspirate smears, cytochemical stains, blood smears and body fluids; (2) the proper technique of performing bone marrow aspirations and biopsies; (3) cellular antigen analysis of leukemias, lymphomas, and fine needle aspirates by flow cytometry and immunohistochemical techniques; (4) interpretation of molecular diagnostic assays; (5) classical and molecular cytogenetics, including FISH; (6) analysis of problems in coagulation medicine; and (7) involvement in management issues associated with the various laboratories that support the hematopathology program.
The programs faculty consists of three full-time hematopathologists, an additional clinical pathologist who specializes in coagulation medicine, the Director of Molecular Diagnostics, and the Director of Cytogenetics. The fellow is exposed to a wide variety of clinical and basic investigation at this world-renowned medical center and is expected to participate in research activities, and take advantage of the extensive opportunities for technical support and scientific interaction present within the medical center
Requirements: Applicants should be Board eligible or certified in AP / CP or AP.
Stipends: Stipends are commensurate with level of training.
Applications: Send a cover letter, personal statement, CV, and three letters of recommendation to: Bachir Alobeid, MD, Director of Hematopathology, Department of Pathology, Columbia University, 630 W. 168th St., VC-14-229, New York, NY 10032
Phone: (212) 305-5697 • **E-mail:** cw324@columbia.edu
*Applications should be received by December 1st (19 months prior to start of the position) http://pathology.columbia.edu/education/residency/hematopathology.shtml

NEW YORK-PRESBYTERIAN HOSPITAL WEILL CORNELL CAMPUS

Hematopathology Fellowship

Description: The Department of Pathology and Laboratory Medicine at Weill Cornell Medical College-New York Presbyterian Hospital offers a one- or two-year ACGME approved hematopathology fellowship under the directorship of Dr Attilio Orazi. The fellowship is designed to prepare individuals for an academic career in hematopathology. During their training, the fellows are responsible for the clinical diagnostic service of the hematopathology laboratory where they learn an integrated morphologic, immunologic and molecular approach to the diagnosis and classification of hematopoietic neoplasms. The fellows have the opportunity to evaluate more than 3,500 in-house adult and pediatric specimens and an additional 1000 hematologic malignancies submitted in consultation from outside institutions. The exceptional mixture of cases assures a more than adequate exposure to lymphoid neoplasms as well as bone marrow and spleen pathology. The fellows usually participate in one or more clinical and/or basic science research projects for which ample opportunities exit both within the hematopathology division and through collaborative projects with other laboratories within the medical center.

Requirements: Three years of training in anatomic or four years in anatomic and clinical pathology.

Types and Numbers of Appointments: Two positions are available.

Facilities: New York Presbyterian Hospital is the major clinical affiliate and teaching hospital of Weill Cornell Medical College. Its New York Weill Cornell Center, an 824-bed facility, is centrally located in a highly sophisticated medical community surrounded by the Hospital for Special Surgery, Memorial-Sloan Kettering Cancer Center and the Rockefeller University.

Community: The Medical Center is located in a beautiful residential neighborhood along the East River in Manhattan within walking distance of Central Park and the midtown entertainment and shopping areas.

Staff: Ethel Cesarman MD, PhD; **Scott A. Ely** MD, MPH; **Daniel M. Knowles** MD; **Susan Mathew** PhD; **Attilio Orazi** MD; **Rita Shaknovich** MD, PhD; **Wayne Tam** MD, PhD; **Julia Turbiner** MD; **Lynn Wang** MD, PhD.

Applications: Please address inquiries to: Attilio Orazi, MD c/o Jessica Pfeifer, Administrative Specialist, Dept of Pathology and Laboratory Medicine, New York Presbyterian Hospital-Weill Cornell Campus, 525 East 68th Street, New York, NY 10065.

Phone: (212) 746-6464 • **Fax:** (212) 746-8192

UNIVERSITY OF NORTH CAROLINA HOSPITALS

Hematopathology Fellowship

Description: The Division of Hematopathology offers a broadly based, one-year training program in diagnostic hematopathology. The program is directed by a full-time hematopathologist and is fully accredited by the ACGME. Hematopathology is a diverse specialty, employing a wide variety of technologies, and our Fellowship program is organized in such a way as to provide appropriate training in all of these areas. Trainees gain experience in the management and medical supervision of a high volume hematology laboratory (1000 CBCs/day), the evaluation of peripheral blood smears, bone marrow and lymph node biopsies and the various procedures conventionally grouped together as special hematology. The Division of Hematopathology prepares comprehensive diagnostic reports on all hematological samples, incorporating morphological, histochemical, flow cytometric, cytogenetic and molecular genetic data. The Hematopathology Fellowship Program works closely with other laboratory areas to provide practical training in diagnostic flow cytometry, cytogenetics and blood coagulation. Trainees participate in a wide range of regularly scheduled conferences that stress clinicopathologic correlation. They also play a crucial role in teaching hematopathology to medical students, as well as to pathology, hematology and oncology residents. While the fellowship is geared primarily to hematological diagnosis, research activities are strongly encouraged, with numerous research opportunities available within the Division of Hematopathology and the Pathology Department as a whole.

Requirements: MD degree and minimum two years accredited residency training in AP and/or CP.

Stipends: Fellowship stipends are based on the trainee's number of years of postdoctoral training.

Applications: For downloadable application forms, please visit our website.
For further information, please contact the Director:

Dr. Cherie Dunphy, CB #7525, UNC, Chapel Hill, 27599.

Phone: (919) 843-0718 • **Fax:** (919) 843-0733 • **E-mail:** cdunphy@unch.unc.edu
Web site: http//www.pathology.unc.edu/fellowsp/hemepath.htm

THE OHIO STATE UNIVERSITY MEDICAL CENTER

Department of Pathology

Hematopathology Fellowship

Description: The Department of Pathology at The Ohio State University Medical Center offers a one-year accredited fellowship in hematopathology. The fellowship is designed to provide the trainee with a broad-based experience in clinical hematopathology, including experience in routine laboratory hematology, bone marrow morphology, coagulation, flow cytometry, solid tissue hematopathology, pediatric hematopathology, cytogenetics and diagnostic molecular pathology. The trainee is actively involved in all diagnostic evaluations, clinical consultations and teaching programs of the department. The clinical material reflects the breadth of hematopathology and includes over 2,400 bone marrow biopsies, 730 lymph node biopsies, 3,000 diagnostic flow cytometry cases, 1,500 manual smear reviews, 750 hemoglobinopathy evaluations, 1,600 coagulation evaluations and 3,500 body fluid samples on an annual basis. Elective time is available for pursuit of research interests.

Requirements: Candidates should have completed pathology residency training (AP and/or CP) in an accredited program. They must have successfully completed USMLE Step 3 prior to their Medical Staff appointment to The Ohio State University Medical Center.

Stipends: The stipend is commensurate with the number of years of postgraduate training.

Applications: Inquiries should be addressed to

Frederick K. Racke, MD, PhD, Director, Division of Hematopathology, Department of Pathology, The Ohio State University, S-301 Rhodes Hall, 450 W 10th Ave., Columbus, OH 43210.

Phone: (614) 293-6512 • **Fax:** (614) 293-2075 • **E-mail:** frederick.racke@osumc.edu
Web site: http://pathology.osumc.edu/ext

OREGON HEALTH & SCIENCE UNIVERSITY

Hematopathology Fellowship

Description: Oregon Health & Science Univ. Dept. of Pathology offers a one year ACGME-accredited fellowship program in hematopathology. The program provides broad experience in diagnosing hematologic diseases and utilizing ancillary diagnostic techniques. Rotations include hematology, bone marrow, lymph node, flow cytometry, coagulation, cytogenetics, molecular diagnosis and research. Clinical material includes cases from OHSU, Doernbecher Children's Hospital, the Portland VA Med. Center, as well as hematopathology consult cases. There were approximately 2200 in-house bone marrows and approximately 750 lymph node/tissue biopsies examined during 2005. Among them there were over 500 consultation cases, and over 1000 cases with flow cytometry analysis.
The Hematopathology Section is staffed by six OHSU hematopathologists, and two hematopathologists from our affiliated Kaiser Permanente facility. The Hematopathology Service works very closely with the hematology-oncology team at OHSU, including Dr. Brian Druker, Co-director of the Center for Hematologic Malignancies at OHSU, and Dr. Richard Maziarz, Director of the Adult Bone Marrow Transplant Center. The fellows are encouraged to particpate in ongoing clinical activities in pathology and other depts.

Requirements: Applicants must have successfully completed a residency in anatomic and clinical pathology (AP/CP board eligible).

Types and Numbers of Appointments: 2 fellowship positions are available each year.

Stipends: The stipend is commensurate with the year of postgraduate training.

Applications: Applications will be accepted up to two years in advance and will be reviewed as rolling admissions. Please submit a cover letter, applicationf orm from our website, your CV and three letters of recommendation to:

Anna Wedeking, Training Programs Coordinator, Department of Pathology, Oregon Health & Science University, 3181 SW Sam Jackson Park Rd., Mail Code L113, Portland, OR 97239-3098.
E-mail: ferencea@ohsu.edu
Web site: http://www.ohsu.edu/pathology/win/Fellhemato.htm

UNIVERSITY OF PENNSYLVANIA MEDICAL CENTER

Department of Pathology & Laboratory Medicine

Hematopathology Fellowship

Description: The goal of this one- or two-year accredited fellowship is to provide the diagnostic skills and in-depth knowledge of both pediatric and adult hematopathology and molecular skills needed for successful careers in academic hematopathology.

Year 1: The fellow, with staff, is responsible for work-up and sign-out of bone marrows, lymph nodes, and other surgical pathology specimens with suspected lymphoproliferative disorders, including review of relevant hematologic data, peripheral smears, bone marrow aspirate smears, histologic sections, cytochemistry, immunohistochemistry, immunophenotyping by four color flow cytometry, molecular analysis for gene rearrangement, and cytogenetics. The fellow is responsible for diagnostic evaluation and triage of fresh material sent to surgical pathology for frozen sections for possible lymphoproliferative disorders. The fellow also serves as the primary point of communication between hematopathology and hematology/oncology. The fellow obtains hands-on experience in laboratory hematology and coagulation, including interpretation of laboratory studies and laboratory management. Two months of elective time in either immunopathology or molecular pathology, or clinical research are provided. Participation in projects is strongly encouraged.

Year 2: An additional year *(or years)* is offered to highly qualified applicants to pursue in-depth research on a problem in hematology or neoplasia. Clinical responsibility during this time is limited to two months as a junior hematopathology attending, to allow the fellow to continue to develop his/her diagnostic skills while conducting research. Preference will be given to candidates interested in the two year program.

Requirements: Applicants must have completed pathology training in an AMA-approved pathology residency program in the United States or Canada, and be Board eligible by the start of the Hematopathology Fellowship. Combined AP/CP training is recommended, but highly qualified AP or CP only applicants will also be considered. A strong interest in laboratory investigation and/or previous research experience is desirable.

Facilities: The Hematopathology Section provides services to the Hospital of the University of Pennsylvania, Presbyterian Hospital, Children's Hospital of Pennsylvania, and many affiliated hospitals in the region through a busy consultation service.

Stipends: Commensurate with level of postgraduate training.

Applications: Mail or e-mail letters of inquiry to:
Nger Ong (c/o Mariusz Wasik, MD), University of Pennsylvania, 422 Curie Blvd., 413A Stellar-Chance Building, Philadelphia, PA 19104-6100.

Phone: (215) 573-5468 • **E-mail:** Nger.Ong@uphs.upenn.edu

UNIVERSITY OF PITTSBURGH MEDICAL CENTER

Hematopathology Fellowship

Description: This 1- or 2-year fellowship offers training in lymph node and bone marrow interpretation, flow cytometry, molecular pathology, cytogenetics, immunohistochemistry, laboratory hematology and coagulation. It is expected that the fellow will participate in a research project in the division. More extensive research opportunities can be arranged for fellows spending two years. The fellowship is approved by the ACGME and upon completion of the one-year program, a fellow is eligible for the American Board of Pathology subspecialty examination in Hematology.

Requirements: Candidate must have completed training in an approved residency in combined Anatomic and Clinical pathology, straight Anatomic Pathology or straight Clinical Pathology. Eligibility for Pennsylvania licensure is required.

Facilities: Hematopathology Services are provided by 8 hematopathologists based at UPMC Presbyterian Hospital. The Division of Hematopathology is responsible for an adult and pediatric bone marrow service, a solid tissue (lymph node) hematopathology service, a flow cytometry laboratory and hematology laboratories. Fellows also rotate in the Division of Molecular Diagnostics, in the University of Pittsburgh's Clinical Cytogenetics Laboratory and on a specialized coagulation service.

Stipends: Stipends are commensurate with year of postgraduate training.

Staff: Steven H. Swerdlow MD, Fellowship Director; **Raymond Felgar** MD, Associate Fellowship Director; **Lydia Contis** MD; **Fiona Craig** MD; **Miroslav Djokic** MD; **Christine Garcia** MD; **Sara Monaghan** MD; **Lisa Robinson** MD.

Applications: Submit application online at http://path.upmc.edu/fellowship/app-form.htm More information can be obtained from Steven H. Swerdlow MD, Director, Division of Hematopathology, UPMC Presbyterian, 200 Lothrop Street, Suite G-300, Pittsburgh, PA 15213-2582.

Phone: (412) 647-5191

SAINT LOUIS UNIVERSITY SCHOOL OF MEDICINE

Hematopatholgy Fellowship

Description: Our ACGME approved one year Hematopathology Fellowship at Saint Louis University School of Medicine is one of an apprenticeship in academic hematopathology. The trainee is the junior member of the hematopathology staff and during training becomes competent in all aspects of hematopathology, developing technical, managerial, consultative, diagnostic, and scientific skills. Integral to the trainee's education is the correlation of the cytomorphological and histologic findings with the patients clinical presentation and other pathological findings including those seen in other areas of the laboratory, for example, the flow cytometric immunophenotypic findings, molecular diagnostic findings, as well as immunophenotypic analysis by immunoperoxidase and enzyme cytochemical techniques and the performance, interpretation, and application of coagulation testing.

Requirements: Candidates must have had at least two years of training in anatomic pathology in an accredited program and be eligible for a Missouri Medical License.

Types and Numbers of Appointments: One per year.

Stipends: Commensurate with postgraduate training. A travel and book allowance are provided.

Applications: Address inquires to: Director, Hematopathology Residency Training Program, Director - Dr. Leonard Grosso, Department of Pathology, 1402 S. Grand Blvd., St. Louis, MO 63104

Phone: (314) 577-8482 • **Fax:** (314) 977-7879 • **E-mail:** grossole@slu.edu
Web site: http://path.slu.edu

UNIVERSITY OF ROCHESTER MEDICAL CENTER

Hematopathology Fellowship

Description: We aim to provide our trainee the skills necessary to practice all aspects of diagnostic pathology with confidence, and to position him or her to obtain what he or she considers the most satisfying job at the end of the fellowship be it private practice or an academic setting. The training is built around morphologic-based diagnosis and the use of flow cytometry and genetic methods. In addition, there is a structured didactic program and clinical involvement in all aspects of "benign hematology" particularly coagulation. Through directed readings and conferences, our program strives to give the trainee the intellectual tools and habits which we all need in order to stay abreast of this quickly evolving field. There is a systematic approach to "graded responsibility" with the goal that by April of the fellowship year the trainee will be able to independently review and appropriately workup most cases. The curriculum and scheduling is intentionally flexible: the program can be modified to fit the interests of a specific trainee. While at least nine months must focus on morphologic-based diagnostics, we would consider any reasonable use of the remaining time that might fit a trainee's needs. For a trainee interested in an academic career, we will provide opportunities to participate in ongoing projects which are likely to produce data in time for job interviews by January of the fellowship year. In addition, a second year of funding is available for individuals for whom that would enhance his/her career.

Requirements: Board certification or eligibility in AP, CP, or AP/CP.

Facilities: Care of both adults and children with hematologic diseases is a particular strength of the University of Rochester Medical Center. In particular, the lymphoma program is nationally prominent. The hospital and its system is the largest facility in an urban area providing our trainees with an ample supply of routine node and marrow biopsies appropriate for training. The marrow transplant program performs over 100 transplants annually. Golisano Children's Hospital, the largest in upstate NY and its only pediatric marrow transplant program, is on site. Hematopathology has a newly renovated core facility which includes the marrow and flow cytometry labs, research space, and trainee/faculty offices. The space has been designed to maximize interactions between the trainee and the teaching staff, to allow the trainee to be "hands-on" in the flow lab, and to foster the ability of the trainee to participate in research projects.

Community: Rochester, with a population in the metropolitan statistical area of 1.1 million, provides all the amenities of a large urban area with surrounding open spaces giving the trainee the option of urban or rural living and a large range of outdoor activities. "Places Rated Almanac" 2008 ranking of 379 metropolitan areas found that Rochester has some of the finest cultural, educational and recreational assets in the country. Ranked at #6, it was one of only two small metropolitan areas to make the top 10. Of particular importance on a trainee's stipend, excellent housing is affordable and the public schools are outstanding.

Stipends: Commensurate to the number of relevant postgraduate years of training and experience. The department supports the fellow's professional development with an educational fund of $1500.

Staff: **W. Richard Burack** MD, PhD, Assoc Prof. Director, Hematopathology section and Fellowship Program; research: molecular mechanisms of lymphoma progression; **John Bennett** MD Prof; editor-in-chief Leukemia Research; research: myelodysplastic syndrome; **Archibald Perkins** MD PhD Prof Pathology & Lab Medicine; research: Evil induced leukemia and AML drug development; **Michael Petzar** MD Asst Prof, Pathology & Lab Medicine; **Dan Ryan** MD Prof and Chair, Pathology & Lab Medicine.

Applications: Send CV, personal statement focusing on your career goals and what you need in the fellowship to achieve those goals, a letter from your current residency program director, and two additional letters of recommendation to Betsy McDonald, Medical Education in Pathology, University of Rochester Medical Center, 601 Elmwood Ave Box 626, Rochester NY 14642.

SCOTT & WHITE HOSPITAL AND CLINIC

Hematopathology Fellowship

Description: The Scott and White Clinic and Hospital Department of Pathology and Laboratory Medicine and the Texas A&M College of Medicine offer a one-year fellowship in hematopathology. The program has the goal of training individuals who will, after completion of the program, be able to direct a hematology laboratory; consult with clinicians on hematopathology; have the morphologic expertise to accurately render hematologic diagnosis on any appropriate specimens, including lymph nodes, spleen, bone marrow aspirate/biopsies, and properly interpret peripheral smears. The program will prepare them to qualify and successfully complete the American Board of Pathology Hematology Board certification examination. The fellow will be exposed to routine and special hematology testing, routine and special coagulation testing, cytochemistry, histochemistry, flow cytometry, cytogenetics and molecular techniques as they apply to the diagnosis and differential diagnosis of hematologic malignancies, morphologic evaluation of peripheral smears, bone marrow aspirates and biopsies, lymph node and other tissue biopsies for the diagnosis of hematologic malignancies. The program emphasizes the practical aspects of the hematopathology practice in regard to morphologic skills, laboratory management and clinical consultation.

Requirements: Completed training in anatomic, clinical, or combined anatomic/clinical pathology.

Facilities: The Scott and White system is very conducive to such exposure because of the complex practice involving 667 physicians, including primary care and specialists and a system that includes 2 hospitals and 29 regional clinics within a 5-150 mile radius.

Stipends: Salary is commensurate with the year of postgraduate training.

Applications: William Koss, MD, Director of Hematopathology Fellowship, Scott and White Hospital and Clinic, 2401 South 31st Street, Temple, TX 76508.

Phone: (254) 724-7354 • **Fax:** (254) 724-6329 • **E-mail:** cdixon@swmail.sw.org
Web site: http://www.sw.org

SCRIPPS CLINIC - SCRIPPS GREEN HOSPITAL

Hematopathology Fellowship

Description: The Scripps Clinic Hematopathology program provides a comprehensive training experience in all aspects of hematopathology. The overarching philosophy of the program is to prepare fellows for tertiary care practice. The program emphasizes the microscopic pathology of hematolymphoid disease, mirroring the primary importance of this aspect of hematopathology in most practice situations. The interpretation and oversight of ancillary methods including cytochemical stains, immunophenotypic studies, both paraffin-based and by flow cytometry, cytogenetic studies and molecular analyses is a second major point of emphasis because of the vital role these analyses play in the interpretation of biopsy specimens. The third major focal point of the program is the pathologist-clinician relationship and the critical nature of information exchange regarding the diagnosis, treatment, and evaluation of the effectiveness of therapy in the management of patients with hematologic disease.
The program director is Dr. Kelly Bethel, and the assistant program director is Dr. Robert Sharpe.

Requirements: Board-certified or Board-eligible in AP/CP or AP. California medical licensure required during fellowship.

Types and Numbers of Appointments: Accredited for two one-year training spots. Usually accept one candidate per year.

Stipends: Commensurate with postgraduate level of training.

Applications: Application deadline is December 1, one and a half years prior to the anticipated July 1 start date.
Inquiries to: Kathy Nobles, Graduate Medical Education Office, Mail Code 403C, Green Hospital, 10666 N. Torrey Pines Rd., La Jolla, CA 92037.

Phone: (858) 554-3234 • **E-mail:** nobles.kathleen@scrippshealth.org

MEDICAL UNIVERSITY OF SOUTH CAROLINA

Hematopathology Fellowship

Description: The Medical University of South Carolina, Department of Pathology and Laboratory Medicine offers a one-year fellowship in hematopathology. The program is designed for the fellow to have experience in interpretation of bone marrow aspirates, biopsies, cytochemical staining and cell surface marking using flow cytometry. In addition, rotations in routine hematology, coagulation, cytogenetics and molecular diagnostics laboratories are required. The trainee will be expected to participate in the coagulation consultation service as well as the bone marrow transplantation team. The amount of time spent in each area can be tailored to the applicant's individual needs and desires. The program is designed to provide eligibility for the subspecialty certification in Hematology given by the American Board of Pathology.

Requirements: Four or more years of training in anatomic, clinical or combined anatomic/clinical pathology. Applications should be received by March 1st of the year preceding the year of the fellowship (15 months prior to the beginning of the fellowship).

Stipends: Salary is commensurate with PGY 5 level of postgraduate training.

Applications: Address inquiries to John Lazarchick, MD, Director of Hematopathology, Department of Pathology and Laboratory Medicine, Medical University of South Carolina, 171 Ashley Avenue, MSC 908, Charleston, SC 29425.

Phone: (843) 792-2933 • **Fax:** (843) 792-1248 • **E-mail:** lazarj@musc.edu

---

STANFORD UNIVERSITY MEDICAL CENTER

Department of Pathology

Hematopathology Fellowship

Description: The fellowship includes broad experience in both neoplastic and non-neoplastic hematologic disorders. There are more than 2,400 bone marrow and 2,000 lymph node cases annually, drawn from Stanford University Hospital and Lucile Packard Children's Hospital, as well as cases submitted in consultation. Experience with neoplastic disorders includes immunophenotyping (using both flow cytometry and immunohistochemistry), cytogenetic and molecular diagnostic techniques. Non-neoplastic hematopathology experience includes evaluation of coagulation and red cell disorders. Rotations include lymph node consultation service, bone marrow and flow cytometry service, molecular pathology, cytogenetics and elective time. Cases are examined individually with faculty including Drs. Arber, Atwater, Cornbleet, George, Natkunam, Tan and Warnke. A multidisciplinary approach allows the fellows to become proficient in, and integrate into the evaluation of cases, all aspects of diagnostic testing in hematopathology.

Requirements: AP, CP or AP/CP training and eligibility for California medical license.

Stipends: Commensurate with experience, plus additional $8,400 per year housing allowance.

Applications: Submit to:
Daniel Arber MD, Director of Hematology, Department of Pathology, Stanford University Medical Center, 300 Pasteur Drive, Room H1507C, Stanford, CA 94305-5627.

Phone: (650) 725-5604 • **Fax:** (650) 736-1473 • **E-mail**: darber@stanford.edu

UNIVERSITY OF TENNESSEE AND AFFILIATED HOSPITALS

Hematopathology Fellowship

Description: The 1-year ACGME-accredited fellowship offered by the Department of Pathology starts July 1. The fellow would rotate at the 670-bed Methodist University Hospital and the world famous St. Jude Children's Research Hospital, allowing very wholesome training in all aspects of adult and pediatric Hematopathology.The training emphasizes graduated responsbility and aims to produce a life-long learner with expertise in Hematopathology. There exist ample opportunities to develop expertise in bone marrow and lymph node pathology, peripheral smears, coagulation, red cell enzymatic disorders, flowcytometry, immunohistochemistry and conventional and molecular cytogenetics, with a generous case-load and under the supervision of highly trained and experienced Hematopathologists and Molecular Geneticist. The fellow would interact with residents and technologists and clinicians in a close collaborative setting. There would be opportunities to participate in clinical and basic research studies, residency-related conferences and adult and pediatric Hematopathology tumor boards and Coagulation meetings. Memphis is a mid-sized city with a temperate climate and a low cost of living.

Requirements: Board eligibility or certification in AP and CP.

Stipends: Commensurate with the level of training.

Staff: Nadeem Zafar MD Fellowship Director; **Alan D. Boon** MD; **Margarita Delaossa** MD; **David K. McGregor** MD; **Mihaela Onciu** MD; **Sheila Shurtleff** PhD; **Frank L. White** MD.

Applications: Applicants should submit a copy of the CV, personal statement of interest and goals, and three letters of reference (directly) to the Residency Program Coordinator, University of Tennessee at Memphis, Department of Pathology- 930 Madison #500, Memphis, TN 38163.

Phone: (901) 448-6344 • **Fax:** (901) 448-6979
Completed applications must be received by October 31 of the of the year preceding anticipated start date.

UT is an EOAA Employer.

THE UNIVERSITY OF TEXAS HEALTH SCIENCE CENTER AT SAN ANTONIO

Hematopathology Fellowship

Description: The Department of Pathology at the University of Texas Health Science Center at San Antonio (UTHSCSA) offers a one-year, fully accredited fellowship in hematology/hematopathology with an optional second year. Training includes laboratory hematology, interpretation of tissue biopsies performed for hemato-lymphoid disorders and experimental hematology. The first year of fellowship training includes core rotations in the clinical hematology laboratories at University Hospital, San Antonio and the South Texas Veterans Health Care System and the flow cytometry, molecular diagnostics and cytogenetics laboratories in the South Texas Reference Laboratories at UTHSCSA. Clinical training includes interpretation of peripheral blood films, body fluid preparations, bone marrow aspirates and biopsies, lymph node diagnosis, work-up of patients with coagulation disorders, flow cytometry immunophenotyping, cytogenetics, molecular diagnostics, immunohistochemistry and electron microscopy. The fellow actively participates in teaching medical students and residents, and makes a presentation to the San Antonio Society of Pathologists. The second year of fellowship training includes nine months dedicated to research in hematopathology and three months signing out as a junior attending. The hematology fellowship program is directed by Dr. Marsha C. Kinney. The fellow is jointly supervised by the faculty in hematopathology.

Requirements: Board eligibility or certification in anatomic and clinical pathology.

Stipends: Commensurate with level of training.

Staff: Siddarth Adhvaryu PhD; **Aamir Ehsan** MD; **Hongxin Fan** MD; **Shelly R. Gunn** MD, PhD; **Russell A. Higgins** MD; **Marsha C. Kinney** MD; **John D. Olson** MD, PhD; **Ryan S. Robetorye** MD, PhD.

Applications: Send inquiries to
Dr. Marsha C. Kinney, Department of Pathology, Mail Code 7750, University of Texas Health Science Center at San Antonio, 7703 Floyd Curl Drive, San Antonio, TX 78229-3900.

Phone: (210) 567-6731 • **E-mail:** kinneym@uthscsa.edu

UNIVERSITY OF TEXAS SOUTHWESTERN MEDICAL SCHOOL

Hematopathology Fellowship

Description: Training will include experience in bone marrow and lymph node pathology, immunophenotyping by flow cytometry and immunohistochemistry, molecular diagnostics, coagulation, cytogenetics and other areas of laboratory hematology. Following initial experience, it is expected that the fellow will assume responsibility comparable to a junior faculty member. Numerous conferences as well as teaching opportunities with students and residents are an integral part of the program. It is anticipated that an area of research interest will be identified early in the fellowship and that one or more clinical research projects will be completed during the training. There is a high level of interaction with the clinical department of hematology.

Requirements: Candidates must have satisfactorily completed pathology training from an approved program in anatomic pathology, clinical pathology or combined AP/CP. This previous training should include at least six months in hematopathology and laboratory hematology. Candidate must be eligible for a Texas Instutitional Permit.

Stipends: Support will be commensurate with the applicant's level of training.

Staff: Nitin J Karandikar MD, PhD Director; **Arnaldo A Arbini** MD; **Weina Chen** MD, PhD; **Franklin Fuda** DO.

Applications: Applications should be made no later than 18 months prior to the intended fellowship. Address inquiries to: Nitin J. Karandikar, MD, PhD University of Texas Southwestern Medical Center, 5323 Harry Hines Blvd, Dallas, TX 75390-9072.

Phone: (214) 648-1190
Web site: http://pathcuric1.swmed.edu

THOMAS JEFFERSON UNIVERSITY

Hematopathology Fellowship

Description: This is an accredited one year program covering all areas of hematopathology, including bone marrow and lymph node histology/cytology. Excellent ancillary services are available (e. g. immunohistochemistry, molecular diagnostics, oncocytogenetics). All diagnostic specimens from Jefferson's bone marrow transplantation service are reviewed. The trainee will also be exposed to the clinical hematology aspect including special coagulation (rotation through Jefferson's well known Cardeza foundation) and hemoglobinopathy diagnostics (Jefferson has a sickle cell disease clinic). Abnormal peripheral blood smears are reviewed daily. Interested applicants have the opportunity to engage in collaborative research. Very active educational program and clinical conferences.

Staff: Eric Behling MD, Director, Hematopathoogy Fellowship Program.

Applications: Please send inquiries to:

Eric Behling, MD, Director, Hematopathology Fellowship Program, 125 S 11th Street, Suite 301 Pavilion Building, Philadelphia, PA 19107.

Phone: (215) 955-6304 • **Fax:** (215) 955-2604 • **E-mail:** Eric.Behling@jefferson.edu

TULANE UNIVERSITY HEALTH SCIENCES CENTER SCHOOL OF MEDICINE

Department of Pathology

Hematopathology Fellowship

Description: This one year ACGME-accredited fellowship in hematopathology emphasizes on diagnostic hematopathology and laboratory hematology. The program includes training in peripheral blood and bone marrow morphology interpretation, lymph node pathology, laboratory pathology, coagulation, flow cytometry, cytogenetics and molecular pathology. The fellow is encouraged to participate in ongoing research projects.

Requirements: Applicants should be Board eligible in anatomic and/or clinical pathology.

Stipends: Stipends are commensurate with the year of postgraduate training in pathology.

Staff: John R. Krause MD, Hematopathology Fellowship Director.

Applications: Applications include curriculum vitae, personal statement, ECFMG certificate if applicable and three letters of references and should be submitted 18 months prior to the year of the fellowship.
Submit application to:
Bea DeLucca
Program Coordinator
1430 Tulane Ave. SL-79
New Orleans, LA 70112

Phone: (504) 988-2436 • **Fax:** (504) 988-7389 • **E-mail:** bdelucc@tulane.edu

---

UNIVERSITY OF UTAH MEDICAL CENTER

Department of Pathology

Hematopathology/Hematology Fellowship

Description: In a flexible one or two-year program designed to meet the needs of the successful candidate, this fellowship offers a broad experience in diagnostic and experimental hematopathology. Liquid hematology, bone marrow aspriate and biopsy examination, lymph node pathology, immunohistochemistry, flow cytometry and molecular pathology are all available to the fellow. Through an active consultation service, an affiliated national reference laboratory, and study cases from Children's Oncology Group and Southwestern Oncology Group, the Hematopathology section processes approximately 4,500 cases per year including both adult and pediatric patients with a wide variety of tissue, blood and bone marrow cases. Special training is available in coagulation and transfusion medicine. The fellow is encouraged to be involved with research projects and participate in teaching.

Requirements: Fellows are accepted for a training period of one to two years and must be Board eligible in anatomic and clinical pathology.

Stipends: Commensurate with year of postgraduate training.

Staff: Sherrie L. Perkins MD, PhD, Fellowship Program Director, Hematopathology and Transplant Pathology; **David Bahler** MD, PhD, Flow Cytometry and Molecular Hematopathology; **Albert Ho** MD, PhD, Hematopathology and Molecular Hematopathology; **Todd Kelley** MD, Hematopathology and Molecular Hematopathology; **Carl R. Kjeldsberg** MD, Hematopathology; **Chris M. Lehman** MD, Laboratory Hematology; **Rodney Miles** MD, PhD, Hematopathology; **George Rogers** MD, PhD, Hemostasis and Thrombosis; **Mohamed Salama** MD, Hematopathology; **Kristi Smock** MD, Hemostasis and Thrombosis; **Ron Weiss** MD, Hematopathology.

Applications: Should be made before December 15 to Sherrie L. Perkins, MD, PhD, Department of Pathology, University of Utah Health Sciences, 500 Chipeta Way - Medical Directors, Salt Lake City, UT 84108.

Website: http://www.path.utah.edu/education/fellowships/hematopathology/
E-mail: sherrie.perkins@hsc.utah.edu

VANDERBILT UNIVERSITY SCHOOL OF MEDICINE

Hematopathology Fellowship

Description: Dr. Robert D. Collins started the Hematopathology Division in the early 1970s. The primary focus of the program is to provide 1) state-of-the-art diagnostic services that integrate morphologic, immunophenotypic, molecular genetic, and ultrastructural studies, 2) resident training in the basics of hematopathology, 3) fellowship training that emphasizes the development of academic hematopathologists, and 4) research opportunities with hematopathology faculty. Current areas of investigation include the molecular basis of leukemias and lymphomas, application of molecular and flow cytometric technology to the diagnosis of hematolymphoid neoplasia, the pathogenesis of myelodysplasia, and the role of extra-cellular matrix receptors in platelet/vascular biology and in the innate immune response. Space is available in the divisional core laboratory and in the laboratories of independent investigators for both clinical/translational, as well as basic research projects. The diagnostic immunopathology and molecular genetics laboratories are an integral part of the division and provide opportunities for training and research for both residents and fellows. In 2008, the Hematopathology Division evaluated approximately 4200 cases including 1800 bone marrows, 1000 consults and referrals, 1400 lymph node and tissue biopsies, and 3000 flow cytometry cases per year from Vanderbilt University Hospital and Monroe Carell Jr. Children's Hospital at Vanderbilt. The Division also reviews an additional 500 morphology cases and 600 flow cytometry cases per year from the VA Tennessee Valley Healthcare System. Data from flow cytometry, immunohistochemistry and molecular genetics are integrated into a single, final diagnosis. Students, residents, and fellows actively participate with the faculty and with clinical colleagues in clinical conferences and clinical-pathologic case analyses.

Requirements: Applicants must have completed either AP/CP or AP or CP training prior to acceptance in this fellowship.

Types and Numbers of Appointments: The division offers both a one-year and a two-year ACGME-accredited fellowship that emphasizes diagnostic hematopathology in the first year and research in the second year.

Facilities: Vanderbilt University Hospital, Monroe Carell Jr. Children's Hospital at Vanderbilt, and the adjacent Nashville VA Medical Center comprise a total of 1,070 licensed beds. There are approximately 46,785 admissions per year with an average length of stay at 5.4 days. There are over one million ambulatory visits (including off-site) and nearly 91,000 emergency room visits per annum. Vanderbilt University Hospital and Vanderbilt Clinic consistently rank among the premier health care facilities in the United States. U.S. News & World Report has ranked Vanderbilt University Medical Center among the foremost programs in the nation. Constructed in 2004, The Monroe Carell Jr. Children's Hospital at Vanderbilt is a leading provider of pediatric care and ranked as one of the 10 best children's hospitals in the country and among the top 10 in the nation for pediatric cancer services by Child magazine. In the 2008 issue of America's Best Hospitals the Monroe Carell Jr. Children's Hospital ranked 23rd in the nation and the Vanderbilt University Hospital 15th in the nation. In fact, U.S. News & World Report has listed Vanderbilt Medical Center on its ''Honor Roll'' of best hospitals — an honor reserved for a select group of 19 institutions labeled by the magazine as the ''best of the best.'' In FORTUNE magazine's 2009 annual survey of US workplaces, Vanderbilt was named one of the Top 100 Best Places to Work. Vanderbilt is the only university to ever achieve this honor.

Community: Nashville (Davidson County) has a population of 619,626 (2007) and is located in the rolling hills of central Tennessee. It is the site of numerous colleges and universities, two medical schools, and several large teaching hospitals. The city has an extensive parks system, a symphony orchestra, opera, ballet, performing arts center, zoo, several museums, and the Grand Ole Opry. The city offers a wide variety of cultural, educational, and recreational opportunities, including professional football and hockey teams.

Stipends: Commensurate with relevant experience and previous training.

Staff: Claudio A. Mosse MD, PhD, Assistant Professor of Pathology, Director of the Hematopathology Fellowship Training Program; **Mary M. Zutter** MD, Professor of Pathology and Cancer Biology, Ingram Professor of Cancer Research, Director of Hematopathology; **Mary Ann Thompson Arildsen** MD, PhD, Assistant Professor of Pathology, Director of Hematology Laboratories; **David Gailani** MD, Associate Professor of Pathology and Medicine, Medical Director of Clinical Coagulation Laboratory and Point of Care Testing; **David R. Head** MD, Professor of Pathology; **Thomas L. McCurley** MD, Associate Professor of Pathology and Director of Immunopathology Laboratory; **Adam Seegmiller** MD, PhD, Assistant Professor of Pathology; **Cindy Vnencak-Jones** Associate Professor and Director of Molecular Genetics Laboratory.

Applications: Interested applicants should submit a cover letter, application, curriculum vitae, personal statement, and three letters of recommendation, to Holly Spann, Hematopathology Administrative Assistant, Department of Pathology, Division of Hematopathology, Vanderbilt University School of Medicine, 4605 TVC, 1301 Medical Center Drive, Nashville, TN 37232. Application and submission information is located at http://www.mc.vanderbilt.edu/root/vumc.php?site=gme
E-mail: holly.spann@vanderbilt.edu

VIRGINIA COMMONWEALTH UNIVERSITY MEDICAL CENTER

Hematopathology Fellowship

Description: This program provides intensive training in **hematopathology**. It is aimed at those who have fulfilled a standard pathology residency and wish to specialize in hematopathology. Emphasis is placed on handling of critical biopsy material and complex specimens with correlation with ancillary techniques, such as flow cytometry, immunohistochemistry, and molecular diagnostics. There is extensive hands-on experience in performing bone marrow aspirates/ biopsies. Intensive training is provided in bone marrow and lymph node pathology, coagulation, clinical correlation, and molecular diagnostics. Training in the use of, and investigative and clinical projects utilizing, molecular diagnostics are also available to the fellow.

Requirements: Preference will be given to applicants who have completed AP/CP training, or are board eligible in anatomic and/or clinical pathology.

Stipends: Stipends usually are those of a sixth year postgraduate level and may be adjusted according to the individual's previous experience and need.

Applications: Interested individuals should contact the training program coordinator, Ms. Violet Brown, Department of Pathology, P.O. Box 980662, Richmond, VA 23298-0662 for additional information. The program accepts the CAP Standardized Application form. Completed applications and letters of recommendation should be addressed to Jonathan Ben-Ezra, MD, Director of Hematopathology, PO Box 980662, Richmond, VA 23298-0662.

Phone: (804) 827-0561 • **E-mail:** vbrown3@mcvh-vcu.edu.

UNIVERSITY OF VIRGINIA SCHOOL OF MEDICINE

Hematopathology Fellowship

Description: The Department of Pathology at the University of Virginia Health System in Charlottesville, Virginia offers one fellowship position in Hematopathology. The fellowship includes one year of training in diagnostic Hematopathology, which is ACGME accredited, and an optional second year of research. The first year is designed to offer the trainee an extensive exposure to all aspects of diagnostic Hematopathology, including lymph node and bone marrow pathology, immunohistochemistry, flow cytometry, molecular genetics, cytogenetics, general hematology and coagulation. The second year is primarily devoted to a research project in the field of hemopoietic or lymphoid disorders under the supervision of a senior faculty member.

Requirements: Applicants must have an MD degree (or foreign equivalent with ECFMG certification) and be Board-eligible or Board-certified in anatomic and clinical pathology.

Types and Numbers of Appointments: One position per year.

Stipends: Commensurate with the applicant's postgraduate training in pathology.

Applications: Interested candidates should submit a letter of interest, current curriculum vitae and three letters of recommendation by January 1st, 18 months prior to the start of fellowship to: John B. Cousar, MD, Department of Pathology, University of Virginia Health System, P.O. Box 800214, Charlottesville, VA, 22908.
E-mail: jcousar@virginia.edu

WAKE FOREST UNIVERSITY BAPTIST MEDICAL CENTER

Hematopathology Fellowship

Description: This one year Hematopathology Fellowship training program provides comprehensive training experience in all aspects of hematopathology, including diagnostic testing, multi-level teaching, an understanding of the principles of biomedical research, and to prepare fellows for tertiary care practice with the ability to manage a large clinical hematology hospital laboratory and provide competent consultation services to clinical colleagues.
The fellow will become proficient in the clinical and laboratory evaluation of blood, bone marrow and lymph nodes, with comprehensive, integrated diagnostic training, including a wide spectrum of benign and neoplastic disorders in pediatric and adult patients. Fundamental microscopic pathology of hematopoietic diseases is combined with the interpretation and oversight of ancillary diagnostic methods, including both phenotypic studies (cytochemistry, immunohistochemistry, and flow cytometry), and genotypic analyses (in situ hybridization, PCR analyses, conventional cytogenetics techniques). Experience in coagulation includes exposure to procedures used in the coagulation laboratory and clinical training in diagnosis, management and treatment of patients with coagulation disorders.

Requirements: The program is offered to pathology residents who have satisfactorily completed their Board eligibility requirements for anatomic pathology (AP) or anatomic and clinical pathology (AP/CP).

Types and Numbers of Appointments: Only one fellow will be accepted per year.

Staff:
Michael W. Beaty MD, Director Hematopathology Fellowship; **A. J. Garvin** MD, PhD, Chair; **David D. Grier** MD, Assistant Professor; **Jennifer Laudadio** MD, Assistant Professor; **Changlee Pang** MD, Assistant Professor.

Applications: All applicants must submit a current curriculum vita, a personal statement, and three letters of recommendation, including one from the chairman of their department as part of the application processs.
Contact: Michael W. Beaty, MD Director, Hematopathology Fellowship Program, Department of Pathology Wake Forest University School of Medicine Medical Center Boulevard, Winston-Salem, North Carolina 27157-1072
Web site: http://www.wfubmc.edu/pathology/training/hemepath.htm

---

UNIVERSITY OF WASHINGTON

Department of Laboratory Medicine

Hematopathology Fellowship

Description: ACGME-accredited two-year program that provides training in the clinical and laboratory diagnosis of hematologic malignancies, hemoglobinopathies and hemolytic syndromes, hemostasis and thrombosis, and general hematology. Training is provided in all the major diagnostic techniques, including flow cytometry and clinical molecular diagnosis. The fellowship consists of a year-long structured intensive core rotation through the clinical areas listed above. In general, fellows follow this clinical year by one or more years of research during which clinical duties are reduced. A major goal of the fellowship is mastery of a hematopathology area leading to publication in quality journals. The fellowship should prepare the trainee for successful completion of the hematology examination given by the American Board of Pathology.

Requirements: Applicants are selected for interview based on academic excellence and interest in the subspecialty. Applicants are expected to have completed the training required for certification in clinical and/or anatomic pathology by the American Board of Pathology must be eligible for a Washington State license.

Facilities: UW Medicine, among the most successful academic medical centers in the US, provides tertiary medical care and medical education to the five-state region of Washington, Wyoming, Alaska, Montana and Idaho. Our program is located in new facilities at Seattle Cancer Care Alliance and at the University of Washington Medical Center.

Stipends: Appointment is for one year and is subject to renewal for subsequent years. Salary is based on the schedule for residents at an equivalent level (R5=$55,032). Fellows are encouraged to apply for extramural funding if additional years of research training are desired. (2 positions)

Staff: D. Sabath Director; **S. Cherian**; **J. Fromm**; **H. Greisman**; **B. Wood**; **D. Wu**.

Applications: Daniel E. Sabath, MD PhD at dsabath@u.washington.edu
Available at the web site or contact Michelle Rickard, Academic Programs Manager, Hematopathology Fellowship Program, at the email address below. Application materials must be received by February 1 with selected interviews to follow until the position is filled.

Phone: (206) 598-4933 • **Fax:** (206) 598-7321 • **E-mail:** fellowship@pathology.washington.edu
Web site: www.pathology.washington.edu/academics/fellowship/

The University of Washington is an equal opportunity institution.

WASHINGTON UNIVERSITY SCHOOL OF MEDICINE

Hematopathology/Hematology Fellowship

Description: The hematopathology section of the Department of Pathology and Immunology, Washington University School of Medicine, announces an opening for a one- or two-year accredited fellowship starting **July 1, 2011**. The first year will emphasize diagnostic hematopathology and laboratory hematology with training in peripheral blood smears, body fluid cytopathology, bone marrow and lymph node morphology, coagulation, flow cytometric immunophenotyping, immunohistochemistry, molecular diagnosis, and cytogenetics. Funding for an additional year is offered to highly qualified applicants to pursue in-depth research in a laboratory of their choice.
The large referral quaternary care and urban hospital system associated with Washington University in St. Louis provides a broad range of cases comprising >2400 marrows (cores and aspirates), >600 lymph nodes and other surgical specimens, and >1200 consult cases per year. These referral cases are largely generated by the Adult and Pediatric Bone Marrow Transplant services that together perform approximately 300 transplants annually. Due to the diversity of cases, the fellow will gain extensive diagnostic experience in the field of hematopathology, including uncommon disease entities, such as mature T-cell and NK-cell neoplasms and immunodeficiency associated lymphoproliferative disorders.
The fellow's responsibilities are broad and at a level of training where an independent approach to case work-up is welcomed. The fellow is regarded as the initial pathologist on all cases and will write pathology reports integrating morphologic description and all ancillary studies (molecular, cytogenetic, and flow cytometric results). The fellow is seen as the primary contact for referring pathologists and will be working closely with the clinical hematology/oncology faculty, gaining insights into the clinical management of patients. The fellow will be presenting weekly at both the lymphoma and leukemia conferences. Additionally, a monthly journal club aids in learning about new developments in this rapidly changing field. During the first year the fellow will be expected to participate in hematopathology-related translational projects, for which funding is provided. Furthermore, trainees with strong academic interests who are offered a 2-year fellowship will be able to choose among many outstanding research laboratories both within and outside the Department of Pathology and Immunology, and will be part of a stimulating and collegial research community with top-notch facilities and resources.
In summary, this program provides a strong basis for clinical practice including challenging cases in both adult and pediatric hematopathology, as well as opportunities for cutting-edge basic and translational research. Upon completion of the program, the fellow will have the necessary skills and experience to successfully pursue a clinical and/or academic career in hematopathology.

Requirements: Applicants must be Board eligible or certified in anatomic and/or clinical pathology. To apply, please submit all materials by email and/or hard copy. Required materials are: 1. Online application 2. CV with names of 3 references. 3. Three letters directly mailed and/or emailed by your references to the program. 4. Personal Statement 5. USMLE test scores. 6. Transcript(s).

Applications: Mail CV and reference letters to: Mary Madden - Fellowship Coordinator, Washington University School of Medicine, Department of Pathology and Immunology, 660 South Euclid Avenue, Campus Box 8118, St. Louis, MO 63110. If you have specific questions about the application process or the program, please contact Mary Madden.

Phone: (314) 747-0687 • **Fax:** (314) 747-2663 • **E-mail:** mmadden@path.wustl.edu
Web site: http://www.pathology.wustl.edu/training/hema.php

WAYNE STATE UNIVERSITY/DETROIT MEDICAL CENTER

Hematopathology Fellowship

Description: The Department of Pathology of Wayne State University School of Medicine, and the Detroit Medical Center offers two one-year, ACGME-accredited fellowships in hematopathology, beginning July 1, annually. The program is based at 3 institutions located on campus: 1. Detroit Medical Center University Laboratories: centralized 24-hour core clinical laboratory run by the Pathology Department, providing major clinical laboratory services to five on-campus and four off-campus hospitals, clinics and non-DMC hospitals, as well as private physician practices. Training includes running a large core hematology laboratory with 1,200,000 tests/year and blood and fluid morphology, coagulation, chemical hematology and a consultation service for bone marrows and lymph nodes. 2. Harper University Hospital: the seat of adult hematology/oncology, includes Karmanos Cancer Center and a large bone marrow transplant program. Specialized laboratories for bone marrows, flow cytometry, immunohistochemistry, molecular DNA analysis and histocompatibility are housed here. Rotation through these laboratories and a cytogenetic laboratory are part of the training. There are 1,000 bone marrows and 400 lymph nodes and other tissues. 3. Children's Hospital: This rotation covers pediatric hematology/oncology and hemoglobinopathies and enzyme deficiencies. Participation in laboratory management, hospital conferences and medical student teaching is expected. Fellow participates in clinically related research, writing two or more papers.

Requirements: Board eligible or certified in anatomic or anatomic and clinical pathology.

Stipends: Commensurate with year of pathology postgraduate training; determined by Wayne State University School of Medicine

Applications: Deadline August 1 of preceding year. Direct inquiries, CV and letter to Margarita Palutke, MD, Director Fellowship Program, Professor of Pathology, c/o Ms. Cynthia Connors, University Laboratories, 4201 St. Antoine, Detroit, MI 48201.

Phone: (313) 993-0535 • **E-mail:** cconnors@dmc.org

WEST VIRGINIA UNIVERSITY SCHOOL OF MEDICINE

Hematopathology Fellowship

Description: This one year Hematopathology Fellowship training program is based on the philosophy of accurate diagnosis through the integration of morphology with advanced state-of-the-art diagnostic studies. Fellows initially receive focused training in these laboratory methods and subsequently focus on globally integrating these methodologies with a patient's morphology and clinical history. The Program's goal is to provide Fellows with clinically-oriented expertise in hematopathology through participation in these laboratories on a daily basis as the cases are initially assessed and ultimately diagnosed. The Program provides advanced training in the interpretation of blood, bone marrow aspirates/biopsies and lymph node biopsies, including the evaluation of enzyme cytochemistry, flow cytometry, immunohistochemistry, cytogenetics and molecular studies. In addition to a strong focus on clinical hematopathology, the Program provides the Fellow with exposure to scholarly clinical research.

Requirements: Applicants must have successfully completed 48 months of combined clinical and anatomic pathology prior to the start of their fellowship year and be eligible to obtain a West Virginia Medical License.

Stipends: Stipend is dependent on the level of prior post-graduate training.

Applications: Applications consist of a personal statement, CV, USMLE Scores, letters of reference, ECFMG certificate for international graduates and other relevant documentation. Applications will be accepted until the one position for a given year is filled. Mail or e-mail applications to: James E. Coad, MD (c/o Linda Tomago) Robert C, Byrd Health Sciences Center of West Virginia University, Department of Pathology, Mail stop 9203, Morgantown, WV 26506.

Phone: (304) 293-3212 • **E-mail:** jcoad@hsc.wvu.edu
Web site: www.hsc.wvu.edu/som/pathology

WILLIAM BEAUMONT HOSPITAL

Hematopathology Fellowship

Description: This comprehensive one year ACGME accredited fellowship training program is based in a 1061 bed tertiary care teaching hospital and it accepts two hematopathology fellows yearly. The fellowship program offers subspecialty training in the multiple aspects of diagnostic hematopathology, laboratory hematology and coagulation. Trainees will gain experience in the following: laboratory management and quality control in a high volume hematology laboratory (2200 CBCs/day), comparative assessment of methodology analysis, coagulation consultation for bleeding and thrombotic disease, and detailed interpretation of peripheral blood smears, bone marrow, lymphoid tissues, body fluid (including the appropriate use and intergration of cytochemistry, immunohistochemistry, flow cytometry, cytogenetic/FISH, and molecular genetic data). Training includes dedicated rotations in flow cytometry, molecular diagnostic and cytogenetics as well. Fellow will also be expected to participate in medical technologist, medical student and resident teaching, as well as clinical and/or basic research.

Requirements: The applicant must possess an MD or DO degree and be board eligible in anatomic and/or clinical pathology at the time of acceptance into the program. They must also hold a license (or be eligible) to practice medicine in the State of Michigan.

Stipends: Salary is commensurate with the level of postgraduate training.

Applications: Should be addressed to
Vonda K. Douglas-Nikitin, MD, Director, Hematopathology Fellowship, Flow Cytometry, Department of Clinical Pathology, William Beaumont Hospital, 3601 W 13 Mile Rd Royal Oak, MI 48073-6769.

Phone: (248) 551-2935 • **Fax:** (248) 551-3694
Web site: http://www.beaumonthospitals.com/gme

MEDICAL COLLEGE OF WISCONSIN

Department of Pathology

Hematopathology Fellowship

Description: The Department of Pathology at the Medical College of Wisconsin offers a one-year ACGME-accredited fellowship in hematopathology, with emphasis on diagnostic hematopathology and laboratory hematology. The program includes training in peripheral blood and bone marrow morphology/interpretation, lymph node pathology, flow cytometric immunophenotyping, cytogenetics, laboratory hematology including hemoglobin electrophoresis, cytochemistry, immunohistochemistry, coagulation, and molecular pathology. The fellow is the primary consultant for the Hematology Laboratory and interacts closely with fellows and staff on an active Hematology/Oncology Service. The Medical College of Wisconsin is a major bone marrow transplant center and maintains the International Bone Marrow Transplant Registry. Major affiliated teaching institutions include Froedtert Memorial Lutheran Hospital, Children's Hospital of Wisconsin, Zablocki VA Medical Center and the Blood Center of Wisconsin. Numerous opportunities for research are available. Participation in ongoing investigative projects in hematopathology is highly encouraged, with support for presentation of research at a national meeting. Active participation in student and resident education and in clinicopathologic conferences is an integral part of the program.

Requirements: Board eligible/Board certified in both AP and CP.

Stipends: Salary commensurate with the year of postgraduate training.

Applications: To apply, submit current curriculum vitae, personal statement and three letters of recommendation to:
Steven Kroft MD, Hematopathology Fellowship Program Director; ATTN: Marie Hardy, Hematopathology Fellowship Coordinator, Department of Pathology, Medical College of Wisconsin, P.O. Box 26509, 9200 West Wisconsin Avenue, Milwaukee WI 53226.

Phone: (414) 805-8459 or (414) 805-6987 • **E-mail:** skroft@mcw.edu or mhardy@mcw.edu

UNIVERSITY OF WISCONSIN HOSPITAL AND CLINICS

Hematopathology Fellowship

Description: The Department of Pathology and Laboratory Medicine at the University of Wisconsin, Madison offers a one year ACGME-accredited Hematopathology fellowship program. Training takes place at the University of Wisconsin Hospital and Clinics, a tertiary care center affiliated with the NCI designated University of Wisconsin Paul P. Carbonne Comprehensive Cancer Center, the American Family Children's Hospital, and the University of Wisconsin School of Medicine and Public Health. Pathology material mainly comes through active adult and pediatric hematology and bone marrow transplant programs, including a consultation service to the Cancer Center. Fellows are exposed to a wide range of benign and malignant hematology specimens including bone marrows, blood smears, body fluids, lymph node and tissue biopsies. Fellows are trained to integrate morphology with immunohistochemistry, flow cytometry, cytogenetics, molecular, and FISH results into the final diagnosis. Graduated responsibility in sign out is given over the year with the goal of the fellow becoming fully independent by the end of training. The fellow rotates through the special coagulation laboratory and is taught coagulation medicine by a clinical hematologist with special interest in thrombotic and bleeding disorders. Fellows, in addition, spend dedicated hands-on time in the flow cytometry, molecular diagnostics, and cytogenetics laboratories. The exact rotation schedule is tailored to fit the individual fellow's needs. Protected time is provided for participation in on-going research projects, with the goal that every fellow submits an abstract or paper by the end of the fellowship. The Department of Pathology supports a Translational Research Laboratory as well as funding for fellow initiated projects in order to promote translational research. The Translational Research lab includes tissue microarrays, immunohistochemistry, automated quantitative immunofluorescence (AQUA), molecular diagnostics, and access to flow cytometry. In addition, a Lymphoma Translational Research Lab provides a collaborative setting focused on human lymphoma/leukemia with numerous ''up and running'' projects in which fellows may become involved.

Requirements: Board-eligible or certified in AP, AP/CP, or CP.

Stipends: Commensurate with year of postgraduate training (i.e. $55,437 (PGY5); $57,120 (PGY6)). There is a $500 book allowance, 15 days vacation and funding available for presentation of a paper at a national meeting.

Staff: **Catherine Leith** MB, BChir, (Univ Cambridge, UK), AP/CP Univ of Arizona, HP Univ New Mexico, Director of Fellowship Program, Division Chief, Hematopathology, Medical Director Flow Cytometry and Bone Marrow Laboratories; **Erik A. Ranheim** MD, PhD, (Univ Minnesota), AP Stanford, HP Stanford, Director of Residency Training Program, Director of Translation Research for Lymphoma Lab; **Ken H. Young** MD, PhD, (Zhejiang Univ, China), AP/CP OHSU, HP Nebraska, Medical Director, Hematology Laboratory; **David Yang** M.D (Loma Linda), AP/CP Univ Utah, HP Univ Utah, Medical Director, Molecular Diagnostics; **Eliot Williams** MD, PhD (Univ Wisconsin), Int Med/Heme Univ Wisconsin, Medical Director, Coagulation Laboratory.

Applications: Amanda Paus, Hematopathology Fellowship Program Coordinator, University of Wisconsin Hospital & Clinics, 600 Highland Ave., B4/243 CSC, Madison, WI 53792-2472.
Preferred deadline: December 1, 19 months prior to anticipated start date.

Phone: (608) 262-7158 • **E-mail:** apaus@uwhealth.org
Web site: http://www.pathology.wisc.edu/clinfellowship/hematopathology

YALE - NEW HAVEN HOSPITAL
YALE UNIVERSITY SCHOOL OF MEDICINE
Hematopathology Fellowship

Description: The Departments of Laboratory Medicine and Pathology at Yale offer a one- year ACGME-accredited fellowship in diagnostic and investigative hematopathology. The fellow receives comprehensive training in all aspects of diagnostic hematology including: morphologic interpretation of blood, marrow and lymph nodes; flow cytometry; cytogenetics; molecular diagnostics including quantitative amplification, FISH, and in situ hybridization; immunohistochemistry; evaluation of hemoglobinopathies; and state-of-the-art genomic and proteomic evaluation of disorders of thrombosis/hemostasis. The fellow is an integral part of a multi-disciplinary patient-care team in an NCI-designated Comprehensive Cancer Center with extensive pediatric and adult patient populations and active stem cell transplantation service. The fellow is encouraged to take advantage of opportunities for basic science, translational and clinical research working with mentors from the departments of Laboratory Medicine and Pathology or with faculty from other basic science and clinical departments at the Yale School of Medicine. In addition, physician-scientist track research opportunities extending investigative training beyond the clinical year are available through a specific institutional research training program in immunohematology.

Requirements: Candidates should be Board-eligible in AP, CP or AP/CP.

Stipends: Support is commensurate with level of postgraduate training.

Applications: Address inquiries to

Brian R. Smith, MD, Yale University School of Medicine, 333 Cedar Street, PO Box 208035, New Haven, CT 06520-8035.

Phone: (203) 688-2286 • **Fax:** (203) 688-7340 • **E-mail:** brian.smith@yale.edu
Web site: http://info.med.yale.edu/labmed/fellowships.html

UNIVERSITY OF MIAMI SCHOOL OF MEDICINE

Department of Pathology

Transplant Pathology and Immunopathology Fellowship

Description: A one year fellowship in transplantation pathology, renal pathology and immunopathology is available effective July 1, 2010. The program is a combined, one-year clinical and research program in clinical immunology, transplant pathology, renal pathology and immunopathology. Flow cytometric, molecular biological and other advanced techniques are routinely used in the Immunopathology Laboratories. Research emphasis of the fellowship director includes areas of transplantation immunobiology and clinical immunology.

Requirements: Candidates must have completed three (3) years of residency training in pathology at the time of the initial appointment.

Applications: Applicants should submit a curriculum vitae and three (3) letters of reference to:
Phillip Ruiz, MD, PhD, Director of Division of Immunopathology, Department of Pathology, University of Miami School of Medicine, 1611 NW 12th Avenue, Jackson Memorial Hospital - Holtz Center #2101, Miami, FL 33136.

Phone: (305) 585-7344 • **Fax:** (305) 585-7262 • **E-mail:** pruiz@med.miami.edu

---

UNIVERSITY OF PITTSBURGH MEDICAL CENTER

Transplant Pathology Fellowship

Description: We offer a one or two year fellowship that can be tailored to provide any combination of clinical or basic research training desired by the applicant. Clinical training emphasizes the interpretation of liver, kidney, heart and gastrointestinal specimens derived from solid organ transplant recipients, and telepathology. Approximately 7,000 such specimens are accessioned annually and handled in state-of-the-art laboratories equipped with all modern investigative tools. The Division of Transplantation Pathology has eight faculty members engaged in a variety of research studies at the clinical, organ, cellular and molecular level. Areas of particular emphasis include cytokine participation in acute rejection, immune mechanisms of chronic graft vasculopathy, malignancies following solid organ transplantation, viral infections such as hepatitis C, cytomegalovirus, BK virus, and Epstein-Barr virus, dendritic cell biology, microchimerism after organ transplantation and tolerance induction. An overview of our clinical services, training programs, ongoing research activities, and professional staff is available on the World Wide Web at http://path.upmc.edu/divisions/transpath.html. The Division of Transplantation Pathology also maintains an educational Web site at http://tpis.upmc.edu

Requirements: Completion of AP or AP/CP residency and all 3 steps of USMLE.

Stipends: Commensurate with the level of postgraduate training.

Staff: Erin Rubin Ochoa MD, Fellowship Director; **Anthony Demetris** MD; **Rene Duquesnoy** PhD; **Michael Nalesnik** MD; **Parmjeet Randhawa** MD; **Eizaburo Sasatomi** MD, PhD; **Tong Wu** MD, PhD; **Adriana Zeevi** PhD.

Applications: Submit application online at http://path.upmc.edu/fellowship. Six to twelve months in advance of starting date, please send current CV and three letters of recommendation to Erin Ochoa, MD, Transplant Pathology Fellowship Director, Department of Pathology, E-733 UPMC Montefiore, 200 Lothrop Street, Pittsburgh, PA 15213.

Phone: (412) 647-9568 • **Fax:** (412) 647-5237 • **E-mail:** ochoaer@upmc.edu

JOHNS HOPKINS MEDICAL INSTITUTIONS

Informatics Fellowship

Description: The Informatics Division of the Department of Pathology offers a one- or two-year fellowship in informatics. The goals and organization of this fellowship can be tailored to the interests of the trainee. Areas of interest in medical informatics include: 1. Tools for integrating data stored in multiple medical databases; 2. Generation of medical knowledge bases using techniques for extracting and synthesizing information from clinical data; 3. Web tools for pathology and laboratory order-entry and result reporting; 4. Natural language retrieval systems; 5. Open source software in health care.

Requirements: This program is intended primarily for individuals with residency training in pathology, although candidates with other professional backgrounds may be considered. Previous computer experience is required.

Stipends: Commensurate with number of years of relevant postgraduate training and experience.

Applications: Send a curriculum vitae and a description of computer background and career objectives, and four letters of reference to
Robert E. Miller, MD, Department of Pathology, Johns Hopkins Hospital, Meyer B-119, 600 N Wolfe Street, Baltimore, MD 21287-6417.

Phone: (410) 955-5429 • **Web site:** http://pathology.jhu.edu

The Johns Hopkins University does not discriminate on the basis of race, color, sex, religion, national or ethnic origin, age,handicapped or veteran status in any student program or activity administered by the University or with regard to admission or employment.

UNIVERSITY OF MICHIGAN MEDICAL CENTER

Informatics Fellowship

Description: A one to two-year Pathology Informatics and Pathology Data Architecture fellowship is available for those with strong interest in information technology as applied towards the collective specialties of both anatomic and clinical pathology. The program is structured to allow the fellow to rapidly gain proficiency with the use of information technology, process automation, asset tracking technology, and high-throughput computational methodologies, thus creating opportunities where project-lead roles may be quickly assumed. Emphasis is placed on important subspecialties including: Laboratory Information System (LIS) operational and design concepts, design and implementation strategies for optimal database architecture, issues intrinsic to massive database repositories, user interface design, automated tracking of workflow including use of the latest-generation barcoding technologies, natural language / lexical analysis / regular expression / heuristic analysis tools and their deployment to reduce error and improve patient safety and outcomes. Additional areas of focus, based upon individial career goals, include: information delivery using Web-based architectures, collaborative cloud/grid-based computation, scripting and 4GL programming, image repository management, digital imaging and whole-slide imaging, bioinformatics and high-throughput computation (in partnership with the Translational Pathology Division), content-based image retrieval, automated report generation, federation of data sources / federated architectures and, finally, use of information technology to enhance educational initiatives. The above curriculum will be tailored to meet the specific needs and interests of each fellow. Core competencies in each of the major areas of applied clinical informatics, research/investigative informatics and education will be covered throughout the year, in the form of both didactic content and project-oriented exercises. Fellows will work with the staff of a well-established, pathology-based informatics division, in concert with pathologists and staff throughout the department and in the University Hospital at large. Frequently, the informatics fellow will be called upon to act as a liaison and team lead for challenging information technology and data architecture issues, working shoulder to shoulder with pathology residents, department staff and members of a large and complex health system. It is expected that fellows will participate in original informatics research during their fellowship, with such efforts leading to quality publications in high-impact journals, and presentations at national/international meetings.

Requirements: Applicants must be Board-certifed or Board-eligible, in Clinical Pathology or Anatomic and Clinical Pathology and be eligible for a license in Michigan.

Stipends: Salary will be commensurate with the candidate's level of training.

Applications: Interested applicants should forward a curriculum vitae and three letters of recommendation to: Ulysses J. Balis, MD, Associate Professor and Director, division of Pathology Informatics, 1301 Catherine, Ann Arbor, Michigan 48109-5602. Applications should be received no later than March 4th of the same year of commencement of the fellowship, which has a start date of July 1st. Early applications are encouraged.

UNIVERSITY OF PITTSBURGH MEDICAL CENTER

Informatics Fellowship

Description: Pathology Informatics is a developing discipline that focuses on the management and analysis of clinical and research oncology and pathology data using modern computing and communications techniques. The field includes the components of biomedical informatics and Imaging that relate to clinical pathology and research. The Division of Pathology Informatics at the University of Pittsburgh train pathologists and oncologists to be leaders in the development and application of informatics in academic, industry or community practice settings. Because the field of informatics is broad, the training experience is flexible based on the trainee's goals and interests. Research fellowships, a one-year certificate program, or degree programs leading to an MS or PhD are available in collaboration with the University of Pittsburgh Department of Biomedical Informatics.

Requirements: Trainees may have clinical backgrounds in Pathology (three years of anatomic or clinical pathology, or four years of combined AP/CP training), equivalent training in another clinical specialty with a strong orientation to Oncology, or graduate training in biomedical science. Some experience in clinical or research computing applications or development is desirable but not required.

Types and Numbers of Appointments: The program supports one pathology informatics trainee per year.

Stipends: Commensurate with level of training.

Staff: **Anil Parwani** MD, PhD, Fellowship Director; **Michael Becich** MD, PhD; **Gary Blank** PhD; **Jeff Fine** MD; **Jon Ho** MD; **Drazen Jukic** MD, PhD; **Zoltan Oltvai** MD.

Applications: Submit application online at https://secure.opi.upmc.edu/path/fellowship/app-form.cfm. More information can be obtained from Anil Parwani, MD, PhD, Division of Pathology Informatics, UPMC Shadyside, Room WG 07, 5230 Centre Avenue, Pittsburgh, PA 15232.

Phone: (412) 623-1326 • **Fax:** (412) 682-6450

ARIZONA HEALTH SCIENCES CENTER
SOUTHERN ARIZONA VA HEALTH CARE SYSTEM

Molecular Diagnostics Fellowship

Description: The ACGME accredited fellowship provides postdoctoral training in molecular genetic pathology to prepare individuals to direct a molecular diagnostics laboratory for clinical or anatomic pathology. Training will include molecular biology theory and applications, lab management, clinical consultations, and method and procedure development. The fellow will gain experience with lab robotics, nucleic acid extraction, traditional and real-time PCR, amplicon detection techniques, FISH, rep-PCR, SNP analysis, and capillary electrophoresis. Training includes rotations that focus on molecular hematopathology, infectious disease, and oncology with additional rotations in cytogenetics, HLA laboratories, DNA sequencing core, microarray facility, and bioinformatics core. Experience with flow cytometry, confocal microscopy, immunohistochemistry, and laser-capture microdissection techniques will also be available as options. Potential research projects include basic, translational or clinical research with primary focus on hematopathology, infectious disease, or molecular oncology. Manuscript preparation and written and oral presentations will be encouraged. The program has affiliations with the Arizona Cancer Ctr, the Arizona Hlth Sci Ctr, the Biomedical Research Foundation of Southern Arizona, the Institute for Bioscience and Biotechnology, and Veteran's Affairs National Biorepository.

Requirements: Applicants must possess a MD or DO degree. Candidates should have completed 4 years of AP/CP or 3 years of AP residency.

Stipends: Commensurate with year of postgraduate training.

Staff: Ronald Schifman MD; **Donna Wolk** PhD; **Lisa Rimsza** MD; **Anil Prasad** MD; **Stephen Renner** MD; **Catherine Spier** MD; **Christopher Cunniff** MD; **Donald Shepley** MPH; **Carrene Plummer** MS; **Doug Trego** CT (ASCP); **Kelly Boesenber** MS; **Rosemarie Neiman** MT (ASCP).

Applications: Deadline is November 1 for the fellowship beginning July 1 of the following year. Interested applicants should submit a cover letter, curriculum vitae, and three reference letters to: Tammy Umstott, Program Coordinator, Department of Pathology, University of Arizona, 1501 N. Campbell Avenue, P.O. Box 245108, Tucson, AZ 85724-5108.

Phone: (520) 626-6830 • **Fax:** (520) 626-2521 • **E-mail:** umstott@email.arizona.edu

---

BRIGHAM AND WOMEN'S HOSPITAL

Molecular Genetic Pathology Fellowship

Description: The Harvard Medical School Molecular Genetic Pathology Training Program represents a collaboration of the major Harvard teaching hospitals. The overall goals of this one-year accredited training program are: 1. Provide extensive training in broad areas of molecular diagnostics and molecular genetics including inherited genetic disorders, disorders of human development, infectious disease, neoplasia, and identity testing. 2. Provide training in the performance and interpretation of molecular and cytogenetic laboratory tests. 3. Provide training as a medical consultant in Molecular Genetic Pathology to assist clinicians in the diagnosis and care of patients. 4. Provide training and direct exposure to laboratory management, quality-assurance, troubleshooting of molecular tests, assay development and evaluation, and instrument evaluation. 5. Provide training and direct exposure to clinical genetic practice through active participation in genetics clinics with the aim of better understanding the clinical implications of genetic testing.
Ensure that the fellows achieve the following: Acquire a sound knowledge base of the basic science of molecular biology and molecular genetics. Learn to integrate molecular and clinical data and calculate genetic risk. Develop research skills and participate in a research project. Demonstrate good communications skills with laboratory and clinical physicians, patients, technologists, and ancillary staff. Demonstrate sensitivity to ethical issues in genetics, particularly those raised by molecular diagnostic testing.To achieve this end, the trainees rotate through 5 Harvard-affiliated teaching hospitals, including the Brigham and Women's Hospital, Beth Israel Deaconess Medical Center, Children's Hospital and the Massachusetts General Hospital and the Dana-Farber Cancer Center.

Requirements: Board-eligible or certified in Pathology or Medical Genetics. Applicants must be eligible for a Massachusetts medical license.

Types and Numbers of Appointments: Accredited for 4 one-year clinical Molecular Genetic Pathology fellowships.

Stipends: Commensurate with level of postgraduate training

Staff: There are over 40 faculty members acroos 5 institutions including pathologists, geneticists, clinicians and physician-scientists. Further details on faculty, rotations and applications can be obtained from the program coordinator.

Applications: Inquiries and applications should be sent to: Dr. Janina Longtine, Director, Molecular Diagnostics, Department of Pathology, Shapiro 5 Room 020, Brigham and Women's Hospital, 75 Francis Street, Boston, MA 02115.

Phone: (857) 307-1539 • **Fax:** (857) 307-1544 • **E-mail:** jlongtine@partners.org.

BAYLOR COLLEGE OF MEDICINE

Departments of Pathology and Molecular and Human Genetics

Molecular Genetic Pathology Fellowship

Description: This ACGME-accredited fellowship offers comprehensive training in Molecular Genetic Pathology at the Baylor College of Medicine (BCM), Texas Children's Hospital (TCH; 715 beds), and Ben Taub General Hospital (BTGH; 650 beds). In the Baylor Department of Molecular and Human Genetics, diagnostic laboratory activities will be performed in the DNA Diagnostic Laboratory (BCM, Director, Christine Eng, MD), Cytogenetics Laboratory (BCM, Director, Sau Wai Cheung, PhD, MBA), and Human Genome Center (BCM, Director, Richard Gibbs, PhD). In the Baylor Department of Pathology, rotations will take place in the Division of Molecular Pathology headed by James Versalovic, MD, PhD and including the Molecular Oncology (TCH, Director, Dolores López-Terrada, MD, PhD), the Molecular Microbiology (TCH, Director, James Versalovic, MD, PhD), and Molecular Neuropathology (TCH, Director, Adekunle Adesina, MD, PhD) Laboratories at TCH, and the Microbiology Laboratory at BTGH (Director, Charles Stager, PhD). Fellows also rotate at the M.D. Anderson Cancer Center (Raja Luthra, PhD) and (Su Chen, MD, PhD). Fellows will rotate among participating laboratories during the core 12-month fellowship period, and opportunities for a second year of translational or basic research are offered by the MGP faculty in the Departments of Pathology or Molecular and Human Genetics. Opportunities for case review and participation with the Departments of Internal Medicine, Obstetrics and Gynecology and Pediatrics (Hematology-Oncology and Genetics) will be available to enrich the educational experience of the fellow. In addition to diagnostic laboratory activities, fellows will be expected to participate in the Molecular Pathology course for residents/fellows and attend the Human Genetics course in the graduate school. Weekly conferences in pathology and genetics are included in the program.

Program Director is Dolores López-Terrada, MD, PhD.

Requirements: MD with board eligibility in AP, CP, AP/CP, or Medical Genetics.

Stipends: Commensurate with experience level.

Applications: Submit statement of interest, curriculum vitae and at least three letters of recommendation to Dr. Dolores López-Terrada, Department of Pathology, MC 315, Baylor College of Medicine, One Baylor Plaza, Houston, TX, 77030.

Phone: (832) 824-1864 • **Fax:** (832) 825-0164 • **E-mail:** rosariog@bcm.edu

Baylor College of Medicine is an Equal Opportunity/Affirmative Action/Equal Access Employer.

UNIVERSITY OF CALIFORNIA, LOS ANGELES

Molecular Genetic Pathology Fellowship

Description: The Department of Pathology & Laboratory Medicine offers a one-year accredited fellowship in Molecular Genetic Pathology that provides intensive training in all aspects of molecular diagnostics, including DNA and RNA analysis in cancers, genetic disorders, infectious disease, and identity testing. The fellow will learn diagnostic skills during exposure to internal cases as well as a large number of referral cases sent to UCLA for consultations. The fellow interacts with Pathology and Laboratory Medicine residents, as well as fellows, residents and faculty in the Medical Genetics and Hematology-Oncology services, among others. The fellow participates in teaching, conferences, and genetics clinics. Fellows are encouraged to develop scholarly or research activities. One fellowship position is offered each academic year.

Requirements: Applicants must be BE/BC in anatomic and/or clinical pathology or medical genetics. A California medical license is required.

Stipends: Support is commensurate with the candidate's level of training.

Applications: Please contact Fellowship Coordinator (Ms. Annetta Pierro) for list of requirements and application. In addition, submit curriculum vitae and three letters of recommendation to Wayne W. Grody, MD, PhD, Program Director, Molecular Genetic Pathology, Department of Pathology & Laboratory Medicine, 10833 Le Conte Ave., Rm: 13-145G CHS, Los Angeles, CA 90095-1732. (310) 825-5648.

Applications should be submitted 1 1/2 years prior to desired fellowship or by February 1st of the year preceding the fellowship; although applications are considered on a rolling basis. Fellowship Coordinator: Ms. Annetta Pierro

Phone: (310) 825-5719 • **Fax:** (310) 267-2058 • **E-mail:** apierro@mednet.ucla.edu
Web site: www.pathology.ucla.edu

UNIVERSITY OF CALIFORNIA, SAN FRANCISCO

Molecular Genetic Pathology Fellowship

Description: The UCSF Departments of Pathology and Laboratory Medicine offer a one year ACGME-accredited Molecular Genetic Pathology Fellowship. The fellowship includes training in the areas of cancer genetics (solid tumors and hematopathology), inherited disease, infectious disease, forensics, pharmacogenomics and cytogenetics. Fellows learn the methodologies used to perform molecular testing, how to interpret and report test results, how to develop and validate new testing, how to oversee a molecular pathology laboratory, and how to serve as consultants to the clinical services. In addition, fellows actively participate in the clinical practice of Medical Genetics during their time in the Genetics Clinics. Fellows are expected to actively participate in an academic research project. A second year of fellowship is available by arrangement to allow more in depth research pursuits.

Requirements: Completed residency training in AP, CP, AP/CP, or medical genetics and eligibility for a California medical license.

Stipends: Commensurate with level of postgraduate training.

Staff: There are over 50 faculty members including pathologists, geneticists, clinicians and basic scientists. Faculty profiles are available on the following Departmental Websites:
http://pathology.ucsf.edu/about/faculty/pathology.html;
http://medicine.ucsf.edu/genetics/faculty.html; http://www.pediatrics.medschool.ucsf.edu/medicalgenetics/faculty/index.aspx

Applications: Please send your application along with a CV, Statement of Interest, and 3 letters of Recommendation to: Dr. Anna B. Berry, Director, Molecular Genetic Pathology, Department of Pathology, University of California San Francisco, 185 Berry Street, Lobby 2, Suite 100, Box 0506, San Francisco, CA 94107-0506, Attention: Ira Lezcano. Fellowship coordinator is Ira Lezcano, she can be reached at

Phone: (415) 885-7376 • **Fax:** (415) 514-8193 • **E-mail:** ira.lezcano@ucsf.edu.

CEDARS-SINAI MEDICAL CENTER

Molecular Genetic Pathology Fellowship

Description: The Cedars-Sinai Medical Center Division of Molecular Pathology and the Medical Genetic Institute jointly offer a one year fellowship to pathologists and medical geneticists. Cedars-Sinai is a 969 bed quaternary hospital with over 35,000 molecular and 3000 cytogenetic and FISH samples evaluated in 2006. The Diagnostic Molecular Laboratory offers tests in exquisitely sensitive quantitative PCR, oncology, hematology, microbiology, and medical genetics. The Cytogenetics and HLA-typing Laboratories offer state-of-the art testing. Test results are integrated with relevant clinicopathological data. In addition, the Medical Genetic Institute offers training in clinical genetics and genetic conseling through rotations in pediatric and adult clinical genetics, metabolic clinic, and the internationally renowned skeletal dysplasia clinic. Trainees are expected to function as junior attendings and will gain hands-on experience with a broad range of molecular techniques including nucleic acid extraction, Southern blotting, hybrid capture, Invader technology, PCR, quantitative PCR, capillary electrophoresis, sequencing, cytogenetics, and FISH.

Requirements: Candidates must be board eligibile in Anatomic and/or Clinical Pathology or Molecular Genetics. A California medical license is required at the time of appointment.

Stipends: Commensurate with level of training, go to http://www.csmc.edu.2810.html

Staff: **Rena Falk** MD; **Jean Lopategui** MD; **Rhona Schreck** PhD.

Applications: For an application, information and correspondence, contact the program coordinator: LeeTanya Marion-Murray, Dept. of Pathology, Cedars-Sinai Medical Center, 8700 Beverly Blvd., S.Tower Room 8709, Los Angeles, CA 90048.

Phone: (310) 423-6941 • **Fax:** (310) 423-5881 • **E-mail:** marionl@cshs.org

---

EMORY UNIVERSITY HOSPITAL

Department of Pathology and Laboratory Medicine

Molecular Genetic Pathology Fellowship

Description: The molecular genetic pathology fellowship is a one-year ACGME board-accredited clinical fellowship designed to train pathologists for a career in molecular genetic pathology. The trainee will get a thorough exposure to all aspects of molecular genetic pathology including hematopathology, infectious diseases, tissue typing, oncology, and medical genetics. Emory Medical Laboratories have a state-of-the art molecular diagnostic facility that performs more than 56,000 tests annually. The trainee will gain hands-on experience with a broad range of molecular techniques including nucleic acid extraction, nucleic acid amplification (conventional and real-time PCR, NASBA, and SDA), Southern blotting, cytogenetics, FISH, microarray technology, SSCP, bone marrow engraftment studies and nucleic acid sequencing. Trainees are expected to participate in laboratory test development and translational research. The fellows will assume progressively more responsibility for interactions with clinicians and other pathologists, and test interpretation as the training progresses.

Requirements: USMLE Step 3, Eligible for Georgia medical licensure, completed AP and/or CP, or Medical Genetics. Hands on experience in molecular biology and/or molecular testing is highly desired.

Stipends: Commensurate with year of postgraduate training.

Staff: **Karen P. Mann** MD, PhD, Director; **Charles Hill** MD, PhD, Co-director; **Angela Caliendo** MD, PhD; **David Ledbetter** PhD; **Christa Martin** PhD, FACMG, and numerous other faculty in pathology, genetics and research laboratories.

Applications:

Phone: (404) 727-4283 • **Fax:** (404) 727-2519 • **E-mail:** mmojonn@emory.edu
Web site: www.emory.edu/PATHOLOGY/

UNIVERSITY OF IOWA HOSPITALS AND CLINICS

Molecular Genetic Pathology Fellowship

Description: TThe University of Iowa Hospitals and Clinics (UIHC) offers a one-year ACGME-accredited fellowship in molecular genetic pathology. The fellowship program combines training in the analytical, clinical, and administrative aspects of molecular pathology with exposure to clinical genetics as well as related clinical or basic research. The training is designed to prepare the candidate for a career in academic medicine as a director of a molecular diagnostics laboratory with a strong emphasis on basic research. The core training faculty is comprised of individuals with primary interest in molecular, biochemical and clinical genetics, and molecular microbiology and oncology. The transitional or basic research component of the training can take place either in the diagnostic laboratory, or in the laboratories of several dozen faculty members who are associated with the program. With the exception of 12 days of biochemical genetics training at the Iowa Hygienic Laboratory in Ankeny, the fellowship training occurs at the UIHC within the Department of Pathology's Medical Microbiology Division.
Requirements: Eligibility for ACGME certification in anatomic and/or clinical pathology or pediatrics (successful completion of ACGME-accredited training program in CP, AP/CP, or Pediatrics), or PhD in the biological sciences with preferable postdoctoral experience.
Facilities: Our laboratory is a state-of-the-art molecular pathology laboratory that currently performs in excess of 30 different molecular tests using a variety of platforms including capillary electrophoresis, dHPLC, real-time PCR. Our laboratory is a state-of-the-art molecular pathology laboratory that currently performs in excess of 30 different molecular tests using a variety of platforms including capillary electrophoresis, dHPLC, real-time PCR. Trainees have access to the technology and technical expertise in any of the labs they choose for research training, as well as to core facilities. For more information, please see: http://www.healthcare.uiowa.edu/pathology/path_folder/education/fellowships/mole_gene_fellow.html
Stipends: Support is commensurate with the candidate's level of postgraduate training.
Staff: Aaron Bossler MD, PhD Molecular Microbiology; **Jonathan W Heusel** MD, PhD Molecular Pathology; **Peter Nagy** MD, PhD Molecular Oncology; **Val Sheffield** MD, PhD Clinical Genetics.
Applications: Inquiries should be addressed to: Peter Nagy, MD, PhD The University of Iowa, Department of Pathology, 354 MRC, Iowa City, IA 52242
Phone: (319) 356-2990 • **Fax:** (319) 356-4916 • **E-mail:** peter-nagy@uiowa.edu
Curriculum vitae, personal statement, 3 letters of reference sent to: Ms. Linda Elliott, University of Iowa Hospitals and Clinics, Department of Pathology, Medical Microbiology Division, 200 Hawkins Drive, Room C606, Iowa City, IA 52242, linda-elliott@uiowa.edu

JOHNS HOPKINS MEDICAL INSTITUTIONS

Molecular Genetic Pathology Fellowship

Description: The molecular genetic pathology fellowship is an ACGME-accredited, two-year flexible program designed to train individuals for academic careers including disease-oriented basic research, development of molecularly-based diagnostic technologies, and molecularly-oriented clinical research. More than 44 faculty members in the Department of Pathology, Human Genetics and others teach or mentor research in this program. Training consists of a didactic course in molecular biology, introductory rotations through selected basic and applied laboratories, and an in-depth research-oriented experience under the direction of a faculty mentor. Current research activities include: molecular oncology including diagnostic development and fundamental neoplastic mechanisms, renal pathology, transplantation, immunopathology including HIV-related research, neuropathology focusing upon mechanisms of degenerative disorders, immunohematology, clinical chemistry, molecular microbiology, and comparative pathology. Fellows may incorporate genomic and proteomic approaches into their research making use of available departmental core facilities.
Requirements: Applicants should possess MD or equivalent doctoral degree and have completed one or more years of training in general pathology or genetics. Exceptional PhD applicants with extensive clinical laboratory experience may also be considered.
Stipends: Commensurate with relevant experience and previous training.
Applications: Address correspondence to: Christopher Gocke, MD, Associate Professor, Johns Hopkins Medical Institutions, 600 N. Wolfe Street, Park Bldg. SB202, Baltimore, MD 21287. Applications can be obtained from Mrs. Penny Spencer (pspence3@jhmi.edu).
Phone: (410) 955-8363
Web site: http://pathology.jhu.edu

The Johns Hopkins University does not discriminate on the basis of race, color, sex, religion, national or ethnic origin, age, handicapped or veteran status in any student program or activity administered by the University or with regard to admission or employment.

MAYO SCHOOL OF GRADUATE MEDICAL EDUCATION

Molecular Genetic Pathology Fellowship

Description: The Molecular Genetic Pathology Fellowship provides a structured educational experience for pathologists and other physicians to obtain proficiency in various aspects of molecular pathology. The Fellowship Program is jointly administered by the Divisions of Laboratory Genetics and Anatomic Pathology. Areas of training include molecular microbiology, molecular oncology (solid tumors), congenital molecular genetics, molecular hematology, molecular histocompatibility, cytogenetics, forensics, and pharmacogenomics. Fellows will learn about the methodologies used to perform testing, how to report and interpret test results, how to manage a molecular pathology laboratory, and how to develop and implement new tests. Fellows completing this training will be eligible to take the Molecular Genetic Pathology board examination that is jointly administered by the American Board of Pathology and American Board of Medical Genetics.
Requirements: Applicants should have a MD or DO degree, a U.S. medical license and have completed a residency by the time the fellowship begins.
Applications: www.mayo.edu/msgme/application.html Submit no later than January 15th of the year preceding the fellowship year which begins in July.
Phone: (507) 284-2404 • **E-mail:** pathologyeducation@mayo.edu
Web site: www.mayo.edu/msgme/molec-gen-rch.html

Mayo Clinic is an affirmative action and equal opportunity educator and employer.

UNIVERSITY OF MICHIGAN MEDICAL CENTER

Molecular Genetic Pathology Fellowship

Description: The Department of Pathology offers a one-year fellowship in molecular genetic pathology with emphasis on molecular-based diagnostic techniques. The program includes training in all areas of molecular genetic pathology, including molecular hematopathology, oncology, infectious diseases, tissue typing, pharmacogenomics, inherited disorders, cytogenetics and medical genetics. Each year, the laboratories perform approximately 50,000 molecular infectious disease tests, 7,000 genetic screening tests, and 2,000 molecular hematopathology/oncology tests. The fellow will gain experience in a broad range of state-of-the-art molecular and cytogenetic techniques including nucleic acid extraction, hybridization technologies, FISH, amplification technologies (PCR, RT-PCR, quantitative PCR), capillary electrophoresis, DNA sequencing, and high throughput molecular genetic testing. Trainees will have significant clinical laboratory responsibilities during the course of the training program, being actively involved in test interpretation and reporting, test development and validation, and serving as consultants to clinicians in a variety of disciplines. Numerous opportunities for research experience are available with the Department of Pathology and the Department of Human Genetics.
Requirements: Applicants must be board-certified or eligible in anatomic and/or clinical pathology or medical genetics. Prior experience in molecular biology is recommended.
Stipends: Support is commensurate with the candidate's level of training.
Applications: Applications should be submitted with curriculum vitae to: Kojo S.J. Elenitoba-Johnson, MD, University of Michigan, Department of Pathology, 1301 Catherine, M5242D, Ann Arbor, Michigan 48109-0602. Applications should be made by October 1st of the year prior to the fellowship start date of July 1st. Early applications are encouraged.

UNIVERSITY OF MINNESOTA AFFILIATED HOSPITALS

Molecular Genetic Pathology Fellowship

Description: Molecular Genetic Pathology (MGP) Training Program at University of Minnesota Medical Center (UMMC) is an ACGME accredited one-year fellowship. This MGP program is designed to train pathologists to be an expert in molecular diagnosis. The MGP graduate will be in excellence to provide comprehensive diagnostic, management and counseling services for inherited diseases and the genetic factors pertinent to all diseases. Trainees will refine their skills in laboratory management, quality assurance and quality control. Trainees will constantly involve and become a critical player in the development, validation and implementation of new tests. The training experience also emphasizes the role of research in molecular pathology so that trainees can pursue investigator-initiated research upon completion of the program. The UMMC Molecular Diagnostics Laboratory is the home base of this program. The molecular lab currently provides 45 clinical molecular tests. Its test menu covers broad inherited diseases, hematological disorders, and solid tumors. MGP fellows will learn and master the molecular techniques including DNA and RNA extraction, Southern blot, variety PCR amplification methods including sequencing, methylation specific PCR and real-time PCR. These technologies are applied in a wide spectrum of clinical tests in cancer, inherited disease, infectious disease, and identification. Fellows will learn to analyze and interpret molecular data from clinical cases, and to compose diagnostic reports. Fellows will engage in correlations with clinical, morphologic, immunophenotypic, and cytogenetic findings. Fellows will be exposed to lab administration procedures, such as QA&QC, CAP surveys, test development, and ethical issues related to clinical service and research in molecular pathology. Fellows will learn to design and carry out research projects aimed at understanding the molecular basis of diseases or translating such basic discoveries into improved patient care. Departmental Research Fund is available for every fellow.
Requirements: MD plus at least 3 years of CP or 4 years of AP/CP training.
Stipends: Commensurate with the level of postgraduate training.
Staff: Michelle Dolan MD, Program Director.
Applications: Mail applications to: Michelle Dolan, MD, Molecular Genetics Fellowship Program Director, Dept. of Lab, Medicine and Pathology, University of Minnesota, 420 Delaware St. SE, MMC 609, Minneapolis, MN 55455
Fax: (612) 625-3976
Web site: http://residency.pathology.umn.edu

UNIVERSITY OF NEW MEXICO

Molecular Genetic Pathology

Description: A comprehensive training in Molecular Genetic Pathology (MGP) is provided at the University of New Mexico Health Science Center and TriCore Reference Laboratories in all areas of Molecular Pathology including Molecular Oncology, HLA typing, Post Bone Marrow Transplantation Chimerism, Hereditary Genetic Tests, Molecular Microbiology/Virology and Cytogenetics/FISH. Training in Medical Genetics and Genetic Counseling is provided in Dysmorphology Clinics in Department of Pediatrics with close interaction of MGP fellow with pediatric dysmorphologist and geneticist including participation in medical rounds. The MGP fellow will be trained in a structured manner with active involvement in the interpretation of molecular pathology test results, preparation of molecular pathology reports prior to sign out and discussion of results with referring physicians. An integrated approach will be taught and used. The fellow will attend ongoing education conferences and didactic presentations. The fellow will also present conferences including interesting, classic or challenging cases in molecular pathology. The fellow will participate in QA/QC aspects of molecular pathology as well as in laboratory management meetings. Graduated responsibility will be given to the fellow as the fellow accrues acceptable competency levels. Ample opportunities for research projects and publications are provided and the fellow is encouraged to present his/her work in molecular pathology-related national meetings. Length of Program: 12 months; July 1st through June 30th.
Requirements: MD plus residency training in pathology or medical genetics.
Facilities: The molecular tests are mainly performed at TriCore Reference Laboratories and include over 70,000 molecular diagnostic tests, 1,300 molecular oncology and 4,400 cytogenetics/FISH assays. A range of technologies is employed that include RT-PCR, qualitative PCR, allelic discrimination PCR, quantitative real time PCR, direct DNA sequencing, high resolution melting curve analysis, fluorescent and chromogenic in situ hybridization, and capillary electrophoresis.
Staff: Mohammad A Vasef Program Director; **Brad Brimhall**; **Carol Clericuzio**; **Thomas Cushing**; **James Gale**; **Nancy Gough** Program coordinator; **Randall Heidenreich**; **John Hozier**; **Barbara Masten**; **Kaaren Reichard**; **Thomas Williams**; **Stephen Young**.
Applications: CV, personal statement and 3 letters of reference to be received no later than November 1 of each year for positions commencing July 1 two years later. Interviews will be conducted in January. Application Deadline: November 1st Visas Accepted: J1 For further information contact either: Mohammad Vasef, MD, Molecular Genetic Pathology Fellowship Program Director or Nancy Gough, Molecular Genetic Pathology Fellowship Program Coordinator Address: 1001 Woodward Place NE Albuquerque, NM 87102
Phone: (505) 938-8456 • **Fax:** (505) 938-8414

UNIVERSITY OF NORTH CAROLINA AT CHAPEL HILL

Molecular Genetic Pathology Fellowship

Description: The University of North Carolina Hospitals offers a one year fellowship in molecular genetic pathology. The fellow gains a working knowledge of molecular procedures including Southern blot, in situ hybridization/FISH, sequencing, protein truncation test, amplification, tissue microdissection, and array technologies including gene expression profiling and comparative genomic hybridization. These procedures are applied in a wide spectrum of clinical settings including oncology, inherited disease, infectious disease, HLA-typing, identification, and pharmacogenetics. The fellow learns to analyze and interpret molecular data from clinical cases and to compose pathology reports. Results are correlated with clinical, morphologic, immunophenotypic, biochemical, and cytogenetic findings. The fellow learns to design and carry out research aimed at understanding the molecular basis of disease and translating fundamental discoveries into improved patient care. Ethical issues, quality assurance, and lab administration are discussed as they relate to clinical practice. Consider applying for our combined 2-year Surgical and Molecular Pathology Fellowship Program. UNC Hospitals has the longest track record of board certifications among all ACGME-accredited molecular genetic pathology training programs. Program Director: Margaret L. Gulley, MD, Dept of Pathology, University of North Carolina, Chapel Hill, NC 27599-7525. A description of UNC molecular programs and facilities is available online, http://www.pathology.unc.edu/fellowsp/molecular_genetic_path.htm

Requirements: Candidates must have an MD degree. AP/CP board eligibility is preferred.

Types and Numbers of Appointments: One MGP fellow trains alongside many other fellows; see list of training programs at UNC at http://www.pathology.unc.edu/resident/fellowsp.htm

Facilities: UNC Hospitals

Community: Chapel Hill is a manageable university town in the vibrant Research Triangle region of North Carolina.

Stipends: Fellowship stipends are based on the trainee's number of years of postdoctoral training and the current UNC Hospitals' Housestaff salary scale.

Applications: Applications should be made no later than October 1 prior to the intended fellowship start date of July 1. For further information and application forms, please contact: Ms. Janice Badstein, McLendon Clin Labs, Rm 1106 UNC Hospitals, Chapel Hill, NC, 27514.

Phone: (919) 966-2318 • **E-mail:** jbadstei@unch.unc.edu

UNIVERSITY OF OKLAHOMA HEALTH SCIENCES CENTER

Molecular Genetic Pathology Fellowship

Description: The Molecular Genetic Pathology (MGP) Program at the University of Oklahoma Health Sciences Center is an ACGME-accredited one year fellowship. It provides structured training in all aspects of molecular pathology, including laboratory management and clinical consultation. The fellow will assume progressive responsibility for the molecular diagnosis of a wide variety of genetic, infectious, and oncologic diseases. The program also provides rotations in molecular HLA typing, paternity testing, and forensics. Techniques available include automated nucleic acid extraction, real-time PCR, capillary electrophoresis, sequencing, Hybrid Capture, and FISH. Trainees attend genetics clinic and participate in test development.

Requirements: AP/CP, AP, CP or Medical Genetics residency training and eligibility for Oklahoma medical licensure.

Stipends: Support will be commensurate with the applicant's level of training.

Staff: Michael L. Talbert MD, Program Director.

Applications: Applicants should submit the universal fellowship application form listed on the CAP website, a personal statement, CV, copies of USMLE scores, and if applicable, an ECFMG certificate. A residency program director's letter and two other letters of recommendation are required. Send all materials to:

Dianne Wright, Residency Program Coordinator, Department of Pathology, University of Oklahoma Health Sciences Center, P.O. Box 26901, BMSB 401, Oklahoma City, OK 73126-0901.

Phone: (405) 271-2451 • **E-mail:** dianne-wright@ouhsc.edu

OREGON HEALTH & SCIENCE UNIVERSITY

Molecular Genetic Pathology Fellowship

Description: The Dept. of Pathology offers an ACGME-accredited one-year fellowship in Molecular Genetic Path., a new subspecialty jointly accredited by the American Board of Path. and the American Board of Med. Genetics. The MGP fellow will gain a working knowledge of all current clinical molecular diagnostic procedures including DNA and RNA extraction, Southern blots, in situ hybridization/FISH, mutation scanning methods, and qualitative and quantitative amplification methods. These technologies are applied in a wide spectrum of clinical settings (and in multiple clinical diagnostic lab sections) including cancer, inherited disease (Mendelian, trinucleotide repeats, and complex), infectious disease, HLA-typing, and identification. The MGP fellow will learn to analyze and interpret molecular data from our wealth of clinical cases, and to compose and communicate diagnostic reports. These molecular results will be correlated with clinical, laboratory, morphologic, immunophenotypic, and cytogenetic findings. Exposure to ethical issues, lab quality assurance, and lab administration are an additional part of the MGP curriculum. The MGP fellow will also learn to design and implement research projects aimed at understanding the molecular basis of disease or translating such basic discoveries into improved patient care. An optional second year of full time research may be available to interested and eligible fellows.

Requirements: Candidates must have an MD degree (or equivalent), and have either completed training in an ACGME accredited residency in Medical Genetics or Pathology (AP and/or CP), or be certified by the American Board of Medical Genetics.

Stipends: The stipend is comensurate with the year of postgraduate training.

Staff: Richard D. Press MD, PhD Program Director; **Sue Richards** PhD, Program Co-director.

Applications: Applications will be accepted up to two years in advance of the annual July 1 start date and will be reviewed as rolling admissions. Admissions are typically made more than 12 months prior to matriculation. Please submit a cover letter, your CV, a completed OHSU application form from our web site, and three letters of recommendation to: Anna Wedeking, Training Programs Coordinator, Department of Pathology, Oregon Health & Science University, 3181 SW Sam Jackson Park Rd., L113, Portland, Oregon 97239-3098.

E-mail: ferencea@ohsu.edu
Web site: http://www.ohsu.edu/pathology/win/Fellmolgen.htm

UNIVERSITY OF PITTSBURGH MEDICAL CENTER

Molecular Genetic Pathology Fellowship

Description: Outstanding training is offered in all areas of molecular diagnostics. The Division of Molecular Diagnostics and Molecular Anatomic Pathology Laboratory are primary sites for molecular testing of inherited, infectious and neoplastic diseases in the UPMC Health System and coordinate molecular sendout testing for the Health System and Children's Hospital of Pittsburgh. Over 80 procedures employ a range of technologies including qualitative/quantitative PCR and RT-PCR, restriction enzyme analysis, fragment sizing, LOH analysis, Southern and dot blots, direct DNA sequencing, and commercial assay kits. Exposure is maximized efficiently since most assays are performed in a single laboratory area. The fellow functions as a junior attending with significant responsibility for clinical interactions, assay interpretation, report preparation and conference presentations. Bench experience and opportunities for research projects and publication are provided in the initial and (sometimes arranged) subsequent years. The fellow participates actively in administrative and developmental activities and meetings to learn a range of practical and management skills necessary to oversee a modern clinical molecular diagnostics laboratory. The MGP fellowship is ACGME-accredited and starts in July.

Requirements: Applicants must be a Doctor of Medicine and upon commencing the fellowship have completed residency training in Pathology or Human Genetics in the United States or Canada. Evidence of past achievement and future potential are essential. Prior molecular biology experience is desirable but not required.

Staff: Jeffrey Kant MD, PhD, Fellowship Director; **Marie DeFrances** MD, PhD; **Zoltan Oltvai** MD; **Tim Oury** MD, PhD; **Xiao-Ming Yin** MD, PhD; **Yuri Nikiforov** MD, PhD; **Marina Nikiforova** MD; **Suneeta Madan-Kheterpal** MD; **Gerald Vockley** MD, PhD; **K. Michael Gibson** PhD; **Urvashi Surti** PhD; **Melissa Melan** PhD; **Jamie M. Moore** MS; **Denise Bell** BS; **Geeta Mantha** PhD; **Michelle Clemens** MS; **Elizabeth Gettig** MS; **Jacqueline Hoover** MS; **Darcy Thull** MS; **John Uhrmacher**.

Applications: Jeffrey A. Kant, MD, PhD, Division of Molecular Diagnostics, Department of Pathology, S-701 Scaife Hall, 3550 Terrace St., Pittsburgh, PA 15261.

Phone: (412) 648-8519 • **Fax:** (412) 383-9594 • **E-mail:** kantja@upmc.edu
Web site: http://path.upmc.edu/divisions/mdx/diagnostics.html
Submit application online at http://path.upmc.edu/fellowship

UNIVERSITY OF PENNSYLVANIA MEDICAL CENTER

Department of Pathology & Laboratory Medicine

Molecular Genetic Pathology Fellowship

Description: The Molecular genetic pathology (MGP) fellowship is a one-year ACGME-accredited post-residency training program. The fellow learns molecular pathology through practical experience, didactic lectures, teaching of residents, presentations at conferences, and by participating in laboratory administration and test development/research. The fellow assumes significant and increasing clinical and laboratory responsibility in an active molecular pathology service that performs testing for inherited disorders, hematopathology, solid tumors, infectious diseases, and identity testing. Service entails the involvement of the fellow and the Pathology residents in all aspects of molecular testing in order to provide optimal patient care. Fellows assist in the training of the residents during the each three-month rotation, with the residents responsible for the majority of the service work after the first month. Requests for molecular testing are assessed on a daily basis to ensure the appropriateness of the requested test in the context of the clinical scenario. Test results are reviewed in preparation for reporting by the faculty and communication of critical results to health care providers. Afternoon case review sessions are an excellent opportunity for teaching and learning about the application of molecular technologies and the role of molecular diagnosis in clinical decision-making. Fellows also participate in the diagnosis, management, and treatment of patients with genetic disorders and in the counseling of the patient and family during a one-month rotation in the Division of Medical Genetics. A one-month rotation at the Children's Hospital of Philadelphia provides the opportunity to observe and participate in the counseling and care of pediatric genetics patients in areas including general genetics, dysmorphology, metabolic and biochemical genetics. The program also includes rotations in cancer cytogenetics, prenatal cytogenetics, and molecular HLA. Additional electives are available. Fellows entering the fellowship without prior training in Pathology will participate in surgical and autopsy pathology. Upon successful completion of the training program, the fellow will be Board eligible in MGP.

Requirements: Candidates must be Board-eligible in either Anatomic and/or Clinical Pathology or Medical Genetics and have passed the USMLE Part 3 exam prior to the start of the program. They must also be licensed or eligible for Pennsylvania licensure.
Prior experience in genetics and/or molecular biology is recommended.

Types and Numbers of Appointments: One position is available each year.

Stipends: Stipend is commensurate with the year of postgraduate clinical training.

Staff: Vivianna Van Deerlin MD, PhD (Lab and Fellowship Director); **Warren Pear** MD, PhD; **Robert B. Wilson** MD, PhD; **Frederick Barr** MD, PhD; **Antonia Sepulveda** MD; **Adam Bagg** MD.

Applications: The academic year begins each year on the first of July. Application forms can be obtained from the laboratory website (www.uphs.upenn.edu/path/molecular.html) or by calling (215) 662-6550 and can be submitted between 16-24 months prior to the start of the program. The position will be filled on or after March 1 of the year preceding the program start date. Candidates considered for the program will be asked to interview with the program director and selected faculty and staff.

STANFORD UNIVERSITY MEDICAL CENTER

Department of Pathology

Molecular Genetic Pathology Fellowship

Description: This ACGME-accredited fellowship offers comprehensive training in Molecular Genetic Pathology. The program serves adult and pediatric populations at Stanford and also sees referrals from Northern California and the rest of the U.S. The approach to training is interdisciplinary, including faculty from Departments of Pathology, Medicine, Pediatrics (Division of Medical Genetics) and Genetics. Fellows are trained in assay development, quality assurance and result interpretation in the Molecular Pathology Laboratory at Stanford and also at Kaiser-Permanente Regional Molecular Diagnosis Laboratory, a large reference laboratory. Other rotations include Biochemical Genetics and Cytogenetics. Fellows are expected to initiate a research project during the fellowship. This project can be performed in any appropriate laboratory at Stanford, which offers unmatched opportunities for research in Molecular Pathology and Molecular Genetics. Departmental funding is available for suitable research projects. Moreover, subject to the approval of the Pathology chair (Stephen Galli, MD), additional funding may be available for qualified fellows, who are graduates of our CP only or AP only residency program and who wish to pursue an academic career devoted primarily to extramurally-funded research, to continue their research beyond the period of the formal fellowship.

Requirements: CP, AP or AP/CP training and eligibility for California medical license.

Stipends: Commensurate with experience plus additional $8,400 per year housing allowance.

Applications: Submit to: Iris Schrijver, MD, Director of Molecular Pathology, Department of Pathology, Stanford University Medical Center, 300 Pasteur Drive, Room L235, Stanford, CA 94305-5324.

Phone: (650) 724-2403 • **Fax:** (650) 724-1567 • **E-mail:** ischrijver@stanfordmed.org

UNIVERSITY OF TEXAS SOUTHWESTERN MEDICAL CENTER

Molecular Genetic Pathology Fellowship

Description: The fellowship program is flexible and includes training in basic and advanced molecular biology techniques as applied to modern pathology. The fellow would assume significant clinical and laboratory responsibility in a molecular diagnostics laboratory that provides testing for hematopoietic malignancies, infectious diseases, solid tumors, and inherited disorders. Viral qualitative and quantitation assays provide the opportunity for extensive interaction with the infectious disease clinicians, hepatologists and transplant specialists (both pediatric and adult). Development of "real-time" PCR, MLPA, clinical sequencing and solid tumor theranostic tests is ongoing. Assays for genetic tests include: Factor V Leiden variant detection, prothrombin variant detection and MTHFR variant detection. Rotation through other clinical laboratories providing additional molecular testing based on FISH and in-situ hybridization techniques is available. Opportunity exists for collaborative projects with faculty directing excellent research laboratories within the Department of Pathology. The fellow will actively support the resident rotation in Molecular Diagnostics. Numerous student, resident and faculty conferences provide ample teaching opportunities.

Requirements: Candidates should have satisfactorily completed pathology training from an approved program in anatomic, clinical pathology, or combined AP/CP or have a strong background in a relevant scientific discipline. Physician must be eligible for a Texas Institutional Permit.

Stipends: Support will be commensurate with the year of postgraduate training.

Staff: **Deborah A Payne** PhD, D(ABMM). DABCC; **Huan-You Wang** MD, PhD.

Applications: Applications should be made no later than October 1 prior to the intended fellowship beginning the following July 1. Address inquiries to: Dr. Deborah Payne, PhD, Laboratory for Molecular Diagnostics, Department of Pathology, University of Texas Southwestern Medical Center, 5323 Harry Hines Blvd., Dallas, TX 75390-8840 or email deborah.payne@utsouthwestern.edu.

Phone: (214) 645-7078
Web site: http://pathcuric1.swmed.edu/Teaching/fellowship/molec_fellowship.htm

UNIVERSITY OF UTAH MEDICAL CENTER

Molecular Genetic Pathology Fellowship

Description: The Department of Pathology at the University of Utah Health Sciences Center offers a one or two-year fellowship in molecular genetic pathology to qualified applicants. This fellowship provides comprehensive training in molecular testing for human genetic and inherited disease, infectious disease, hematopathology, solid tumor oncology, histocompatability and rotations in cytogenetics, biochemical genetics and clinical genetics. Training includes didactic lectures in molecular pathology, rotations through a variety of clinical laboratories performing molecular testing at the ARUP Laboratories, active consultation on clinical problems related to molecular tests and applied research. A large variety and volume of molecular assays are received from the University of Utah Health Sciences Center and the ARUP Laboratories reference testing network. Opportunities for gaining competence in clinical/pathological correlation for a variety of molecular assays are abundant. Active development of new molecular assays is ongoing incorporating a broad range of traditional and cutting edge technologies. Fellows are required to participate in projects of assay development and validation. Fellows also gain exposure to laboratory management and quality control and assurance topics pertinent to the operation of a molecular diagnostic laboratory. The second year of the fellowship is devoted to pursuit of research projects and is oriented towards fellows interested in pursuing an academic career.

Requirements: Candidates should have completed pathology training in an approved AP and/ or CP program. Prior experience in molecular biology or genetics is preferred.

Stipends: Commensurate with level of training and experience.

Staff: David W. Bahler MD, PhD; **Pinar Bayrak-Toydemir** MD, PhD; **Phil Bernard** MD; **Arthur Brothman** PhD; **David Eckels** PhD; **David Hillyard** MD; **Elaine Lyon** PhD; **Rong Mao** MD; **Karl V Voelkerding** MD; **Patrice K Held** PhD; **Marzia Pasquali** PhD; **Mohamed E Salama** MD; **Sarah South** PhD.

Applications: Please go to the following website http://www.path.utah.edu/education/fellowships/molecular-genetic/, fill out the application and send to :

Karl V. Voelkerding MD, Department of Pathology/ARUP Laboratories, 500 Chipeta Way, Salt Lake City, UT 84108.

Phone: (801) 583-2787 ext. 2190 • **E-mail:** voelkek@aruplab.com

---

VIRGINIA COMMONWEALTH UNIVERSITY MEDICAL CENTER

Division of Molecular Diagnostics/Department of Pathology

Molecular Genetic Pathology Fellowship

Description: The molecular genetic pathology fellowship is a one-year ACGME-accredited clinical fellowship which trains pathologists and medical geneticists for a career in molecular genetic pathology. The trainee receives a thorough exposure to all aspects of molecular genetic pathology including infectious diseases, hematopathology, oncology, human identity testing, and medical genetics. The VCU Molecular Diagnostics Laboratory is a state-of-the art, 6,400 sq ft facility that performs more than 25,000 tests annually. Fellows participate in laboratory test development and translational research. The fellows are responsible for interactions with clinicians and other pathologists, and test interpretation as the training progresses. Fellows rotate through the human genetics clinical services and in the biochemical genetics laboratory. Hands-on experience is obtained with a broad range of molecular techniques including nucleic acid extraction, real-time PCR and reverse transcriptase PCR, cytogenetics, FISH, SNP analysis, Affymetrix microarray technology, bone marrow engraftment chimerism studies, and nucleic acid sequencing.

Requirements: Passed USMLE Step 3, completion of residency in AP and/or CP, or Medical Genetics.

Stipends: Commensurate with year of postgraduate training.

Staff: David S. Wilkinson MD, PhD, Department Chair; Director; **Andrea Ferreira-Gonzalez** PhD, Associate Director; **Carleton T. Garrett** MD, PhD, Associate Director; **Colleen Jackson-Cook** PhD, Director of Cytogenetics; **Jonathan Ben-Ezra** MD, Director Hematopathology; **Joann N. Bodurtha** MD, PhD; **Catherine I. Dumur** PhD.

Applications: Interested individuals should submit a CV and the Standardized Application for Pathology Fellowship form found on the CAP website (www.cap.org), the VCU Pathology website (www.pathology.vcu.edu), or for more information, contact the training coordinator, Ms. Violet Brown, Department of Pathology, P.O. Box 980662, Richmond, VA 23298-0662.

Phone: (804) 827-0561 • **Fax:** (804) 827-1078 • **E-mail:** vbrown3@mcvh-vcu.edu

VANDERBILT UNIVERSITY SCHOOL OF MEDICINE

Molecular Genetic Pathology Fellowship

Description: Vanderbilt University School of Medicine offers a 1-year ACGME-accredited Fellowship in Molecular Genetic Pathology at Vanderbilt University Medical Center, which includes Vanderbilt University School of Medicine, The Vanderbilt Hospital, and Monroe Carell Jr. Children's Hospital at Vanderbilt. This comprehensive program provides training in all aspects of molecular genetic pathology including the diagnosis of inherited and acquired genetic diseases, hematologic and non-hematologic malignancies, the detection of infectious agents by molecular approaches, as well as medical and biochemical genetics. The program integrates several departments and centers throughout the medical center including the Departments of Pathology, Medicine and Pediatrics; and includes a Center for Human Genetic Research (CHCR) and Center for Genetics and Health Policy. The molecular genetics laboratory performs over 60,000 billable tests annually and the molecular infectious disease laboratory performs 27,000 billable tests annually. The fellow will benefit from interdepartmental relationships while gaining experience in the diagnosis and management of patients with inherited metabolic diseases through work with the Division of Medical Genetics at Monroe Carell Jr. Children's Hospital at Vanderbilt. The curriculum includes didactic courses offered through the CHRC. In addition to developing skills required to direct a clinical molecular genetics laboratory, the fellow will be instrumental in test development and implementation and will conduct clinically-based research. The fellow will gain experience in the following molecular techniques: nucleic acid extraction, routine PCR, fluorescent PCR, reverse transcriptase PCR and real time PCR, invader technology, Southern blot analysis, gel and capillary electrophoresis, SNP studies, microarray, MSI and LOH analysis and DNA sequencing, as well as exposure to HLA testing, cytogenetics and FISH techniques.

Requirements: Completion of AP/CP; AP or CP training

Types and Numbers of Appointments: 1-Year ACGME-Accredited Fellowship

Facilities: Vanderbilt University Hospital, Monroe Carell Jr. Children's Hospital at Vanderbilt, and the adjacent Nashville VA Medical Center comprise a total of 1,070 licensed beds. There are approximately 46,785 admissions per year with an average length of stay at 5.4 days. Ambulatory visits (including off-site) are 1,019,715 and emergency room visits 90,870. Vanderbilt University Hospital and Vanderbilt Clinic consistently rank among the premier health care facilities in the United States. U.S. News & World Report has ranked Vanderbilt University Medical Center among the foremost programs in the nation. Constructed in 2004, The Monroe Carell Jr. Children's Hospital at Vanderbilt is a leading provider of pediatric care and ranked as one of the 10 best children's hospitals in the country and among the top 10 in the nation for pediatric cancer services by Child magazine. It is ranked 23rd in the nation by U.S. News & World Report. Vanderbilt ranked 15th in the nation in the 2008 issue of America's Best Hospitals. Only 19 hospitals made the honor roll. U.S. News & World Report is listing Vanderbilt Medical Center on its ''Honor Roll'' of hospitals — an honor reserved for a select group of institutions labeled by the magazine as the ''best of the best.'' For the first time Vanderbilt was named one of the top 100 best places to work in 2009 in the United States in FORTUNE magazine's annual survey. Vanderbilt was the first university to ever be named to the list.

Community: Nashville (Davidson County) has a population of 619,626 (2007) and is located in the rolling hills of central Tennessee. It is the site of numerous colleges and universities, two medical schools, and several large teaching hospitals. The city has an extensive parks system, a symphony orchestra, opera, ballet, performing arts center, zoo, several museums, and the Grand Ole Opry. The city offers a wide variety of cultural, educational, and recreational opportunities, including professional football and hockey teams.

Stipends: Commensurate with level of training.

Staff: Mary M. Zutter MD Director of Hematopathology, Program Director of Molecular Genetic Pathology Fellowship; **Cindy L. Vnencak-Jones** PhD Director of Molecular Genetics, Assistant Program Director of Molecular Genetic Pathology Fellowship; **Sarki Abdulkadir** MD, PhD Director of Graduate Studies, Pathology; **Mary Ann Thompson Arildsen** MD, PhD Assistant Professor of Pathology, Director of Hematology; **Brendan Lanpher** MD Director of ACGME Clinical Genetics Fellowship Program; **Claudio A. Mosse** MD, PhD Assistant Professor of Pathology; **John A. Phillips III** MD Director of Division of Medical Genetics; **Alison Woodworth** PhD Director of Esoteric Chemistry.

Applications: Interested applicants should submit a cover letter, application, curriculum vitae, personal statement, USMLE scores, passport size photo, three letters of recommendation, and ECFMG certificate (if applicable) to:
Mary M. Zutter, MD, Department of Pathology, Vanderbilt University Medical Center, C2102C MCN, 1161 21st Avenue South, Nashville, TN 37232. Application and submission information is located at http://www.mc.vanderbilt.edu/root/vumc.php?site=gme

WASHINGTON UNIVERSITY MEDICAL CENTER

Molecular Genetic Pathology Fellowship

Description: The Molecular Genetic Pathology fellowship program is a joint undertaking between the Divisions of Anatomic and Molecular Pathology, Laboratory and Genomic Medicine, and Neuropathology. The fellowship offers 1 year positions (1 clinical year) as well as 3 year positions (1 clinical year followed by 2 research years). The fellowship is accredited by the ACGME, and is designed to meet the needs of individuals interested in a career in academic pathology focused on the application of molecular genetic techniques in basic science, translational, or clinical research settings. Upon completion of the program, the fellow will have the skills necessary to pass the American Board of Pathology subspecialty exam in Molecular Genetic Pathology.

The large, referral, quaternary care hospital system associated with Washington University School of Medicine and Barnes-Jewish Hospital provides the clinical material for the program. The fellowship includes laboratory rotations through the clinical Molecular Diagnostic Laboratory, Microbiology Laboratory, HLA Laboratory, and FISH Laboratory of Barnes-Jewish Hospital; the Microbiology Laboratory of St. Louis Children's Hospital; and the Cytogenetics Laboratory, Microarray Laboratory, and Bioinformatics section of the Department of Pathology. The fellowship also includes clinical rotations through the general pediatric genetics clinic and the general adult genetics clinic (as well as elective rotations through the neurogenetics, Down syndrome, or Beckwith-Wiedemann clinics). Fellows will be active participants in reviewing cases submitted to the various molecular genetics laboratories. Particular emphasis will be placed on correlating molecular testing with traditional laboratory analysis. Fellows will also participate in regular didactic teaching sessions with faculty, and contribute to departmental conferences and journal clubs.

For those individuals interested in a 3 year position, a wide spectrum of research opportunities exists within the Medical School, including those that focus on utilization of state-of-the-art technologies for genome-wide analysis; application of molecular analysis in the settings of oncology, infectious diseases, medical genetics, and internal medicine; and development of testing paradigms for optimized provision of diagnostic, prognostic, and therapeutic information. The goal of the 2 years of research is to provide the fellow with the opportunity to focus on a specific area of investigation with the aim of developing a research program that leads to a faculty position at an academic medical center, and that can be supported by extramural funding. It is possible for trainees to extend their time in the lab depending on their long term career goals, availability of an appropriate mentor, and funding.

Requirements: Applicants must be Board certified/Board eligible in Anatomic and/or Clinical Pathology, or Medical Genetics, and meet the requirements for medical licensure in Missouri.

Stipends: Support will be commensurate with the applicant's level of training.

Applications: John D. Pfeifer, MD, PhD, Division of Anatomic and Molecular Pathology, Department of Pathology and Immunology, Washington University School of Medicine, 660 South Euclid Avenue, Box 8118, St. Louis, MO 63110

Phone: (314) 747-0276 • **Fax:** (314) 747-2663 • **E-mail:** pfeifer@path.wustl.edu

UNIVERSITY OF NORTH CAROLINA AT CHAPEL HILL

Molecular Pathology Fellowship

Description: The McLendon Clinical Laboratories of UNC Hospitals offer training in Clinical Molecular Genetics, leading to eligibility for certification by the American Board of Medical Genetics (ABMG). The usual training period is two years. The Molecular Diagnostic Laboratory at UNC provides experience with tests including cystic fibrosis, fragile X mental retardation, hemochromatosis, factor V Leiden and prothrombin, MCAD, Prader Willi and Angelman syndromes, a1-antitrypsin deficiency, connexin 26 and 30 mutations, hereditary cancers, EBV, CMV and BK viral loads, T and B-cell clonality, and chromosomal breakpoints in leukemias, as well as monitoring of bone marrow transplants with polymorphic microsatellite markers. State-of-the-art technologies and instrumentation are used in all of these tests, and the laboratory has a strong research foundation. Our postdoctoral training programs in medical genetics are provided by collaboration among individuals from numerous academic units including Anatomy & Cell Biology, Biochemistry, Genetics, Medicine, Obstetrics & Gynecology, Pathology & Laboratory Medicine, Pediatrics, the Curriculum in Genetics and Molecular Biology, the School of Public Health, the Cancer Center, the Center for Genomics, the Neuroscience Center, the Gene Therapy Center, and the Birth Defects Center. The University of North Carolina Hospitals, with a statewide referral base, provide a rich source for clinical experience in all subspecialty areas. Our medical genetics programs have been a focus for statewide referrals since 1970.

Requirements: PhD in an area related to genetics or MD required.

Stipends: Fellowship stipends are based on the trainee's number of years of postdoctoral training.

Applications: Applications are due on December 1 for a start date on July 1 of the following year. Send a cover letter, curriculum vitae, and the names of three references to Jessica Booker, PhD Department of Pathology and Laboratory Medicine CB#7525, Brinkhous-Bullitt Bldg. University of North Carolina at Chapel Hill Chapel Hill, NC 27599-7525

Phone: (919) 966-7894 • **E-mail:** jbooker@unch.unc.edu

VANDERBILT UNIVERSITY SCHOOL OF MEDICINE

Clinical Molecular Genetics Fellowship

Description: Vanderbilt University School of Medicine offers a 2-year ABMG-accredited Fellowship in Clinical Molecular Genetics at Vanderbilt University Medical Center, which includes Vanderbilt University School of Medicine, The Vanderbilt Hospital, and Monroe Carell Jr. Children's Hospital at Vanderbilt. This comprehensive program provides training in all aspects of clinical molecular genetics including the diagnosis of inherited and acquired genetic diseases, hematologic and non-hematologic malignancies by molecular approaches, as well as medical and biochemical genetics. The program integrates several departments and centers throughout the medical center including the Departments of Pathology, Medicine and Pediatrics; and includes a Center for Human Genetic Research (CHCR) and Center for Genetics and Health Policy. The molecular genetics laboratory performs over 60,000 billable tests annually. The fellow will benefit from interdepartmental relationships while gaining experience in the diagnosis and management of patients with inherited metabolic diseases through work with the Division of Medical Genetics at Monroe Carell Jr. Children's Hospital at Vanderbilt. The curriculum includes didactic courses offered through the CHRC. In addition to dev eloping skills required to direct a clinical molecular genetics laboratory, the fellow will be instrumental in test dev elopment and implementation and will conduct clinically-based research. The fellow will gain experience in the following molecular techniques: nucleic acid extraction, routine PCR, fluorescent PCR, reverse transcriptase PCR and real time PCR, invader technology, Southern blot analysis, gel and capillary electrophoresis, SNP studies, microarray, MSI and LOH analysis and DNA sequencing, as well as exposure to HLA testing, cytogenetics and FISH techniques.

Requirements: Applicants should possess a PhD in genetics, pathology or a related field. Applicants with an MD should have completed residency training in AP/CP; AP or CP.

Stipends: Commensurate with level of training.

Staff: **Cindy Vnencak-Jones** PhD, Director, Molecular Genetics Lab; Director, ABMG Clinical Molecular Genetics Fellowship Program; **Mary Ann Thompson Arildsen** MD, PhD, Assistant Professor of Pathology, Director of Hematology; **Brendan Lanpher** MD, Director of ACGME Clinical Genetics Fellowship Program; **Claudio A. Mosse** MD, PhD, Assistant Professor of Pathology; **John A. Phillips III** MD, Director of Division of Medical Genetics; **Alison Woodworth** PhD, Director of Esoteric Chemistry.

Applications: Interested applicants should submit a cover letter, application, curriculum vitae, personal statement, three letters of recommendation and USMLE scores and ECFMG certificate (if applicable) to: Cindy Vnencak-Jones, PhD, Vanderbilt University Medical Center, 4606 TVC, 1301 Medical Center Drive, Nashville, TN 37232.

E-mail: Cindy.Vnencak-Jones@Vanderbilt.edu.

UNIVERSITY OF ALABAMA AT BIRMINGHAM

Neuropathology Fellowship

Description: The neuropathology fellowship at the University of Alabama at Birmingham is accredited by the ACGME and meets the requirements towards Board certification in neuropathology. The program accepts one fellow in each year of training for the two-year fellowship program. We seek to train pathologists or other physicians with appropriate neuroscience training for careers in academic neuropathology. One year of fellowship is on clinical service, and the second provided as a year of research experience. The UAB Division of Neuropathology has a broad cachement area, with specimens originating from University Hospital, the Birmingham Veterans Affairs Medical Center, The Children's Hospital of Alabama, and the Medical Examiner's System of Alabama, as well as an active consultation service. Research opportunities in many different disciplines are available, with numerous neuroscience subcenters in the University.

Requirements: Board eligibility or certification in anatomic pathology or AP/CP. A license to practice medicine in Alabama, which requires successful completion of USMLE Steps 1, 2 and 3, is needed.

Stipends: Commensurate with year of postgraduate training.

Staff: **Steven L. Carroll** MD, PhD Professor and Director, Division of Neuropathology; **Cheryl Ann Palmer** MD Professor; **Richard E. Powers** MD Associate Professor; **Kevin A. Roth** MD, PhD Professor; **John J. Shacka** PhD; **Jianhua Zhang** PhD.

Applications: Curriculum vitae should be sent to
Cheryl Ann Palmer, MD, Neuropathology Fellowship Director, University of Alabama at Birmingham, 1960 6th Avenue South; PD6A 175E, Birmingham, AL 35249-4550.

Phone: (205) 934-2164 • **Fax:** (205) 975-7548 • **E-mail:** capalmer@uab.edu

---

BAYLOR COLLEGE OF MEDICINE AFFILIATED HOSPITALS

Neuropathology Fellowship

Description: This is a rigorous two year program which prepares our trainees to be competent in both diagnostic and investigational neuropathology. The fact that this is a combined program between the Baylor College of Medicine and MD Anderson Cancer Center allows access to a high volume of surgical and autopsy material including approximately 3,000 brain and spinal cord biopsies (~1,800 nervous system tumors), 450 autopsies and 200 pediatric/adult neuromuscular biopsies per year. Our clinical material is varied since we serve a large adult private hospital, **The Methodist Hospital**; the largest children's hospital in the United States, **Texas Children's Hospital**; a public general hospital, **Ben Taub General Hospital**; and one of the largest oncology centers in the United States, **MD Anderson Cancer Center**. In addition, we have close relationship with the Harris County Medical Examiner's Office at Houston, and a broad case referral base. Research experience is required during the fellowship and may be pursued within the Neuropathology Program with faculty members with the following areas of interest: **Dr. Adekunle Adesina** - molecular pathology of pediatric brain tumors and molecular genetic pathology; **Dr. Meena Bhattacharjee** - developmental neuropathology with an emphasis on autism and mental retardation; **Dr. J. Clay Goodman** - molecular foundations of neural injury in stroke and trauma; **Dr. Suzanne Powell** - neurodegenerative disorders; **Dr. Emilie Rouah** - diagnostic neuropathology; **Dr. Greg Fuller** - molecular pathology of brain tumors; **Dr. Ken Aldape** - molecular pathology of brain tumors; **Dr. Lauren Langford** - diagnostic neurooncology and **Dr. Janet Bruner** - diagnostic neurooncology.

Requirements: Applicants must be Board eligible in anatomic and clinical pathology, or anatomic pathology. It is also possible for applicants having Board eligibility in neurology or neurosurgery to enter the fellowship after one year of training in anatomic pathology.

Types and Numbers of Appointments: We have three accreditied neuropathology fellowship positions.

Stipends: Stipend is commensurate with the training level of the applicant.

Applications: Direct inquiries to:
Adekunle M. Adesina, MD, PhD, Department of Pathology, Baylor College of Medicine, One Baylor Plaza, Room 286A, Houston, TX 77030.

Phone: (832) 824-5859 • **E-mail:** aadesina@bcm.tmc.edu

ALBERT EINSTEIN COLLEGE OF MEDICINE
MONTEFIORE MEDICAL CENTER
Neuropathology Training Program

Description: This program provides two years of intensive training in various aspects of neuropathology, and an optional third year as a research fellow may be arranged. One new residency position is usually available every other year. Preference in the selection of candidates is given to those seeking a career in neuropathology, but individuals in training in anatomic pathology or neurology or neurosurgery may be considered. Foreign medical graduates must have ECFMG certification. The program is fully accredited by the Accreditation Council of Graduate Medical Education. The trainee is responsible for neurosurgical specimens, nerve and muscle biopsies, and for removing and examining the brains and spinal cords in autopsies of neuropathological interest. The first year is largely devoted to diagnostic neuropathology. During this period, the trainee plans and, if possible, begins a research project that can be carried into the second year with a remaining commitment to some diagnostic work.

Facilities: The Albert Einstein College of Medicine consists of an East and a West Campus: the Weiler Division of Montefiore Medical Center, and the Medical School buildings are on the East Campus; Moses Division of Montefiore Medical Center is on the West Campus. A shuttle bus operates on an hourly basis between the two campuses. The neuropathology training program uses both campuses. The trainees share the facilities of the two campuses by attending joint clinical and research conferences, and by rotation through laboratories on both campuses. This institution has long been known for its strength in the neurosciences, and neuropathology groups participate fully and collaborate with members of several other Departments. Each year about 150 brains are examined at autopsy. Approximately 800 neurological surgical specimens are processed, most on the West campus, including nerve and muscle biopsies. A large number of brains are sent to Einstein as part of ongoing studies in aging and dementia and in AIDS. The Department maintains a brain bank. Some specimens, especially cases of AIDS, neoplasia, motor neuron disorders, dementia, storage diseases, and demyelinating conditions, are received each year for consultation. The diagnostic and research facilities include fully equipped laboratories for electron microscopy, immunocytochemistry, histochemistry, biochemistry and molecular biology, immunology, and tissue culture. All diagnostic work is reviewed with an attending neuropathologist. Cross indexing of all cases allows easy retrieval and retrospective studies. All trainees are encouraged to participate in research with a member of the faculty who fosters further development in such areas as electron microscopy, enzyme and immunohistochemistry, Golgi technique, biochemistry, image analysis, tissue culture, and molecular biology. Our faculty members are active in research on aging, dementia, motor neuron diseases, demyelinating diseases, developmental neuropathology, neurovirology, and neurotoxicology.

Community: The campuses are located in the north Bronx, adjacent to Westchester County communities. Nearby rapid transportation, including express bus service from the campus, provides ready access to midtown Manhattan. New York City provides numerous opportunities for unsurpassed cultural experiences of the highest order. Concerts, opera, theaters and museums are all accessible on a daily basis. Professional activities in the field of pathology comprise two very active pathology societies (The New York Pathological Society and The Pathologists' Club). The New York Association of Neuropathologists meets monthly. The New York Academy of Medicine, the New York Academy of Sciences, and frequent scientific meetings at this and nearby medical schools, provide residents and trainees with outstanding opportunities for education.

Stipends: Stipends for 2009 range from $52,000 to $69,500 (PGY1-8). In addition, house staff members are provided with 4 weeks vacation; disability, medical and life insurance; and benefits for optical, psychiatric and dental care; legal aid; meal and laundry allowances; and an allowance for conference expenses.

Staff: Celia Brosnan PhD Prof; in vivo and in vitro models of demyelination; neuroimmunology; **Barbara Cannella** PhD Assoc Prof; cell biology; neuroimmunology; **Peter Davies** PhD Prof; neurochemical studies in aging and dementia; **Asao Hirano** MD Prof; electron microscopy; immunocytochemical studies of degenerative diseases (ALS-Parkinson's disease); **Christian Keller** MD Assistant Prof; diagnostic neuropathology and surgical pathology; **Sunhee C. Lee** MD Prof; immunobiology of microglia and astrocytes in inflammation and host defense; **Josefina F. Llena** MD Assoc Prof; diagnostic neuropathology; clinicopathologic studies; **Cedric S. Raine** PhD, DSc Prof; experimental neuropathology, neuroimmunology; demyelinating diseases; **Pearl S. Rosenbaum** MD Clinical Prof; ophthalmic pathology; **Herbert H. Schaumburg** MD Prof; peripheral nerve pathology; **Bridget Shafit-Zagardo** PhD Prof; developmental expression and molecular organization ofmicrotubule associated proteins; **Alfred J. Spiro** MD Prof; muscle pathology; **Steven Walkley** DVM, PhD Prof; animal models of neuronal storage disease; Golgi studies; **Karen W. Weidenheim** MD Prof; clinical neuropathology, developmental neurobiology, electron microscopy.

Applications: Applications should be received by January 1 for appointments beginning July of the following year. Selection of candidates is made in late fall and early spring.

Address inquiries to:
Karen M. Weidenheim, MD
Department of Pathology
Montefiore Medical Center
111 East 210th Street (Central 2)
Bronx, NY 10467

Phone: (718) 920-4446 • **E-mail:** kweidenh@montefiore.org

BRIGHAM AND WOMEN'S HOSPITAL
CHILDREN'S HOSPITAL

Neuropathology Fellowship

Description: This is an ACGME fully-accredited, two-year training program in neuropathology based at the Brigham and Women's Hospital, with joint programming at Children's Hospital Boston, and affiliated with Harvard Medical School. Fellows also rotate at the Massachusetts General Hospital, Massachusetts Eye and Ear Infirmary (eye pathology), and either the Office of the Chief Medical Examiner, City of New York, or Office of the Chief Medical Examiner, State of Vermont (forensic neuropathology). The trainee is expected to develop skills in diagnostic surgical and autopsy neuropathology including the interpretation of lesions by light and electron microscopy, enzyme histochemistry, immunohistochemistry and molecular/cytogenetic methods. Trainees also participate in teaching fellow residents in related disciplines and medical students at Harvard Medical School. The latter part of the second year of training is devoted to an extensive experience in a research laboratory. Opportunities for research collaboration with staff members are available in the areas of degenerative diseases, neuro-oncology, and developmental and neuromuscular neurobiology. Faculty members of the Medical School and The Massachusetts Institute of Technology with additional research interests also accept fellows for research training.

Requirements: Candidates should be Board-"eligible" or certified in anatomic pathology or neurology.

Stipends: Based on postgraduate level of trainee.

Staff: **Rebecca Folkerth** MD Director; **Matthew P. Anderson** MD, PhD Consultant; **Elizabeth Bundock** MD Consultant; **Umberto De Girolami** MD; **Ivana Delalle** MD, PhD Consultant; **Mel B. Feany** MD, PhD; **Matthew P. Frosch** MD, PhD Consultant; **Hannah C. Kinney** MD; **Hart G. W. Lidov** MD, PhD; **Keith L. Ligon** MD, PhD; **Rolf M. Pfannl** MD Consultant; **Sandra Santagata** MD, PhD; **William C. Schoene** MD.

Applications: Applications should be addressed to
Rebecca D. Folkerth, MD, Neuropathology Program Director, Department of Pathology (Neuropathology Division), Brigham and Women's Hospital, 75 Francis Street, Boston, MA 02115.

Phone: (617) 732-7532

BROWN UNIVERSITY

Neuropathology Fellowship

Description: This accredited program provides two years of training in neuropathology in preparation for certification by the American Board of Pathology. Trainees will master gross and microscopic description of neuropathologic material obtained at autopsy or surgery, and electron microscopic evaluation of brain, nerve and muscle biopsies. They will serve as laboratory consultants to, and will participate in teaching conferences with, the Department of Clinical Neuroscience (Neurology/Neurosurgery). General facilities are described under the Brown University Pathology Program. Clinical rotations will include forensic neuropathology (Medical Examiner's Office), and neonatal neuropathology (Women & Infants Hospital). A wide range of research opportunities are also available in the 5 affiliated teaching hospitals or in conjunction with the Brown campus faculty.

Requirements: MD with two years of anatomic pathology training, or one year anatomic pathology and neurology or neurosurgery board eligibility.

Stipends: Stipends are commensurate with the year of postgraduate training (See Brown University scale). Stipends are adjusted yearly on July 1. Benefits include health and professional liability insurance and four weeks annual vacation.

Staff: **Edward G. Stopa** MD Director; Alzheimer's Disease; **Suzanne de la Monte** MD Alzheimer's Disease; **John E Donahue** MD Blood Brain Barrier; **Conrad Johanson** PhD Choroid Plexus Function; **James Gilchrist** MD Neuromuscular Diseases; **Cynthia Jackson** PhD Molecular Biology; **M. Halit Pinar** MD Pediatric/Perinatal Neuropathology; **Thomas Gilson** MD Forensic Neuropathology; **Mary Ambler** MD Emeritus Faculty; **Stanley Aronson** MD Emeritus Faculty.

Applications: Should be sent to: Edward Stopa, MD, Director Neuropathology Training Program, Rhode Island Hospital, 593 Eddy Street, Providence, RI 02903.

E-mail: EStopa@Lifespan.org

UNIVERSITY OF CALIFORNIA, LOS ANGELES

Department of Pathology and Laboratory Medicine

Neuropathology Fellowship

Description: This accredited training program in neuropathology includes training in diagnostic and experimental neuropathology including neuromuscular disease. *Clinical training:* Encompasses surgical neuropathology, frozen section diagnosis, autopsy pathology and evaluation of nerve and muscle biopsies with appropriate histochemical and morphometric techniques. Weekly brain cutting conferences, clinicopathologic sessions, brain tumor board, neuromuscular disease conferences and histopathology review sessions are held. The program has special interest in AIDS, Alzheimer and non-Alzheimer dementia, cerebrovascular pathology, nerve and muscle pathology, epilepsy, neurotrophic and growth factors and biology of brain tumors. Routine diagnostic and research laboratories are centered around electron microscopy, tissue culture and brain tumor biology, neurochemistry and molecular studies. *Experimental training:* Is provided to teach physician investigators basic science with reference to molecular neurobiology, tissue culture, oncogene activation, and programmed cell death. Fellows may, if interested, attend diagnostic neuropathology sessions at Cedars-Sinai Medical Center and Wadsworth VAMC.

Requirements: A California medical license is required.

Stipends: Commensurate with support level of residency program and candidate's level of training.

Staff: Paul S. Mischel MD; **M.A. Verity** MB, BS (Emeritus); **Harry V. Vinters** MD; **W. H Yong** MD.

Applications: Please contact Fellowship Coordinator for list of requirements and application, Send to Harry V. Vinters, MD, Director of Neuropathology. Department of Pathology and Lab Medicine, UCLA Center for the Health Sciences, 10833 Le Conte Ave., Rm: A7-149 CHS, Los Angeles, CA 90095-1732. Applications must be received by December 31 preceding intended start date of July 1. Fellowship Coordinator: Annetta Pierro (310) 825-5719 / **Fax:** (310) 267-2058

Phone: (310) 825-6191 • **Fax:** (310) 206-8290 • **E-mail:** hvinters@mednet.ucla.edu

---

UNIVERSITY OF CALIFORNIA, SAN FRANCISCO

Department of Pathology

Neuropathology Fellowship

Description: A two-year accredited fellowship in clinical and research neuropathology is offered. Clinical cases are obtained from the very active neurosurgical and neurology services at the Moffitt-Long Hospital; from the autopsy services of Moffitt-Long, San Francisco Veterans Affairs Medical Center, San Francisco General Hospital; and from numerous consultations. The goals of the clinical training are to provide a broad fund of knowledge in neuroanatomy; gross and microscopic neuropathology; CNS, PNS, and muscle ultrastructure; current hypotheses about the pathogenesis of neoplastic and non-neoplastic neurological disorders; clinical-neuropathological correlations; and neurohistological, enzyme histochemical, and immunohistochemical techniques. The diagnostic service is particularly strong in neurooncology, epilepsy, nerve and muscle disorders, and infections. Research training is tailored for each fellow. The faculty research interests include molecular neurooncology, neurodegenerative diseases, including prion diseases, and developmental neurobiology.

Stipends: Commensurate with applicants level of training.

Staff: Andrew W. Bollen DVM, MD; **Stephen J. DeArmond** MD, PhD; **Eric J. Huang** MD, PhD; **Marta Margeta** MD, PhD; **Joanna Phillips** MD, PhD; **Tarik Tihan** MD, PhD; **Scott R. VandenBerg** MD, PhD.

Applications: An interview is required. Address inquiries to
Andrew Bollen DVM, MD, Director of Neuropathology Fellowship, Department of Pathology, University of California, School of Medicine, 505 Parnassus Ave., M551, San Francisco, CA 94143-0102.

Phone: (415) 476-5236 • **Fax:** (415) 476-7963

EMORY UNIVERSITY AFFILIATED HOSPITALS

Department of Pathology and Laboratory Medicine

Neuropathology Fellowship

Description: A neuropathology fellowship program of two years duration is offered. Activities are centered at the Emory University Hospital, with additional responsibilities at Crawford Long Hospital, Grady Memorial Hospital, Egleston Children's Hospital, and the Veterans Affairs Medical Center. Together, these hospitals provide a large volume of surgical and autopsy neuropathology, including approximately 500 brain tumors and 360 muscle biopsies per year. Planning and participation in departmental and interdepartmental conferences are a part of the fellowship, as is the instruction of residents and medical students. The first year is generally devoted to developing competence in diagnostic surgical and autopsy neuropathology. The second year is flexible with opportunities for research in a variety of areas. Specialized training in ophthalamic pathology, molecular pathology and forensic neuropathology is available. Resources available for research include an Alzheimer's Disease Research Center, an active brain tumor molecular biology group, and a neuromuscular research lab.

Requirements: USMLE step 3; applicants must have completed at least one year of anatomic pathology and one additional year of either anatomic pathology, neurology, or neurosurgery.

Stipends: Commensurate with level of training and experience. Reappointment to the second year is contingent upon successful completion of the first year.

Staff: Daniel Brat MD, PhD Fellowship Director; **Stephen Hunter** MD Co-director; **Marla Gearing** PhD; **Jonathan Glass** MD; **Hans Grossniklaus** MD; **Charles Hao** MD, PhD; **John Sladky** MD.

Applications: Mary Lou Mojonnier, Education Coordinator

Phone: (404) 727-4283 • **E-mail:** mmojonn@emory.edu
Web site: www.emory.edu/PATHOLOGY/

UNIVERSITY OF FLORIDA

Neuropathology Fellowship

Description: This accredited program provides up to two years of training in neuropathology, with the aim of Board certification and preparation for a career in academic neuropathology. Under supervision, trainees are responsible for primary diagnosis of all neurosurgical, muscle and nerve biopsies, as well as the brain, spinal cord, nerve, and muscle removed at autopsy. Trainees participate in daily sign-out of cases and in brain-cutting conferences held twice weekly, and the weekly neurosurgical pathology and neuropathology CPC conferences. They are expected to participate in continuing or original research activities and will train in immunocytochemical, electron microscopic, enzyme histochemical and molecular biological techniques used in neuropathology. Opportunities for research are enriched by the broad clinical and investigative interactions between the Unit and the Departments of Neurology, Neurosurgery, Neuroscience and the McKnight Brain Institute. Participation in medical student and house staff teaching is expected.

Requirements: The fellow will be selected by the Program Director. It is one of five competitive subspecialty fellowship positions offered annually by the Department. Two years of accredited anatomic pathology residency are required, and candidates must meet the application requirements described in the main Directory entry of the University of Florida.

Stipends: Appointment is for one year subject to renewal for a 2nd year. Salary is comparable to those of residents at this institution with equivalent years of postdoctoral training.

Applications: Applications and interviews completed before January 1. Appointment begins July 1. Direct inquiries and requests for applications to
Anthony T. Yachnis, MD, Department of Pathology, University of Florida College of Medicine, PO Box 100275, Gainesville, FL 32610-0275.

Phone: (352) 265-0238 • **Fax:** (352) 265-0437
Web site: http://www.pathology.ufl.edu/fellowship.htm

INDIANA UNIVERSITY SCHOOL OF MEDICINE

Neuropathology Fellowship

Description: A two-year fellowship program is offered. Activities are centered at the Indiana University School of Medicine and its main teaching facilities (University and Methodist Hospitals, and the Riley Hospital for Children). The medical center provides a large volume of surgical and autopsy cases in neuropathology and ocular pathology. Planning and participation in departmental and interdepartmental conferences are a part of the program, as is the instruction of residents and medical students. Diagnostic neuropathology is generally emphasized during the first year. Active participation in research projects is the main goal during the second year. Research opportunities in a variety of areas are numerous and include Alzheimer's disease, prion diseases and brain tumors. One month rotation in Neurology, Neurosurgery and Neuroradiology are optional.

Requirements: Applicants must have completed two years of accredited anatomic pathology training. Applicants with board certification in clinical pathology or other specialties must have one year of accredited training in anatomical pathology.

Stipends: Commensurate with level of training. Reappointment to the second year is contingent upon successful completion of the first year.

Staff: Jose Bonnin MD Program Director; **Bernardino Ghetti** MD; **Eyas Hattab** MD; **Saeed Vakili** MD; **Jill Murrell** PhD; **Ruben Vidal** PhD.

Applications: A letter of interest, curriculum vitae, and three letters of recommendation (including one from the training director) should be sent to Dr. Jose Bonnin. Additional information may be obtained by writing to Dr. Jose Bonnin, IU School of Medicine, Clarian Pathology Laboratory, 350 W. 11th Street, Rm 4038, Indianapolis, IN 46202
E-mail: jbonnin@iupui.edu

JOHNS HOPKINS MEDICAL INSTITUTIONS

Neuropathology Fellowship

Description: We offer training programs in diagnostic and experimental neuropathology (NP). The diagnostic training program, accredited by the American Board of Pathology and the ACGME, leads to eligibility for board certification in NP (for specifics contact http://www.abpath.org). The two year diagnostic program focuses on studies of neurosurgical and neuromuscular biopsies, autopsy material from hospital cases and research programs, and forensic cases. The experimental NP program is designed to teach young investigators (MDs or PhDs) basic science approaches to neurological disorders. Under faculty supervision, trainees work on projects to become familiar with methods of cell/molecular neurobiology, cloning, neurochemistry, ultrastructure, immunocytochemistry, and the use of transgenic and gene-targeting strategies to model diseases. The faculty has background in neurology, neuropathology, pathology, neuroscience, biochemistry, cellular/molecular biology and behavioral studies. Research efforts focus on neurodegenerative diseases, i.e., Alzheimer's, Parkinson's and Huntington's diseases, ALS, brain tumors, traumatic brain injury, and relevant animal and transgenic models, as well as therapeutics including the use of trophic factors, genetic approaches, and stem cells.

Requirements: One or more years of training in neurology, general pathology or special experience in neurological sciences is required. NIH training grant positions are limited to U.S. citizens or permanent residents. A medical degree is required for individuals applying to the diagnostic training program. These individuals should also have training in AP, preferably before entering the NP Fellowship, in order to fulfill the requirements for board certification in NP (for specifics contact http://www.abpath.org).

Stipends: Salaries follow NIH guidelines and are commensurate with level of previous training.

Applications: Juan C. Troncoso, MD, Professor, Pathology and Neurology, Division of Neuropathology, 558 Ross Bldg, Johns Hopkins School of Medicine, 720 Rutland Avenue, Baltimore MD 21205-2196.

Phone (410) 955-5632 • **Fax** (410) 955-9777 • **E-mail** kwall2@jhmi.edu
Web site http://pathology.jhu.edu

The Johns Hopkins University is an EOE.

LAC+USC MEDICAL CENTER/KECK SCHOOL OF MEDICINE AT THE UNIVERSITY OF SOUTHERN CALIFORNIA/VETERANS AFFAIRS GREATER LOS ANGELES HEALTHCARE SYSTEM

Neuropathology Fellowship

Description: The neuropathology program includes training in diagnostic and experimental neuropathology. Gross and microscopic examination of adult and pediatric autopsy, CSF cytology, forensic neuropathology, neuromuscular pathology and neurosurgical specimens provides extensive experience. Understanding mechanisms of disease in the nervous system is integrated through comprehensive lectures on neuroanatomy, neurohistology, immunohistochemistry and ultrastructure of the CNS. Opportunities for basic research in cell and molecular neurobiology are available. Major research efforts focus on degenerative diseases including Alzheimer's Disease, as well as neuropathology of the visual system. The two-year accredited program will prepare the fellow for the American Board of Pathology subspecialty examination in neuropathology.

Requirements: Candidates must have completed a residency in anatomic pathology or a residency in neurology plus one year of anatomic pathology.

Stipends: Support will be commensurate with the applicant's level of training.

Staff: Valerie Askanas MD, PhD; **Deborah Commins** MD, PhD; **Floyd Gilles** MD; **David R. Hinton** MD; **Carol A. Miller** MD.

Applications: Send to
Carol A. Miller MD, Chief of Neuropathology, LAC+USC Medical Center, 2051 Marengo Street, IPT-C1G104, Los Angeles, CA 90033. Appointments to fellowship positions for the 2010-2011 academic year starting July 1, 2010 will be concluded byOctober 1, 2009. The deadline for receipt of completed applications is July 1, 2009. Early applications are encouraged.

Phone: (323) 442-1602 • **Fax:** (323) 442-1808 • **E-mail:** carolmil@usc.edu

---

MASSACHUSETTS GENERAL HOSPITAL

Neuropathology Laboratory, Department of Pathology

Neuropathology Fellowship

Description: The first year of this fully accredited two-year training program is spent acquiring a strong base in diagnostic surgical and autopsy neuropathology. In the second year fellows consolidate their clinical expertise, gain greated exposure to the neurodegenerative disease autopsy service and have time to work on a research project. Approximately 1,100 neurosurgical specimens, 100 muscle and nerve biopsies and 300 brains are examined per year at Massachusetts General Hospital. There is also a large volume of consultation cases as well as extensive archives for additional educationsl exposure. One month is spent at Children's Hospital for additional exposure to pediatric neuropathology. Fellows teach neurology, neurosurgery, neuroradiology and pathology residents as well as students at Harvard Medical School. Close interactions are maintained with neurology, neurosurgery, and neuroradiology. Within the neuropathology service active funded research areas include neurodegenerative diseases and neuro-oncology. Collaborative activities with other investigators in basic and clinical neuroscience are encouraged.

Requirements: At least two years of anatomic pathology, or one year of anatomic pathology following neurology or neurosurgery training.

Stipends: Determined by hospital policy; commensurate with level of previous training.

Staff: Matthew P. Frosch MD, PhD; **E. Tessa Hedley-Whyte** MD; **David N. Louis** MD; **Anat Stemmer-Rachamimov** MD.

Applications: Candidates should submit a letter of interest,their curriculum vitae, USLME scores and three letters of recommendation by December 1st 18 months prior to the starting date of the fellowship (July 1) to: Matthew P. Frosch, MD, PhD Neuropathology Laboratory, Department of Pathology, Massachusetts General Hospital, 55 Fruit Street, Boston, MA 02114-2696.

Phone: (617) 726-5156

MAYO SCHOOL OF GRADUATE MEDICAL EDUCATION

Department of Laboratory Medicine and Pathology

Neuropathology Fellowship

Description: The Mayo Clinic offers a two-year ACGME-accredited Neuropathology Fellowship Program that provides intensive training in diagnostic surgical and autopsy neuropathology and extensive research opportunities leading to eligibility for certification in neuropathology by the American Board of Pathology (ABP). During the first year of training, the major emphasis is focused on developing diagnostic expertise in neuropathology, including the interpretation of gross and microscopic features, the utility of special stains and procedures, electron microscopy, and immunohistochemistry. The trainee is expected to initiate research that can be completed during the second year of training. Opportunities for research in neuroimmunology, neurovirology, neurogenetics, molecular biology, tumor neuropathology, and demyelinating and neurodegenerative diseases are available. The annual volume of specimens include approximately 500 autopsy brain, 3200 neurosurgical, 1000 skeletal muscle, 500 peripheral nerve, and 200 eye specimens.

Requirements: Positions are available on a competive basis every two years. Applicants must meet ABP requirements for qualification for training in neuropathology.

Staff: **J. E. Parisi** MD, Program Director; **C. Giannini** MD, PhD; **F. J. Rodriguez** MD; **B. W. Scheithauer** MD.

Applications: www.mayo.edu/msgme/application.html
Applications should be completed by January 1 (18 months prior) to the start of the academic year, which begins in July. Applicants are responsible for ensuring that all necessary materials are received by us prior to consideration for an interview. Positions will be offered beginning March 1 of the previous year. Our next available position (1) for candidates interested in the program will begin July 2012. Address inquiries to: Tasha Gilbertson, Education Program Coordinator, Mayo Clinic, 200 First Street SW, Stabile SL-16 Education, Rochester, MN 55905.

Phone: (507) 538-6453 • **E-mail:** pathologyeducation@mayo.edu
Web site: www.mayo.edu/msgme/lm-neuropath-rch.html

McGAW MEDICAL CENTER OF NORTHWESTERN UNIVERSITY

Neuropathology Fellowship

Description: The Neuropathology Division is a two-year fellowship at Northwestern University McGaw Medical Center has a program dedicated to providing excellence in clinical service, research, and teaching. Our faculty includes nationally and internationally recognized experts, particularly in the fields of neurodegenerative neuropathology and gene regulation of nervous system development and function. The goal of the neuropathology training program is to prepare our fellows for all aspects of a highly successful career in academic neuropathology. One new fellow is accepted into the program every other year. At least two years of prior postgraduate training are required. Preference is given to individuals who are either board-eligible in Anatomic/Clinical Pathology, or have had two years of Anatomic Pathology training; however, those who are board eligible in other medical specialties, such as Neurology, and who have had one year of Anatomic Pathology training also are considered. Candidates will also be considered for combined Anatomic Pathology and Neuropathology training.

Requirements: The candidate must be Board eligible or certified in either Anatomic Pathology or Anatomic and Clinical Pathology, or in some other medical specialty such as Neurology **and** have had one year Anatomic Pathology training. Candidates for combined training in Anatomic Pathology and Neuropathology will be considered.

Stipends: The stipend is determined by previous pathology training and experience.

Applications: Please send CV, cover letter which includes a paragraph describing career goals, and 2 letters of recommendation to program coordinator:

Irene Galace
Northwestern University, Department of Pathology
Ward 3-140 W127 Pathology
303 East Chicago Avenue
Chicago, IL 60611

Electronic submission encouraged.

Phone: (312) 503-8223 • **Fax:** (312) 503-8240 • **E-mail:** i-galace@northwestern.edu

THE METHODIST HOSPITAL AND M.D. ANDERSON CANCER CENTER

Department of Pathology

Neuropathology Fellowship

Description: This is a new ACGME-accredited rigorous two-year neuropathology fellowship program shared equally by the two institutions that is designed to prepare trainees to practice neuropathology competently and independently in both diagnostic and investigative neuropathology. An extensive and busy surgical neuropathology service at the participating institutions evaluates approximately 2300 brain tumors (788 at TMH, 1400 at M. D. Anderson) annually, including in-house surgical cases and referral consultations. The autopsy service at TMH is heavily weighted toward the examination of neurodegenerative disease, and participation in Alzheimer's disease and amyotrophic lateral sclerosis (ALS) research with Baylor College of Medicine and the Neurological Institute at The Methodist Hospital is a major investigative avenue available to trainees. Neuropathologists at TMH also provide consultative expertise to the Harris County Medical Examiner's Office, reviewing approximately 150 forensic neuropathologic cases annually. Rotations in pediatric neuropathology at the University of Texas — Houston are provided and the experience also includes neuromuscular biopsies. Participation in a weekly neuropathology journal club, twice weekly microscopic consensus conferences, a twice monthly Neuropathology Conference (attended by medical students and residents throughout the Texas Medical Center), neuroncology tumor boards, and a monthly Houston Area Neuropathology Society Meeting comprise only a few of the many opportunities open to trainees. The University of Texas M. D. Anderson Cancer Center (MDACC) is an internationally recognized cancer center with a very active multidisciplinary Brain Tumor Center staffed by over 50 faculty members and four neuropathologists. All contemporary laboratory research approaches are available and utilized in brain tumor research, including genomics (cDNA arrays), proteomics (protein lysate arrays), molecular and cell biologic techniques, experimental and clinical translational gene therapy techniques and high-density tissue microarrays, providing trainees with a broad range of laboratory research opportunities. The faculty and staff of all participating institutions of the training program interact regularly with each other and also with the faculty and staff of the Neuropathology Fellowship Training Program at Baylor College of Medicine. Fellows in both training programs interact on a daily basis. There are currently 14 neuropathologists in the Texas Medical Center and 17 neuropathologists that are members of the Houston Area Neuropathology Society.

Requirements: Two (2) positions are available. Potential applicants must have completed at least two (2) years of training in anatomic pathology or in a combined anatomic and clinical pathology program (AP/CP) or have completed training in neurology or neurosurgery. Must hold or be eligible for a Texas Physician In Training Permit or Licensure.

Stipends: Commensurate with the level of training.

Staff: Min Wang MD Assistant Professor, University of Texas, Houston, Neurodegenerative disease and pediatric neuropathology; **Kenneth D. Aldape** MD, PhD Professor, M.D. Anderson Cancer Center, Neuro-oncology and molecular genetics of brain tumors; **Janet M. Bruner** MD Professor, M.D. Anderson Cancer Center, Neuro-oncology, Chair of Pathology; **Gregory N. Fuller** MD, PhD Professor, Chief of Neuropathology, M.D. Anderson Cancer Center, Neuro-oncology and molecular genetics of brain tumors; **Lauren L. Langford** MD Associate Professor, M.D. Anderson Cancer Center, Neuro-oncology, education and electron microscopy; **Sozos Papasozomenos** Professor, Chief of Neuropathology, University of Texas, Houston, Neuromuscular diseases; **Suzanne Z. Powell** MD Associate Professor, Weill Medical College, The Methodist Hospital, Neurodegenerative diseases and forensic neuropathology.

Applications: Address inquires to Suzanne Z. Powell, MD, Co-director, Neuropathology Fellowship Program, Department of Pathology, 6565 Fannin M227, Houston, TX 77030.

Phone: (713) 441-3496 • **Fax:** (713) 441-3489 • **E-mail:** ljozwiak@tmhs.org
Web site: http://www.methodisthealth.com

NEW YORK UNIVERSITY MEDICAL CENTER

Neuropathology Fellowship

Description: Two fellowships. Our two-year ACGME accredited program provides training in all aspects of neuropathology, including extensive exposure to surgical neuropathology at one of the nation's largest adult and pediatric neurosurgical centers. Specimens derive from four hospitals, including Tisch Hospital (the university hospital of NYUMC) and Bellevue Hospital Center, New York City's flagship public hospital, as well as an active referral practice. The laboratory accessions over 1900 neurosurgical specimens a year, including over 550 tumors, ranging from stereotaxic biopsies to gross resections and including many infectious and epileptic cases. Muscle biopsies derive from diverse populations, including the NYUMC muscular dystrophy center. We examine over 200 diverse pediatric and adult autopsy brains a year. Research activities focus on clinical-pathological and basic science neurooncology, but also involve the Aging & Dementia Research Center. Substantial AIDS-related material is available. Associations with neurology, basic neuroscience, and neurosurgery, allow diverse clinical and basic research opportunities. New York City has an active neuropathology community, including regular bimonthly neuropathology meetings.

Requirements: Preference is given to candidates who have completed at least 2 years of Anatomic Pathology residency, or to those with completed Neurology or Neurosurgery training. Candidates requiring additional AP training must also apply to the general pathology program of the Department and must hold a NY State License.

Stipends: Commensurate with candidate's level of training.

Applications: Applications for positions beginning on July 1 should be received by December 1 the preceding year. Requests for information or applications should be addressed to:Thomas Wisniewski, MD, PhD, Neuropathology, NYU Medical Center, Room HN-419 Milhauser Labs, 550 First Avenue, New York, NY 10016.

Phone: (212) 263-7993 • **Fax:** (212) 263-7528 • **E-mail:** thomas.wisniewski@med.nyu.edu

---

UNIVERSITY OF NORTH CAROLINA AT CHAPEL HILL

Department of Pathology and Laboratory Medicine

Neuropathology Fellowship

Description: This is a fully accredited, two-year training program in diagnostic and experimental neuropathology under the direction of Dr. Thomas W. Bouldin, a board-certified neuropathologist. All aspects of diagnostic neuropathology are covered, including autopsy and surgical neuropathology, nerve and muscle biopsies, and ophthalmic pathology. Specimens are drawn from UNC Hospitals and from an active outside consultation service. Trainees participate in a full range of regularly scheduled conferences that stress gross and microscopic pathology and clinicopathologic correlation. There are considerable opportunities for teaching experience and close working relationships with the Neurology, Neurosurgery and Neuroradiology services. Research opportunities include the characterization of the molecular genetic mechanisms responsible for the heterogeneity of patient responses to cancer chemotherapy and the exploration of clinicopathologic correlations in nervous-system disease.

Requirements: An MD degree with at least two years of training in anatomic pathology.

Stipends: Based on trainee's years of postdoctoral training and UNC Hospitals' Housestaff salary scale.

Staff: **Thomas W. Bouldin** MD; **Nadia N. Malouf** MD; **C. Ryan Miller** MD, PhD; **Leigh Thorne** MD.

Applications: Applications should be made no later than October 1 prior to the intended July 1 start date. To apply, please send a cover letter, curriculum vitae, and the names of three references to Dr. Bouldin. Electronic applications are preferred. For further information, please contact:
Thomas W. Bouldin, MD, Department of Pathology and Laboratory Medicine, CB #7525, The University of North Carolina at Chapel Hill, Chapel Hill, NC 27599-7525.

Phone: (919) 843-1074 • **E-mail:** tbouldin@med.unc.edu
Web site: http://www.pathology.unc.edu/fellowsp/neuropath.htm

SUNY DOWNSTATE MEDICAL CENTER AT BROOKLYN

Department of Pathology

Neuropathology Fellowship

Description: SUNY Downstate's fully accredited program (five year accreditation by ACGME in 2007) offers an exciting opportunity for those interested in a rich training experience in neuropathology. The department is chaired by neuropathologist Suzanne S. Mirra MD, The training program has a faculty of three additional neuropathologists as well as a molecular pathologist and several neuroscientists based at the College of Medicine and our two major teaching affiliates, University Hospital of Brooklyn and Kings County Medical Center. Neuropathology training under Program Director, Chandrakant Rao, MD, provides exposure to a wide array of material that is further enhanced by specialty rotations. These include rotations in ophthalmic pathology at the New York Eye and Ear Infirmary, in neuromuscular pathology at Columbia University Medical Center, in forensic neuropathology in the Office of the Chief Medical Examiner of New York City, and in community neuropathology at Staten Island University Hospital.
Trainees have many opportunities to conduct research. Downstate is recognized as an international center for basic and clinical investigation on hippocampal function and pathophysiology with implications for epilepsy and memory disturbance. Within the department, trainees may work with faculty members on research projects related to Alzheimer's and other neurodegenerative diseases, synaptic function, neurogenesis, and basic mechanisms of memory formation.

Requirements: Board eligibility or certification in Anatomic Pathology preferred. A minimum of one year of Anatomic Pathology is required. A combined anatomic and neuropathology AP/NP program is offered (see ABP website http://www.abpath.org/BIReqForCert.htm#NP for certification requirements).

Stipends: Based on postgraduate level of trainee.

Staff: Chandrakant Rao MD, Director, Neuropathology Training Program and Clinical Professor of Pathology; **Suzanne S. Mirra** MD, Chair, Department of Pathology; Professor of Pathology and Neurology; **Arthur P. Hays** MD, Professor of Clinical Pathology and Cell Biology, Neuromuscular Pathology, Columbia University; **Mena Hernando** MD, Clinical Associate Professor of Forensic Neuropathology, Chief Medical Examiner's Office (OCME); **Felicitas Lacbawan** MD, Director, Molecular Pathology and Associate Professor of Pathology; **Jenny M. Libien** MD, PhD, Director, Autopsy Service, UHB; Assistant Professor of Pathology; **Steven A. McCormick** MD, Director of Pathology, New York Eye and Ear Infirmary; **Charles Y. Shao** MD, PhD, Clinical Associate Professor of Pathology; **Kurenai Tanji** MD, PhD, Associate Professor of Clinical Pathology and Cell Biology, Columbia University; **Monika Wrzolek** MD, Clinical Assistant Professor of Pathology, Staten Island University Hospital.

Applications: Chandrakant Rao, MD, Director, Neuropathology Training Program, Department of Pathology, SUNY Downstate Medical Center, 450 Clarkson Avenue, Box 25, Brooklyn, NY 11203.

Phone: (718) 245-5320 • **E-mail:** rao91@aol.com or Chandrakant.Rao@downstate.edu

For further information, contact Ms. Denise Leggard, Program Coordinator.

Phone: (718) 270-1288 • **Fax:** (718) 613-8774 • **E-mail:** Denise.Leggard@downstate.edu

NEW YORK-PRESBYTERIAN HOSPITAL
COLUMBIA UNIVERSITY MEDICAL CENTER

Neuropathology Fellowship

Description: This program, accredited by the American Board of Pathology, qualifies candidates for Board certification in neuropathology and prepares them for academic careers in diagnostic neuropathology and research. Fellows spend two years in the Division of Neuropathology. The Division examines all nervous system tissues from autopsies at the Columbia campus of the New York Presbyterian Hospital, Children's Hospital of New York, and the New York Neurological Institute. This large and varied volume of material is supplemented by brains sent to Columbia for consultation, particularly in the areas of Parkinson's disease, dementing disorders, and other neurodegenerative diseases. There is a large volume of neurosurgical specimens, about 1,800 per year. These also are varied, and include tumors, brain biopsies for degenerative diseases, and muscle and nerve biopsies. Fellows examine all specimens and sign out with an attending physician. Teaching conferences are held regularly, including weekly brain cuttings, weekly microscopic conferences to review surgical and autopsy cases with all of the staff, weekly brain tumor board conferences, muscle biopsy reviews, and CPCs. Neuropathology fellows, along with residents from Pathology, Neurology, and Neurosurgery, organize and present material at most of the conferences. Centralized departmental laboratories for electron microscopy and immunocytochemistry facilitate the use of these techniques for studying specimens. Fellows will receive training in EM and immunocytochemical techniques. In general, fellows will be expected to spend much of the first year in clinical studies. The second year should be spent in basic or clinical investigative work, in affiliation with a faculty member.

Facilities: In addition to a busy and widely diverse clinical service, the Division of Neuropathology and the Department of Pathology and Cell Biology contain a large number of neuroscience research programs (see staff list). Particular areas of strength include developmental neurobiology, cellular interactions in brain development, growth factors, cytoskeletal protein chemistry and molecular biology, myelination, and neurodegenerative diseases, particularly Alzheimer's and Parkinson's diseases. The Department has close ties to the Departments of Neurology, Neurosurgery, and Psychiatry and the Depratment of Neuroscience. Many of our members belong to the interdisciplinary Taub Center for Alzheimer Disease and the Aging Brain. A number of our faculty also belong to the Columbia University Stem Cell Initiative. Thus, we are involved in a large number of excellent programs in neuroscience research at Columbia.

Stipends: Stipends are commensurate with support levels for residency programs at this institution and the fellow's level of training (see general listing).

Staff: **Asa Abeliovich** MD, PhD Associate Professor. Pathophysiology of familial Parkinson's disease genes; alpha-synuclein, parkin; **Ottavio Arancio** MD, PhD Assistant Professor. Hippocampal function, neurodegenerative diseases; **Peter D. Canoll** MD, PhD Assistant Professor. Molecular mechanisms of glioma migration; **Lorraine N. Clark** PhD Assistant Professor. Molecular genetic analysis of neurodegenerative diseases, Parkinson disease, genomics; **Christopher G. Conrad** PhD Assistant Professor. Genetics of Alzheimer's disease, pathobiology of Alzheimer's disease and related disorders; **Gilbert DiPaolo** PhD Assistant Professor. Molecular mechanisms of synaptic function and neuronal endocytosis in normal CNS and neurodegenerative diseases; **Fiona K. Doetsch** PhD Assistant Professor. Neurogenesis, neural stem cells; **Karen E. Duff** PhD Professor. Molecular pathogenesis o neurodegenerative diseases, genetic mouse models; **Andrew Dwork** MD Associate Professor. Psychiatric and neurodegenerative diseases, cerebral iron metabolism; **Phyllis L. Faust** MD, PhD Associate Professor. Peroxisomal diseases, neuronal migration, developmental neurobiology; **James E. Goldman** MD, PhD Professor and Director. Developmental neurobiology, differentiation and pathological reactions of glial cells, molecular mechanisms of neurodegenerative diseases; **Lloyd Greene** PhD Professor. Developmental biology and neurochemistry, actions of nerve growth factor, oncogenes in regulation and differentiation; **Arthur P. Hays** MD Professor. Peripheral nerve, muscle diseases, immune-mediated neuropathies; **Tae-Wan Kim** PhD Associate Professor. Molecular pathogenesis of Alzheimer disease; proteomics analysis of Alzheimer CNS; presenilins; **Ronald Liem** PhD Professor. Cellular and molecular biology of neuronal cytoskeleton, molecular biology of neuro-glial interaction molecules; **Carol Mason** PhD Professor. Developmental neurobiology; axon pathfinding, axon-target cell interactions, development of axonal arbors and formation of synaptic connections in mammalian CNS; **Michael Shelanski** MD, PhD Chairman and Professor of Pathology. Neuropathology of aging, molecular biology of the neuronal cytoskeleton and neuronal cell surface; **Kurenai Tanji** MD, PhD Associate Professor. Muscle & Nerve pathology, mitochondrial encephalomyopathies; **Carol Troy** MD, PhD Associate Professor. Molecular mechanisms of neuronal dysfunction and death; **Benjamin Tycko** MD, PhD Associate Professor. DNA alterations in neoplasia, role of genetic imprinting in embryonal tumors; **Richard Vallee** PhD Professor of Pathology. Molecular motors, cell migration, neuronal migration disorders; **Jean Paul Vonsattel** MD Professor. Pathology of neurodegenerative and cerebrovascular diseases; **Hynek Wichterle** PhD Assistant Professor. Neural stem cells, motor neuron disorders.

Applications:
James Goldman, MD, PhD
Department of Pathology
Columbia College of Physicians & Surgeons
630 West 168th Street
New York, NY 10032

Phone: (212) 305-4531

Columbia University adheres to affirmative action and equal opportunity principles.

OREGON HEALTH & SCIENCE UNIVERSITY

Neuropathology Fellowship

Description: Oregon Health & Science University Department of Pathology is provisionally accredited by the ACGME for two fellowship positions in neuropathology. The standard fellowship lasts two years. The clinical component of the fellowship program covers all aspects of neuropathology, including examination and study of diseases of the central nervous system, peripheral nervous system, and muscle. This involves surgical pathology, cytopathology, and autopsy specimens and procedures. Fellows are responsible for initial interpretation of frozen sections, surgical specimens, autopsy brain cutting, and all aspects of the clinical service. Participation in clinical or basic science research projects is an essential part of the training program. The neuropathology section sees an average of 650 CNS surgical pathology specimens, 300 muscle and nerve biopsies, and more than 200 autopsy brains each year. An active Alzheimer Disease Research Center and brain bank provide excellent exposure to degenerative diseases. Experience in forensic pathology is primarily obtained through the Oregon State Medical Examiners Office. OHSU has a dedicated Ophthalmic Pathology service at the Casey Eye Institute, and the fellow attends applicable conferences there and has access to their study sets. Fellows participate in teaching medical student laboratory sessions for neuroanatomy and neuroembryology. The fellow is exposed to a full spectrum of neuropathology including adult and pediatric neoplastic, inflammatory, traumatic and degenerative disorders.

Requirements: Applicants must have successfully completed a residency in anatomic pathology or anatomic and clinical pathology (AP/CP board eligible).

Stipends: The stipend is communsurate with the year of post-graduate training.

Staff: Marjorie Grafe MD, PhD Program Director, Neuropathologist; **S. Humayun Gultekin** MD Neuropathologist; **Randall Woltjer** MD, PhD Neuropathologist; **David Wilson** MD Ophthalmologist; **Edward Culper** MD Neurologist (Neuromuscular Diseases).

Applications: Applications for the 2011 position will be accepted between January and July 2009. Please submit a cover letter, OHSU Application Form from our web site, curriculum vitae, and three letters of recommendation to: Marjorie Grafe, MD, PhD, Neuropathology Fellowship Director, c/o Training Programs Coordinator, Oregon Health and Science University, Department of Pathology L-113, 3181 SW Sam Jackson Park Road, Portland, OR 97239.

For additional information visit our web site, or contact Anna Wedeking, Training Programs Coordinator.

E-mail: ferencea@ohsu.edu
Web site: www.ohsu.edu/pathology

UNIVERSITY OF PENNSYLVANIA MEDICAL CENTER

Department of Pathology & Laboratory Medicine

Neuropathology Fellowship

Description: A two-year ACGME approved clinical training program is offered to qualified candidates with an MD degree and prior training in anatomic pathology. First-year residents are responsible for approximately 200 brain specimens and ~775 surgical, nerve, and muscle biopsies at the Hospital of the University of Pennsylvania. Second-year residents rotate through the Children's Hospital of Philadelphia and the Center for Neurodegenerative Diseases, supervise junior residents and are exposed to ongoing research projects in the Division, the Department, and the Medical Center. State-of-the-art cellular and molecular approaches are applied in fully-equipped laboratories occupying approximately 13,000 sq ft.

Requirements: Trainees are selected by the Division of Neuropathology in conjunction with the Resident Applicant Committee.

Stipends: Stipends are commensurate with the year of postgraduate training.

Staff: Jeffrey A. Golden MD: Pediatric neuropathology, developmental neurobiology; **Nicholas K. Gonatas** MD: The Golgi apparatus, amyotrophic lateral sclerosis; **Brian Harding** MD, PhD: Pediatric neuropathology; **Alexander Judkins** MD: Pediatric neuropathology, CNS tumors, forensic neuropathology; **Virginia Lee** PhD: Cellular and molecular studies of neurodegenerative diseases; **Zissimos Mourelatos** MD: microRNAs, piRNAs, RNA-mediated gene expression regulation; **Lucy Rorke-Adams** MD: Pediatric CNS tumors and trauma, forensic neuropathology; **Mariarita Santi** MD, PhD: Pediatric neuropathology, muscle pathology; **Gerard Schellenberg** Neurogenetics; **William W. Schlaepfer** MD: Gene expression, RNA stability, cytoskeleton; **John Q. Trojanowski** MD, PhD: Neurodegenerative diseases.

Applications: For application and further information contact:

Zissimos Mourelatos, MD, 613B Stellar-Chance Laboratories, 422 Curie Boulevard, Philadelphia, PA 19104-6079.

Phone: (215) 746-0014
Web site: http://www.uphs.upenn.edu/path

UNIVERSITY OF PITTSBURGH MEDICAL CENTER

Neuropathology Fellowship

Description: This is a two-year ACGME-accredited program, staffed by nine neuropathologists. The University of Pittsburgh Medical Center is one of the largest academic health centers in the country and is ranked 6th in NIH funding. With numerous affiliated hospitals and over 30 staff neurosurgeons there is an abundance of surgical neuropathology specimens for review. We adhere to a Center of Excellence design that allows staff and trainees to concentrate their service work at a single site. We collaborate extensively with other divisions in the Department of Pathology (e.g. Molecular Diagnostics) along with the Departments of Neurology, Neurosurgery, Ophthalmology, Western Psychiatric Institutes and Clinic, Center for Neuroscience and Allegheny County Medical Examiners Office. Complete facilities are available for patient care and research activities including telepathology, electron microscopy, immunocytochemistry, in-situ hybridization, proteomics, laser confocal microscopy, PET, tissue culture, extensive banking of neoplastic and neurodegenerative patient brain specimens, bioinformatics, and the entire spectrum of molecular biology such as gene microarrays. Trainees are encouraged to pursue academic research careers. In addition to training fellows as competent board-certified neuropathologists, we offer mentorship to facilitate development of funded research programs.

Requirements: Applicants to UPMC Anatomical Pathology are encouraged to pursue the 3-year track followed by 2 years of Neuropathology fellowship. For more information on the residency research track, see http://www.pathology.pitt.edu/pirt/

Staff: **Clayton A. Wiley** MD, PhD Division Director of Neuropathology; **Robert Bowser** PhD; **Charleen Chu** MD, PhD; **Ronald L. Hamilton** MD; **Scott Kulich** MD, PhD; **David Lacomis** MD; **Katherine McFadden** MD; **Geoffrey Murdoch** MD, PhD; **Gutti R. Rao** MD.

Applications: Clayton A. Wiley, MD, PhD, Division Director of Neuropathology, Department of Pathology, A-506 UPMC Presbyterian, 200 Lothrop Street, Pittsburgh, PA 15213.

Phone: (412) 647-9417
Division Web site: http://neuro.pathology.pitt.edu/
Submit application online at http://path.upmc.edu/fellowship

STANFORD UNIVERSITY MEDICAL CENTER

Department of Pathology

Neuropathology Fellowship

Description: This two-year, ACGME-accredited neuropathology training program is designed to foster the careers of future leaders in neuropathology and neuroscience. One position is available each year. The neuropathology service annually receives over 800 biopsies, 300 muscle biopsies, 600 consultations, and 200 brains obtained from autopsies at Stanford, Palo Alto VA Medical Center and regional private and forensic institutions. Under close supervision of the Director and other faculty neuropathologists, the trainee is responsible for the gross and microscopic examination of all neurosurgical specimens, which includes in depth exposure to frozen sections, muscle histochemistry, FISH, immunohistochemistry and electron microscopy, as well as examining the brains and spinal cords removed at autopsy. The trainee participates actively in joint conferences with the clinical neuroscience departments and is encouraged to pursue research projects which can be pursued in greater depth the second, predominantly research-oriented year of training. Candidates with a strong background or interest in neuroscience are especially encouraged to apply. Moreover, subject to the approval of the Pathology chair (Stephen Galli, MD), additional funding may be available for qualified fellows, who are graduates of Stanford's AP/NP residency program and who wish to pursue an academic career devoted primarily to extramurally-funded research, to continue their research beyond the period of the formal fellowship.

Requirements: AP or AP/CP training and eligibility for California medical license.

Stipends: Commensurate with experience, plus additional $8,400 per year housing allowance.

Applications: Submit to: Hannes Vogel, MD, Director of Neuropathology, Department of Pathology, Stanford University Medical Center, 300 Pasteur Drive, Room R241, Palo Alto, CA 94305-5324.

Phone: (650) 723-6041 • **Fax:** (650) 498-5394 • **E-mail:** hvogel@stanford.edu

UNIVERSITY OF ROCHESTER MEDICAL CENTER

Department of Pathology & Laboratory Medicine

Neuropathology Fellowship

Description: Our ACGME-accredited two year training program provides one fellow training in neurosurgical, neuromuscular and autopsy neuropathology. The first year is devoted principally to diagnostic neuropathology at which time the trainee is responsible, under supervision, for neurosurgical cases, muscle biopsies, occasional nerve biopsies, and diagnostic workups of brain and spinal cords, including forensic and pediatric cases. We receive between 600 and 700 neurosurgical specimens, excluding intervertebral discs, and approximately 200 autopsy cases per year. Participation in the Neuro-oncology, Neuroradiology, Neuromuscular and Neurosurgery Conferences is also expected. Teaching opportunities include instruction of rotating medical students, and resident trainees from Pathology, Neurosurgery and Neurology. In addition, during the first year, an individual is expected to plan and, if possible, begin a research project. The research project and participation in the Neuropathology and Neuromuscular Consultation services become the major responsibilities during the second year of the program.

Requirements: Candidates must have satisfactorily completed at least two years of an ACGME-accredited anatomic pathology training program and be ABP eligible.

Facilities: The University of Rochester Medical Center consists of the School of Medicine & Dentistry, School of Nursing and Strong Memorial Hospital. The faculty of the School of Medicine serves as the staff of Strong Memorial Hospital, a 750-bed facility and Level 3 trauma center. Our facility processes over 5 million laboratory examinations annually. Departmental research facilities and programs offer opportunities for applied and basic research. The medical center houses a modern library with 240,000 volumes and subscriptions to over 2,300 print and electronic journals. Our in-house Fitness & Wellness Center offers fitness training classes, personal training, aerobics, team sports and is open 24/7.

Community: Picture a city with miles of lakeshore, a central-city riverfront sprinkled with waterfalls, and a historic canal that flows through the heart of the small-town Americana. Now imagine that same city surrounded by glacier-carved lakes, one of the largest collections of cobblestone homes in the country, and world-class wine country. Welcome to the Rochester/Finger Lakes Region of Upstate New York. Monroe County, named after James Monroe, fifth president of the United States, is comprised of 19 towns, 10 villages and the City of Rochester, the third largest city in the state, with a combined population of approximately 750,000 residents and a land area of nearly 664 square miles. Monroe County has been a world leader in imaging technology. Today, we're not only on the cutting edge of imaging, but biotechnology, telecommunications, optics, photonics, and much more. We rank among the top three communities in the nation in the number of patents granted per capita. Monroe County and the City of Rochester are home to the University of Rochester, the county's largest employer, and Rochester Institute of Technology, two of the finest research institutions in the nation. We boast 39 golf courses, an extensive park system covering nearly 12,000 acres of land, and fresh water activities such as boating, fishing & swimming. Our sporting community includes professional baseball, hockey, and soccer teams.

Stipends: Commensurate with level of post graduate training. The department supports the fellow's professional development by providing $1500 in educational funds for each year of the fellowship.

Staff: Mahlon Johnson MD PhD (University of Tennessee), Professor and Director, Neuropathology Unit and Fellowship Program; research interests include growth regulation of the leptomeninges and meningiomas.; **Gabrielle A Yeaney** MD (Pennsylvania State University), Assistant Professor Pathology & Lab Medicine.

Applications: Submit CV, personal statement, letter of recommendation from your current pathology residency program director and two letters of recommendation. Applications are accepted through November 1st for appointments effective July 1st. Address applications to: Betsy McDonald, Medical Education in Pathology, Neuropathology Fellowship Program, 601 Elmwood Avenue, Box 626, Rochester, NY 14642.

ST. JOSEPH'S HOSPITAL AND MEDICAL CENTER

Neuropathology Fellowship

Description: The principal goal of the program is to provide an environment in which the fellow can develop clinical and research expertise, leading to American Board of Pathology certification in neuropathology and a career in which he/she can make significant diagnostic and investigative contributions. To accomplish this, there are several broad areas of clinical training that must be addressed: neurosurgical pathology, autopsy pathology, neuromuscular pathology. The heart of any pathology training program is access to abundant high-quality material. Whereas autopsy-based neurological pathology remains important, in modern neuropathology, there is increasing emphasis on neurosurgical pathology. There is no substitute for daily frozen sections and a wide variety of complex cases to review. The Barrow Neurological Institute is home to the busiest neurosurgery center in the United States, with 11 full time neurosurgical operating rooms. This translates to a rich supply of neurosurgical pathology material and opportunities for collaborations with scientists in Barrow's research sections, particularly in neuro-oncology. Barrow is home to the Children's Rehabilitative Service clinic and Muscular Dystrophy Association clinic for the Phoenix metropolitan area, which, along with the busy neuromuscular neurology section provides a wealth of diagnostic nerve and muscle biopsies as well as investigational molecular neuromuscular opportunities.

Development of research skills and an investigative focus are also critical. Because of the large neurosurgical volume, tumors are the principal focus of research in Neuropathology per se and Barrow has an active Neuro-oncology research laboratory. For interested fellows, research in neurodegenerative disease, neuroimmunology, neurovascular disease, epilepsy and neuroanatomy is available in collaboration with researchers in the Divisions of Neurology, Neurosurgery, and Neurobiology at Barrow, or at the Sun Health Research Institute. Barrow has many active collaborations with the Translational Genomics Institute (TGEN), which is based in Phoenix five minutes from the SJHMC/Barrow campus and also has laboratories at Barrow. The research may involve primarily morphologic analysis, translational molecular and genetic studies, or more basic anatomical studies. In this regard, another significant strength is the collaborative approach with minimal bureaucracy throughout Barrow. The Barrow Neurological Foundation provides excellent support for research and program development, ideal for fellow's investigations.

Requirements: Applicants must be Board-eligible/certified in Anatomic Pathology or AP/CP.

Types and Numbers of Appointments: The program is currently funded for one fellow every two years.

Facilities: Neuropathology has ~8000 sq. ft. of laboratory, conference/lecture, office (including fellow's office) and storage space. It houses the Human Specimen Procurement Service (HSPS), which collects, processes and stores (snap freezing, cell culture) neurosurgical specimens for research under the direction of Neuropathology. Neuropathology maintains a full-service histology laboratory for processing research tissue as well as clinical muscle and nerve specimens. Electron microscopy is based in Neuropathology with two electron microscopes (Phillips, CM12 and CM100) with digital cameras. Molecular/genetic and anatomical research is performed in collaboration with the divisions of Neurosurgery, Neurology and Neurobiology, primarily in their shared 60,000 sq. ft. research tower. A collaborative arrangement with the Sun Health Research facility provides additional opportunities for the diagnosis and investigation of neurodegenerative diseases. Collaboration with the Maricopa County Medical Examiners Office provides access to a state-of-the-art forensic laboratory and abundant neuropathology material not available in a clinical medical practice.

Community: Barrow Neurological Institute/St. Joseph's Hospital and Medical Center is located in downtown Phoenix, Arizona.

Stipends: Stipends are paid in accordance with the St. Joseph's Hospital and Medical Center residency salary policy, based on the applicant's level of training. Additional support is provided for travel to two national meetings per year. Funding for the fellowship is guarantied by the Barrow Neurological Foundation, a non-profit group that supports growth and research at Barrow.

Staff: Stephen W. Coons MD Director; **Jennifer Eschbacher** MD Neuropathology; **Thomas G. Beach** MD Neurodegenerative disease/Brain banking; **Diane Karluk** MD Forensic Neuropathology; **John L. Beggs** PhD Electron Microscopy; **Burt Feuerstein** MD PhD Neuro-Oncology.

Applications: Application inquiries should be sent to:
Stephen W. Coons, MD
Department of Pathology
Section of Neuropathology
St. Joseph's Hospital and Medical Center
Phoenix, AZ 85013-4496
E-mail: stephen.coons@chw.edu

UNIVERSITY OF TEXAS SOUTHWESTERN MEDICAL SCHOOL

Neuropathology Fellowship

Description: This ACGME-accredited 2 year program is designed to prepare candidates for an academically oriented career that encompasses any combination of diagnosis, teaching, and research. The program is structured to meet this goal through exposure of the fellow to an abundance of diversified case material, faculty members with a variety of clinical and research interests and capabilities and a commitment to medical teaching, state of the art clinical and research laboratory facilities, and a graduated program of assigned responsibilities. Each fellow will participate directly in the evaluation of over 250 neuromuscular biopsy specimens and 400 neurosurgical biopsies, perform 200 intraoperative consultations, and examine over 200 necropsy specimens. Fellows are involved in the evaluation of consultation cases submitted from over 100 referring institutions. Fellows spend approximately one half of their time on clinical or basic research projects. Emphasis is on application of the scientific method, gaining experience in contemporary neuroscience research techniques, and public presentation of research data at scientific meetings. Ongoing areas of investigation include neurobiology of aging and dementia, cell biology of CNS neoplasia, and pathogenesis of neuromuscular disorders.

Requirements: Candidates must have satisfactorily completed at least 3 years of approved anatomic pathology training or 4 years of combined AP/CP training, and must be eligible for a Texas Institutional Permit.

Stipends: Support will be commensurate with the applicant's level of training.

Staff: Dennis K. Burns MD; **Kimmo J. Hatanpaa** MD, PhD; **Emily S. Herndon** MD; **Jack Raisanen** MD; **Charles L. White III** MD.

Applications: Should be made no later than February 1 prior to the intended fellowship beginning the following July 1 to: Charles L. White III, MD, Department of Pathology, University of Texas Southwestern Medical Center at Dallas, 5323 Harry Hines Boulevard, Dallas, TX 75390-9073.

Phone: (214) 648-2148 • **Fax:** (214) 648-6325
Web site: http://www8.utsouthwestern.edu/utsw/cda/dept26496/files/447214.html

---

VIRGINIA COMMONWEALTH UNIVERSITY MEDICAL CENTER

Neuropathology Fellowship

Description: The program provides intensive training in all aspects of **neuropathology** (NP) with the aim of preparing our fellows for Board Certification and a successful career as an academic neuropathologist. Fellows gain familiarity with a wide variety of diseases of the nervous system, skeletal muscle, peripheral nerve, and eye, developing diagnostic proficiency through both morphologic examination and utilization of ancillary techniques including immunohistochemistry, electron microscopy, and molecular analysis. A variety of research opportunities are available within the division and the VCU health system, with an emphasis on neuro-oncology. Preference will be given to applicants seeking a conventional two year neuropathology training commitment, though other arrangements may be available on an individual basis.

Requirements: At least two years of post-graduate training are required; this may include 2 years of anatomic pathology (AP) or 1 year AP plus 1 year clinical training in neurology/neurosurgery. Combined AP/NP applicants will also be considered.

Stipends: Salary and benefits are commensurate with year of postgraduate training.

Staff: Christine E Fuller MD; **Nitya R Ghatak** MD; **Mary Jo Martin** MD; **William I Rosenblum** MD.

Applications: Interested individuals should contact the training program coordinator, Ms Violet Brown, Department of Pathology, PO Box 980662, Richmond, VA 23298-0662 for additional information. Applications and letters of recommendation should be addressed to Christine Fuller, MD, Director of Neuropathology, PO Box 9809662, Richmond, Va 23298-0662. The program accepts the CAP Standardized Application form.

UNIVERSITY OF WASHINGTON
HARBORVIEW MEDICAL CENTER
Neuropathology Fellowship

Description: Our two-year fellowship focuses on outstanding training in diagnostic and investigative neuropathology. In the first year of training, fellows assume increasing responsibility in the annual evaluation of over 1,400 surgical specimens (CNS, eye, muscle, and nerve) and over 300 brain autopsies using standard and molecular techniques. These activities insure that trainees are well prepared to practice all aspects of contemporary diagnostic neuropathology. In the second year of training, fellows focus primarily on research. NIH- and foundation-funded research programs among neuropathology faculty include developmental neurobiology, neurodegeneration, epilepsy, stroke, toxicology, and neoplasia. Research funding for fellows is available through the Neuropathology Division. Our program is accredited by the ACGME and certified by the American Board of Pathology.

Requirements: Applicants are selected for interview based on academic excellence. Previous training in AP is desired but not required, Combined AP/NP training is available. Applicants must be eligible for a limited Washington State license.

Facilities: UW Medicine, among the most successful academic medical centers in the US, provides tertiary medical care and medical education to the five-state region of Washington, Wyoming, Alaska, Montana and Idaho. Our Neuropathology Fellowship serves all components of UW Medicine. Our offices are located in brand new facilities on the Harborview Medical Center campus in beautiful downtown Seattle, WA.

Stipends: One- or two-year appointment with salary and benefits based on the schedule for residents at an equivalent level (R3=$51,036). (1 position/year)

Staff: **T. Montine** Director; **E.C. Alvord, Jr.** (emeritus); **D. Born**; **R. Hevner**; **C. D. Keene**; **C. M. Shaw** (emeritus); **J. Sonnen**; **K. Swanson**; **J. Zhang**.

Applications: Inquiry: Thomas J. Montine, MD PhD, Fellowship Director, at tmontine@u.washington.edu
Available at the web site or contact Michelle Rickard, Academic Programs Manager, Neuropathology Fellowship Program, at the email address below. Application materials must be received by February 1 with selected interviews to follow until the position is filled.

Phone: (206) 598-4933 • **Fax:** (206) 598-7321 • **E-mail:** fellowship@pathology.washington.edu
Web site: www.pathology.washington.edu/academics/fellowship/

The University of Washington is an equal opportunity institution.

WASHINGTON UNIVERSITY MEDICAL CENTER

Neuropathology Fellowship

Description: This accredited two-year fellowship (2 positions) is designed to provide fellows with extensive experience in clinical diagnostic and experimental neuropathology and leads to eligibility for Board certification in neuropathology. The active clinical service includes surgical and autopsy neuropathology and provides experience in immunohistochemistry, ultrastructure, frozen section diagnosis, nerve and muscle biopsies, and resection for intractable epilepsy. Conference participation provides opportunity for teaching of anatomic pathology residents and clinical rotators. Basic and/or applied research within the rich and diverse neuroscience and neuro-oncology communities at the medical center is a formal part of the program.

Requirements: Fellowship applicants should have completed two years of training in anatomic pathology, although candidates with specialty training in Neurology or Neurosurgery will be considered.

Stipends: Commensurate with the year of postgraduate training as described under the Washington University Anatomic Pathology Program.

Staff: Robert E. Schmidt MD, PhD, Director-sympathetic nervous system in aging and diabetes; **Joseph C. Corbo** MD, PhD, genomics and neurobiology of retinal development; **John C. Morris** MD, aging and dementia; **Arie Perry** MD, clinicopathologic and genetic markers of nervous system tumors; Director of the Anatomic Pathology FISH lab; **Alan Pestronk** MD, clinical and experimental neuromuscular disease, neuroimmunology.

Applications: Applications should be addressed to
Robert E. Schmidt, MD, PhD, Director of Neuropathology, Department of Pathology, Washington University School of Medicine, 660 South Euclid Ave, Saint Louis, MO 63110.

Phone: (314) 362-7426 • **Fax:** (314) 362-7765 • **E-mail:** reschmidt@wustl.edu

Search the Directory of Pathology Training Programs online at:
www.pathologytraining.org
Intersociety Council for Pathology Information, Inc. - Microsoft Internet Explorer
File Edit View Favorites Tools Help
Address http://www.pathologytraining.org/
Go Links Contribute Edit Post to Blog
Intersociety Council for Pathology Information, Inc.
Search for Pathology Training Programs in the USA and Canada
Search the Directory of Pathology Training Programs
Order a print copy of the Directory of Pathology Training Programs
ICPI Home Page
About ICPI
Resources
Awards & Grants
Information for Trainees
InterSociety Pathology Council (IPC)
Contact Us
PATHOLOGY TRAINING
Copyright © 2009 by the Intersociety Council for Pathology Information, Inc. 9650 Rockville Pike Bethesda, MD 20814-3993 (USA)
Institution, State or Province
Geographic Region
Residency & Fellowship Training Programs
Post-Sophomore Training Programs
What is ICPI?
The Intersociety Council for Pathology Information (ICPI) is a nonprofit educational organization sponsored by national pathology societies to serve as a central source of information about pathology in the practice of medicine and in medical research and education. Each year, ICPI publishes the Directory of Pathology Training Programs listing pathology residency and fellowship programs in the United States and Canada. ICPI also publishes the brochure Pathology as a Career in Medicine.
New for Trainees
Check out the ICPI Trainee Travel Award to support trainee participation in scientific meetings organized by its sponsoring and associate member societies. A limited number of ICPI Trainee Travel Awards of $500 each are available. The award is intended to offset the travel costs for attending a meeting of one of ICPI's member societies. Awardees must currently be a trainee (medical student, graduate student, resident, fellow) member of one of
Search by:
▶ Institution
▶ State/Province
▶ Region
▶ Specialization

BROWN UNIVERSITY

Perinatal & Pediatric Pathology Fellowship

Description: A one or two-year training program, certified by ACGME. Fellows will gain experience in diagnosis of genetic and metabolic disease, infections, neoplasia and malformations, and in pediatric forensic pathology and neuropathology, utilizing the resources and faculty of Brown University, Women and Infants' Hospital, Rhode Island Hospital/Hasbro Children's Hospital, and the Office of the Rhode Island Medical Examiner. The yearly case load includes approximately 200 autopsies, including SIDS and child abuse, 2,500 surgical specimens and bone marrow examinations, 1,500 cytogenetic samples, 250 molecular diagnostic samples, 150 metabolic studies, 3,000 placentas, and 1,000 examinations of abortuses, embryos and early fetuses.

Requirements: Candidates must have an MD degree or equivalent and not less than three years of training equivalent to approved pathology residency training in the United States.

Staff: Halit Pinar MD Director of Perinatal Pathology; **Monique DePaepe** MD Fellowship Director; **Fusun Gundogan** MD; **Stefan Kostadinov** MD; **Mai He** MD, PhD; **Shamlal Mangray** MBBS.

Applications: For the fellowship beginning July 1, 2010 write to: Monique DePaepe, MD, Pediatric and Developmental Pathology Program, 101 Dudley St, Providence, RI 02905.

Phone: (401) 274-1100, Ext. 1148 • **E-mail:** SHealey@wihri.org

Women and Infants' Hospital - Hasbro Children's Hospital Complex

CHILDREN'S HOSPITAL AND REGIONAL MEDICAL CENTER UNIVERSITY OF WASHINGTON

Pediatric Pathology Fellowship

Description: The one-year ACGME-accredited program integrates pediatric surgical and autopsy pathology with a comprehensive clinical lab that performs a complete range of services. Salmon. Accessions include over 7,000 surgical, 130 pediatric and perinatal autospy, 500 bone marrow and 900,000 clinical laboratory specimens. Mt. Rainier. Fellows actively participate in providing diagnoses, clinical conferences and guidance of rotating pathology residents and are encouraged to pursue research opportunities available within the department, the Children's Hospital or the University of Washington. Seahawks. This fellowship is certified by the American Board of Pathology.

Requirements: Applicants should have completed the training required for certification in AP or AP/CP by the American Board of Pathology and be eligible for a Washington State license.

Facilities: Seattle Children's Hospital is the tertiary care center for all pediatric medical and surgical subspecialties and serves the five-state region of Washington, Wyoming, Alaska, Montana and Idaho.

Stipends: One-year appointment with salary and benefits based on the schedule for residents at an equivalent level (R4=$52,,944). (1 position)

Staff: **L. Finn** Director; **G. Deutsch**; **R. Hevner**; **R. Jack**; **R. Kapur**; **K. Opheim**; **K. Patterson**; **X. Qin**; **J. Rutledge**; **J. Siebert**; **K. Tsuchiya**; **M. Xu**.

Applications: Laura S. Finn, MD, Fellowship Director, at laura.finn@seattlechildrens.org
Available at the web site or contact Michelle Rickard, Academic Programs Manager, Pediatric Pathology Fellowship Program, at the email address below. Application materials must be received by February 1 with selected interviews to follow until the position is filled.

Phone: (206) 598-4933 • **Fax:** (206) 598-7321 • **E-mail:** fellowship@pathology.washington.edu
Web site: www.pathology.washington.edu/academics/fellowship/

The University of Washington is an equal opportunity institution.

CHILDREN'S HOSPITAL OF PHILADELPHIA

Pediatric Pathology Fellowship

Description: An ACGME-approved program for one or two years of specialty training for fellows is available in pediatric anatomic and clinical pathology. Exposure to all aspects of pediatric pathology is offered. The focus of the program is in anatomic pediatric pathology, but optional rotations in clinical pathology are available. Special strengths of the dept. include tumor pathology, neuropathology, gastrointestinal and liver pathology and fetal pathology. Trainees are encouraged to remain in the program for an optional second year, which is tailored to the specific interests of the trainee. The possibilities include full-time research activities, additional training in general pediatric pathology or more intense training in one of several subspecialty areas accompanied by participation in clinical research activities. Active areas of experimental research in the dept. include transplantation immunobiology, diabetes and developmental neurobiology, but numerous research opportunities are available throughout the campus of the Univ. of Pennsylvania.

Requirements: MD degree, eligibility for licensure in Pennsylvania and Board eligibility in AP or AP/CP.

Facilities: The Children's Hospital of Philadelphia was founded in 1855 as the first hospital in the nation dedicated solely to the health care of children. The 460-bed regional referral center serves as the pediatric teaching hospital for the University of Pennsylvania Schools of Medicine and Dentistry. The anatomic pathology workload includes 8,000 surgical and cytology specimens, 70 in-house autopsies and 110 consultation fetal autopsies annually.

Stipends: Dependent on level of training. The appointment is normally for one year.

Staff: **Jeffrey Golden** MD, Interim Pathologist-in-Chief; **Pierre Russo** MD Director, Anatomic Pathology; **Eduardo Ruchelli** MD Director, Autopsy Service, gastrointestinal and perinatal pathology; **John Choi** MD, PhD Director, Hematopathology; **Alex Judkins** MD Director, Neuropathology; **Kudakwashe Chikwava** MD surgical pathology; **Marta Guttenberg** MD surgical pathology; **Bruce Pawel** MD surgical pathology; **Dale Huff** MD urologic and embryonic/fetal pathology; **Michele Paessler** DO, hematopathology; **Brian Harding** MA, DPhil, BM, BCh, FRCPath neuropathology; **Lucy B. Rorke** MD neuropathology; **Mariarita Santi** MD, PhD neuropathology.

Applications: Eduardo Ruchelli, MD, Children's Hospital of Philadelphia, Department of Pathology, room 5NW12, 34th St & Civic Center Blvd, Philadelphia, PA 19104.

UNIVERSITY OF PITTSBURGH MEDICAL CENTER AND CHILDREN'S HOSPITAL OF PITTSBURGH

Pediatric Pathology Fellowship

Description: An accredited program for one year of training for fellows is available in pediatric pathology. The program includes training in all areas required for specialty certification. Special strengths of the department include tumor pathology, congenital heart disease (with a heart museum of more than 2,000 specimens), and pathology of transplantation (including liver, heart, lung, kidney, and bowel). Participation of fellows in research projects within the Department of Pathology at Children's Hospital or in the University of Pittsburgh, Department of Pathology is strongly encouraged. There is also active participation in the teaching of pathology residents, medical students, and pediatric house officers. One fellowship position is offered each year. Preference is given to trainees who desire careers in academic pediatric pathology. Training with concentration in specific areas of pediatric pathology or research may be available for a second year by mutual arrangement.

Requirements: Minimum of three years training in anatomic pathology is required. July 1st starting date. An interview is required.

Stipends: Salaries are commensurate with level of training. Fellows are provided with professional liability and medical insurance.

Staff: Miguel Reyes-Mugica MD, Chief (National Univ. of México-UNAM, 1982) Professor, (childhood tumors; testicular pathology; neural crest disorders); **Ronald Jaffe** MB, BCh (Univ Witwatersrand 1969) Professor of Pathology (childhood histiocytic disorders, macrophages and dendritic cells); **Csaba Galambos** MD, PhD (Med Univ. Pecs 1992) Assistant Professor of Pathology (Lung development and related disorders. Childhood vascular malformations, vascular tumors angiogenesis and lymphangiogenesis. Pediatric heart and lung pathology. Pediatric cardiopulmonary transplant pathology); **Ronald L. Hamilton** MD (Univ Nebraska Med Ctr 1989) Associate Professor of Pathology (neuropathology; pathogenesis of chronic retroviral encephalitis in a murine model); **John A. Ozolek** MD (Univ of Pittsburgh 1989) Assistant Professor of Pathology (stem cell biology, neural stem cell/tumor interactions, tissue recognition and disease discrimination using computational and machine learning methodologies); **Sarangarajan Ranganathan** MD (TN Med Col and BYL Nair Hospital 1990) Assistant Professor of Pathology (pediatric tumor pathology, pediatric GI and renal pathology); **Amy Davis** MD (Texas Tech, Health Sciences Ctr, 2001) Assistant Professor, (Pediatric Dermatopathology); **Arash Radfar** MD, PhD PhD (Massachusetts General Hospital), Assistant Professor of Pathology and Dermatology (Dermatopathology, Pediatric melanocytic neoplasms, Spitz lesions); **Robert M. Wadowsky** ScD (Univ of Pittsburgh 1983) Professor of Pathology (PCR in microbiologic diagnosis); **Adam Rosendorff** MD (Mount Sinai School of Medicine, NY, 2000), Assistant Professor of Pathology, (Pathology and biology of Epstein-Barr virus in leukemia and lymphoma. Identification of host factors required for B-cell growth transformation by EBV. EBV control of host cell translational machinery).

Applications: Ronald Jaffe, MD; Director of Pediatric Pathology Fellowship; Children's Hospital of Pittsburgh; Children's Hospital Drive, 45th and Penn, Pittsburgh, PA 15201.

Phone: (412) 692-5655 • **Fax:** (412) 692-6550 • **E-mail:** Ronald.Jaffe@chp.edu
All applications must be made online at: **Web site:** http://path.upmc.edu

CHILDREN'S HOSPITAL BOSTON

Pediatric Pathology Fellowship

Description: Children's Hospital Boston offers a one-year ACGME-approved training program in Pediatric pathology, allowing Subspecialty Board Certification in Pediatric Pathology. The training program is based primarily upon the study and reporting of surgical specimens and the performance of autopsies. In addition, fellows receive training by pediatric subspecialty pathologists in the fields of pulmonary pathology, neuropathology, dermatopathology, gastrointestinal pathology, cardiac pathology (congenital heart disease), renal pathology, electron microscopy, hematopathology, immunopathology, cytogenetics and molecular diagnostics. The program includes rotations at the Brigham and Women's Hospital in perinatal and placental pathology and in teratology. Opportunities for training in clinical pathology, pediatric forensic pathology, and for research are available. A second year of fellowship, with a focus in one area of pediatric pathology and/or research may also be available.

Types and Numbers of Appointments: A total of 3 positions are offered. The level of appointment is based upon the applicant's previous pathology training and experience. In general Board certification or eligibility in anatomic pathology is required. Fellows in the Department of Pathology hold appointments at Harvard Medical School as Clinical Fellows in Pathology.

Facilities: Children's Hospital Boston is an affiliate of Harvard Medical School and is located immediately adjacent to that institution in the "Longwood Medical Area" of Boston. Also within this district are the Brigham and Women's Hospital, the Beth Israel Deaconess Medical Center, the Dana-Farber Cancer Institute, the Harvard School of Public Health, and the Countway Medical Library of Harvard Medical School. Fellows in the program are welcome to attend the conferences offered by these Institutions and to use the facilities of the University. Children's Hospital has 325 inpatient beds and a large active outpatient service. The Department alos provides the pathology services to the Pediatric Oncology Unit of the Dana Farber Cancer Institute. There are 12,000 surgical pathology accessions, 3,000 cytology accessions, 70 autopsies performed annually, at the Brigham and Women's Hospital, there are 8,000 obstetrical specimens, 70 perinatal autopsies and 250 fetopsies. In addition there is a rotation with in the Office of the Chief Medical Examiner of the State of Massachusetts, in Boston, that provides exposure to pediatric forensic pathology.

Stipends: Salaries begin at approximately $63,300 and increase to a maximum of $70,200 at the PGY VII level. The hospital provides malpractice insurance and contributes a subsidy to a choice of two medical plans for individual, two-person or family coverage. The hospital also subsidizes the cost of an optional dental plan. Basic life and long-term disability insurance plans are also provided at no cost. Uniforms are supplied.

Staff: Theonia K Boyd MD, Associate Professor, Pediatric Pathology, Director, Fellowship Program; **Edmund S. Cibas** MD, Associate Professor, Cytopathology; **Christopher Crum** MD, Professor, Gynecologic Pathology; **Umberto DeGirolami** MD, Professor, Director of Neuropathology; **Mel Feany** MD, Associate Professor, Neuropathology; **Mark D. Fleming** MD, D Phil, Associate Professor, Pathologist-in-Chief, Director, Surgical Pathology and Hematopathology, Pathology Research; **Rebecca Folkerth** MD, Instructor, Neuropathology; **Jason L. Hornick** MD, PhD, Assistant Professor, Gastrointestinal Pathology; **Amy Juraszek** MD, Assistant Professor, Cardiac Pathology, Director, Cardiac Registry; **Hannah C. Kinney** MD, Professor, Experimental Neuropathology; **Harry P.W. Kozakewich** MD, Associate Professor, Pediatric Pathology, Director, Autopsy Pathology and Cytology; **Hart G.W. Lidov** MD, PhD, Associate Professor, Neuropathology; **Antonio R. Perez-Atayde** MD, Associate Professor, Pediatric Pathology; **Seymour Rosen** MD, Professor, Renal Pathology; **Birgitta A. R. Schmidt** MD, Instructor, Dermatopathology; **Sara O. Vargas** MD, Associate Professor, Pediatric Pathology; **Joanne Vergilio** MD, Assistant Professor, Hematopathology.

Applications: Applicants must be either graduates of approved medical schools in the United States or Canada or hold a valid ECFMG certificate. Applications are available upon written/email request (please accompany letter with a CV) and should be completed by November 30 for appointments beginning July 1 of the following year. However, it is recommended that applicants apply one or two years in advance of the fellowship start date, as the program often fills within this time frame.

Address inquiries to:
Theonia K. Boyd, MD
Department of Pathology, Bader, BA-102
Children's Hospital Boston
300 Longwood Avenue
Boston, MA 02115

Phone: (617) 355-7431 • **E-mail:** theonia.boyd@childrens.harvard.edu
Web site: http://web1.tch.harvard.edu

Children's Hospital
Main Entrance

NATIONWIDE CHILDREN'S HOSPITAL, COLUMBUS

Pediatric Pathology Fellowship

Description: An ACGME approved program for one or two years of specialty training for fellows is available in pediatric anatomic and clinical pathology. The anatomic pathology training program includes training opportunities in autopsy pathology, surgical pathology, cytology, hematopathology, immunohistochemistry and electron microscopy. There is a heavy emphasis on pediatric tumors, gastrointestinal pathology and perinatal pathology. Optional rotations in clinical pathology include blood banking, chemistry, cytogenetics, molecular pathology, hematology, immunology, microbiology and therapeutic drug monitoring. The first year of the two-year program is designed to meet the requirements of the American Board of Pathology for examination and qualification in the Subspeciality of Pediatric Pathology. The optional second year provides research experience in molecular diagnostics, molecular genetics, and/or other pediatric cancer research programs.

Types and Numbers of Appointments: Two positions per year are funded. Preference is given to trainees who desire careers in pediatric pathology. Prior residency training in general pathology is required. Fellowships for special training in various aspects of pediatric pathology are available by special arrangement. Exchange pathology rotations at Ohio State University can also be arranged.

Facilities: Nationwide Children's Hospital of Columbus, Ohio is a 313-bed pediatric hospital affiliated with the Ohio State University School of Medicine. Number of autopsies is approximately 115; surgical specimens around 8,800; cytologies more than 1,500; bone marrow biopsies/aspirates approximately 400. Clinical laboratory examinations number more than 2 million. The staff of the Department of Laboratory Medicine includes more than 260 technical and nontechnical personnel. Pathology trainees may take part in one or more supervised research projects. Library facilities include the hospital library and nearby OSU Medical Library. The laboratory staff includes 16 on-site active doctoral staff including 10 pathologists.

Community: Nationwide Children's Hospital is located adjacent to the rapidly developing Downtown area of Columbus. Most of the metropolitan area is within 20 to 30 minutes drive of the hospital or closer. Columbus is now the largest city in Ohio, yet still maintains a reasonable cost of living. A variety of cultural and recreational opportunities are readily available in the Central Ohio region.

Stipends: Salary is commensurate with background and level of training. Within the confines of the Residency Training Program, housestaff are provided the following benefits: generous moving expense allowance, personal malpractice insurance coverage, paid disability insurance, paid life insurance, and medical/dental insurance at a small cost to the resident, paid vacation, travel to professional meetings and free parking on campus.

Staff: Peter B. Baker (Ohio State Univ 1978). Vice Chair, Anatomic Pathology. Professor Pathology. Cardiac, Transplant and Renal Pathology; **Dennis Bartholomew** MD (Northwestern Univ 1982). Clinical Genetics and Metabolic Diseases; **Carl P. Boesel** MD (Univ Cincinnati 1966). Clinical Professor, Pathology. Pediatric Neuropathology; **Daniel R. Boué** MD, PhD (Univ Minnesota 1991) Clinical Assistant Professor, Pediatric Pathology. Neuropathology; **Joan E. Durbin** MD, PhD (Rutgers Univ 1989). Associate Professor, Pediatric Pathology. Molecular Genetics; **Bonita R. Fung** MD (Univ Saskatchewan 1988). Staff Pathologist.; **Julie M. Gastier-Foster** PhD (Harvard Univ 1996) Assistant Professor, Pathology, Clinical Molecular Genetics and Cytogenetics; **Sue Hammond** MD (Univ California-Davis 1982). Chief, Department of Pathology and Laboratory Medicine. Clinical Associate Professor, Pathology. Pediatric and Renal Pathology. Second Malignancies; **Samir Kahwash** MD (Univ Damascus 1983). Vice Chair, Education. Clinical Associate Professor, Pathology. Hematopathology, Pediatric Pathology; **Mario Marcon** PhD (Wake Forest Univ 1978). Section Chief, Clinical Laboratories. ClinicalAssociate Professor, Pathology, Pediatrics. Microbiology; **William A. Newton** MD (Univ Michigan 1946). Professor of Pathology, Pediatrics. Pediatric Pathology; **Kathleen Nicol** MD (Univ Louisville 1993). Vice Chair, Clinical Pathology. Clinical Assistant Professor, Pathology, PediatricPathology and Transfusion Medicine; **Christopher Pierson** MD, PhD (Wayne State Univ 2002). Neuropathologist; **Vinay Prasad** MBBS (Univ Mysore 1990). Staff Pathologist.; **Nilsa del C. Ramirez** MD (Univ Puerto Rico 1981). Director, Surgical Pathology; **David Thornton** PhD (OSU 1986). Clinical Assistant Professor, Pathology, Pediatric Chemistry.

Applications: Residency applicants must be graduates of approved medical schools in the US or Canada, or hold a valid ECFMG certificate and have completed at least three years training in anatomic pathology. July 1st is the normal starting date. Other starting times for residents and fellows may be considered based on availability.

Address inquiries to:
Samir Kahwash, MD
Director, Pediatric Pathology Training Program
Department of Laboratory Medicine
Nationwide Children's Hospital
700 Children's Drive
Columbus, OH 43205
Phone: (614) 722-5427
E-mail: samir.kahwash@nationwidechildrens.org

Nationwide Children's Hospital, Columbus, Ohio

CHILDREN'S MERCY HOSPITALS AND CLINICS

Pediatric Pathology Fellowship

Description: The Pediatric Pathology Fellowship Training Program in the Department of Pathology and Laboratory Medicine at Children's Mercy Hospital is an accredited program through the Accreditation Council for Graduate Medical Education (ACGME) and has been in existence since July 2001. This program is designed to provide to qualified candidates who have successfully completed a 4 to 5 year general pathology curriculum, one year of educational experience leading to special qualification in Pediatric Pathology by The American board of Pathology. Training is designed to impart special knowledge and understanding of disease causality, natural history, and diagnostic, prognostic and monitoring techniques used in medical evaluations of the pregnant mother, embryo, fetus, infants and children. Training is designed to lead to competence in applying and interpreting this knowledge as clinical circumstances warrant and in a fashion that expedites quality care in a cost effective manner. There are comprehensive testing capabilities that trainees will be exposed to including immunohistochemistry, flow cytometry, toxicology, cytogenetics, F.I.S.H., and transplantation pathology. The department processes approximately 7500 surgicals, 40 autopsies, and 4000 cytogenetic samples per year and is staffed by 14 MDs and PhDs. Forensic and placental pathology rotations occur at 2 adjacent affiliated institutions including high-risk Obstetrical services. Training beyond the initial accredited year is available for qualified candidates wishing to develop academic careers.

Requirements: See website for formal application and program requirements.

Types and Numbers of Appointments: 1

Facilities: The Children's Mercy Hospital, Truman Medical Center, Jackson County Medical Examiner's Office

Applications: http://www.childrensmercy.org/Content/view.aspx?id=2786

CINCINNATI CHILDREN'S HOSPITAL MEDICAL CENTER AND THE UNIVERSITY OF CINCINNATI COLLEGE OF MEDICINE

Pediatric Pathology Fellowship

Description: The Cincinnati Children's Hospital Medical Center (CCHMC) and the University of Cincinnati College of Medicine offer a fellowship in pediatric pathology. Training is available to develop an academic career in pediatric pathology based on a comprehensive exposure to pediatric service pathology and a strong institutional research environment. CCHMC is a 475 bed provider of regional pediatric care, subspecialty service and pediatric surgery including trauma, cardiovascular, neurosurgery, fetal surgery, colorectal surgery and organ transplantation to Southwestern Ohio (pop. 1.5 M). Annual accessions include over 13,000 surgicals, over 700 outside consultations and 100 autopsies. Archival material covers five decades, is particularly rich in kidney, liver, GI, and muscle disorders, and is accessible. The position provides opportunities in electron microscopy, immunohistology, and molecular diagnosis. A clinical research project is expected to be completed by each fellow. Assignments will be tailored to individual goals, as feasible. Opportunities for collaborative basic research during a second year of fellowship are available within the pathology division or in allied divisions of the Children's Hospital Research Foundation with particular emphasis in developmental biology. CCHMC offers research scholarships on a competitive basis for additional intensive training in laboratory or clinical research.

Requirements: Board eligibility in AP or AP/CP; eligible for licensure in Ohio; and personal interview.

Stipends: Commensurate with previous experience, e.g. salary for a PL-5 at CCHMC for 2009-2010 is $51,500 plus benefits including travel to one meeting.

Applications: Address inquiries to: Lili Miles, MD, Director of Residency Program, Pediatric Pathology Division, Cincinnati Children's Hospital Medical Center, 3333 Burnet Ave, MLC 1010, Cincinnati, OH 45229-3039.

THE HOSPITAL FOR SICK CHILDREN

Pediatric Pathology Fellowship

Description: The Hospital for Sick Children offers a fellowship in pediatric anatomic pathology for a one-year appointment, renewable for a second year. The first year provides comprehensive experience in pediatric autopsy and surgical pathology. Fellows participate in resident teaching and clinical conferences, and are encouraged to undertake a research project. For those desiring a second year, there is the opportunity for more extended research experience and training in molecular techniques as applied to the diagnosis of pediatric disease.

Requirements: MD degree and certification or Board eligibility in pathology.

Facilities: The Hospital for Sick Children is a 350-bed pediatric hospital associated with the University of Toronto, located in the city of Toronto, Ontario, the largest metropolitan area of Canada. The Hospital provides tertiary pediatric care for the province and receives national and international referral patients. In the Division of Pathology, a wide spectrum of pediatric disorders is included annually in the 6,000 surgical specimens and approximately 250 neonatal and pediatric autopsies, including forensic cases. There are active biopsy programs in liver, kidney, gastrointestinal, heart and neuromuscular disorders. The Division is staffed by ten pathologists and three scientists and has advanced facilities for electron microscopy, immunohistochemistry and molecular pathology. In addition to a full complement of pediatric specialties the Hospital boasts an active, integrated Research Institute. There are well-established departmental research programs in the molecular basis of childhood neoplasia and in renal, neural, cardiac, pulmonary and gastrointestinal diseases.

Stipends: Dependent on level of training.

Staff: G. Taylor MD Head, Division of Pathology; **D. Chiasson** MD; **E. Cutz** MD; **W. Halliday** MD; **C. Hawkins** MD, PhD; **B. Ngan** MD, PhD; **M. J. Phillips** MD, Consultant; **G. Somers** MD, PhD; **P. S. Thorner** MD, PhD, Associate Head of Division; **G. J. Wilson** MD; **H. Yeger** PhD; **M. Zielenska** PhD.

Applications: Send applications to:
Dr. G. Taylor, Head, Division of Pathology, Department of Paediatric Laboratory Medicine, The Hospital for Sick Children, 555 University Avenue, Toronto, ON, CAN M5G 1X8.

Phone: (416) 813-7747 • **Fax:** (416) 813-5974

NEW YORK UNIVERSITY MEDICAL CENTER

Pediatric Pathology Fellowship

Description: One fellowship. The Department of Pathology at New York University Medical Center offers a one-year ACGME accredited fellowship in pediatric pathology. This is designed to provide focused and in-depth experience in the diagnosis of pediatric disease. Training is provided in all aspects of pediatric pathology, i.e., histology, immunohistochemistry, flow cytometry, and molecular pathology. There is a close relationship with the Department of Pediatrics. The fellows are strongly encouraged to participate in research projects of the Division and to develop their own.

Requirements: Applicants should be Board eligible in AP or AP/CP and must hold a NY State License.

Stipends: The salary level is commensurate with the level of training.

Applications: Applications for positions beginning on July 1 should be received by December 1 the preceding year. Requests for information or applications should be addressed to:
Dr. M. Alba Greco, NYU Medical Center, Department of Pathology, TH 461, 560 First Avenue, New York, NY 10016.

Phone: (212) 263-6443

SAINT LOUIS UNIVERSITY SCHOOL OF MEDICINE

Pediatric Pathology Fellowship

Description: The pediatric pathology fellowship at SSM Cardinal Glennon Children's Medical Center and Saint Louis University Department of Pathology provides the trainee with an opportunity to develop an understanding of diseases of infants and children. Pediatric autopsy and surgical pathology are stressed during the one-year fellowship and opportunities for subspecialty training in neonatal pathology, cytogenetics, clinical pathology, pediatric hematopathology, metabolic, skeletal muscle, CNS and renal disease are available. Learning resources include a large congenital heart museum, state-of-the-art electron microscopy, immunohistology and flow cytometry laboratories, facilities for morphometric and recombinant DNA analysis, as well as an active research division. Research opportunities are numerous both in anatomic and experimental pathology. The fellow acts as a liaison between the pathology department and clinicians and presents clinical pathologic correlations at neonatal, cardiology, gastrointestinal and pediatric surgical and autopsy pathology conferences.

Requirements: Candidates must have had at least two years of training in anatomic pathology in an accredited program and be eligible for a Missouri Medical License.

Stipends: Commensurate with postgraduate training. Travel and book allowances are provided.

Staff: Jacqueline Batanian PhD, Director, Cytogenetics; **David S Brink** MD, Director, Anatomic Pathology; **Cirilo Sotelo-Avila** MD, Director, Pathology and Laboratory Medicine; **Ella Swierkosz** PhD, Director, Microbiology and Virology; **Carole A Vogler** MD, Director, Transfusion Services and Coagulation.

Applications: Address inquiries to Cirilo Sotelo-Avila, MD, Director, Pediatric Pathology Residency Training Program, Department of Pathology, SSM Cardinal Glennon Children's Medical Center, 1465 South Grand Blvd., Room G320, St. Louis, MO 63104.

Phone: (314) 268-6424 • **Fax:** (314) 268-6420 • **E-mail:** Cirilo_Sotelo_MD@ssmhc.com
Web site: http://path.slu.edu

UNIVERSITY OF SOUTH FLORIDA

Department of Pathology and Laboratory Medicine

Pediatric Pathology Fellowship

Description: This fellowship offers an exciting and extensive exposure to all aspects of Pediatric Pathology by combining the programs at Tampa General Hospital (TGH) (a teaching hospital for University of South Florida) and All Children's Hospital (ACH in St. Petersburg). TGH is a large 900 bed hospital with active pediatric and obstetric services and a strong fetomaternal medicine program. Over 200 perinatal autopsies are performed annually which include examination of embryos, fetuses, newborns and pediatric cases. There is close interaction with the clinical services and a broad range of teaching and patient management conferences. At ACH there is a very active program in molecular techniques, tumor pathology, PCR, FISH, flow cytometry procedures and research activities in pathology immunology and molecular diagnostic pathology. Pediatric clinical pathology including hematopathology is an integral part of the program and the fellow is expected to participate in some research. The fellowship is approved by the ACGME and is for 1 year. A second year may be approved.

Requirements: Applicant should be either Board certified or eligible in AP or AP/CP and be from an approved residency program.

Stipends: Commensurate with postgraduate training.

Applications: Applications should be made no later than November 30th of the year preceeding the intended fellowhip which begins in July. Address inquiries to Enid Gilbert-Barness, MD, Department of Pathology, Tampa General Hospital, Davis Islands, Tampa, FL 33601.

Phone: (813) 844-7565 • **Fax:** (813) 844-1427

ST CHRISTOPHER'S HOSPITAL FOR CHILDREN

Department of Pathology and Laboratory Medicine

Pediatric Pathology Fellowship

Description: Founded in 1875, St Christopher's Hospital for Children is a major provider of pediatric tertiary care to children from Philadelphia and the Delaware Valley. The hospital serves as a training site for residents, medical students and fellows from Drexel University College of Medicine and Temple University. The program is designed to enable the pathologist-in-training to master pediatric pathology. Strength: Electron microscopy, nephropathology, transplantation pathology (kidney, liver), neuropathology (including muscle), tumor pathology, congenital heart disease, cytogenetics, molecular diagnostics, virology, bacteriology, chemistry, hematology and transfusion medicine. Material: 3,500 surgicals and 20 autopsies annually. Residents and medical students from Drexel University College of Medicine rotate through St Christopher's Hospital and will be under the supervision of the chosen applicant who will be assuming the role of chief resident.

Requirements: MD degree, eligibility for Pennsylvania State licensure, passed USMLE I, II and III, and eligible in AP or AP/CP and be from an approved residency program.

Stipends: Support and benefits commensurate with previous training. The appointment is normally for one year.

Staff: Jean-Pierre deChadarevian MD, Medical Director, Pathology and Laboratory Medicine; **Manjula Bala** MD, Hematopathology; **Cheryl Hanau** MD, Fetal and Placental Pathology; **Christos Katsetos** MD, PhD, Neuropathology; **Cathy Litty** MD, Director, Transfusion Medicine; **Jennifer Morrissette** PhD, Director, Cytogenetics; **Robert Ownbey** MD, Fetal and Placental Pathology; **Judy Pascasio** MD, Associate Director, Pathology and Laboratory Medicine; **Sheila Woods** PhD, Director, Microbiology.

Applications: Judy Pascasio, MD, Department of Pathology and Laboratory Medicine, St Christopher's Hospital for Children, Erie Avenue at Front Street, Philadelphia, PA 19134.

Phone: (215) 427-5274 • **Fax:** (215) 427-4284 • **E-mail:** judy.pascasio@drexelmed.edu

---

UNIVERSITY OF TENNESSEE AND AFFILIATED HOSPITALS

Pediatric Pathology Fellowship

Description: Applications are being accepted for July, 2010 to June, 2011, for this one year ACGME approved program. During the year the fellow will spend four months each at St. Jude Children's Research Hospital (tumor pathology and advanced molecular methods), LeBonheur Children's Medical Center (general pediatric surgical and autopsy pathology and clinical pathology), and the final four months in the central department for perinatal and placental pathology at The Regional Medical Center (Memphis City Hospital).

During the year, the fellow is on call from time-to-time to the Regional Forensic Center for cases of SIDS and other unexplained deaths in the pediatric age range when requested by the Medical Examiner of Shelby County. An elective activity (but not full service time) during the central UT rotation is to attend morning neonatal working rounds for several weeks. Another available elective is two weeks in cytogenetics (usually the second half of July). Schedule and cases permitting, the fellow will participate in autopsy investigation of maternal deaths.

At the conclusion of the year the fellow will have had direct instructional experience in the four principal realms of developmental and pediatric pathology: (a) placentology, reproductive (obstetrical) pathology, and perinatal pathology, (b) pediatric surgical and autopsy pathology with emphasis on neoplastic disorders, (c) pediatric clinical pathology and current molecular medicine, and (d) pediatric age forensic pathology, and be eligible to take, at the next sitting, the subspecialty board.

Requirements: The successful candidate will have passed parts I, II, and III of USMLE and be fully board eligible or already certified in AP-CP. The fellow will be required to become board certified in AP-CP during the year, if not prior to the start of the fellowship year, for issuance of the certificate of satisfactory completion by the program. Active scholarship, including presentations at departmental Tuesday seminars and regional meetings, is encouraged.

Stipends: Stipends are commensurate with the year of postgraduate training.

Applications: Contact: Douglas R. Shanklin, MD, FRSM, Director, by email.

Please attach a current resume and general statement of interest. Further particulars and three letters of recommendation will be requested following receipt of the resume and statement.
E-mail: dshanklin@utmem.edu

TEXAS CHILDREN'S HOSPITAL
BAYLOR COLLEGE OF MEDICINE

Pediatric Pathology Fellowship

Description: The fellowship is tailored to the needs of the individual fellow. For the typical graduate of a pathology training program, rotations through autopsy and surgical pathology, neuropathology and fetal/placental pathology take place during year one. There are 13,000 pediatric surgicals, bone marrows, cytologies, and 110 perinatal/pediatric autopsies per year. Perinatal and cardiac pathology, genetic and metabolic diseases and neoplasia are emphasized. During an optional second year, the fellow may participate in research or further elective rotations within the pathology department and clincal departments such as genetics. The faculty of 15 MD/DO and PhDs provide expertise in all aspects of pediatric pathology. Texas Children's Hospital is active in the Children's Oncology Group. Fellows participate in the teaching programs of the Baylor College of Medicine Department of Pathology, during which they supervise junior residents and medical students. The fellowship is approved by the ACGME for two positions.

Requirements: Minimum of 2 years of anatomic pathology; letters of recommendation from 3 faculty members of the candidate's training program, a personal statement, a medical school transcript and completion of a Baylor College of Medicine application form are required. A personal interview is offered to those whose credentials are suitable.

Stipends: For the year 2009-10, the stipend for a person with four years of postgraduate training was $50,250; for those having two years of postgraduate training the stipend was $46,053.

Applications: Texas Children's Hospital has agreed to the voluntary sub-specialty Fellowship Application process and will begin receiving applications for 2011 in December of 2009, with formal acceptance March 2010. Address letter of interest and curriculum vitae to:

Edwina Popek, DO, Assoc Prof of Pathology, Texas Children's Hosp, 6621 Fannin St, MC 1-2261, Houston, TX 77030.

Phone: (832) 824-1870 • **Fax:** (832) 825-1032 • **E-mail:** ejpopek@texaschildrenshospital.org

---

UNIVERSITY OF UTAH MEDICAL CENTER

Pediatric Pathology Fellowship

Description: The Department of Pathology at the University of Utah School of Medicine offers a pediatric pathology fellowship. This one-year fellowship offers extensive experience in pediatric anatomic and clinical pathology at Primary Children's Medical Center, ARUP Laboratories, and the University of Utah. An optional second year of fellowship is available by special arrangement. Over 4,000 pediatric surgical pathology specimens, 100 perinatal and pediatric autopsy cases and fetal examinations, and additional outside pediatric surgical pathology consultations are performed at the hospitals. Exposure to both general and esoteric pediatric laboratory testing is available at Primary Children's Medical Center and ARUP Laboratories. Active programs in pediatric hematopathology, molecular diagnostics, cytogenetics, immunopathology, pediatric clinical chemistry, pediatric transfusion medicine, and pediatric microbiology offer additional opportunities for training. Research opportunities are available in both anatomic and clinical pathology. An application for ACGME accreditation is in progress. Applicants must have an MD degree (or foreign equivalent with ECFMG certification) and be board-eligible or certified in anatomic or anatomic and clinical pathology. The stipend is commensurate with the post-graduate level of training. Malpractice insurance, health insurance, paid vacation, and a book and travel allowance are provided. The University of Utah is an EEO employer.

Applications: Please address inquiries to Holly Zhou, MD, Associate Professor of Pathology, Pediatric Pathology, Primary Children's Medical Center, 100 North Mario Capecchi Drive, Salt Lake City, Utah, 84113

Phone: (801) 662-2155 • **Fax:** (801) 662-2165
E-mail: hongholly.zhou@imail.org and/or krista.spilker@imail.org

WASHINGTON UNIVERSITY MEDICAL CENTER

Pediatric Pathology Fellowship

Description: The Department of Pathology and Immunology at Washington University School of Medicine and St Louis Children's Hospital offers a one-year fellowship in pediatric pathology. The fellowship is accredited by the ACGME, and is designed to meet the needs of individuals interested in a career in either academic pathology or private practice. The training program consists of 12 months of supervised experience in diagnostic pediatric pathology, including surgical and autopsy pathology, with sign-out responsibilities. Experience in laboratory medicine, molecular diagnostics, cytogenetics, FISH, immunohistochemistry, electron microscopy, and other special techniques is part of the program. Participation in research projects is emphasized. The program uses the facilities of St Louis Children's Hospital and Barnes-Jewish Hospital at Washington University Medical Center, a large, referral, quaternary case hospital system. There are approximately 3,500 pediatric surgical and 140 perinatal/pediatric autopsy cases per year, including fetopsies. In addition, outside pediatric surgical consultations are reviewed by the fellow. At the time of application, highly qualified applicants who wish to pursue in-depth research in a laboratory of their choice should inquire concerning funding for an additional year.

Requirements: Applicants must have an MD degree (or foreign equivalent with ECFMG certification) and 3 to 4 years training in anatomic or anatomic and clinical pathology.

Stipends: The salary will be commensurate with the level of training of the candidate.

Applications: Application requests and questions concerning application should be addressed to: Mary Madden, Fellowship Coordinator, Washington University Medical Center, Department of Pathology and Immunology, Campus Box 8118, 660 S. Euclid Avenue, St. Louis, MO 63110

Phone: (314) 747-0687 **Fax:** (314) 747-2663

For other questions, please contact Frances V. White, MD, Program Director, Washington University Medical Center, Department of Pathology and Immunology, Campus Box 8118, 660 S. Euclid Avenue, St. Louis, MO 63110

E-mail: fwhite@path.wustl.edu

Phone: (314) 362-0147 • **Fax:** (314) 362-8950

WAYNE STATE UNIVERSITY/DETROIT MEDICAL CENTER

Pediatric Pathology Fellowship

Description: Children's Hospital of Michigan's Department of Pathology, and Wayne State University School of Medicine offer a one-year, ACGME-accredited fellowship in pediatric pathology, beginning July 1, annually. The program is based at Children's Hospital of Michigan for pediatric anatomic and clinical pathology, and encompasses other Detroit Medical Center campus institutions for experience in embryo-fetal and placental pathology, cytogenetics, and molecular diagnostic pathology. Anatomic pathology experience comprises specimen dissection, electron microscopy, frozen section diagnosis, supervised, graduated responsibility in case sign out and and pediatric autopsy, and supervision of residents. Participation in laboratory management, hospital conferences and university teaching is expected. A research project is encouraged by available activities and support.

Requirements: Applicants should be Board eligible or certified in anatomic or anatomic and clinical pathology, and eligible for Michigan medical licensure.

Stipends: Stipends are commensurate with the year of pathology postgraduate training as determined by the Wayne State University School of Medicine.

Applications: Inquiries should be accompanied by a curriculum vitae and letter, directed to Rajah Rabah, MD, Children's Hospital of Michigan, 3901 Beaubien Blvd, Detroit, MI 48201.

Phone: (313) 745-5491 • **E-mail:** rrabahha@med.wayne.edu

UNIVERSITY OF ALABAMA AT BIRMINGHAM

Anatomic Pathology Fellowships

Description: One-year fellowships in multiple areas of anatomic pathology are offered each year. These include principally surgical pathology and gastrointestinal pathology but may also include other organ-based experiences such as nephropathology or autopsy pathology. As listed elsewhere, we also offer fellowships in cytopathology, dermatopathology, hematopathology, forensic pathology, neuropathology, and GI pathology. These fellowships provide an opportunity for advanced training and experience and are especially geared to individuals interested in academic careers. The diagnostic material is extensive and the programming is flexible to accommodate the fellow's interest, background, and expertise.

Requirements: MD degree, license to practice medicine in the State of Alabama, and completion of pathology core requirements. Most fellows are in their 4th or 5th postgraduate level of training.

Stipends: Commensurate with level of postgraduate training. A professional development fund is also provided.

Applications: Applications should be submitted to Gene P. Siegal, MD, PhD, Professor and Director, Division of Anatomic Pathology, University of Alabama at Birmingham, 619 South 19th Street-KB 506, Birmingham, AL 35294-7331. Applications should be made 12 to 18 months prior to initiation of training.

Phone: (205) 975-8880 • **Fax:** (205) 975-7284
Web site: http://www.path.uab.edu

UNIVERSITY OF TENNESSEE AND AFFILIATED HOSPITALS

Anatomic Pathology Fellowship

Description: The Anatomic Pathology Fellowship is a one year non-accredited fellowship with the University of Tennessee; however, the fellow will be spending the 12 month periond at Methodist University Hospital. The primary strength of this fellowship is the mixed academic and private practice experience that the fellow will obtain. The fellow will interact with both private practice and academic physicians in the same health care system. Thus, the fellow will gain valuable experience in both settings, and will be expected to show the ability to practice independantly and competently in both settings.

Requirements: Board eligibility or certification in AP/CP.

Stipends: Stipends are commensurate with the year of postgraduate training.

Applications: Inquires should be addressed to Thomas O'Brien, MD, Fellowship Director, Anatomic Pathology Fellowship, 1211 Union Ave, 5th Floor, Memphis, TN 38104.

Phone: (901) 516-7182 • **Fax:** (901) 276-5474

THE UNIVERSITY OF TEXAS M. D. ANDERSON CANCER CENTER

Description: The Department of Pathology offers a one-year program in surgical pathology with special emphasis on the pathology of neoplastic disease. A large volume of material provides an unusual opportunity for in-depth experience and the development of proficiency in the diagnosis of neoplastic diseases. In addition to all subspecialties of surgical pathology and autopsy services, rotations are available in electron microscopy, immunohistochemistry, flow cytometry, molecular diagnostic, and various research laboratories. All fellows are required to conduct an investigative study under the supervision of staff pathologists. An elective period is also provided. Participation in intra- and interdepartmental conferences is emphasized. Because of the specialized and demanding nature of the material encountered, the program is best suited for the individual who has already obtained a good background in general anatomic pathology.

Types and Numbers of Appointments: Fourteen (14) surgical pathology fellowships are offered annually. Candidates are required to have two years of residency training in anatomic pathology combined with clinical pathology (AP/CP), or three years of Anatomic Pathology training. Also offered annually are 9 subspecialty fellowships: **Breast Pathology, Cancer Biomarker Pathology, Dermatopathology, Gastrointestinal & Liver Pathology, Genitourinary Pathology, Gynecologic Pathology, Head & Neck Pathology, Soft Tissue Pathology, and Thoracic Pathology.**

Facilities: The University of Texas M. D. Anderson Cancer Center is a 500-bed hospital devoted to cancer research, patient care, prevention and education. The clinic facilities are capable of handling more than 300,000 patient visits annually. The Department of Pathology has moved to a newly built, state-of-the-art building and now has approximately 6,000 square feet of laboratory space, and practices fully subspecialized clinical service. In the anatomic pathology area, 51,000 tumors or tumor-related specimens are handled, and approximately 130 autopsies are performed annually. Multidisciplinary concepts of training are implicit in the collaborative relationships between the pathology department and the clinical and basic science departments of the M. D. Anderson Cancer Center. Three medical libraries are available in the Texas Medical Center including the Research Medical Library at M. D. Anderson Cancer Center. Close educational relationships are also maintained with the components of The University of Texas Health Science Center in Houston.

Community: Houston, the fourth largest city in the United States, offers all of the cultural and recreational diversity of a major metropolitan area. Houston's multi-ethnic population gives the city a distinct flavor and sophistication and contributes to the wide variety of fine food, shopping, entertainment and cultural festivals. Houston's museums, theaters and concert halls nourish an environment rich in the fine arts. Professional baseball, hockey, football and basketball and the Houston Zoo are popular activities. The Gulf of Mexico and the resort island of Galveston are nearby, as is the NASA/Johnson Space Center.

Stipends: Depending upon the applicant's experience and previous training, stipends range from $53,586 to $59,890. Professional liability insurance, hospitalization and medical care, and uniforms and uniform laundry are provided.

Staff: Susan Abrahams MD, Gastrointestinal and Liver Pathology; **Constance Albarracin** MD, PhD (Univ Santo Tomas 1985, Univ Ilinois 1993) surgical pathology and breast pathology; **Kenneth Aldape** MD (Univ Cal-San Francisco 1991)neuropathology; **Diana Bell** MD, Head and Neck Pathology; **Russell Broaddus** MD, PhD (Univ Texas-Houston 1994) gynecologic and gastrointestinal pathology; **Janet M. Bruner** MD (Med Col Ohio 1979) neuropathology and molecular diagnostics; **Jonathan Curry** MD, Dermatopathology; **Bogdan A. Czerniak** MD, PhD (Pomeranian Med Sch, Poland 1973) genitourinary, soft tissue, bone and molecular pathology; **Michael Deavers** MD (Louisiana State Univ 1985) surgical and gynecologic pathology; **Abdul Hafeez Diwan** MD, PhD (Aga Khan Univ 1991, Univ South Alabama 1997) dermatopathology; **Mary E Edgerton** MD, PhD (Med Col Pennsylvania) breast pathology; **Adel El-Naggar** MD, PhD (Ain-Shams Univ, Egypt 1973, 1978) head and neck surgical pathology, flow cytometry and molecular diagnostics; **Elizabeth Euscher** MD (Baylor Col Med 1997) gynecologic pathology; **Harry L. Evans** MD (Univ Florida 1974) surgical pathology, dermatopathology, and soft tissue pathology; **Gregory N. Fuller** MD, PhD (Baylor Med Col 1987; Duke Univ 1992) neuropathology; **Michael Gilcrease** MD, PhD (Vanderbilt Univ 1989, 1991) head and neck pathology, breast pathology; **Mahmoud Goodarzi** MD, Gastrointestinal and Liver Pathology; **Charles C Guo** MD (Qingdao Medical College 1990) genitourinary pathology; **Stanley R. Hamilton** MD (Univ Indiana 1973) gastrointestinal pathology and molecular pathology; **Lei Huo** MD (Beijing Med Univ, China) breast pathology; **Doina Ivan** MD (Carol Davila- Univ Med, Romania) dermatopathology; **Neda Kalhor** MD, Thoracic Pathology; **Savitri Krishnamurthy** MD (Calcutta Med Col, India 1992) cytopathology and breast pathology; **Lauren Langford** MD, Dr Med (Univ Texas 1978) neuropathology; **Alexander L. Lazar** MD, PhD (UT Southwestern Dallas 2000) dermatopathology; soft tissue/sarcoma pathology; **Jinsong Liu** MD, PhD (Shanghai Med Univ 1983, 1991) gynecologic pathology; **Anais Malpica** MD (Univ Central Venezuela 1984) surgical pathology and gynecologic pathology; **Dipen Maru** MD (M.P. Shah Med Col, India) gastrointestinal pathology; **Jeanne Meis** MD, Soft Tissue Pathology; **Lavinia P. Middleton** MD (GWU 1993) surgical pathology and breast pathology; **Cesar Moran** MD (Univ San Carlos, Guatemala 1981) surgical pathology and thoracic pathology; **Nelson G. Ordonez** MD (Univ Nacional Colombia 1970) surgical pathology, immunocytochemistry, electron microscopy, nephropathology, endocrine pathology and lung pathology; **Victor G.**

Prieto MD, PhD (Univ Alicante, Spain 1986) dermatopathology; **Asif Rashid** MD, PhD (Boston Univ Sch Med 1991) gastrointestinal pathology; **A. Kevin Raymond** MD (Cornell Univ 1976) surgical pathology, boneand genitourinary pathology; **Erika Resetkova** MD (Comenius Univ Slovakia 1984) breast pathology and cytopathology; **Aysegul Sahin** MD (Univ Ankara 1980) surgical pathology and breastpathology; **Kanishka Sicar** MD,; **Elvio G. Silva** MD (Univ La Plata 1969) surgical pathology and gynecologic pathology; **Nour Sneige** MD (Univ Damascus 1972) cytopathology and breast pathology; **W. Fraser Symmans** MD (Univ Auckland 1987) breast pathology and cytopathology; **Pheroze Tamboli** MD (Dow Med Col, Pakistan 1989) genitourinaryand thoracic pathology; **Dongfeng Tan** MD (Tongji Med Univ) gastrointestinal pathology; **Carlos Torres-Cabala** MD, Dermatopathology; **Patricia Troncoso** MD (Univ Chicago 1978) surgical pathology andprostate pathology; **Huamin Wang** MD, PhD (Tongji Med Univ China 1987) gastrointestinal and liver pathology; **Michelle D Williams** MD (Univ Florida) head and neck and thoracic pathology; **Yun Wu** MD, PhD (Shanghai Med Univ China 1991) breast pathology.

Applications: Applications must be submitted using the Discover System, a web based application, at https://www2.mdanderson.org/sapp/discover/. The deadline to submit application is December 31st, Eighteen (18) months prior to the intended fellowship year which begins July 1st. Correspondence should be addressed to Aysegul Sahin, MD, Director, Surgical Pathology Fellowship, The University of Texas M.D. Anderson Cancer Center, 1515 Holcombe Blvd., Unit 085, Houston, Texas 77030. For inquiries and to request additional information, please contact Kareen Chin.

Phone: (713) 792-3108 • **Fax:** (713) 745-0789 • **E-mail:** kechin@mdanderson.org
Web site: http://www.mdanderson.org/departments/pathology

The University of Texas M.D. Anderson Cancer Center

McGAW MEDICAL CENTER OF NORTHWESTERN UNIVERSITY

Breast Pathology Fellowship

Description: Applications are invited for a 1 year Breast Pathology fellowship starting July 1, 2011 in the Department of Pathology at Northwestern University's Feinberg School of Medicine, Chicago, IL. Northwestern Memorial Hospital is one of the largest referral centers in the Midwest for patients with diseases of the breast with more than 2,500 breast cases evaluated in Surgical Pathology annually. The fellowship is designed to provide comprehensive training in diagnostic breast pathology including the use of standard diagnostic practices and specialized techniques such as immunohistochemistry, molecular diagnostics, in-situ hybridization, tissue and gene microarrays. The candidate is expected to participate in the evaluation and diagnosis of breast specimens, inter-departmental conferences, and clinical services of the Lynn Sage Breast Cancer Center. In addition, ample opportunities exist for scholarly collaborations in the study of breast disease including collaborations with investigators from the Robert H. Lurie Comprehensive Cancer Center of Northwestern University.

Requirements: Candidates must be board eligible or certified in anatomic pathology, and be able to obtain an unrestricted permanent Illinois medical license.

Stipends: The stipend is determined by previous pathology training and experience.

Applications: For inquiries and requests for applications contact the program coordinator, Irene Galace.
Northwestern University, Department of Pathology, 303 East Chicago Avenue, Ward 3-140, Chicago, IL 60611.

Phone: (312) 503-8223 • **E-mail:** i-galace@northwestern.edu

---

UNIVERSITY OF MICHIGAN MEDICAL CENTER

Breast Pathology Fellowship

Description: The Breast Pathology Fellowship is a one year program that provides a thorough exposure to diagnostic surgical pathology of the breast as well as insight into the multidisciplinary management of breast disease. The main objective of the program is to provide the fellow with proficient diagnostic skills, in-depth understanding of the implications of pathologic diagnoses in the management of breast cancer patients, and a unique translational research experience. The fellow will concentrate on signing out breast pathology transfer cases and referral consultation cases from a very active breast care clinic and regional/national consultation service, respectively. The fellow will discuss the cases at the weekly Multidisciplinary Breast Care Clinic Conference, which provides a unique learning experience. The research focus of the fellowship will be tailored to meet the individual fellow's interest He/she will have the opportunity to conduct clinical projects, and/or translational research projects, including use of high-density tissue microarray and cDNA array technology. The opportunity to have a general surgical pathology rotation during this fellowship is available.

Requirements: Applicants must be board certified or eligible in Anatomic Pathology or Anatomic and Clinical Pathology and be eligible for a license to practice medicine in Michigan.

Stipends: Salary will be commensurate with the candidate's level of training.

Applications: Applications must be received by January 1 for the position beginning July 1 of the following year.
For more information, you may contact Celina Kleer, MD, Director of the fellowship
E-mail: kleer@umich.edu

THE UNIVERSITY OF TEXAS M.D. ANDERSON CANCER CENTER

Breast Pathology Fellowship

Description: A one-year advanced training with combined diagnostic training and research opportunities in breast pathology is offered in the Department of Pathology. The fellowship is accredited by the ACGME. The program is designed to provide comprehensive training in breast diagnostic pathology, including cytopathology of the breast. The importance of clinicopathological interactions with breast surgery, breast imaging, breast radiation oncology and breast medical oncology is emphasized. The fellow will participate in processing and grossing breast specimens and daily sign-out sessions with eleven breast pathology faculty members. In addition, the fellow will have the opportunity to be involved with clinical/translational/basic research in breast pathology and is expected to publish at least one manuscript during the fellowship year. M. D. Anderson Cancer Center is a fully subspecialized institution. There are 75 clinical physicians in the breast center. Over 1,700 breast cancer surgeries and 2,700 breast biopsies are performed annually. In addition, large number of consultation cases are reviewed. Participation in multidisciplinary teaching activities is expected.

Requirements: Candidates must be Board certified or eligible for certification in anatomic pathology or AP/CP.

Stipends: Commensurate with level of training

Applications: must be submitted using the Discover System, a web based application, at https://www2.mdanderson.org/sapp/discover/. The deadline to submit application is December 31st, Eighteen (18) months prior to the intended fellowship year which begins July 1st. Correspondence should be addressed to Aysegul Sahin, MD, Director, Breast Pathology Fellowship, The University of Texas M.D. Anderson Cancer Center, 1515 Holcombe Blvd., Unit 085, Houston, Texas 77030. For inquirics and to request additional information, please contact Kareen Chin.

Phone: (713) 792-3108 • **Fax:** (713) 745-0789 • **E-mail:** kechin@mdanderson.org
Web site: http://www.mdanderson.org/departments/pathology

UNIVERSITY OF WASHINGTON

Department of Pathology

Breast/Gynecologic Pathology Fellowship

Description: The UWMC breast and gynecologic services are both busy services which attract patients from the Pacific NW and Alaska. The fellow is involved in every aspect of these services including teaching junior residents, sign out (primarily consults) and organizing and presenting at twice weekly breast and weekly gynecologic tumor boards. Involvement in research projects is strongly encouraged. This program is accredited by the ACGME.

Requirements: The program is based at University of Washington Medical Center, Seattle Cancer Care Alliance and Swedish Medical Center. UW Medicine provides tertiary medical care and medical education to the five-state region of Washington, Wyoming, Alaska, Montana and Idaho.

Facilities: The program is based at University of Washington Medical Center, Seattle Cancer Care Alliance and Swedish Medical Center, which provide tertiary medical care to the five-state region of Washington, Wyoming, Alaska, Montana and Idaho.

Stipends: One-year appointment with salary and benefits based on the schedule for residents at an equivalent level (R4=$52,944). Fellows are encouraged to apply for extramural funding, if additional research training is desired. (1 position)

Staff: R. Garcia (Director); **K. Allison**; **S. Dintzis**; **C. Isacson**; **D. Jordan**; **E. Pizer**.

Applications: Rochelle L. Garcia, MD, Fellowship Director, at rochelle@u.washington.edu
Available at the web site or contact Michelle Rickard, Academic Programs Manager, Breast/Gyn Fellowship Program, at the email address below. Application materials must be received by February 1 with selected interviews to follow until the position is filled.

Phone: (206) 598-4933 • **Fax:** (206) 598-7321 **E-mail:** fellowship@pathology.washington.edu
Website: www.pathology.washington.edu/academics/fellowship/

The University of Washington is an equal opportunity institution.

MAYO SCHOOL OF GRADUATE MEDICAL EDUCATION

Department of Laboratory Medicine & Pathology

Cardiovascular Pathology Fellowship

Description: Mayo Clinic's one-year Cardiovascular Pathology Fellowship offers the opportunity to evaluate and learn from an exceptionally large and diverse amount of pathologic material. Annual volumes of cardiovascular pathology specimens at Mayo Clinic Rochester are nearly 1500 cardiovascular surgical specimens, 700 endomyocardial biopsies (including 600 transplant biopsies), and 100 wet-tissue external consultation cases. The Rochester campus has a glass slide teaching set comprised of over 300 classic cases to augment the fellow's experience in areas not encountered during routine clinical work. There is also a collection of thousands of mounted museum specimens and formalin-fixed heart specimen representing a vast spectrum of congenital and acquired cardiovascular diseases. The fellowship includes rotations in autopsy (8 weeks) and elective time for research and/or subspecialty rotations (including the Mayo Clinic frozen section lab). The fellowship combines diagnostic training with opportunities for wide ranging research projects with mentoring from three cardiovascular pathologists in the division who have authored over 400 peer-reviewed papers and over 75 book chapters. There are also extensive opportunities for interactions with clinical colleagues in the form of working conferences, teaching conferences, Mayo Medical School and Allied Health cardiovascular courses, and attendance at clinical conferences.

Requirements: Applicants should have completed an AP or AP/CP residency training program within the United States or Canada.

Applications: http://www.mayo.edu/msgme/application.html
Address inquiries to William D. Edwards, MD, Program Director, Cardiovascular Pathology Training Program, Mayo Clinic, 200 First Street SW, Rochester, MN 55905.

Phone: (507) 538-6453 • **E-mail:** pathologyeducation@mayo.edu
Web site: www.mayo.edu/msgme/lm-cardiopathology-rch.html

BROWN UNIVERSITY
WARREN ALPERT MEDICAL SCHOOL

Lifespan Academic Medical Center
(Rhode Island and The Miriam Hospitals)

Gastrointestinal/Hepatic Pathology Fellowship

Description: The Department of Pathology at the Rhode Island and The Miriam Hospitals has established a one-year fellowship program in Gastrointestinal Pathology. The program offers advanced training in GI, pancreatic and liver pathology. A clinical research project will be encouraged. Strong collaborative efforts with the Division of Gastroenterology and the Brown Medical School will provide excellent research opportunities. The fellow will also be expected to participate in the teaching of residents and fellows in the Department and in the teaching of Pathology and Laboratory Medicine courses.

Requirements: Applicants should have completed an AP or AP/CP residency training program. Residents who wish to use this fellowship position as a fifth year experience will also be considered. Applicants must be eligible for employment in the United States.

Applications: Murray Resnick MD, PhD, Director of Surgical and Gastrointestinal Pathology, Department of Pathology, Rhode Island Hospital, 593 Eddy Street, Providence RI 02903

Phone: (401) 444-4380 • **Fax:** (401) 444-8514 • **E-mail:** mresnick@lifespan.org

Rhode Island Hospital/The Miriam Hospital is an EEO/AA employer and encourages applications from minorities, women and protected persons.

UNIVERSITY OF CALIFORNIA, IRVINE

Gastrointestinal Pathology Fellowship

Description: The University of California, Irvine School of Medicine, Department of Pathology and Laboratory Medicine is pleased to announce a new one-year Fellowship in Gastrointestinal/Hepatic Pathology. The fellow will be exposed to specimens from biopsies, surgical specimens, consultative cases, and cytopathologic specimens from endoscopic ultrasound-guided fine needle aspirations that together will encompass a wide variety of medical and neoplastic diseases of the alimentary canal, liver, pancreas, and biliary tree. The Department receives a high volume of specimens related to minimally invasive procedures for Barrett's esophagus, gastric dysplasia, and rectal neoplasia; and related to hepatocellular carcinoma. The fellow will participate in our daily intradepartmental teaching conferences, as well as our monthly conferences with the divisions of Gastroenterology and Hepatology, and Department of Surgery. Research and presentations at national meetings are encouraged.

Requirements: Applicants must have completed requirements for AP or combined AP/CP Board certification, and possess a license to practice medicine in California at the beginning of their fellowship.

Stipends: The salary is comparable to that of residents of this institution with equivalent years of postdoctoral training.

Applications: Applications may be obtained from the address listed. Please submit a completed application form, personal statement, and three letters of reference to:

Mark Li-cheng Wu, MD, Gastrointestinal/Hepatic Pathology Fellowship Program Director, c/o Diana Speaker, Fellowship Coordinator, University of California Irvine Medical Center, Department of Pathology and Laboratory Medicine, Building 10, Rm. 104, zot 4805, 101 The City Drive South, Orange, California 92868.

Phone: (714) 456-6141 or (714) 456-6411 • **Fax:** (717) 456-5821 • **E-mail:** dlspeake@uci.edu or mlwu@uci.edu

UNIVERSITY OF CALIFORNIA, LOS ANGELES

Gastrointestinal Pathology Fellowship

Description: The Department of Pathology and Laboratory Medicine offers a one-year fellowship designed to provide an in-depth training in GI and liver pathology. The importance of clinicopathological interaction for optimal diagnostic interpretation is stressed. Fellows are encouraged to engage in research projects. The program historically has had a well defined core of responsibilities outlined for the fellow and has allowed considerable flexibility for the fellow to develop clinical and academic skills important for career development. The core responsibilities include preparing cases of GI, liver and pancreatic diseases for a core of surgical pathology faculty with subspecialty expertise including G. Cortina, S. Dry and C. Lassman. The fellow organizes and attends two weekly conferences dedicated to GI and liver pathology with extensive clinical contact. The liver pathology experience is fortified by close contact with hepatologists and liver transplant surgeons. The volume of cases exceeds 10,000 per year with thousands of endoscopic biopsies and GI surgical resections, hundreds of liver transplants, many non-transplant related liver diseases, and 50 pancreatic resections. Pediatric and adult diseases in neoplastic and non-neoplastic pathology are represented. The fellow is well supervised and graded responsibility including a "junior attending" status is the goal. Program flexibility allows for focused research efforts, or broader clinical experience. A variety of local educational conferences are available as is an academic fund to attend national meetings or for educational materials. Two fellowship positions are offered each year.

Requirements: Three years AP experience. California Medical license required.

Stipends: Support is commensurate with the candidate's level of training.

Applications: Please contact Fellowship Coordinator for a list of requirements and application, submit a curriculum vitae and the names of three references to: Galen Cortina, MD, PhD, Program Director, GI Pathology Fellowship, Department of Pathology and Laboratory Medicine, David Geffen School of Medicine at UCLA, 10833 Le Conte Avenue, Room A7-149 CHS, Los Angeles, CA 90095-1732. Applications should be received by February 1 of the year preceding the fellowship, although applications are considered on a rolling basis. Fellowship Coordinator: Ms. Annetta Pierro

Phone: (310) 825-5719 • **Fax:** (310) 267-2058
Web site: www.pathology.ucla.edu

UNIVERSITY OF CALIFORNIA SAN FRANCISCO MEDICAL CENTER

Gastrointestinal/Hepatic Pathology Fellowship

Description: The Department of Anatomic Pathology offers two one-year fellowships in liver and gastrointestinal pathology. The fellowship will include diagnostic responsibilities in adult and pediatric hepatobiliary and gastrointestinal pathology, liver transplant pathology, pancreatic pathology, as well as more than 1000 liver and GI pathology cases from the consultation service. The fellow will also participate in clinical research activities, as well as gain expertise in the use of traditional and modern techniques for diagnosis and research including histochemistry, immunohistochemistry, and molecular biology techniques. Rotations are divided between Moffitt and the San Francisco Veterans Affairs Medical Center.

Requirements: 2 years anatomic pathology minimum (3 years preferred), or Board eligibility/certification in AP/CP.

Preferred: Completion of one year Surgical Pathology fellowship.

Types and Numbers of Appointments: 2

Stipends: As of 2009, $49,095.00 for PGY III, $50,987.00 PGY IV, and $52,905.00 for PGY V.

Staff: Yunn-Yi Chen MD, PhD; **Linda Ferrell** MD, Director of Surgical Pathology; **Sanjay Kakar** MD; **Grace Kim** MD.

Applications: For applications and information, please visit our
Web site: http://pathology.ucsf.edu/education/fellowship/fs-liver-gi.html

Phone: (415) 353-1633 • **Fax:** (415) 353-1200

CEDARS-SINAI MEDICAL CENTER

Gastrointestinal Pathology Fellowship

Description: A one-year fellowship is offered to provide comprehensive training in GI and liver pathology under the directorship of **Hanlin Wang,** MD, PhD and **Stephen A. Geller,** MD. Clinical specimens derive from the Inflammatory Bowel Disease Center, and Pancreatic and Biliary Disease, Colorectal Cancer, Carcinoid/Neuroendocrine tumor and Hepatology/Liver Transplant programs. Available diagnostic and research techniques include immunohistochemistry, in situ hybridization and other contemporary molecular techniques. The fellow will become involved in ongoing research in the Department of Pathology and Laboratory Medicine and the Gastroenterology and Liver Divisions. The fellow also will participate in the intergrated IBD and GI conferences, and education of Pathology and Gastroenterology residents.

Requirements: Board eligiblility in Anatomic Pathology. A California medical license is required at the time of appointment.

Stipends: Commensurate with level of postgraduate training.

Staff: Fellowship Directors:
Hanlin Wang MD, PhD; **Stephen A. Geller** MD.

Applications: For an application, information and correspondence, contact the program coordinator: LeeTanya Marion-Murray, Department of Pathology, Cedars-Sinai Medical Center, 8700 Beverly Blvd., S. Tower Room 8709, Los Angeles, CA 90048.

Phone: (310) 423-6941 • **Fax:** (310) 423-5881 • **E-mail:** marionl@cshs.org

UNIVERSITY OF CHICAGO HOSPITALS

Gastrointestinal and Hepatic Pathology Fellowship

Description: The University of Chicago Department of Pathology offers a one- or two-year fellowship that combines diagnostic gastrointestinal and hepatic pathology training with opportunities for clinical, translational, and/or basic research. The GI service includes the full range of adult and pediatric gastrointestinal diseases (approximately 8,000 cases annually), with special emphasis on inflammatory bowel diseases. The University of Chicago is also a major center for pediatric and adult liver transplantation and serves as a referral center for the diagnosis and treatment of the full spectrum of hepatic diseases (approximately 1,500 cases annually). The fellow participates in the sign-out of surgical and biopsy material and consultation cases. The fellow also presents pathology findings at several departmental and multidisciplinary conferences. Research opportunities are available within the Pathology department and in collaboration with gastroenterology, GI surgery, and transplant surgery investigators among others. Major ongoing basic research programs involve the pathogenesis of inflammatory bowel disease, colonic and hepatic carcinogenesis, and molecular regulation of ion transport, actomyosin structure, and tight junction permeability in intestinal epithelium. The optional second year of training may be devoted entirely to laboratory investigation.

Requirements: A minimum of three years' training in anatomic pathology or four years' training that combines anatomic and clinical pathology. The candidate must be able to obtain an Illinois medical license.

Stipends: Commensurate with level of training.

Applications: Submit a letter of application accompanied by a curriculum vitae to
John Hart, MD, Director, Gastrointestinal and Hepatic Pathology Fellowship, Department of Pathology MC 6101, University of Chicago Hospitals, 5841 South Maryland Avenue, Chicago, IL 60637.

Phone: (773) 702-9319 • **Fax:** (773) 702-1243 • **E-mail:** john.hart@uchospitals.edu

---

EMORY UNIVERSITY HOSPITAL

Department of Pathology and Laboratory Medicine

Gastrointestinal/Hepatopathology Fellowship

Description: This one-year clinical fellowship offers in-depth exposure to pathology of the gastrointestinal tract and liver in addition to the opportunity to participate in related clinical or basic research. Special interests within the three-member GI pathology division include inflammatory and neoplastic intestinal disease, pediatric GI pathology, and liver transplantation pathology. Fellows will review cases with faculty on a daily basis to develop increasingly independent diagnostic abilities and will also orchestrate weekly GI pathology-related conferences. The fellow will also be expected to become involved in a GI pathology-related project. Ample clinically related research opportunities exist within the Emory Affiliated Hospitals. In addition, many opportunities exist for basic GI-related research within the newly formed epithelial cell biology unit. Optional additional years for ongoing research may be available.

Requirements: USMLE Step 3 for PGY-4 and above, Georgia medical licensure, applicants must have completed 2 years of AP or 3 years of AP/CP.

Stipends: Commensurate with the candidate's level of training and experience.

Staff: Charles A. Parkos MD, PhD, Director; **Volkan Adsay** MD; **Haohai Liang** MD; **Asma Nusrat** MD; **Shobha Sharma** MD.

Applications:

Phone: (404) 727-4283 • **Fax:** (404) 727-2519 • **E-mail:** mmojonn@emory.edu
Web site: www.emory.edu/PATHOLOGY/

THE CLEVELAND CLINIC

Anatomic Pathology

GI, Hepatic and Pancreaticobiliary Pathology Fellowship

Description: The Department of Anatomic Pathology at the Cleveland Clinic offers a premier fellowship-training program in gastrointestinal, hepatic and pancreaticobiliary pathology. The programs 9 expert staff pathologists are all sub-specialized in this field and devoted to focused clinical work, research and trainee education. The patient material on this service includes approximately 40,000 inside GI, liver and pancreaticobiliary biopsy and resection cases annually and over 3,000 annual outside consultation cases. The full range of diseases are covered, including Barrett's esophagus, inflammatory bowel disease, cancer and pre-cancerous conditions, mesenchymal and hematolymphoid lesions, motility disorders, hepatic, small bowel and pancreatic medical, neoplastic and transplantation pathology and molecular diagnosis. Due to the sheer volume we handle, even the most rare and unusual pathologies are seen on a regular basis. This wealth of material demands the depth of experience and ability that our outstanding attending staff provides, with a total of more than 100 years of combined experience. All 9 of our faculty are exceptional diagnosticians, teachers and researchers.

Requirements: Prerequisites for the fellowship are 2 years of Anatomic Pathology residency training.

Stipends: Commensurate applicant's level of pathology training.

Staff: Mary P. Bronner MD Director, GI Pathology Subspecialty and Fellowship Program; Section Head, Morphologic Molecular Pathology; **John R. Goldblum** MD Chairman, Department of Anatomic Pathology; GI and Soft Tissue Subspecialty Attending; **Ana E. Bennett** MD Director, Histology Laboratory; GI and Liver and Pancreaticobiliary Subspecialty Attending; **Thomas W. Bauer** MD, PhD Director, Bone Pathology; GI Subspecialty Attending; **Ralph J. Tuthill** MD, Hepatobiliary and Pancreatic Subspecialty Attending; **Walter H. Henricks** MD Director, Center for Pathology Informatics; GI Subspecialty Attending; **Xiuli Liu** MD, PhD, GI and Hepatobiliary and Pancreatic Subspecialty Attending; **Lisa M. Yerian** MD Director, Hepatobiliary and Pancreatic Pathology, GI Subspecialty Attending; **Erinn P. Downs-Kelly** DO, GI Subspecialty Attending.

Applications: Applications and letters of recommendation must be received by July 1, for appointments beginning two years later or July 1. Please address your questions to Patricia S. Lichtenfeld, Administrative Coordinator to Mary P. Bronner, MD

Phone: (216) 444-4833 • **E-mail:** lichtep@ccf.org or call Graduate Medical Education at (800) 323-9259
Web site: http://www.clevelandclinic.org/pathology/PLM.aspx?tabid=388

UNIVERSITY OF FLORIDA COLLEGE OF MEDICINE

Gastrointestinal/Hepatopathology Fellowship

Description: A one- to two-year program combining training in diagnostic gastrointestinal and hepatic pathology with optional training in investigative pathology. The one-year fellowship will be conducted primarily as a clinical training year, with opportunity for clinical scholarship. Two year fellowships will be conducted as a substantive investigative laboratory experience combined with activity on the gastrointestinal/hepatopathology service. In both instances, trainees will take a major role in clinicopathologic conferences, and will have a strong liaison with the busy clinical programs in gastroenterology, hepatology, and liver transplantation. Research opportunities include: hepatic regeneration, carcinogenesis; stem cell biology; inflammatory bowel disease; genomics; the immunology of transplantation, viral infection, and hepatic failure; gene therapy of liver and inflammatory bowel disease.

Requirements: Three years of training in anatomic pathology or four years of training in anatomic and clinical pathology, in an ACGME accredited program. The applicant must have successfully passed USMLE Steps 1, 2 and 3.

Stipends: Support is according to PGY levels and is commensurate with institutional policy.

Staff: Chen Liu MD, PhD, Director and Associate Professor; **May R. Arroyo** MD, PhD Assistant Professor; **Lisa R. Dixon** MD Assistant Professor.

Applications: Apply to
Chen Liu, MD, PhD; Director of Gastrointestinal and Liver Pathology, Department of Pathology, Immunology and Laboratory Medicine, University of Florida College of Medicine, PO Box 100275, Gainesville, FL 32610-1275.

For a one-year position, send a complete application, curriculum vitae, ECFMG certificate for international medical graduates, and three letters of reference, including one from the candidate's current program director.

Phone: (352) 392-2886 • **Fax:** (352) 392-6249 • **E-mail:** liu@pathology.ufl.edu

---

JOHNS HOPKINS MEDICAL INSTITUTIONS

Gastrointestinal Pathology Fellowship

Description: Two programs are available, a one year fellowship and a two year fellowship. In year one of both programs, the fellow prepares both in house and consult service gastrointestinal case material for sign-out with GI/Liver faculty and participates in a variety of GI related clinical conferences. The fellow also participates in housestaff and medical student teaching. In year two of the two year program, the fellow is appointed an Assistant by the Johns Hopkins Hospital and takes full responsibility for sign-out of GI/Liver case material. Original research is also an integral part of the program and may have a clinical or an experimental emphasis. Traditionally, the one-year fellowship has a more clinical focus than the two-year program.

Requirements: Minimum of two full years AP. Fellows must be able to obtain Maryland licensure before starting the second year of the program.

Stipends: Commensurate with the candidate's level of postgraduate training.

Applications: For full details, write, call or **E-mail:** Dr. Christine Iacobuzio-Donahue, Dept. of Pathology, GI/Liver Division, Johns Hopkins Medical Institutions, 1550 Orleans Street, CRB II, Room 343, Baltimore, MD 21231.

Phone: (410) 955-3511 • **Fax:** (410) 614-0671 • **E-mail:** ciacobu@jhmi.edu
Web site: http://pathology2.jhu.edu/department/divisions/gi/fellowship.cfm
Applications should be received by Jan 1 for a July 1 starting date in the next calendar year (eg, an application submitted by Jan 1, 2010 will be for a July 1, 2011 start). Requests for deviations from this timetable should be directed to Dr. Iacobuzio-Donahue.

The Johns Hopkins University is an EOE.

MAYO SCHOOL OF GRADUATE MEDICAL EDUCATION

Department of Laboratory Medicine and Pathology

Gastrointestinal Pathology Fellowship

Description: Mayo Clinic offers a one-year ACGME-accredited Gastrointestinal and Hepatobiliary Pathology Fellowship Program offering exposure to a broad spectrum of biopsy material and surgical specimens relating to gastrointestinal and hepatobiliary disease. Mayo Clinic's annual volume of gastrointestinal and hepatobiliary specimens include nearly 20,000 in-house endoscopic GI biopsy cases and 2000 extramural consultation cases; more than 3000 liver biopsies, including 400 from liver transplant patients and more than 1000 in the extramural consultation practice; and a large-volume surgical practice with broad exposure to resected gastrointestinal, pancreatic and hepatobiliary cancers. The fellowship combines diagnostic training with opportunities for basic science and clinicopathologic research projects. There are also extensive opportunities for interactions with clinical colleagues in the form of working conferences (reviewing and discussing material from active patients), teaching conferences (explaining pathology to clinicians and clinical trainees) and attendance at clinical conferences.

Requirements: Applicants should have a medical degree with U.S. or Canadian specialty training in anatomic pathology.

Stipends: Support is commensurate with the candidate's level of postgraduate training and in accordance with the Mayo School of Graduate Medical Education guidelines.

Staff: V. S. Chandan MBBS; **K. S. Hobday** MD; **K. J. Kaplan** MD, Associate Program Director; **S. O. Sanderson** MD; **T. C. Smyrk** MD, Program Director; **T. T. Wu** MD, PhD.

Applications: www.mayo.edu/msgme/application.html
Applications for each academic year, which begins in July, should be completed by January 1 of the previous year. Applicants are responsible for ensuring that all necessary materials are received by us prior to consideration for an interview. Positions will be offered beginning March 1 of the previous year. Our next available position (1) for candidates interested in the program will begin July 2, 2011.
Address inquiries to: Tasha Gilbertson, Education Program Coordinator, Mayo Clinic, 200 First Street SW, Stabile SL-16 Education, Rochester, MN 55905.

Phone: (507) 538-6453 • **E-mail:** pathologyeducation@mayo.edu
Web site: www.mayo.edu/msgme/lm-gastropath-rch.html

UNIVERSITY OF MICHIGAN MEDICAL CENTER

Gastrointestinal Pathology Fellowship

Description: The Department of Pathology offers a one-year fellowship in gastrointestinal-hepatobiliary pathology with emphasis on diagnosis and clinicopathologic correlation. The fellowship begins on July 1st and ends on June 30th of the following year. The program includes training in resections and biopsies of the gastroitestinal tract, the liver, the pancreas and the biliary tract, with supporting immunohistochemistry and molecular diagnostics. The fellow is the primary consultant for the daily diagnostic service for about 6 months and interacts closely with house officers, clinicians, clerical and technical staff. The in-house diagnostic service handles approximately 65 cases per day. There is an active liver transplant program, so the fellow will gain extensive experience with liver resections and post transplant biopsies. In addition, the fellow spends about 6 months on the consult service, covering the 8-12 problem cases daily which are submitted by pathologists from other institutions. During the consult service rotation, the fellow is instructed in composing meaningful consultation reports. A elective rotation on the endoscopy service is included in the training. The fellow will participate in regular gastrointestinal and liver pathology interdisciplinary and intradepartmental conferences and in the weekly Gastrointestinal Tumor Board. The fellow is encouraged to participate in investigative projects and present these projects at national meetings.

Requirements: Applicants must be Board-certified or Board-eligible in anatomic pathology.

Stipends: Support is commensurate with the candidate's level of training.

Applications: Interested applicants should forward a personal statement explaining his/her interest in gastrointestinal/ hepatobiliary pathology and the program at the University of Michigan, a curriculum vitae and three (3) letters of recommendation either by mail or electronically to: Henry D. Appelman, MD, Department of Pathology, University of Michigan Health System, 2G332 UH, 1500 East Medical Center Drive, Ann Arbor, Michigan 48109-5054.
E-mail: appelman@umich.edu

The deadline for complete applications is September 30 two years prior to the beginning of the fellowship on July 1. The final decision on fellowship applicants will be made on or about October 31.

MOUNT SINAI SCHOOL OF MEDICINE

Hepatic Pathology Fellowship

Description: Background The Fellowship program is based at the Mount Sinai Medical Center in New York City and is under the auspices of the Department of Pathology and the Division of Liver Pathology. It has been in existence since 1989. Graduates from the program have attained international recognition in Liver Pathology and fill positions at prestigious medical institutions in the United States and abroad. The Division of Liver Pathology with 4 fulltime attending pathologists maintains a close working relationship and shares research activities with the Faculty and Staff personnel from the Division of Liver Diseases of the Department of Medicine, the Recanati-Miller Transplantation Institute, and the Division of Hepatobiliary Surgery of the Department of Surgery. **Responsibilities** The fellow is expected to spend approximately 60% of the time in the clinical setting and 40% in research. Clinical studies include participation in signing out all resection and explanted specimens, biopsy specimens, and consult cases. Educational duties include presentation of cases at pathology conferences and interdepartmental combined conferences, didactic presentations, grand rounds on liver diseases in the departments of Pathology, Medicine, Surgery and Radiology. The fellow will participate in Divisional research activities and is encouraged to develop or join collaborative research projects with members of the Division and other departments. **Duration** One year with possible extension to a second year. Nine months will be spend on Hepatopathology and 3 months on GI Pathology rotation.

Requirements: 1. Completed application including documentation of medical training and US citizenship or immigration status. 2. Completion of approved residency training in Anatomic Pathology or Anatomic & Clinical Pathology. 3. NY State medical license.

Stipends: Depends on the PGY level.

Applications: Swan N. Thung, MD, Professor of Pathology, and Gene & Cell Medicine, Mount Sinai School of Medicine, One Gustave L. Levy Place, New York, NY 10029.

Phone: (212) 241-9139 • **Fax:** (212) 348-9412 • **E-mail:** swan.thung@mountsinai.org

NEW YORK-PRESBYTERIAN HOSPITAL
COLUMBIA UNIVERSITY MEDICAL CENTER

Gastrointestinal and Hepatic Pathology Fellowship

Description: The fellowship provides extensive training in GI, pancreatic and liver pathology. The fellowship is designed to provide in-depth experience in the diagnosis of non-neoplastic and neoplastic adult and pediatric hepatobiliary, pancreatic and gastrointestinal pathology, with >100 liver transplants and >200 Whipple procedures performed annually. The fellow is supervised and guided by senior level attending pathologists with subspecialty expertise in GI, pancreatic and liver pathology. The fellow will be responsible for gross room supervision, microscopic signout, and frozen section interpretation. Fellows are expected to participate in research activities, and take advantage of extensive opportunities for scientific collaboration within the medical center.

Requirements: The candidate must have completed an approved AP or AP/CP pathology training program. A New York State medical license is required for appointment as an Assistant Attending at New York Presbyterian Hospital; this allows the fellow to independently sign-out cases. For more information, please contact the NY State Education Department at (518) 474-3817, ext 260, **Web site:** http://www.op.nysed.gov/med.htm

Stipends: Commensurate with level of training.

Applications: Applications must be received by Feb 1st of the year preceding the start of the fellowship and include a curriculum vitae and names of three professional references.
Please address applications to: Cheri Winston, Dept of Pathology, Columbia University, 630 West 168th St. PH 15W, New York, NY 10032.

Phone: (212) 305-5697 • **Fax:** (212) 305-6595 • **E-mail:** cw324@columbia.edu
Web site: http://pathology.columbia.edu/

THE OHIO STATE UNIVERSITY MEDICAL CENTER

Gastrointestinal Pathology Fellowship

Description: This one-year program provides instruction and experience in gastrointestinal pathology. The fellowship will allow fellows to integrate their medical knowledge with the use of traditional and modern techniques for the diagnosis of gastrointestinal and liver disorders. The fellow will become proficient in the use of ancillary studies such as immunohistochemistry and molecular testing. There is a large volume of GI and liver cases including a wide spectrum of medical and neoplastic disease. Additionally, OSUMC treats many patients with pancreatic disease and the fellow will have ample opportunity to evaluate this disease material. The fellowship is also designed to develop investigational skills through ongoing research projects in gastrointestinal pathology as well as expand teaching and presentation skills.

Requirements: Candidates must successfully complete USMLE Step III prior to their Medical Staff appointment to The Ohio State University Medical Center. They must also be AP/CP Board eligible or Board certified.

Stipends: The stipend is commensurate with the number of years of postgraduate training.

Applications: Applications should be sent to Gretchen Staschiak, Pathology Education Manager, The Ohio State University, N-308 Doan Hall, 410 West 10th Ave., Columbus, OH 43210.

Phone: (614) 293-3055 • **Fax:** (614) 293-7273 • **E-mail:** Gretchen.Staschiak@osumc.edu
Web site: http://pathology.osumc.edu/ext

UNIVERSITY OF PENNSYLVANIA MEDICAL CENTER

Department of Pathology

Gastrointestinal and Liver Pathology Fellowship

Description: This one year ACGME accredited program is aimed toward the development of academically oriented surgical pathologists with a subspecialty interest in gastrointestinal and liver pathology. To that end, the first year is devoted to clinical duties including the development of research projects while the second year is fully devoted to research endeavors the choice of which may come from the entire university community. During the first year, the fellow is responsible for the GI and Liver pathology consult service within the section of surgical pathology and numerous conferences involving the departments of medicine, surgery, and radiology. The clinical service encounters a wide variety of cases from the very active liver transplant, inflammatory bowel disease, hepatology, and oncology programs. The diverse and strong academic research environment of the Medical Center serves as rich source from which the fellow may chose a research project to be carried out during the second year. This optional second year devoted to research is possible dependent upon the director and funding options.

Applications: Send inquires and CV to:
Emma E. Furth, MD, Director GI and Liver Pathology Fellowship Program
Associate Director Surgical Pathology
6 Founders
Hospital of the University of Pennsylvania
3400 Spruce St.
Philadelphia, Pa 19104

Phone: (215) 662-6503 • **E-mail:** eef@mail.med.upenn.edu

NEW YORK-PRESBYTERIAN HOSPITAL WEILL CORNELL CAMPUS

GI/Liver Pathology Fellowship

Description: The Department of Pathology and Laboratory Medicine of Weill Cornell Medical Center (WCMC) and Department of Pathology at Memorial Sloan-Kettering Cancer Center (MSKCC) offer a joint 1-year Gastrointestinal Pathology Fellowship Program. The fellowship emphasizes a multidisciplinary team approach to patient management as well as clinicopathologic and translational research. Fellow responsibilities include slide review and preparation of reports for selected in-house and submitted consultation cases, with increasing independence as the fellowship progresses, teaching and supervision of trainees, and participation in conferences and journal clubs. Fellows also participate in research projects under the guidance of the attending faculty or in collaboration with members of other departments, as necessary. The case material at MSKCC is largely related to neoplastic diseases, and is especially rich in hepatic and pancreatic neoplasms. The case material at WCMC covers the full range of gastrointestinal diseases, including a substantial amount of non-neoplastic hepatic pathology. The program is directed by Dr. Rhonda Yantiss (WCMC) and Dr. David Klimstra (MSKCC).

Requirements: All fellows should have completed residency training in anatomic pathology and be certified (or eligible for certification) by the American Board of Pathology.

Types and Numbers of Appointments: The fellows spend 6 months at each institution and two positions are available.

Facilities: New York Presbyterian Hospital is the major clinical affiliate and teaching hospital of Weill Cornell Medical College. Its New York Weill Cornell Campus, an 824-bed facility, is centrally located in a highly sophisticated medical community surrounded by the Hospital for Special Surgery, the Memorial Sloan-Kettering Cancer Center and the Rockefeller University.

Community: The Medical Center is located in a beautiful residential neighborhood along the East River in Manhattan within walking distance of Central Park and the midtown entertainment and shopping areas.The major museums, concert halls and opera house are nearby.

Stipends: Salaries are commensurate with the level of training.

Staff: Debra Beneck MD (WCMC); **Yao-Tseng Chen** MD, PhD (WCMC); **David Klimstra** MD (WCMC); **Jinru Shia** MD (MSKCC); **Laura Tang** MD (MSKCC); **Shu-Yuan Xiao** MD (WCMC); **Rhonda K Yantiss** MD (WCMC).

Applications: Please address inquiries to: Rhonda K. Yantiss, MD c/o Jessica Pfeifer, Administrative Specialist, Department of Pathology and Laboratory Medicine, New York Presbyterian Hospital-Cornell Campus, 525 East 68th Street, New York, NY 10065.

Phone: (212) 746-6464 • **Fax:** (212) 746-8192

UNIVERSITY OF PITTSBURGH MEDICAL CENTER

Gastrointestinal Pathology Fellowship

Description: The Department of Pathology offers an ACGME-accredited one-year fellowship program in Gastrointestinal Pathology. The emphasis of the program is in both clinical diagnostic training and research activities; a second year focused on research may be arranged upon special request. Gastrointestinal Pathology is one of the Centers of Excellence of the Department and handles more than 15,000 GI cases annually. Cutting edge research and training in up-to date technologies is available (gene microarrays, proteomics, tissue arrays, etc.). The GI fellow has access to and has the opportunity to contribute to numerous didactic and clinical conferences. Five gastrointestinal pathologists and additional pathologists with an interest in GI pathology provide clinical service, contribute to the research program of the GI section, and support the GI Pathology Fellowship.

Requirements: Completion of AP or AP/CP residency and all 3 steps of USMLE.

Stipends: Commensurate with the level of postgraduate training in Pathology.

Staff: Alyssa M. Krasinskas MD, Fellowship Director; **Sheldon Bastacky** MD; **Simon Chiosea** MD; **Sanja Dacic** MD, PhD; **Jon Davison** MD; **Douglas Hartman** MD; **Larry Kiss** MD; **Shih-Fan Kuan** MD, PhD; **Sarah Navina** MD; **Scott Owens** MD; **Robert Peel** MD; **Karen Schoedel** MD; **Raja Seethala** MD.

Applications: Submit electronic application at http://path.upmc.edu/fellowship. Send a letter of interest and CV to Alyssa M. Krasinskas MD, Director, Gastrointestinal Pathology Fellowship, Department of Pathology, Room A-610 PUH, 200 Lothrop Street, Pittsburgh, PA 15213.

Phone: (412) 647-3935 • **E-mail:** krasinskasam@upmc.edu

RUSH UNIVERSITY COLLEGE OF MEDICINE

Gastrointestinal Pathology Fellowship

Description: The Department of Pathology at Rush University Medical Center offers a one-year fellowship in gastrointestinal and liver pathology starting July 1, 2008. The program provides in-depth training in diagnostic interpretation of broad spectrum of in-house and consult cases including endoscopic biopsies (>4000 specimens), resected GI specimens (>1000), liver biopsies (>1000) and liver transplants (>100). Close interaction with clinical services, participation in clinical research and clinico-pathological conferences and supervision of grossing is expected. Opportunities for teaching residents and medical students, posting educational material on web-site, virtual microscopy consultation, advanced training in liver transplantation and pediatric gastrointestinal pathology and presenting research studies at national conferences are available. Assistance will be provided for securing specialized GI/Liver pathologists' jobs for qualified candidates.

Requirements: Eligibility: Successful completion of 4-year AP/CP pathology residency program. License:Valid permanent license from the state of Illinois.

Applications: Send CV and 3 letters of recommendation to:
Shriram Jakate, MD, FRCPath
Director, GI/Liver pathology fellowship
Rush University Medical Center
1750 West Harrison St
Chicago, IL 60612

Phone: (312) 942-5227, (312) 942-5260 **Page:** (312) 249-9284
Fax: (312) 942-4228 • **E-mail:** sjakate@rush.edu

THE UNIVERSITY OF TEXAS M.D. ANDERSON CANCER CENTER

Gastrointestinal Pathology Fellowship

Description: The Department of Pathology offers a one-year ACGME accredited fellowship in gastrointestinal and liver pathology. The Department currently accessions over 10,000 gastrointestinal, pancreatic and hepatobiliary cases, including complex surgical resection specimens, mucosal and liver biopsies, and outside referrals and consultation specimens from a wide variety of neoplastic and non-neoplastic conditions. The fellowship is designed to prepare individuals for a career in an academic setting. The fellow will be expected to spend the majority of his/her time performing clinical duties such as surgical signout, and participating in intradepartmental and multidisciplinary conferences. In addition, the fellow is encouraged and expected to participate in clinical or laboratory-based research projects.

Requirements: Candidate must be Board-certified or eligible for certification in Anatomic Pathology or AP/CP

Stipends: Commensurate with the candidate's level of training

Applications: must be submitted using the Discover System, a web based application, at https://www2.mdanderson.org/sapp/discover/. The deadline to submit application is December 31st, eighteen (18) months prior to the intended fellowship year which begins July 1st. Correspondence should be addressed to Asif Rashid, MD PhD, Director, Gastrointestinal and Liver Pathology Fellowship, The University of Texas M.D. Anderson Cancer Center, 1515 Holcombe Blvd., Unit 085, Houston, Texas 77030. For inquiries and to request additional information, please contact Kareen Chin.

Phone: (713) 792-3108 • **Fax:** (713) 745-0789 • **E-mail:** kechin@mdanderson.org
Web site: http://www.mdanderson.org/departments/pathology

UNIVERSITY OF WASHINGTON

Department of Pathology

GI & Hepatic Pathology Fellowship

Description: This ACGME accredited program offers advanced subspecialty training in GI and hepatic pathology. The fellow participates in all activities of the GI pathology service including approx. 1,500 outside consult cases, presentations at hospital-wide clinical conferences, and teaching residents and medical students. Each fellow is expected to complete one or more research projects.

Requirements: Applicants are selected for interview based on academic excellence and interest in the subspecialty. Applicants need to be board eligible for Anatomic Pathology certification by the American Board of Pathology and must be eligible for a Washington State license.

Facilities: The program is based at University of Washington Medical Center. UW Medicine, among the most successful academic medical centers in the US, provides tertiary medical care and medical education to the five-state region of Washington, Wyoming, Alaska, Montana and Idaho.

Stipends: One year appointment with salary and benefits based on the schedule for residents at an equivalent level (R5=$55,032). Fellows are encouraged to apply for extramural funding under the guidance of the attendings, if additional research training is desired. (2 positions)

Staff: M. Upton Director; **S. Dintzis**; **C. Rubin**; **P. Swanson**; **K. Tham**; **M. Yeh**.

Applications: Melissa P. Upton, MD, Fellowship Director, at mupton@u.washington.edu
Available at the web site or contact Michelle Rickard, Academic Programs Manager, GI & Hepatic Pathology Fellowship Program, at the email address below. Application materials must be received by February 1 with selected interviews to follow until the position is filled.

Phone: (206) 598-4933 • **Fax:** (206) 598-7321 • **E-mail:** fellowship@pathology.washington.edu
Web site: www.pathology.washington.edu/academics/fellowship/

The University of Washington is an equal opportunity institution.

WASHINGTON UNIVERSITY MEDICAL CENTER

Liver/Gastrointestinal Pathology Fellowship

Description: The Liver/ Gastrointestinal Pathology Fellowship at Washington University School of Medicine is a one year program aimed at focusing on and training individuals for academic practice. There is the possibility of expansion to 2 years, for research, depending level of interest and funding availability. The Clinical Year takes advantage of the the presence of strong clinical programs in Hepatology, GI, Liver Surgery and Transplant, Colorectal and Hepatobiliary/ Pancreatic Surgery at Washington University. Fellows will participate in patient as well as the monthly to weekly interdisciplinary conferences shared amongst our Departments. By the end of this Clinical Year, the fellow should be comfortable with the evaluation, clinical correlations and future research questions pertaining to a wide variety of specimens related to Liver and Gastrointestinal Diseases. The large referral, quaternary care hospital system associated with Washington University School of Medicine includes Barnes-Jewish Hospital, St. Louis Children's Hospital, and Barnes-Jewish West County Hospital. Additionally, the "outside" referral biopsies for Liver and GI are included. There are over 7500 specimens and 1000 FS specimens for the adult and pediatric L/GI services. The Liver/GI Fellow will also gain experience by participation in rotations covering frozen sections, oversight and specimen handling of the large Gross Room, and the "Hot Seat". Through these services, the Fellow will work with the diagnostic general surgical pathologists of Anatomic and Molecular Pathology to allow the Fellow to continue to build their general pathology clinical acumen, grossing skills and rapid diagnostic abilities from the large variety of surgical pathology material. Specifically oriented for the Liver/GI Fellow will be the referred Liver and GI biopsies, participation in the in-house L/GI sign-outs, participation in Liver Transplant coverage and participation in the weekly and monthly clinico-pathologic conferences involving Hepatology, GI, Hepatobiliary Surgery, Colorectal Surgery and Hepatic Imaging. There are 2 faculty members dedicated to L/GI sign-out for adult material, and 3 for pediatric material. For Fellows in the Clinical Year who are not pursuing further research opportunities, opportunities for clinical research within the Department or in collaboration with clinical colleagues are encouraged. The Department has a supported Research Laboratory that includes standard histochemical and immunohistochemical processing, as well as access to the Molecular Diagnostic Laboratory within the Department, and potentially the core services provided through the Siteman Cancer Center. For Fellows interested in an academically-focused research program, opportunities for discussion are available.

Requirements: Applicants must be able to apply successfully for medical licensure in the state of Missouri.

Applications: Inquires should be addressed to Elizabeth M. Brunt, MD, c/o Mary Madden, Fellowship Coordinator, at the Washington University School of Medicine, 660 South Euclid Avenue, Campus Box 8118, St. Louis, MO 63110.

Phone: (314) 747-0687 • **Fax:** (314) 747-2663

YALE UNIVERSITY SCHOOL OF MEDICINE

Department of Pathology

Gastrointestinal Pathology Fellowship

Description: A one year program combining training in diagnostic gastrointestinal, pancreaticobiliary, and hepatic pathology with clinical research. There is an opportunity to spend additional years in funded research, if arranged. The clinical activities of the Program in Gastrointestinal Pathology include reporting on approximately 10,000 gastrointestinal and pancreatobiliary specimens and over 500 liver biopsies per year. The fellow will take a major role in clinicopathologic conferences and will assist in the training of first and second year residents. Strengths of the program include the dedicated nature of the gastrointestinal pathology service, the strong and diverse clinical gastroenterology and hepatology programs at Yale, and extensive teaching materials within the department. Research may be undertaken as part of active interdepartmental research programs aimed at understanding the pathobiology and improving the diagnosis and management of gastrointestinal diseases. There is a strong and long established interest in diseases of the gastrointestinal tract, liver, biliary tract, and pancreas at Yale, with outstanding research programs in each area.

Requirements: Three years of training in anatomic pathology or four years combined anatomic and clinical pathology.

Stipends: Stipends commensurate with hospital policy.

Applications: Apply to Marie Robert, MD, Director of Program in Gastrointestinal Pathology, Department of Pathology, Yale University School of Medicine, PO Box 208023, New Haven, CT 06520-8023.
Director: Marie E. Robert, MD, Director of Program in Gastrointestinal Pathology

Phone: (203) 785-5486 • **Fax:** (203) 737-1064 • **E-mail:** marie.robert@yale.edu

---

CEDARS-SINAI MEDICAL CENTER

Genitourinary Pathology Fellowship

Description: The Department of Pathology offers a one-year fellowship in genitourinary pathology at Cedars-Sinai Medical Center under the direction of Dr. Mahul Amin. Cedars-Sinai is a 969-bed hospital which houses the Louis Warschaw Prostate Cancer Center and is a large referral center for outreach prostate biopsies. Its Minimally Invasive Urology Institute is a leader in endoscopic and laparoscopic management of neoplasms and medical diseases of the genitourinary tract. The case material is further enhanced by Dr. Amin's extramural consultation practice. The fellow will be provided with comprehensive training in diagnostic genitourinary pathology and given graduated responsibility for signing out cases including consultation cases. The fellow is expected to become involved in ongoing clinical and, depending on career interests, in basic science research in the Departments of Pathology and Urology, including initiation and completion of at least one research project during the course of the year. Available diagnostic and research techniques include immunohistochemistry, in situ hybridization and other contemporary molecular techniques. The fellow also will participate in the integrated urologic conferences and education of pathology and urology residents.

Requirements: Board eligibility in anatomic patholgy. Must have California medical license at the time of appointment.

Stipends: Commensurate with applicant's previous pathology training and experience.

Staff: Mahul B Amin MD; **Daniel J Luthringer** MD; **Sijian Wang** MD.

Applications: For an application, information and correspondence, contact the program coordinator: LeeTanya Marion-Murray, Department of Pathology, Cedars-Sinai Medical Center, 8700 Beverly Blvd., S. Tower Room 8709, Los Angeles, CA 90048

Phone: (310) 423-6941 • **Fax:** (310) 423-5881 • **E-mail:** marionl@cshs.org

JOHNS HOPKINS MEDICAL INSTITUTIONS

Urologic Pathology Fellowship

Description: A one-year ACGME program combining diagnostic urologic pathology with research. The fellow will be under the supervision of Dr Jonathan I. Epstein. The material comprises radical prostatectomy specimens, teaching sets covering the entire spectrum of urologic pathology, and a heavy personal consultation service. Approximately 60 consults are received every day. Consults are split between three urological pathology fellows and senior residents in pathology. Fellows will also participate in several multidisciplinary urologic conferences and in Urological Pathology Journal Club. A major role of the fellow will be participating in various and diverse research projects in genitourinary pathology. The fellow will attend at least one national meeting per year to present research.

Requirements: Minimum of three years of AP training or four years of AP/CP training.

Stipends: Commensurate with the number of years of relevant postgraduate training and experience.

Applications: For all details, write or call
Jonathan I. Epstein, MD, Department of Pathology, The Johns Hopkins Hospital, Weinberg Building, 2nd floor, Room 2242, 401 N Broadway, Baltimore, MD 21231.

Phone: (410) 955-5043
Web site: http://pathology.jhu.edu

The Johns Hopkins University does not discriminate on the basis of race, color, sex, religion, national or ethnic origin, age, handicapped or veterans status in any student program or activity administered by the University or with regard to admission or employment.

McGAW MEDICAL CENTER OF NORTHWESTERN UNIVERSITY

Genitourinary Pathology

Description: Applications are invited for a 1 year Genitourinary Pathology fellowship starting July 1, 2011 in the Department of Pathology at Northwestern University's Feinberg School of Medicine, Chicago, IL. Northwestern Memorial Hospital (McGaw Medical Center), situated in the magnificent downtown Chicago, is one of the premier referral medical centers in the Midwest for patients with urologic diseases with 17 full-time urologists. More than 4,000 GU cases are evaluated in Surgical Pathology annually. The fellowship is designed to provide comprehensive training in diagnostic GU pathology including standard diagnostic practices. The fellow will learn specialized techniques such as immunohistochemistry, molecular diagnostics, in situ hybridization, tissue-microarrays, cDNA microarrays and flow cytometry. The candidate is expected to participate in the diagnosis of GU specimens from a wide range of benign and malignant urologic conditions and inter-departmental clinical conferences. In addition, ample opportunities exist for scholarly collaborations in all areas of GU pathology including collaborations with investigators from Robert H. Lurie Comprehensive Cancer Center at Northwestern.

Requirements: Candidates must be board eligible or certified in anatomic pathology.

Stipends: The stipend is determined by previous pathology training and experience.

Applications: For inquiries and requests for applications contact the program coordinator: Irene Galace at i-galace@n-orthwestern.edu Address correspondence and references to: Ximing J. Yang, MD, PhD, Professor of Pathology and Chief of Urologic Pathology
Feinberg 7-338, Surgical Pathology, Northwestern Memorial Hospital
Northwestern University Feinberg School of Medicine
251 E. Huron Street, Chicago, IL 60611

Phone: (312) 926-3213 • **E-mail:** xyang@northwestern.edu
We encourage early applications.

UNIVERSITY OF MICHIGAN MEDICAL CENTER

Genitourinary Pathology Fellowship

Description: The Departments of Pathology and Urology, offer a one-year fellowship in genitourinary surgical pathology with emphasis on diagnostic uropathology. This program has both strong clinical and research components. The fellow will act as the primary consultant for the genitourinary pathology service, which handles a wide variety of biopsies and resection specimens. The University of Michigan has a federally funded Specialized Program of Research Excellence (SPORE) in prostate cancer. The fellow is expected to pursue research projects in addition to ongoing clinical and teaching activities.

Requirements: Applicants must be board-certified or eligible in anatomic and/or clinical pathology. J-1 visa candidates are not eligible for this position. Candidates interested in an academic career are strongly encouraged to apply.
Applications must include:
1) curriculum vitae with bibliography and minimum 2 references
2) letter expressing interest in the fellowship

Stipends: Support is commensurate with the candidate's level of training.

Applications: Applications must by received by January 1 for fellowships beginning July 1 of the following year.
Submit the above documents to:
Rajal B. Shah, MD / L. Priya Kunju, MD
Department of Pathology
2G332 UH/1500 East Medical Center Drive
Ann Arbor, Michigan 48109-5054

Phone: (734) 647-9125 • **E-mail:** rajshah@med.umich.edu

NEW YORK-PRESBYTERIAN HOSPITAL
WEILL CORNELL CAMPUS

Genitourinary Pathology Fellowship

Description: The New York Presbyterian Hospital-Weill Cornell Campus offers a one year fellowship in urological pathology. This fellowship will provide the trainees with exposure to a very active clinical urological service. The Department in 2008 accessioned 3,035 cases, resulting in 8,950 parts including a wide variety of benign and malignant lesions of the prostate, bladder, kidney, testis and other urological organs. The fellowship is designed to prepare individuals for a career in an academic setting. The fellow will be expected to spend a significant amount of time performing clinical duties such as surgical sign out, supervising the activities of junior residents on service, and participating in intradepartmental and multidisciplinary conferences. The fellow will also have the opportunity to review a large teaching set including more than 1,000 selected cases of the entire GU system. In addition, the fellow will participate in clinical and translational research activities and gain experience in the use of traditional and modern techniques for clinical diagnosis and scientific inquiry.
Requirements: 3 years of anatomic pathology, or board eligibility/certification in anatomic and clinical pathology.
Types and Numbers of Appointments: There is one position available.
Facilities: New York Presbyterian Hospital is the major clinical affiliate and teaching hospital of Weill Cornell Medical College. It's New York Weill Cornell Campus, is an 824-bed facility and is centrally located in a highly sophisticated medical community surrounded by the Hospital for Special Surgery, Memorial Sloan Kettering Cancer Center and Rockefeller University.
Community: The Medical Center is located in a beautiful residential neighborhood along the East River in Manhattan within walking distance of Central Park and the midtown entertainment and shopping areas. The major museums, concert halls and opera houses are close by.
Stipends: Commensurate with level of training.
Staff: Mohammad Akhtar MD; **Mark Rubin** MD; **Maria Shevchuk** MD.
Applications: Please address inquiries to: Mark Rubin,MD, c/o Jessica Pfeifer, Administrative Specialist, Department of Pathology and Laboratory Medicine, New York Presbyterian Hospital-Cornell Campus, 525 East 68th Street, New York, NY 10065.
Phone: (212) 746-6464 • **Fax:** (212) 746-8192

UNIVERSITY OF PITTSBURGH MEDICAL CENTER

Genitourinary Pathology Fellowship

Description: This 1-to 2-year fellowship prepares trainees to function independently as academic genitourinary (GU) surgical pathologists. It provides a large case volume, junior staff responsibilities, and clinical/ basic science research opportunities. Primary responsibility is for patient material derived from urologic oncology with an emphasis on prostate disease, bladder neoplasia, inflammatory urothelial disease, kidney tumors, neo-adjuvant therapy of GU malignancies and materials derived from cystoscopic and GU surgical services. The clinical service also provides exposure to new developing molecular techniques. We have recently implemented UroVysion molecular testing for urine surveillance of patients with Urothelial carcinoma. In addition molecular Fluorescence in-situ hybridization (FISH) studies are now routinely performed to help in the exact classification of renal epithelial neoplasms. The fellow learns immunofluorescence and electron microscopy as part of the medical renal biopsy pathology service (750 cases per year). The fellow coordinates the weekly GU multidisciplinary conference with the Division of Urology and is responsible for all GU consultation cases and prepares and maintains a GU teaching collection. The trainee will collaborate in research studies and present the research to at least one national meeting each year. Training opportunities include (1) helping maintain an institutional and national prostate tissue bank (2) gene chip array based molecular classification of tumors and various molecular and cell biological techniques (3) Paraffin Tissue Arrays (4) epithelial cell culture techniques and (5) Immunohistochemistry and quantitative image analysis and morphometry. Additional years of training may be arranged. *Annual Volume:* 5,000 GU surgicals, biopsies and consults from a network of hospitals in Western Pennsylvania.

Requirements: Three years experience in Anatomic Pathology.

Stipends: Commensurate with the level of postgraduate training in Pathology.

Staff: Rajiv Dhir MD, Fellowship Director; **Sheldon Bastacky** MD; **Walid Khalbuss** MD; **Lawrence Kiss** MD; **William LaFramboise** PhD; **Anil Parwani** MD, PhD.

Applications: Rajiv Dhir, MD, Associate Professor of Pathology, Department of Pathology, 5230 Center Avenue, Pittsburgh, PA 15213.

E-mail: dhirr@upmc.edu

For more information, please contact Eileen Misencik.

Phone: (412) 623-3002 • **Fax:** (412) 682-6450 • **E-mail:** misencikev@upmc.edu

Web site: http://path.upmc.edu/fellowship

UNIVERSITY OF ROCHESTER MEDICAL CENTER

Genitourinary Pathology Fellowship

Description: This is a one-year genitourinary pathology fellowship under the supervision of P. Anthony di Sant'Agnese MD and is divided into three primary activities: clinically oriented work, clinical/pathologic research, and teaching/ conference presentations. The fellow is actively involved in supervising gross specimen examination, sign-out of cases and review of consultation cases with an emphasis on genitourinary specimens. Research includes the construction/ use of tissue microarrays, immunohistochemical methods and other molecular techniques for clinical and translational research. Basic bench research is also encouraged. The fellow is expected to successfully complete at least one research project during the course of the year, and encouraged to present at a national meeting. The Urology and Pathology departments have a wide range of clinical and basic research activities with particular strengths in prostate and bladder cancer research. Many of the projects are collaborations between the two departments including the investigation of neuroendocrine differentiation in androgen independent prostate cancer, the focus of research being performed by the co-directors of the fellowship.

Requirements: Minimum of three years AP training or four years of AP/CP training. A New York State medical license is not required but will be necessary for sign out privileges.

Facilities: The University of Rochester Medical Center is a regional referral center with a strong Urology Department. The Department of Pathology accessions over 45,000 surgical cases a year with a significant number of complex and unusual genitourinary specimens.

Community: Picture a city with miles of lakeshore, a central-city riverfront sprinkled with waterfalls, and a historic canal that flows through the heart of the small-town Americana. Now imagine that same city surrounded by glacier-carved lakes, one of the largest collections of cobblestone homes in the country, and world-class wine country. Welcome to the Rochester/Finger Lakes Region of Upstate New York. Monroe County, named after James Monroe, fifth president of the United States, is comprised of 19 towns, 10 villages and the City of Rochester, the third largest city in the state, with a combined population of approximately 750,000 residents and a land area of nearly 664 square miles. Monroe County has been a world leader in imaging technology. Today, we're not only on the cutting edge of imaging, but biotechnology, telecommunications, optics, photonics, and much more. We rank among the top three communities in the nation in the number of patents granted per capita. Monroe County and the City of Rochester are home to the University of Rochester, the county's largest employer, and Rochester Institute of Technology, two of the finest research institutions in the nation. We boast 39 golf courses, an extensive park system covering nearly 12,000 acres of land, and fresh water activities such as boating, fishing & swimming. Our sporting community includes professional baseball, hockey, lacrosse and soccer teams.

Stipends: Commensurate to the number of relevant postgraduate years of training and experience. A fund for travel expenses to present research projects at national meetings is available.

Staff: **P. Anthony di Sant'Agnese** MD (Columbia University); research interests include investigation of prostatic neuroendocrine cell and neuroendocrine differentiation in prostatic carcinoma.; **Hiroshi Miyamoto** MD (Yokohama Shiritsu Daigaku Igakubu, Japan) PhD (Yokohama City Univ Sch of Medicine) Asst Prof Pathology & Lab Medicine; research: genitourinary carcinomas; **Jorge Yao** MD (Univ of the East Ramon Magsaysay Memorial Medical Center); research interests include role of neuroendocrine cells in benign and neoplastic prostate, pathogenesis and characterization of small cell carcinoma of the prostate, and construction and use of tissue microarrays.

Applications: Send curriculum vitae, personal statement, a letter from your current residency program director and three letters of recommendation to Betsy McDonald, University of Rochester Medical Center, Pathology & Laboratory Medicine at 601 Elmwood Ave Box 626, Rochester NY 14642.

Web site: http://www.urmc.rochester.edu/pathology_lab_medicine/

THE UNIVERSITY OF TEXAS M.D. ANDERSON CANCER CENTER

Genitourinary Pathology Fellowship

Description: The Department of Pathology offers a one-year ACGME accredited fellowship in Genitourinary Pathology. The fellowship is designed to provide comprehensive training in diagnostic Genitourinary Pathology with emphasis in the multidisciplinary team approach to the treatment of GU malignancies and opportunities in clinical, translational and basic research. The fellow will participate in the diagnostic sign-out of biopsies, surgical specimens, referral and consultation cases with the faculty members of the Genitourinary Pathology Section. In addition, the fellow will have the opportunity to work with complex GU specimens, and participate in the evaluation of intraoperative frozen section consultations. Research opportunities in addition to clinical research include participation in all levels of translational research including ongoing clinical trials and basic research. The fellow is expected to complete one clinical/translational/basic research project during the fellowship.

Requirements: Candidates must be Board-certified or Board-eligible for certification in Anatomic or AP/CP Pathology.

Stipends: Commensurate with level of training

Applications: must be submitted using the Discover System, a web based application, at https://www2.mdanderson.org/sapp/discover/. The deadline to submit application is December 31st, Eighteen (18) months prior to the intended fellowship year which begins July 1st. Correspondence should be addressed to Patricia Troncoso, MD, Director, Genitourinary Pathology Fellowship, The University of Texas M.D. Anderson Cancer Center, 1515 Holcombe Blvd., Unit 085, Houston, Texas 77030. For inquiries and to request additional information, please contact Kareen Chin.

Phone: (713) 792-3108 • **Fax:** (713) 745-0789 • **E-mail:** kechin@mdanderson.org

Web site: http://www.mdanderson.org/departments/pathology

BROWN UNIVERSITY WOMEN AND INFANTS HOSPITAL

Stuart C. Lauchlan Fellowship in Gynecologic Pathology, Cytology & Breast Pathology

Description: A two-year program in diagnostic gynecologic pathology, breast pathology and gynecologic cytopathology with time devoted to research. The resources available include a case load of 22,000 surgical specimens a year, upwards of 100,000 cytology accessions and 1100 consultation cases. Research facilities include space in a number of active research laboratories, and include flow cytometry, molecular, endocrine and genetic facilities. Active participation in weekly prospective multidisciplinary gynecologic and breast tumor boards, telemedicine and gynecologic oncologic pathology conference further enhances training. The fellow participates in teaching of pathology residents and medical students at the Warren Alpert Medical School of Brown University.

Requirements: Candidates must have an MD degree or equivalent, and should have at least three years of training in an approved pathology residency in the US.

Stipends: Stipend is communsurate with year of postgraduate training.

Staff: Katrine Hansen MD; **John Kasznica** MD; **Geralyn Lambert-Messerlian** PhD; **W. Dwayne Lawrence** MD; **Michele M. Lomme** MD; **Latha Pisharodi** MD; **M. Ruhul Quddus** MD; **Margaret M. Steinhoff** MD; **C. James Sung** MD; **Uma Tantravahi** PhD; **JinJun Xiong** MD; **Cunxian Zhang** MD, PhD.

Applications: For entry in July 2011, send a CAP Standardized Application for Pathology Fellowships, curriculum vitae, a personal statement, USMLE Steps 1, 2, & 3 scores, visa status and three letters of recommendation to: C. James Sung, MD, Department of Pathology, Women and Infants Hospital, 101 Dudley Street, Providence, RI 02905-2499. For inquiry contact Fellowship Coordinator Susan Healey.

E-mail: shealey@wihri.org

BRIGHAM AND WOMEN'S HOSPITAL

Gynecologic, Obstetric & Perinatal Pathology Fellowship

Description: Advanced training in gynecologic, obstetrical and perinatal pathology is offered in the Women's and Perinatal Pathology Division. Included in the ACGME-approved program is intensive training in the pathology of benign and neoplastic gynecologic diseases, trophoblastic neoplasia, teratology, obstetrical complications, and placental diseases. Additional elective time in breast pathology, cytogenetics, laboratory research and image analysis may be available. Fellows are expected to participate in clinical, translational and/or basic research, and teaching.

The Division accessions over 16,500 surgical specimens, consultations and HPV tests, and 50 perinatal autopsies annually; 400 new cases of female genital tract malignancy are diagnosed each year. Consultation is readily available from experts in all subspecialties in pathology. Brigham and Women's Hospital (BWH) is a 698 bed tertiary care hospital (including 105 obstetric beds) with comprehensive women's health services that also provides pathology services for the Dana Farber Cancer Institute.

The clinical training program is a one year commitment, however, qualified career-minded candidates may be eligible for additional training in the division's gynecologic cancer research laboratory and elsewhere, including Brigham and Women's Hospital, Harvard Medical School (HMS), The Dana Farber Cancer Institute (DFCI), Whitehead Institute and Massachusetts Institute of Technology. Individuals seeking this pathway will maintain their relationship with the division, combining laboratory research and diagnostic responsibilities. Collaborating investigators include Drs. George Mutter (endometrial carcinogenesis), Christopher Crum (early cervical neoplasia and pelvic serous carcinogenesis); Bradley Quade (molecular genetics of smooth muscle tumors), Daniela Dinulescu (animal models of ovarian cancer); Tan Ince (cell culture models of gynecologic neoplasia); Jonathan Fletcher (molecular genetics of neoplasia); Ronny Drapkin (DFCI; ovarian carcinogenesis); Peter Howley (HMS; cervical carcinogenesis); Frank McKeon (HMS; p63 and development), and others.

Requirements: Applicants must have satisfactorily completed residency training in anatomic pathology and have specific interests in gynecologic and obstetric pathology. Applicants interested in a career in academic medicine are preferred.

Stipends: Depend on previous training.

Staff: **Christopher P. Crum** Professor, Harvard Medical School, and Director; **Frederick R. Bieber**; **Daniela Dinulescu**; **Ronny I. Drapkin**; **Michelle S. Hirsch** Associate Director, Women's & Perinatal Fellowship Program; **Tan A. Ince**; **David Kindelberger**; **Kenneth R. Lee**; **George L. Mutter** Director, Gynecologic Cancer Research Laboratory; **Marisa R. Nucci**; **Bradley J. Quade**; **William R. Welch**; **Theonia Boyd** (Consultant); **Robert Padera** (Consultant).

Applications: Application and inquiries should be sent to Michelle S. Hirsch, MD, PhD, Associate Director, Women's and Perinatal Fellowship Training Program, Brigham and Women's Hospital, 75 Francis Street, Boston, MA 02115.
Phone: (617) 525-7256 • **Fax:** (617) 277-9015 • **E-mail:** mhirsch1@partners.org
Web site: http://www.obgynpath.org

JOHNS HOPKINS MEDICAL INSTITUTIONS

Gynecologic Pathology Fellowship

Description: The program is ideal for individuals pursuing academic careers in surgical pathology and/or gynecologic pathology but is not restricted to such individuals. It is designed to be a combination of a fellowship and a junior faculty assistant position of two years duration. Variations of the program are possible, ranging from a single fellowship year to two full years as a faculty assistant. The program combines advanced training in diagnostic gynecologic pathology with clinical/translational/basic research and teaching. Clinical responsibilities: sign-out of in-house material and evaluation of consultation cases. Research: the fellows are engaged in research activities, which include clinicopathologic and immunohistochemical studies as well as basic and translational research. Current staff research interests: cervical, endometrial, and ovarian neoplasia; trophoblastic disease; HPV; and tumor genetics. Teaching: supervision and instruction of residents; presentation of cases at the gynecologic oncology tumor board, colposcopy correlation conference, and reproductive endocrinology and infertility conference.

Requirements: Minimum of two full years AP (three years preferred). Fellows must be able to obtain a Maryland license prior to starting the second year of the fellowship program. Only U.S. Nationals and Foreign Nationals with a permanent resident visa will be considered. The applicant must have passed USMLE Step 3 prior to our review of the application.

Stipends: At prevailing level for clinical fellows in the SOM according to relevant experience.

Applications: For full details, write or call: Dr. Russell Vang, Associate Professor of Pathology, The Johns Hopkins Hospital, Department of Pathology, Weinberg Building, Room 2242, 401 N Broadway, Baltimore, MD 21231. A cover letter, application form, CV, and three letters of recommendation should be received before April 1 of the calendar year prior to a July 1 starting date (i.e., 15 months in advance). Selections will be made by July 1 of the year preceding the start of the fellowship program.

Phone: (443) 287-4996

Web site: http://pathology.jhu.edu/gynecologic/index.cfm

The Johns Hopkins University is an EOE.

NEW YORK UNIVERSITY MEDICAL CENTER

Gynecologic and Obstetrical Pathology Fellowship

Description: The one-year fellowship provides an intensive experience in diagnostic Gynecologic and Obstetric pathology. The fellowship is based at Bellevue Hospital in New York, which accessions approximately 10,000 Ob-Gyn cases per year. The nature and variety of the case material is outstanding, as it comes from a variety of sources, including Tisch Hospital, Gouvernier Hospital, out patient clinics, and Bellevue Hospital. Bellevue Hospital is part of New York University Hospitals Center, which is a tertiary care medical center with an active Cancer Center. The Fellow works as an attending in training: supervising junior residents, reviewing consult cases, presenting at conferences, grossing, participating in studies, and teaching residents and medical students. The hospital is located in mid-Manhattan, which is a vibrant part of the city by the East River, with many ethnic restaurants in close vicinity.

Requirements: At least two years of training in Anatomic Pathology. USMLE III, and NY State license by the start date.

Stipends: Commensurate with candidate's level of training.

Applications: Send your CV, including USMLE I, II, and III scores, with a cover letter, preferably via e-mail, to Khush Mittal, MD, Director of Obstetric-Gynecologic Pathology, 4W1, 462 First Avenue, New York, NY 10016.

Fax: (212) 263-2041 • **E-mail:** khush.mittal@med.nyu.edu

Have two letters of recommendation sent separately.

UNIVERSITY OF PITTSBURGH MEDICAL CENTER AND MAGEE-WOMENS HOSPITAL

Gynecologic & Breast Pathology Fellowship

Description: Three positions are offered in this ACGME-approved fellowship for gynecologic and breast pathology. There is some exposure to perinatal/obstetrical surgical pathology. Fellows rotate on surgical benches devoted to breast and gynecologic specimens as well as cytology, cytogenetics, and molecular pathology. Magee-Womens Hospital is the Center of Excellence for women's health in the UPMC health system. The surgical load is 27,000 and the cytology load is 110,000. State of the art resources are available system-wide for academic pursuits.

Requirements: MD degree or equivalent plus not less than 4 years of approved training in pathology, a Pennsylvania medical license, and for foreign medical graduates appropriate visa and certification (ECFMG, etc).

Stipends: Stipend and benefits are competitive with other training programs for 4th-6th year training.

Staff: David Dabbs MD, Fellowship Director; **R. Marshall Austin** MD, PhD; **Rohit Bhargava** MD; **Gloria Carter** MD; **Mamatha Chivukula** MD; **Esther Elishaev** MD; **Jeff Fine** MD; **Mirka Jones** MD; **Anisa Kanbour** MD; **Amal Kanbour-Shakir** MD, PhD; **Trevor Macpherson** MD; **Olga Navolotskaia** MD; **W. Tony Parks** MD; **Giuliana Trucco** MD; **Jing Yu** MD, PhD; **Chengquan Zhao** MD.

Applications: Submit application online, preferably before September 1st of the year preceding the July 1st fellowship, to: David Dabbs, MD, Magee-Womens Hospital, 300 Halket St, Pittsburgh, PA 15213.

Web site: http://path.upmc.edu/fellowship/app-form.htm

THE UNIVERSITY OF TEXAS M.D. ANDERSON CANCER CENTER

Gynecologic Oncology Pathology Fellowship

Description: The one-year Gynecologic Oncology Pathology fellowship program is accredited by ACGME. The fellowship offers a combined diagnostic training and research opportunities in Gynecologic Pathology with an Oncologic emphasis. The department of Gynecologic Oncology at The University of Texas M.D. Anderson Cancer Center has always ranked among one of the first three institutions in the management of gynecologic cancer. The department is responsible for approximately 4,500 cases per year, which include 1,500 outside referrals, 1,500 biopsies, 750 outside consultations and 750 in-house surgical cases. Clinical responsibilities include daily sign-out sessions with the gynecologic pathology staff. The sign-out sessions alternate between the inside service, such as frozen section, biopsies and surgical cases; and the outside service, which include referral and consultation cases. The fellow participates with the staff in the preparation of cases to be discussed in the Gynecologic Oncology Planning Clinic and in the quality assurance program. A one-month rotation in the Cytopathology Section is mandatory. Research opportunities are numerous and range from clinicopathologic studies to basic research projects in molecular pathology.

Requirements: Candidates must be Board-certified or eligible for certification in Anatomic Pathology or AP/CP.

Stipends: Commensurate with the candidate's level of training.

Applications: must be submitted using the Discover System, a web based application, at https://www2.mdanderson.org/sapp/discover/. The deadline to submit application is December 31st, eighteen (18) months prior to the intended fellowship year which begins July 1st. Correspondence should be addressed to Anais Malpica, M.D. Director, Gynecologic Oncology Pathology Fellowship, The University of Texas M.D. Anderson Cancer Center, 1515 Holcombe Blvd., Unit 085, Houston, Texas 77030. For inquiries and to request additional information, please contact Kareen Chin.

Phone: (713) 792-3108 • **Fax:** (713) 745-0789 • **E-mail:** kechin@mdanderson.org

Web site: http://www.mdanderson.org/departments/pathology

UNIVERSITY OF VIRGINIA SCHOOL OF MEDICINE

Gynecologic Pathology Fellowship

Description: This post-residency fellowship emphasizes gynecologic pathology in the context of general surgical pathology. This one year experience will provide in depth exposure to consultation, referral and routine diagnostic material. In addition, the fellow will actively participate in clinical conferences, teach residents and be expected to participate in ongoing translational research utilizing the outstanding faculty and resources of the University of Virginia.

Requirements: Applicants should be Board-certified or Board-eligible in AP or AP/CP.

Types and Numbers of Appointments: One position per year.

Facilities: The Department of Pathology provides an extensive training resource based on annual accessions (including extramural consultations) of over 31,000 surgicals and over 30,000 cytologies, including approximately 1,200 fine needle aspirations. More than 5000 surgical specimens are in the area of gynecologic pathology. Excellent intradepartmental laboratories including immunohistochemistry, molecular biology, tissue procurment and others provide all the necessary support for research productivity.

Stipends: Commensurate with the applicant's postgraduate training in pathology.

Applications: Complete applications (cover letter, curriculum vitae, three letters of recommendation) should be received by May 1 of the prior year and addressed to: Mark H. Stoler, MD, Professor, Associate Director of Surgical Pathology and Cytopathology, Department of Pathology, P.O. Box 800214, University of Virginia Health System, Charlottesville, VA 22908.

Phone: (434) 982-0284 • **Fax:** (434) 924-9492 • **E-mail:** mhs2e@virginia.edu

---

YALE UNIVERSITY SCHOOL OF MEDICINE

Gynecological Pathology Fellowship

Description: A one- or two-year program combining training in diagnostic gynecologic and breast pathology with potential for training in translational research. The fellow will have a primary commitment to an active clinical service, with opportunities to conduct translational research in gynecologic and breast pathology. The fellowship benefits from the outstanding quality and variety of approximately 15,000 gynecologic and breast surgical specimens at Yale-New Haven Hospital, supplemented by a wide range of lesions reviewed in consultation. The fellow will take a major role in tumor board conferences and will assist in the training of first and second year residents during their rotation in gynecologic pathology. Fellows are expected to conduct research projects aimed at understanding the pathobiology and improving the diagnosis and management of gynecologic diseases under the supervision of senior faculty.

Requirements: Three years of training in anatomic pathology or four years combined anatomic and clinical pathology.

Stipends: Commensurate with hospital policy.

Applications: Apply to F. A. Tavassoli, MD, Professor of Pathology/Obstetrics & Gynecology. Director of Women's Health Program/Gynecologic and Breast Pathology, Yale University School of Medicine, Department of Pathology, P.O. Box 208023, New Haven, CT 06520-8070

Phone: (203) 785-5439 • **Fax:** (203) 737-2470 • **E-mail:** fattaneh.tavassoli@yale.edu

UNIVERSITY OF PITTSBURGH MEDICAL CENTER

Head and Neck Pathology Fellowship

Description: One-year intensive training in head and neck pathology, with three months of elective rotations in other specialized areas of pathology (oral pathology, molecular diagnostics, cytopathology, etc.). A research project leading to publication in a peer-reviewed journal is expected.

Requirements: Completion of an accredited three or four-year program in Anatomic Pathology or combined Anatomic-Clinical Pathology program.

Stipends: Commensurate with the level of postgraduate training in Pathology.

Staff: E. Leon Barnes MD, Fellowship Director; **Simion Chiosea** MD; **Robert Peel** MD; **Raja Seethala** MD.

Applications: Submit application online at http://path.upmc.edu/fellowship Current curriculum vitae and three letters of recommendation should be forwarded 12 months in advance of starting date (July 1 of each year) to Leon Barnes, MD, Department of Pathology, A-608 UPMC Presbyterian, 200 Lothrop Street, Pittsburgh, PA 15213.

Phone: (412) 647-3732 • **Fax:** (412) 647-6251 • **E-mail:** barnesel@upmc.edu

---

THE UNIVERSITY OF TEXAS M.D. ANDERSON CANCER CENTER

Head and Neck Pathology Fellowship

Description: The one-year ACGME accredited fellowship offers an advanced training in oncologic head and neck pathology at The University of Texas M.D. Anderson Cancer Center, and is accredited by the ACGME. The Section receives approximately 4,500 new cases per year including general and personal consultations. Additional rotations at the UT-Dental Branch and The Methodist Hospital are required for training in non-oncologic and odontogenic lesions. Clinical responsibilities include handling, reviewing and pathologic evaluations of complex surgical resection specimens and frozen section practice. Fellows will also be responsible for preparing and presenting head and neck pathology, clinical and planning conferences. Attendance, participation and preparation of multidisciplinary planning clinic, and journal clubs are integral component of the training. Emphasis will be placed on integrating, pathology, molecular and biomarkers in head and neck tumors. Training of an extensive collection of salivary, mucosal and rare tumors of the head and neck regions are available. Fellows will be assigned a research project with a faculty member typically of translational nature and will be required to submit a written manuscript. At the completion of the program, fellows are expected to master gross, intra-operative and surgical pathology diagnostic interpretation of both rare and common entities in head and neck pathology and be familiar with the most up-to-date parameters for pathology reporting including prognostic factors and special studies.

Requirements: Candidates must be Board-certified or eligible for certification in A natomic Pathology or AP/CP

Stipends: Commensurate with level of training

Applications: must be submitted using the Discover System, a web based application, at https://www2.mdanderson.org/sapp/discover/. The deadline to submit application is December 31st, eighteen (18) months prior to the intended fellowship year which begins July 1st. Correspondence should be addressed to Adel El-Naggar, MD PhD, Director, Head and Neck Pathology Fellowship, The University of Texas M.D. Anderson Cancer Center, 1515 Holcombe Blvd., Unit 085, Houston, Texas 77030. For inquiries and to request additional information, please contact Kareen Chin.

Phone: (713) 792-3108 • **Fax:** (713) 745-0789 • **E-mail:** kechin@mdanderson.org

Web site: http://www.mdanderson.org/departments/pathology

FOX CHASE CANCER CENTER AND THOMAS JEFFERSON UNIVERSITY

Oncologic Surgical Pathology Fellowship

Description: The Department of Pathology offers three one-year fellowships in oncologic surgical pathology at our 100-bed NCI-designated multidisciplinary comprehensive cancer center. Fox Chase processes over 13,000 surgical, 2,500 frozen sections, and 4,000 non-gyn cytology specimens a year, all of which are cancer or cancer-related. There is extensive material in pulmonary, head and neck, gastrointestinal, urologic, gynecologic, breast and hematolymphoid tumors. The faculty includes six surgical pathologists, two hematopathologists, a dermatopathologist, three cytopathologists, one molecular pathologist and one cytogeneticist, who have active consultation services. Ample time for scholarly activities is facilitated by two full time pathologists' assistants whose gross room activities include frozen section preparation. The department has an affiliation with Thomas Jefferson University; a 600-bed medical school hospital with over 20,000 surgical specimens, 26,000 gyn cytology and 8,000 non-gyn cytology specimens, and a month-long rotation at this hospital is available.

Requirements: Applicants must have completed at least two years of anatomic pathology and be eligible for a Pennsylvania medical license.

Stipends: Commensurate with level of training plus excellent benefits.

Staff: Tahseen Al-Saleem MD; **Harry S. Cooper** MD; **Hormoz Ehya** MD; **Douglas B. Flieder** MD; **Andrew Godwin** PhD; **Karen S. Gustafson** MD, PhD; **Min Huang** MD, PhD; **Andres Klein-Szanto** MD; **Arthur S. Patchefsky** MD; **Valentin G. Robu** MD, PhD; **Joseph Testa** PhD; **Hong Wu** MD, PhD.

Applications: Write to: Douglas B. Flieder, MD, Chief of Surgical Pathology and Fellowship Director, Department of Pathology, Fox Chase Cancer Center, 333 Cottman Avenue, Philadelphia, Pennsylvania 19111.

Phone: (215) 728-4092. • **E-mail:** Douglas.Flieder@fccc.edu.

Web site: http://www.fccc.edu/medical/fellowships/pathology.html.

H. LEE MOFFITT CANCER CENTER AT THE UNIVERSITY OF SOUTH FLORIDA

Oncologic Surgical Pathology Fellowship

Description: The Department of Pathology and Laboratory Medicine at the University of South Florida offers two one-year fellowships in oncologic surgical pathology at the NIH-designated H. Lee Moffitt Cancer Center and Research Institute beginning July 1. The Department accessions approximately 19,250 (11,200 in-house and 8,050 reviews) surgical pathology cases and 8,700 frozen sections. Along with 8,050 cytology specimens including, 1,780 FNAs and approximately 720 cytological consultations annually. A broad range of specialties is represented with emphasis on breast, genitourinary, gastrointestinal, pulmonary, gynecologic, head and neck, and soft tissue pathology. The fellow will have supervised signout responsibilities and will be involved in multidisciplinary conferences. Experience in special techniques and opportunities for focused clinical research are provided.

Requirements: At least three years of AP or four years of AP/CP training.

Stipends: Commensurate with level of postgraduate training.

Applications: Must be completed by November 30th of the year preceding the intended fellowship which begin in July. Request application at sbeacham@health.usf.edu or snicosia@hsc.usf.edu.

Director: Ardeshir Hakam, MD, Director of Oncological Surgical Pathology Fellowship, H. Lee Moffitt Cancer Center & Research Institute and the University of South Florida.

THE UNIVERSITY OF TEXAS M.D. ANDERSON CANCER CENTER

Cancer Biomarker Pathology Fellowship Oncologic Surgical Pathology

Description: The Department of Pathology offers a one-year fellowship in Cancer Biomarker Pathology.

The goal of the Cancer Biomarker Pathology training program is to provide fellows with expertise in integrating traditional microscopic diagnostic skills with technical skills required for the discovery and validation of clinically useful pathology biomarkers for cancer patients. The program will also adequately prepare pathology trainees for a successful career in academic medicine.

The Cancer Biomarker Pathology fellow will identify a specific cancer type for more detailed study and an appropriate Program faculty supervisor. The fellow will participate in traditional microscopic sign-out of cases in this sub-specialty field. Available sub-specialties at MDACC include GI Pathology, GU Pathology, Gynecologic Pathology, Breast Pathology, Neuropathology, Hematopathology, Dermatopathology, Soft Tissue Pathology, and Lung Pathology. For example, trainees interested in colon cancer biomarker development will participate in GI Pathology clinical sign-out; trainees interested in ovarian cancer biomarker discovery will participate in Gynecological Pathology clinical sign-out. In addition to acquiring focused, diagnostic experience in such sub-specialty areas, the fellow will gain knowledge and skills in molecular techniques useful for cancer biomarker discovery, such as genomic technologies (cDNA microarray, PCR, qRT-PCR), proteomic technologies, tissue microarrays, and protein lysate arrays. All of these technologies are already established in the Division of Pathology & Laboratory Medicine at MDACC. Particular emphasis will be placed on the integration of such molecular data with already established clinical and pathological indicators of tumor behavior. The trainees will be expected to participate in relevant tumor board planning treatment conferences at MDACC, where discussion of the utility of such molecular assays frequently occurs.

Applications: must be submitted using the Discover System, a web based application, at https://www2.mdanderson.org/sapp/discover/. The deadline to submit application is December 31st, Eighteen (18) months prior to the intended fellowship year which begins July 1st. Correspondence should be addressed to Russell Broaddus, MD PhD, Director, Cancer Biomarker Pathology Fellowship, The University of Texas M.D. Anderson Cancer Center, 1515 Holcombe Blvd., Unit 085, Houston, Texas 77030. For inquiries and to request additional information, please contact Kareen Chin.

Phone: (713) 792-3108 • **Fax:** (713) 745-0789 • **E-mail:** kechin@mdanderson.org

Web site: http://www.mdanderson.org/departments/pathology

ROSWELL PARK CANCER INSTITUTE, BUFFALO

Oncologic Surgical Pathology Fellowships

Description: Roswell Park Cancer Institute (RPCI) offers an ACGME-accredited one-year Fellowship in Oncologic Surgical Pathology beginning each July. RPCI, founded in 1898, is the oldest NCI-funded Comprehensive Cancer Center. The environment is fast-paced, dynamic, collegial, and exciting! The **Oncologic Surgical Pathology Fellowship** provides advanced training in neoplastic diseases of the GYN, Breast, GI, GU, Pulmonary, Head and Neck, Endocrine, Skin, Brain, Bone, Soft Tissue, and Hematopoietic systems. Fellows will spend 7 months on the surgical pathology service and will have 2 months of protected time for research. There is an opportunity to gain additional skills in diagnostic molecular pathology, or in one of the world's best flow cytometry labs, or in solid tumor cytogenetics with capabilities in FISH and interphase analysis during your elective time. Elective rotations in cytopathology and hematopathology are also possible. Additionally, Fellows are complemented by Residents and Medical Students enabling ample opportunity for teaching and graduated responsibility. The Fellows are an integral part of patient care at RPCI, and their participation in disease site specific multidisciplinary tumor boards, while serving an educational purpose, also ensures the optimum quality of patient care. Seminars from Faculty within and outside the Department will supplement the Fellow's education. The complexity of cases coupled with the large volume (14,000+ cases) allows Fellows to become proficient in the diagnosis of neoplastic diseases. Fellowships may be individualized, and a second year as Chief Fellow is possible.

Requirements: Because of the demanding nature of the diseases encountered, only Residents who will complete their training in an ACGME-accredited Program by the Fellowship start date will be considered. In addition, candidates must be eligible for a New York State Medical License or Limited Permit.

Types and Numbers of Appointments: (Year 1) **Oncologic Surgical Pathology Fellowship**: 6 ACGME-accredited Positions

(Potential Year 2) **Chief Fellow**: 1 Non-accredited Position (Combined Subspecialty & Oncologic Surgical Pathology)

Facilities: The campus spans 25 acres in downtown Buffalo and consists of 15 buildings with about 1 million square feet of space. The new hospital was completed in 1998 and houses a comprehensive diagnostic and treatment center. In addition, the Institute built a new medical research complex and renovated existing education and research space to support its future growth and expansion. RPCI is dedicated to providing total care to the cancer patient; to conducting research into the causes, treatment, and prevention of cancer; and to educating the public and the next generation of those who study and treat cancer.

Community: Buffalo has 4 wonderful seasons and a great economic, intellectual, and cultural life. It is a treasure to discover and is an exceptional place to live, work, and raise a family. Buffalo is an area of geographic beauty offering temperate summers for boating, camping, bicycling, sports, amusement and water parks, and other activities. During the winter, one can ice skate, ski, snowmobile, snowshoe, or just take a walk. Unlike some cities, traffic is hardly an issue. The average commute time is just 20 minutes! Nearby "getaways" include Niagara Falls and Toronto, Canada.

Stipends: Stipends are commensurate with postgraduate year of training.

Applications: A **Personal Statement, CV, RPCI Fellowship Application Form**, and **3 Letters of Reference** should be sent by February 28th (**16 months prior to the beginning of your Fellowship**) to: Christine Hegarty; Fellowship Coordinator; Department of Pathology; Roswell Park Cancer Institute; Elm & Carlton Streets; Buffalo, New York 14263.

Phone: (716) 845-7700 • **Fax:** (716) 845-3427 • **E-mail:** christine.hegarty@roswellpark.org

THE METHODIST HOSPITAL

Department of Pathology

Ophthalmic Pathology Fellowship

Description: The Methodist Hospital in Houston TX offers an ACGME accredited (selective pathology) one-year Ophthalmic Pathology fellowship. The fellowship is available for Pathology or Ophthalmology trained residents. The fellowship is tailored for each background to assure adequate training. For example, pathology trained fellows will have rotations in the oculoplastics/oncology service while ophthalmology trained fellows will have rotations in surgical pathology. Fellows will have the opportunity to review approximately 1,000 ocular specimens (adult and pediatric) that include enucleated eyes, exenterations of the orbit, eyelid, conjunctiva, lacrimal sac, lacrimal gland, orbit and intraocular biopsies. Cytology training is part of the program and includes interpretation of vitrectomy specimens, anterior chamber taps, corneal and conjunctival scrapings and occasional fine needle aspirations of intraocular lesions. In addition, the fellow will have the opportunity to review outside consultation of ophthalmic pathology cases that are routinely received in the department. The department has a fund available to support research projects (immunohistochemistry, in situ hybridization, and other molecular pathology techniques may be used) or case series reports for interested fellows during the year of training. The fellows will attend and participate in the didactic lectures, grand rounds, retinoblastoma tumor board and neuropathology/ophthalmic pathology case conference.

Requirements: At least two years of training in Anatomic Pathology. Preferably AP or AP/CP board-eligible. Ophthalmology trained applicants must be PGY3 or higher. Applicants must hold or be eligible for a Texas Physician In Training Permit or Licensure.

Stipends: Commensurate with level of post-graduate training.

Applications: Send inquiries to Patricia Chévez-Barrios, MD, Director, Ophthalmic Pathology Program, The Methodist Hospital, Department of Pathology, 6565 Fannin, M227, Houston, TX 77030.

Phone: (713) 441-3496 • **Fax:** (713) 441-3489 • **E-mail:** ljozwiak@tmhs.org

Web site: http://www.methodisthealth.com

UNIVERSITY OF CHICAGO

Orthopaedic Pathology (Bone & Soft Tissue) Fellowship

Description: The University of Chicago is a major tertiary referral center for orthopaedic tumors; the Laboratory of Surgical Pathology processes over 1500 orthopaedic specimens a year, including 500 oncologic specimens representing both pediatric and adult bone and soft tissue tumors. Over 100 orthopaedic tumor cases a year have intraoperative frozen sections and over 40 have cytologic specimens. A weekly multi-disciplinary work conference reviews all active patients, providing clinical and radiologic correlation. The fellow participates in the processing of major excision specimens, the sign-out of biopsies, excisions and consults, and has primary responsibility for the weekly oncology conference. Ample time for research is available, and a close working relationship with the Orthopaedic Molecular Oncology Laboratory provides the opportunity for translational and bench research. A two-year fellowship including a major commitment to bench research is also possible.

Requirements: A minimum of three years' training in anatomic pathology or four years' training that combines anatomic and clinical pathology. The candidate must be able to obtain an Illinois medical license.

Stipends: Commensurate with level of training.

Applications: Submit a letter of application accompanied by a curriculum vitae to: Anthony Montag, MD, Director Orthopaedic Pathology Fellowship, Department of Pathology MC 6101, University of Chicago Medical Center, 5841 S. Maryland Avenue, Chicago, IL 60637.

Phone: (773) 702-9318 • **Fax:** (773) 834-7644 • **E-mail:** amontag@bsd.uchicago.edu

NEW YORK UNIVERSITY MEDICAL CENTER
NYU HOSPITAL FOR JOINT DISEASES

Orthopedic Pathology Fellowship

Description: One Fellowship. We offer a one-year fellowship of training in Orthopedic Pathology. This program provides a wide experience in the pathology of bone, soft tissues and joint diseases, including tumors, tumor-like lesions, inflammatory and degenerative processes. The attending staff consists of 3 full-time orthopedic pathologists who are actively involved in the teaching program. There are 2 orthopedic oncologists who provide a large number of bone and soft tissue tumors to the department. The department of Radiology specializes in musculoskeletal disorders. The fellow is exposed to CT-Guided biopsies of bones and soft tissues that are performed by radiologists. He/She will learn the processing of large resection specimens including dissection, x-raying and mapping of tissue slabs. Particular emphasis is given to radiologic-pathologic correlation. The teaching program also includes monthly topics of orthopedic pathology that are discussed with the fellow using the existing files of the department. There are weekly inter-disciplinary conferences with bone radiologists and orthopedic oncologists, as well as intradepartmental conferences. The department houses documented study sets of teaching material that is available to the fellow for review. Our hospital has merged with New York University Hospitals Center and the fellow has access to the NYUHC library and other facilities. He/ she is encouraged to participate in clinical research activities. This fellowship program is accredited for one year of training in anatomic pathology by the Accreditation Council for Graduate Medical Education.

Requirements: Minimum of 2 years of previous experience in AP is required and must hold a NY State License.

Stipends: Commensurate with candidate's level of training.

Applications: Applications for positions beginning on July 1 should be received by December 1 the preceding year. Requests for information or applications should be addressed to:

Dr. German Steiner, NYU Hospital for Joint Disease, Department of Pathology, 301 East 17th Street, New York, NY 10013.

Phone: (212) 598-6231 • **Fax:** (212) 598-6057

NYU HOSPITAL FOR JOINT DISEASES

Department of Pathology

Orthopaedic Pathology Fellowship

Description: We offer a one-year fellowship in Orthopaedic Pathology which provides a wide experience in bone, soft tissue and joint pathology, including tumors, tumor-like lesions, inflammatory and degenerative processes. The attending staff consists of 3 full-time orthopaedic pathologists who are actively involved in the teaching program. There is a substantial number of bone and soft tissue tumors processed in our department. The fellow is exposed to CT-Guided biopsies of bone and soft tissue which are performed by radiologists. He/She will learn the processing of large resection specimens including dissection, x-raying and mapping of tissue slabs. Particular emphasis is given to radiologic-pathologic correlation. There are inter-disciplinary conferences with bone radiologists and orthopaedic oncologists, as well as intradepartmental conferences with active participation of the fellow. The department houses documented study sets of teaching material which are available to the fellow for review. Our hospital merged with New York University Medical Center and the fellow has access to the NYUMC library and other facilities. This program is accredited for one year of training in anatomic pathology by the Accreditation Council of Graduate Medical Education.

Requirements: A minimum of 2 years of previous experience in anatomic pathology is required.

Stipends: Salary is appropriate for the year of postgraduate training.

Applications: Application should be made to

German C. Steiner, MD, Program Director, NYU Hospital for Joint Diseases, 301 East 17th Street, New York, NY 10003.

Phone: (212) 598-6231 • **Fax:** (212) 598-6057 • **E-mail:** german.steiner@nyumc.org

UNIVERSITY OF CALIFORNIA, LOS ANGELES

Cardiovascular Pulmonary Pathology Fellowship

Description: The Department of Pathology and Laboratory Medicine at the UCLA Center for Health Sciences offers a one or two year fellowship in clinical and experimental Cardiovascular and Pulmonary Pathology starting July 1st. UCLA is a leading center of clinical practice and research in cardiac transplantation, congenital heart disease, and atherosclerotic cardiovascular disease, as well as lung cancer and interstitial lung disease. The fellow will participate in these programs and other scholarly activities related to teaching and research. The fellow will daily review cardiovascular pathology specimens. The fellow will participate in autopsy evaluation of cardiovascular specimens from adults and children, including congenital malformations, and all forms of acquired heart disease. The fellow will be encouraged to design and carry-out independent research. The fellow will participate in teaching cardiovascular pathology to medical and dental students, clinical and pathology residents and fellows, and cardiovascular physicians. One fellowship position is offered per academic year.

Requirements: The applicant should be board eligible in Anatomic Pathology and eligible for licensure in California. California medical license must be active by start of fellowship.

Stipends: Support is commensurate with the candidate's level of training.

Applications: Please contact Fellowship Coordinator for a list of requirements and application, submit curriculum vitae, and 3 letters of reference to Michael C. Fishbein, MD, Program Director of Cardio/Pulmonary Pathology Fellowship, David Geffen School of Medicine at UCLA, Department of Pathology and Laboratory Medicine, Room 13-145G CHS, 10833 Le Conte Avenue, Los Angeles, CA 90095.

UCLA is an Affirmative Action/Equal Opportunity employer. Applications are accepted on a rolling basis, and should be submitted one and one-half years preceding requested fellowship. **Fellowship Coordinator:** Annetta Pierro

Phone: (310) 825-5719 • **Fax:** (310) 267-2058 • **E-mail:** apierro@mednet.ucla.edu

Web site: www.pathology.ucla.edu

MAYO SCHOOL OF GRADUATE MEDICAL EDUCATION

Department of Laboratory Medicine and Pathology

Pulmonary Pathology Fellowship

Description: Mayo Clinic offers a one-year, ACGME-accredited Pulmonary Pathology Fellowship Program during which the fellow works with a broad spectrum of biopsy materials and surgical specimens relating to pulmonary, pleural and thoracic diseases. The fellowship experience includes the interpretation of interstitial, infectious, lymphoproliferative, immunologic and transplant-related lung disease and neoplastic pulmonary, thymic and pleural disease. When necessary, a variety of immunohistochemical and in-situ hybridization techniques will be applied as diagnostic tools. Mayo Clinic Rochester material averages 2,400 lung and pleural biopsies and resections, and approximately 1,900 pulmonary cytology specimens (including FNAs, sputa, secretions, and fluids). This is in addition to over 6,900 pulmonary pathology consults in Rochester and Scottsdale combined. The fellow also participates in clinicopathologic projects and a variety of clinical and pathological conferences. Opportunities for basic research also exist.

Requirements: Applicants must have completed an AP or AP/CP residency training program within the United States or Canada.

Stipends: Commensurate with level of training.

Applications: www.mayo.edu/msgme/application.html

Address inquiries to Marie-Christine Aubry, MD, Director, Pulmonary Pathology Training Program, Department of Pathology, Hilton 11, Mayo Clinic, 200 First Street, SW, Rochester, MN 55905.

Phone: (507) 293-3839 • **E-mail:** pathologyeducation@mayo.edu

Web site: www.mayo.edu/msgme/lm-pulmonarypath-rch.html

UNIVERSITY OF MICHIGAN MEDICAL CENTER

Pulmonary Pathology Fellowship

Description: The pulmonary pathology fellowship is a one-year program that begins on July 1 and continues through June 30 of the following year. Opportunities also exist for additional training in a basic research setting, depending on the interests and career goals of the applicant.The core curriculum includes a robust combination of both institutional and consultation cases covering a diverse range of problems in neoplastic and non-neoplastic lung diseases. The emphasis is on histopathologic and cytologic diagnosis as well as clinically oriented resarch. Fellows will work closely with a number of faculty who have a collective experience of over 70 years in diagnostic pulmonary pathology and cytopathology, an established track record of academic achievement, and a strong commitment to education. Partnering with colleagues in Thoracic Surgery and Pulmonary and Critical Care Medicine, fellows will have multiple opportunities for clinical-pathologic correlation in the course of case review as well as multidisciplinary conferences and collaborative projects. At the conclusion of this fellowship, incumbents will be well positioned for a career in any practice setting.

Requirements: Applicants must be board certified or eligible in Anatomic Pathology by the beginning of the fellowship and be eligible for a license in the State of Michigan.

Applications must include: 1) a letter expressing interest in the fellowship, 2) a resume or curriculum vita with bibliography, and 3) letters from 3 references, all from the postgraduate training period.

Stipends: Salary will be commensurate with the candidate's level of training.

Applications: Applications must be received by January 1 for the position beginning July 1 of the following year. Submit the above documents to: Jeffrey L. Myers, MD

A. James French Professor and Director, Division of Anatomic Pathology, Department of Pathology, 2G332 University Hospitals, 1500 east Medical Center Drive, Ann Arbor, Michigan 48109-5054.

E-mail: myerjeff@umich.edu

UNIVERSITY OF PITTSBURGH MEDICAL CENTER

Thoracic Pathology Fellowship

Description: This program offers an ACGME-accredited one-year fellowship focused on thoracic pathology, based largely at UPMC Presbyterian. The Thoracic Pathology Fellowship focuses on three aspects of pulmonary and mediastinal pathology: pleuropulmonary inflammatory disease, pleuropulmonary neoplasia, and diseases of the mediastinum. The fellow receives exposure to all three aspects of thoracic pathology, including an active thoracic surgery program in pulmonary neoplasia which is supported by a Lung SPORE, a vibrant and research oriented program in inflammatory lung disease focusing on idiopathic pulmonary fibrosis (supported by the Simmons Center for Interstitial Lung Disease) and the world's largest lung transplant surgery program, and finally a busy consultation service. This thoracic pathology fellowship program is unique in providing exposure to each of these areas of thoracic lung disease, in addition to having active basic and translational research programs associated with them. In addition, the department through its surgical pathology and autopsy service provides tremendous exposure to occupational lung disease due to Western Pennsylvania 's long standing commitment to the steel and mining industries.

Requirements: Completion of an accredited three-year program in Anatomic Pathology or four year program in Combined Anatomic-Clinical Pathology. Residents completing fellowships in general surgical pathology who desire subspecialty training in thoracic pathology are especially encouraged to apply.

Stipends: Salary is commensurate with year of postgraduate training.

Staff: Samuel Yousem MD, Fellowship Director; **Sanja Dacic** MD, PhD; **N. Paul Ohori** MD.

Applications: Submit online application at http://path.upmc.edu/fellowship. Send letter of interest to Samuel A. Yousem, MD, Department of Pathology, A-610 UPMC Presbyterian, 200 Lothrop Street, Pittsburgh, PA 15213.

Phone: (412) 647-6193 • **Fax:** (412) 647-3399 • **E-mail:** yousemsa@upmc.edu

THE UNIVERSITY OF TEXAS M.D. ANDERSON CANCER CENTER

Thoracic Pathology Fellowship

Description: The Thoracic Pathology fellowship program at MD Anderson Cancer Center is a one- year fellowship with an optional second year geared towards training fellows in all aspects of thoracic pathology, with emphasis on neoplastic lung disease. The selected individual will rotate the first year in the clinical service rendering provisional microscopic diagnosis and supervising the gross pathology dictation and sampling of thoracic cases. The fellow will be responsible for previewing and establishing the diagnosis for each case seen in the department (in house biopsies, resections, referrals and general consults). The fellow will also assist in the gross examination of complex surgical resection specimens, correlate the results of cytogentics and molecular testing with the final diagnosis of cases, interact with clinical colleagues from Head and Neck Oncology, and Thoracic Surgery departments to obtain additional pertinent clinical information, as well as, supports the multidisciplinary conferences. In addition, the fellow will be exposed to non-neoplastic pathology, which includes 10-15% of our daily practice. The ranges of non-neoplastic disease include infectious, fibrotic and rejection processes among other things. The second year will be devoted to laboratory translational research. The trainee is expected to participate in different molecular pathology studies with clinicopathologic correlations directed to gain more knowledge in thoracic pathology. These studies are designed to gain experience in molecular pathology laboratory studies of thoracic malignancies to be presented at national and international meetings with the goal of publication in medical journals.

Requirements: Candidates must be board certified or board eligible for certification in Anatomic or AP/CP Pathology.

Stipends: Commensurate with level of training.

Applications: must be submitted using the Discover System, a web based application, at https://www2.mdanderson.org/sapp/discover/. The deadline to submit application is December 31st, eighteen (18) months prior to the intended fellowship year which begins July 1st. Correspondence should be addressed to Cesar Moran, MD Director, Thoracic Pathology Fellowship, The University of Texas M.D. Anderson Cancer Center, 1515 Holcombe Blvd., Unit 085, Houston, Texas 77030. For inquiries and to request additional information, please contact Kareen Chin.

Phone: (713) 792-3108 • **Fax:** (713) 745-0789 • **E-mail:** kechin@mdanderson.org

Web site: http://www.mdanderson.org/departments/pathology

CEDARS-SINAI MEDICAL CENTER

Renal Pathology Fellowship

Description: The renal biopsy service at Cedars-Sinai Medical Center accessions in excess of 2400 kidney biopsies per year for comprehensive evaluation by sophisticated light microscopy, immunofluorescence and electron microscopy. Roughly 20% of the total are transplant biopsies and the others are a mixture of adult (predominantly) and pediatric biopsies. The fellow will be instructed in depth and detail concerning diagnostic renal pathology, and will become skilled in electron microscopy and evaluation of specimens by immunofluorescence. Once proficient, the fellow will work reasonably independently, including communications with referring nephrologists. The fellow will be expected to present at renal pathology conferences and participate in at least one or two investigative projects during the year. These activities ideally will lead to one or more presentations at national meetings and/or publications.

Requirements: Board eligibility in Anatomic Pathology. A California medical license is required at the time of appointment.

Stipends: Commensurate with level of training.

Staff: **Arthur H Cohen** MD; **Mark Haas** MD, PhD; **Cynthia C Nast** MD.

Applications: For an application, information and correspondence, contact the program coordinator: LeeTanya Marion-Murray, Department of Pathology, Cedars-Sinai Medical Center, 8700 Beverly Blvd., S. Tower Room 8709, Los Angeles, CA 90048.

Phone: (310) 423-6941 • **Fax:** (310) 423-5881 • **E-mail:** marionl@cshs.org

UNIVERSITY OF CHICAGO

Renal Pathology Fellowship

Description: The Department of Pathology offers a one or two year fellowship in diagnostic medical renal pathology training with opportunities for clinical or basic research during an optional second year of training. The service includes the full range of medical renal diseases (approximately 900 cases annually). These cases represent largely native (70%) as well as transplant (30%) renal biopsies from both adult and pediatric patients. Approximately 70% of cases are consult cases from referring hospitals in the region. The University of Chicago is also a major center for adult kidney transplantation. The fellow participates in the full evaluation of biopsies, which includes light, immunofluorescence and electron microscopy. The fellow also presents pathology findings at the departmental and multidisciplinary conferences. Research opportunities are available within the Pathology department and in collaboration with nephrology, rheumatology, and transplant surgery investigators among others. Funding is available to attend either the American Society of Nephrology or USCAP meeting. Major ongoing research programs involve the role of complement in renal diseases and autoantibodies in lupus nephritis.

Requirements: A minimum of three years' training in anatomic pathology or four years' training that combines anatomic and clinical pathology. The candidate must be able to obtain an Illinois medical license.

Stipends: Commensurate with level of training

Staff: Shane Meehan, MB, BCh, Associate Professor, Director Renal Pathology Fellowship; Anthony Chang, MD, Assistant Professor

Applications: Submit a letter of application accompanied by a curriculum vitae to: Shane Meehan, MB, BCh, Director Renal Pathology Fellowship, Department of Pathology MC6101, University of Chicago Medical Center, 5841 S. Maryland Avenue, Chicago, IL 60637.

Phone: (773) 702-8997 • **Fax:** (773) 834-7644 • **E-mail:** shane.meehan@uchospitals.edu

Web site: http://pathology.bsd.uchicago.edu

JOHNS HOPKINS MEDICAL INSTITUTIONS

Renal Pathology Fellowship

Description: This one or two year program offers formal clinical training in Renal Pathology. The possibility of a second year with more time devoted to research is available on a case by case base. In the first year, the fellow evaluates renal case material for signout by the faculty. This includes kidney biopsies as well as nephrectomy specimens with 1200-1400 specimens annually, including renal allograft biopsies. The fellow is responsible for examination of the material using light, immunofluorescence and electron microscopy. The fellow will also participate in clinical rounds with the Department of Medicine, Division of Nephrology, and the Department of Surgery, Division of Transplant Surgery. In the first year, there will be opportunity for case-based/translational research. In the second year, the fellow takes full responsibility for signout of renal case material on a rotating basis. Research is an integral part of the fellowship program and may have either a clinical or experimental emphasis, with potential for interdepartmental collaboration as well. The fellow will also be trained in technical and administrative aspects of IF and EM laboratories. The first year of this program is accredited as a "Special Pathology" program by the ACGME.

Requirements: Minimum of two full years AP.

Stipends: Commensurate with the candidate's level of postgraduate training in pathology.

Applications: Address correspondence to
Serena Bagnasco, MD, Department of Pathology, Ross 632, 720 Rutland Avenue, Baltimore, Maryland 21205

Phone: (410) 502-0812 • **E-mail:** sbagnas1@jhmi.edu

Web site: http://pathology.jhu.edu

The Johns Hopkins University does not discriminate on the basis of race, color, sex, religion, national or ethnic origin, age, handicapped or veteran status in any student program or activity administered by the University or with regard to admission or employment.

UNIVERSITY OF NORTH CAROLINA AT CHAPEL HILL

Renal Pathology Fellowship

Description: A one- to two-year formal fellowship training in renal pathology is offered in the nephropathology laboratory at the University of North Carolina, campus Chapel Hill. One or two fellows are accepted into the program. The laboratory, which is part of the Department of Pathology, has three faculty members (V. Nickeleit, MD; HK Singh, MD; JC Jennette, MD); it is directed by Volker Nickeleit. The fellows are directly involved in the diagnostic evaluation of over 1800 renal biopsies/nephrectomies (both native and transplants) examined annually. All fellows are integrative members of our dynamic team and receive intensive training. Fellows are expected to be enthusiastic, highly motivated, and to work independently. They prepare cases for sign out by the faculty using all standard techniques (light microscopy, immunofluorescence microscopy, immunohistochemistry and electron microscopy). Part of the fellows' responsibility is to organize clinicopathologic and biopsy review conferences for medical faculty and housestaff, and to teach renal pathology to medical students, residents and fellows. Teaching conferences and continuous education series offered by the nephrology and transplant divisions at UNC provide additional ample learning opportunities. Although emphasis is placed on the development of diagnostic skills, fellows are expected to carry out clinicopathological and/or basic research projects and to present their data at national meetings, such as the ASN or USCAP. Research projects will focus on the pathogenesis of glomerulonephritis, allograft rejection, or polyomavirus infections. All state-of-the-art facilities (including laser microdissection) are available in the department. Appropriate research studies will be funded by the nephropathology laboratory. Clinicopathological studies are facilitated by the Glomerular Disease Collaborative Network, which is a well established network of over 200 nephrologists participating in clinical data collection. For further information, visit our website at www.uncnephropathology.org.

Requirements: MD degree. Board eligibility or certification in anatomic pathology. Both U.S. and foreign candidates are considered.

Types and Numbers of Appointments: One to two fellowship positions are offered. Appointments vary and are based on training background and licensing.

Stipends: Commensurate with training and medical license. Limited funds are available to support foreign visiting scholars.

Applications: Send letter of interest and CV to V. Nickeleit, MD; Professor of Pathology; Director: Nephropathology Unit, The University of North Carolina; Department of Pathology, Campus Box #7525, Chapel Hill, NC 27599-7525

Phone: (919) 966-2421 • **Fax:** (919) 966-4542 • **E-mail:** volker_nickeleit@med.unc.edu

---

THE OHIO STATE UNIVERSITY MEDICAL CENTER

Department of Pathology

Renal and Transplant Pathology Fellowship

Description: The Department of Pathology at The Ohio State University Medical Center (OSUMC) invites applications for a two-year renal pathology/transplant pathology fellowship. The Department of Pathology has a busy renal biopsy referral service receiving biopsies from several states. OSUMC has outstanding academic nephrology and transplant divisions. The transplant division performs kidney, pancreas, heart, lung and liver transplants. The kidney transplant program is one of the most active in the country with approximately 250 renal transplantations performed in a year. The fellow is expected to spend 50% of his/her time doing clinical work; the other 50% of the fellow's time will be devoted to clinical and/or basic research projects, but the fellowship can be tailored according to individual needs.

Requirements: Candidates must successfully complete USMLE Step III prior to their Medical Staff appointment at The Ohio State University Medical Center. They must also be AP/CP Board eligible or Board certified.

Stipends: The stipend is commensurate with the number of years of postgraduate training.

Applications: Send letter of application and curriculum vitae to: Tibor Nadasdy, MD, Department of Pathology, The Ohio State University, M018 Starling Loving Hall, 320 W. 10th Ave., Columbus, OH 43210.

Phone: (614) 293-9258 • **Fax:** (614) 293-4255 • **E-mail:** tibor.nadasdy@osumc.edu

Web site: http://pathology.osumc.edu/ext

VANDERBILT UNIVERSITY SCHOOL OF MEDICINE

Renal Pathology Fellowship

Description: The Division of Renal Pathology/Electron Microscopy in the Department of Pathology at Vanderbilt University Medical Center, Nashville, Tennessee, offers a Fellowship in Renal Pathology each year starting on July 1. Either a one-year fellowship with clinical focus or a two-year fellowship with clinical experience and in-depth clinicopathologic or basic research is available. The fellowship is under the direction of Agnes Fogo, MD, Professor of Pathology, Medicine and Pediatrics, at Vanderbilt University Medical Center. Juan Iturregui, MD, Assistant Professor of Pathology, and Candice Frederick, MD, Instructor of Pathology, are faculty members of the Division of Renal Pathology who participate actively in the fellow's training. The Fellow will be directly involved in the diagnostic evaluation of all renal biopsies received annually by the Renal Pathology Laboratory at Vanderbilt. These cases represent largely native (70%) as well as transplant (30%) renal biopsies, with both adult and pediatric cases. Current volume is about 1,000 cases/year, of which 70% are consult cases from outside hospitals in the region and other countries.

Requirements: The Fellow will be expected to work independently in preparing cases for sign-out by the faculty, using light, immunofluorescence and electron microscopy. Fellows will also present cases at clinical conferences held jointly with the Nephrology and Renal Transplant Divisions, have ample exposure to clinical teaching conferences, actively participate in teaching renal pathology to medical students, residents and nephrology fellows, and attend weekly departmental surgical pathology slide conferences. Fellows are expected to pursue an academic project, e.g., clinical teaching case reports. Fellows are encouraged and funds are available to attend a yearly scientific meeting during their training. Applicants must be ECFMG certified if graduates of a foreign medical school, and should have a minimum of two years' training in AP or three years in AP/CP, or equivalent renal morphological exposure through renal research. Applications are accepted through March of each year for positions starting the following year. Competitive applicants will then be invited for interview, and final decisions made by July one year ahead of start date.

Stipends: Commensurate with relevant experience and previous training.

Staff: Agnes B. Fogo MD, Professor of Pathology; **Juan Iturregui** MD, Assistant Professor of Pathology; **Candice Frederick** MD, Instructor of Pathology.

Applications: Address correspondence with CV to: Agnes B. Fogo, MD, Director, Division of Renal Pathology/ Electron Microscopy, Department of Pathology, Vanderbilt University Medical Center, C-3310 Medical Center North, 1161 21st Ave South, Nashville, TN 37232-2561, or via e-mail at a gnes.fogo@vanderbilt.edu

---

UNIVERSITY OF WASHINGTON

Department of Pathology

Renal Pathology Fellowship

Description: This ACGME-accredited fellowship provides an intensive experience in diagnostic renal pathology, with broad experience in the special evaluation techniques relevant to the clinical diagnosis of renal native and transplant biopsy material (currently accesioning 1,300/year). The fellow will participate in all aspects of the routine diagnostic work-up of all renal biopsies and gain management experience of hospital laboratories. The fellow would have sufficient diagnostic experience after one year to function independently as a diagnostic renal pathologist in an academic medical center. An important component is engagement in clinical and/or basic research. Additional years of research training may be available, under different funding mechanisms.

Requirements: Applicants are selected for interview based on academic excellence and interest in the subspecialty. Applicants need to be board eligible for AP or AP/CP certification by the American Board of Pathology and must be eligible for a Washington State license

Facilities: The program is based at University of Washington Medical Center, which provides tertiary medical care to the five-state region of Washington, Wyoming, Alaska, Montana and Idaho.

Stipends: One-year appointment with salary and benefits based on the schedule for residents at an equivalent level (R5=$55,032). Fellows are encouraged to apply for extramural funding, if additional research training is desired. (1 position)

Staff: C. Alpers Director; **L. Finn**; **J. Kowalewska**; **R. Nicosia**; **K. Smith**.

Applications: Charles E. Alpers, MD, Fellowship Director, at calp@u.washington.edu
Available at the web site or contact Michelle Rickard, Academic Programs Manager, Renal Pathology Fellowship Program, at the email address below. Application materials must be received by February 1 with selected interviews to follow until the position is filled.

Phone: (206) 598-4933 • **Fax:** (206) 598-7321 • **E-mail:** fellowship@pathology.washington.edu
Web site: www.pathology.washington.edu/academics/fellowship/

The University of Washington is an equal opportunity institution.

EMORY UNIVERSITY HOSPITAL

Department of Pathology and Laboratory Medicine

Soft Tissue Pathology Fellowship

Description: A dedicated one-year soft tissue fellowship is offered. Fellows will have the opportunity to review the over 3,000 soft tissue consultation cases referred annually to Dr. Sharon Weiss, as well as the over 200 primary bone and soft tissue tumors treated in the Emory Healthcare, Emory Children's Center, and Grady Memorial Hospital. In addition to daily diagnostic activities, fellows will participate in sarcoma conference and engage in one or more research projects on a clinical or basic science topic. The Department has abundant resources to support investigative endeavors including facilities for performing immunocytochemistry, in situ hybridization, polymerase chain reaction, flow cytometry, and computer facilities. (One position per year.)

Requirements: USMLE Step 3 for PG-3 and above, Georgia medical licensure, applicants may apply for the elective or credential years, must have completed 3 years of AP/CP or 2 years of AP.

Stipends: Commensurate with training and experience.

Applications: A letter of application, curriculum vitae, and three letters of reference, including one from the candidate's program director, should be sent to Sharon W. Weiss, MD, Director Soft Tissue Pathology, or Andrea Deyrup, MD, Co-Director, H-185A EUH, 1364 Clifton Road, NE, Atlanta, GA 30322. Applications should be received by January 1 of year preceding fellowship. Notification of acceptance will be made by April 1 of year preceding fellowship.

Phone: (404) 727-4283 • **Fax:** (404) 727-2519 • **E-mail:** mmojonn@emory.edu

MAYO SCHOOL OF GRADUATE MEDICAL EDUCATION

Soft Tissue Pathology Fellowship

Description: This new ACGME-accredited one-year fellowship exposes you to a comprehensive and multidisciplinary approach to the diagnosis of benign and malignant bone and soft tissue tumors.

This intensive training program is designed to prepare you for a career in an academic or large private referral center. You will review all of Mayo Clinic's consultation cases seen by members of the Bone and Soft Tissue team, approximately 5000 cases per year.

In-house ancillary studies are utilized extensively and include immunohistochemistry, in situ hybridization, cytogenetics, molecular genetics, and electron microscopy. The bone and soft tissue pathology service supports a large multidisciplinary practice, including surgery, oncology, radiation therapy, radiology and nuclear medicine.

You will be responsible for reviewing all clinical material and radiological studies, and will participate in the daily Orthopedic Pathology-Radiology Conference and the weekly multidisciplinary sarcoma conference. Clinicopathological research is strongly encouraged and extensive diagnostic resources (e.g., IHC, FISH, RT-PCR) are available to you.

Requirements: Applicants should have completed an AP or AP/CP residency training program within the United States or Canada.

Types and Numbers of Appointments: One position is available each year on a competitive basis.

Applications: http://www.mayo.edu/msgme/application.html

Applications for each academic year, which begins in July, should be completed by January 1st (18 months before). Positions will be offered beginning March 1 the previous year.

Address inquiries to Andrew L. Folpe, MD, Program Director, Bone and Soft Tissue Pathology Training Program, Mayo Clinic, 200 First Street SE, Rochester, MN 55905.

Phone: (507) 293-3839 • **E-mail:** pathologyeducation@mayo.edu

Web site: http://www.mayo.edu/msgme/bonesofttissue-rch.html

PENNSYLVANIA HOSPITAL

Department of Pathology

Soft Tissue Pathology Fellowship

Description: A one-year fellowship in Soft tissue and Bone Pathology with Dr. John S. J. Brooks at Pennsylvania Hospital (PAH), a University of Pennsylvania Health System member, serves the largest sarcoma practice in the Delaware Valley. The successful candidate will be exposed to nearly 1000 soft tissue and bone pathology service cases per year; in addition, personal consult cases are reviewed daily. Time for clinical research activities is built into the fellowship, and some elective time is available at the Hospital of the University of Pennsylvania.

Requirements: Four years of training in pathology (combined AP-CP) or straight AP; Pennsylvania medical license.

Stipends: Commensurate with the year of postgraduate training.

Applications: Candidates should forward their CV together with three letters of reference to Dr. John S. J. Brooks, Chair of Pathology, Pennsylvania Hospital, 800 Spruce Street, Philadelphia, PA 19107. CVs may be Faxed; however, applications will not be processed nor will interviews be scheduled until the three reference letters are received.

Fax: (215) 829-7564

UNIVERSITY OF PITTSBURGH MEDICAL CENTER

Bone & Soft Tissue Pathology Fellowship

Description: The bone and soft tissue pathology fellowship is based at UPMC-Shadyside, and receives over 5,000 specimens and consultations from all UPMC hospitals. The fellowship program offers a broad-based experience in benign, and malignant soft tissue and bone lesions, and stresses the importance of ancillary techniques such as immunohistochemistry, in situ hybridization, molecular and cytogenetic investigations, often required for diagnosis of these lesions. The bone and soft tissue section is very well supported in these areas and has three pathologists deeply interested in this subspeciality.
The fellowship is a nine month rotation devoted to this subspeciality and a three month elective rotation in related molecular diagnostics, routine and molecular cytogenetics, informatics and quality assurance. The precise duration of each of the elective rotations is flexible. The fellow will be involved in a daily case sign out and intra operative consultations with the bone/soft tissue pathologist. The fellow is also expected to participate in the teaching of medical students and pathology residents. The fellowship program also emphasizes the importance of a multidisciplinary approach required for the diagnosis of these tumors, and the fellow is expected to actively participate in orthopaedic oncology teaching conferences. The fellow will also interact with surgical and medical oncologists, and the department of radiology based at UPMC Shadyside and the University of Pittsburgh Cancer Institute.
The bone and soft tissue pathology fellow will take advantage of the department's informatics resources including image archiving, electronic medical record and the World Wide Web. Fellows are expected to undertake at least one investigational project and are strongly encouraged to publish and present at national meetings. The nature of the project will depend on the fellow's interest and the amount of time they wish to devote to it.
The fellowship program has been approved by the ACGME.

Requirements: Candidate must have completed training in an approved residency in combined Anatomic and Clinical Pathology or straight Anatomic Pathology, must have passed all three steps of USMLE, and should be board certified or board eligible in Pathology. Eligibility for Pennsylvania licensure is required.

Stipends: Commensurate with the level of postgraduate training in Pathology.

Staff: **Uma Rao** MD, Fellowship Director; **Alka Palekar** MD; **Anil Parwani** MD, PhD; **Karen Schoedel** MD.

Applications: Submit application online at http://path.upmc.edu/fellowship. Current curriculum vitae and three letters of recommendation should be forwarded 12 months in advance of starting date (July 1 of each year) to Uma N.M. Rao, MD; Director, Bone & Soft Tissue Pathology Fellowship Program; Rm. 2.9 West Wing; UPMC-Shadyside; Pittsburgh, PA 15232.

Phone: (412) 623-2319 • **Fax:** (412) 682-6450 • **E-mail:** raounm@upmc.edu

THE UNIVERSITY OF TEXAS M.D. ANDERSON CANCER CENTER

Soft Tissue Pathology Fellowship

Description: The Department of Pathology offers a one-year ACGME accredited fellowship in Soft Tissue Pathology. This program provides an extensive immersive experience in soft tissue pathology. The focus can vary with the interests of the individual, but the fellow will be responsible for previewing and establishing the diagnosis for cases seen in the department (in house biopsies, resections, referrals and consults), correlate the results of cytogenetics and molecular testing with the final diagnosis, interact with clinical colleagues, and support the multidisciplinary conferences. At least one major academic project leading to submission for publication is required. Resources for presentation at a national meeting are provided. Soft tissue sarcomas are rare tumors representing approximately 1% of malignant tumors, however, the differential diagnosis of these tumors is broad and there are numerous benign and malignant mimics of sarcomas. M.D. Anderson Cancer Center, the largest sarcoma treatment center in the United States, has long been recognized for the excellent multidisciplinary, oncologic and surgical care it provides for sarcoma patients and provides a uniquely rich opportunity for translational research. The broad range of pathologic material available at this institution and the large consultation services of several of our faculty are excellent sources for learning diagnostic skills and the clinical aspects of these tumors and their treatment. The fellow will obtain strong skills in the diagnosis and multidisciplinary treatment of these tumors. Rotations in the cytogenetics and molecular diagnostics labs and continual involvement with the sarcoma molecular diagnosis service are required. Ample time and resources are available for academic pursuits. Exposure to the bone sarcoma service can also be arranged as suits the interests of the fellow.

Requirements: Candidate must be Board-certified or eligible for certification in Anatomic Pathology or AP/CP

Stipends: Commensurate with the candidate's level of training

Applications: must be submitted using the Discover System, a web based application, at https://www2.mdanderson.org/sapp/discover/. The deadline to submit application is December 31st, eighteen (18) months prior to the intended fellowship year which begins July 1st. Correspondence should be addressed to Alexander Lazar, MD, PhD, Director, Soft Tissue Pathology Fellowship, The University of Texas M.D. Anderson Cancer Center, 1515 Holcombe Blvd., Unit 085, Houston, Texas 77030. For inquiries and to request additional information, please contact Kareen Chin.

Phone: (713) 792-3108 • **Fax:** (713) 745-0789 • **E-mail:** kechin@mdanderson.org
Web site: http://www.mdanderson.org/departments/pathology

UNIVERSITY OF WASHINGTON

Department of Pathology

Bone and Soft Tissue Pathology Fellowship

Description: This ACGME-accredited training program exposes the fellow to a comprehensive and multidisciplinary approach to the diagnosis of bone and soft tissue tumors including the use of special diagnostic techniques. The bone and soft tissue pathology service supports a large multidisciplinary group including surgery, oncology, radiation therapy, radiology, and nuclear medicine. There is a large diversity of in-house as well as consult material. The fellow will be responsible for reviewing all clinical material and radiological studies, and running the weekly multidisciplinary sarcoma conference. Clinicopathological research is strongly encouraged.

Requirements: Applicants are selected for interview based on academic excellence and interest in the subspecialty. Applicants are expected to have completed at least two years of Anatomic Pathology training in an ACGME-accredited program and must be eligible for a Washington State license.

Facilities: The program is based at University of Washington Medical Center. UW Medicine, among the most successful academic medical centers in the US, provides tertiary medical care and medical education to the five-state region of Washington, Wyoming, Alaska, Montana and Idaho.

Stipends: One-year appointment with salary and benefits based on the schedule for residents at an equivalent level (R5= $55,032). Fellows are encouraged to apply for extramural funding, if additional research training is desired. (1 position)

Staff: B. Hoch Director; **P. Swanson**.

Applications: Inquiry : Benjamin Hoch, MD, Fellowship Director, at bhoch@u.washington.edu
Available at the web site or contact Michelle Rickard, Academic Programs Manager, BST Fellowship Program, at the email address below. Application materials must be received by February 1 with selected interviews to follow until the position is filled.

Phone: (206) 598-4933 • **Fax:** (206) 598-7321 • **E-mail:** fellowship@pathology.washington.edu
Web site: www.pathology.washington.edu/academics/fellowship/

The University of Washington is an equal opportunity institution.

UNIVERSITY OF ALABAMA AT BIRMINGHAM

Surgical Pathology Fellowship

Description: A one-year fellowship is being offered in Surgical Pathology. This fellowship provides an opportunity for advanced training and experience (**including potential individual sign out responsibilities**) in all aspects of Surgical Pathology and is especially geared to individuals interested in academic careers. The diagnostic material is extensive and the programming is flexible to accommodate the fellow's interest, background, and expertise. Strengths are multiple among the faculty in the Division and include, but are not limited to, Gyn, GI and liver, Breast, Male GU, Cardiac, Kidney, Perinatal and Bone Pathology.

Requirements: MD degree, license to practice medicine in the State of Alabama, and completion of pathology core requirements (**3 yrs of AP or 4 yrs of combined AP/CP training**). Most fellows are in their 5th postgraduate level of training. Stipends: Commensurate with level of postgraduate training. A professional development fund is also provided.

Stipends: Salary levels are commensurate with the level of postgraduate training.

Staff: Applications should be submitted to Gene P. Siegal, MD, PhD, Professor and Director, Division of Anatomic Pathology, University of Alabama at Birmingham, 619 South 19th Street, Birmingham, AL 35249-7331. Applications should be made 12 to 18 months prior to initiation of training.
Phone: (205) 975-8880 • **Fax:** (205) 975-7284
Web site: http://www.path.uab.edu

ALLEGHENY GENERAL HOSPITAL

Department of Pathology and Laboratory Medicine

Surgical Pathology Fellowship

Description: A one-year fellowship is offered to provide advanced training and experience in general surgical pathology. Allegheny General Hospital (AGH) is a 698-bed tertiary medical center serving southwestern Pennsylvania. Approximately 20,000 surgical and 18,000 cytology specimens are accessioned annually with an expanding fine needle aspiration biopsy program. Besides general surgical pathology, special areas of excellence include breast, urologic, pulmonary, liver/GI, gyn and neuropathology. The NSABP is located at AGH with opportunities for collaboration. Elective time is available in cytology/FNA biopsy, as well as for clinical and translational research. There are also excellent facilities for ancillary techniques including immunohistochemistry, flow cytometry, cytogenetics, molecular diagnostics and digital imaging.

Requirements: Applicants should be Board certified or eligible in AP or AP/CP. The appointment is for one year.

Staff: **Jan F. Silverman** MD (Med Col Virginia 1970) Chairman and Director of Anatomic Pathology, Department Pathology and Laboratory Medicine; surgical pathology, fine needle aspiration biopsy, cytopathology; **Henry G. Brown** MD,PhD (Univ Illinois 1992) Director, Neuropathology; surgical pathology; **Karen Clary** MD (SUNY at Syracuse 1995) cytopathology, surgical pathology; **Anna Estop** PhD (Autonomous Univ of Barcelona 1979) Director of Cytogenetics; **Karl R. Fox** MD (Univ Iowa1967) Director, Hematology; flow cytometry, hematopathology; **Katherine M. Jasnosz** MD (SUNY at Buffalo 1980) Director, Autopsy Pathology; perinatal pathology, ob/gyn pathology, cytopathology, forensic pathology; **Yulin Liu** MD,PhD (Hunan Medical Univ, China) cytology, fine needle aspiration, surgical pathology; **Ileana Lopez-Plaza** MD (Univ Central del Caribe 1985) transfusion medicine; **Walter Mastropaolo** PhD (Univ Rochester) Director Clinical Chemistry; chemistry, toxicology; **Girija Nathan** MD (Stanley Med Col 1969) surgical pathology, cytology, breast pathology, gastrointestinal pathology; **Peter R. Olson** MD (Univ Minnesota 1969) Director Clinical Pathology; urologic pathology, transfusion medicine; **Stanley Shackney** MD (Harvard Med Sch 1964) Adjunct Faculty, Professor; molecular diagnostics; **Darrell Triulzi** MD (Albany Med Col 1985) transfusion medicine.

Applications: Letter of application and curriculum vitae should be sent to Jan F. Silverman, MD, Chairman and Director of Anatomic Pathology, Allegheny General Hospital, Department of Pathology and Laboratory Medicine, 320 East North Avenue, Pittsburgh, PA 15212-4772.

Phone: (412) 359-6886 • **Fax:** (412) 359-3598 • **E-mail:** JSilverm@wpahs.org

ARIZONA HEALTH SCIENCES CENTER

Department of Pathology

Surgical Pathology Fellowship

Description: The Department of Pathology at the University of Arizona Health Sciences Center/University Medical Center is accepting applications for a one-year fellowship position in Surgical Pathology to begin July 1. This fellowship will provide advanced training in diagnostic Surgical Pathology with all the specialties, including Transplantation Pathology, Neuropathology, and Immunopathology. A clinical research project will be encouraged. The University of Arizona has pathology faculty with expertise in Gastrointestinal Pathology, Heart and Lung Pathology, Neuropathology/ Muscle Disease, Hematopathology, Renal Pathology, and Obstetrics and Gynecologic Pathology. The hospital is a tertiary care medical center with an adjacent Comprehensive Cancer Center that draws in patients from throughout the western United States. The candidate will be expected to participate in clinical conferences and teach residents, medical students, and fellows, as appropriate. Our outreach surgical pathology cases, which arrive daily from other parts of the state, will be the fellow's special responsibility and will prepare the fellow for independent practice.

Requirements: Applicants should have completed either an Anatomic Pathology or an Anatomic Pathology/Clinical Pathology residency training program.

Stipends: Salary and benefits are commensurate with the level of training of the individual.

Applications: Interested candidates should submit a letter of intent, a curriculum vitae, and three letters of reference to: Achyut Bhattacharyya, MD, Director of Surgical Pathology, Department of Pathology, Arizona Health Sciences Center, Tucson, AZ 85724-5108.

Phone: (520) 626-6830 • **Fax:** (520) 626-2521 • **E-mail:** abhattac@email.arizona.edu

---

BROWN UNIVERSITY
WARREN ALPERT MEDICAL SCHOOL

Lifespan Academic Medical Center
(Rhode Island and The Miriam Hospitals)

Surgical Pathology Fellowship

Description: The Department of Pathology at the Rhode Island and The Miriam Hospitals have established a one-year fellowship program in Surgical Pathology. The program offers advanced training in all aspects of surgical pathology. A clinical research project will be encouraged. Strong collaborative efforts with the Brown Medical School will provide excellent research opportunities. The fellow will also be expected to participate in the teaching of residents and fellows in the Department and in the teaching of Pathology and Laboratory Medicine courses.

Requirements: Applicants should have completed an AP or AP/CP residency training program. Residents who wish to use this fellowship position as a fifth year experience will also be considered. Applicants must be eligible for employment in the United States.

Applications: Shamlal Mangray, MD, Director of Surgical Pathology Fellowship, Department of Pathology, Rhode Island Hospital, 593 Eddy Street, Providence RI 02903.

Phone: (401) 444-3847 • **Fax:** (401) 444-8514 • **E-mail:** smangray@lifespan.org

Rhode Island Hospital/The Miriam Hospital is an EEO/AA employer and encourages applications from minorities, women and protected persons.

UNIVERSITY OF CALIFORNIA, DAVIS

Surgical Pathology Fellowship

Description: The program is designed to train fellows in the interpretation of all surgical pathology specimens. Expertise will include; frozen section interpretation, intraoperative consultations - gross examination, biopsy diagnosis/ interpretation and appropriate work-up of cancer resections. The fellow in Surgical Pathology will develop an analytical approach to diagnoses, which will include the appropriate use of ancillary techniques such as electron microscopy, immunohistochemistry and molecular pathology. Training in this program will encompass consultation to health care providers, teaching/staffing medical students, residents, pathologist's and clinicians with occasional conferences. The fellow is encouraged to participate in a research project, which leads to publication in a peer reviewed journal.

Requirements: At least two years of Training in an ACGME accredited Anatomic or, four years in a combined AP/ CP Pathology training program.

Types and Numbers of Appointments: 3- one year appointments.

Stipends: Stipends are commensurate with appropriate postgraduate levels established by the University of California at Davis.

Staff: Rajendra Ramsamooj MD, Director Surgical Pathology Fellowship, Residency Training Program; **Penny Young** penny.young@ucdmc.ucdavis.edu; **Alaa Afify** MD, Director of Cytopathology Fellowship; **John Bishop** MD, Director, Surgical Pathology; **Alexander Borowsky** MD, Breast Pathology; **Dariusz Borys** MD, Soft Tissue and Bone, Pediatric Pathology; **William Ellis** MD, Neuropathology; **Regina Gandour-Edwards** MD, Head and Neck Pathology; **Claudia Greco** MD, Neuropathology; **Lydia Howell** MD, Cytopathology; **Lee-Way Jin** MD, Neuropathology and Research; **Malathy Kapali** MD, Breast and Gyn Pathology; **Thomas Konia** MD, Dermatopathology; **Ramez Saroufeem** MD, Gastrointestinal Pathology; **Cindy Yu** MD, Surgical Pathology.

Applications: Completed applications consist of; CV, personal statement and, 3 letters of recommendation (1 must be from current Program Director) sent to: Penny Young, Fellowship and Residency Training Program Coordinator, Department of Pathology and Laboratory Medicine, University of California, Davis, Medical Center, PATH Building, 4400 V Street, PATH Building, Sacramento, California 95817.
Web site: http://ucdmc.ucdavis.edu/pathology

UNIVERSITY OF CALIFORNIA, LOS ANGELES

Department of Pathology

Surgical Pathology Fellowship

Description: The Department of Pathology and Laboratory Medicine offers one-year fellowships in surgical pathology. Fellows rotate through various month-long assignments in surgical pathology at a senior or supervisorial level. As frozen section/gross room supervisor, the fellow will oversee the preparation and interpretation of intraoperative consults and will guide residents and physician assistants in gross analysis and processing of specimens. As junior attending, the fellow will rotate on many of our numerous surgical pathology specialty services directly checking and preparing cases with the resident on service. The fellows will also rotate at UCLA Santa Monica Hospital and at Olympia Hospital as junior attending, independently reviewing cases, preparing reports, performing frozen sections and bone marrow biopsies under the guidance of UCLA faculty at those institutions. The fellows participate in and are responsible for preparing and presenting at numerous clinical conferences, tumor boards, and teaching conferences. In addition, fellows may choose to rotate at a fellow level on a number of specialty services including hematopathology, neuropathology, GI pathology and cytopathology. The program remains flexible for those with specific interests or requirements. Vacation and elective time is built in. We are committed to making this a meaningful, well-rounded experience in surgical pathology, with a goal of engendering a sense of confidence in the practice of surgical pathology. Between three and five fellowship positions are offered each year.

Requirements: These positions are open to residents or applicants who have completed their training in AP and are Board eligible or certified. A California medical license is required.

Stipends: Support is commensurate with the candidate's level of training.

Applications: Please contact Fellowship Coordinator to obtain the requirements and application, submit a curriculum vitae and the names of three references to: Charles R. Lassman, MD, PhD, Vice Chair for Clinical Education, Department of Pathology and Laboratory Medicine, David Geffen School of Medicine at UCLA, Room A7-149 CHS, Los Angeles, CA 90095-1732. Applications should be received by February 1 for the year preceding the fellowship, although applications are considered on a rolling basis. Fellowship Coordinator: Ms. Annetta Pierro

Phone: (310) 825-5719 • **Fax:** (310) 267-2058
Web site: www.pathology.ucla.edu

UNIVERSITY OF CALIFORNIA
SAN DIEGO MEDICAL CENTER
Surgical Pathology/Cytopathology Fellowship

Description: A one-year fellowship in general surgical (with extensive exposure to cytopathology) is offered by the Division of Anatomic Pathology (UCSD). Up to four positions are available for AP or AP/CP residents who are interested in receiving focused and intensive training in diagnostic surgical pathology and cytopathology. The specific rotations include: 1) Provisional "hot seat" diagnosis (with sign-out of outside consults), 2) Gross Room and Frozen Section Supervisor, 3) Rotation at Children's Hospital, San Diego, and 4) Rotation at the Southern California Kaiser Permanente Medical Group (~50,000 surgical specimens). Each rotation will comprise one-fourth of the 12-month-long fellowship; and, with the exception of the Kaiser Permanente and Children's Hospital rotations, all rotations will be at the UCSD teaching hospitals (Hillcrest and La Jolla with ~16,000 surgical specimens and ~25,000 cytology specimens).

Requirements: Two years of anatomic pathology residency before starting the fellowship; eligibility to train in California.

Stipends: As of 2009, $49,095 for PGY III, $50,987 for PGY IV, $52,905 for PGY V.

Applications: For applications and additional information, please contact
Noel Weidner, MD, Director of Anatomic Pathology, Department of Pathology, Mail Code 8720; University of California, San Diego, Medical Center, 200 West Arbor Drive, San Diego, CA 92103-8320.

Phone: (619) 543-2616 • **Fax:** (619) 543-5249 • **E-mail:** noweidner@ucsd.edu

---

UNIVERSITY OF CALIFORNIA
SAN FRANCISCO MEDICAL CENTER
Surgical Pathology Fellowship

Description: A one-year fellowship in general surgical pathology is offered by the Division of Surgical Pathology. Up to seven positions a year are available for AP or AP/CP residents who are interested in receiving focused and intensive training in diagnostic surgical pathology. The specific rotations include: 1) provisional "hot seat' diagnosis, 2) supervision of the gross room and frozen sections, 3) outside consult cases, 4) renal biopsies, transplant biopsies, and those cases submitted for electron microscopy, immunohistochemistry, or molecular diagnostics 5) a surgical pathology rotation within the Department, and 6) elective time (i.e., choice of cytology, dermatopathology, neuropathology, molecular diagnostics, and/or research). All rotations are at the UCSF/Mt.Zion campuses, which include all general surgical pathology specimens from both Moffitt and Mt. Zion Cancer Center Hospitals (about 30,000 surgicals).

Requirements: Two years of anatomic pathology residency are required before starting the fellowship.

Types and Numbers of Appointments: 7

Stipends: As of 2009, $49,095.00 for PGY III, $50,987.00 for PGY IV, and $52,905.00 for PGY V.

Applications: Director: Linda Ferrell, MD, Professor and Vice Chair, Director of Surgical Pathology
Associate Director: Joseph Rabban, MD, MPH
For applications and information, please visit our website.

Phone: (415) 353-1633 • **Fax:** (415) 353-1200
Web site: http://pathology.ucsf.edu/education/fellowship/fs-surgical.html

CEDARS-SINAI MEDICAL CENTER

Surgical Pathology Fellowship

Description: A one-year fellowship is offered to provide advanced training and experience in surgical pathology. Cedars-Sinai is a 969-bed tertiary medical center at which approximately 50,000 surgical pathology specimens are accessioned annually in the Department of Pathology. All specialty areas of surgical pathology are represented with a fully subspecialized AP structure. The fellowship provides 2 months of elective during which a research project may be done or expertise gained in one or two specialty areas. Training and experience in cytopathology, electron microscopy, immunohistochemistry, flow cytometry, and molecular diagnostics also are available. The fellow is expected to participate in a clinically applied or translational research effort, present at tumor board and other conferences, and engage in resident teaching and departmental administrative functions. Two fellows are selected each year.

Requirements: A minimum of two years of training in anatomic pathology. A California medical license is required at the time of appointment.

Stipends: Commensurate with level of postgraduate training.

Applications: For an application, information and correspondence, contact the program coordinator: LeeTanya Marion-Murray, Department of Pathology, Cedars-Sinai Medical Center, 8700 Beverly Blvd., S. Tower Room 8709, Los Angeles, CA 90048

Phone: (310) 423-6941 • **Fax:** (310) 423-5881 • **E-mail:** marionl@cshs.org

---

UNIVERSITY OF CHICAGO HOSPITALS

Surgical Pathology Fellowship

Description: The University of Chicago Department of Pathology offers a one- to two-year fellowship in surgical pathology with opportunities for either clinical or translational research. The fellowship offers training in an academic, tertiary care center receiving 29,000 cases annually. The diagnostic material includes specimens from most fields of pathology with a relatively high proportion of gastrointestinal, liver, gynecologic, bone and soft tissue, breast, urologic and head and neck cases. Large numbers of specimens are also received for consultant opinions. The University of Chicago is an active transplant center (kidney, liver, heart, lung and bone marrow). The fellow supervises junior residents, assists in frozen sections, participates in the daily diagnostic sign-out and handles a portion of consultation material. The fellow also presents cases at various clinicopathologic conferences and assumes some responsibility for teaching of residents and medical students. We offer an active basic scientific, translational and clinicopathologic research program. The optional second year of training may be devoted entirely to laboratory investigation. Research training is tailored to each fellow.

Requirements: A minimum of three years training in anatomic pathology or four years training that combines anatomic and clinical pathology. The candidate must be able to obtain an Illinois medical license.

Stipends: Commensurate with level of training.

Applications: Submit a letter of application accompanied by a curriculum vitae to
Thomas Krausz, MD, FRCPath, Director, Surgical Pathology Fellowship, Department of Pathology MC 6101, University of Chicago Hospitals, 5841 South Maryland Avenue, Chicago, IL 60637.

Phone: (773) 834-8541 • **Fax:** (773) 834-7644 • **E-mail:** thomas.krausz@uchospitals.edu

UNIVERSITY OF COLORADO DENVER SCHOOL OF MEDICINE

Surgical Pathology Fellowship

Description: The Surgical Pathology Fellowship at the University of Colorado is a one-year fellowship program with 2 positions per year which provides the trainee with advanced training and experience in general surgical pathology at a busy academic medical center. The department sees approximately 21,000 surgical pathology specimens per year and an addtional 4,500 non-gynecologic cytology specimens, as well as 1,500 fine needle aspirations. The fellowship consists of 10 months of structured training, predominantly as a "hot-seat" fellowship, such that the fellow previews all surgical cases and initiates appropriate workup of them. Additionally, the fellow is responsible for reviewing all outside cases sent to this institution for consultations and review, as well as graduated responsibility for covering the frozen section laboratory. Additional opportunities include teaching medical students in small group sessions. The remaining months of the fellowship can be individually tailored to meet the needs of the fellow and spent in clinical or basic research or used for more rigorous training in various areas of surgical pathology.

Requirements: Applicants must have completed a minimum of 3 years of post-graduate training at an ACGME-accredited residency program.

Stipends: Commensurate with level of post-graduate training.

Applications: The CAP standardized fellowship application form is preferred. Applications accepted until December of the year before the fellowship begins.

Please address all inquiries to:

Patricia Braund, Residency/Fellowship Coordinator, University of Colorado Denver School of Medicine, Dept of Pathology, 12631 E. 17th Avenue, Box B216, Mail Stop 6511, Aurora, CO 80045. patricia.braund@ucdenver.edu

Phone: (303) 724-3483 • **Fax:** (303) 724-1105
Web site: www.uchsc.edu/pathology

CREIGHTON UNIVERSITY MEDICAL CENTER AND AFFILIATED HOSPITALS

Surgical Pathology Fellowship

Description: A one-year fellowship is offered in general diagnostic surgical pathology. The program is designed to provide a concentrated experience in diagnostic surgical pathology and to allow increasing clinical responsibility in preparation for independent practice. The department sees a wide range of material and has excellent resources for immunohistochemistry, flow cytometry, image analysis, electron microscopy, and molecular pathology. The fellow will participate in resident teaching, function as a consultant to the clinical staff, and participate in interdisciplinary conferences, in addition to the supervision of the gross laboratory, signing out cases, and providing frozen section diagnoses. Nine months will be spent on surgical pathology rotation with up to 3 months in dedicated elective rotations (EM, Molecular pathology, renal pathology, cytopathology, dermatopathology, etc.). Active participation in translational research is encouraged and supported.

Requirements: Completed 3 years of AP training or 4 years of AP/CP training. Must have passed USMLE step 3 and be eligible for a Nebraska medical license.

Stipends: Commensurate with level of postgraduate training (HO-5= $56,000.00)

Applications: Applications can be downloaded from the department Web site (http://pathology.creighton.edu/index.php). The application and supporting documents should be submitted by July 1, 2008 for July 1, 2009 start date addressed to Pathology Residency Program Director, Creighton University Medical Center, 601 North 30th Street, Omaha, NE 68131.

Phone: (402) 280-3436 • **Fax:** (402) 280-5247 • **E-mail:** patholres@creighton.edu
For more information please contact: Residency Program Director, Department of Pathology, Creighton University Medical Center, 601 North 30th Street, Omaha, NE 68131.

EMORY UNIVERSITY AFFILIATED HOSPITALS

Department of Pathology and Laboratory Medicine

Surgical Pathology & Subspecialty Fellowship

Description: Three fellowship positions are offered, each for a one-year period, with activities centered at Emory University and Grady Memorial Hospitals. The combined number of surgical specimens processed is over 63,394 annually. Responsibilities of each fellow include independent diagnostic activities, including frozen section consultations, instruction of residents and medical students, participation in the departmental quality assurance program, and the planning and execution of a research project. The program is designed to develop general expertise in surgical pathology for residents desiring to enter private practice or to achieve special competence in an area of surgical pathology for individuals planning an academic career. Research resources include electron microscopy, image analysis, immunohistology, tissue microarrays, in situ hybridization, polymerase chain reaction, flow cytometry, eDNA microarray facility. All subspecialty areas of surgical and medical pathology are represented by the case material in the Emory health care system. Depending on the career goals of the fellows, the diagnostic and research activities may additionally center on a subspecialty area such as gastrointestinal, pulmonary, renal and genitourinary, pulmonary, GYN and breast pathology.

Requirements: Completion of 2-3 years of AP and 3-4 years of AP/CP, USMLE Step 3 for PG-3

Stipends: Commensurate with training and experience.

Staff: Sanjay Logani MD, Program Director.

Applications: See Emory University Residency listing.

Phone: (404) 727-4283 • **E-mail:** mmojonn@emory.edu
Web site: www.emory.edu/Pathology/

GEORGE WASHINGTON UNIVERSITY MEDICAL CENTER

Surgical Pathology Fellowship

Description: The Division of Anatomic Pathology offers a one-year fellowship position in surgical pathology. The program offers the fellows advanced comprehensive training in diagnostic surgical pathology, and is designed to provide the necessary skills for a successful transition to an attending pathologist. The fellow signs out cases with appropriate supervision and instruction by the senior faculty. Participation in quality assurance, intraoperative consultations, intra- and inter-departmental conferences and teaching is required. Two months of elective time in a specialized area is provided, and participation in research is encouraged.

Requirements: Applicants for the program should have completed at least three years of straight AP or four years of combined AP/CP training and must be eligible for a District of Columbia medical license.

Stipends: Commensurate with level of training.

Applications: Inquiries concerning the program should be received at the latest by December 31 one year before the anticipated starting date. Write to Sana O. Tabbara, MD, Director Division of Anatomic Pathology, The George Washington University Medical Center, Ross Hall #502, 2300 Eye Street, NW, Washington, DC 20037.

Phone: (202) 994-3391 • **Fax:** (202) 994-2618

MEDICAL COLLEGE OF GEORGIA HOSPITAL AND CLINICS

Surgical Pathology Fellowship

Description: A one-year fellowship in surgical pathology is offered by the Division of Surgical Pathology. Based in a tertiary care university hospital and Children's Medical Center, the program provides advanced training and responsibility in diagnostic surgical pathology through teaching conferences, rotations which include preliminary diagnosis of all cases, frozen section interpretation, gross room supervision, consult service, and elective time for subspecialty and/or research experience. The laboratory examines 12,000 surgical specimens and 1,500 frozen sections per year. The fellow is given responsibility in signing out with appropriate supervision by senior faculty. Teaching activities include unknown case conferences, journal club, case presentations, conference presentations, and research presentations where applicable. The Department has a close relationship with the Center for Biotechnology & Genomic Medicine, and the Director and Associate Director of this Center have their academic affiliaton in the Department of Pathology.

Requirements: Applicants should have completed four years of an AP/CP or three years of AP residency program. USMLE Step III must be completed prior to beginning the fellowship.

Types and Numbers of Appointments: Surgical Pathology Fellowships: 1

Stipends: Commensurate with PGY5 pay level or candidate's level of training.

Staff: Paul W Biddinger MD (Univ Cincinnati 1979) Director Surgical Pathology Fellowship Program, Chief, Section of Anatomic Pathology, Director Autopsy Services, Director Immunopathology; **Michael Boyd** MD (Univ of California at Davis 1985) pathologists' assistant; **John H Crosby** MD (Univ Tennessee 1967) anatomic pathology, cytopathology; **D. Greer Falls** MD (Med Univ South Carolina 1979) anatomic pathology, Director Pathology Residency Program; **Anita S Kulkarya** PhD (Univ North Texas 1990) anatomic pathology; Director Cancer Cytogenetics Laboratory; **Jeffrey R Lee** MD (Northwestern Univ 1975) Chief, Laboratory Service, VA Hospital, Augusta; **Nidia Messias** MD (Faculdade de Medicina da Universidade Federal do Ceara 1988) anatomic pathology; **Cuong Nguyen** MD (Uninformed Services Univ of Health Sciences, The F. Edward Hebert Sch of Med 1994) anatomic pathology; **Preetha Ramalingam** MBBS (Rajah Muthiah Med Col, India 1992) anatomic pathology; Associate Director Pathology Residency Program; **Michelle D Reid-Nicholson** MBBS (Univ West Indies 1995) anatomic pathology; Director Cytopathology; **Suash Sharma** MD (All India Inst of Med Sciences 1992) anatomic pathology, Director Neuromuscular Laboratory; **Daniel Sheehan** MD (Washington Univ School of Medicine 2001) dermatopathology.

Applications: Inquiries and requests for application should be addressed to Shannon Williford, Fellowship Coordinator, Medical College of Georgia, Department of Pathology, 1120 15th Street, BA-2576, Augusta, GA 30912.

Phone: (706) 721-5118 • **Fax:** (706) 721-7781 • **E-mail:** swillifo@mail.mcg.edu
Web site: http://www.mcg.edu/som/pathology

HARBOR-UCLA MEDICAL CENTER

Department of Pathology

Surgical Pathology Fellowship

Description: This one-year fellowship is designed to provide practice-level experience and responsibility in diagnostic surgical pathology. The Fellow will participate in the daily activities of the division of Surgical Pathology as a Junior Attending staff, assuming responsibility for first-look review of all surgical cases with junior residents and sign-out of uncomplicated surgical pathology cases. Other rotations include intraoperative frozen section experience and the opportunity for sign-out of referred cases with senior staff. The program provides for elective months of additional advanced training in subspecialty areas such as GI pathology, GYN pathology, dermatopathology, hematopathology, neuropathology, cytopathology, electron microscopy and molecular biology. Research opportunities are also available in a variety of subspecialty areas of surgical pathology. The Fellow will be able to participate in a wide variety of clinically and research-oriented intra- and inter-departmental educational conferences.

Requirements: Applicant will have completed at least three years in straight AP or four years combined AP/CP training by the time the fellowship starts. A California medical license will be needed.

Stipends: Fellows will be paid at the level of fifth-year residents ($61,443) at this institution.

Applications: For application and additional information, please contact

Shi-Kaung Peng, MD, PhD, Director of Surgical Pathology, Harbor-UCLA Medical Center, 1000 W Carson St, Torrance, CA 90509.

Phone: (310) 222-2201 • **Fax:** (310) 222-5333 • **E-mail:** adflores@dhs.lacounty.gov
Web site: http://www.harbor-ucla.org/pathology

HARTFORD HOSPITAL

Department of Pathology and Laboratory Medicine

Surgical Pathology Fellowship

Description: The Department of Pathology at Hartford Hospital sponsors four advanced level one-year fellowships in surgical pathology. The Division of Anatomic Pathology represents an extensive training resource based on more than 37,000 surgical accessions. The program features, in addition to the general surgical pathology rotations, opportunities for extensive experience in all subspecialty areas. Experience in Immunohistochemistry and Molecular Pathology is available as elective rotations. Opportunities for teaching at the student and resident levels are available as are opportunities for presentation of diagnostic material at clinical pathological conferences. Investigative work and clinical-pathologic research activities are encouraged and such opportunities are readily available.

Requirements: Candidates must be Board -certified or eligible in AP or AP/CP and must have passed USMLE Step 3.

Stipends: See general description of Hartford Hospital Residency Program.

Applications: Fellowship appointments are effective July 1 of each academic year. Inquiries regarding applications should be addressed to:

Srinivas Mandavilli, MD, Surgical Pathology Fellowship Program Director, Department of Pathology, Hartford Hospital, 80 Seymour St, PO Box 5037, Hartford, CT 06102-5037.

Phone: (860) 545-6113 • **E-mail:** cdavids @clpct.com
Web site: http://www.harthosp.org/education

UNIVERSITY OF ILLINOIS COLLEGE OF MEDICINE

Surgical Pathology Fellowship

Description: A one-year fellowship in general surgical pathology is offered by the Section of Surgical Pathology at the University of Illinois Medical Center at Chicago. The Medical Center is a 441-bed, tertiary care, university hospital, which receives 12,000 surgical pathology specimens yearly. A wide variety of specimens are encountered, with special emphasis on melanoma, ophthalmic, soft tissue, hepatic, gastrointestinal, dermatologic and transplantation (heart, lung, liver, kidney, small bowel and pancreas) pathology. The fellowship is designed to provide a broad and intensive experience in diagnostic Surgical Pathology with emphasis on independent thought. The fellow will be responsible for participating in sign-out sessions and frozen section interpretation, presenting cases at hospital-wide clinicopathologic conferences, supervising residents and pathology assistants, and teaching medical students and residents. Resources for diagnostic and research activities include immunohistochemistry, flow cytometry, electron microscopy, laser capture microdissection, tissue mircroarrays and molecular pathology. Elective months are available. Research experience is strongly encouraged.

Requirements: Applicants should have completed four years of training in a combined AP/CP residency or three years in AP, USMLE Step 3 and must be eligible for a permanent Illinois license.

Stipends: Commensurate with level of training. The Web site of the Graduate Medical Education Office (http://www.uic.edu/com/gme/) contains specific information regarding stipends and benefits.

Applications: Address letter of interest with curriculum vitae to:
Elizabeth L. Wiley, MD, Department of Pathology, University of Illinois at Chicago (MC 847), 840 S. Wood Street, Suite 130 CSN, Chicago, IL 60612-7335.

Phone: (312) 996-3879
Web site: http://pathology.uic.edu

INDIANA UNIVERSITY SCHOOL OF MEDICINE

Surgical Pathology Fellowship

Description: The goal of this program is to provide one year of advanced training in surgical pathology through exposure to a wide range of diverse cases at an academic medical center. The trainee will actively participate in all aspects of surgical pathology, including the signout of in-house and consultation cases, as well as participation in an active frozen section service. The applicant will be expected to take periodic frozen section call, with faculty back-up. The case material (approximately 60,000 cases) is enriched in oncological, transplantation-related and GI specimens that originate from 7 hospitals. There is subspecialty sign-out in urological, hepatic and medical kidney that are available as electives. Attendance at teaching conferences, including a daily consensus conference, is expected. Participation in one or more research projects is encouraged.

Requirements: Candidates must have completed an AP or AP/CP pathology residency and hold (or be eligible for) a medical license in the state of Indiana. If candidates are not citizens of the U.S., they must hold a valid visa.

Stipends: Stipends are commensurate with the year of postgraduate training in pathology.

Staff: Oscar W Cummings MD, Director, Division of Surgical Pathology; **Thomas M Ulbright** MD, Director Anatomic Pathology; **Narasimham Agaram** MBBS; **Sunil Badve** MBBS; **Jose Bonnin** MD; **Jey-Hsin Chen** MD; **Liang Cheng** MD; **Rosen Dimitrov** MD; **Robert Emerson** MD; **Rong Fan** MD; **Philip Faught** MD; **Eyas Hattab** MBBS; **Muhammad Idrees** MBBS; **Lisbeth Larsson** MD; **Helen Michael** MD; **Paul Musto** MD; **Carrie Phillips** MD; **Romil Saxena** MD; **Don John Summerlin** DMD; **Xiaoyan Wang** MD,PhD.

Applications: Applications (CV + 3 letters of reference) should be submitted (preferably by email) by June 30 of the year prior to the intended fellowship. Apply to Oscar W. Cummings, MD, Division of Surgical Pathology, Department of Pathology and Laboratory Medicine, Clarian Pathology Laboratory, 350 W. 11th Street, Indianapolis, IN 46202

Phone: (317) 491-6486 • **Fax**: (317) 491-6419 • **E-mail**: ocumming@iupui.edu
Web site: http://www.pathology.iupui.edu

UNIVERSITY OF IOWA HOSPITALS AND CLINICS

Surgical Pathology Fellowship

Description: A one-year fellowship in surgical pathology (three or four positions) is offered by the Division of Surgical Pathology. Based in a 772-bed quaternary care university hospital, the program provides advanced training and responsibility in diagnostic surgical pathology through teaching conferences, rotations which include preliminary diagnosis of all cases, frozen section interpretation, gross room supervision, consult service, and elective time for subspecialty and/or research experience. Special laboratory expertise may be gained in molecular pathology, and immunopathology. The laboratory examines 32,000 surgical specimens and approximately 4,000 frozen sections per year.

Requirements: Applicants should have completed an AP or AP/CP residency program.

Stipends: Commensurate with level of training.

Staff: **Ryan Askeland** MD; **Jo Benda** MD; **Laila Dahmoush** MD; **Barry DeYoung** MD, Director; **Chris Jensen** MD; **Pat Kirby** MD; **Frank Mitros** MD; **Robert Robinson** MD, PhD.

Applications: Should be made to

Barry R. De Young MD, Director, Surgical Pathology, Department of Pathology, 200 Hawkins Drive, 5244 RCP University of Iowa, Iowa City, IA 52242.

Phone: (319) 356-4433 • **Fax:** (319) 384-8052 • **E-mail:** deyoungb@healthcare.uiowa.edu

JACKSON MEMORIAL HOSPITAL/JACKSON HEALTH SYSTEM/ UNIVERSITY OF MIAMI SCHOOL OF MEDICINE

Surgical Pathology Fellowship

Description: A one-year fellowship is offered to provide advanced training and experience in diagnostic surgical pathology and immunohistochemistry. The program is designed to provide opportunities in intraoperative consultations and sign out sessions in surgical pathology subspecialty areas including GU, GYN, Breast, GI, Lung, and Head and Neck pathology.

Participation in departmental conferences, medical student and resident teaching, and research activities is integral to the program.

Requirements: Candidates must be board certified or eligible in anatomic pathology or anatomic and clinical pathology and able to obtain a Florida medical license.

Stipends: Commensurate with level of training.

Applications: A letter of intent, curriculum vitae, and three letters of reference should be submitted to: Carmen Gomez-Fernandez, MD
Department of Pathology
Holtz Building, Room 2050
1611 NW 12 Avenue
Miami, FL. 33136

Phone: (305) 243-5229 • **Fax:** (305) 243-3704 • **E-mail:** cgomez3@med.miami.edu

JOHNS HOPKINS MEDICAL INSTITUTIONS

Surgical Pathology Post Residency Experience

Description: While Johns Hopkins does not offer a fellowship in Surgical Pathology we do offer a one-year program that provides advanced experience and responsibility on a surgical pathology service which accessions close to 80,000 specimens per year. The successful applicant will be appointed as a junior faculty member in the Johns Hopkins University School of Medicine and a medical Staff appointment in the Johns Hopkins Hospital and the Johns Hopkins Bayview Medical Center. Responsibilities include interpretation and reporting of frozen sections, sign out of surgical cases and consult cases, and supervision of residents in the surgical pathology cutting area. There will also be exposure to numerous ancillary techniques utilized in surgical pathology including immuno histochemistry, cytogenetic, and molecular biologic studies. There will be opportunities for research and for electives in surgical pathology-related subspecialty areas. The appointed individuals will participate in a few clinical interdepartmental conferences, including surgical and medical grand rounds.

Requirements: Four years of AP training or four years of AP/CP training. A Maryland medical license is required prior to starting date. Non-U.S. citizens must hold or be able to obtain the appropriate employment visa. A J-1 visa is not appropriate for the position.

Stipends: Commensurate with applicant's level of training and experience.

Applications: Application, including supporting documents, should be submitted by September 1 of the year preceding the following July 1st start date. Please send curriculum vitae and four letters of recommendation to
William H. Westra, MD, Professor, Surgical Pathology, The Johns Hopkins Hospital, Weinberg Bldg, 2nd Floor, Rm 2242, 401 N Broadway, Baltimore, MD 21231.

Phone: (410) 955-5043 • **Fax:** (443) 287-3818
Web site: http://pathology.jhu.edu

EOE

UNIVERSITY OF KENTUCKY MEDICAL CENTER

Department of Pathology and Laboratory Medicine

Surgical Pathology Fellowship

Description: A one-year fellowship in surgical pathology is offered at the University of Kentucky Chandler Medical Center. The Division accessions over 18,000 cases per year and performs approximately 3,000 frozen sections. A high proportion of surgical accessions are related to the diagnosis and staging of neoplasms and specialized experiences are available in hematologic, cardiac, renal, neuro, gynecologic and uropathology in addition to immunopathology, molecular pathology, electron microscopy and flow cytometry. The program includes 9 months of surgical pathology and 3 months of elective. Approximately one month of vacation/travel is included. A combined 2 year surgical pathology/cytopathology fellowship leading to Cytopathology Board eligibility is offered.

Requirements: Individuals should have completed Board requirements in anatomic pathology and must be eligible for licensure in the state of Kentucky.

Stipends: Commensurate with year of postgraduate training in pathology plus $1,200 per year available for attending meetings and purchasing books.

Staff: **Michael Cibull** MD; Director, Fellowship Program; **Kimberly Absher** MD; **Yolanda M. Brill** MD; **Rouzan Karabakhtsian** MD; **Melissa V Kesler** MD, Associate Director Fellowship Program; **Eun Y. Lee** MD; **Bonnie Mitchell** MD (VAMC); **William O'Connor** MD; **Luis M Samayoa** MD (VAMC); **Dianne Wilson** MD.

Applications:

Universal Application, including CV and letters of recommendation, should be sent to Michael Cibull, MD, Director, Surgical Pathology Fellowship, Department of Pathology and Laboratory Medicine, University of Kentucky Medical Center, 800 Rose Street, Suite MS-117, Lexington, KY 40536-0298.

Phone: (859) 257-9548

UNIVERSITY OF KANSAS MEDICAL CENTER

Surgical Pathology Fellowship

Description: This one-year accredited program is designed to train up to two well-rounded academically oriented surgical pathologists and to provide advanced training in diagnostic surgical pathology. The fellowship will provide extensive training in all aspects of surgical pathology, including head and neck, neuropathology, endocrine, GYN, GU, GI, breast, bone and soft tissue, liver, transplant pathology, dermatopathology and hematopathology. Approximately, 17,500 surgical specimens are evaluated each year in our hospital-based laboratory.

Particularly strong interdepartmental programs exist in cancer prevention and control, epidemiology and biostatistics; and fellows have the opportunity to participate in clinical and basic research in addition to diagnostic cases. After a training period, the fellow is expected to assume graded sign-out responsibilities under supervision. The fellow has first-hand experience in signing out cases, intra operative consultations, including frozen sections and review of outside consultations. Participation in conferences and teaching pathology residents are required. The program is designed to provide the successful candidate with an in-depth experience that will include immunohistochemistry, immunofluorescence, electron microscopy, molecular diagnostics, flow cytometry and health services research. Fellows are encouraged to design and complete a research project.

Requirements: Candidates must be Board eligible or certified in anatomic pathology or anatomic and clinical pathology and must have or be eligible for an unrestricted license to practice medicine in Kansas. Preference will be given to candidates who have demonstrated an interest in pursuing an academic career in anatomic pathology.

Stipends: Commensurate with the level of training and experience.

Staff: Mark Cunningham MD (Univ Minnesota 1989) Associate Professor; hematopathology; **Ivan Damjanov** MD, PhD (Zagreb Univ, Yugoslavia 1964) Professor; Director of autopsy, surgical pathology, renal pathology, liver pathology, transplant pathology, fertility and testicular parthology, GI pathology and electron microscopy; **Fang Fan** MD, PhD (Univ Shanghai 1989) Associate Professor; Director Cytopathology; breast and gynecologic pathology, Head & Neck pathology, thyroid and salivary gland pathology; **Timothy Fields** MD, PhD (Duke Univ 1997) Associate Professor; renal pathology, transplant pathology; **James Fishback** MD (Univ Kansas 1983) Associate Professor; autopsy, infectious diseases; **Garth Fraga** MD (Univ Chicago 1994) A&C Pathologist; dermatopathology; **Roy Jensen** MD (Vanderbilt Univ 1984) Director of Cancer Center; breast pathology; **Rashna Madan** MD, (Kasturba Medical College 1996) Assistant Professor; cytopathology, surgical pathology, GI pathology, lung pathology soft tissue pathology and thyroid pathology; **Kathy Newell** MD (Univ Kansas 1992) Assistant Professor; nerve and muscle pathology; neuropathology; **Ossama Tawfik** MD, PhD (Univ Cairo 1978) Program Director, surgical pathology, cytopathology, breast pathology, GYN pathology, GU pathology, interstitial lung diseases, immunohistochemistry, image analysis and telepathology; **Patricia Thomas** MD, MA (NYC 1986) Chair; Professor, surgical pathology, cytopathology, breast pathology, pediatric pathology, GYN pathology; **Lowell Tilzer** MD, PhD (Univ Kansas 1976) Professor; Director Clinical Labs;hematopathology, chemistry, flow cytometry, molecular pathology & transfusion medicine; **Da Zhang** MD (Shandong Univ, China 1985) Assistant Professor; surgical pathology, renal pathology, electron microscopy, hematopathology, molecular pathology.

Applications: Send or email completed standardized application to: Charla Tunget, Program Coordinator, University of Kansas School of Medicine, Department of Pathology and Laboratory Medicine, Division of Surgical Pathology, 3901 Rainbow Blvd, 2006 Wahl Hall West, Mail Stop 3045, Kansas City, KS 66160-7410. (Have letters of recommendation addressed to: Ossama Tawfik, MD, PhD, Professor, Vice Chairman, Director of Anatomic and Surgical Pathology). Additional information may be obtained at the number listed below.

Phone: (913) 588-7076 • **Fax:** (913) 588-7073 • **E-mail:** ctunget@kumc.edu

LOUISIANA STATE UNIVERSITY HEALTH SCIENCES CENTER SHREVEPORT

Surgical Pathology Fellowship

Description: The Department of Pathology of LSUHSC-S offers a one-year surgical pathology fellowship designed to provide a comprehensive training under the close supervision of experienced attending pathologists. The goal of the program is to train a well-rounded general surgical pathologist through extensive exposure to diverse and interesting clinical material and active research experience, preparing the fellow for either an academic career or private practice. The fellowship is structured to achieve advanced diagnostic skills through an integrated approach in a setting of academic excellence. The fellow participates in, and is responsible for presenting at interdepartmental clinical conferences, multidisciplinary tumor board and resident teaching conferences. The candidate can expect graded responsibilities. This will begin with gross room supervision, preparation and interpretation of intraoperative consultations, independently reviewing and working-up routine surgical and consultation cases with ancillary techniques, preparing reports and ultimately assuming independent sign-out responsibility. The fellowship program also offers elective rotations that include cytopathology, molecular pathology, hematopathology/flow cytometry, renal pathology, neuropathology muscle pathology, and forensic pathology. Completion of a research project is expected by the end of the fellowship year with a presentation to faculty, staff, and peers at the Annual Albert G. Smith Resident Research Forum.

Requirements: Applicants must have completed their AP or AP/CP training and be AP or AP/CP Board eligible/ certified by July 1 of year of training. A Louisiana medical license will be needed. Additionally, the qualified applicant must have good English language skills to effectively communicate with clinicians and to satisfy their teaching responsibilities. Foreign Medical Graduates must have an ECFMG Certificate and a valid J-1 Visa.

Types and Numbers of Appointments: One position is available.

Stipends: Depending on PGY level. Professional allowance also provided.

Staff: Stephen M. Bonsib MD, AP/CP, Chairman of the Department of Pathology, renal pathology, male genitourinary, surgical pathology, electron microscopy; **Jaiyeola Thomas-Ogunniyi** MD, Director of Surgical Pathology; cytopathology; **Fleurette Abreo** MD, renal pathology, cytopathology, breast pathology; **Marjorie Fowler** MD, Residency Program Director; neuropathology, endocrine pathology, electron microscopy; **Xin Gu** MD, renal pathology, genitourinary pathology, electron microscopy; **James Cotelingam** MD, Director of Clinical Pathology Division; hematopathology, lymphomas, leukemias; **Diana Veillon** MD, flow cytometry, hematopathology, molecular pathology; **Mary Lowery-Nordberg** PhD, molecular pathology; **Songlin Zhang** MD, cytopathology, surgical pathology, GYN pathology.

Applications: Address inquiries to:
Lisa LaChance, BA
Department of Pathology, LSUHSC-Shreveport
P.O. Box 33932
Shreveport, LA 71130-3932
E-mail: llacha@lsuhsc.edu
Web site: http://www.sh.lsuhsc.edu/pathology

LOYOLA UNIVERSITY MEDICAL CENTER

Department of Pathology

Surgical Pathology Fellowship

Description: The surgical pathology fellowship is designed to provide a broad and in depth exposure to surgical pathology material as well as diagnostic molecular techniques at Loyola University Medical Center. It also provides opportunities for development of sub-specialty training in other branches of surgical pathology such as dermatopathology, neuropathology, hematopathology, cytolopathology, renal, gastrointestinal, head and neck, pulmonary, breast and transplant pathology. The fellow will also be involved in QA and QC evaluation. Opportunities are also available for training in molecular pathology for individuals interested in academic careers including disease-oriented basic research, development of molecularly-based diagnostic technologies, and molecularly-oriented clinical research. This training will consist of rotations through selected basic and applied laboratories, and an in-depth research-oriented experience under the supervision of faculty members.

Requirements: Applicants should have completed four years of training in AP or AP/CP.

Stipends: Commensurate with the year of postgraduate training.

Applications: Send cover letter, CV, and three letters of recommendation to:
Vicki Baertschi, Fellowship Training Program, Loyola University Medical Center, Department of Pathology, Bldg., 103, room 0177, 2160 S First Avenue, Maywood, IL 60153. Additional information may be obtained from the Pathology Education office at the number listed below.

Phone: (708) 216-5591 • **Fax:** (708) 216-8225
Web site: http://www.stritch.luc.edu/depts/path/index.htm

UNIVERSITY OF MASSACHUSETTS MEDICAL SCHOOL

Surgical (Selective) Pathology Fellowship

Description: This one-year fellowship is designed to provide experience in signing out surgical pathology cases for the transition from residency to practice. The Division of Anatomic Pathology accessions 57,000 surgical specimens and 64,000 cytology specimens per year. The attending staff includes 17 full-time specialty-oriented surgical pathologists, dermatopathologists and a neuropathologist. The fellow will be responsible for signing out general surgical pathology cases. In addition, he/she will perform frozen sections at various UMass Memorial campuses. There are opportunities for rotations through the specialty services, signing out cases under the supervision of the attending specialist. The fellow will teach grossing skills to beginning residents. The fellow will present cases at multi-disciplinary hospital conferences. There will be opportunities for experience in the diagnostic application of special techniques such as flow cytometry, immunohistochemistry and molecular diagnostics.

Requirements: Applicants must have completed a four-year AP/CP residency or three years of a straight AP residency and have passed Step III of the USMLE.

Stipends: Commensurate with the year of postgraduate training.

Applications: Send CV with names of three references and a letter describing career goals to Patti Davis, Pathology Residency/Fellow Coordinator, UMass Memorial Medical Center, Biotech Three, One Innovation Drive, Worcester, MA 01605.

Phone: (508) 793-6156 • **E-mail:** Patricia.Davis@umassmemorial.org.

McGAW MEDICAL CENTER OF NORTHWESTERN UNIVERSITY

Surgical Pathology Fellowship

Description: Applications are invited for a 1 year general Surgical Pathology fellowship with emphasis of gastrointestinal pathology starting July 1, 2011 in the Department of Pathology at Northwestern University's Feinberg School of Medicine (FSM), Chicago, IL. Northwestern Memorial Hospital, the main teaching hospital of FSM located in the magnificent ''gold coast'' area of downtown Chicago, is one of the largest referral centers in the midwest for patients with gastrointestinal, liver, pancreatic, urologic, and gynecologic/breast disorders. The pathology department accesses over 40,000 in-house and 2,300 consultation cases per year. The anatomic pathology staff includes experts in the fields of gastrointestinal/liver/pancreaticobiliary tract, urologic, breast, gynecologic, pulmonary, and soft tissue/bone pathology. The fellowship is designed to provide comprehensive training in diagnostic surgical pathology including standard diagnostic practices, immunohistochemistry, and specialized techniques. As the gastrointestinal, liver, and pancreaticobiliary tract pathology services constitute a major proportion of in-house and referral cases, fellowship training in these areas will be emphasized and translational research opportunities in gastrointestinal and liver pathology available. Additionally, the fellow may participate in the activities of the Neuropathology and Dermatopathology Departments, if desired. The candidate is expected to participate in the diagnosis of surgical pathology specimens, inter-departmental clinical conferences, frozen section analysis, and training of anatomic pathology residents. In addition, ample opportunities exist for scholarly collaborations in all areas of surgical pathology and for teaching 2nd year FSM medical students.

Requirements: Candidates must be board eligible or certified in anatomic pathology.

Stipends: The stipend is determined by previous pathology training and experience.

Applications: For inquiries and requests for applications contact the program coordinator: Irene Galace at i-galace@northwestern.edu

Address correspondence and references to:
William B. Laskin, MD, Associate Professor of Pathology
Feinberg 7-325, Surgical Pathology, Northwestern Memorial Hospital
Northwestern University Feinberg School of Medicine
251 E. Huron Street, Chicago, IL 60611

Phone: (312)926-1367 • **E-mail:** wbl769@northwestern.edu

For inquires regarding gastrointestinal/liver aspect of fellowship: Guang-Yu Yang, MD, PhD, Associate Professor of Pathology

Phone: (312) 503 0645 • **E-mail:** g-yang@northwestern.edu

MEMORIAL SLOAN-KETTERING CANCER CENTER
NEW YORK

Description: The Department of Pathology at MSKCC offers the following fellowship programs to individuals who have completed their basic training in pathology and who are interested in a concentrated and intensive exposure to a particular aspect of human tumor pathology.

ONCOLOGIC PATHOLOGY FELLOWSHIP

This is a one-year ACGME accredited program in tumor pathology, during which the fellows are actively engaged in the examination of the anatomic pathology material submitted to the Department, under the supervision of the Attending staff. The material comprises over 50,000 surgical specimens (including departmental consults, personal consults, and electron microscopic specimens) and approximately 40 autopsies per year. The program incorporates dedicated rotations in intraoperative consultation (frozen sections) and by subspecialty (bone/soft tissue, breast, dermatopathology, GI, GU, GYN, head and neck, hematopathology, and thoracic). An elective period is also provided. Participation by the fellows in either clinical or basic research projects during this year is highly encouraged.

CYTOPATHOLOGY FELLOWSHIP

This is a one-year ACGME accredited program in diagnostic cytopathology offered by the Cytology Service of the Department. During this period, the fellow is engaged in the examination of the cytopathologic material submitted to the service, under the supervision of the Attending staff. The material comprises approximately 35,000 specimens per year (17,000 gynecologic, 14,000 nongynecologic, and 4,000 FNAs). The program includes participation in the intraoperative cytology consultation service and interaction with the School of Cytotechnology run by the Cytology Service. Fellows are encouraged to participate in research projects with members of the Department and/or in cooperation with clinicians. There is a cytology-based Fine Needle Aspiration Service.

DIAGNOSTIC MOLECULAR PATHOLOGY FELLOWSHIP

This is a one-year program in diagnostic molecular pathology. During this period, the fellow will receive training in the performance and interpretation of various molecular diagnostic tests in the Laboratory of Diagnostic Molecular Pathology of the Department. The material submitted to the Laboratory consists of over 2,000 cases per year, including both hematopoietic and solid neoplasms, and marrow samples for monitoring of post-transplant engraftment status. Correlation with clinical and morphologic parameters is stressed, and ample opportunity is given for participation in research projects.

SURGICAL PATHOLOGY SUBSPECIALTY FELLOWSHIPS

Advanced training in the following subspecialty areas is available: Breast Pathology, Gastrointestinal Pathology, Genitourinary Pathology, Gynecologic Pathology, Head and Neck Pathology, Dermatopathology (ACGME accredited), Thoracic Pathology (ACGME accredited), and Hematopathology (ACGME accredited). These one-year programs provide intensive exposure to all the components of the respective subspecialty, concentrating on the investigative aspects. Clinical responsibilities are kept at a minimum in order to maximize the time to be devoted to projects carried out under supervision. Exposure to the various techniques used in that subspecialty (immunohistochemical, cytogenetic, molecular, etc.) and interaction with other clinical and basic departments working in the field are an integral part of the program. The basic research work is carried out in one of the laboratories of the Division of Molecular Pathology.

Facilities: Memorial Hospital for Cancer and Allied Diseases is a 425-bed hospital devoted to the care of patients with neoplastic diseases. The hospital is part of the Memorial Sloan-Kettering Cancer Center which also includes the Sloan-Kettering Institute for Cancer Research. There is an affiliation and close interaction between the clinical and research units of the Center and the Weill Medical College of Cornell University, as well as with Rockefeller University.

Stipends: The stipend is commensurate with the year of postgraduate training. Housing is available; professional liability insurance and health coverage are provided.

Staff: Marc K. Rosenblum MD Attending Pathologist and Chairman; Chief, Neuropathology and Autopsy Service; Chief, Cytopathology Service; **Cristina Antonescu** MD Associate Attending Pathologist; **Violetta V. Barbashina** MD Assistant Attending Pathologist; **Edi Brogi** MD, PhD Associate Attending Pathologist; **Klaus J. Busam** MD Attending Pathologist; **Diane L. Carlson** MD Assistant Attending Pathologist; Associate Director, Fellowship Training Programs; **Daniel A. Filippa** MD Attending Pathologist; Director, Hematopathology Fellowship Program; **Samson Fine** MD Assistant Attending Pathologist; **Ronald A. Ghossein** MD Associate Attending Pathologist; **Dilip Giri** MD Associate Attending Pathologist; **Anuradha Gopalan** MD Instructor; **Cyrus V. Hedvat** MD, PhD Assistant Attending Pathologist; **Nora Katabi** MD Instructor; **David S. Klimstra** MD Attending Pathologist; Chief, Surgical Pathology; **Marc Ladanyi** MD Attending Pathologist; Chief, Molecular Diagnostic Pathology Service; **Oscar Lin** MD, PhD Associate Attending Pathologist; **Andre L. Moreira** MD, PhD Assistant Attending Pathologist; **Melissa P. Murray** DO Instructor; **Kay J Park** MD Assistant Attending; **Victor E. Reuter** MD Attending Pathologist and Vice-Chairman; **Jinru Shia** MD Associate Attending Pathologist; **Robert A. Soslow** MD Attending Pathologist; **Lee K. Tan** MD Associate Attending Pathologist; **Laura H. Tang** MD, PhD Assistant Attending Pathologist; **Julie Teruya-Feldstein** MD Associate Attending Pathologist; **Satish Tickoo** MD Associate Attending Pathologist; **William Travis** MD Attending Pathologist; Director,

Thoracic Pathology Fellowship; **Cristina Vallejo** MD Assistant Attending Pathologist; **Maureen F. Zakowski** MD Attending Pathologist; Director, Fellowship Training Programs; **Karuna Garg** MD Instructor; **Melissa Pultzer** MD Assistant Attending; **Hikmait Al-Ahmadie** MD Assistant Attending; **Meera Hameed** MD Assistant Attending; **Natasha Rekhtman** MD Assistant Attending; **Efsevia Vakiani** MD Assistant Attending.

Applications: All fellowships are available to those who have completed their basic training in pathology, either AP or combined AP-CP, with at least two years of AP training in an accredited US or Canadian program. Dermatopathology fellowship applicants must have completed a residency in Dermatology, Anatomic Pathology or Anatomic and Clinical Pathology. All qualified applicants are welcome, but preference will be given to those committed to an academic career in pathology. An attempt will be made to identify individuals interested in combining two of these fellowships, under the assumption that this experience should provide them with a strong basis for a successful career in academic pathology. Application deadline: Oncologic Pathology-April 1, Cytopathology-March 1, other fellowships-April 1. Early application is encouraged.

Address inquiries to

Sophia Oreste, Department of Pathology
Memorial Sloan-Kettering Cancer Center, 1275 York Avenue, New York, NY 10065

Phone: (212) 639-6336 • **E-mail:** orestes @mskcc.org
Web site: http://www.mskcc.org/pathologyfellowships

MAYO SCHOOL OF GRADUATE MEDICAL EDUCATION

Department of Laboratory Medicine and Pathology

Surgical Pathology Fellowship

Description: Mayo Clinic's one-year, ACGME-accredited Surgical Pathology Fellowship offers the opportunity to evaluate and learn from an exceptionally large and diverse amount of pathologic material. Mayo processes over 330,000 specimens annually including 194,000 surgical; 76,000 cytology; and 61,000 consultative cases. Your rotation schedule will include intensive training in our frozen section lab practice where you will examine both routine and unusual neoplastic and non-neoplastic specimens. Fellows also assist in the sign-out of consultation cases and a variety of biopsy services. Elective rotations are also available in a variety of subspecialty areas including bone and soft tissue pathology, breast pathology, cardiovascular pathology, cytopathology, dermatopathology, endocrine pathology, gastrointestinal and hepatobiliary pathology, genitourinary and gynecologic pathology, hematopathology, molecular biology, cytogenetics and flow cytometry, neuropathology, ophthalmic, renal, and pulmonary pathology.

Requirements: Applicants should have completed an AP or AP/CP residency training program within the United States or Canada.

Stipends: Commensurate with level of training.

Applications: http://www.mayo.edu/msgme/application.html
Applications for each academic year, which begins in July, should be completed by January 1 of the previous year. Applicants are responsible for ensuring that all necessary materials are received by us prior to consideration for an interview. Positions will be offered beginning March 1 of the previous year. Address inquiries to Diva Salomao, MD, Director, Surgical Pathology Fellowship Program, Department of Pathology, Hilton 11, Mayo Clinic, 200 First Street, S.W., Rochester, MN 55905.

Phone: (507) 284-1196 • **E-mail:** pathologyeducation@mayo.edu
Web site: www.mayo.edu/msgme/lm-surgpath-rch.html

THE METHODIST HOSPITAL

Department of Pathology

General Surgical Pathology

Description: A one-year ACGME-accredited fellowship in Surgical Pathology is offered at The Methodist Hospital, a tertiary referral academic medical center, with over 30,000 annual surgical accessions. In addition to advanced training in general surgical pathology, the fellowship provides experiences in a broad spectrum of subspecialty areas under the guidance of faculty experts. Electives in surgical subspecialty areas, as well as in immunohistochemistry, flow cytometry, molecular diagnostics, hematopathology, and cytopathology are available. Rotation on a busy consultation service is included. Experience in quality management, laboratory management, teaching junior residents, and tumor board participation are part of the fellowship. Special rotations elsewhere in the Texas Medical Center may be arranged, e.g., The University of Texas-Houston, M.D. Anderson Cancer Center. The fellow will assume responsibility commensurate with his/her level of training experience. The fellow will be expected to participate in scholarly activities leading to publication.

Requirements: At least two years of training in Anatomic Pathology. Preferably AP or AP/CP Board-eligible. Must hold or be eligible for a Texas Physician In Training Permit or Licensure.

Stipends: Commensurate with level of postgraduate training.

Applications: Send inquiries to Mary R. Schwartz, MD, The Methodist Hospital, Department of Pathology, 6565 Fannin, M227, Houston, TX 77030.

Phone: (713) 441-3496 • **Fax:** (713) 441-3489 • **E-mail:** ljozwiak@tmhs.org
Web site: www.methodisthealth.com

UNIVERSITY OF MICHIGAN MEDICAL CENTER

Surgical Pathology Fellowship

Description: This one-year fellowship is designed to provide comprehensive training in diagnostic surgical pathology of both neoplastic and non-neoplastic diseases. The University of Michigan has a strong oncologic service with a full range of cancer-related clinical and research programs, and is also an active transplant center. A busy tertiary referral center, University Hospital generates over 65,000 surgical specimens annually. Transferred cases and a busy extramural consultant practice contribute to a total of nearly 80,000 cases accessioned annually in the surgical pathology laboratories. A large staff with a range of clinical and research interests allows fellows to gain unparalleled clinical experience while also participating in collaborative research projects. In addition to participation in a busy and varied general surgical pathology service with frozen section responsibility, the fellowship includes rotations on the following subspecialty services: Gastrointestinal Pathology, Genitourinary Pathology, Gynecologic Pathology, and Breast Pathology, with opportunities for signout of extramural consultation cases, and involvement in clinicopathologic conferences. In addition, ample time for electing experience in other areas of Anatomic Pathology, such as Dermatopathology and Cytopathology, is available. Teaching of residents and medical students is an important component of the experience. The laboratory is fully computerized which allows easy retrieval of specimens for teaching and research.

Requirements: Candidates must be board certified or eligible in anatomic pathology or AP/CP and must be eligible for a license to practice in Michigan.

Stipends: Support is commensurate with the candidate's level of training.

Applications: Applications should be received no later than October 31st for fellowships beginning July 1st of the following year. To apply for this fellowship, a letter of interest, a curriculum vitae, and three letters of reference from faculty from the candidate's residency program should be sent to:
Barbara J. McKenna, MD, Surgical Pathology Fellowship Director, Department of Pathology, University of Michigan Medical Center, Room 2G332/Box 5054, 1500 E. Medical Center Drive, Ann Arbor, Michigan 48109-5054.

UNIVERSITY OF NEBRASKA MEDICAL CENTER

Department of Pathology and Microbiology

Surgical Pathology Fellowship

Description: The Department of Pathology and Microbiology at the University of Nebraska Medical Center is accepting applications for a one year fellowship position in Surgical Pathology to begin July 1. This fellowship will provide advanced training in diagnostic Surgical Pathology. The goal of the fellowship is to improve and learn diagnostic skills so as to ease the transition from residency to independent sign-out. Fellows will be expected to signout independently in the last three months of the fellowship. Attention will be given to fulfill the needs of the individual fellow in terms of gaining skills towards pursuing a career in either private practice or academics. There will be several months of elective time which could be tailored to suit the needs of the fellow. The Surgical Pathology division at the Nebraska Medical Center accessions more than 32,000 specimens with a wide range of neoplastic and non-neoplastic pathology. The 20+ pathologists on staff have a wide variety of subspecialty expertise to further enhance the fellow's training. The Nebraska Medical Center is a world-renowned transplant center and the Eppley Institute for Research in Cancer and Allied Diseases is one of only a few in the country that holds the designation of NCI. There is also full access to state-of-the-art facilities in molecular and ultrastructural techniques.

Requirements: Board eligible or certified in anatomic or combined anatomic and clinical pathology.

Stipends: Commensurate with level of postgraduate training.

Applications: Apply with curriculum vitae and three letters of recommendation to:

Subodh M Lele, MD
Department of Pathology and Microbiology
983135 Nebraska Medical Center
Omaha, NE 68198-3135

Phone: (402) 559-7760 • **Fax:** (402) 559-6018 • **E-mail:** slele@unmc.edu
Web site: http://www.unmc.edu/pathology

MILTON S. HERSHEY MEDICAL CENTER
PENN STATE COLLEGE OF MEDICINE
Surgical Pathology Fellowship

Description: The Surgical Pathology Fellowship Program offers the fellow very broad and enriched clinical, research, and educational experience in surgical pathology under the guidance of dedicated and experienced educators. The program will provide an important step between residency and practice, preparing the trainee for future practice in an academic or private practice setting.

Requirements: Applicants should be board-certified or board-eligible in combined Anatomic/Clinical Pathology or Anatomic Pathology only.

Types and Numbers of Appointments: The Surgical Pathology Fellowship Program offers one position per academic year.

Facilities: The faculty, residents/fellows, and main laboratory facilities are housed in the Penn State Milton S. Hershey Medical Center. The hospital has a capacity of approximately 500 beds. The surgical pathology service accessions exceed 42,000 cases per year and reflect the broad variety of subspecialties practiced at the medical center. There is also a large representation of case material sent in by non-PSMSHMC clinical practitioners and pathologists for primary diagnosis or consultation.

Community: Hershey, in the foothills of the Blue Ridge Mountains, is a community of approximately 20,000 people. Harrisburg, the state capital, is 12 miles away. There are over one million people within a fifty-mile radius. Surrounded by rich farm lands and close to urban centers of the eastern seaboard, Hershey can be described as a suburban community in a rural setting. It has excellent educational and recreational programs and facilities, outstanding musical and stage performances, and numerous fine arts and cultural opportunities. Outdoor activities are readily available and include golf, swimming, fishing, hunting, mountain climbing, skiing, and ready access to the Appalachian Trail. Philadelphia, Baltimore, Washington, New York City, and the Pennsylvania Dutch country are just short distances by automobile or train. The Harrisburg International Airport (MDT) is 15 minutes away from Hershey, and airports in both Baltimore and Philadelphia are about 1.5-2 hours away by car.

Stipends: Salaries are comparable with salaries in the northeast as well as the rest of the United States, and fellows are provided with professional liability insurance, health insurance, disability insurance, uniforms, laundry, and four weeks paid vacation per year. The Department also provides yearly stipends that can be used for support of continuing medical education expenses, dues and membership, books, and subscriptions.

Applications: The Penn State Milton S. Hershey Medical Center and College of Medicine of the Pennsylvania State University are currently soliciting applications for academic year 2009-2010. This is a fully-funded, one year, ACGME-accredited position. Applications are evaluated on an on-going basis and will be accepted until the position is filled. Applications should include the standardized application for pathology fellowships, a cover letter with a personal statement, curriculum vitae, a letter from the current/most recent program director, and three additional letters of recommendation.

Applications materials and/or inquiries should be directed to:

Francesca M. Ruggiero, MD, Program Director, Surgical Pathology Fellowship, Department of Pathology - H179, Room C7628A, Penn State Milton S. Hershey Medical Center, 500 University Drive, P.O. Box 850, Hershey, PA 17033-0850.

E-mail: fruggiero@hmc.psu.edu

MOUNT SINAI MEDICAL CENTER OF GREATER MIAMI

Surgical Pathology Fellowship

Description: The Arkadi M. Rywlin, MD Department of Pathology and Laboratory Medicine at Mount Sinai Medical Center offers a one year surgical pathology fellowship program which emphasizes Breast and GI pathology along with the highly diverse range of general surgical pathology specimens expected to be encountered in both tertiary-care and community hospital settings. The unique demographics of South Florida as well as the department's national and international pathology consultation service provides a gamut of common and uncommon diseases for diagnostic review.

With nearly 20,000 in-house surgical specimens processed annually, additional glass slide consults, and non-gynecologic cytology specimens, the strength of the fellowship program is derived not only from the wealth of material but also from a staff of pathologists whose diagnostic acumen is complemented by an enthusiasm to teach. Affiliation with consulting pathologists in virtually every pathology sub-specialty renders an invaluable array of knowledge to the department's impressive resource of combined experience.

Opportunities for the fellow to perform at an advanced and independent level in sign-out and frozen section diagnosis are available and fostered with an appropriate level of attending guidance. Individual interests are accommodated while maintaining a focus on creating a balanced and well-rounded experience. The fellow assumes primary responsibility for diagnosing and reporting all of the outside consultation material. The fellow participates in and is responsible for a variety of clinico-pathologic conferences allowing for excellent clinical interactions and review of essentially all organ system pathology. All consultation sign outs and conferences are conducted with attending supervision. Of note is a well-established ''Pathology/Radiology Correlation Breast Conference" that helps integrate the benefits of an evidence-based approach to patient medical care with current concepts of breast pathology. Teaching of residents, rotating clinical residents and medical students is encouraged. Required student teaching includes the University of Miami School of Medicine and Florida International University's College of Medicine. A strong interest in research and publication is engendered within the fellowship program and is supported by full sponsorship to conferences in which accepted works are presented.

The hospital's spectacular location adjacent to the waters of Biscayne Bay in Miami Beach enhances an unrivaled lifestyle throughout the year.

Requirements: The desirable candidate will be BC/BE in Anatomic Pathology or Anatomic and Clinical Pathology and will have or be eligible for Florida medical licensure. A successful history of published research is preferred.

Types and Numbers of Appointments: A single position for a one-year fellowship is offered.

Stipends: Commensurate to the level of pathology training.

Staff: Robert J. Poppiti MD, AP and CP, Chairman Department of Pathology; **Morton J. Robinson** MD, AP and CP, Autopsy Pathology; **John B. Alexis** MB, ChB, AP and CP, Dermatopathology; **Lydia Howard** MD, AP and CP, Transfusion Medicine and Program Director; **Antonio Martinez** MD, AP and CP Hematopathology and GI Pathology; **Monica Recine** MD, AP and CP, Cytopathology and Gynecological Pathology; **Vathany Sriganeshan** MD, AP and CP, Hematopathology; **Y umna Omarzai** MD.

Applications: Applications with supporting documentation and two letters of recommendation should be submitted to Luisa Cruz, Residency Program Coordinator, Mount Sinai Medical Center, 4300 Alton Road, Miami Beach, FL 33140. **E-mail:** cruzl@msmc.com

UNIVERSITY OF NEW MEXICO

Surgical Pathology Fellowship

Description: The University of New Mexico Health Sciences Center provides an enterprising fellow a wide variety of surgical pathology, as it serves as the major tertiary hospital for the state. The goal of this fellowship is to provide advanced training in practical surgical pathology with the opportunity to engage in clinically related research. The fellow is posted at the University Hospiital for the year. He/she reviews a diversity of surgical specimens deriving in part from consult cases (approximately 900 per year), and in-house cases (about 17,000 per year). In addition, the fellow helps instruct pathology residents in appropriate gross dissection techniques and also provides histopathology training to the residents in the form of periodic didactic or microscope tutorial sessions on selected topics. There is also the opportunity to participate in medical student teaching. The fellow will actively participate in case presentation at surgical pathology tumor boards. Because of the affiliation of the University Hospital with TriCore Reference Laboratories, a very large regional not-for-profit laboratory, the fellow also will have the opportunity to learn about histology laboratory management. What sets this program apart are the close working relationship the fellow develops with the surgical pathology faculty, a very attractive mixture of more common with more esoteric cases encompassing all areas of surgical pathology, and the friendly, supportive atmosphere of the department. The fellow is accorded time for research. Projects conducted with fellows include access to molecular technology such as FISH and variants of PCR. By the end of the year, the fellow will have reviewed more than 1,500 cases personally, should have completed a publishable research project, and will have learned basic aspects of histology laboratory management. One fellow is accepted per year.

Requirements: MD or DO and at least three years of anatomic pathology residency training or four years of combined anatomic/clinical pathology residency. U.S. citizens or J-1 visa, USMLE Step 3 required.

Stipends: Postgraduate year five salary for 2008-2009 academic year is $52,649.

Applications: Please contact Nancy Joste, MD, Fellowship Director
E-mail: njoste@salud.unm.edu

NEW YORK UNIVERSITY MEDICAL CENTER

Surgical Pathology Fellowship

Description: Three fellowships. The one-year fellowship is intended to provide an intensive experience in general diagnostic surgical pathology, along with opportunities for electives and subspecialty areas. The fellowship is based at Tisch (University) Hospital which accessions approximately 22,000 cases per year. The nature and variety of the case material is outstanding. New York University Medical Center is a quaternary/tertiary care medical center with an active Cancer Center. Fellows are involved in the grossing and sign-out of specimens, the performance and interpretation of frozen sections, presentation at conferences, and the teaching of residents and medical students. The opportunity for sign-out responsibility is available and special projects are encouraged.

Requirements: At least four years of AP/CP training or 3 years of AP training and must hold a NY State License.

Stipends: Commensurate with candidate's level of training.

Applications: Standardized dates for applications and interviews ("months before matriculation" given in parentheses): December 1 (19 months before): Receipt of Standardized Form by Program January 1 (18 months before): Receipt of Letters of Recommendation February 28 (16 months before): Completion of Interviews Standardized date for issuance of offers March 1 (16 months before): Issuance of Offers Application forms can be obtained from:

Adrienne Fabiano, Program Coordinator, Department of Pathology, NYU Medical Center, 522 First Avenue, SRB 301C, New York, NY 10016.

Phone: (212) 263-7916 • **E-mail:** adrienne.fabiano@nyumc.org
For further information, contact Jonathan Melamed, MD, Director of Immunohistochemistry and Surgical Pathology Fellowship.
E-mail: jonathan.melamed@nyumc.org

OREGON HEALTH & SCIENCE UNIVERSITY

Surgical Pathology Fellowship

Description: The Department of Pathology of Oregon Health & Science University fills 2 Surgical Pathology Fellowship positions per year. As the major tertiary care referral center for the entire state of Oregon, OHSU offers a full spectrum of surgical pathology material, including substantial numbers of soft tissue, bone and pediatric cases. Assigned responsibilities include initial interpretation of biopsies and frozen sections, and oversight of the cutting room. Up to three months of elective time are offered, including optional rotations at the Portland VA Medical Center and the Northwest Kaiser Regional Laboratory. Other available elective rotations include hematopathology, dermatopathology, renal pathology, neuropathology, cytopathology, cytogenetics and molecular pathology. Participation in clinical research activities and teaching conferences is encouraged. Located on a scenic hill overlooking downtown Portland, the OHSU campus is less than 90 minutes from Mt. Hood, the Columbia River Gorge and the beautiful Oregon coast, providing endless opportunities for outdoor recreation. OHSU is an Equal Opportunity, Affirmative Action Employer.

Stipends: The stipend is comensurate with the year of post graduate training.

Applications: Applications will be accepted up to two years in advance and reviewed as rolling admissions. Interested applicants should send a cover letter, personal CV, OHSU application form from our web site, and three letters of recommendation to:
Christopher L. Corless, Director, Surgical Pathology, c/o Training Programs Coordinator, OHSU L-113, 3181 SW Sam Jackson Park Rd, Portland, OR 97239-3098.
For more information about our program, please visit our web site.
E-mail: ferencea@ohsu.edu
Web site: http://www.ohsu.edu/pathology/win/Fellsurgpath.htm

PENNSYLVANIA HOSPITAL

Department of Pathology

Surgical Pathology Fellowship

Description: A one-year fellowship provides advanced training in surgical pathology, with sign-out experience under supervision. Elective time is available at the Hospital of the University of Pennsylvania. The laboratory accessions approximately 12,000 surgical specimens annually.

Requirements: Four years of training in pathology (combined AP-CP) or straight AP; Pennsylvania medical license.

Stipends: Commensurate with the year of postgraduate training.

Applications: Candidates should forward their CV along with three to four letters of reference to Tunde A. Farkas, MD, Director of Pathology Residency Training, Pennsylvania Hospital, Ayer Laboratory, 8th & Spruce Streets, Philadelphia, PA 19107. CVs may be faxed or e-mailed; however, applications will not be processed nor will interviews be scheduled until the reference letters are received.

Phone: (215) 829-6992 • **Fax**: (215) 829-7564 • **E-mail**: anmccl@pahosp.com

HOSPITAL OF THE UNIVERSITY OF PENNSYLVANIA

Department of Pathology and Laboratory Medicine

Surgical Pathology Fellowship

Description: Seven one-year fellowships are offered to provide advanced experience in surgical pathology. These positions have received ACGME special selective accreditation. The surgical pathology practice of the Hospital of the University of Pennsylvania functions in a subspecialty model. The responsibilities of the fellow include supervised signout of a comprehensive range of medical and oncologic surgical specimens and responsibility for frozen section diagnoses. Fellows rotate through all of the surgical pathology subspecialty rotations and choose a subspecialty of particular interest for additional concentration. Development of a translational research project during the fellowship hear is strongly encouraged. The laboratory accessions approximately 34,000 surgical specimens a year. Candidates who demonstrate excellence in diagnostic skills, a firm commitment to teaching, and completion of a research project related to human disease may be eligible for the H. T. Enterline Fellowship Award.

Requirements: Successful completion of the Residency requirements for certification in Anatomic Pathology.

Stipends: Stipends are commensurate with the year of postgraduate training.

Applications: Must be made by January 1 of the year preceding the intended fellowship (begins July 1). Applications will be accepted until all positions are filled. Apply to Antonia Sepulveda, MD, PhD, Director of Surgical Pathology, Hospital of the University of Pennsylvania, 3400 Spruce Street, Philadelphia, PA 19104.

Phone: (215) 615-4361
Web site: www.uphs.upenn.edu/path/residency/SurgicalPathology.doc

---

PITT COUNTY MEMORIAL HOSPITAL
BRODY SCHOOL OF MEDICINE
EAST CAROLINA UNIVERSITY

Department of Pathology & Laboratory Medicine

Surgical Pathology Fellowship

Description: The department offers a one-year fellowship in surgical pathology. The fellowship will provide extensive training in all aspects of surgical pathology, including dermatopathology, hematopathology, gynecologic, gastrointestinal, renal, and genitourinary pathology. The surgical pathology cases number over 21,000 per year, and include an active frozen section service. The fellow has first-hand experience in signing out cases and reviews all consultation cases, with progressive independent sign out responsibility built into the program. Contemporary diagnostic techniques are utilized including immunofluorescence microscopy, electron microscopy, immunohistochemistry, flow cytometry and molecular techniques. Research opportunities are available in a variety of subspecialty areas of surgical pathology.

Requirements: 3 years AP or 4 years AP/CP minimum; and eligible for North Carolina medical license.

Stipends: The stipend is that of a comparable year resident at Pitt County Memorial Hospital and competitive with others in the region. Benefit package includes health insurance for the fellow, retirement benefits, term life insurance, accident insurance, disability insurance and malpractice liability insurance. Benefits may vary depending on level of training.

Applications: Should be made to:
Karlene Hewan-Lowe, MD, Director of Surgical Pathology Fellowship, Department of Pathology & Laboratory Medicine, Brody School of Medicine, East Carolina University, Greenville, NC 27834.

Phone: (252) 744-5911

UNIVERSITY OF PITTSBURGH MEDICAL CENTER

Surgical Pathology Fellowship

Description: One-year intensive training in general surgical pathology, organized as core of subspecialty pathology rotations (GI, thoracic, ENT, GU, bone and soft tissue, gynecologic, transplant, dermatopathology). Three months of elective rotations in other specialized areas of pathology (informatics, molecular diagnostics, cytopathology, neuropathology, medical renal biopsy) are provided. Graded responsibility is emphasized. A research project leading to publication in a peer-reviewed publication is expected.

Requirements: Completion of an accredited residency program in Anatomic Pathology or combined Anatomic / Clinical Pathology.

Stipends: Commensurate with the level of postgraduate training in Pathology.

Staff: Sheldon Bastacky MD, Fellowship Director; **R. Marshall Austin** MD, PhD; **E. Leon Barnes** MD; **Rohit Bhargava** MD; **Gloria Carter** MD; **Mamatha Chivukula** MD; **David Dabbs** MD; **Sanja Dacic** MD, PhD; **Anthony Demetris** MD; **Rajiv Dhir** MD; **Esther Elishaev** MD; **Jeff Fine** MD; **Mirka Jones** MD; **Drazen Jukic** MD; **Anisa Kanbour** MD; **Amal Kanbour-Shakir** MD, PhD; **Larry Kiss** MD; **Alyssa Krasinskas** MD; **Shih-Fan Kuan** MD; **Michael Nalesnik** MD; **Sarah Navina** MD; **Olga Navolotskaia** MD; **Larry Nichols** MD; **Erin Ochoa** MD; **N. Paul Ohori** MD; **Scott Owens** MD; **Alka Palekar** MD; **Anil Parwani** MD, PhD; **Robert Peel** MD; **Uma Rao** MD; **Karen Schoedel** MD; **Raja Seethala** MD; **Lisa Teot** MD; **Guiliana Trucco** MD; **Tong Wu** MD, PhD; **Samuel Yousem** MD; **Chengquan Zhao** MD.

Applications: Submit application online at http://path.upmc.edu/fellowship Current curriculum vitae and three letters of recommendation should be forwarded 12 months in advance of starting date (July 1 of each year) to Sheldon Bastacky, MD, Department of Pathology, C-622 UPMC Presbyterian, 200 Lothrop Street, Pittsburgh, PA 15213.

Phone: (412) 647-9612 • **Fax:** (412) 647-3455 • **E-mail:** bastackysi@upmc.edu

MEDICAL UNIVERSITY OF SOUTH CAROLINA

Surgical Pathology Fellowship

Description: The Surgical Pathology Service of the Department of Pathology and Laboratory Medicine at the Medical University of South Carolina in Charleston offers a one year program of non-ACGME accredited subspecialty training in surgical pathology. During this time, fellows are given primary responsibility for examination and diagnosis of surgical pathology specimens. The surgical pathology fellow must be board eligible and will function as a junior attending. The Medical University of South Carolina Surgical Pathology Laboratory examines 26,000 surgical pathology specimens (including neuropathology and dermatopathology specimens). Many cases involve immunocytochemical, ultrastructural or flow cytometric examination. The surgical pathology fellowship offers opportunity for teaching residents, medical students, and for participation in interdepartmental conferences. Depending on interest and previous experience, the fellow may participate in ongoing research projects within the Section of Surgical Pathology. Many of these projects would expose the fellow to newer diagnostic/research methodologies such as image analysis, immunohistochemistry, in situ hybridization, tissue culture, flow cytometry and nucleic acid chemistry (DNA/RNA extraction, hybridization, etc.) and telepathology exposure.

Requirements: Candidates must have completed an AP or AP/CP residency. Candidates must hold or be eligible to hold a medical license in South Carolina. Applications should be received January 1st of the year preceding the year of the fellowship (18 months prior to the beginning of the fellowship).

Stipends: Salary is commensurate with year of postgraduate training.

Applications: Inquiries should be directed to Mary Richardson, MD, Director of Surgical Pathology, Department of Pathology and Laboratory Medicine, Medical University of South Carolina, 171 Ashley Avenue, Suite 309, MSC 908, Charleston, SC 29425

Phone: (843) 792-3121 • **Fax:** (843) 792-0555 • **E-mail:** richardm@musc.edu

STATEN ISLAND UNIVERSITY HOSPITAL

Surgical Pathology Fellowship

Description: Staten Island University Hospital is a member of the North Shore-Long Island Jewish Healthcare System. This one year fellowship program is designed to provide advanced training in diagnostic pathology in the setting of a university medical center affiliated hospital. The Department of Pathology examines over 27,000 surgical specimens annually, and has a staff of 14 pathologists and clinical scientists. Active morphometric analysis, immunohistochemistry, and flow cytometry laboratories are maintained, and ongoing research in the area of tumor biology, is actively pursued. The fellow will participate in the surgical pathology activities of the department, and responsibilities will include frozen section diagnoses, final histopathologic diagnoses, consultations with surgery, medicine and subspecialty services, clinical-pathologic conferences, and teaching of clinical house staff. The opportunity for a clinically oriented research project is available. Emphasis is placed on the achievement of confidence, as well as accuracy in diagnostic surgical pathology.

Requirements: Applicants must have successfully completed at least two years of anatomic pathology training, and be Board eligible/certified in AP or AP/CP.

Stipends: Commensurate with training and experience.

Applications: A letter of application, curriculum vitae, and 3 letters of reference should be sent, prior to December 1, to

Henry Simpkins, PhD, MD, Chairman of Pathology and Laboratory Medicine, Staten Island University Hospital, 1 Edgewater Plaza, Staten Island, NY 10305.

Phone: (718) 226-4133

THE UNIVERSITY OF TEXAS HEALTH SCIENCE CENTER AT SAN ANTONIO, UNIVERSITY HOSPITAL AUDIE MURPHY VETERANS AFFAIRS HOSPITAL

Surgical Pathology Fellowship

Description: This program is designed to give the fellow experience working at the junior faculty level. Clinical duties include serving as first-line consultant to resident trainees in surgical pathology, frozen section interpretation, organization of conferences, participation in surgical pathology quality improvement activities, and review of faculty consult cases. Participation with faculty in scholarly activities is essential. Electives are available in cytopathology, hematopathology, pulmonary pathology, immunocytochemistry, molecular pathology, nephropathology or neuropathology. The combined hospitals process 23,000 surgical cases and 25,000 cytology cases; the latter include 3,000 non-Paps and 1,000 FNAs.

Requirements: Three years of straight AP training, or four years of combined AP/CP training.

Stipends: Commensurate with level of training.

Applications: Send inquiries to: Jaishree Jagirdar, MD, Director, The University of Texas Health Science Center, 7703 Floyd Curl Drive, San Antonio, TX 78229-3900.

Phone: (210) 567-4034 • **Fax:** (210) 567-2478 • **E-mail:** jagirdar@uthscsa.edu

THE UNIVERSITY OF TENNESSEE MEDICAL CENTER

Surgical Pathology Fellowship

Description: One, one-year fellowship is available beginning each July 1. The program emphasizes the achievement of competence in interpreting frozen sections (approximately 2,000 cases per year) and surgical pathology material (greater than 22,000 accessions per year), and associated cytopathology material (greater than 35,000 accessions per year). The fellow is given responsibility in signing out with appropriate supervision by senior faculty. Teaching activities include an unknown case conference, journal club, case presentations, conference presentation, and research presentations where applicable. Rotations include gross room and sign-out, special techniques: electron microscopy, molecular pathology, flow cytometry, etc. A wide spectrum of specimens (GU, GI, renal, lung, liver, muscle, brain, skin, etc.) provide extensive experience. The fellow participates in interdepartmental conferences and has an active role in supervising and teaching pathology residents. A research project is not a requirement during the fellowship year, however it is highly encouraged, and supported. The Department of Pathology, which includes over twenty faculty, has an excellent information technology base (Cerner/ PowerChart/ CoPath) and incorporates state-of-the-art facilities.

Requirements: Candidates must have completed, prior to entering the fellowship, three years of AP or four years of AP/CP. USMLE Step III must be completed prior to beginning the fellowship. Those accepted into the fellowship must acquire their Tennessee medical license by the completion of the third month of their fellowship. The candidate must have completed requirements to sit for the ABP, AP examination, prior to starting the fellowship. USMLE Step III must be completed prior to beginning the fellowship.

Stipends: Commensurate with year of postgraduate level of training.

Staff: Alan Grindstaff MD, Director.

Applications: Should be submitted by September 1 of the proceeding year to: Alan Grindstaff, MD, Surgical Pathology Fellowship Program Director. Application consists of cover letter, CV, and three letters of evaluation including one from program director.

Address inquiries:
Ms. Pamela C. Guider, Program Coordinator
Department of Pathology
The University of Tennessee Medical Center Knoxville
1924 Alcoa Highway
Box 108
Knoxville, TN 37920

Phone: (865) 305-8994 • **Fax:** (865) 305-8563 • **E-mail:** Pguider@utmck.edu
Web site: www.utmedicalcenter.org/pathology/

UNIVERSITY OF TEXAS SOUTHWESTERN MEDICAL SCHOOL

Department of Pathology

Surgical Pathology Assistant Instructorship (Fellowship)

Description: Our one-year program offers a year of transition in which ones surgical pathology skills and confidence can be improved prior to entering practice. Our Assistant Instructors will be primarily responsible for daily sign out of surgical pathology cases with our residents at Parkland Health & Hospital System (25,000 surgicals). A staff of experienced attending surgical pathologists is available for back up and support, as one's confidence and skills improve. The year may also include two to four months of grossing responsibilities at our tertiary care center, University Hospital - Zale Lipshy (3,500 surgicals).

Requirements: Applicants must have completed an approved straight anatomic or AP/CP residency program, and obtain a license to practice medicine in Texas.

Types and Numbers of Appointments:

Three assistant instructorships (fellowships) are available each year.

Stipends: Salary will be commensurate with the applicant's level of training.

Staff: Kyle Molberg MD; **Sara Milchgrub** MD; **Thomas Rogers** MD; **Jyoti Balani** MD; **Lauri Campagna** MD; **Kelley Carrick** MD; **Gene Ewing** MD; **Yisheng Fang** MD; **Nicholas Feliciano** MD; **Erika Fong** MD; **Wareef Kabbani** MD; **Payal Kapur** MD; **Yuri Lemeshev** MD; **Dwight Oliver** MD; **Yan Peng** MD; **Venetia Sarode** MD.

Applications: Applications should be made no later than June 1 of the year prior to the intended instructorship year which normally begins July 1. Address inquiries to:
Kyle H. Molberg, MD, Medical Director of Anatomic and Clinical Pathology, Department of Pathology, University of Texas Southwestern Medical Center at Dallas, 5323 Harry Hines Boulevard, Dallas, TX 75390-9073.

Phone: (214) 590-8185
Web site: http://pathcuric1.swmed.edu

UNIVERSITY OF UTAH HEALTH SCIENCES CENTER

Department of Pathology

Surgical Pathology Fellowship

Description: The Department of Pathology at the University of Utah Hospitals and Clinics offers a one year Surgical Pathology Fellowship. The fellowship is designed to give the Fellow experience at the junior faculty level, including sign out of surgical pathology cases. The Fellowship is based at the Huntsman Cancer Hospital at the University of Utah. Training in general surgical pathology is emphasized. A variety of interesting and challenging general surgical pathology cases are seen on a daily basis, including breast, gynecologic, gastrointestinal, genitourinary, pulmonary, head and neck, skin and soft tissue/bone pathology. Electives are available in hematopathology, neuropathology, gastrointestinal and renal pathology. Research activities are available and encouraged.

Requirements: Applicants should have completed an Anatomic Pathology or combined Anatomic/Clinical Pathology residency training program, be board eligible or board certified, and able to obtain a Utah State medical license.

Stipends: Commensurate with level of training.

Applications: Send inquiries to

Steven S. Chin, MD, PhD,Department of Pathology, Division of Anatomic Pathology, Huntsman Cancer Hospital, 1950 Circle of Hope Room 3860, Salt Lake City, UT 84112

Phone: (801) 581-2507 • **Fax:** (801) 581-7035 • **E-mail:** steven.chin@path.utah.edu
Web site: http://www.path.utah.edu/education/fellowships/surgical-pathology/

UNIVERSITY OF VERMONT COLLEGE OF MEDICINE

Surgical Pathology Fellowship

Description: The Department of Pathology and Laboratory Medicine offers a one-year fellowship in surgical pathology. The Medical Center campus of Fletcher Allen Health Care is the primary site of fellowship training. The program provides extensive training in all areas of surgical pathology and will provide the senior level resident with the necessary skills for the transition to an attending pathologist. Four to six months are devoted to the "Hot Seat" provisional diagnosis rotation. This rotation provides graduated responsibility through gross room supervision, frozen section interpretation, and providing provisional diagnoses with appropriate attending faculty supervision. Two months may be devoted to independent sign-out with the level of responsibility geared to the resident's experience and confidence level. The remaining months are devoted to subspecialty selective rotations with options including: cytopathology, dermatopathology, breast pathology, gastrointestinal pathology, hematopathology, neuropathology, pulmonary pathology, or soft tissue pathology. Elective research in the experimental pathology laboratory is possible and encouraged and may provide additional exposure to special techniques including molecular diagnostics, immunohistochemistry, electron microscopy, and flow cytometry. The Department accessions at least 36,000 surgicals, 5,000 non-gyn and fine needle aspirate cytology specimens, and over 55,000 gyn cytology specimens per year.

Requirements: Completion of three years of AP training or four years of AP/CP training. Stipends: The appointment is for one year and the stipend is based on the applicant's level of postgraduate training.

Applications: Should be received prior to December 15 and addressed to:

Donald L. Weaver, MD, Director of Surgical Pathology Fellowship Program, Fletcher Allen Health Care, Dept of Pathology & Laboratory Medicine, 111 Colchester Avenue, Burlington, VT 05401.

Phone: (802) 847-0392 • **E-mail:** Jane.murray@vtmednet.org

VIRGINIA COMMONWEALTH UNIVERSITY MEDICAL CENTER

Surgical Pathology Fellowship

Description: This is a one year program designed for individuals who wish to pursue intense training in **Surgical Pathology** in an environment that allows graduated responsibility and independent work necessary to build diagnostic confidence and maturity. The Surgical Pathology laboratory at VCU Medical Center processes over 16,000 specimens/year representing benign and malignant pathology, biopsies as well as large complex resections from all organ systems. Sign-out in Surgical Pathology is subspecialized, assuring trainee interaction with faculty with expertise in specific organ system pathology. The general framework of this fellowship includes: one month introduction to the subspecialty services, gross room operation, frozen section procedure, eight months rotations through various subspecialty services (GI/Liver-2 months, GYN/GU-2 months, Breast/Heart/Lung-2 months, ENT/General-2 months) and three months of elective rotations. The fellowship allows flexibility in the schedule, depending on the fellow's subspecialty interest. While on a subspecialty service rotation, the fellow signs-out the cases as a junior attending with the resident only, handles frozen sections and consultation cases, instructs the residents in handling complex specimens, and presents at interdisciplinary conferences. Elective rotations are available in Dermatopathology, Neuropathology, Cytopathology, Molecular Pathology, or other clinical pathology services (Hematopathology, Blood Bank). The fellow is expected to participate in one of the many departmental research projects and presentation at national meetings and publication in a peer reviewed journal will be encouraged. This fellowship is designed to provide the necessary skills for the fellow to function as an academic pathologist with responsibilities in service, teaching, and research or as a community-based pathologist with responsibilities primarily in service and laboratory management.

Requirements: Candidates must have satisfactorily completed an accredited training program in AP or AP/CP.

Stipends: Salary and benefits are commensurate with level of training.

Applications: Interested individuals should contact the training program coordinator, Ms. Violet Brown, Department of Pathology, P.O. Box 980662, Richmond, VA 23298-0662 for additional information. The program accepts the CAP Standardized Application form. Completed applications and letters of recommendation should be addressed to Ema Dragoescu, MD, Director of Surgical Pathology Fellowship Program, VCU Medical Center, PO Box 980662, Richmond, VA 23298-0662.

Phone: (804) 827-0561 • **E-mail:** vbrown3@mcvh-vcu.edu.

WASHINGTON UNIVERSITY MEDICAL CENTER

Surgical Pathology Fellowship

Description: The Division of Anatomic Pathology at Washington University Medical Center (WUMC), St Louis, Missouri, has openings for six surgical pathology fellows. Fellows are given a high degree of case-management responsibility in this program, during general surgical pathology rotations as well as subspecialty experience in gynecologic pathology and intraoperative consultation. Approximately 52,000 surgical specimens are seen per year at WUMC, covering all facets of modern clinical practice. Thirty full-time faculty members comprise the division of Anatomic Pathology, and are the recipients of approximately 3,500 referral cases per year. These are evaluated independently by fellows during their consultation rotations. Experience with immunohistology, electron microscopy, flow cytometry, molecular diagnostics, and other special techniques is integrated into the workup of diagnostic cases throughout the training period. Opportunities for involvement in clinical research projects are numerous and strongly encouraged.

Requirements: Applicants must possess the MD degree (or foreign equivalent) and must have completed at least 18 months of training in anatomic pathology in an accredited postgraduate program, in order to qualify for fellowship training.

Applications: Inquiries should be addressed to
Phyllis C. Huettner MD, c/o Mary Madden, Fellowship Coordinator, at the Washington University School of Medicine, 660 South Euclid Ave, Campus Box 8118, St Louis, MO 63110.

Phone: (314) 747-0687 • **Fax:** (314) 747-2663

UNIVERSITY OF WASHINGTON

Department of Pathology

Surgical Pathology Fellowship

Description: This one-year ACGME accredited fellowship offers a diverse experience in diagnostic surgical pathology designed to train the fellow in all facets of current anatomic pathology practice to successfully bridge to independent practice in either a community-based or academic environment, by building on core competencies achieved in earlier years of training. This level of professional growth is accomplished through an integration of several key elements: exposure to complicated surgical pathology cases and consults; experience with teaching and supervision, both within the pathology residency program and within the broader UWMC medical community; practical application of laboratory management skills; responsibility for critical elements of program administration; and enhanced exposure to a subspecialty of their choosing.

Requirements: Applicants are selected for interview based on academic excellence and interest in the subspecialty. Applicants are expected to have completed at least 2 years of Anatomic Pathology training in an ACGME-accredited program and be eligible for a limited Washington State license.

Facilities: The program is based at University of Washington Medical Center, which provides tertiary medical care to the five-state region of Washington, Wyoming, Alaska, Montana and Idaho.

Stipends: One-year appointment with salary and benefits based on the schedule for residents at an equivalent level (R5=$55,032). Four positions per year.

Staff: **R. Garcia** Fellowship Director; **P. Swanson** Director, Anatomic Pathology; **K. Allison**; **S. Dintzis**; **C. Fligner**; **E. George**; **J. Haas**; **B. Hoch**; **D. Jordan**; **T. Norwood**; **R. Schmidt**; **L. True**; **M. Upton**; **M. Yeh**.

Applications: Inquiry: Rochelle L. Garcia, MD, Fellowship Director, at rochelle@u.washington.edu
Available at the web site or contact Michelle Rickard, Academic Programs Manager, Surgical Pathology Fellowship Program, at the email address below. Application materials must be received by February 1 with selected interviews to follow until the position is filled.

Phone: (206) 598-4933 • **Fax:** (206) 598-7321 • **E-mail:** fellowship@pathology.washington.edu
Web site: www.pathology.washington.edu/academics/fellowship/

The University of Washington is an equal opportunity institution.

WAYNE STATE UNIVERSITY/DETROIT MEDICAL CENTER

Surgical Pathology Fellowship

Description: The Department of Pathology of Wayne State University School of Medicine, and the Detroit Medical Center, offers a one-year fellowship in surgical pathology beginning July 1, annually. The program is offered at the central campus of the Detroit Medical Center — Harper University Hospital, which also includes the Karmanos Cancer Institute, Hutzel Women's Hospital and the Children's Hospital of Michigan. The surgical pathology annual workload includes over 25,000 specimens with a heavy concentration in oncologic pathology. The fellowship rotations are tailored to the interests of the individual fellow with a minimum of 6 months allocated to the general surgical pathology service. Opportunities exist for elective rotations in pediatric pathology, renal & transplant pathology, hematopathology, cytopathology, and neuropathology. Fellows are expected to participate in translational research activities and the department has consistently been among the top 10 institutions for scientific presentations by trainees at the USCAP annual meeting.

Requirements: Candidates must be Board certified or eligible by the American Board of Pathology in AP or AP/CP. Individuals with an interest in pursuing a career in academic pathology are preferred.

Stipends: Stipends are commensurate with the year of pathology postgraduate training as determined by Wayne State University School of Medicine.

Applications: Applications should be completed by August 1 of the preceding year. Direct your inquiries, CV, and letter to Wael Sakr, MD Director Fellowship Program, Professor of Pathology, c/o Markel Washington, Wayne State University School of Medicine, Department of Pathology, 540 E. Canfield Avenue, Detroit, MI 48201.

Phone: (313) 745-2525 • **E-mail:** wsakr@dmc.org

UNIVERSITY OF WISCONSIN HOSPITAL AND CLINICS

Surgical Pathology Fellowship

Description: The program is designed to provide intense training in general surgical pathology and subspecialty areas to prepare the fellow for a successful career in private or academic practice. The University of Wisconsin Hospital and Clinics is a leading academic tertiary care medical center with a NCI-designated comprehensive cancer center. The fellow actively participates in frozen section diagnosis, grossing room supervision, and surgical pathology sign-out. Several departmental and inter-departmental conferences afford an opportunity for interaction with clinical colleagues. Opportunities also exist for resident and medical student teaching. A flexible schedule can be arranged for subspecialty electives in gastrointestinal/liver, genito-urinary, gynecologic, transplantation and renal pathology. There is ample opportunity for intra and inter-departmental research collaborations. A pathology core laboratory provides instrumentation, technical staffing and funding for research projects involving advanced pathology techniques such as tissue microarrays, laser microdissection and quantitative real-time PCR.
(see also: http://www.pathology.wisc.edu/clinfellowship/surgical.aspx)

Requirements: Certification or Board eligibility in combined Clinical and Anatomic Pathology or in Anatomic Pathology.

Stipends: Commensurate with postgraduate training.

Staff: Rashmi Agni MD; **Andres Friedl** MD, Director of Surgical Pathology; **G. Reza Hafez** MD; **Jo Harter** MD; **Wei Huang** MD; **Agnes Loffler** MD, PhD; **Igor Slukvin** MD; **Jose Torrealba** MD; **Thomas Warner** MD.

Applications: Due February 1 (1 yr. & 5 mo. prior to start date). Send application (download at http://www.pathology.wisc.edu/clinfellowship/surgical.aspx), cover letter, CV and three letters of recommendation to Andreas Friedl, MD, Director of Surgical Pathology, c/o Amanda Paus, University of Wisconsin Hospital & Clinics, 600 Highland Ave., B4/243-2472, Madison, WI 53792-2472.

Phone: (608) 262-7158 • **Fax:** (608) 262-6337 • **E-mail:** apaus@uwhealth.org
Web site: http://www.pathology.wisc.edu/clinfellowship/surgical

YALE UNIVERSITY SCHOOL OF MEDICINE

General Surgical Pathology Fellowship

Description: This one year fellowship is designed to develop diagnostic expertise in general surgical pathology for either academic or community settings. The year includes core rotation experiences on General Surgical Pathology (academic and community settings), "Hot-Seat" and Frozen Section. Elective time is available for focused subspecialty rotations in areas such as breast, gynecologic, or gastrointestinal pathology, among others. Fellow responsibilities vary with rotation, but in general include: workup of consultation cases, supervision of pathology residents, sign-out experiences and teaching. The fellow is a vital member of multi-disciplinary tumor boards, and presents at departmental and interdepartmental clinical conferences. Protected time is provided for fellows to complete a personal research project under the supervision of senior faculty. The scientific environment is particularly well suited to encourage translational research bringing advances in the basic sciences to clinical investigation.

Requirements: Three years of training in anatomic pathology or four years training in combined anatomic and clinical pathology.

Stipends: Commensurate with hospital policy.

Applications: Apply to G. Kenneth Haines III, MD, General Surgical Pathology Fellowship Program, Department of Pathology, Yale University School of Medicine, PO Box 208070, New Haven, CT 06520-8070.

Phone: (203) 785-3937 • **Fax:** (203) 737-2922 • **E-mail:** k.haines@yale.edu

42nd Edition

Post-Sophomore Fellowships in Pathology 2010–2011

A number of medical schools offer "year out" student fellowships in pathology for medical students, usually following the sophomore year. These programs were initiated because it has become evident that the opportunity to work in a pathology department with a pathologist before or during medical school is often influential in a person's decision to become a pathologist.

Detailed descriptions of these programs are shown on the following pages, with requirements, stipends, and application information. Interested students should also check other medical schools for additional programs.

The Intersociety Council for Pathology Information, Inc.

ALBERT EINSTEIN COLLEGE OF MEDICINE AND MONTEFIORE MEDICAL CENTER

Description: This one-year fellowship consists of intensive exposure to the fields of anatomic and clinical pathology with opportunities for research or training in selected subspecialties of pathology. Fellows will spend a minimum of eight months in the "hands-on" practice of pathology, including rotations in autopsy pathology, surgical pathology, and rotations in clinical pathology including microbiology, hematology, blood banking or chemistry. The remaining four months will be spent in either basic research or in a subspecialty area of pathology. Fellows will attend all the teaching conferences of the Department of Pathology.

Requirements: Open to qualified medical students who have completed at least two years in an accredited U.S. medical school.

Stipends: $12,000 per year.

Applications: For information and applications, contact
Jacob J. Steinberg, MD, Department of Pathology, Albert Einstein College of Medicine/Montefiore Medical Center, Central Bldg, Room 312, 111 East 210 St, Bronx, NY 10467.
Phone: (718) 920-6573 • **Fax:** (718) 547-8349
E-mail: jsteinbe@montefiore.org or beedward@montefiore.org
Web site: http://www.aecom.yu.edu

UNIVERSITY OF CALIFORNIA, LOS ANGELES

Description: The Department of Pathology and Laboratory Medicine offers one-year post-sophomore and post-junior fellowships in pathology. After a brief orientation and introduction, fellows will rotate on various surgical and clinical pathology services and the autopsy service at UCLA Medical Center. Fellows are given responsibilities similar to first year residents. Elective for research experience is also available.

Requirements: Applicants must have completed at least two years in an accredited medical school prior to the fellowship.

Stipends: Stipend is $25,000 per year (with tuition paid by the department for UCLA students only), and $750 book allowance. Insurance benefits and meal cards are provided.

Applications: Deadline is March 30th for fellowships beginning the following July. A curriculum vitae, two letters of recommendation and a current transcript are required. Interview is desirable. Send to: Charles R. Lassman, MD, PhD, Residency Training Program Director, Department of Pathology and Laboratory Medicine, 10833 Le Conte Avenue, Room A7-149 Center for the Health Sciences, Los Angeles, CA 90095-1732. Fellowship Coordinator: Ms. Annetta Pierro
Phone: (310) 825-5719 • **Fax:** (310)267-2058
Web site: www.pathology.ucla.edu

UNIVERSITY OF CALIFORNIA, SAN FRANCISCO

Description: The Department of Pathology has one to two positions for post-sophomore fellows beginning May 1 or July 1, for 12 months. Each anatomic pathology fellow will do rotations of autopsy pathology, surgical pathology, and research or electives in pathology. Rotations are at Moffitt Hospital, Mt. Zion Medical Center and San Francisco General Hospital. The student can select a faculty member as their advisor for the research block. Fellows essentially function as first-year residents after the first few months of initial training. Participation in medical and dental student teaching is part of the rotation.

Requirements: Applicants must have completed at least two years in an accredited medical school in the United States or Canada prior to beginning the fellowship.

Stipends: $25,189.00 per year.

Applications: For information and applications, contact
Henry Sanchez, MD, Post-Sophomore Fellowship, Department of Pathology, Box 0102, University of California, San Francisco, CA 94143. Applications are due by February 1.
Phone: (415) 514-2068
Web site: http://pathology.ucsf.edu/education/other/post-sophomore.html

UNIVERSITY OF MASSACHUSETTS MEDICAL SCHOOL

Description: The Department of Pathology sponsors two one-year post-sophomore fellowships for medical students who have successfully completed their basic sciences or students who are in their clinical training period. Students actively participate, under faculty supervision, in the surgical pathology rotation (six months) neuropathology (one month) and autopsy rotation (three months). Fellows are also given 2 months of elective time to actively pursue personal areas of interest and/or research. Students function as junior residents, participate in all anatomic pathology conferences and participate in laboratory teaching sessions for the second-year pathology course. Each student is assigned a faculty member to be his/her professional and personal advisor during the year.

Requirements: Qualified medical students completing at least 2 years in accredited US institution.

Stipends: Funding for the year-long position is $28,000 per annum.

Applications: Send application, biographical sketch and brief statement of medical career interests to
Patti Davis, Residency Coordinator, Dept of Pathology, UMass Memorial Health Care, Biotech 3, One Innovation Drive, Worcester, MA 01605.
Phone: (508) 793-6156 • **E-mail:** Patricia.Davis@umassmemorial.org.

UNIVERSITY OF NEW MEXICO

Description: The fellowship consists of four three-month rotations on various Pathology Services. These rotations are comparable in responsibilities and structure to rotations of beginning residents in pathology, except that the Fellow receives more intense faculty supervision and instruction. Two rotations (six months) are devoted to Anatomic Pathology Services at the University Hospital and/or VA Medical Center. One rotation (three months) consists of learning and performing autopsy pathology at the Office of the Medical Investigator. The other rotation (three months) is an elective, which may involve an additional anatomic pathology training, laboratory medicine rotation or research rotation.

Requirements: Open to qualified medical students who have completed at least two years in an accredited US Medical School.

Stipends: $19,500.00, 15 days paid annual leave, 15 days sick leave, $600 text book fund.

Applications: Contact
Jeanne Lay, Univ of New Mexico Health Sciences Center, Dept of Pathology, 1 University of New Mexico, MSC08-4640, Albuquerque, NM 87131.
Phone: (505) 272-3696 • **Fax:** (505) 925-7399 • **E-mail:** jlay@salud.unm.edu
Web site: http://hsc.unm.edu/pathology/residency/

SAINT LOUIS UNIVERSITY SCHOOL OF MEDICINE

Description: The post-sophomore pathology fellowship at Saint Louis University provides an educational experience to medical students interested in a career in pathology and in furthering their understanding of mechanisms of disease. During the fellowship, the student has service, conference and teaching activities similar to those of a first-year pathology resident. With faculty, the post-sophomore fellow performs autopsies and examines surgical specimens. Research opportunities in clinical and experimental pathology and elective experiences in subspecialty areas in pathology are available and the fellowship will be "tailor-made" to suit each student's interests.

Requirements: The applicant must have completed his/her second year of medical school by the beginning of the fellowship year.

Stipends: $18,000, plus travel and book allowance.

Applications: Address inquiries to
Carole Vogler, MD, Director, Residency Training Program, Department of Pathology, Saint Louis University School of Medicine, 1402 South Grand Blvd, St Louis, MO 63104. Application deadline is December 15th of the current academic year. **Phone:** 314.577.8694 • **Fax:** 314.268.5641 • **E-mail:** voglerca@slu.edu • **Web site:** http://path.slu.edu

---

UNIVERSITY OF PENNSYLVANIA MEDICAL CENTER

Description: Two positions in Anatomic Pathology (AP), combined Anatomic/Clinical Pathology (AP/CP), or Clinical Pathology (CP) are offered. Each student fellow, under appropriate supervision, is given training and responsibilities similar to those of a first-year resident. In the AP student fellowship, a minimum of three months each will be spent on the Autopsy and Surgical Pathology Services, and up to three months on the Cytopathology Service. In the combined AP/CP student fellowship, the student will spend time rotating on each of the above rotations, as well as rotate through one to three of the major laboratories in Laboratory Medicine (Chemistry, Coagulation, Hematology, Transfusion Medicine, Tissue Typing/Immunology, Molecular Diagnosis, or Microbiology). The student typically rotates through two of these service areas as pre-arranged with the Director and Laboratory Medicine faculty, in addition to rotations in AP. For the AP and AP/CP student fellowships, three months are set aside for pursuing a problem in disease etiology and diagnosis under staff guidance, the results of which are presented at a conference to the Division's staff and residents. The Laboratory Medicine work study experience is spent in one to three of the major laboratories (as listed above) within the Division of Laboratory Medicine. The student typically rotates through two of these service areas as pre-arranged with the Director and Laboratory Medicine faculty, and then spends up to six months in intensive study and research within a third area in addition to participating in various divisional conferences. One or more publications typically result from these projects.

Requirements: Completion of basic medicine and surgery clinical rotations prior to start of year-out.

Stipends: $27,000 for year-out which may be paid as a monthly salary or awarded following completion of year-out as a tuition fellowship. The cost of student fees and health insurance equivalent to that charged by Penn's School of Medicine are also provided.

Applications: Cindy McGrath MD, Director of Student Fellowship Program, c/o Pamela Mammarelli, Fellowship Coordinator, Pathology Training Program/6 Founders, Department of Pathology and Laboratory Medicine, University of Pennsylvania Medical Center, 3400 Spruce Street, Philadelphia, PA 19104-4283. Applications preferred prior to Feb 1 for the upcoming June/July, but will be accepted throughout the year.
Phone: (215) 662-4829 Pamela Mammarelli • **E-mail:** mammarep@uphs.upenn.edu.
Web site: http://www.uphs.upenn.edu/path/TOCbroch.html

UNIVERSITY OF SOUTH FLORIDA COLLEGE OF MEDICINE

Description: The Department of Pathology and Laboratory Medicine at the University of South Florida College of Medicine offers a one-year post-sophomore medical student fellowship, beginning July 1. This fellowship is designed to provide the fellow with a significant educational experience in the practice of pathology. Experience will be gained through rotations in surgical pathology, cytopathology and autopsy services as well as selected areas of clinical pathology including hematopathology and microbiology. Opportunities to participate in mentored research with a faculty member as advisor.

Requirements: Applicants must have completed two or more years of studies in an accredited U.S. or Canadian medical school.

Stipends: The annual stipend is $14,000 plus travel and book allowance.

Applications: Must be completed by November 30th of the year precceding the intended fellowship which begins in July. Request application at sbeacham@health.usf.edu or snicosia@hsc.usf.edu.
Director: Santo V. Nicosia, MD, Professor and Chairman, Department of Pathology, University of South Florida.

WEST VIRGINIA UNIVERSITY SCHOOL OF MEDICINE

Description: The Department of Pathology at West Virginia University School of Medicine offers two post sophomore fellowships each year. Fellows spend portions of their time in surgical pathology, autopsy pathology and clinical pathology, and assist with medical student teaching. Research opportunities are available through individual arrangements with faculty members.

Requirements: Students must have completed their second year of medical school to be eligible for the program. Starting date will be July 1 unless other arrangements are made with the program director.

Stipends: The annual stipend is $21,000. A book allowance, health insurance, uniforms, and uniform laundry are also provided.

Applications: Please send to
James Coad, MD, Director, Post-Sophomore Fellowship, Department of Pathology, Robert C. Byrd Health Sciences Center of West Virginia University, PO Box 9203, Morgantown, WV 26506-9203.

42nd Edition

Faculty Index
2010–2011

The Intersociety Council for Pathology Information, Inc.

FACULTY INDEX